Contemporary Mathematics
for Business and Consumers

5th Edition

Annotated Instructor's Edition

Contemporary Mathematics
for Business and Consumers

5th Edition

Robert Brechner
Miami-Dade College

Australia • Brazil • Canada • Mexico • Singapore • Spain • United Kingdom • United States

AIE Contemporary Mathematics for Business and Consumers, Fifth Edition
Robert Brechner

VP/Editorial Director: Jack Calhoun

VP/Editor-in-Chief: Alex von Rosenberg

Sr. Acquisitions Editor: Charles McCormick, Jr.

Developmental Editor: Katie Yanos

Sr. Marketing Manager: Bryant Chrzan

Sr. Content Project Manager: Tamborah Moore

Manager, Editorial Media: John Barans

Managing Technology Project Manager: Matt McKinney

Technology Project Manager: Robin Browning

Marketing Communications Manager: Libby Shipp

Sr. Manufacturing Coordinator: Diane Gibbons

Production House: LEAP Publishing Services, Inc.

Compositor: Newgen

Art Director: Stacy Jenkins Shirley

Cover and Internal Designer: Joe Devine, Red Hangar Design

Cover Image: Getty Images

Photography Manager: Deanna Ettinger

Photo Researcher: Rose Alcorn

For product information and technology assistance, contact us at
Cengage Learning Academic Resource Center, 1-800-423-0563

For permission to use material from this text or product,
submit all requests online at **www.cengage.com/permissions**
Further permissions questions can be emailed to
permissionrequest@cengage.com

Library of Congress Control Number: 2008921202

AIE Package ISBN 13: 978-0-324-65867-5
AIE Package ISBN 10: 0-324-65867-2

AIE Book only ISBN 13: 978-0-324-65865-1
AIE Book only ISBN 10: 0-324-65865-6

South-Western Cengage Learning
5191 Natorp Boulevard
Mason, OH 45040
USA

Cengage Learning products are represented in Canada by Nelson Education, Ltd.

For your course and learning solutions, visit **academic.cengage.com**
Purchase any of our products at your local college store or at our preferred online store **www.ichapters.com**

Printed in the United States of America
1 2 3 4 5 6 7 12 11 10 09 08

Robert Brechner

Dear Colleague:

Today's dynamic business world requires dynamic tools to prepare students for success. To that end, ***Contemporary Mathematics for Business and Consumers*** and the **MathCue.Business** student tutorial software were written as the main components of a learning system designed to help business students achieve that success.

With an emphasis on applications that reflect real-world situations, the text provides sound and comprehensive coverage of the topics considered essential for students going on to courses and careers in accounting, marketing, retailing, banking, office administration, finance, insurance, real estate, and business administration. In addition, it is ideal for use in small businesses or for personal consumer needs. This is not just a textbook, but a "reference manual" for consumers and businesspeople, alike.

Contemporary Mathematics and MathCue.Business, along with their support ancillaries, are designed to meet the needs of traditional college students as well as those returning to school after some time away from the classroom.

- To reduce math anxiety, each chapter is divided into sections, and each section is subdivided into clear and manageable Performance Objectives.
- A page-referenced list of these objectives at the beginning of each chapter provides students with an overview of what lies ahead and how to best schedule their study time.

This modular approach allows instructors the flexibility to customize their courses' content and order of presentation to best meet the educational requirements and the specific learning needs of their students. In addition to customary classroom presentations, the text and software format are easily adaptable to self-paced labs and distance learning courses.

Realistic chapter material and explanations reflect current dates, names, and trends. This gives each topic immediate relevance and encourages students to see mathematics as an integral part of their daily lives.

- To emphasize vocabulary, all newly introduced math terminology appears in bold letters in the textual definitions as well as being displayed in an easy-to-reference Marginal Glossary. This helps to familiarize students with the language they need to know in order to master the concepts.
- In keeping with the philosophy that "practice makes perfect," the text contains more than 2,000 realistic business math exercises—many with multiple parts—designed to prepare students to use math to make business decisions. Odd-numbered answers to these exercises are listed in Appendix A.

Even before reaching the newly updated Section Review Exercises and numerous new Business Decisions in each chapter, students are given many opportunities to "see and try" each new topic: in the textual explanations, in the step-by-step boxes, in the Solution Strategies of each Example, and in the Try It Exercise Solutions. Not just the answers, but the worked-out solutions!

Also new to this edition, each end-of-chapter Assessment Test begins with a set of Concept Review fill-in questions designed to test student's comprehension of the basic concepts and important vocabulary. Each Assessment Test ends with a new Collaborative Learning Activity to help develop student's critical-thinking, research, and problem solving skills.

It is my sincere hope that *Contemporary Mathematics* will make your students better problem solvers and provide a solid mathematical foundation to help them succeed in further business courses and future careers. Of course, any book is only as strong as the service and commitment behind it. As part of my personal commitment to your success, I encourage you to contact me with questions or comments using my dedicated toll-free number 1-888-284-MATH or through email at bizmath@aol.com.

Thank you for making this book a success. I look forward to working together with you to ensure a rewarding business math experience for you and your students.

Warmest regards,

Robert Brechner

Robert Brechner

Brechner's *Contemporary Mathematics, 5e*

Real Business. Real Math. Real Life.

***Contemporary Mathematics, 5e* helps students overcome math anxiety and confidently master key concepts and their practical application to mathematics!**

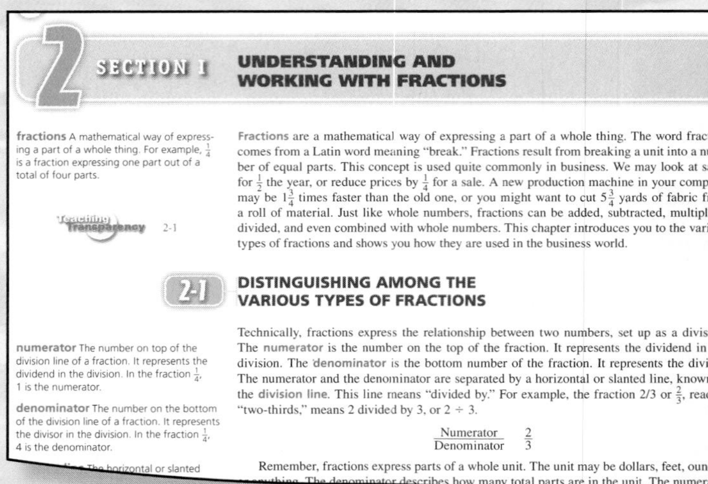

2 SECTION I **UNDERSTANDING AND WORKING WITH FRACTIONS**

fractions A mathematical way of expressing a part of a whole thing. For example, $\frac{1}{4}$ is a fraction expressing one part out of a total of four parts.

Teaching Transparency 2-1

Fractions are a mathematical way of expressing a part of a whole thing. The word fract
comes from a Latin word meaning "break." Fractions result from breaking a unit into a nu
ber of equal parts. This concept is used quite commonly in business. We may look at sa
for $\frac{1}{2}$ the year, or reduce prices by $\frac{1}{4}$ for a sale. A new production machine in your compa
may be $1\frac{3}{4}$ times faster than the old one, or you might want to cut $5\frac{3}{4}$ yards of fabric fr
a roll of material. Just like whole numbers, fractions can be added, subtracted, multipli
divided, and even combined with whole numbers. This chapter introduces you to the vari
types of fractions and shows you how they are used in the business world.

2-1 **DISTINGUISHING AMONG THE VARIOUS TYPES OF FRACTIONS**

numerator The number on top of the division line of a fraction. It represents the dividend in the division. In the fraction $\frac{1}{4}$, 1 is the numerator.

denominator The number on the bottom of the division line of a fraction. It represents the divisor in the division. In the fraction $\frac{1}{4}$, 4 is the denominator.

Technically, fractions express the relationship between two numbers, set up as a divisi
The **numerator** is the number on the top of the fraction. It represents the dividend in
division. The **denominator** is the bottom number of the fraction. It represents the divis
The numerator and the denominator are separated by a horizontal or slanted line, known
the **division line**. This line means "divided by." For example, the fraction 2/3 or $\frac{2}{3}$, read
"two-thirds," means 2 divided by 3, or 2 ÷ 3.

$$\frac{\text{Numerator}}{\text{Denominator}} \quad \frac{2}{3}$$

Remember, fractions express parts of a whole unit. The unit may be dollars, feet, ounc

From Motivation to Mastery

Brechner's **accessible and engaging style** begins with a business-oriented review of basic math operations, including whole numbers, fractions, and decimals. After students master these operations, they move to basic equations and their use in solving business problems.

Reflecting the Latest in Real Business

Brechner incorporates numerous **realistic** and **current** problems that are designed to develop problem-solving and critical thinking skills.

- Coverage of personal finances addresses the newest ways to manage finances, including online bills and banking, debit cards, and e-management of accounts.
- Realistic business and government forms, checks, bank statements, financial statements, credit card statements, and invoices are featured throughout.
- Stock, bond, and mutual fund tables are taken from *The Wall Street Journal Online.*

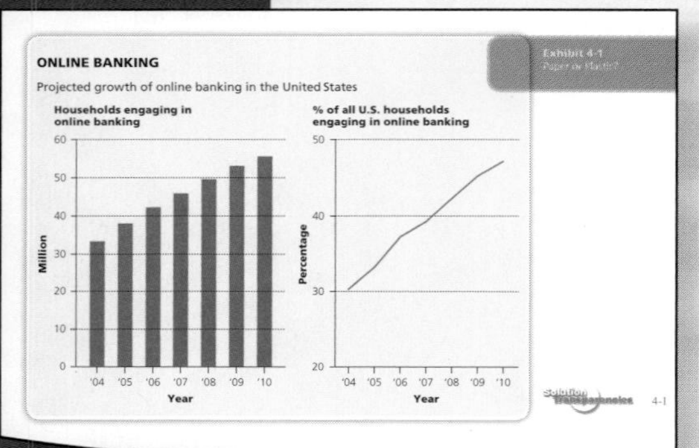

Step into the Real Business World

Brechner's unique modular approach **breaks each chapter into separate learning components,** allowing you to customize the material and order of coverage to meet the specific learning needs of your students.

Enhance Student Learning

Created specifically to accompany this text, **MathCue.Business** is a tutorial and assessment software that enhances student learning. With an endless supply of practice problems keyed to each performance objective, you can use MathCue.Business as a seamless course management tool or as a comprehensive student tutorial.

MC MathCue. Business

MORE THAN 2,000 EXERCISES!

Realistic business math exercises encourage critical thinking and problem-solving as students use math to make business decisions. Exercises cover a full range of difficulty, and many of them have multiple steps and answers.

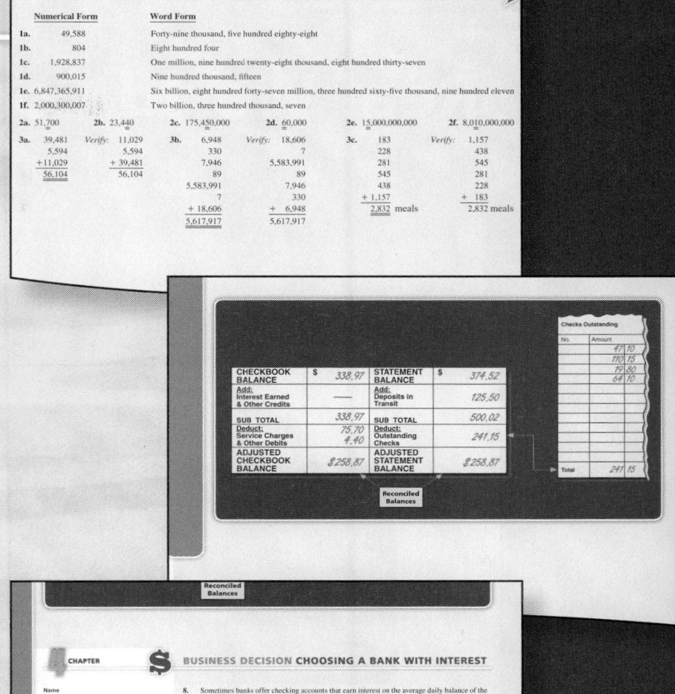

TRY IT EXERCISE SOLUTIONS FOR CHAPTER 1

	Numerical Form	Word Form
1a.	49,588	Forty-nine thousand, five hundred eighty-eight
1b.	804	Eight hundred four
1c.	1,928,837	One million, nine hundred twenty-eight thousand, eight hundred thirty-seven
1d.	900,015	Nine hundred thousand, fifteen
1e.	6,847,365,911	Six billion, eight hundred forty-seven million, three hundred sixty-five thousand, nine hundred eleven
1f.	2,000,300,007	Two billion, three hundred thousand, seven

2a. 51,700 2b. 23,440 2c. 175,450,000 2d. 60,000 2e. 15,000,000,000 2f. 8,010,000,000

3a. 39,481 + 5,594 + 11,029 = 56,104 *Verify:* 11,029 + 5,594 + 39,481 = 56,104

3b. 6,948 + 330 + 7,946 + 89 + 5,583,991 + 7 + 18,606 = 5,617,917 *Verify:* 18,606 + 7 + 5,583,991 + 89 + 7,946 + 330 + 6,948 = 5,617,917

3c. 183 + 228 + 281 + 545 + 438 + 1,157 = 2,832 meals *Verify:* 1,157 + 438 + 545 + 281 + 228 + 183 = 2,832 meals

CHECKBOOK BALANCE	$ 338.97	STATEMENT BALANCE	$ 374.52
Add: Interest Earned & Other Credits	—	Add: Deposits in Transit	125.50
SUB TOTAL	338.97	SUB TOTAL	500.02
Deduct: Service Charges & Other Debits	75.70 4.40	Deduct: Outstanding Checks	241.15
ADJUSTED CHECKBOOK BALANCE	$258.87	ADJUSTED STATEMENT BALANCE	$258.87

Checks Outstanding

No.	Amount
	47 10
	110 15
	19 80
	64 10
Total	241 15

Reconciled Balances

CHAPTER

Name

Class

Opportunity cost is the sacrifice of benefits from the next-best alternative when you make a financial or economic decision. To fully evaluate how much a checking account with a required minimum balance costs, calculate the opportunity cost.

Consider a bank that requires an average monthly balance of $1,500. If you can earn 3% a year in interest in a savings account, maintaining this checking account means giving

BUSINESS DECISION CHOOSING A BANK WITH INTEREST

8. Sometimes banks offer checking accounts that earn interest on the average daily balance of the account each month. This interest is calculated using a formula known as the simple interest formula. The formula is written as:

Interest = Principal × Rate × Time I = PRT

The formula states that the amount of **Interest** earned on the account is equal to the **Principal** (average daily balance) multiplied by the **Rate** (interest rate per year—expressed as a decimal) multiplied by the **Time** (expressed in years—use $\frac{1}{12}$ to represent one month of a year).

a. If you have not already done so, complete the Business Decision, Choosing a Bank, in Section II, page 120.

b. Use the simple interest formula to calculate the amount of interest you would earn per month if the Intercontinental Bank was offering 2 percent (.02) interest per year on checking accounts. (Note that your average daily balance changes from $900 to $2,400 in the last six months of the year.)

First 6 Months $I = 900 \times .02 \times \frac{1}{12} = \$1.50$ Per month

Last 6 Months $I = 2,400 \times .02 \times \frac{1}{12} = \$4.00$ Per month

- **Try It Exercises with Worked-out Solutions** encourage students to work out their own exercises for immediate feedback as they evaluate their comprehension of each new topic.

- Each chapter includes 8–12 new **Excel Exercises,** with three levels of difficulty—beginner, intermediate, or advanced—making it simple to provide hands-on practice with realistic business calculations. Student and instructor versions of the Excel templates are available on accompanying CDs.

- In-depth **Business Decision** exercises at the end of each section and each Assessment Test challenge students' comprehension and stimulate critical thinking as students work through a realistic multi-step business situation.

STEP-BY-STEP LEARNING SYSTEM

The step-by-step approach for each Performance Objective makes math accessible to students.

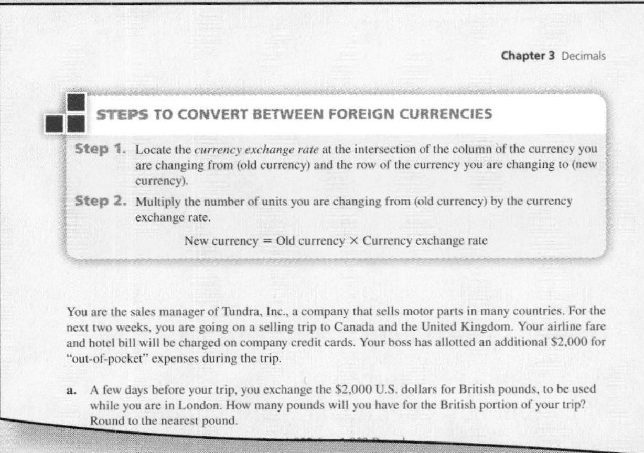

Chapter 3 Decimals

STEPS TO CONVERT BETWEEN FOREIGN CURRENCIES

Step 1. Locate the *currency exchange rate* at the intersection of the column of the currency you are changing from (old currency) and the row of the currency you are changing to (new currency).

Step 2. Multiply the number of units you are changing from (old currency) by the currency exchange rate.

New currency = Old currency × Currency exchange rate

You are the sales manager of Tundra, Inc., a company that sells motor parts in many countries. For the next two weeks, you are going on a selling trip to Canada and the United Kingdom. Your airline fare and hotel bill will be charged on company credit cards. Your boss has allotted an additional $2,000 for "out-of-pocket" expenses during the trip.

a. A few days before your trip, you exchange the $2,000 U.S. dollars for British pounds, to be used while you are in London. How many pounds will you have for the British portion of your trip? Round to the nearest pound.

- Detailed and up-to-date **Explanations** guide students through the topic.

- **Step-by-Step Boxes** overview important procedures for quick review.

- **Examples** with step-by-step **Solution Strategies** offer explanations and notes to ensure student understanding.

- **Calculator Sequences** walk students through difficult computations.

- **Section Review Exercises**—A set of 25–50 numeric and word problem exercises at the end of each section allow instructors to assign practice problems or homework for immediate review without waiting to complete the entire chapter.

Real World Connections

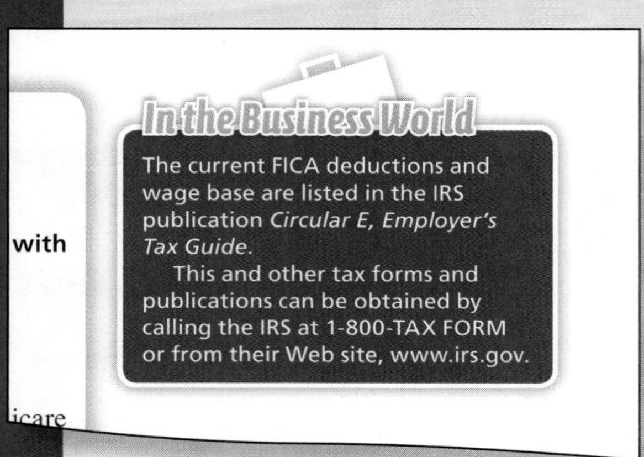

In the Business World

Useful and interesting connections to the real business world. Many have useful information to help students manage their own personal finance situations.

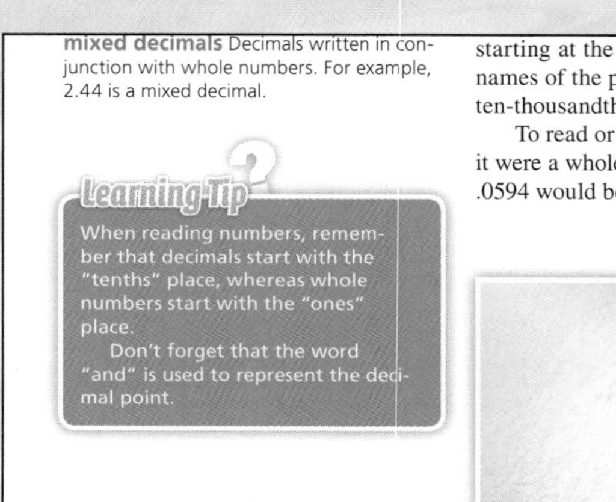

Learning Tips

Helpful mathematical hints, shortcuts, and reminders to enhance students' understanding of the chapter material.

Formula Recap Charts

Lists of all-important formulas provide students with a quick reference for homework or test preparation.

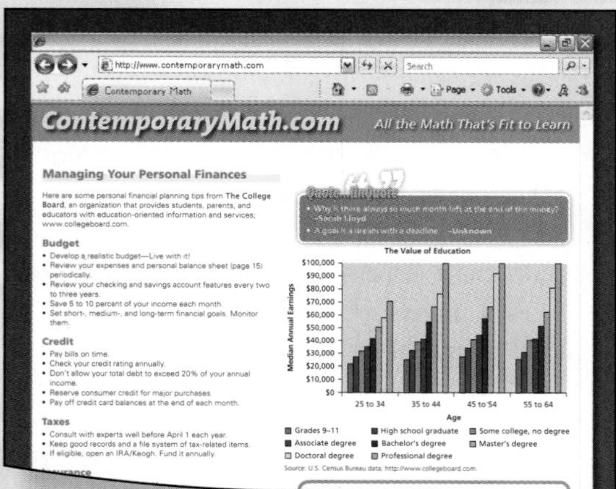

WWW.CONTEMPORARYMATH.COM

Appearing every three chapters, a page of current news items, cartoons, famous business and inspirational quotes, career information, and many other interesting facts and figures related to business topics.

END-OF-CHAPTER FEATURES PREPARE STUDENTS FOR THE REAL WORLD

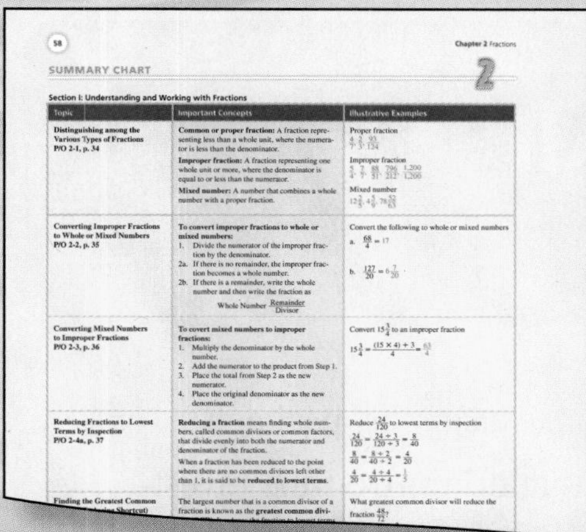

Chapter Summary Chart

This comprehensive review of each Performance Objective emphasizes important chapter concepts, steps, and formulas with illustrative examples, worked-out solutions, and specific page references. This is an invaluable reference for students reviewing or studying for an exam.

Concept Review

A set of fill-in questions designed to test students' comprehension of the basic concepts and important vocabulary of each chapter.

Assessment Test

Many exercises within the Assessment Tests involve multiple parts that build on previous answers and previously learned material to encourage critical thinking and problem solving.

Pages are perforated for easy removal and grading!

Collaborative Learning Activity

Multi-part individual or team activities designed to supplement and enhance student's comprehension of the chapter topics and their relevance in real world scenarios.

Grading Panel

This distinctive panel in the margin of the Assessment Tests allows students to record their answers for easy evaluation. Grading is simple with an answer template.

Answers to Odd-Numbered Exercises

Answers to all of the odd-numbered Section Review Exercises and Assessment Test questions (except Business Decisions) allow students to easily check their progress on class assignments or homework.

The Package that Does It All

This edition's comprehensive support package stands alone with tools that minimize time investment and make it easier to transition to this edition from a previous edition or another book. Traditional and technology-driven tools throughout the entire package make it easy to start using this edition immediately.

Contemporary Mathematics
for Business and Consumers
5TH EDITION

Robert Brechner

Full Edition or Brief Edition student texts are available to fit your specific course needs.

INSTRUCTOR TOOLS

Annotated Instructor's Edition

Student pages are surrounded by margin notes that provide comprehensive teaching tips, collaborative learning activities, classroom activities, and icons that indicate where to use solution and teaching transparencies. Worked-out solutions to all exercises are indicated in blue in the text. Appendix B contains solutions too large to fit on chapter pages.

Section III Multiplication and Division of Fractions 55

Review Exercises SECTION III 2

Multiply the following fractions and reduce to lowest terms. Use cancellation whenever possible.

1. $\frac{2}{3} \times \frac{4}{5} = \frac{8}{15}$
2. $\frac{5}{6} \times \frac{1}{4} = \frac{5}{24}$
3. $\frac{1}{2} \times \frac{4}{9} = \frac{2}{9}$
4. $\frac{7}{8} \times \frac{1}{3} \times \frac{4}{7} = \frac{1}{6}$
5. $\frac{16}{19} \times \frac{5}{8} = \frac{10}{19}$
6. $\frac{25}{51} \times \frac{2}{5} = \frac{10}{51}$
7. $\frac{8}{11} \times \frac{33}{40} \times \frac{4}{1} = \frac{12}{5}$
8. $\frac{2}{3} \times \frac{2}{3} \times \frac{6}{1} = \frac{8}{3} = 2\frac{2}{3}$
9. $8\frac{1}{5} \times 2\frac{2}{3}$ $\quad \frac{41}{5} \times \frac{8}{3} = \frac{328}{15} = 21\frac{13}{15}$
10. $\frac{1}{2} \times \frac{2}{3} \times \frac{4}{5} \times \frac{3}{4} \times \frac{5}{1} = \frac{1}{1} = 1$
11. $\frac{1}{5} \times \frac{1}{5} \times \frac{1}{5} = \frac{1}{125}$
12. $\frac{2}{3} \times 5\frac{4}{5} \times 9$ $\quad \frac{2}{3} \times \frac{29}{5} \times \frac{9}{1} = \frac{174}{5} = 34\frac{4}{5}$
13. A recent market research survey showed that $\frac{3}{8}$ of the people interviewed preferred decaffeinated coffee over regular.
    a. What fraction of the people preferred regular coffee?
    $\frac{8}{8} - \frac{3}{8} = \frac{5}{8}$ Preferred regular
    b. If 4,400 persons were interviewed, how many preferred regular coffee?
    $\frac{4,400}{1} \times \frac{5}{8} = \frac{2,750}{1} = 2,750$ People preferred regular
14. Katrina Byrd planned to bake a triple recipe of chocolate chip cookies for her office party. If the recipe calls for $1\frac{3}{4}$ cups of flour, how many cups will she need?
    $1\frac{3}{4} \times 3 = 5\frac{1}{4}$ cups
15. A driveway requires $9\frac{1}{2}$ truckloads of gravel. If the truck holds $4\frac{5}{8}$ cubic yards of gravel, … total cubic yards of gravel are used for the driveway?

Solution Transparencies

Getty Images

Instructor's Resource CD

This comprehensive electronic resource contains the following **(ISBN-10: 0-324-65853-2 / ISBN-13: 978-0-324-65853-8)**:

- **Instructor's Manual** offers a general introduction and walk-through of the text and entire ancillary package, suggestions for preparing a course syllabus, chapter notes and teaching tips, lecture launcher for each chapter, additional collaborative learning activities, and homework assignments.
- **"Questions Students Always Ask"** is a helpful feature at the end of each chapter in the Instructor's Manual that is ideal for adjunct instructors or those teaching from this text for the first time.
- **PowerPoint® Slides** for electronic classroom presentation contain solutions to all Section Review Exercises, and selected tables, charts, and other relevant graphics from the chapters.
- **ExamView® Electronic Test Bank** allows instructors to select problems at random by level of difficulty (easy, medium, or difficult levels are available for each question) or by type of problem. Instructors can customize or add test questions and create multiple versions of the same test.
- **Instructor's Edition of Excel templates**

MathCue.Business with Course Management and Quick-Pick Assignments

MathCue.Business provides both tutorial and assessment support for your course. Instructors can utilize the software for assignments and tests using the course management system or by taking advantage of the new Quick-Pick Assignment feature. (Please see pages xii-xv for details.)

Printed Test Bank

The test bank contains more than 2,400 problems, including vocabulary reviews, true/false, drill, and word problems. All questions now offer three levels of difficulty from which to choose. For each chapter, the test bank also contains a section with three "ready-made" quizzes built from test bank questions.

ISBN-10: 0-324-65862-1
ISBN-13: 978-0-324-65862-0

Teaching Transparencies

More than 100 two- and four-color Teaching Transparencies display figures, exhibits, tables, and Try It Exercises from the text in an easy display format to reinforce important concepts. Icons in the Annotated Instructor's Edition indicate when to use these.

ISBN-10: 0-324-65956-3
ISBN-13: 978-0-324-65956-6

Solution Transparencies

More than 275 Solution Transparencies can be used in class to illustrate worked-out solutions for Section Review Exercises. Icons in the Annotated Instructor's Edition indicate when these are best used.

ISBN-10: 0-324-65957-1
ISBN-13: 978-0-324-65957-3

An instructor-only Web site offers numerous downloadable instructor resources!

Contemporary Mathematics, 5e Web Site

ACADEMIC.CENGAGE.COM/BMATH/BRECHNER

This dedicated Web site provides comprehensive tutorial tools and business links for students. Students find Performance Objectives from the book, interactive quizzes, flashcards, and other dynamic learning links that make business math come alive.

STUDENT TOOLS

Student Resource CD

This important resource includes **MathCue.Business** self-study tutorial software, student Excel templates, and Chapter 22, an extra chapter covering U.S. and metric business measurements and currency conversion. This CD accompanies each ***new text*** or is available for purchase separately.

ISBN-10: 0-324-65985-7 / ISBN-13: 978-0-324-65985-6

BizMath Tutorial Videos

Available within the **MathCue.Business** software these Flash tutorials focus on core topics of business math. They utilize the three methods of learning: Define, Demonstrate, and Do. Each segment focuses on a core topic to help students master the most critical skills necessary for success in the business math course. Available on the Student Resource CD, which accompanies each ***new text*** or is available for purchase separately.

Contemporary Mathematics, 5e Web Site

ACADEMIC.CENGAGE.COM/BMATH/BRECHNER

This dedicated Web site provides comprehensive tutorial tools and business links for students. Students find Performance Objectives from the book, interactive quizzes, flashcards, and other dynamic learning links that make business math come alive.

Both you and your students will find MathCue.Business easy to use! Take a look at what MathCue.Business can do for your course.

Created specifically to accompany this text, **MathCue.Business** offers the ultimate in flexibility for instructors. There are now three ways to utilize **MathCue. Business** in your course:

- **Self-Study Student Tutorial**
- **Quick-Pick Assignments**
- **Comprehensive Course Management**

SELF-STUDY TUTORIAL FOR STUDENTS

Use **MathCue.Business** as a self-study tool and student resource for tutoring and practice.

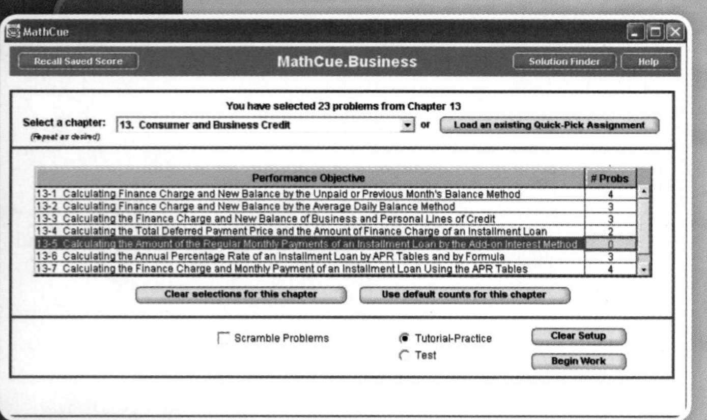

- **Sessions are easily customized** to include problems from one or more Performance Objectives allowing users to create highly targeted tutorial sessions, practice tests, and exams.
- In **Tutorial Practice Mode,** the software presents problems, evaluates answers, and gives immediate feedback. In Test Mode, problem answers and results are given only when students finish the entire session.
- **Algorithms randomly generate** carefully designed problems keyed to Performance Objectives in the text.

- Each problem is accompanied by a complete, **step-by-step solution.** Students can also get help starting a problem. Students can back up sessions and resume them later if they are unable to finish in one sitting.

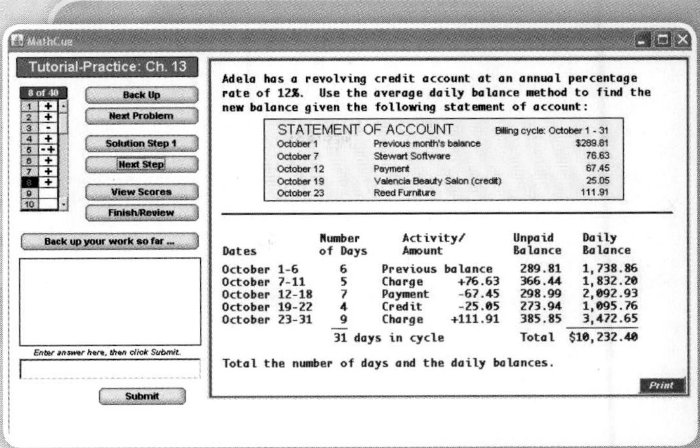

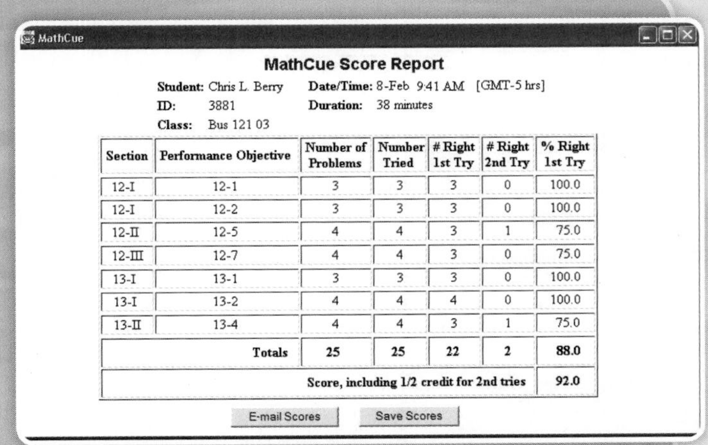

MathCue Score Report

Student: Chris L. Berry Date/Time: 8-Feb 9:41 AM [GMT-5 hrs]
ID: 3881 Duration: 38 minutes
Class: Bus 121 03

Section	Performance Objective	Number of Problems	Number Tried	# Right 1st Try	# Right 2nd Try	% Right 1st Try
12-I	12-1	3	3	3	0	100.0
12-I	12-2	3	3	3	0	100.0
12-II	12-5	4	4	3	1	75.0
12-III	12-7	4	4	3	0	75.0
13-I	13-1	3	3	3	0	100.0
13-I	13-2	4	4	4	0	100.0
13-II	13-4	4	4	3	1	75.0
	Totals	25	25	22	2	88.0
	Score, including 1/2 credit for 2nd tries					92.0

E-mail Scores Save Scores

- **Result Summaries** provide a detailed record of a student's performance with results linked to specific Performance Objectives so instructors and students can determine areas of strength and improve areas of weakness.

- **Solution Finder** is a unique feature that allows students to ***enter their own basic math problems.*** Like a personal tutor, the software guides students through solving the problem with a complete step-by-step explanation.

- A link from within MathCue.Business provides direct access to the **BizMath Tutorial Videos.**

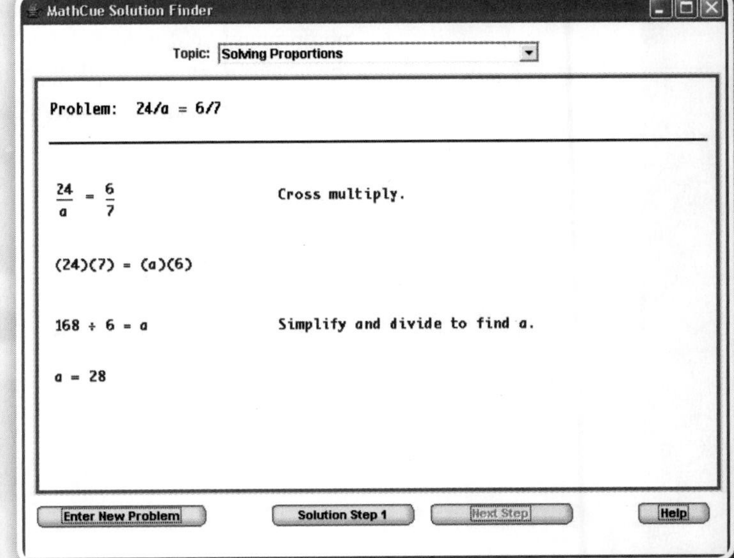

QUICK-PICK ASSIGNMENTS

Now, without the need to register or set up online rosters or syllabi, instructors can create customized, targeted tutorial practice or test sessions and assign them to students via the Internet.

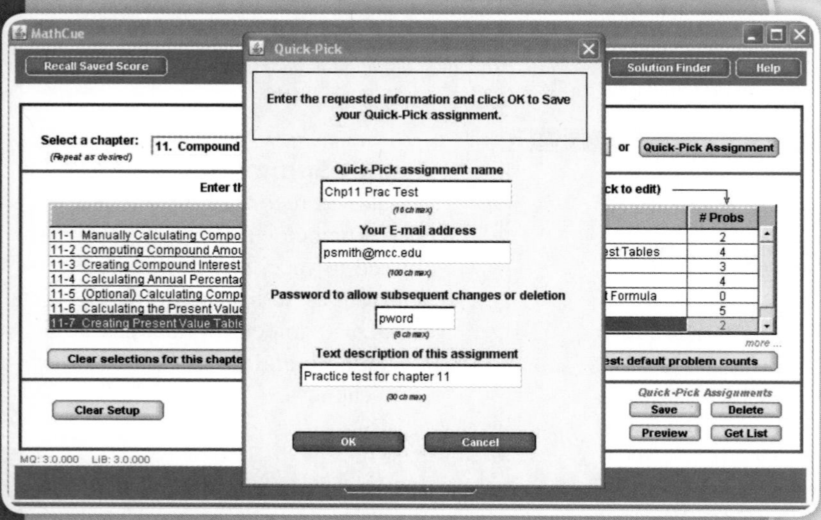

- **Quick-Pick Assignments** are great for make-ups, extra credit and remediation for individuals, groups, or an entire class. They can be initiated at any time during a course with little effort and no preplanning. Students launch their sessions by simply entering the assignment name and their instructor's e-mail address. Scores are sent back using the **MathCue.Business** secure e-mail-scores feature.

COMPREHENSIVE COURSE MANAGEMENT

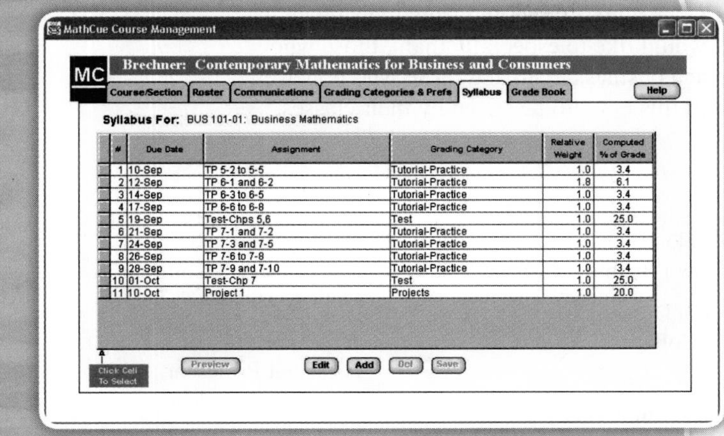

#	Due Date	Assignment	Grading Category	Relative Weight	Computed % of Grade
1	10-Sep	TP 5-2 to 5-5	Tutorial-Practice	1.0	3.4
2	12-Sep	TP 6-1 and 6-2	Tutorial-Practice	1.8	6.1
3	14-Sep	TP 6-3 to 6-5	Tutorial-Practice	1.0	3.4
4	17-Sep	TP 6-6 to 6-8	Tutorial-Practice	1.0	3.4
5	19-Sep	Test-Chps 5,6	Test	1.0	25.0
6	21-Sep	TP 7-1 and 7-2	Tutorial-Practice	1.0	3.4
7	24-Sep	TP 7-3 and 7-5	Tutorial-Practice	1.0	3.4
8	26-Sep	TP 7-6 to 7-8	Tutorial-Practice	1.0	3.4
9	28-Sep	TP 7-9 and 7-10	Tutorial-Practice	1.0	3.4
10	01-Oct	Test-Chp 7	Test	1.0	25.0
11	10-Oct	Project 1	Projects	1.0	20.0

- **MathCue.Business Syllabus –** Instructors can schedule customized, highly targeted sessions for students to practice specific Performance Objectives. Instructors can specify practice quizzes or tests.

- **Grade Book Management –** The MathCue.Business Grade Book automatically tracks student progress with a listing of session grades for all students in a section and session-by-session details. Assess class-wide strengths and weaknesses with various grading options.

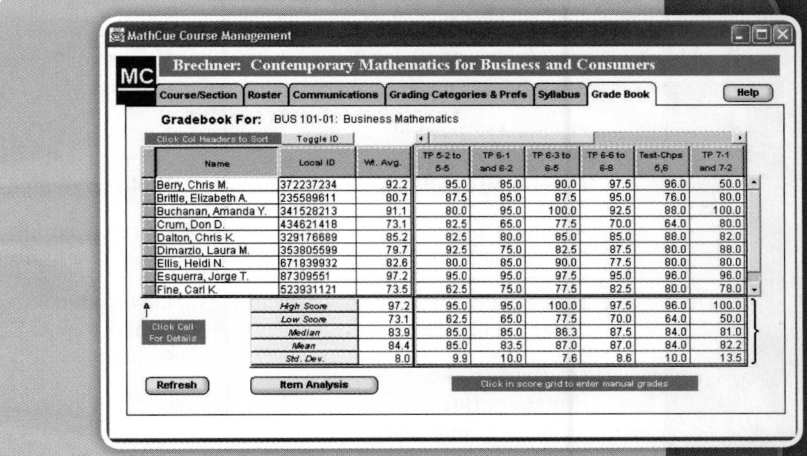

Name	Local ID	Wt. Avg.	TP 5-2 to 5-5	TP 6-1 and 6-2	TP 6-3 to 6-5	TP 6-6 to 6-8	Test-Chps 5,6	TP 7-1 and 7-2
Berry, Chris M.	372237234	92.2	95.0	85.0	90.0	97.5	96.0	50.0
Brittle, Elizabeth A.	235589611	80.7	87.5	85.0	87.5	95.0	76.0	80.0
Buchanan, Amanda Y.	341528213	91.1	80.0	95.0	100.0	92.5	88.0	100.0
Crum, Don D.	434621418	73.1	82.5	65.0	77.5	70.0	64.0	80.0
Dalton, Chris K.	329176689	85.2	82.5	80.0	85.0	85.0	88.0	82.0
Dimarzio, Laura M.	353805599	79.7	92.5	75.0	82.5	87.5	80.0	88.0
Ellis, Heidi N.	671839932	82.6	80.0	85.0	90.0	77.5	80.0	80.0
Esquerra, Jorge T.	87309551	97.2	95.0	95.0	97.5	95.0	96.0	96.0
Fine, Carl K.	523931121	73.5	62.5	75.0	77.5	82.5	80.0	78.0
	High Score	97.2	95.0	95.0	100.0	97.5	96.0	100.0
	Low Score	73.1	62.5	65.0	77.5	70.0	64.0	50.0
	Median	83.9	85.0	85.0	86.3	87.5	84.0	81.0
	Mean	84.4	85.0	83.5	87.0	87.0	84.0	82.2
	Std. Dev.	8.0	9.9	10.0	7.6	8.6	10.0	13.5

- **MathCue.Business Communications –** Create effective, immediate instructor-student communications with this software that can send messages to the entire class or selected groups of individuals.

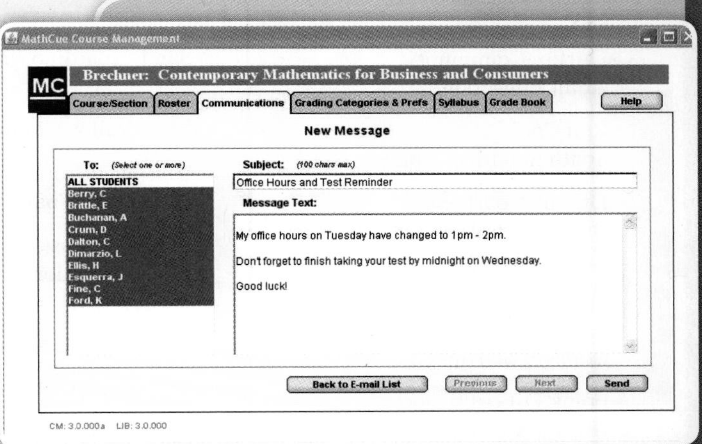

Acknowledgments

Contemporary Mathematics for Business and Consumers benefited from the valuable input of instructors throughout the country. I would like to especially thank those who responded to our questions about how they teach business math and those who reviewed various parts of the manuscript and/or allowed this book to be tested by their classes.

Reviewers:

Alton Amidon,
Pamlico Community College

Carol Baker,
Napa Valley Community College

Michael J. Batali,
Yakima Valley
Community College

Leon G. Bean, J.D.,
International Business College
El Paso, Texas

Christine F. Belles,
Macomb Community College

George H. Bernard,
Professor, Seminole
Community College

Yvonne Block,
College of Lake County

Don Boyer,
Jefferson College

Dr. Barry Bunn,
Professor, Business,
Valencia Community College

Natalie Card,
Utah Valley State College

Janet P. Ciccarelli,
Professor, Herkimer County
Community College

Milton Cohen,
Fairfax Community
Adult Education

Ron Cooley,
South Suburban College

Dr. Sue Courtney,
Business Professor, Kansas City,
Kansas Community College

Toby Deal,
Patrick Henry Community
College, Martinsville, VA

Frank DiFerdinando,
Hudson County
Community College

Mary Jo Dix,
Jamestown Business College

Elizabeth Domenico,
Gaston College

J. D. Dulgeroff,
San Bernardino Valley
Community College

Acie B. Earl,
Black Hawk Community College

Susan Emens,
Kent State University—Trumbull
Campus

Rene Garcia,
Miami-Dade Community College,
Wolfson Campus

Patricia Gardner,
San Bernardino Valley College

Glen Gelderloos,
Grand Rapids Community
College

Cecil Green,
Riverside Community College

Stephen W. Griffin,
Tarrant County Junior College,
South Campus

James Grigsby,
Lake Sumter Community College

Paul Grutsis,
San Bernardino Valley College

Julie Hall,
Napa Valley Community College

Giselle Halpern,
El Camino Community College

John Heinsius,
Modesto Junior College

Jana Hosmer,
Blue Ridge Community College

Dr. Harry T. Kolendrianos,
Danville Community College,
Danville, VA

Phil C. Kopriva,
San Francisco Community
College District

Jeffrey Kroll,
Assistant Professor,
Brazosport College

Sherry Jones,
Glenville State College

Janis Lawrence,
Northwestern Business College

Rosemarie LeFebvre,
Mohave Community College

Diana Lee Lloyd,
Hesser College

Gwendolyn Loftis,
Rose State College

Joyellen Lottie,
Glendale Community College

Marvin Mai,
Empire College

Paul H. Martin,
Business, Aim Community
College, Greeley, CO

Loretta A. McAdam,
Professor Information Systems,
Business and Legal Studies,
Seminole Community College

Sharon M. Meyer,
Pikes Peak Community College

Zo Miller,
Rose State College

Linda Mosley,
Coordinator/Instructor of Business Programs, Tarrant County
College, Southeast Campus

Jack L. Nelson,
Ferris State University

Wayne A. Paper,
Hawkeye Institute of Technology

Cynthia L. Phipps, CPA,
Lake Land College

Lana L. Powell,
Valencia Community College

Wayne Price,
Napa Valley Community College

Barbara Rosenthal,
Miami-Dade Community College,
Wolfson Campus

Ben Sadler,
Miami-Dade Community College,
Wolfson Campus

Charles R. Shatzer, Ph.D.,
Solano College

Jane C Shatzer,
Solano Community College

Jo-Anne Sheehan,
Briarcliffe College

Amy Shinoki,
Kapiolani Community College

Kent Smith,
Texas State Technical College
West Texas

Natalie E. Smith,
Okaloosa Walton
Community College

Carl J. Sonntag,
Pikes Peak Community College

David D. Stringer,
DeAnza College

Lynette Teal,
Western WI Technical College

Steven Teeter,
Utah Valley State College

Charles Webb,
Miami-Dade Community College,
Wolfson Campus

Gregory J. Worosz,
Schoolcraft College

James T. Yamamoto,
Hawaii Business College

Phone Survey Respondents:

Jeffrey Abrams,
Newport Business Institute

Terry Alexander,
Denver Technical College

Charles Anderson,
TN Technology Center
at Livingston

David Blum,
Moraine Park Technical College

Rita Boetell,
Bakersfield College

Barry Brandbold,
Aaker's Business College

Norma Broadway,
Hinds Community College

Howard Bryan,
Santa Rosa Junior College

Dr. Bob Bulls,
J.S. Reynolds County College

Roy Bunek,
Fugazzi College

Patricia Calloway, East Mississippi County College

Lisa Campenella,
ICSI (Allentown, PA)

John H. Carpenter,
Polk Community College

Roger D. Chagnon,
Jamestown Business College

Victor Clearsuas,
Holyoke Community College

Carol Coeyman,
Yorktown Business Institute

George Converse,
Stone Academy

Ron Cooley,
South Suburban College

William S. Dahlman,
Premier Career College

Nancy Degnan,
Sawyer School

Karen Desele,
Gillette

Joe D. DiCostanzo,
Johnson County
Community College

Stephen Ernest,
Baton Rouge School
of Computers

Carol Ferguson,
Rock Valley College

Mark Finger,
Madison Area Technical College

Dennis Franklin,
Culinary Arts Institute

Rachael Freuche,
Indiana Business College

Rick Gallardo,
International Business College

Miriam Gateley,
Valencia Community College

Cynthia Gerber,
Indiana Business College

Jeff Gordon,
San Joaquin Valley College

Carolyn Green,
Universal Business
& Media School

Bob Grenier,
Vatterott College

Ray Hale,
Rets Medical & Business Institute

Michael Hlebik,
Erie Business School

Bill Holbrook,
Owensboro Junior College
of Business

Brenda Holmes,
Northwest Mississippi
Community College

John Hudson,
National Business College

Jared Jay,
American Commercial College

Joanne Kaufman,
Metro Business College

Patti Koluda,
Yakima Valley County College

Janice Lawrence,
Northwestern Business College

Suzann Lewison,
Southwestern WI
Technical College

Marvin Mai,
Empire College

Jackie Marshall,
Ohio Business College

Faye Massey,
Northwest Mississippi
Community College

Cheryl McGahee,
Guilford Community College

Mary Jo McKinney,
American School of Business

Hugh McNiece,
Lincolnland County College

Rose Miller,
Milwaukee Area
Technical College

Charlene Mulleollan,
Dubois Business College

Jim Murray,
Western WI Technical College

Steve O'Rourke,
Newcastle Business School

Peggy Peterson,
Rasmussen College

Barbara Portzen,
Mid State Technical College

Edward Pratowski,
Dorsey Business School

Rose Ramirez,
MTL Business College of Stockton

Bill Rhodarmer,
Haywood County College

Linda Rockwall,
Ridley Lowell Business & Technical Institute

Steve Shaw,
Tidewater Tech

Susan Shaw,
Southwestern Business College

Chuck Sherrill,
Community College of Aurora

Forrest Simmons,
Portland Community College

Eileen Snyder,
Harrisburg Area Community College

Adina Solomon,
Vatterott College

Walter Soroka,
Newcastle School of Trade

Teresa Stephenson,
Indianapolis Business School

Mary Susa,
Mid-State Technical College

Kermit Swanson,
Rasmussen College

Paula Terrones,
College of Office Technology

Arthur Walter,
Suffolk Community College

Winston Wrenn,
Draughton Junior College

Gaylon Wright,
Angelina College

Sandra Young,
Business Institute of Pennsylvania

I would like to extend personal thanks to the many academic and business information contributors who helped me develop this book:

Santiago Alan
Bob Albrecht
John Aldrich
John Anderson
Vince Arenas
Marcie Bader
Christine Balmori
Robert Barton
Charlie Beavin
Jessica Bergeman
Ed Blakemore
Joan Braverman
Martha Cavalaris
Gilbert S. Cohen
Patricia Conroy
Dave Cook
Ralph Covert
Nancy De La Vega
Elliott Denner
George DiOrio
John Dunham
Ivan Figueroa
Mario Font
Butch Gemin
John Godlewski
Abdul Hamza
Lionel Howard
Scott Isenberg
Al Kahn
Joseph Kreutle
Kimberly Lipscomb
Jaime Lopez
Marvin Mai
Jane Mangrum
Paul Marx
Jim McHugh
Noemi McPherson
Sharon Meyer
Rolando Montoya
Joseph Moutran
Sylvia Ratner
Cheryl Robinson
Brian Rochlin
Michael Rohrer
Howard Schoninger
Steven Steidel
Bill Taylor
Richard Waldman
Joseph Walzer
Kathryn Warren
Larry Zigler

Also, I would like to thank the corporate and government organizations that I used as examples and sources of information in preparing and developing this book:

7-11
Aamco
Ace Hardware
Aetna
Amazon.com
AMR Corporation
Ann Taylor
Apple
Arthur Andersen & Company
Auto Zone
Bank of America
Baskin & Robbins
Best Buy
Board of Governors, Federal Reserve System
Brinker International
Bureau of Labor Statistics
CarMax
Center
Chili's
Circuit City
Citicorp Financial Services
Dairy Queen
Darden Restaurants
Dell
Dominos Pizza
Dow Jones, Inc., The Wall Street Journal
EBay
Federal Express
General Motors/Saturn
Goodrich
Google
Harley-Davidson
Home Depot
Hotels.com
Insurance Information Institute
Internal Revenue Service
Jiffy Lube
Kellogg
KFC
Kinko's
Knight-Ridder, Inc., The Miami Herald
Kodak
Long John Silvers
Lowe's Home Improvement Center
Macaroni Grill
Macy's
MasterCard International
McDonald's
The Miami Herald

Microsoft
New York Times
Nike
Nissan
Office Depot
Olive Garden
On the Border
Panasonic
Pizza Hut
Popular Bank of Florida
Radio Shack
Red Lobster
Reebok, Inc.
Ryder
Sea Ray Boats
Sirius Satellite Radio
Smith Barney Shearson
Sony
Sprint/Nextel
Starbucks
State of Florida, Department of Revenue
Taco Bell
Target
Time, Inc., Fortune Magazine
Town & Country
Toyota Motors
Toys 'R' Us, Inc.
Transamerica Life Companies
Transocean
Travelocity.com
Tribune
TruValue Hardware
Tupperware
U.S. Census Bureau
U.S. Department of Commerce
U.S. Department of Housing and Urban Development
U.S. Government Printing Office, Statistical Abstract of the United States
U.S. Postal Service
U.S. Timber
U-Haul
USA Today
Wall Street Journal
Wall Street Journal Online
Wal-Mart, Inc.
Walt Disney Company
Wendy's
West Marine
XM Satellite Radio
Yum Brands

I would like to gratefully acknowledge and thank the editorial, production, and marketing teams at South-Western, a part of Cengage Learning for their continued support over the years and great Fifth Edition. I am honored and thrilled to be associated with such talented and dedicated professionals.

Special thanks to Jack W. Calhoun, VP/Editorial Director; Charles McCormick, Jr., senior acquisitions editor; Bryant Chrzan, marketing manager; Katie Yanos, developmental editor; Rose Alcorn, photo editor; Malvine Litten, LEAP Publishing Services, Inc.; Tamborah Moore, senior content project manager; Stacy Shirley, art director; Robin Browning, technology project manager; and Libby Shipp, marketing communications manager.

I would also like to thank Mike Gordon and Fernando Rodriguez for their creativity, business acumen, and wonderful research.

Finally, I would like to acknowledge my dear friend and colleague, George Bergeman. Many thanks for your continued support and blockbuster new edition of MathCue.Business.

Robert Brechner
December 2007

Dedication

To my wife, Shari Joy.
I'll love you forever and a day!

About the Authors

Robert Brechner

Robert Brechner is Professor, School of Business, at Miami-Dade College, the largest multi-campus community college in the country. For the past 42 years, he has taught Business Math, Principles of Business, Marketing, Advertising, Public Relations, Management, and Personal Finance. He has been Adjunct Professor at Florida Atlantic University, Boca Raton, International Fine Arts College, Miami, and Florida International University School of Journalism and Mass Communications.

Bob holds a Bachelor of Science degree in Industrial Management from the Georgia Institute of Technology in Atlanta, Georgia. He also has a Masters of Business Administration from Emory University in Atlanta. He consults widely with industrial companies and has published numerous books covering a variety of business topics.

Bob lives in Coconut Grove, Florida, with his wife, Shari Joy. His passions include travel, photography, sailing, tennis, and running. Bob encourages feedback and suggestions for future editions from those who use the text. Students, as well as instructors, can contact him toll-free at 1-888-284-MATH or e-mail him at bizmath@aol.com.

George Bergeman, **author of MathCue.Business**

The author of numerous software packages, George Bergeman has taught mathematics for more than 25 years. His teaching career began at a small college in West Africa as a Peace Corps volunteer and continued at Northern Virginia Community College, one of the largest multi-campus colleges in the country. Teaching awards have included Faculty Member of the Year honors at his campus.

In an effort to enhance his instruction by incorporating computer support, George developed a small program for use in statistics classes. Students and instructors responded positively, and in 1985 an expanded version was published along with an accompanying workbook. Since then, George has developed a variety of software packages to accompany texts in statistics, calculus, developmental math, finite math, and a special favorite—Robert Brechner's *Contemporary Mathematics for Business and Consumers*.

By drawing upon his teaching experiences and contact with students and faculty, he has endeavored to develop software that provides targeted, effective, and easy-to-use support for instruction.

George lives with his wife, Clarissa, near Washington, D.C., and they have one daughter, Jessica, who recently returned to the east coast after four years in San Francisco and a period of volunteer work in Brazil. In his free time, he enjoys accompanying his wife and their dog, Anny, to dog shows, and he flies an ultralight airplane.

Brief Contents

Contents

Contemporary Mathematics
for Business and Consumers

5th Edition

Annotated Instructor's Edition

CHAPTER 1

Whole Numbers

PERFORMANCE OBJECTIVES

SECTION I THE DECIMAL NUMBER SYSTEM: WHOLE NUMBERS

Numbers are one of the primary tools used in business. The ability to read, comprehend, and manipulate numbers is an essential part of the everyday activity in today's complex business world. To be successful, business students should become competent and confident in dealing with numbers.

We shall begin our study of business mathematics with whole numbers and their basic operations—addition, subtraction, multiplication, and division. The material in this chapter is based on the assumption that you have a basic working knowledge of these operations. Our goal is to review these fundamentals and build accuracy and speed. This arithmetic review will set the groundwork for our study of fractions, decimals, and percents. Most business math applications involve calculations using these components.

1-1 READING AND WRITING WHOLE NUMBERS IN NUMERICAL AND WORD FORM

decimal number system A system using the 10 Hindu-Arabic symbols, 0 through 9. In this place-value system, the position of a digit to the left or right of the decimal point affects its value.

decimal point A dot written in a decimal number to indicate where the place values change from whole numbers to decimals.

The number system most widely used in the world today is known as the Hindu-Arabic, or **decimal number system**. This system is far superior to any other for today's complex business calculations. It derives its name from the Latin words *decimus*, meaning 10th, and *decem*, meaning 10. The decimal system is based on 10s, with the starting point marked by a dot known as the **decimal point**. The decimal system uses the 10 familiar Hindu-Arabic symbols or digits:

0, 1, 2, 3, 4, 5, 6, 7, 8, 9

The major advantage of our decimal system over previous systems is that the position of a digit to the left or right of the decimal point affects its value. This enables us to write any

© Digital Vision/Getty Images

Skills you acquire in this course will be applied frequently in your roles as a consumer and a businessperson.

Exhibit 1-1
Whole Number Place Value Chart

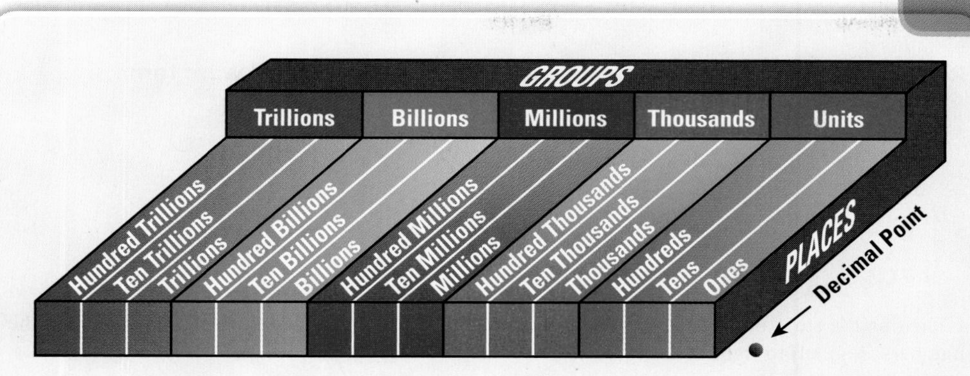

Teaching Transparency 1-1

number with only the 10 single-digit numbers, 0 through 9. For this reason, we have given names to the places or positions. In this chapter we work with places to the left of the decimal point, **whole numbers**. The next two chapters are concerned with the places to the right of the decimal point, fractions and decimals.

whole numbers Any numbers, 0 or greater, that do not contain a decimal or fraction. Whole numbers are found to the left of the decimal point. Also known as an integer. For example, 6, 25, and 300 are whole numbers.

When whole numbers are written, a decimal point is understood to be located on the right of the number. For example, the number **27** is actually

27.

The decimal point is not displayed until we write a decimal number or dollars and cents, such as 27.25 inches or $27.25.

Exhibit 1-1 illustrates the first 15 places, and five groups, of the decimal number system. Note that our system is made up of groups of three places, separated by commas, each with their own name. Whole numbers start at the understood decimal point and increase in value from right to left. Each group contains the same three places: one, ten, and hundred. Note that each place increases by a factor of "times 10." The group names are units, thousands, millions, billions, and trillions.

STEPS FOR READING AND WRITING WHOLE NUMBERS

Step 1. Beginning at the right side of the number, insert a comma every three digits to mark the groups.

Step 2. Beginning from left to right, name the digits and the groups. The units group and groups that have all zeros are not named.

Step 3. When writing whole numbers in word form, the numbers from 21 to 99 are hyphenated (except for the decades, e.g., thirty). For example, 83 would be written eighty-three.

Note: The word *and* should *not* be used in reading or writing whole numbers. It represents the decimal point and will be covered in Chapter 3.

Whole numbers with 4 digits may be written with or without a comma. For example, 3,400 or 3400 would be correct.

EXAMPLE 1 READING AND WRITING WHOLE NUMBERS

Read and write the following whole numbers in numerical and word form.

a. 14296 b. 560
c. 2294857 d. 184910
e. 3004959001 f. 24000064

SOLUTION STRATEGY

Following the steps on page 3, we insert the commas to mark the groups, then read and write the numbers from left to right.

	Number	Numerical Form	Word Form
a.	14296	14,296	fourteen thousand, two hundred ninety-six
b.	560	560	five hundred sixty
c.	2294857	2,294,857	two million, two hundred ninety-four thousand, eight hundred fifty-seven
d.	184910	184,910	one hundred eighty-four thousand, nine hundred ten
e.	3004959001	3,004,959,001	three billion, four million, nine hundred fifty-nine thousand, one
f.	24000064	24,000,064	twenty-four million, sixty-four

In the Business World

In text, large numbers, in the millions and greater, may be easier to read by writing the "zero's portion" in words. For example, 44,000,000,000,000 may be written as 44 trillion.

TRY IT EXERCISE 1

Read and write the following whole numbers in numerical and word form.

a. 49588 b. 804 c. 1928837
d. 900015 e. 6847365911 f. 2000300007

CHECK YOUR ANSWERS WITH THE SOLUTIONS ON PAGE 26.

1-2 ROUNDING WHOLE NUMBERS TO A SPECIFIED PLACE VALUE

rounded numbers Numbers that are approximations or estimates of exact numbers. For example, 50 is the rounded number of the exact number 49.

estimate To calculate approximately the amount or value of something. The number 50 would be an estimate of 49.

rounding all the way A process of rounding numbers to the first digit. Used to prework a problem to an estimated answer. For example, 2,865 rounded all the way is 3,000.

In many business applications, an approximation of an exact number may be more desirable to use than the number itself. Approximations, or **rounded numbers**, are easier to refer to and remember. For example, if a grocery store carries 9,858 items on its shelves, you would probably say that it carries 10,000 items. If you drive 1,593 miles, you would say that the trip is 1,600 miles. Another rounding application in business involves money. If your company has profits of $1,302,201, you might refer to this exact amount by the rounded number $1,300,000. Money amounts are usually rounded to the nearest cent, although they could also be rounded to the nearest dollar.

Rounded numbers are frequently used to **estimate** an answer to a problem, before working that problem. Estimation approximates the exact answer. By knowing an estimate of an answer in advance, you will be able to catch many math errors. When using estimation to prework a problem, you can generally round off to the first digit, which is called **rounding all the way**.

Once you have rounded to the first digit, perform the indicated math procedure. This can often be done quickly and will give you a ballpark or general idea of the actual answer. In the example below, the estimated answer of 26,000 is a good indicator of the "reasonableness" of the actual answer.

Original Calculation	Estimated Solution (rounding all the way)	Actual Solution
19,549	20,000	19,549
+ 6,489	+ 6,000	+ 6,489
	26,000	26,038

If, for example, you had mistakenly added for a total of 23,038 instead of 26,038, your estimate would have immediately indicated that something was wrong.

STEPS FOR ROUNDING WHOLE NUMBERS TO A SPECIFIED PLACE VALUE

Step 1. Determine the place to which the number is to be rounded.

Step 2a. If the digit to the right of the place being rounded is 5 or more, increase the digit in that place by 1.

Step 2b. If the digit to the right of the place being rounded is 4 or less, do not change the digit in the place being rounded.

Step 3. Change all digits to the right of the place being rounded to zeros.

EXAMPLE 2 ROUNDING WHOLE NUMBERS

Round the following numbers to the indicated place.

a. 1,867 to tens
b. 760 to hundreds
c. 129,338 to thousands
d. 293,847 to hundred thousands
e. 97,078,838,576 to billions
f. 85,600,061 all the way

SOLUTION STRATEGY

Following the steps above, locate the place to be rounded, use the digit to the right of that place to determine whether to round up or leave it as is, then change all digits to the right of the place being rounded to zeros.

		Place Indicated	Rounded Number
a.	1,867 to tens	1,867	1,870
b.	760 to hundreds	760	800
c.	129,338 to thousands	129,338	129,000
d.	293,847 to hundred thousands	293,847	300,000
e.	97,078,838,576 to billions	97,078,838,576	97,000,000,000
f.	85,600,061 all the way	85,600,061	90,000,000

CLASSROOM ACTIVITY
Ask students to think of situations in which rounding or estimating would be useful. Typical responses might include
- totaling a check in a restaurant
- deciding how much food and beverages to buy for a party
- planning the purchase of materials for a construction project

TRY IT EXERCISE 2

Round the following numbers to the indicated place.

a. 51,667 to hundreds b. 23,441 to tens c. 175,445,980 to ten thousands
d. 59,561 all the way e. 14,657,000,138 to billions f. 8,009,070,436 to ten millions

CHECK YOUR ANSWERS WITH THE SOLUTIONS ON PAGE 26.

SECTION I Review Exercises

Read and write the following whole numbers in numerical and word form.

	Number	Numerical Form	Word Form
1.	22938	22,938	Twenty-two thousand, nine hundred thirty-eight
2.	1573	1,573	One thousand, five hundred seventy-three
3.	184	184	One hundred eighty-four
4.	984773	984,773	Nine hundred eighty-four thousand, seven hundred seventy-three
5.	2433590	2,433,590	Two million, four hundred thirty-three thousand, five hundred ninety
6.	49081472	49,081,472	Forty-nine million, eighty-one thousand, four hundred seventy-two

Write the following whole numbers in numerical form.

7. One hundred eighty-three thousand, six hundred twenty-two 183,622
8. Two million, forty-three thousand, twelve 2,043,012
9. One thousand, nine hundred thirty-six 1,936

Match the following numbers in word form with the numbers in numerical form.

10. One hundred two thousand, four hundred seventy b a. 11,270
11. One hundred twelve thousand, seven hundred forty-three d b. 102,470
12. Twelve thousand, seven hundred forty-three e c. 102,740
13. Eleven thousand, two hundred seventy a d. 112,743
14. One hundred two thousand, seven hundred forty c e. 12,743

Round the following numbers to the indicated place.

15. 1,757 to tens 1,760
16. 32,475 to thousands 32,000
17. 235,376 to hundreds 235,400

18. 559,443 to ten thousands 560,000
19. 8,488,710 to millions 8,000,000
20. 45,699 all the way 50,000
21. 1,325,669,226 to hundred millions 1,300,000,000
22. 23,755 all the way 20,000
23. 18,750,000,000 to billions 19,000,000,000
24. 860,002 to hundred thousands 900,000

BUSINESS DECISION UP OR DOWN?

25. You are responsible for writing a monthly stockholder's report about your company. Your boss has given you the flexibility to round the numbers to tens, hundreds, thousands, or not at all depending on which is the most beneficial for the company's image. For each of the following monthly figures, make a rounding choice and explain your reasoning:
    a. 75,469—number of items manufactured 100's; 75,500 Items
    b. $245,833—your department's net sales for the month 1000's; $246,000 Sales
    c. 5,648—defective items manufactured 100's; 5,600 Defects
    d. $649,341—total company profit 10,000's; $650,000 Profit
    e. 149 new customers 10's; 150 New customers

TEACHING TIP
Answers may vary. This is a good time to discuss how far numbers should be rounded in various situations.

ADDITION AND SUBTRACTION OF WHOLE NUMBERS

SECTION II 1

Addition and subtraction are the most basic mathematical operations. They are used in almost all business calculations. In business, amounts of things or dollars are often combined or added to determine the total. Likewise, subtraction is frequently used to determine an amount of something after it has been reduced in quantity.

Basic math proficiency without calculators is important. Calculators are not permitted on most employment tests and Civil Service exams.

ADDING WHOLE NUMBERS AND VERIFYING YOUR ANSWERS

1-2

Addition is the mathematical process of computing sets of numbers to find their sum, or total. The numbers being added are known as **addends**, and the result or answer of the addition is known as the **sum**, **total**, or **amount**. The "+" symbol represents addition and is called the **plus sign**.

1,932	addend
2,928	addend
+ 6,857	addend
11,717	total

addition The mathematical process of computing sets of numbers to find their sum or total.

addends Any of a set of numbers being added in an addition problem. For example, 4 and 1 are the addends of the addition problem 4 + 1 = 5.

STEPS FOR ADDING WHOLE NUMBERS

Step 1. Write the whole numbers in columns so that you line up the place values—units, tens, hundreds, thousands, and so on.

Step 2. Add the digits in each column, starting on the right with the units column.

Step 3. When the total in a column is greater than nine, write the units digit and carry the tens digit to the top of the next column to the left.

sum, total, or amount The result or answer of an addition problem. The number 5 is the sum or total of 4 + 1 = 5.

plus sign The symbol "+" representing addition.

Once you become proficient at verifying addition, you can speed up your addition by recognizing and combining two numbers that add up to 10, such as 1 + 9, 2 + 8, 6 + 4, 5 + 5, and so on. After you have mastered combining two numbers, try combining three numbers that add up to 10, such as 3 + 3 + 4, 2 + 5 + 3, 4 + 4 + 2, and so on.

Verifying Addition

Generally, when adding the digits in each column, we add from top to bottom. An easy and commonly used method of verifying your addition is to add the numbers again, but this time from bottom to top. By adding the digits in the *reverse* order, you will check your answer without making the same error twice.

For illustrative purposes, addition verification will be rewritten in reverse. In actuality, you do not have to rewrite the numbers; just add them from bottom to top. As mentioned earlier, speed and accuracy will be achieved with practice.

Addition	Verification
8	6
3	3
+ 6	+ 8
17	17

A Word about Word Problems

In business math, calculations are only a part of the story! Business math, most importantly, requires the ability to (a) understand and analyze the facts of business situations; (b) determine what information is given and what is missing; and (c) decide what strategy and procedure is required to solve for an answer. (d) Verify your answer. Business application word problems are an important part of each chapter's subject matter. As you progress through the course, your ability to analyze and solve these business situations will improve. Now, start slowly, and relax!

EXAMPLE 3 ADDING WHOLE NUMBERS

Add the following sets of whole numbers. Verify your answers by adding in reverse.

a.
```
  40,562
  29,381
+ 60,095
```

b. 2,293 + 121 + 7,706 + 20 + 57,293 + 4

c. Galaxy Industries, a furniture manufacturing company, has 229 employees in the design and cutting department, 439 employees in the assembly department, and 360 in the finishing department. There are 57 warehouse workers, 23 salespeople, 4 bookkeepers, 12 secretaries, and 5 executives. How many people work for this company?

SOLUTION STRATEGY

a.

```
   1 1 2
  40,562
  29,381
+ 60,095
 130,038

Verification:
   1 1 2
  60,095
  29,381
+ 40,562
 130,038
```

Step 1. Write the numbers in columns so that the place values line up. In this example they are already lined up.

Step 2. Add the digits in each column, starting with the units column.

<u>*Units column:*</u> 2 + 1 + 5 = 8 Enter the 8 under the units column.

<u>*Tens column:*</u> 6 + 8 + 9 = 23 Enter the 3 under the tens column and carry the 2 to the hundreds column.

<u>*Hundreds column:*</u> 2 + 5 + 3 + 0 = 10 Enter the 0 under the hundreds column and carry the 1 to the thousands column.

<u>*Thousands column:*</u> 1 + 0 + 9 + 0 = 10 Enter the 0 under the thousands column and carry the 1 to the ten thousands column.

<u>*Ten thousands column:*</u> 1 + 4 + 2 + 6 = 13 Enter the 3 under the ten thousands column and the 1 under the hundred thousands column.

b.

Addition	Verification
1 1 2 1	1 1 2 1
2,293	4
121	57,293
7,706	20
20	7,706
57,293	121
+ 4	+ 2,293
67,437	67,437

c.

Addition	Verification
2 3	2 3
229	5
439	12
360	4
57	23
23	57
4	360
12	439
+ 5	+ 229
1,129	1,129

TRY IT EXERCISE 3

Add the following sets of whole numbers and verify your answers.

a.
```
   39,481
    5,594
 + 11,029
```

b. 6,948 + 330 + 7,946 + 89 + 5,583,991 + 7 + 18,606

c. Anthony's Italian Restaurant served 183 meals on Monday, 228 meals on Tuesday, 281 meals on Wednesday, 545 meals on Thursday, and 438 meals on Friday. On the weekend they served 1,157 meals. How many total meals were served that week?

CHECK YOUR ANSWERS WITH THE SOLUTIONS ON PAGE 26.

SUBTRACTING WHOLE NUMBERS AND VERIFYING YOUR ANSWERS

1-3

Subtraction is the mathematical computation of taking away, or deducting, an amount from a given number. Subtraction is the opposite of addition. The original or top number is the **minuend**, the amount we are subtracting from the original number is the **subtrahend**, and the answer is the **remainder**, or **difference**. The "−" symbol represents subtraction and is called the **minus sign**.

```
  2,495  minuend
−   320  subtrahend
  2,175  difference
```

subtraction The mathematical process of taking away, or deducting, an amount from a given number.

minuend In subtraction, the original number. The amount from which another number, the subtrahend, is subtracted. For example, 5 is the minuend of the subtraction problem 5 − 1 = 4.

subtrahend The amount being taken or subtracted from the minuend. For example, 1 is the subtrahend of 5 − 1 = 4.

difference or remainder The number obtained when one number is subtracted from another. The answer or result of subtraction. For example, 4 is the difference or remainder of 5 − 1 = 4.

minus sign The symbol "−" representing subtraction.

STEPS FOR SUBTRACTING WHOLE NUMBERS

Step 1. Write the whole numbers in columns so that the place values line up.

Step 2. Starting with the units column, subtract the digits.

Step 3. When a column cannot be subtracted, you must "borrow" a digit from the column to the left of the one you are working in.

Verifying Subtraction

An easy and well-known method of verifying subtraction is to add the difference and the subtrahend. If you subtracted correctly, this total will equal the minuend.

Subtraction	Verification
200 minuend	150 difference
− 50 subtrahend	+ 50 subtrahend
150 difference	200 minuend

COLLOBORATIVE LEARNING ACTIVITY

In groups, have students formulate a strategy and complete this addition problem. Each letter represents a different digit.

```
  NUT
+ SUN
 NEAR
```

where U = 3 and T = 4

SOLUTION:

The strategy is to find the value of "N" first.

```
  134
+ 931
1,065
```

Learning Tip

Because each place value increases by a factor of 10 as we move from right to left (units, tens, hundreds, etc.), when we borrow a digit, we are actually borrowing a 10.

EXAMPLE 4 SUBTRACTING WHOLE NUMBERS

Subtract the following whole numbers and verify your answers.

a.
```
  4,968
−   192
```

b. 189,440 − 1,347

c. On Monday morning, Appliance Depot had 165 microwave ovens in inventory. During the week the store had a clearance sale and sold 71 of the ovens. How many ovens remain in stock for next week?

SOLUTION STRATEGY

a.
```
     8
  4,9̸68
−   192
  4,776
```

Verification:

```
     1
  4,776
+   192
  4,968
```

Write the numbers in columns so that the place values are lined up. In this problem they are already lined up.

Starting with the units column, subtract the digits.

Units column: 8 − 2 = 6. Enter the 6 under the units column.

Tens column: 6 − 9 can't be subtracted so we must borrow a digit, 10, from the hundreds column of the minuend. This reduces the 9 to an 8 and gives us a 10 to add to the 6, making it 16.

Now we can subtract 9 from 16 to get 7. Enter the 7 under the tens column.

Hundreds column: 8 − 1 = 7. Enter the 7 under the hundreds column.

Thousands column: This column has no subtrahend, so just bring down the 4 from the minuend to the answer line.

b. **Subtraction** / **Verification**

```
      3 3            11
  189,4̸4̸0      188,093
−   1,347    +   1,347
  188,093      189,440
```

c. **Subtraction** / **Verification**

```
   0          1
  1̸65        94
 − 71      + 71
   94       165
```

TRY IT EXERCISE 4

Subtract the following whole numbers and verify your answers.

a. 98,117
 −7,682

b. 12,395 − 5,589

c. Joe Montgomery has $4,589 in his checking account. If he writes a check for $344, how much will be left in the account?

CHECK YOUR ANSWERS WITH THE SOLUTIONS ON PAGE 27.

Review Exercises

SECTION II

Add the following numbers.

1. 45
 27
 + 19
 91

2. 548
 229
 4,600
 + 62,660
 68,037

3. 339
 1,236
 5,981
 3,597
 + 8,790
 19,943

4. 2,359
 8,511
 + 14,006
 24,876

5. 733
 401
 1,808
 24,111
 + 10,595
 37,648

6. 2,339 + 118 + 3,650 + 8,770 + 81 + 6 = 14,964

 2,339
 118
 3,650
 8,770
 81
 + 6
 14,964

7. 12,554 + 22,606 + 11,460 + 20,005 + 4,303 = 70,928

 12,554
 22,606
 11,460
 20,005
 + 4,303
 70,928

Estimate the following by rounding each number all the way, then add to find the exact answer.

		Estimate	Rounded Estimate	Exact Answer
8.	288	300	6,800	6,694
	512	500		
	3,950	4,000		
	+ 1,944	+ 2,000		
	6,694	6,800		
9.	38,599	40,000	43,100	41,844
	3,116	3,000		
	+ 129	+ 100		
	41,844	43,100		

		Estimate	**Rounded Estimate**	**Exact Answer**
10.	318,459	300,000	600,000	601,864
	+ 283,405	+ 300,000		
	601,864	600,000		

11. Stuffedanimals.com sold 2,594 stuffed animals in January; 2,478 in February; and 1,863 in March.

a. Round each number to the nearest hundred, and add to get an *estimate* of the production.

```
  2,600
  2,500
 +1,900
  7,000
```

b. What was the *exact* amount of production for the three-month period?

```
  2,594
  2,478
 +1,863
  6,935
```

12. While shopping, Tyler Hammond purchases items for $3, $24, $13, $2, and $175. How much did he spend?

```
     3
    24
    13
     2
 + 175
  $217   Total spent
```

© Tanya Constantine/Digital Vision/Getty Images

The Service Sector
According to the Bureau of Labor Statistics, service sector businesses, such as dry cleaners, account for 50% of the U.S. economy. Other sectors include: manufacturing, 18%; retailing, 17%; and government, 15%. Between 2000 and 2014, the service sector is projected to grow by almost 19 million new jobs.

13. The following chart shows the output of Royal Cleaners for last week. Total each column to get the *daily totals*. Total each row to get the *total items* per clothing category. What is the week's *grand total*?

Royal Cleaners

	Monday	Tuesday	Wednesday	Thursday	Friday	Total Items
Shirts	342	125	332	227	172	1,198
Pants	298	267	111	198	97	971
Suits	66	85	121	207	142	621
Dresses	98	48	79	118	103	446
Daily Totals	804	525	643	750	514	**Grand Total** 3,236

14. At Green Acres Farm, a farmer plants 350 acres of soybeans, 288 acres of corn, 590 acres of wheat, and 43 acres of assorted vegetables. In addition, the farm has 9 acres for grazing and 4 acres for the barnyard and farmhouse. What is the total acreage of the farm?

```
   350
   288
   590
    43
     9
 +   4
 1,284   Total acres
```

15. Rainbow Cosmetics pays its sales staff a salary of $575 per month, plus commissions. Last month Kelly Holiday earned commissions of $129, $216, $126, $353, and $228. What was Kelly's total income for the month?

    575
    129
    216
    126
    353
    + 228
    $1,627 Total income

Subtract the following numbers.

16. 354 − 48 = 306
17. 5,596 − 967 = 4,629
18. 95,490 − 73,500 = 21,990
19. 339,002 − 60,911 = 278,091
20. 2,000,077 − 87,801 = 1,912,276

21. $185 minus $47

    185
    − 47
    $138

22. 67,800 − 9,835

    67,800
    − 9,835
    57,965

23. $308 less $169

    308
    − 169
    $139

24. Subtract 264 from 1,893

    1,893
    − 264
    1,629

25. Subtract 8,906,000 from 12,396,700

    12,396,700
    − 8,906,000
    3,490,700

26. The U.S. Postal Service delivers billions of pieces of mail each year. Use the graph to answer the following questions.

    a. How many pieces were delivered in 2005 and 2006 combined?

    212
    + 213
    425 Billion

    b. How many more pieces were delivered in 2006 than in 2004?

    213
    −206
    7 Billion

    c. Write the number of pieces of mail for 2003 in numerical form?

    202,000,000,000

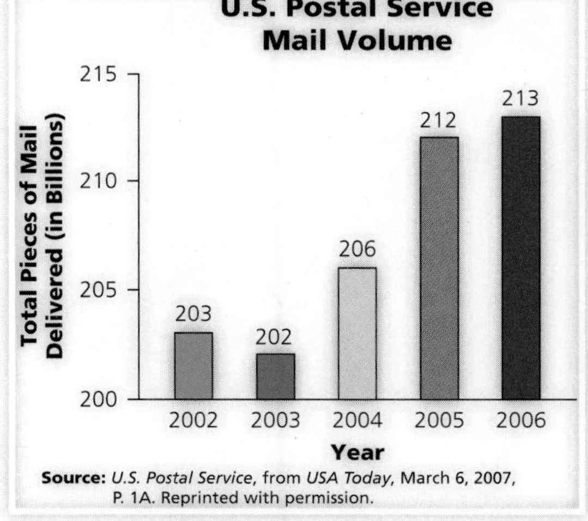

Source: *U.S. Postal Service*, from *USA Today*, March 6, 2007, P. 1A. Reprinted with permission.

27. Michele Clayton is planting her flower beds. She initially bought 72 bedding plants at Home Depot.

    a. If she plants 29 in the front bed, how many plants remain unplanted?

    72
    −29
    43 Plants

    b. Michele's remaining flower beds have room for 65 bedding plants. How many more plants must she buy to fill up the flower beds?

    65
    −43
    22 Plants

    c. How many total plants did she buy?

    72
    +22
    94 Plants

28. The beginning inventory of the European Shoe Salon for August was 850 pairs of shoes. On the 9th, they received a shipment from the factory of 297 pairs. On the 23rd, another shipment of 188 pairs arrived. When inventory was taken at the end of the month, there were 754 pairs left. How many pairs of shoes were sold that month?

850	Beginning inventory
297	Purchases
+ 188	Purchases
1,335	Total inventory

1,335	Total inventory
− 754	Ending inventory
581	Pairs sold

29. An electrician starts the day with 650 feet of wire on his truck. In the morning he cuts off pieces 26, 78, 45, and 89 feet long. During lunch he goes to an electrical supply warehouse and buys another 250 feet of wire. In the afternoon he uses lengths of 75, 89, and 120 feet. How many feet of wire are still on the truck at the end of the day?

26
78
45
+ 89
238 Morning feet used

650
− 238
412 Morning feet left

412
+ 250
662 Afternoon start

75
89
+ 120
284 Afternoon feet used

662
− 284
378 Feet left end of day

30. A moving company's truck picks up loads of furniture weighing 5,500 pounds, 12,495 pounds, and 14,562 pounds. The truck weighs 11,480 pounds and the driver weighs 188 pounds. If a bridge has a weight limit of 42,500 pounds, is the truck within the weight limit to cross the bridge?

5,500
12,495
14,562
11,480
+ 188
44,225 Pounds total weight

44,225
− 42,500
1,725 Pounds over weight limit

No, the truck is overweight

BUSINESS DECISION PERSONAL BALANCE SHEET

31. A personal *balance sheet* is the financial picture of how much "wealth" you have accumulated, as of a certain date. It specifically lists your *assets* (i.e., what you own) and your *liabilities* (i.e., what you owe.) Your current *net worth* is the difference between the assets and the liabilities.

Net worth = Assets − Liabilities

Randy and Christine Simpson have asked for your help in preparing a personal balance sheet. They have listed the following assets and liabilities: current value of home, $144,000; audio/video equipment, $1,340; automobiles, $17,500; personal property, $4,350; computer, $3,700; mutual funds, $26,700; 401k retirement plan, $53,680; jewelry, $4,800; certificates of deposit, $19,300; stock investments, $24,280; furniture and other household goods, $8,600; Wal-Mart and Sears charge accounts balance, $4,868; automobile loan balance, $8,840; home mortgage balance, $106,770; Visa and MasterCard balances, $4,211; savings account balance, $3,700; Christine's night school tuition loan balance, $2,750; checking account balance, $1,385; signature loan balance, $6,350.

Use the data provided and the personal balance sheet that follows to calculate the following for the Simpsons.

a. Total assets $313,335

b. Total liabilities $133,789

c. Net worth $179,546

d. Explain the importance of the personal balance sheet. How often should this information be updated?
Monthly—or at least quarterly; answers will vary.

PERSONAL BALANCE SHEET

ASSETS			**LIABILITIES**		
CURRENT ASSETS			**CURRENT LIABILITIES**		
Checking account	1,385		Store charge accounts	4,868	
Savings account	3,700		Credit card accounts	4,211	
Certificates of deposit	19,300		Other current debt		
Other			**Total Current Liabilities**		9,079
Total Current Assets		24,385	**LONG-TERM LIABILITIES**		
LONG-TERM ASSETS			Home mortgage	106,770	
Investments			Automobile loan	8,840	
Retirement plans	53,680		Education loan	2,750	
Stocks	24,280		Other loan	6,350	
Bonds			Other loan		
Mutual funds	26,700		**Total Long-Term Liabilities**		124,710
Other			**TOTAL LIABILITIES**		$133,789
Personal					
Home	144,000				
Automobiles	17,500				
Furniture	8,600				
Personal property	4,350				
Jewelry	4,800		**NET WORTH**		
Other	1,340				
Other	3,700		**Total Assets**	313,335	
Total Long-Term Assets		288,950	**Total Liabilities**	−133,789	
TOTAL ASSETS		$313,335	**NET WORTH**		$179,546

© Digital Vision/Getty Images

Just as with corporate statements, **personal financial statements** are an important indicator of your financial position. The balance sheet, income statement, and cash flow statement are the most commonly used. When compared over a period of time, they tell a story of where you have been, and where you are going, financially.

MULTIPLICATION AND DIVISION OF WHOLE NUMBERS

SECTION III 1

Multiplication and division are the next two mathematical procedures used with whole numbers. Both are found in business as often as addition and subtraction. In reality, most business problems involve a combination of procedures. For example, invoices, which are a detailed list of goods and services sold by a company, require multiplication of items by the price per item, and then addition to reach a total. From the total, discounts are frequently subtracted, or transportation charges added.

MULTIPLYING WHOLE NUMBERS AND VERIFYING YOUR ANSWERS

Multiplication of whole numbers is actually a shortcut method for addition. Let's see how this works. If a clothing store buys 12 pairs of jeans at $29 per pair, what is the total cost of the jeans? One way to solve this problem is to add $29 + $29 + . . . , 12 times. It's not hard to see how tedious this repeated addition becomes, especially with large numbers. By using multiplication, we get the answer in one step: 12 × 29 = 348.

multiplication The combination of two numbers in which the number of times one is represented is determined by the value of the other.

multiplicand In multiplication, the number being multiplied. For example, 5 is the multiplicand of 5 × 4 = 20.

multiplier The number by which the multiplicand is multiplied. For example, 4 is the multiplier of 5 × 4 = 20.

product The answer or result of multiplication. The number 20 is the product of 5 × 4 = 20.

times sign The symbol "×" representing multiplication. Also represented by a dot "·" or parentheses "( )".

Multiplication is the combination of two whole numbers in which the number of times one is represented is determined by the value of the other. These two whole numbers are known as factors. The number being multiplied is the **multiplicand**, and the number by which the multiplicand is multiplied is the **multiplier**. The answer to a multiplication problem is the **product**. Intermediate answers are called partial products.

258	multiplicand or factor
× 43	multiplier or factor
774	partial product 1
10 32	partial product 2
11,094	product

In mathematics, the **times sign**—represented by the symbols "×" and "·" and "( )"—is used to indicate multiplication. For example, 12 times 18 can be expressed as

12 × 18 12 · 18 (12)(18) 12(18)

Note: The symbol · is *not* a decimal point.

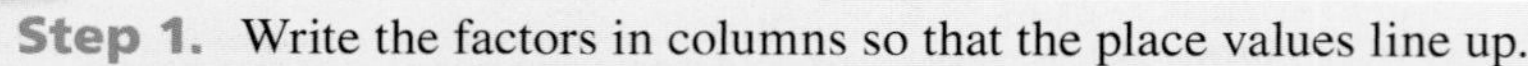

STEPS FOR MULTIPLYING WHOLE NUMBERS

Step 1. Write the factors in columns so that the place values line up.

Step 2. Multiply each digit of the multiplier, starting with units, times the multiplicand. Each will yield a partial product whose units digit appears under the corresponding digit of the multiplier.

Step 3. Add the digits in each column of the partial products, starting on the right with the units column.

Teaching Transparency 1-4

Learning Tip

In multiplication, the factors are interchangeable. For example, 15 times 5 gives the same product as 5 times 15.

Multiplication is usually expressed with the larger factor on top as the multiplicand and the smaller factor placed under it as the multiplier.

Multiplication Shortcuts

The following shortcuts can be used to make multiplication easier and faster.

1. **When multiplying any number times zero,** the resulting product is *always* zero. For example,

   573 × 0 = 0 0 × 34 = 0 1,254,779 × 0 = 0

2. **When multiplying a number times one, the product is that number itself.** For example,

   1,844 × 1 = 1,844 500 × 1 = 500 1 × 894 = 894

3. **When a number is multiplied by 10, 100, 1,000, 10,000, 100,000, and so on,** simply add the zeros of the multiplier to the end of that number. For example,

   792 × 100 = 792 + 00 = 79,200 9,345 × 1,000 = 9,345 + 000 = 9,345,000

Teaching Transparency 1-5

4. **When the multiplier has a 0 in one or more of its middle digits,** there is no need to write a whole line of zeros as a partial product. Simply place a 0 in the next partial

product row, directly below the 0 in the multiplier, and go on to the next digit in the multiplier. The next partial product will start on the same row, one place to the left of the 0, and directly below its corresponding digit in the multiplier. For example, consider 554 times 103.

Shortcut:		*Long way:*	
	554		554
	× 103		× 103
	1 662		1 662
	55 40		0 00
	57,062		55 4
			57,062

5. **When the multiplicand and/or the multiplier have zeros at the end,** multiply the two numbers without the zeros, and then add that number of zeros to the product. For example,

130 × 90 = 13
× 9
117 + 00 = 11,700

5,800 × 3,400 = 58
× 34
232
1 74
1,972 + 0000 = 19,720,000

Verifying Multiplication

To check your multiplication for accuracy, divide the product by the multiplier. If the multiplication was correct, this will yield the multiplicand. For example,

Multiplication	Verification	Multiplication	Verification
48		527	
× 7		× 18	
336	336 ÷ 7 = 48	4 216	
		5 27	
		9,486	9,486 ÷ 18 = 527

EXAMPLE 5 MULTIPLYING WHOLE NUMBERS

Multiply the following numbers and verify your answers by division.

a. 2,293 × 45   b. 59,300 × 180   c. 436 × 2,027   d. 877 × 1   e. 6,922 × 0

f. Ransford Industries has a new aluminum parts molding machine which produces 85 parts per minute. How many parts can this machine produce in an hour? If a company has 15 of these machines and they run for 8 hours per day, what is the total output of parts per day?

SOLUTION STRATEGY

a.
2,293
× 45
11 465
91 72
103,185

This is a standard multiplication problem with two partial products. Always be sure to keep your columns lined up. The answer, 103,185, can be verified by division: 103,185 ÷ 45 = 2,293

b.
```
      593
   ×   18
    4 744
    5 93
   10,674 + 000 = 10,674,000
```
In this problem we remove the three zeros, multiply, and then add back the zeros.
Verification: 10,674 ÷ 18 = 593

c.
```
    2,027
   ×  436
   12 162
   60 81
  810 8
  883,772
```
This is another standard multiplication problem. Note that the larger number was made the multiplicand (top), and the smaller number became the multiplier. This makes the problem easier to work.
Verification: 883,772 ÷ 436 = 2,027

d. 877 × 1 = 877 — Remember, any number multiplied by 1 is that number.

e. 6,922 × 0 = 0 — Remember, any number multiplied by 0 is 0.

f. 85 parts per minute × 60 minutes per hour = 5,100 parts per hour
5,100 parts per hour × 15 machines = 76,500 parts per hour, all machines
76,500 parts per hour × 8 hours per day = 612,000 parts per day, total output

TRY IT EXERCISE 5

Multiply the following numbers and verify your answers.

a.
```
   8,203
 ×   508
```
b.
```
   5,400
 ×   250
```
c.
```
   3,370
 × 4,002
```
d. 189 × 169

e. Dave Peterson, a plasterer, can finish 150 square feet of interior wall per hour. If he works 6 hours per day
- How many square feet can he finish per day?
- If a contractor hires four plasterers, how many feet can they finish in a 5-day week?

CHECK YOUR ANSWERS WITH THE SOLUTIONS ON PAGE 27.

1-6 DIVIDING WHOLE NUMBERS AND VERIFYING YOUR ANSWERS

1-6

division The mathematical process of determining how many times one number is contained within another number.

dividend In division, the quantity being divided. For example, 20 is the dividend of 20 ÷ 5 = 4.

divisor The quantity by which another quantity, the dividend, is being divided. The number doing the dividing. For example, 5 is the divisor of 20 ÷ 5 = 4.

quotient The answer or result of division. The number 4 is the quotient of 20 ÷ 5 = 4.

Just as multiplication is a shortcut for repeated addition, division is a shortcut for repeated subtraction. Let's say while shopping you want to know how many $5 items you can purchase with $45. You could get the answer by finding out how many times 5 can be subtracted from 45. You would begin by subtracting 5 from 45 to get 40; then subtracting 5 from 40 to get 35; 5 from 35 to get 30; and so on, until you got to 0. Quite tedious, but it does give you the answer, 9. By using division, we simply ask, how many $5 are contained in $45? By dividing 45 by 5 we get the answer in one step (45 ÷ 5 = 9). Because division is the opposite of multiplication, we can verify our answer by multiplying 5 times 9 to get 45.

Division of whole numbers is the process of determining how many times one number is contained within another number. The number being divided is called the **dividend**, the number doing the dividing is called the **divisor**, and the answer is known as the **quotient**. When the divisor has only one digit, as in 100 divided by 5, it is called short division. When the divisor has more than one digit, as in 100 divided by 10, it is known as long division.

The "÷" symbol represents division and is known as the **division sign**. For example, 12 ÷ 4 is read "12 divided by 4." Another way to show division is

$$\frac{12}{4}$$

This is also read as "12 divided by 4." To actually solve the division, we use the sign $\overline{)\quad}$. The problem is then written as $4\overline{)12}$. As in addition, subtraction, and multiplication, proper alignment of the digits is very important.

$$\frac{\text{Divided}}{\text{Divisor}} = \text{Quotient} \qquad \begin{array}{r}\text{Quotient}\\ \text{Divisor}\overline{)\text{Dividend}}\end{array}$$

When the divisor divides evenly into the dividend, it is known as even division. When the divisor does not divide evenly into the dividend, the answer then becomes a quotient plus a **remainder**. The remainder is the amount left over after the division is completed. This is known as uneven division. In this chapter, a remainder of 3, for example, will be expressed as R 3. In Chapter 2, remainders will be expressed as fractions, and in Chapter 3, remainders will be expressed as decimals.

division sign The symbol "÷" representing division.

remainder In uneven division, the amount left over after the division is completed. For example, 2 is the remainder of 22 ÷ 5 = 4, R 2.

Verifying Division

To verify even division, multiply the quotient by the divisor. If the problem was worked correctly, this will yield the dividend. To verify uneven division, multiply the quotient by the divisor, and add the remainder to the product. If the problem was worked correctly, this will yield the dividend.

Even Division Illustrated

$$\frac{850 \text{ (dividend)}}{25 \text{ (divisor)}} = 34 \text{ (quotient)}$$

$$\begin{array}{r} 34\\ 25\overline{)850}\\ \underline{75}\downarrow\\ 100\\ \underline{100}\\ 0 \end{array}$$

Verification: 34 × 25 = 850

Uneven Division Illustrated

$$\frac{850 \text{ (dividend)}}{20 \text{ (divisor)}} = 42 \text{ R } 10 \text{ (quotient)}$$

$$\begin{array}{r} 42 \text{ R } 10\\ 20\overline{)850}\\ \underline{80}\downarrow\\ 50\\ \underline{40}\\ 10 \end{array}$$

Verification: 42 × 20 = 840
+ 10
850

Division Shortcut

When both the dividend and the divisor end in one or more zeros, you can remove an *equal* number of zeros from each and then divide. This gives the same answer with much less work. For example, 7,000 divided by 200 is the same as 70 divided by 2. *Note:* Although 7,000 has three zeros, you can't remove three zeros, because 200 has only two zeros.

$$\frac{70\not{0}\not{0}}{2\not{0}\not{0}} = 35 \qquad \frac{70}{2} = 35$$

CLASSROOM ACTIVITY

Have students practice the division shortcut with this example:

Last year the U.S. Postal Service delivered 213 billion pieces of mail. If there are 125 million households in the country, on the average, how many pieces were delivered to each house?

SOLUTION:

Hint: Drop six zeros from each number.

$$\frac{213{,}000{,}000{,}000}{125{,}000{,}000} = \frac{213{,}000}{125}$$
$$= 1{,}704 \text{ pieces of mail}$$

1-7

STEPS FOR DIVIDING WHOLE NUMBERS

Step 1. Determine the first group of digits in the dividend that the divisor will divide into at least once. Divide, and place the partial quotient over the last digit in that group.

Step 2. Multiply the partial quotient by the divisor. Place it under the first group of digits and subtract.

Step 3. From the dividend, bring down the next digit after the first group of digits.

Step 4. Repeat Steps 1, 2, and 3 until all of the digits in the dividend have been brought down.

EXAMPLE 6 DIVIDING WHOLE NUMBERS

Divide the following numbers and verify your answers.

a. $210 \div 7$ b. $185 \div 9$ c. $\frac{1,508}{6}$ d. $\frac{14,000}{3,500}$

e. On an assembly line, a packing machine uses rolls of rope containing 650 feet. How many 8-foot pieces can be cut from each roll?

SOLUTION STRATEGY

a.

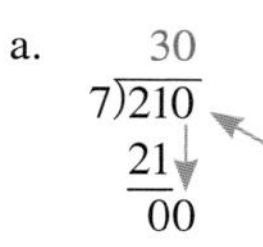

```
   30
7)210
  21
   00
```

This is an example of even division. Note that there is no remainder.

Verification: $30 \times 7 = 210$

b.

```
   20 R 5
9)185
  18
    5
```

This example illustrates uneven division. Note that there is a remainder.

Verification: $20 \times 9 = 180$
$+\ 5$
185

c.

```
   251 R 2
6)1508
  12
   30
   30
    08
     6
     2
```

This is another example of uneven divison. Be sure to keep the digits properly lined up.

Verification: $251 \times 6 = 1,506$
$+\quad 2$
$1,508$

d.

```
     4
35)140
   140
     0
```

In this example, we simplify the division by deleting two zeros from the dividend and the divisor.

Verification: $4 \times 35 = 140$

e.

```
   81 R 2
8)650
  64
   10
    8
    2
```

In this word problem, we want to know how many 8-foot pieces of rope are contained in a 650-foot roll. The dividend is 650 and the divisor is 8. The quotient, 81 R 2, means that 81 whole pieces of rope can be cut from the roll, with some left over, but not enough for another whole piece.

Verification: $81 \times 8 = 648$
$+ 2$
650

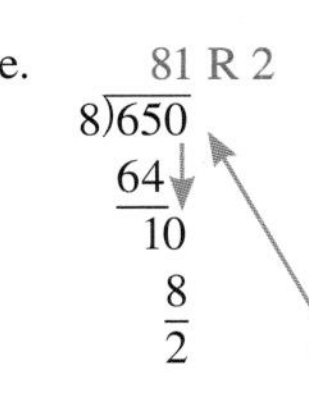

TRY IT EXERCISE 6

Divide the following numbers and verify your answers.

a. $910 \div 35$ b. $1{,}503 \div 160$ c. $\frac{3{,}358}{196}$ d. $\frac{175{,}000}{12{,}000}$

e. Fortune Industries has 39 production line workers, each making the same amount of money. If last week's total payroll amounted to \$18,330, how much did each employee earn?

CHECK YOUR ANSWERS WITH THE SOLUTIONS ON PAGE 27.

Review Exercises

Multiply the following numbers and verify your answers.

1. $589 \times 19 = 11{,}191$
2. $1{,}292 \times 158 = 204{,}136$
3. $327 \times 900 = 294{,}300$
4. $76{,}000 \times 45 = 3{,}420{,}000$
5. $56{,}969 \times 1{,}000 = 56{,}969{,}000$
6. Multiply \$4 by 501
   $501 \times 4 = \$2{,}004$
7. 23×570
   $570 \times 23 = 13{,}110$
8. What is 475 times 12?
   $475 \times 12 = 5{,}700$

Estimate the following by rounding each number all the way, then multiply to get the exact answer.

		Estimate	Rounded Estimate	Exact Answer
9.	$202 \times 490 = 98{,}980$	$200 \times 500 = 100{,}000$	100,000	98,980
10.	$515 \times 180 = 92{,}700$	$500 \times 200 = 100{,}000$	100,000	92,700
11.	$17 \times 11 = 187$	$20 \times 10 = 200$	200	187

12. Dazzling Designs made custom drapery for a client using 30 yards of material.
    a. At $5 per yard, what is that cost of the material?

    $30 \times 5 = \$150$

    b. If the company received 4 more orders of the same size, how much material will be needed to fill the orders?

    $30 \times 4 = 120$ Yards

13. For traffic engineering purposes, the **traffic load** is the number of vehicles passing a point in 12 hours. If a particular intersection averages 1,080 vehicles an hour, what is its traffic load?

    $1{,}080 \times 12 = 12{,}960$

14. To earn extra money while attending college, you work as a cashier in a restaurant.
    a. Find the total bill for the following food order: three sirloin steak dinners at $12 each; two baked chicken specials at $7 each; four steak burger platters at $5 each; two extra salads at $2 each; six drinks at $1 each; and tax of $7.

Steaks	$3 \times 12 =$	36
Chicken	$2 \times 7 =$	14
Burgers	$4 \times 5 =$	20
Salads	$2 \times 2 =$	4
Drinks	$6 \times 1 =$	6
Tax		+ 7
		$87 Total

    b. How much change will you give back if the check is paid with a $100 bill?

    $100 - 87 = \$13$ Change

15. A consulting electrical engineer is offered two different jobs. Abbott Industries has a project that pays $52 per hour and will take 35 hours to complete. Micro Systems has a project that pays $44 per hour and will take 45 hours to complete. Which offer has a greater gross income and by how much?

    Abbott Industries: $52 × 35 hours = $1,820
    Micro Systems: $44 × 45 hours = $1,980
    1,980 − 1,820 = $160
    The Micro Systems project has the greater income by $160.

Divide the following numbers.

16. 4,500 ÷ 35

    128 R 20
    35)4500
    35
    100
    70
    300
    280
    20

17. 74,77Ø ÷ 5,7ØØ

    13 R 67
    570)7477
    570
    1777
    1710
    67

18. $\frac{60{,}0\text{Ø}\text{Ø}}{25\text{Ø}}$

    240
    25)6000
    50
    100
    100
    00

19. $\frac{236{,}5\text{ØØ},\text{ØØØ}}{4{,}3\text{ØØ},\text{ØØØ}}$

    55
    43)2365
    215
    215
    215
    0

Estimate the following by rounding each number to hundreds, and then divide to get the exact answer.

	Estimate	Rounded Estimate	Exact Answer
20. 890 ÷ 295	$\frac{900}{300}$	3	3 R 5
21. 1,499 ÷ 580	$\frac{1,500}{600}$	2 R 300	2 R 339
22. 57,800 ÷ 102	$\frac{57,800}{100}$	578	566 R 68

23. Ace Roofing has 50,640 square feet of roofing material on hand. If the average roof requires 8,440 square feet of material, how many roofs can be installed?

$\frac{50,640}{8,440} = 6$ Roofs

24. A calculator uses eight circuit boards, each containing 450 parts. A company has 421,215 parts in stock.
   a. How many calculators can it manufacture?

450
× 8
3,600 Parts per calculator

$\frac{421.215}{3,600} = 117 \text{ R } 15$

117 Calculators

   b. How many parts will be left?

15 Parts left

25. Howard Silver borrows $24,600 from the Hamilton Bank and Trust Co. The interest charge amounts to $8,664. What equal monthly payments must Howard make in order to pay back the loan, with interest, in 36 months?

24,600
+ 8,664
$33,264 Total payback

$\frac{33,264}{36} = \$924$ Per month

26. A 16-person college basketball team is going to a tournament in Boston. As the team manager, you are trying to find the best price for hotel rooms. The Empire Hotel is quoting a price of $108 for 2 people in a room and $10 for each extra person. The Liberty Hotel is quoting a price of $94 for 2 people in a room and $15 for each extra person. If the maximum number of people allowed in a room is 4, which hotel would be more economical?

Rooms needed: $\frac{16}{4} = 4$ rooms
Empire Hotel $108 room rate + 2 extra people @ $10 each = $128 per room
4 rooms × $128 per room = $512
Liberty Hotel: $94 room rate + 2 extra people @ $15 each = $124 per room
4 rooms × $124 per room = $496
The Liberty Hotel is more economical.

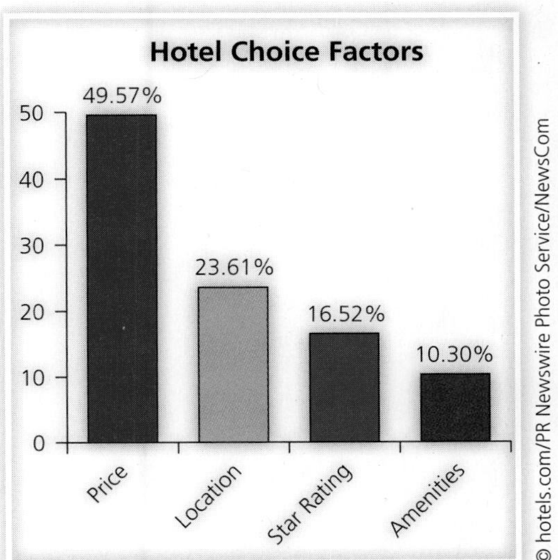

Hotels.com Survey: When selecting a hotel, what do you consider most important?

27. You have just purchased a 65-acre ranch for a price of $780 per acre. In addition, the house was valued at $125,000 and the equipment amounted to $22,300.
   a. What was the total price of your purchase?

65 × 780 = 50,700 Land
125,000 House
22,300 Equipment
$198,000 Total price

   b. Since the owner was anxious to sell, he offered to finance the ranch for you with a no-interest mortgage loan. What would your monthly payments be to pay off the loan in 10 years?

$\frac{198,000}{120} = \$1,650$ Monthly payment

c. Besides the mortgage payment, you are required to make monthly property tax and insurance payments. If property tax is $3,000 per year and insurance is $2,400 per year, how much would these items add to your monthly expenses for the ranch?

$\frac{3{,}000 + 2{,}400}{12} = \$450$ Additional expense

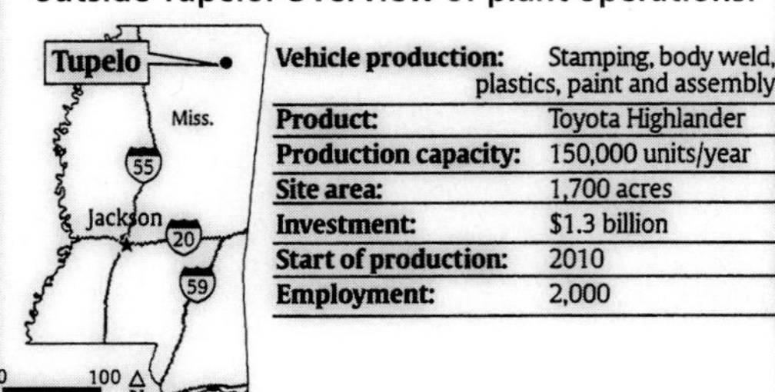

Toyota will open its eighth North American vehicle assembly plant in Blue Springs, Miss., outside Tupelo. Overview of plant operations:

Vehicle production:	Stamping, body weld, plastics, paint and assembly
Product:	Toyota Highlander
Production capacity:	150,000 units/year
Site area:	1,700 acres
Investment:	$1.3 billion
Start of production:	2010
Employment:	2,000

Source: *USA Today*, February 28, 2007. Reprinted with permission.

28. Toyota's new manufacturing plant near Tupelo, Mississippi, will produce 150,000 Highlander crossover utility vehicles per year.

a. On average, how many Highlanders will the plant produce each month?

$\frac{150{,}000}{12} = 12{,}500$

b. Toyota reports that the 2,000 employees will be paid an average $20 per hour after 3 years on the job, not counting benefits. How much will this payroll rate cost the company per hour?

$$\begin{array}{r} 2{,}000 \\ \times \quad 20 \\ \hline \$40{,}000 \end{array}$$

c. Express your answer from part b. in words.

forty thousand dollars

BUSINESS DECISION ESTIMATING A TILE JOB

29. You are the owner of The Tile Mart. Todd and Claudia have asked you to give them an estimate for tiling four rooms of their house. The living room is 15 feet × 23 feet; the dining room is 12 feet × 18 feet; the kitchen is 9 feet × 11 feet; and the study is 10 feet × 12 feet.

a. How many square feet of tile are required for each room? (Multiply the length by the width.)

Living Room	Dining Room	Kitchen	Study
23	18	11	12
× 15	× 12	× 9	× 10
345 sq ft	216 sq ft	99 sq ft	120 sq ft

b. What is the total number of square feet to be tiled?

$$\begin{array}{r} 345 \\ 216 \\ 99 \\ +\ 120 \\ \hline 780 \end{array}$$ Total sq ft

c. If the tile for the kitchen and study costs $4 per square foot, and the tile for the living and dining rooms costs $3 per square foot, what is the total cost of the tile?

99	Kitchen	345	Living Room	876	
+ 120	Study	+ 216	Dining Room	+ 1,683	
219	sq ft	561	sq ft	$2,559	Total cost of tile
× 4	Price	× 3	Price		
$876		$1,683			

d. If your company charges $2 per square foot for installation, what is the total cost of the tile job?

780	sq ft	1,560	
× 2	Price	+ 2,559	
$1,560	Installation charge	$4,119	Total cost of job

e. If Todd and Claudia have saved $4,500 for the tile job, by how much are they over or under the amount needed?

4,500	Saved
− 4,119	Cost
$381	Over amount needed

CHAPTER SUMMARY

1

Section I: The Decimal Number System: Whole Numbers

Topic	Important Concepts	Illustrative Examples
Reading and Writing Whole Numbers in Numerical and Word Form **Performance Objective (P/O) 1-1, p. 2**	1. Insert the commas every three digits to mark the groups, beginning at the right side of the number. 2. From left to right, name the places and the groups. Groups that have all zeros are not named. 3. When writing whole numbers in word form, the numbers from 21 to 99 are hyphenated. *Note:* The word *and* should not be used in reading or writing whole numbers.	Write each number in numerical and word form. The number 15538 takes on the numerical form 15,538 and is read, "fifteen thousand, five hundred thirty-eight." The number 22939643 takes on the numerical form 22,939,643 and is read, "twenty-two million, nine hundred thirty-nine thousand, six hundred forty-three." The number 1000022 takes on the numerical value 1,000,022 and is read, "one million, twenty-two."
Rounding Whole Numbers to a Specified Place Value **P/O 1-2, p. 4**	1. Determine the place to which the number is to be rounded. 2a. If the digit to the right of the one being rounded is 5 or more, increase the digit in the place being rounded by 1. 2b. If the digit to the right of the one being rounded is 4 or less, do not change the digit in the place being rounded. 3. Change all digits to the right of the place being rounded to zeros.	Round as indicated. 1,449 to tens = 1,450 255 to hundreds = 300 345,391 to thousands = 345,000 68,658,200 to millions = 69,000,000 768,892 all the way = 800,000

Section II: Addition and Subtraction of Whole Numbers

Topic	Important Concepts	Illustrative Examples
Adding Whole Numbers and Verifying Your Answers **P/O 1-3, p. 7**	1. Write the whole numbers in columns so that the place values line up. 2. Add the digits in each column, starting on the right with the units column. 3. When the total in a column is greater than 9, write the units digit and carry the tens digit to the top of the next column to the left. To verify addition, add the numbers in reverse, from bottom to top.	Add 2 11 1,931 addend 2,928 addend + 5,857 addend 10,716 sum Verification: 2 11 5,857 2,928 + 1,931 10,716
Subtracting Whole Numbers and Verifying Your Answers **P/O 1-4, p. 9**	1. Write the whole numbers in columns so that the place values line up. 2. Starting with the units column, subtract the digits. 3. When a column cannot be subtracted, borrow a digit from the column to the left of the one you are working in. To verify subtraction, add the difference and the subtrahend; this should equal the minuend.	Subtract 34,557 minuend − 6,224 subtrahend 28,333 difference Verification: 28,333 + 6,224 34,557

Section III: Multiplication and Division of Whole Numbers

Topic	Important Concepts	Illustrative Examples
Multiplying Whole Numbers and Verifying Your Answers **P/O 1-5, p. 16**	1. Write the multiplication factors in columns so that the place values are lined up. 2. Multiply each digit of the multiplier, starting with units, times the multiplicand. Each will yield a partial product whose units digit appears under the corresponding digit of the multiplier. 3. Add the digits in each column of the partial products, starting on the right, with the units column. To verify multiplication, divide the product by the multiplier. If the multiplication is correct, it should yield the multiplicand.	Multiply 258 × 43 258 multiplicand or factor × 43 multiplier or factor 774 partial product 1 10 32 partial product 2 11,094 product Verification: $\frac{11,094}{43} = 258$
Dividing Whole Numbers and Verifying Your Answers **P/O 1-6, p. 18**	1. The number being divided is the dividend. The number by which we are dividing is the divisor. The answer is known as the quotient. Divisor) Dividend = Quotient 2. If the divisor does not divide evenly into the dividend, the quotient will have a remainder. To verify division, multiply the divisor by the quotient and add the remainder. If the division is correct, it will yield the dividend.	Divide six hundred fifty by twenty-seven. $650 \div 27 = \frac{650}{27} =$ 27) 650 = 24 R 2 54 110 108 2 Verification: 27 × 24 = 648 + 2 = 650

TRY IT EXERCISE SOLUTIONS FOR CHAPTER 1

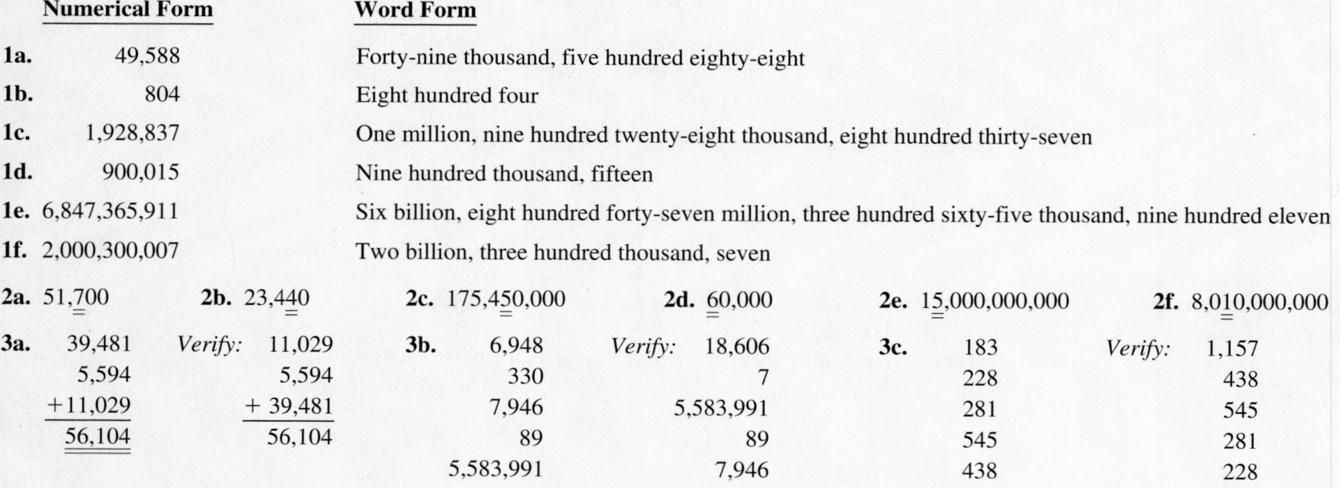

	Numerical Form	Word Form
1a.	49,588	Forty-nine thousand, five hundred eighty-eight
1b.	804	Eight hundred four
1c.	1,928,837	One million, nine hundred twenty-eight thousand, eight hundred thirty-seven
1d.	900,015	Nine hundred thousand, fifteen
1e.	6,847,365,911	Six billion, eight hundred forty-seven million, three hundred sixty-five thousand, nine hundred eleven
1f.	2,000,300,007	Two billion, three hundred thousand, seven

2a. 51,700 **2b.** 23,440 **2c.** 175,450,000 **2d.** 60,000 **2e.** 15,000,000,000 **2f.** 8,010,000,000

3a. 39,481 + 5,594 + 11,029 = 56,104
Verify: 11,029 + 5,594 + 39,481 = 56,104

3b. 6,948 + 330 + 7,946 + 89 + 5,583,991 + 7 + 18,606 = 5,617,917
Verify: 18,606 + 7 + 5,583,991 + 89 + 7,946 + 330 + 6,948 = 5,617,917

3c. 183 + 228 + 281 + 545 + 438 + 1,157 = 2,832 meals
Verify: 1,157 + 438 + 545 + 281 + 228 + 183 = 2,832 meals

4a. 98,117
− 7,682
90,435

Verify: 90,435
+ 7,682
98,117

4b. 12,395
− 5,589
6,806

Verify: 6,806
+ 5,589
12,395

4c. $4,589
− 344
$4,245 left in account

Verify: $4,245
+ 344
$4,589

5a. 8,203
× 508
65 624
4 101 50
4,167,124

Verify:
$\frac{4,167,124}{508} = 8,203$

5b. 5,400
× 250
270 000
1 080 00
1,350,000

Verify:
$\frac{1,350,000}{250} = 5,400$

5c. 3,370
× 4,002
6 740
13 480 00
13,486,740

Verify:
$\frac{13,486,740}{4,002} = 3,370$

5d. 189 × 169

189
× 169
1701
1134
189
31,941

Verify:
$\frac{31,941}{169} = 189$

5e. 150
× 6
900 sq ft per day

900
× 4 plasterers
3,600 sq ft per day

3,600
× 5 days
18,000 sq ft in 5 days

6a. 35)910 = 26
70
210
210
0

Verify:
26 × 35 = 910

6b. 160) 1,503 = 9 R63
1 440
63

Verify:
160 × 9 = 1,440
+ 63
1,503

6c. 196) 3,358 = 17 R26
1 96
1 398
1 372
26

Verify:
196 × 17 = 3,332
+ 26
3,358

6d. 12) 175 = 14 R7
12
55
48
7

Verify:
12 × 14 = 168
+ 7
175

6e. $\frac{18,330}{39} =$ $470 per employee

39)18,330 = 470
15 6
2 73
2 73
0

Verify: 39 × 470 = 18,330

CONCEPT REVIEW

1. The number system most widely used in the world today is known as the Hindu-Arabic or ____ number system. (1-1)
decimal

2. Our number system utilizes the ten Hindu-Arabic symbols, ____ through ____, to write any number. (1-1)
0.9

3. The set of numbers 1,2,3,4 . . . are known as ____ numbers. (1-1)
whole

4. On the place-value chart, whole numbers appear to the ____ of the decimal point. (1-1)
left

5. A ____ number is an approximation or estimate of an exact number. (1-2)
rounded

6. Rounding all the way is a process of rounding numbers to the ____ digit. (1-2)
first

7. In addition, the numbers being added are known as ____; the answer is known as the ____. (1-3)
addends; sum, total, or amount

8. When performing addition, we write the addends in columns so that the place values are aligned ____. (1-3)
vertically

9. The mathematical process of taking away, or deducting, an amount from a given number is known as ____. (1-4)
subtraction

10. In subtraction, when a column cannot be subtracted, we must ____ a digit from the column to the left. (1-4)
borrow

11. In multiplication, the product of any number and zero is ____. (1-5)
zero

12. In multiplication, the product of any number and ____ is the number itself. (1-5)
one

13. The amount left over after division is completed is known as the ____. (1-6)
remainder

14. Show four ways to express 15 divided by 5. (1-6)
15÷5, 15/5, $\frac{15}{5}$, $5\overline{)15}$

ASSESSMENT TEST

Name ____________________

Class ____________________

Answers

1. 200,049 Two hundred thousand, forty-nine
2. 52,308,411 Fifty-two million, three hundred eight thousand, four hundred eleven
3. 316,229
4. 4,560,000
5. 18,300
6. 4,000,000
7. 260,000
8. 3,431
9. 99
10. 21,942
11. 44 R 28
12. 1,016,450
13. 22,258
14. 797 R 164
15. 714

Read and write the following whole numbers in numerical and word form.

	Number	Numerical Form	Word Form
1.	200049	200,049	Two hundred thousand, forty-nine
2.	52308411	52,308,411	Fifty-two million, three hundred eight thousand, four hundred eleven

Write the following whole numbers in numerical form.

3. Three hundred sixteen thousand, two hundred twenty-nine 316,229

4. Four million, five hundred sixty thousand 4,560,000

Round the following numbers to the indicated place.

5. 18,334 to hundreds 18,300

6. 3,545,687 all the way 4,000,000

7. 256,733 to ten thousands 260,000

Perform the indicated operation for the following.

8. 1,860 + 429 + 133 + 1,009 = 3,431

9. 927 − 828 = 99

10. 207 × 106
1242
2070
21,942

11. $42\overline{)1876}$ = 44 R 28
168
196
168
28

12. 3,505 × 290
315 450
701 0
1,016,450

13. 6,800 + 919 + 201 + 14,338 = 22,258

14. 150,000 ÷ 188
$188\overline{)150000}$ = 797 R 164
1316
1840
1692
1480
1316
164

15. 1,205 − 491
1205 − 491 = 714

CHAPTER 

Name

Class

Answers

16. 1,450

17. $53,950 Total sales

18. $104 Per acre

19. a. 19 Boats

b. 25 Boats

20. $520 Per week

21. a. $11,340 Total cost

b. $36 Per stockholder

16. The following chart shows Glades Music Shop's product sales for last week. Use addition and subtraction to fill in the blank spaces. What is the week's grand total?

Glades Music Shop

	Monday	Tuesday	Wednesday	Thursday	Friday	Saturday	Total Units
DVDs	82	56	68	57	72	92	427
MP3 Players	29	69	61	58	82	75	374
CDs	96	103	71	108	112	159	649
Daily Totals	207	228	200	223	266	326	**Grand Total** 1,450

17. You are the bookkeeper for Glades, in Exercise 16. If DVDs sell for $19 each, MP3 players sell for $100 each, and CDs sell for $13 each, what was the total dollar sales for last week?

DVDs	MP3 Players	CDs	
427	374	649	8,113
× 19	× 100	× 13	37,400
$8,113	$37,400	$8,437	+ 8,437
			$53,950 Total sales

18. Hazy Dayz Farm, a 1,600-acre farm, was sold for a total of $235,000. If the house and equipment are worth $68,600 and the land represents the balance, what was the price paid per acre for the land?

235,000 Total
− 68,600 House and equipment
166,400 Land

$$\frac{166,400}{1,600} = \$104 \text{ Per acre}$$

19. Camp Minnewonka, a summer camp in the Rocky Mountains, has budgeted $85,500 for a new fleet of sailboats. The boat selected is a deluxe model costing $4,500.

a. How many boats can be purchased by the camp?

$$\frac{85,500}{4,500} = 19 \text{ Boats}$$

b. If instead a standard model was chosen costing $3,420, how many boats could be purchased?

$$\frac{85,500}{3,420} = 25 \text{ Boats}$$

20. Maggie Martin makes a salary of $23,440 per year plus a commission of $300 per month as a sales associate for Midway Corp. What is her weekly income? (There are 52 weeks in a year.)

300
× 12
$3,600 Commission

23,440
+ 3,600
$27,040 Total salary

$$\frac{27,040}{52} = \$520 \text{ Per week}$$

21. You are in charge of organizing the annual stockholder's meeting and luncheon for your company, Tundra Industries, Inc. The meal will cost $13 per person; entertainment will cost $2,100; facility rental is $880; invitations and annual report printing costs are $2,636; and other expenses come to $1,629. If 315 stockholders plan to attend:

a. What is the total cost of the luncheon?

315
× 13
4,095 Meals

4,095
2,100
880
2,636
+1,629
$11,340 Total cost

b. What is the cost per stockholder?

$$\frac{11,340}{315} = \$36 \text{ Per stockholder}$$

Stockholder

Corporation ownership is measured by the number of shares of stock an investor, known as a **stockholder**, owns. One share of stock represents one unit of ownership.

The annual stockholder's meeting is an opportunity for company executives to meet with stockholders and to report on the financial and competitive position of the company.

CHAPTER

Name

Class

Answers

22. $4,325 Per month

23. $1,003 Balance April 30

24. $3,186 Profit

25. $49,260 Profit

26. 5,040 Total in 6 weeks

27. a. $7,119,770 Over budget

b. 17,990,230 Profit

22. New Age Bank requires mortgage loan applicants to have a gross monthly income of five times the amount of their monthly payment. How much monthly income must Shelly Krane have to qualify for a payment of $865?

865
× 5
$4,325 Per month

23. Sandra Furrow had $868 in her checking account on April 1. During the month she wrote checks for $15, $123, $88, $276, and $34. She also deposited $45, $190, and $436. What is the balance in her checking account at the end of April?

Checks	Deposits		
15	45	868	Balance April 1
123	190	− 536	
88	+ 436	332	
276	$671	+ 671	
+ 34		$1,003	Balance April 30
$536			

24. Last week, the *More Joy,* a commercial fishing boat, brought in 360 pounds of tuna, 225 pounds of halibut, and 570 pounds of snapper. At the dock, the catch was sold to Atlantic Seafood Wholesalers. The tuna brought $3 per pound; the halibut, $4 per pound; and the snapper, $5 per pound. If fuel and crew expenses amounted to $1,644, how much profit did Captain Bob make on this trip?

Tuna	Halibut	Snapper		
360	225	570	1,080	
× 3	× 4	× 5	900	
$1,080	$900	$2,850	+ 2,850	
			4,830	Total sales
			− 1,644	Expenses
			$3,186	Profit

25. David Gibson bought 2,000 shares of stock at $62 per share. Six months later he sold the 2,000 shares at $87 per share. If the total stockbroker's commission was $740, how much profit did he make on this transaction?

Buy	Sell		
2,000	2,000	174,000	
× 62	× 87	− 124,000	
$124,000	$174,000	50,000	
		− 740	Commission
		$49,260	Profit

26. The Canmore Mining Company produces 40 tons of ore in an 8-hour shift. The mine operates continuously—three shifts per day, 7 days per week. How many tons of ore can be extracted in 6 weeks?

40 Tons	120 Tons	840 Tons
× 3 Shifts	× 7 Days	× 6 Weeks
120 Tons per day	840 Tons per week	5,040 Total tons in 6 weeks

27. A Hollywood movie was estimated to cost $24,890,000 to produce.

a. If the actual cost was $32,009,770, by how much was the movie over budget?

32,009,770
−24,890,000
$7,119,770 Over budget

b. If ticket sales grossed $50,000,000, how much was the profit?

50,000,000
− 32,009,770
$17,990,230 Profit

Name

Class

Answers

28. a. $4,975 Per month

b. $2,985 Less if paid in 5 years

29. 15 Tons per trailer

30. a. 23 Officers

b. $1,725 Total officer payroll

31. Amount saved: $20

28. The Ashland Corporation purchased a new building for $165,000. After a down payment of $45,600, the balance was paid in equal monthly payments, with no interest.

a. If the loan was paid off in 2 years, how much were the monthly payments?

165,000
−45,600
$119,400 Amount financed

12 Months
× 2 Years
24 Months

$\frac{119,400}{24} = \$4,975$ Per month

b. If the loan was paid off in 5 years, how much *less* were the monthly payments?

12 Months
× 5 Years
60 Months

$\frac{119,400}{60} = \$1,990$ Per month

4,975
−1,990
$2,985 Less if paid in 5 years

29. A flatbed railroad car weighs 150 tons empty and 420 tons loaded with 18 equal-weight trailers. How many tons does each trailer weigh?

420 Total
−150 Railroad car
270 Weight of trailers

$\frac{270}{18} = 15$ Tons per trailer

30. The Porterville Police Department has been asked to provide protection support for a visiting politician. If they have to provide 2 officers at the airport for motorcycle escort, 7 officers for intersection control along the planned route of travel, and 14 officers at the high school auditorium during the speech,

a. How many officers are to be assigned to the protection detail?

2
7
+ 14
23 Officers

b. If each officer is to be paid $75 extra for this duty, what is the total officer payroll for the protection detail?

75
× 23
$1,725 Total officer payroll

31. The following ad for Tire Giant shows the original and sale prices of certain tires. If 2 tires of each size are to be bought, what will be the total amount saved by purchasing at the sale prices rather than at the original prices?

Tire Size	Original Price	Sale Price
14 in.	$36	$32
15 in.	$40	$34

Original Price	Sale Price	
2 tires × 36 = $72	2 tires × 32 = $64	Amount saved:
2 tires × 40 = $80	2 tires × 34 = $68	152 − 132 = $20
72 + 80 = $152	64 + 68 = $132	

CHAPTER

Name

Class

Answers

32. Total cost: $1,030

33. a. Model 800 is $17 less expensive

b. $760 Per year

32. The Scott family reunion is being held at Fantasy World Amusement Park. What will be the total cost if 20 children under 5, 18 children ages 5 to 9, 15 children ages 10 to 17, 40 adults 18 to 55, and 23 adults over 55 attend? The ticket prices are shown below.

Fantasy World Amusement Park Ticket Prices

Children under 5	Free
5–9 years	$5
10–17 years	$10
18–55 years	$14
Over 55	$10

Children under 5	20 × 0 =	0
5 – 9 years	18 × $5 =	$90
10 – 17 years	15 × $10 =	$150
18 – 55 years	40 × $14 =	$560
Over 55	23 × $10 =	$230
		$1,030 Total cost

BUSINESS DECISION CELL PHONE NUMBERS

33. John Rock has narrowed down his selection of a new cell phone to two models with similar features. Model 800 is plug compatible with his existing car charger and remote ear bud/microphone and will cost $140. There is a $35 mail-in rebate for the Model 800. His other choice is the Model 300, which is not plug compatible with his existing accessories. The price of the Model 300 is $89 and it has a $20 mail-in rebate. But if he buys the Model 300, he will also have to buy the car charger for $30 and an ear bud/microphone for $23.

a. All considered, which model would be the least expensive choice? By how much?

Model 800: $140 - 35 = \$105$

Model 300: $89 - 20 + 30 + 23 = \$122$

$122 - 105 = \$17$

Model 800 is $17 less expensive

b. For either cell phone choice, the monthly charge will be $34 per month with a $5 rebate if less than 250 minutes are used during the month. Government fees and taxes will be $9, the access fee is $7, and the Internet connection charge is $15. Based on last year's usage, John estimates that he will use less than 250 minutes in May, June, August, and October. If John's service starts on January 1, how much will he spend in the next year on cellular phone services?

$34 + 9 + 7 + 15 = \$65$
× 8 months
$520

$34 - 5 + 9 + 7 + 15 = \$60$
× 4 months
$240

$520 + 240 = \$760$ Per year

COLLABORATIVE LEARNING ACTIVITY

TEACHING TIP
It is recommended that students break into teams of two, three, or four and work together to accomplish the task. For maximum effectiveness, each team's findings should be shared with the class.

Using Math in Business

As a team, discuss and list the ways that math is used in the following types of business. Report your findings to the class.

a. Supermarket
b. Car dealership
c. Beauty salon
d. Dog-walking service
e. Restaurant
f. Additional team choice ________________

Fractions

PERFORMANCE OBJECTIVES

Section I Understanding and Working with Fractions

2-1: Distinguishing among the various types of fractions (p. 34)

2-2: Converting improper fractions to whole or mixed numbers (p. 35)

2-3: Converting mixed numbers to improper fractions (p. 36)

2-4: Reducing fractions to lowest terms using
a. inspection and the rules of divisibility (p. 37)
b. the greatest common divisor method (p. 38)

2-5: Raising fractions to higher terms (p. 39)

Section II Addition and Subtraction of Fractions

2-6: Determining the least common denominator (LCD) of two or more fractions (p. 42)

2-7: Adding fractions and mixed numbers (p. 43)

2-8: Subtracting fractions and mixed numbers (p. 45)

Section III Multiplication and Division of Fractions

2-9: Multiplying fractions and mixed numbers (p. 51)

2-10: Dividing fractions and mixed numbers (p. 53)

SECTION I UNDERSTANDING AND WORKING WITH FRACTIONS

fractions A mathematical way of expressing a part of a whole thing. For example, $\frac{1}{4}$ is a fraction expressing one part out of a total of four parts.

2-1

Fractions are a mathematical way of expressing a part of a whole thing. The word fraction comes from a Latin word meaning "break." Fractions result from breaking a unit into a number of equal parts. This concept is used quite commonly in business. We may look at sales for $\frac{1}{2}$ the year, or reduce prices by $\frac{1}{4}$ for a sale. A new production machine in your company may be $1\frac{3}{4}$ times faster than the old one, or you might want to cut $5\frac{3}{4}$ yards of fabric from a roll of material. Just like whole numbers, fractions can be added, subtracted, multiplied, divided, and even combined with whole numbers. This chapter introduces you to the various types of fractions and shows you how they are used in the business world.

2-1 DISTINGUISHING AMONG THE VARIOUS TYPES OF FRACTIONS

numerator The number on top of the division line of a fraction. It represents the dividend in the division. In the fraction $\frac{1}{4}$, 1 is the numerator.

denominator The number on the bottom of the division line of a fraction. It represents the divisor in the division. In the fraction $\frac{1}{4}$, 4 is the denominator.

division line The horizontal or slanted line separating the numerator from the denominator. The symbol representing "divided by" in a fraction. In the fraction $\frac{1}{4}$, the line between the 1 and the 4 is the division line.

Technically, fractions express the relationship between two numbers, set up as a division. The **numerator** is the number on the top of the fraction. It represents the dividend in the division. The **denominator** is the bottom number of the fraction. It represents the divisor. The numerator and the denominator are separated by a horizontal or slanted line, known as the **division line**. This line means "divided by." For example, the fraction 2/3 or $\frac{2}{3}$, read as "two-thirds," means 2 divided by 3, or 2 ÷ 3.

$$\frac{\text{Numerator}}{\text{Denominator}} \quad \frac{2}{3}$$

Remember, fractions express parts of a whole unit. The unit may be dollars, feet, ounces, or anything. The denominator describes how many total parts are in the unit. The numerator represents how many of the total parts we are describing or referring to. For example, a pizza (the whole unit) is divided into eight slices (total equal parts, denominator). As a fraction, the whole pizza would be represented as $\frac{8}{8}$. If five of the slices were eaten (parts referred to, numerator), what fraction represents the part that was eaten? The answer would be the fraction $\frac{5}{8}$, read "five-eighths." Because five slices were eaten out of a total of eight, three slices, or $\frac{3}{8}$, of the pizza is left.

$\frac{8}{8}$ 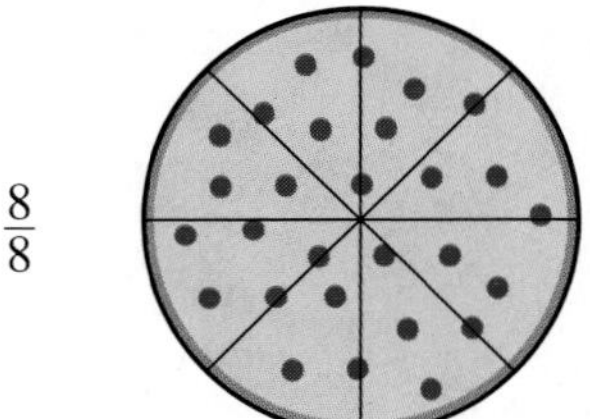 $\frac{5}{8}$ 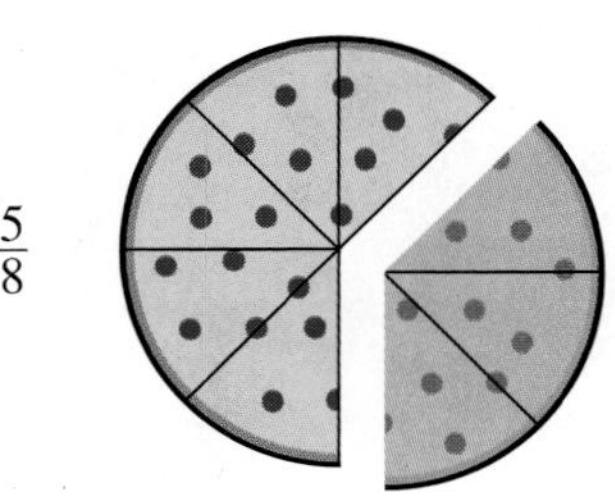 $\frac{3}{8}$

common or proper fraction A fraction in which the numerator is less than the denominator. Represents less than a whole unit. The fraction $\frac{1}{4}$ is a common or proper fraction.

improper fraction A fraction in which the denominator is equal to or less than the numerator. Represents one whole unit or more. The fraction $\frac{4}{1}$ is an improper fraction.

Fractions such as $\frac{3}{8}$ and $\frac{5}{8}$, in which the numerator is smaller than the denominator, represent less than a whole unit and are known as **common**, or **proper fractions**. Some examples of proper fractions would be

$\frac{3}{16}$ three-sixteenths $\frac{1}{4}$ one-fourth $\frac{9}{32}$ nine-thirty-seconds

When a fraction's denominator is equal to or less than the numerator, it represents one whole unit or more, and is known as an **improper fraction**. Some examples of improper fractions are

$\frac{9}{9}$ nine-ninths $\frac{15}{11}$ fifteen-elevenths $\frac{19}{7}$ nineteen-sevenths

A number that combines a whole number with a proper fraction is known as a **mixed number**. Some examples of mixed numbers are

$3\frac{1}{8}$ three and one-eighth $\quad 7\frac{11}{16}$ seven and eleven-sixteenths

$46\frac{51}{60}$ forty-six and fifty-one-sixtieths

mixed number A number that combines a whole number with a proper fraction. The fraction $10\frac{1}{4}$ is a mixed number.

EXAMPLE 1 IDENTIFYING AND WRITING FRACTIONS

For each of the following, identify the type of fraction, and write it in word form.

a. $\frac{45}{16}$ b. $14\frac{2}{5}$ c. $\frac{11}{12}$

SOLUTION STRATEGY

a. $\frac{45}{16}$ This is an improper fraction because the denominator, 16, is less than the numerator, 45. In word form we say, "forty-five sixteenths." It could also be read as "45 divided by 16," or "45 over 16."

b. $14\frac{2}{5}$ This is a mixed number because it combines the whole number 14 with the fraction $\frac{2}{5}$. In word form this is read, "fourteen and two-fifths."

c. $\frac{11}{12}$ This is a common or proper fraction because the numerator, 11, is less than the denominator, 12. This fraction is read, "eleven-twelfths." It could also be read, "11 over 12" or "11 divided by 12."

TRY IT EXERCISE 1

For each of the following, identify the type of fraction, and write it in word form.

a. $76\frac{3}{4}$ b. $\frac{3}{5}$ c. $\frac{18}{18}$ d. $\frac{33}{8}$

CHECK YOUR ANSWERS WITH THE SOLUTIONS ON PAGE 61.

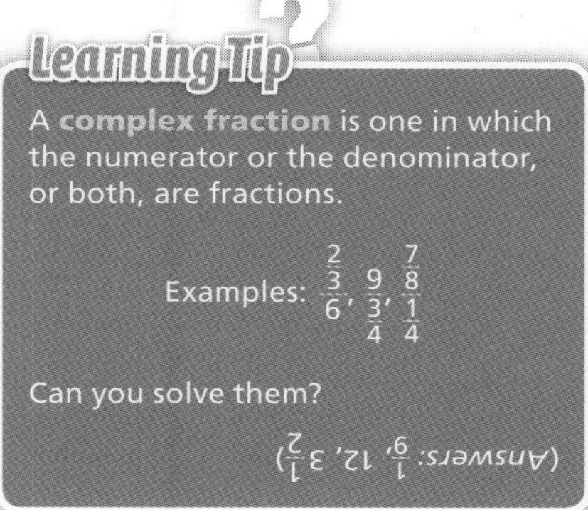

CONVERTING IMPROPER FRACTIONS TO WHOLE OR MIXED NUMBERS

2-2

It often becomes necessary to change or convert an improper fraction into a whole or mixed number. For example, final answers cannot be left as improper fractions; they must be converted.

STEPS FOR CONVERTING IMPROPER FRACTIONS TO WHOLE OR MIXED NUMBERS

Step 1. Divide the numerator of the improper fraction by the denominator.

Step 2a. If there is no remainder, the improper fraction becomes a whole number.

Step 2b. If there is a remainder, write the whole number and then write the fraction as

$$\textbf{Whole number}\ \frac{\textbf{Remainder}}{\textbf{Divisor}}$$

EXAMPLE 2 CONVERTING FRACTIONS

Convert the following improper fractions to whole or mixed numbers.

a. $\frac{30}{5}$ b. $\frac{9}{2}$

SOLUTION STRATEGY

a. $\frac{30}{5} = \underline{\underline{6}}$ When we divide the numerator, 30, by the denominator, 5, we get the whole number 6. There is no remainder.

b. $\frac{9}{2} = 2\overline{)9} = \underline{\underline{4\frac{1}{2}}}$ This improper fraction divides 4 times with a remainder of 1, therefore it will become a mixed number. In this case, the 4 is the whole number. The remainder, 1, becomes the numerator of the new fraction; the divisor, 2, becomes the denominator.

TRY IT EXERCISE 2

Convert the following improper fractions to whole or mixed numbers.

a. $\frac{8}{3}$ b. $\frac{25}{4}$ c. $\frac{39}{3}$

CHECK YOUR ANSWERS WITH THE SOLUTIONS ON PAGE 61.

2-3 CONVERTING MIXED NUMBERS TO IMPROPER FRACTIONS

STEPS FOR CONVERTING A MIXED NUMBER TO AN IMPROPER FRACTION

Step 1. Multiply the denominator by the whole number.

Step 2. Add the numerator to the product from Step 1.

Step 3. Place the total from Step 2 as the "new" numerator.

Step 4. Place the original denominator as the "new" denominator.

Certain calculators have a fraction key, $a\frac{b}{c}$, that allows you to enter fractions. For example, $\frac{2}{3}$ would be entered as [2] [$a\frac{b}{c}$] [3] and would appear as 2⌋3. The mixed fraction $25\frac{2}{3}$ would be entered as [25] [$a\frac{b}{c}$] [2] [$a\frac{b}{c}$] [3] and would appear as 25⌋2⌋3.

Fraction calculators express answers in fractional notation and are a handy tool for measuring materials without having to convert fractions to decimals. They are particularly useful in the construction, medical, and food trades.

EXAMPLE 3 CONVERTING FRACTIONS

Convert the following mixed numbers to improper fractions.

a. $5\frac{2}{3}$ b. $9\frac{5}{6}$

SOLUTION STRATEGY

a. $5\frac{2}{3} = \underline{\underline{\frac{17}{3}}}$ In this example, we multiply the denominator, 3, by the whole number, 5, and add the numerator, 2, to get 17 ($3 \times 5 + 2 = 17$). We then place the 17 over the original denominator, 3.

b. $9\frac{5}{6} = \underline{\underline{\frac{59}{6}}}$ In this example, we multiply the denominator, 6, by the whole number, 9, and add the numerator, 5, to get 59 ($6 \times 9 + 5 = 59$). We then place the 59 over the original denominator, 6.

TRY IT EXERCISE 3

Convert the following mixed numbers to improper fractions.

a. $2\frac{3}{4}$ b. $9\frac{1}{5}$ c. $22\frac{5}{8}$

CHECK YOUR ANSWERS WITH THE SOLUTIONS ON PAGE 61.

REDUCING FRACTIONS TO LOWEST TERMS

Reducing a fraction means finding whole numbers, called common divisors or common factors, that divide evenly into both the numerator and denominator of the fraction. For example, the fraction $\frac{24}{48}$ can be reduced to $\frac{12}{24}$, by the common divisor 2. The new fraction, $\frac{12}{24}$, can be further reduced to $\frac{4}{8}$ by the common divisor 3, and to $\frac{1}{2}$, by the common divisor 4. When a fraction has been reduced to the point where there are no common divisors left, other than 1, it is said to be **reduced to lowest terms**.

The largest number that is a common divisor of a fraction is known as the **greatest common divisor**. It reduces the fraction to lowest terms in one step. In the example of $\frac{24}{48}$ above, we could have used 24, the greatest common divisor, to reduce the fraction to $\frac{1}{2}$.

$$\frac{24 \div 24}{48 \div 24} = \frac{1}{2}$$

reduce to lowest terms The process of dividing whole numbers, known as common divisors or common factors, into both the numerator and denominator of a fraction. Used for expressing fractions as final answers. For example, $\frac{5}{20}$ reduces to $\frac{1}{4}$ by the common divisor, 5.

greatest common divisor The largest number that is a common divisor of a fraction. Used to reduce a fraction to lowest terms in one step. For example, 5 is the greatest common divisor of $\frac{5}{20}$.

a. Reducing Fractions by Inspection

Reducing fractions by inspection or observation is often a trial-and-error procedure. Sometimes a fraction's common divisors are obvious; other times they are more difficult to determine. The following rules of divisibility may be helpful:

RULES OF DIVISIBILITY

A Number Is Divisible by	Conditions
2	If the last digit is 0, 2, 4, 6, or 8.
3	If the sum of the digits is divisible by 3.
4	If the last two digits are divisible by 4.
5	If the last digit is 0 or 5.
6	If the number is divisible by 2 and 3, or if it is even and the sum of the digits is divisible by 3.
8	If the last three digits are divisible by 8.
9	If the sum of the digits is divisible by 9.
10	If the last digit is 0.

2-2

Construction workers must accurately measure and calculate various lengths of building materials by using fractions.

EXAMPLE 4 REDUCING FRACTIONS TO LOWEST TERMS USING INSPECTION

Use observation and the rules of divisibility to reduce $\frac{48}{54}$ to lowest terms.

SOLUTION STRATEGY

$\frac{48}{54} = \frac{48 \div 2}{54 \div 2} = \frac{24}{27}$ Because the last digit of the numerator is 8 and the last digit of the denominator is 4, they are both divisible by 2.

$\frac{24}{27} = \frac{24 \div 3}{27 \div 3} = \frac{8}{9}$ Because the sum of the digits of the numerator, 2 + 4, and the denominator, 2 + 7, are both divisible by 3, the fraction is divisible by 3.

$\frac{48}{54} = \underline{\underline{\frac{8}{9}}}$ Because no numbers other than 1 divide evenly into the new fraction $\frac{8}{9}$, it is now reduced to lowest terms.

TRY IT EXERCISE 4

Reduce the following fractions to lowest terms.

a. $\frac{30}{55}$ b. $\frac{72}{148}$

CHECK YOUR ANSWERS WITH THE SOLUTIONS ON PAGE 61.

When buying gas, the price per gallon is frequently quoted as a fraction. The price of 3.20$\frac{9}{10}$ is read as "three dollars, twenty and 9/10ths cents."

b. Reducing Fractions by the Greatest Common Divisor Method

The best method for reducing a fraction to lowest terms is to divide the numerator and the denominator by the greatest common divisor, because this accomplishes the task in one step. When the greatest common divisor is not obvious to you, use the following steps to determine it:

STEPS FOR DETERMINING THE GREATEST COMMON DIVISOR OF A FRACTION

Step 1. Divide the numerator of the fraction into the denominator.

Step 2. Take the remainder from Step 1 and divide it into the divisor from Step 1.

Step 3. Repeat this division process until the remainder is either 0 or 1.

- **If the remainder is 0, the last divisor is the greatest common divisor.**
- **If the remainder is 1, the fraction cannot be reduced and is therefore in lowest terms.**

EXAMPLE 5 REDUCING FRACTIONS TO LOWEST TERMS USING THE GREATEST COMMON DIVISOR METHOD

Reduce the fraction $\frac{63}{231}$ by finding the greatest common divisor.

SOLUTION STRATEGY

$231 \div 63 = 3$; $3 \times 63 = 189$; $231 - 189 = 42$ — Divide the numerator, 63, into the denominator, 231. This leaves a remainder of 42.

$63 \div 42 = 1$; $63 - 42 = 21$ — Next, divide the remainder, 42, into the previous divisor, 63. This leaves a remainder of 21.

$42 \div 21 = 2$; $42 - 42 = 0$ — Then, divide the remainder, 21, into the previous divisor, 42. Because this leaves a remainder of 0, the last divisor, 21, is the greatest common divisor of the original fraction.

$\frac{63 \div 21}{231 \div 21} = \underline{\underline{\frac{3}{11}}}$ — By dividing both the numerator and the denominator by the greatest common divisor, 21, we get the fraction, $\frac{3}{11}$, which is the original fraction reduced to lowest terms.

CLASSROOM ACTIVITY

Frequently, fractions are used to express a quantity as a part of a whole, such as 4 months equals $\frac{4}{12}$ or $\frac{1}{3}$ of a year.

Ask students to write the following as a fractional part of the whole, reduced to lowest terms:

- 6 hours is what part of a day? $\frac{6}{24} = \frac{1}{4}$
- 9 inches is what part of a foot? $\frac{9}{12} = \frac{3}{4}$
- 2 quarts is what part of a gallon? $\frac{2}{4} = \frac{1}{2}$
- 800 lbs. is what part of a ton? $\frac{800}{2{,}000} = \frac{2}{5}$
- 2 days is what part of a week? $\frac{2}{7}$

TRY IT EXERCISE 5

Reduce the following fractions to lowest terms.

a. $\frac{270}{810}$ b. $\frac{175}{232}$

CHECK YOUR ANSWERS WITH THE SOLUTIONS ON PAGE 61.

RAISING FRACTIONS TO HIGHER TERMS

Raising a fraction to higher terms is a procedure sometimes needed in addition and subtraction. It is the opposite of reducing fractions to lower terms. In reducing, we used common divisors; in raising fractions we use common multiples. To **raise to higher terms**, simply multiply the numerator and denominator of a fraction by a **common multiple**.

For example, if we want to raise the fraction $\frac{3}{4}$ by a factor of 7, multiply the numerator and the denominator by 7. This procedure raises the fraction to $\frac{21}{28}$.

$$\frac{3 \times 7}{4 \times 7} = \frac{21}{28}$$

It is important to remember that the value of the fraction has not changed by raising it; we have simply divided the "whole" into more parts.

STEPS FOR RAISING A FRACTION TO A NEW DENOMINATOR

Step 1. Divide the original denominator into the new denominator. The resulting quotient is the common multiple that raises the fraction.

Step 2. Multiply the numerator and the denominator of the original fraction by the common multiple.

EXAMPLE 6 RAISING FRACTIONS TO HIGHER TERMS

Raise the following fractions to higher terms, as indicated.

a. $\frac{2}{3}$ to fifteenths b. $\frac{3}{5}$ to fortieths

SOLUTION STRATEGY

a. $\frac{2}{3} = \frac{?}{15}$ In this example, we are raising the fraction $\frac{2}{3}$ to the denominator 15.

$15 \div 3 = 5$ Divide the original denominator, 3, into 15. This yields the common multiple, 5.

$\frac{2 \times 5}{3 \times 5} = \underline{\underline{\frac{10}{15}}}$ Now, multiply both the numerator and denominator by the common multiple, 5.

b. $\frac{3}{5} = \frac{?}{40}$ Here, the indicated denominator is 40.

$40 \div 5 = 8$ Dividing 5 into 40, we get the common multiple, 8.

$\frac{3 \times 8}{5 \times 8} = \underline{\underline{\frac{24}{40}}}$ Now raise the fraction by multiplying the numerator, 3, and the denominator, 5, by 8.

TRY IT EXERCISE 6

Raise the following fractions to higher terms, as indicated.

a. $\frac{7}{8}$ to sixty-fourths b. $\frac{3}{7}$ to thirty-fifths

CHECK YOUR ANSWERS WITH THE SOLUTIONS ON PAGE 61.

raise to higher terms The process of multiplying the numerator and denominator of a fraction by a common multiple. Sometimes needed in addition and subtraction of fractions. For example, $\frac{5}{20}$ is the fraction $\frac{1}{4}$ raised to higher terms, 20ths, by the common multiple, 5.

common multiple Whole number used to raise a fraction to higher terms. The common multiple 5 raises the fraction $\frac{1}{4}$ to $\frac{5}{20}$.

Learning Tip

Sometimes it is difficult to determine which of two fractions is the larger or smaller number. By converting them to **like fractions** (same denominator), the answer will become evident.

For example:

Which fraction is larger, $\frac{4}{5}$ or $\frac{5}{6}$?

$\frac{4}{5} = \frac{24}{30}$, whereas $\frac{5}{6} = \frac{25}{30}$

2 SECTION I Review Exercises

For each of the following, identify the type of fraction, and write it in word form.

1. $23\frac{4}{5}$ Mixed; Twenty-three and four-fifths
2. $\frac{12}{12}$ Improper; Twelve-twelfths
3. $\frac{15}{9}$ Improper; Fifteen-ninths
4. $\frac{7}{16}$ Proper; Seven-sixteenths
5. $2\frac{1}{8}$ Mixed; Two and one-eighth

Convert the following improper fractions to whole or mixed numbers.

6. $\frac{26}{8} = 3\frac{2}{8} = 3\frac{1}{4}$
7. $\frac{20}{6} = 3\frac{2}{6} = 3\frac{1}{3}$
8. $\frac{92}{16} = 5\frac{12}{16} = 5\frac{3}{4}$
9. $\frac{64}{15} = 4\frac{4}{15}$
10. $\frac{88}{11} = 8$
11. $\frac{33}{31} = 1\frac{2}{31}$

Convert the following mixed numbers to improper fractions.

12. $6\frac{1}{2} = \frac{13}{2}$ $(6 \times 2 + 1 = 13)$
13. $11\frac{4}{5} = \frac{59}{5}$ $(11 \times 5 + 4 = 59)$
14. $25\frac{2}{3} = \frac{77}{3}$ $(25 \times 3 + 2 = 77)$
15. $18\frac{5}{8} = \frac{149}{8}$ $(18 \times 8 + 5 = 149)$
16. $1\frac{5}{9} = \frac{14}{9}$ $(1 \times 9 + 5 = 14)$
17. $250\frac{1}{4} = \frac{1{,}001}{4}$ $(250 \times 4 + 1 = 1{,}001)$

Use inspection or the greatest common divisor to reduce the following fractions to lowest terms.

18. $\frac{21}{35}$ $\frac{21 \div 7}{35 \div 7} = \frac{3}{5}$
19. $\frac{9}{12}$ $\frac{9 \div 3}{12 \div 3} = \frac{3}{4}$
20. $\frac{18}{48}$ $\frac{18 \div 6}{48 \div 6} = \frac{3}{8}$
21. $\frac{216}{920}$ $\frac{216 \div 8}{920 \div 8} = \frac{27}{115}$
22. $\frac{27}{36}$ $\frac{27 \div 9}{36 \div 9} = \frac{3}{4}$
23. $\frac{14}{112}$ $\frac{14 \div 14}{112 \div 14} = \frac{1}{8}$
24. $\frac{9}{42}$ $\frac{9 \div 3}{42 \div 3} = \frac{3}{14}$
25. $\frac{95}{325}$ $\frac{95 \div 5}{325 \div 5} = \frac{19}{65}$
26. $\frac{8}{23}$ $\frac{8}{23}$ = Lowest terms
27. $\frac{78}{96}$ $\frac{78 \div 6}{96 \div 6} = \frac{13}{16}$
28. $\frac{30}{150}$ $\frac{30 \div 30}{150 \div 30} = \frac{1}{5}$
29. $\frac{85}{306}$ $\frac{85 \div 17}{306 \div 17} = \frac{5}{18}$

Raise the following fractions to higher terms, as indicated.

30. $\frac{2}{3}$ to twenty-sevenths $\frac{2}{3} = \frac{18}{27}$ $\left(\begin{matrix}27 \div 3 = 9\\ 9 \times 2 = 18\end{matrix}\right)$
31. $\frac{3}{4}$ to forty-eighths $\frac{3}{4} = \frac{36}{48}$ $\left(\begin{matrix}48 \div 4 = 12\\ 12 \times 3 = 36\end{matrix}\right)$
32. $\frac{7}{8}$ to eightieths $\frac{7}{8} = \frac{70}{80}$ $\left(\begin{matrix}80 \div 8 = 10\\ 10 \times 7 = 70\end{matrix}\right)$
33. $\frac{11}{16}$ to sixty-fourths $\frac{11}{16} = \frac{44}{64}$ $\left(\begin{matrix}64 \div 16 = 4\\ 4 \times 11 = 44\end{matrix}\right)$
34. $\frac{1}{5}$ to hundredths $\frac{1}{5} = \frac{20}{100}$ $\left(\begin{matrix}100 \div 5 = 20\\ 20 \times 1 = 20\end{matrix}\right)$
35. $\frac{3}{7}$ to ninety-eighths $\frac{3}{7} = \frac{42}{98}$ $\left(\begin{matrix}98 \div 7 = 14\\ 14 \times 3 = 42\end{matrix}\right)$
36. $\frac{3}{5} = \frac{\quad}{25}$ $\frac{3}{5} = \frac{15}{25}$ $\left(\begin{matrix}25 \div 5 = 5\\ 5 \times 3 = 15\end{matrix}\right)$
37. $\frac{5}{8} = \frac{\quad}{64}$ $\frac{5}{8} = \frac{40}{64}$ $\left(\begin{matrix}64 \div 8 = 8\\ 8 \times 5 = 40\end{matrix}\right)$
38. $\frac{5}{6} = \frac{\quad}{360}$ $\frac{5}{6} = \frac{300}{360}$ $\left(\begin{matrix}360 \div 6 = 60\\ 60 \times 5 = 300\end{matrix}\right)$
39. $\frac{9}{13} = \frac{\quad}{182}$ $\frac{9}{13} = \frac{126}{182}$ $\left(\begin{matrix}182 \div 13 = 14\\ 14 \times 9 = 126\end{matrix}\right)$

40. $\frac{23}{24} = \frac{}{96}$

$\frac{23}{24} = \frac{92}{96}\left(\begin{matrix}96 \div 24 = 4\\ 4 \times 23 = 92\end{matrix}\right)$

41. $\frac{2}{9} = \frac{}{72}$

$\frac{2}{9} = \frac{16}{72}\left(\begin{matrix}72 \div 9 = 8\\ 8 \times 2 = 16\end{matrix}\right)$

42. $\frac{3}{8} = \frac{}{4{,}000}$

$\frac{3}{8} = \frac{1{,}500}{4{,}000}\left(\begin{matrix}4{,}000 \div 8 = 500\\ 500 \times 3 = 1{,}500\end{matrix}\right)$

43. A wedding cake was cut into 40 slices. If 24 of the slices were eaten, what fraction represents the eaten portion of the cake? Reduce your answer to lowest terms.

$\frac{24}{40} = \frac{3}{5}$ Was eaten

44. Shawna Tysse's swimming pool holds 16,000 gallons of water, and her spa holds 2,000 gallons of water. Of all the water in the pool and spa,

a. What fraction is the spa water?

$\frac{2{,}000}{2{,}000 + 16{,}000} = \frac{2}{18} = \frac{1}{9}$

b. What fraction is the pool water?

$\frac{16{,}000}{2{,}000 + 16{,}000} = \frac{16}{18} = \frac{8}{9}$

BUSINESS DECISION THE WRENCH SALE

45. You work in the tool department of a Lowes store. Your manager asks you to set up a point-of-purchase display for a set of 10 wrenches that are on sale this week. He asks you to arrange them in order from smallest to largest on the display board. When you open the box, you find the following sizes in inches: $\frac{9}{32}, \frac{5}{8}, \frac{5}{16}, \frac{1}{2}, \frac{3}{16}, \frac{3}{4}, \frac{7}{8}, \frac{5}{32}, \frac{1}{4}, \frac{3}{8}$.

a. Rearrange the wrenches by size, from smallest to largest.

To solve, raise all fractions to the LCD, 32, then arrange and reduce.

$\frac{5}{32}, \frac{3}{16}, \frac{1}{4}, \frac{9}{32}, \frac{5}{16}, \frac{3}{8}, \frac{1}{2}, \frac{5}{8}, \frac{3}{4}, \frac{7}{8}$

b. Next, your manager tells you that the sale will be for "1/3 off" the regular price of $57, and has asked you to calculate the "sale price" to be printed on the sign.

$\frac{2}{3} \times 57 = \$38$

c. After the sale is over, your manager asks you for the sales figures on the wrench promotion. If 150 sets were sold that week, what amount of revenue will you report?

$$\begin{array}{r} 150 \\ \times\ 38 \\ \hline \$5{,}700 \end{array}$$

d. If $6,000 in sales was expected, what reduced fraction represents the sales actually attained?

$\frac{5{,}700}{6{,}000} = \frac{19}{20}$

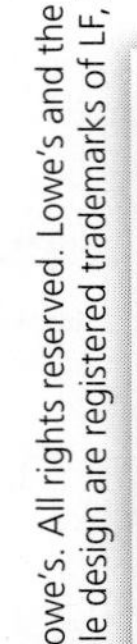

The Home Depot, with 2,147 stores, 364,000 employees and sales of over $90.8 billion, is the world's largest home improvement chain.

Lowe's, the #2 home improvement chain, has more than 1,400 stores, with 210,000 employees. Sales in 2006 were $46.9 billion.

ADDITION AND SUBTRACTION OF FRACTIONS

SECTION II

Adding and subtracting fractions occurs frequently in business. Quite often, we must combine or subtract quantities expressed as fractions. To add or subtract fractions, the denominators must be the same. If they are not, we must find a common multiple, or **common denominator**, of all the denominators in the problem. The most efficient common denominator to use is the least common denominator, or LCD. By using the LCD you avoid raising fractions to terms higher than necessary.

common denominator A common multiple of all the denominators in an addition or subtraction of fractions problem. A common denominator of the fractions $\frac{1}{4} + \frac{3}{5}$ is 40.

2-6 DETERMINING THE LEAST COMMON DENOMINATOR (LCD) OF TWO OR MORE FRACTIONS

least common denominator (LCD) The smallest and, therefore, most efficient common denominator in addition or subtraction of fractions. The least common denominator of the fractions $\frac{1}{4} + \frac{3}{5}$ is 20.

prime number A whole number divisible only by itself and 1. For example, 2, 3, 5, 7, and 11 are prime numbers.

Determining the **least common denominator (LCD)** involves a series of divisions using prime numbers. A **prime number** is a whole number divisible only by itself and 1. Some examples of prime numbers are

2, 3, 5, 7, 11, 13, 17, 19, 23, 29, 31, and so on

STEPS FOR DETERMINING THE LEAST COMMON DENOMINATOR OF TWO OR MORE FRACTIONS

Step 1. Write all the denominators in a row.

Step 2. Find a prime number that divides evenly into any of the denominators. Write that prime number to the left of the row, and divide. Place all quotients and undivided numbers in the next row down.

Step 3. Repeat this process until the new row contains all ones.

Step 4. Multiply all the prime numbers on the left together to get the LCD of the fractions.

EXAMPLE 7 DETERMINING THE LEAST COMMON DENOMINATOR (LCD)

Determine the least common denominator of the fractions $\frac{3}{4}, \frac{1}{5}, \frac{4}{9}$, and $\frac{5}{6}$.

SOLUTION STRATEGY

The following chart shows our solution. Note that the first row contains the original denominators. The first prime number, 2, divides evenly into the 4 and the 6. The quotients, 2 and 3, and the nondivisible numbers, 5 and 9, are brought down to the next row.

The same procedure is repeated with the prime numbers 2, 3, 3, and 5. When the bottom row becomes all ones, we multiply all the prime numbers to get the LCD, 180.

Prime Number	Denominators			
2	4	5	9	6
2	2	5	9	3
3	1	5	9	3
3	1	5	3	1
5	1	5	1	1
	1	1	1	1

$2 \times 2 \times 3 \times 3 \times 5 = \underline{\underline{180}} = \text{LCD}$

Answers to fraction problems should be reduced to lowest terms.

TRY IT EXERCISE 7

Determine the least common denominator of the fractions $\frac{3}{8}, \frac{4}{5}, \frac{4}{15}$, and $\frac{11}{12}$.

CHECK YOUR ANSWER WITH THE SOLUTION ON PAGE 61.

ADDING FRACTIONS AND MIXED NUMBERS

2-7

Now that you have learned to convert fractions to higher and lower terms and find least common denominators, you are ready to add and subtract fractions. We shall learn to add and subtract fractions with the same denominator, fractions with different denominators, and mixed numbers.

Adding Fractions with the Same Denominator

Proper fractions that have the same denominator are known as **like fractions**.

like fractions Proper fractions that have the same denominator. For example, $\frac{1}{4}$ and $\frac{3}{4}$ are like fractions.

STEPS FOR ADDING LIKE FRACTIONS

Step 1. Add all the numerators and place the total over the original denominator.
Step 2. If the result is a proper fraction, reduce it to lowest terms.
Step 3. If the result is an improper fraction, convert it to a whole or a mixed number.

EXAMPLE 8 ADDING LIKE FRACTIONS

Add $\frac{4}{15} + \frac{2}{15}$.

SOLUTION STRATEGY

$$\frac{4}{15} + \frac{2}{15} = \frac{4+2}{15} = \frac{6}{15} = \underline{\underline{\frac{2}{5}}}$$

Because these are like fractions, we simply add the numerators, 4 + 2, and place the total, 6, over the original denominator, 15. This gives us the fraction $\frac{6}{15}$, which reduces by 3 to $\frac{2}{5}$.

TRY IT EXERCISE 8

Add and reduce to lowest terms.

$$\frac{3}{25} + \frac{9}{25} + \frac{8}{25}$$

CHECK YOUR ANSWER WITH THE SOLUTION ON PAGE 61.

Adding Fractions with Different Denominators

Proper fractions that have different denominators are known as **unlike fractions**. Unlike fractions must be converted to like fractions before they can be added.

unlike fractions Proper fractions that have different denominators. For example, $\frac{1}{4}$ and $\frac{1}{3}$ are unlike fractions.

STEPS FOR ADDING UNLIKE FRACTIONS

Step 1. Find the least common denominator of the unlike fractions.
Step 2. Raise all fractions to the terms of the LCD, making them like fractions.
Step 3. Follow the same procedure used for adding like fractions.

EXAMPLE 9 ADDING UNLIKE FRACTIONS

Add $\frac{3}{8} + \frac{5}{7} + \frac{1}{2}$.

SOLUTION STRATEGY

Prime Number	Denominators		
2	8	7	2
2	4	7	1
2	2	7	1
7	1	7	1
	1	1	1

These are unlike fractions and must be converted to obtain the same denominator.

First, find the LCD, 56.

$$2 \times 2 \times 2 \times 7 = 56$$

$$\frac{3}{8} = \frac{21}{56}$$
$$\frac{5}{7} = \frac{40}{56}$$
$$+\frac{1}{2} = \frac{28}{56}$$
$$\frac{89}{56} = 1\frac{33}{56}$$

Next raise each fraction to fifty sixths

Then add the fractions and convert the answer, an improper fraction, to a mixed number

TRY IT EXERCISE 9

Add and reduce to lowest terms.

$$\frac{1}{6} + \frac{3}{5} + \frac{2}{3}$$

CHECK YOUR ANSWER WITH THE SOLUTION ON PAGE 62.

Adding Mixed Numbers

STEPS FOR ADDING MIXED NUMBERS

Step 1. Add the fractional parts. If the sum is an improper fraction, convert it to a mixed number.

Step 2. Add the whole numbers.

Step 3. Add the fraction from Step 1 to the whole number from Step 2.

Step 4. Reduce the answer to lowest terms, if necessary.

EXAMPLE 10 ADDING MIXED NUMBERS

Add $15\frac{3}{4} + 18\frac{5}{8}$.

SOLUTION STRATEGY

$$15\frac{3}{4} = 15\frac{6}{8}$$
$$+\ 18\frac{5}{8} = 18\frac{5}{8}$$
$$33\frac{11}{8} = 33 + 1\frac{3}{8} = \underline{\underline{34\frac{3}{8}}}$$

First add the fractional parts, using 8 as the LCD. Because $\frac{11}{8}$ is an improper fraction, convert it to the mixed number, $1\frac{3}{8}$.

Next add the whole numbers, 15 + 18 = 33. Then add the fraction and the whole number to get the answer, $34\frac{3}{8}$.

TRY IT EXERCISE 10

Add and reduce to lowest terms.

$$45\frac{1}{4} + 16\frac{5}{9} + \frac{1}{3}$$

CHECK YOUR ANSWER WITH THE SOLUTION ON PAGE 62.

COLLABORATIVE LEARNING ACTIVITY

As a review, have students work in pairs to write and solve some word problems using addition and subtraction of fractions.

Next, have them exchange and work those of another group, compare answers, and resolve any differences.

SUBTRACTING FRACTIONS AND MIXED NUMBERS

2-8

In addition, we add the numerators of like fractions. In subtraction, we subtract the numerators of like fractions. If the fractions have different denominators, first raise the fractions to the terms of the least common denominator and then subtract.

STEPS FOR SUBTRACTING LIKE FRACTIONS

Step 1. Subtract the numerators and place the difference over the original denominator.

Step 2. Reduce the answer to lowest terms, if necessary.

EXAMPLE 11 SUBTRACTING LIKE FRACTIONS

Subtract $\frac{9}{16} - \frac{5}{16}$.

SOLUTION STRATEGY

$$\frac{9}{16} - \frac{5}{16} = \frac{9-5}{16}$$
$$= \frac{4}{16} = \underline{\underline{\frac{1}{4}}}$$

In this example, the denominators are the same so we simply subtract the numerators, 9 − 5, and place the difference, 4, over the original denominator, 16. Then reduce the fraction $\frac{4}{16}$ to lowest terms, $\frac{1}{4}$.

TRY IT EXERCISE 11

Subtract $\frac{11}{25} - \frac{6}{25}$.

CHECK YOUR ANSWER WITH THE SOLUTION ON PAGE 62.

Subtracting Fractions with Different Denominators

Unlike fractions must first be converted to like fractions before they can be subtracted.

STEPS FOR SUBTRACTING UNLIKE FRACTIONS

Step 1. Find the least common denominator.

Step 2. Raise each fraction to the denominator of the LCD.

Step 3. Follow the same procedure used to subtract like fractions.

EXAMPLE 12 SUBTRACTING UNLIKE FRACTIONS

Subtract $\frac{7}{9} - \frac{1}{2}$.

SOLUTION STRATEGY

$$\frac{7}{9} = \frac{14}{18}$$

$$-\frac{1}{2} = \frac{9}{18}$$

$$\frac{5}{18}$$

In this example, we must first find the least common denominator. By inspection we can see that the LCD is 18.

Next raise both fractions to eighteenths. Now subtract the numerators, 14 − 9, and place the difference, 5, over the common denominator, 18. Because it cannot be reduced, $\frac{5}{18}$ is the final answer.

TRY IT EXERCISE 12

Subtract $\frac{5}{12} - \frac{2}{9}$.

CHECK YOUR ANSWER WITH THE SOLUTION ON PAGE 62.

Subtracting Mixed Numbers

STEPS FOR SUBTRACTING MIXED NUMBERS

Step 1. If the fractions of the mixed numbers have the same denominator, subtract them and reduce to lowest terms.

Step 2. If the fractions do not have the same denominator, raise them to the denominator of the LCD, and subtract.

Note: When the numerator of the fraction in the minuend is less than the numerator of the fraction in the subtrahend, we must *borrow* one whole unit from the whole number of the minuend. This will be in the form of the LCD/LCD and is added to the fraction of the minuend.

Step 3. Subtract the whole numbers.

Step 4. Add the difference of the whole numbers and the difference of the fractions.

EXAMPLE 13 SUBTRACTING MIXED NUMBERS

Subtract.

a. $15\frac{2}{3} - 9\frac{1}{5}$ b. $7\frac{1}{8} - 2\frac{3}{4}$

SOLUTION STRATEGY

a. $15\frac{2}{3} = 15\frac{10}{15}$ In this example raise the fractions to fifteenths; LCD = 5 × 3 = 15.

$-9\frac{1}{5} = -9\frac{3}{15}$ Then subtract the fractions to get $\frac{7}{15}$.

$6\frac{7}{15}$ Now subtract the whole numbers, 15 − 9, to get the whole number 6,

By combining the 6 and the $\frac{7}{15}$, we get the final answer, $6\frac{7}{15}$.

b. $7\frac{1}{8} = 7\frac{1}{8} = 6\frac{1}{8} + \frac{8}{8} = 6\frac{9}{8}$

$-2\frac{3}{4} = -2\frac{6}{8} = \quad -2\frac{6}{8}$

$4\frac{3}{8}$

In this example, after raising $\frac{3}{4}$ to $\frac{6}{8}$, we find that we cannot subtract $\frac{6}{8}$ from $\frac{1}{8}$. We must *borrow* one whole unit, $\frac{8}{8}$, from the whole number, 7, making it a 6 (8 ÷ 8 = 1).
By adding $\frac{8}{8}$ to $\frac{1}{8}$, we get $\frac{9}{8}$.

Now we can subtract $\frac{9}{8} - \frac{6}{8}$, to get $\frac{3}{8}$

We now subtract the whole numbers, 6 − 2 = 4. By combining the whole number, 4, and the fraction, $\frac{3}{8}$, we get the final answer, $4\frac{3}{8}$.

Learning Tip

Remember, when you borrow "one" in subtraction, you are borrowing a whole unit expressed in terms of the common denominator.

Such as, $\frac{4}{4}, \frac{5}{5}, \frac{8}{8}, \frac{24}{24}$

Don't forget to add this to the existing fraction.

TRY IT EXERCISE 13

Subtract the following mixed numbers and reduce to lowest terms.

a. $6\frac{3}{4} - 4\frac{2}{3}$ b. $25\frac{2}{9} - 11\frac{5}{6}$

CHECK YOUR ANSWERS WITH THE SOLUTIONS ON PAGE 62.

Review Exercises

SECTION II

Solution Transparencies

Find the least common denominator for the following groups of fractions.

1. $\frac{4}{5}, \frac{2}{3}, \frac{8}{15}$

3	5	3	15
5	5	1	5
	1	1	1

3 × 5 = 15 LCD

2. $\frac{1}{3}, \frac{4}{9}, \frac{3}{4}$

3	3	9	4
2	1	3	4
3	1	3	2
2	1	1	2
	1	1	1

3 × 2 × 3 × 2 = 36 LCD

3. $\frac{5}{6}, \frac{11}{12}, \frac{1}{4}, \frac{1}{2}$

2	6	12	4	2
2	3	6	2	1
3	3	3	1	1
	1	1	1	1

2 × 2 × 3 = 12 LCD

4. 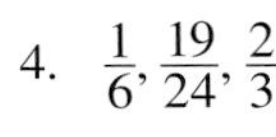 $\frac{1}{6}, \frac{19}{24}, \frac{2}{3}, \frac{3}{5}$

2	6	24	3	5
2	3	12	3	5
2	3	6	3	5
3	3	3	3	5
5	1	1	1	5
	1	1	1	1

2 × 2 × 2 × 3 × 5 = 120 LCD

5. $\frac{21}{25}, \frac{9}{60}, \frac{7}{20}, \frac{1}{3}$

2	25	60	20	3
2	25	30	10	3
3	25	15	5	3
5	25	5	5	1
5	5	1	1	1
	1	1	1	1

2 × 2 × 3 × 5 × 5 = 300 LCD

6. $\frac{5}{12}, \frac{9}{14}, \frac{2}{3}, \frac{7}{10}$

2	12	14	3	10
2	6	7	3	5
3	3	7	3	5
5	1	7	1	5
7	1	7	1	1
	1	1	1	1

2 × 2 × 3 × 5 × 7 = 420 LCD

Add the following fractions, and reduce to lowest terms.

7. $\frac{5}{6} + \frac{1}{2}$

$$\frac{5}{6} + \frac{3}{6} = \frac{8}{6} = 1\frac{2}{6} = 1\frac{1}{3}$$

8. $\frac{2}{3} + \frac{3}{4}$

$$\frac{8}{12} + \frac{9}{12} = \frac{17}{12} = 1\frac{5}{12}$$

9. $\frac{5}{8} + \frac{13}{16}$

$$\frac{10}{16} + \frac{13}{16} = \frac{23}{16} = 1\frac{7}{16}$$

10. $\frac{9}{32} + \frac{29}{32}$

$$\frac{9 + 29}{32} = \frac{38}{32} = 1\frac{6}{32} = 1\frac{3}{16}$$

11. $\frac{1}{2} + \frac{4}{5} + \frac{7}{20}$

$$\frac{10}{20} + \frac{16}{20} + \frac{7}{20} = \frac{33}{20} = 1\frac{13}{20}$$

12. $\frac{3}{4} + \frac{7}{8} + \frac{5}{16}$

$$\frac{12}{16} + \frac{14}{16} + \frac{5}{16} = \frac{31}{16} = 1\frac{15}{16}$$

13. $\frac{11}{12} + \frac{3}{5} + \frac{19}{30}$

$$\frac{55}{60} + \frac{36}{60} + \frac{38}{60} = \frac{129}{60} = 2\frac{9}{60} = 2\frac{3}{20}$$

14. $5\frac{4}{7} + \frac{2}{3}$

$$5\frac{12}{21} + \frac{14}{21} = 5\frac{26}{21} = 5 + 1\frac{5}{21} = 6\frac{5}{21}$$

15. $7\frac{1}{2} + 2\frac{7}{8} + 1\frac{1}{6}$

$$7\frac{12}{24} + 2\frac{21}{24} + 1\frac{4}{24} = 10\frac{37}{24} = 10 + 1\frac{13}{24} = 11\frac{13}{24}$$

16. $13\frac{5}{9} + 45\frac{1}{3} + 9\frac{7}{27}$

$$13\frac{15}{27} + 45\frac{9}{27} + 9\frac{7}{27} = 67\frac{31}{27} = 67 + 1\frac{4}{27} = 68\frac{4}{27}$$

17. Andrea Roderick ran $3\frac{1}{2}$ miles on Monday, $2\frac{4}{5}$ miles on Tuesday, and $4\frac{1}{8}$ miles on Wednesday. What was Andrea's total mileage for the 3 days?

Monday $3\frac{1}{2} = 3\frac{20}{40}$

Tuesday $2\frac{4}{5} = 2\frac{32}{40}$

Wednesday $4\frac{1}{8} = +4\frac{5}{40}$

$9\frac{57}{40} = 9 + 1\frac{17}{40} = 10\frac{17}{40}$ Total miles

18. West Elm shipped three packages to New York weighing $45\frac{1}{5}$, $126\frac{3}{4}$, and $88\frac{3}{8}$ pounds. What was the total weight of the shipment?

$45\frac{1}{5} = 45\frac{8}{40}$

$126\frac{3}{4} = 126\frac{30}{40}$

$+ 88\frac{3}{8} = + 88\frac{15}{40}$

$259\frac{53}{40} = 259 + 1\frac{13}{40} = 260\frac{13}{40}$ Pounds

19. At the Grove Market you buy $6\frac{3}{10}$ pounds of red onions and $4\frac{1}{3}$ pounds of yellow onions. What is the total weight of the purchase?

$6\frac{3}{10} = 6\frac{9}{30}$

$+ 4\frac{1}{3} = + 4\frac{10}{30}$

$10\frac{19}{30}$

20. BrewMasters Coffee Co. purchased $12\frac{1}{2}$ tons of coffee beans in January, $15\frac{4}{5}$ tons in February, and $34\frac{7}{10}$ tons in March. What was the total weight of the purchases?

January $12\frac{1}{2} = 12\frac{5}{10}$

February $15\frac{4}{5} = 15\frac{8}{10}$

March $+ 34\frac{7}{10} = + 34\frac{7}{10}$

$61\frac{20}{10} = 61 + 2 = 63$ Tons

Subtract the following fractions, and reduce to lowest terms.

21. $\frac{5}{6} - \frac{1}{6}$
$= \frac{4}{6} = \frac{2}{3}$

22. $\frac{4}{7} - \frac{1}{8}$
$= \frac{32}{56} - \frac{7}{56} = \frac{25}{56}$

23. $\frac{2}{3} - \frac{1}{18}$
$= \frac{12}{18} - \frac{1}{18} = \frac{11}{18}$

24. $\frac{3}{4} - \frac{9}{16}$
$= \frac{12}{16} - \frac{9}{16} = \frac{3}{16}$

25. $12\frac{3}{5} - 4\frac{1}{3}$
$= 12\frac{9}{15} - 4\frac{5}{15} = 8\frac{4}{15}$

26. $8\frac{1}{4} - 5\frac{2}{3}$
$= 8\frac{3}{12} - 5\frac{8}{12}$
$= 7\frac{15}{12} - 5\frac{8}{12} = 2\frac{7}{12}$

27. $28\frac{4}{9} - 1\frac{4}{5}$
$= 28\frac{20}{45} - 1\frac{36}{45}$
$= 27\frac{65}{45} - 1\frac{36}{45} = 26\frac{29}{45}$

28. $8\frac{11}{12} - 8\frac{3}{8}$
$= 8\frac{22}{24} - 8\frac{9}{24} = \frac{13}{24}$

29. Steve Adams sold $18\frac{4}{5}$ of his $54\frac{2}{3}$ acres of land. How many acres does Steve have left?

$54\frac{2}{3} = 54\frac{10}{15} = 53\frac{25}{15}$
$-18\frac{4}{5} = -18\frac{12}{15} = -18\frac{12}{15}$
$35\frac{13}{15}$ Acres left

30. A particular dress requires $3\frac{1}{4}$ yards of fabric for manufacturing. If the matching jacket requires $\frac{5}{6}$ yard less fabric, how much fabric is needed for both pieces?

$3\frac{1}{4} = \frac{13}{4} = \frac{39}{12}$
$-\frac{5}{6} = -\frac{5}{6} = -\frac{10}{12}$
$\frac{29}{12} = 2\frac{5}{12}$ Yards for jacket

$3\frac{1}{4} = 3\frac{3}{12}$
$+2\frac{5}{12} = +2\frac{5}{12}$
$5\frac{8}{12} = 5\frac{2}{3}$ Total yards for both pieces

31. Julie Moffitt bought a frozen, factory-processed turkey that included the giblets and neck. The package weighed $22\frac{3}{4}$ pounds. Julie thawed the bird and then removed and weighed the giblets and neck, which totaled $1\frac{1}{8}$ pounds. The juice that she drained from the package weighed $\frac{1}{2}$ pound. How much did the turkey weigh going into the oven?

$1\frac{1}{8}$ pounds—giblets and neck
$+\frac{1}{2}$ pounds—juice
$1\frac{5}{8}$ pounds—weight lost in thawing

$22\frac{3}{4} = 22\frac{6}{8}$
$-1\frac{5}{8} = -1\frac{5}{8}$
$21\frac{1}{8}$ Pounds

32. Bill Morrow weighed $196\frac{1}{2}$ pounds when he decided to join a gym to lose some weight. At the end of the first month he weighed $191\frac{3}{8}$ pounds

a. How much did he lose that month?

$196\frac{1}{2} = 196\frac{4}{8}$
$-191\frac{3}{8} = -191\frac{3}{8}$
$5\frac{1}{8}$ Pounds

b. If his goal is $183\frac{3}{4}$ pounds, how much more does he have to lose?

$191\frac{3}{8} = 191\frac{3}{8} = 190\frac{11}{8}$
$-183\frac{3}{4} = -183\frac{6}{8} = -183\frac{6}{8}$
$7\frac{5}{8}$ Pounds

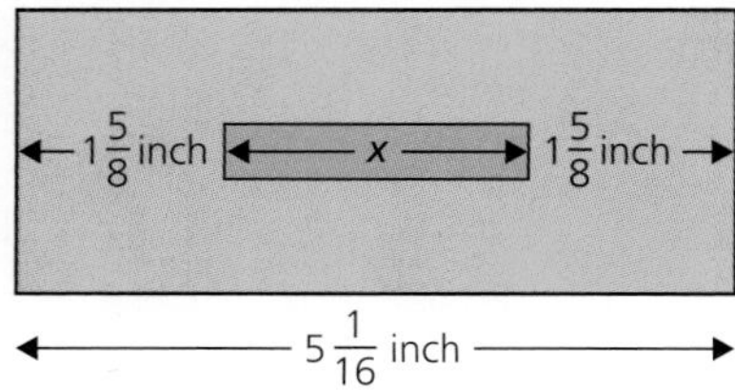

33. Curtis Industries manufactures metal heat shields for light fixture assemblies. What is the length, *x*, on the heat shield?

$$\begin{array}{r} 1\frac{5}{8} \\ +\ 1\frac{5}{8} \\ \hline 2\frac{10}{8} = 3\frac{2}{8} = 3\frac{1}{4} \end{array} \qquad \begin{array}{rcr} 5\frac{1}{16} & = & 4\frac{17}{16} \\ -3\frac{1}{4} & = & -3\frac{4}{16} \\ \hline & & 1\frac{13}{16} \text{ inch} \end{array}$$

34. John Lacey, a painter, used $6\frac{4}{5}$ gallons of paint on the exterior of a house and $9\frac{3}{4}$ gallons on the interior.

   a. What is the total amount of paint used on the house?

$$\begin{array}{rcr} 6\frac{4}{5} & = & 6\frac{16}{20} \\ +9\frac{3}{4} & = & +9\frac{15}{20} \\ \hline & & 15\frac{31}{20} = 16\frac{11}{20} \end{array}$$

   b. If an additional $8\frac{3}{5}$ gallons was used on the garage, what is the total amount of paint used on the house and garage?

$$\begin{array}{rcr} 16\frac{11}{20} & = & 16\frac{11}{20} \\ +\ 8\frac{3}{5} & = & +8\frac{12}{20} \\ \hline & & 24\frac{23}{20} = 25\frac{3}{20} \end{array}$$

   c. Rounding your answer from part b "up" to the next whole gallon, calculate the total cost of the paint, if you paid \$23 for each gallon.

$$\begin{array}{r} 26 \\ \times\ 23 \\ \hline \$\,598 \end{array} \text{ Total cost of paint}$$

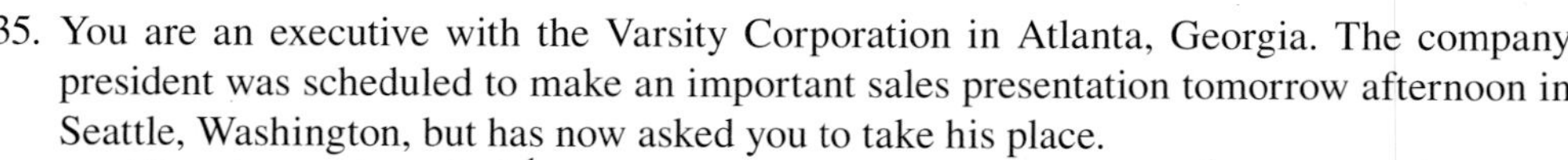

BUSINESS DECISION THE RED-EYE EXPRESS

© Ted S. Warren/Associated Press

35. You are an executive with the Varsity Corporation in Atlanta, Georgia. The company president was scheduled to make an important sales presentation tomorrow afternoon in Seattle, Washington, but has now asked you to take his place.

   The trip consists of a $2\frac{1}{2}$ hour flight from Atlanta to Dallas, a $1\frac{1}{4}$ hour layover in Dallas, and then a $3\frac{3}{4}$ hour flight to Portland. There is a $1\frac{1}{2}$ hour layover in Portland and then a $\frac{3}{4}$ hour flight to Seattle. Seattle is on Pacific Time, which is 3 hours earlier than Eastern Time in Atlanta.

   a. If you depart Atlanta tonight at 11:30 P.M., and all flights are on schedule, what time will you arrive in Seattle?

$$2\frac{1}{2} + 1\frac{1}{4} + 3\frac{3}{4} + 1\frac{1}{2} + \frac{3}{4} = 9\frac{3}{4} \text{ hours}$$

11:30 P.M. + $9\frac{3}{4}$ hours − 3 hour time difference = 6:15 A.M.

b. If your return flight is scheduled to leave Seattle at 10:10 P.M. tomorrow night, with the same flight times and layovers in reverse, what time are you scheduled to arrive in Atlanta?

10:10 P.M. + $9\frac{3}{4}$ hours + 3 hour time difference = <u>10:55 A.M.</u>

c. If the leg from Dallas back to Atlanta is $\frac{2}{3}$ of an hour longer than scheduled due to headwinds, what time will you actually arrive?

$\frac{2}{3}$ hour = 40 minutes

10:55 A.M. + 40 minutes = <u>11:35 A.M.</u>

World's Busiest Airports
12 months ending March 16, 2007 (millions)

Rank	City (Airport)	Total Passengers
1.	Atlanta, GA (ATL)	84.8
2.	Chicago, IL (ORD)	76.2
3.	London, GB (LHR)	67.5
4.	Tokyo, JP (HND)	65.2
5.	Los Angeles, CA (LAX)	61.0
6.	Dallas/Ft Worth, TX (DFW)	60.0
7.	Paris, FR (CDG)	56.8
8.	Frankfurt, DE (FRA)	52.8
9.	Beijing, CN (PEK)	48.5
10.	Denver, Co (DEN)	47.3

www.airports.org

MULTIPLICATION AND DIVISION OF FRACTIONS

SECTION III

2

In addition and subtraction we were concerned with common denominators; however, in multiplication and division common denominators are not required. This simplifies the process considerably.

MULTIPLYING FRACTIONS AND MIXED NUMBERS

STEPS FOR MULTIPLYING FRACTIONS

Step 1. Multiply all the numerators to form the new numerator.

Step 2. Multiply all the denominators to form the new denominator.

Step 3. Reduce the answer to lowest terms, if necessary.

A procedure known as **cancellation** can serve as a useful shortcut when multiplying fractions. Cancellation simplifies the numbers with which we are dealing and often leaves the answer in lowest terms.

cancellation When multiplying fractions, cancellation is the process of finding a common factor that divides evenly into at least one numerator and one denominator. The common factor 2 can be used to cancel

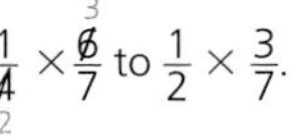

STEPS FOR APPLYING CANCELLATION

Step 1. Find a common factor that divides evenly into at least one of the denominators and one of the numerators.

Step 2. Divide that common factor into the denominator and numerator, thereby reducing it.

Step 3. Repeat this process until there are no more common factors.

Step 4. Multiply the fractions as before.

EXAMPLE 14 MULTIPLYING FRACTONS

Multiply the following fractions.

a. $\frac{5}{7} \times \frac{3}{4}$

b. $\frac{2}{3} \times \frac{7}{8}$

SOLUTION STRATEGY

a. $\frac{5}{7} \times \frac{3}{4}$

In this example, there are no common factors between the numerators and the denominators; therefore we cannot use cancellation.

$\frac{5 \times 3}{7 \times 4} = \underline{\underline{\frac{15}{28}}}$

Multiply the numerators, 5 × 3, to form the new numerator, 15; and multiply the denominators, 7 × 4, to form the new denominator, 28. This fraction does not reduce.

b. $\frac{2}{3} \times \frac{7}{8}$

In this example, the 2 in the numerator and the 8 in the denominator have the common factor of 2.

$\frac{\overset{1}{\cancel{2}}}{3} \times \frac{7}{\underset{4}{\cancel{8}}}$

Dividing each by the common factor reduces the 2 to a 1 and the 8 to a 4.

$\frac{1 \times 7}{3 \times 4} = \underline{\underline{\frac{7}{12}}}$

Now multiply the simplified numbers; 1 × 7 forms the numerator, 7, and 3 × 4 forms the denominator, 12. The resulting product is $\frac{7}{12}$.

TRY IT EXERCISE 14

Multiply and reduce to lowest terms.

$\frac{12}{21} \times \frac{7}{8}$

CHECK YOUR ANSWER WITH THE SOLUTION ON PAGE 62.

Multiplying Mixed Numbers

CLASSROOM ACTIVITY

To demonstrate that fractions raised to higher terms or reduced to lower terms are still the same number, have students multiply a number, say, 60, for example, by $\frac{1}{4}$, $\frac{2}{8}$, and $\frac{4}{16}$.

All calculations will yield the same answer, $\underline{\underline{15}}$.

STEPS FOR MULTIPLYING MIXED NUMBERS

Step 1. Convert all mixed numbers to improper fractions.

Note: When multiplying fractions by whole numbers, change the whole numbers to fractions by placing them over 1.

Step 2. Multiply as before, using cancellation wherever possible.

Step 3. If the answer is an improper fraction, convert it to a whole or mixed number.

Step 4. Reduce the answer to lowest terms, if necessary.

EXAMPLE 15 MULTIPLYING MIXED NUMBERS

Multiply.

a. $3\frac{3}{4} \times 5\frac{1}{2}$ b. $12\frac{5}{6} \times 4$

SOLUTION STRATEGY

a.

$3\frac{3}{4} \times 5\frac{1}{2}$

In this example, convert the mixed numbers to improper fractions; $3\frac{3}{4}$ becomes $\frac{15}{4}$, and $5\frac{1}{2}$ becomes $\frac{11}{2}$.

$\frac{15}{4} \times \frac{11}{2}$

$\frac{15 \times 11}{4 \times 2} = \frac{165}{8} = 20\frac{5}{8}$

After multiplying the numerators together and the denominators together, we get the improper fraction $\frac{165}{8}$, which converts to the mixed number $20\frac{5}{8}$.

b.

$12\frac{5}{6} \times 4$

This example demonstrates a mixed number multiplied by a whole number.

$\frac{77}{6} \times \frac{4}{1}$

The mixed number $12\frac{5}{6}$ converts to the improper fraction $\frac{77}{6}$. The whole number, 4, expressed as a fraction, becomes $\frac{4}{1}$.

$\frac{77}{\underset{3}{\cancel{6}}} \times \frac{\overset{2}{\cancel{4}}}{1}$

Before multiplying, cancel the 4 in the numerator and the 6 in the denominator by the common factor, 2.

$\frac{77 \times 2}{3 \times 1} = \frac{154}{3} = 51\frac{1}{3}$

After multiplying, convert the improper fraction $\frac{154}{3}$ to the mixed number $51\frac{1}{3}$.

TRY IT EXERCISE 15

Multiply and reduce to lowest terms.

a. $8\frac{2}{5} \times 6\frac{1}{4}$ b. $45 \times \frac{4}{9} \times 2\frac{1}{4}$

CHECK YOUR ANSWERS WITH THE SOLUTIONS ON PAGE 62.

DIVIDING FRACTIONS AND MIXED NUMBERS

2-10

In division of fractions, it is important to identify which fraction is the dividend and which is the divisor. In whole numbers, we found that a problem such as 12 ÷ 5 is read, "12 divided by 5." The 12 therefore is the dividend and the 5 is the divisor. Fractions work in the same way. The number *after* the "÷" sign is the divisor. In the problem $\frac{3}{4} \div \frac{2}{3}$, for example, $\frac{3}{4}$ is the dividend and $\frac{2}{3}$ is the divisor.

$$\text{Dividend} \div \text{Divisor} = \frac{\text{Dividend}}{\text{Divisor}} = \text{Divisor}\overline{)\text{Dividend}}$$

Division of fractions requires that we **invert** the divisor. To invert means to turn upside down. By inverting a fraction, the numerator becomes the denominator, and the denominator becomes the numerator. For example, the fraction $\frac{5}{12}$ becomes $\frac{12}{5}$ when inverted. These fractions are also known as **reciprocals**. Therefore $\frac{5}{12}$ and $\frac{12}{5}$ are reciprocals of each other.

As in multiplication, division requires that mixed numbers be converted to improper fractions.

The number *after* the "÷" sign is the divisor.
This is the number that gets inverted when dividing.

invert To turn upside down. For example, $\frac{1}{4}$ inverted becomes $\frac{4}{1}$. In division of fractions, the divisor is inverted.

reciprocals Numbers whose product is 1. Inverted numbers are also known as reciprocals of each other. The fractions $\frac{1}{4}$ and $\frac{4}{1}$ are reciprocals since $\frac{1}{4} \times \frac{4}{1} = 1$.

STEPS FOR DIVIDING FRACTIONS

Step 1. Identify the fraction that is the divisor, and invert.

Step 2. Change the "divided by" sign, ÷, to a "multiplied by" sign, ×.

Step 3. Multiply the fractions.

Step 4. Reduce the answer to lowest terms, if necessary.

EXAMPLE 16 DIVIDING FRACTIONS

Divide the following fractions.

a. $\frac{4}{5} \div \frac{2}{3}$ b. $6\frac{3}{8} \div 2\frac{1}{2}$ c. $12\frac{1}{6} \div 3$

SOLUTION STRATEGY

a. $\frac{4}{5} \div \frac{2}{3} = \frac{4}{5} \times \frac{3}{2}$

In this example, invert the divisor, $\frac{2}{3}$, to form its reciprocal, $\frac{3}{2}$, and change the sign from "÷" to "×."

$\frac{\overset{2}{\cancel{4}}}{5} \times \frac{3}{\underset{1}{\cancel{2}}} = \frac{6}{5} = \underline{\underline{1\frac{1}{5}}}$

Now multiply in the usual manner. Note that the 4 in the numerator and the 2 in the denominator can be reduced by the common factor, 2. The answer, $\frac{6}{5}$, is an improper fraction and must be converted to the mixed number $1\frac{1}{5}$.

b. $6\frac{3}{8} \div 2\frac{1}{2} = \frac{51}{8} \div \frac{5}{2}$

First, convert the mixed numbers to the improper fractions $\frac{51}{8}$ and $\frac{5}{2}$, and state them again as a division.

$\frac{51}{8} \times \frac{2}{5}$

Next invert the divisor, $\frac{5}{2}$, to its reciprocal, $\frac{2}{5}$, and change the sign from "÷" to "×."

$\frac{51}{\underset{4}{\cancel{8}}} \times \frac{\overset{1}{\cancel{2}}}{5} = \frac{51}{20} = \underline{\underline{2\frac{11}{20}}}$

Now multiply in the usual way. Note that the 2 in the numerator and the 8 in the denominator can be reduced by the common factor, 2. The answer, $\frac{51}{20}$, is an improper fraction and must be converted to the mixed number $2\frac{11}{20}$.

c. $12\frac{1}{6} \div 3 = \frac{73}{6} \div \frac{3}{1}$

In this example, we have a mixed number that must be converted to the improper fraction, $\frac{73}{6}$, and a whole number, 3, that converts to $\frac{3}{1}$.

$\frac{73}{6} \times \frac{1}{3}$

The fraction $\frac{3}{1}$ is the divisor and must be inverted to its reciprocal, $\frac{1}{3}$. The sign is changed from "÷" to "×."

$\frac{73}{6} \times \frac{1}{3} = \frac{73}{18} = \underline{\underline{4\frac{1}{18}}}$

The answer is the improper fraction $\frac{73}{18}$, which converts to the mixed number $4\frac{1}{18}$.

In the Business World

According to *The Wall Street Journal*, the problem below was a question on the Jersey City High School admissions exam in June 1885! Try this for practice:

Divide the difference between 37 hundredths and 95 thousandths by 25 hundred-thousandths and express the result in words.

Answer: one thousand, one hundred

TRY IT EXERCISE 16

Divide the following fractions and mixed numbers.

a. $\frac{14}{25} \div \frac{4}{5}$ b. $11\frac{3}{16} \div 8\frac{2}{3}$ c. $18 \div 5\frac{3}{5}$

CHECK YOUR ANSWERS WITH THE SOLUTIONS ON PAGE 62.

Review Exercises

SECTION III

Multiply the following fractions and reduce to lowest terms. Use cancellation whenever possible.

1. $\frac{2}{3} \times \frac{4}{5} = \frac{8}{15}$

2. $\frac{5}{6} \times \frac{1}{4} = \frac{5}{24}$

3. $\frac{1}{\underset{1}{2}} \times \frac{\overset{2}{4}}{9} = \frac{2}{9}$

4. $\frac{\overset{1}{7}}{\underset{2}{8}} \times \frac{1}{3} \times \frac{\overset{1}{4}}{\underset{1}{7}} = \frac{1}{6}$

5. $\frac{\overset{2}{16}}{19} \times \frac{5}{\underset{1}{8}} = \frac{10}{19}$

6. $\frac{\overset{5}{25}}{51} \times \frac{2}{\underset{1}{5}} = \frac{10}{51}$

7. $\frac{\overset{1}{8}}{\underset{1}{11}} \times \frac{\overset{3}{33}}{\underset{5}{40}} \times \frac{4}{1} = \frac{12}{5}$

8. $\frac{2}{3} \times \frac{2}{\underset{1}{3}} \times \frac{\overset{2}{6}}{1} = \frac{8}{3} = 2\frac{2}{3}$

9. $8\frac{1}{5} \times 2\frac{2}{3}$ $\quad \frac{41}{5} \times \frac{8}{3} = \frac{328}{15} = 21\frac{13}{15}$

10. $\frac{1}{\underset{1}{2}} \times \frac{\overset{1}{2}}{\underset{1}{3}} \times \frac{\overset{1}{4}}{\underset{1}{5}} \times \frac{\overset{1}{3}}{\underset{1}{4}} \times \frac{\overset{1}{5}}{1} = \frac{1}{1} = 1$

11. $\frac{1}{5} \times \frac{1}{5} \times \frac{1}{5} = \frac{1}{125}$

12. $\frac{2}{3} \times 5\frac{4}{5} \times 9$ $\quad \frac{2}{\underset{1}{3}} \times \frac{29}{5} \times \frac{\overset{3}{9}}{1} = \frac{174}{5} = 34\frac{4}{5}$

13. A recent market research survey showed that $\frac{3}{8}$ of the people interviewed preferred decaffeinated coffee over regular.

    a. What fraction of the people preferred regular coffee?

    $\frac{8}{8} - \frac{3}{8} = \frac{5}{8}$ Preferred regular

    b. If 4,400 persons were interviewed, how many preferred regular coffee?

    $\frac{\overset{550}{4{,}400}}{1} \times \frac{5}{\underset{1}{8}} = \frac{2{,}750}{1} = 2{,}750$ People preferred regular

14. Katrina Byrd planned to bake a triple recipe of chocolate chip cookies for her office party. If the recipe calls for $1\frac{3}{4}$ cups of flour, how many cups will she need?

    $1\frac{3}{4} \times 3 = 5\frac{1}{4}$ cups

15. A driveway requires $9\frac{1}{2}$ truckloads of gravel. If the truck holds $4\frac{5}{8}$ cubic yards of gravel, how many total cubic yards of gravel are used for the driveway?

    $9\frac{1}{2} \times 4\frac{5}{8} = \frac{19}{2} \times \frac{37}{8} = \frac{703}{16} = 43\frac{15}{16}$ Yards of gravel

16. Molly Malone borrowed \$4,200 from the bank. If she has already repaid $\frac{3}{7}$ of the loan, what is the remaining balance owed to the bank?

    $\frac{\overset{600}{4{,}200}}{1} \times \frac{3}{\underset{1}{7}} = \frac{1{,}800}{1} = \$1{,}800$ Already paid

    4,200 Total
    −1,800
    \$2,400 Still owed

17. Magi Khoo's movie collection occupies $\frac{5}{8}$ of her computer's hard drive. Her photography takes up $\frac{1}{6}$ of the drive. The operating system, application software and miscellaneous files take up another $\frac{1}{12}$ of the drive. If her hard drive's capacity is 120 gigabytes, how many gigabytes of free space remain on the hard drive?

    $\frac{5}{8} + \frac{1}{6} + \frac{1}{12} = \frac{15 + 4 + 2}{24} = \frac{21}{24} = \frac{7}{8}$ Capacity used $\quad \frac{1}{8} \times 120 = 15$ Gigabytes

18. Three partners share a business. Sam owns $\frac{3}{8}$, Anita owns $\frac{2}{5}$, and David owns the rest. If the profits this year are \$150,000, how much does each partner receive?

    Sam $150{,}000 \times \frac{3}{8} = \frac{\overset{18{,}750}{150{,}000}}{1} \times \frac{3}{\underset{1}{8}} = \frac{56{,}250}{1} = \$56{,}250$

    Anita $150{,}000 \times \frac{2}{5} = \frac{\overset{30{,}000}{150{,}000}}{1} \times \frac{2}{\underset{1}{5}} = \frac{60{,}000}{1} = \$60{,}000$

    David 56,250 + 60,000 = 116,250 $\quad$ 150,000 − 116,250 = \$33,750

© Sparky/Stone/Getty Images

Opinion and market research is a multi-billion dollar a year industry dedicated to providing valuable consumer feedback to companies that sell products and services. This information helps companies identify, understand, and meet consumer needs and wants.

According to the Marketing Research Association, almost 72 million Americans per year are interviewed in opinion and marketing research studies.

Divide the following fractions and reduce to lowest terms.

19. $\frac{5}{6} \div \frac{3}{8}$

$\frac{5}{\underset{3}{\cancel{6}}} \times \frac{\overset{4}{\cancel{8}}}{3} = \frac{20}{9} = 2\frac{2}{9}$

20. $\frac{7}{10} \div \frac{1}{5}$

$\frac{7}{\underset{2}{\cancel{10}}} \times \frac{\overset{1}{\cancel{5}}}{1} = \frac{7}{2} = 3\frac{1}{2}$

21. $\frac{2}{3} \div \frac{5}{8}$

$\frac{2}{3} \times \frac{8}{5} = \frac{16}{15} = 1\frac{1}{15}$

22. $7 \div \frac{4}{5}$

$\frac{7}{1} \times \frac{5}{4} = \frac{35}{4} = 8\frac{3}{4}$

23. $\frac{1}{3} \div \frac{5}{6}$

$\frac{1}{\underset{1}{\cancel{3}}} \times \frac{\overset{2}{\cancel{6}}}{5} = \frac{2}{5}$

24. $\frac{9}{16} \div \frac{9}{16}$

$\frac{\overset{1}{\cancel{9}}}{\underset{1}{\cancel{16}}} \times \frac{\overset{1}{\cancel{16}}}{\underset{1}{\cancel{9}}} = \frac{1}{1} = 1$

25. $4\frac{4}{5} \div \frac{7}{8}$

$\frac{24}{5} \times \frac{8}{7} = \frac{192}{35} = 5\frac{17}{35}$

26. $21\frac{1}{2} \div 5\frac{2}{3}$

$\frac{43}{2} \times \frac{3}{17} = \frac{129}{34} = 3\frac{27}{34}$

27. $18 \div \frac{18}{19}$

$\frac{\overset{1}{\cancel{18}}}{1} \times \frac{19}{\underset{1}{\cancel{18}}} = \frac{19}{1} = 19$

28. $12 \div 1\frac{3}{5}$

$\frac{\overset{3}{\cancel{12}}}{1} \times \frac{5}{\underset{2}{\cancel{8}}} = \frac{15}{2} = 7\frac{1}{2}$

29. $\frac{15}{60} \div \frac{7}{10}$

$\frac{15}{\underset{6}{\cancel{60}}} \times \frac{\overset{1}{\cancel{10}}}{7} = \frac{15}{42} = \frac{5}{14}$

30. $1\frac{1}{5} \div 10$

$\frac{\overset{3}{\cancel{6}}}{5} \times \frac{1}{\underset{5}{\cancel{10}}} = \frac{3}{25}$

31. Alpine Homes, Inc., a builder of custom homes, owns $126\frac{1}{2}$ acres of undeveloped land. If the property is divided into $2\frac{3}{4}$-acre pieces, how many homesites can be developed?

$126\frac{1}{2} \div 2\frac{3}{4} = \frac{253}{2} \div \frac{11}{4} = \frac{\overset{23}{\cancel{253}}}{\underset{1}{\cancel{2}}} \times \frac{\overset{2}{\cancel{4}}}{\underset{1}{\cancel{11}}} = \frac{46}{1} = 46$ Homesites

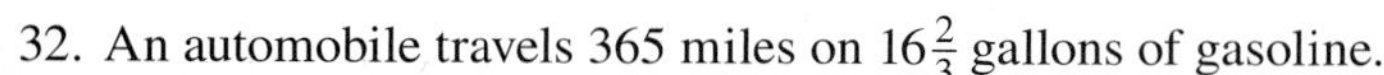

© David Zalubowski/Associated Press

The U.S. Environmental Protection Agency (EPA) and U.S. Department of Energy (DOE) produce the **Fuel Economy Guide** to help car buyers choose the most fuel-efficient vehicle that meets their needs. EPA compiles the fuel economy data and DOE publishes them in print and on the Web at www.fueleconomy.gov.

32. An automobile travels 365 miles on $16\frac{2}{3}$ gallons of gasoline.
   a. How many miles per gallon does the car get on the trip?

   $365 \div 16\frac{2}{3} = \frac{365}{1} \div \frac{50}{3} = \frac{\overset{73}{\cancel{365}}}{1} \times \frac{3}{\underset{10}{\cancel{50}}} = \frac{219}{10} = 21\frac{9}{10}$ Miles per gallon

   b. How many gallons would be required for the car to travel 876 miles?

   $876 \div 21\frac{9}{10} = \frac{876}{1} \div \frac{219}{10} = \frac{\overset{4}{\cancel{876}}}{1} \times \frac{10}{\underset{1}{\cancel{219}}} = \frac{40}{1} = 40$ Gallons

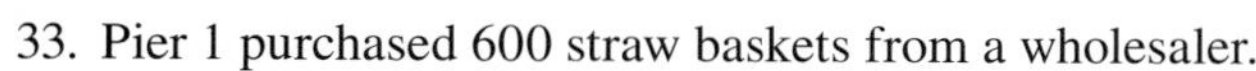

33. Pier 1 purchased 600 straw baskets from a wholesaler.
   a. In the first week, $\frac{2}{5}$ of the baskets are sold. How many are sold?

   $\frac{\overset{120}{\cancel{600}}}{1} \times \frac{2}{\underset{1}{\cancel{5}}} = \frac{240}{1} = 240$ Baskets sold first week

   b. By the third week, only $\frac{3}{20}$ remain. How many baskets are left?

   $\frac{\overset{30}{\cancel{600}}}{1} \times \frac{3}{\underset{1}{\cancel{20}}} = \frac{90}{1} = 90$ Baskets left third week

34. At the Cattleman's Market, $3\frac{1}{2}$ pounds of hamburger are to be divided into 7 equal packages. How many pounds of meat will each package contain?

$3\frac{1}{2} \div 7 = \frac{7}{2} \times \frac{1}{7} = \frac{1}{2}$ Pound

35. Magnum Hardware Supply Company buys nails in bulk from the manufacturer and packs them into $2\frac{4}{5}$-pound boxes. How many boxes can be filled from 518 pounds of nails?

$518 \div 2\frac{4}{5} = \frac{518}{1} \div \frac{14}{5} = \frac{\overset{37}{\cancel{518}}}{1} \times \frac{5}{\underset{1}{\cancel{14}}} = \frac{185}{1} = 185$ Boxes

36. The chef at the Sizzling Steakhouse has 140 pounds of sirloin steak on hand for Saturday night. If each portion is $10\frac{1}{2}$ ounces, how many sirloin steak dinners can be served? Round to the nearest whole dinner. (There are 16 ounces in a pound.)

    140 lbs
    × 16 oz
    2,240 Total ounces

    $2{,}240 \div 10\frac{1}{2} = \frac{2{,}240}{1} \div \frac{21}{2} = \frac{\overset{320}{\cancel{2{,}240}}}{1} \times \frac{2}{\underset{3}{\cancel{21}}} = \frac{640}{3} = 213\frac{1}{3} = \underline{\underline{213}}$ Dinners

37. Royal Reflective Signs makes speed limit signs for the state department of transportation. By law, these signs must be displayed every $\frac{5}{8}$ of a mile. How many signs will be required on a new highway that is $34\frac{3}{8}$ miles long?

    $34\frac{3}{8} \div \frac{5}{8} = \frac{275}{8} \div \frac{5}{8} = \frac{\overset{55}{\cancel{275}}}{\underset{1}{\cancel{8}}} \times \frac{\overset{1}{\cancel{8}}}{\underset{1}{\cancel{5}}} = \underline{\underline{55}}$ Signs

38. Engineers at Fujitsu Electronics use special silver wire to manufacture fuzzy logic circuit boards. The wire comes in 840-foot rolls that cost $1,200 each. Each board requires $4\frac{1}{5}$ feet of wire.

    a. How many circuit boards can be made from each roll?

    $840 \div 4\frac{1}{5} = \frac{840}{1} \div \frac{21}{5} = \frac{\overset{40}{\cancel{840}}}{1} \times \frac{5}{\underset{1}{\cancel{21}}} = \frac{200}{1} = \underline{\underline{200}}$ Circuit boards

    b. What is the cost of wire per circuit board?

    $1{,}200 \div 200 = \underline{\underline{\$6}}$ Each

© Photodisc/Getty Images

39. You are making a batch of corn flake-crusted chicken for a party. The recipe calls for one pound of crushed corn flakes. How many $\frac{11}{16}$ ounce individual-sized boxes will it take to make the chicken? (There are 16 ounces in a pound.)

    $16 \div \frac{11}{16} = \frac{16}{1} \times \frac{16}{11} = \frac{256}{11} = \underline{\underline{23\frac{3}{11}}}$ Boxes

BUSINESS DECISION DINNER SPECIAL

40. You are the owner of The Gourmet Diner. On Wednesday nights you offer a special of "Buy one dinner, get one free dinner—of equal or lesser value." Michael and Ernie come in for the special. Michael chooses chicken Parmesan for $15, and Ernie chooses a $10 barbecue-combo platter.

    a. Excluding tax and tip, how much should each pay for their share of the check?

    Michael $\frac{15}{25} = \frac{3}{5}$ $\quad \frac{3}{5} \times 15 = \underline{\underline{\$9}}$

    Ernie $\frac{10}{25} = \frac{2}{5}$ $\quad \frac{2}{5} \times 15 = \underline{\underline{\$6}}$

    b. If sales tax and tip amount to $\frac{1}{5}$ of the total of the two dinners, how much is that?

    $\frac{1}{5} \times \frac{25}{1} = \underline{\underline{\$5}}$

    c. If they decide to split the tax and tip in the same ratio as the dinners, how much more does each owe?

    $\frac{3}{5} \times 5 = \underline{\underline{\$3}}$

    $\frac{2}{5} \times 5 = \underline{\underline{\$2}}$

SUMMARY CHART

Section I: Understanding and Working with Fractions

Topic	Important Concepts	Illustrative Examples
Distinguishing among the Various Types of Fractions **P/O 2-1, p. 34**	**Common or proper fraction:** A fraction representing less than a whole unit, where the numerator is less than the denominator. **Improper fraction:** A fraction representing one whole unit or more, where the denominator is equal to or less than the numerator. **Mixed number:** A number that combines a whole number with a proper fraction.	Proper fraction $\frac{4}{7}, \frac{2}{3}, \frac{93}{124}$ Improper fraction $\frac{5}{4}, \frac{7}{7}, \frac{88}{51}, \frac{796}{212}, \frac{1,200}{1,200}$ Mixed number $12\frac{2}{5}, 4\frac{5}{9}, 78\frac{52}{63}$
Converting Improper Fractions to Whole or Mixed Numbers **P/O 2-2, p. 35**	**To convert improper fractions to whole or mixed numbers:** 1. Divide the numerator of the improper fraction by the denominator. 2a. If there is no remainder, the improper fraction becomes a whole number. 2b. If there is a remainder, write the whole number and then write the fraction as Whole Number $\frac{\text{Remainder}}{\text{Divisor}}$	Convert the following to whole or mixed numbers a. $\frac{68}{4} = 17$ b. $\frac{127}{20} = 6\frac{7}{20}$
Converting Mixed Numbers to Improper Fractions **P/O 2-3, p. 36**	**To covert mixed numbers to improper fractions:** 1. Multiply the denominator by the whole number. 2. Add the numerator to the product from Step 1. 3. Place the total from Step 2 as the new numerator. 4. Place the original denominator as the new denominator.	Convert $15\frac{3}{4}$ to an improper fraction $15\frac{3}{4} = \frac{(15 \times 4) + 3}{4} = \frac{63}{4}$
Reducing Fractions to Lowest Terms by Inspection **P/O 2-4a, p. 37**	**Reducing a fraction** means finding whole numbers, called common divisors or common factors, that divide evenly into both the numerator and denominator of the fraction. When a fraction has been reduced to the point where there are no common divisors left other than 1, it is said to be **reduced to lowest terms**.	Reduce $\frac{24}{120}$ to lowest terms by inspection $\frac{24}{120} = \frac{24 \div 3}{120 \div 3} = \frac{8}{40}$ $\frac{8}{40} = \frac{8 \div 2}{40 \div 2} = \frac{4}{20}$ $\frac{4}{20} = \frac{4 \div 4}{20 \div 4} = \frac{1}{5}$
Finding the Greatest Common Divisor (Reducing Shortcut) **P/O 2-4b, p. 38**	The largest number that is a common divisor of a fraction is known as the **greatest common divisor (GCD)**. It reduces the fraction to lowest terms in one step. **To find the GCD:** 1. Divide the numerator of the fraction into the denominator. 2. Take the remainder from Step 1 and divide it into the divisor from Step 1. 3. Repeat this division process until the remainder is either 0 or 1. If the remainder is 0, the last divisor is the greatest common divisor. If the remainder is 1, the fraction cannot be reduced and is therefore in lowest terms.	What greatest common divisor will reduce the fraction $\frac{48}{72}$? $72 \div 48 = 1$, $72 - 48 = 24$; $48 \div 24 = 2$, $48 - 48 = 0$ The greatest common divisor is 24.

Section I: (continued)

Topic	Important Concepts	Illustrative Examples
Raising Fractions to Higher Terms **P/O 2-5, p. 39**	**To raise a fraction to a new denominator:** 1. Divide the original denominator into the new denominator. The resulting quotient is the common multiple that raises the fraction. 2. Multiply the numerator and the denominator of the original fraction by the common multiple.	Raise $\frac{5}{8}$ to forty-eighths $\frac{5}{8} = \frac{?}{48}$ $48 \div 8 = 6$ $\frac{5 \times 6}{8 \times 6} = \frac{30}{48}$

Section II: Addition and Subtraction of Fractions

Topic	Important Concepts	Illustrative Examples
Understanding Prime Numbers **P/O 2-6, p. 42**	**A prime number** is a whole number greater than 1 that is divisible only by 1 and itself. Prime numbers are used to find the least common denominator.	Examples of prime numbers: 2, 3, 5, 7, 11, 13, 17, 19, 23, 29
Determining the Least Common Denominator (LCD) of Two or More Fractions **P/O 2-6, p. 42**	1. Write all the denominators in a row. 2. Find a prime number that divides evenly into any of the denominators. Write that prime number to the left of the row, and divide. Place all quotients and undivided numbers in the next row down. 3. Repeat this process until the new row contains all ones. 4. Multiply all the prime numbers on the left together, to get the LCD of the fractions.	Find the LCD of $\frac{2}{9}, \frac{5}{6}, \frac{1}{4}$, and $\frac{4}{5}$. **Prime Number** — **Denominators** 3 — 9 6 4 5 2 — 3 2 4 5 2 — 3 1 2 5 3 — 3 1 1 5 5 — 1 1 1 5 1 1 1 1 LCD $= 3 \times 2 \times 2 \times 3 \times 5 = 180$
Adding Like Fractions **P/O 2-7, p. 43**	1. Add all the numerators and place the total over the original denominator. 2. If the result is a proper fraction, reduce it to lowest terms. 3. If the result is an improper fraction, convert it to a whole or a mixed number.	Add $\frac{8}{9}, \frac{4}{9}$, and $\frac{1}{9}$ $\frac{8+4+1}{9} = \frac{13}{9} = 1\frac{4}{9}$
Adding Unlike Fractions **P/O 2-7, p. 43**	1. Find the least common denominator of the unlike fractions. 2. Raise each fraction to the terms of the LCD, thereby making them like fractions. 3. Add the like fractions.	Add $\frac{2}{3} + \frac{5}{7}$ LCD $= 3 \times 7 = 21$ $\frac{2 \times 7}{21} + \frac{5 \times 3}{21} = \frac{14+15}{21} = \frac{29}{21} = 1\frac{8}{21}$
Adding Mixed Numbers **P/O 2-7, p. 44**	1. Add the fractional parts. If the sum is an improper fraction, convert it to a mixed number. 2. Add the whole numbers. 3. Add the fraction from Step 1 to the whole number from Step 2. 4. Reduce the answer to lowest terms, if necessary.	Add $3\frac{3}{4} + 4\frac{1}{8}$ $3 + 4 = 7$ $\frac{3}{4} + \frac{1}{8} = \frac{(3 \times 2) + 1}{8} = \frac{7}{8}$ $7 + \frac{7}{8} = 7\frac{7}{8}$
Subtracting Like Fractions **P/O 2-8, p. 45**	1. Subtract the numerators and place the difference over the original denominator. 2. Reduce the fraction to lowest terms, if necessary.	Subtract $\frac{11}{12} - \frac{5}{12}$ $\frac{11-5}{12} = \frac{6}{12} = \frac{1}{2}$
Subtracting Unlike Fractions **P/O 2-8, p. 46**	1. Find the least common denominator. 2. Raise each fraction to the denominator of the LCD. 3. Subtract the like fractions.	Subtract $\frac{7}{8} - \frac{2}{3}$ LCD $= 8 \times 3 = 24$ $\frac{21}{24} - \frac{16}{24} = \frac{5}{24}$

Section II: (continued)

Topic	Important Concepts	Illustrative Examples
Subtracting Mixed Numbers P/O 2-8, p. 46	1. If the fractions of the mixed numbers have the same denominator, subtract them and reduce to lowest terms. 2. If the fractions do not have the same denominator, raise them to the denominator of the LCD, and subtract. 3. Subtract the whole numbers. 4. Add the difference of the whole numbers and the difference of the fractions.	Subtract $15\frac{5}{8} - 12\frac{1}{2}$ $15\frac{5}{8} = 15\frac{5}{8}$ $-12\frac{1}{2} = -12\frac{4}{8}$ $= 3\frac{1}{8}$
Subtracting Mixed Numbers, Using Borrowing P/O 2-8, p. 46	When the numerator of the fraction in the minuend is less than the numerator of the fraction in the subtrahend, we must borrow one whole unit from the whole number of the minuend. This will be in the form of the LCD/LCD and is added to the fraction of the minuend. Now, subtract as before.	Subtract $6\frac{1}{7} - 2\frac{5}{7}$ $6\frac{1}{7} = 5\frac{7}{7} + \frac{1}{7} = 5\frac{8}{7}$ $-2\frac{5}{7} \qquad -2\frac{5}{7}$ $= 3\frac{3}{7}$

Section III: Multiplication and Division of Fractions

Topic	Important Concepts	Illustrative Examples
Multiplying Fractions P/O 2-9, p. 51	1. Multiply all the numerators to form the new numerator. 2. Multiply all the denominators to form the new denominator. 3. Reduce the answer to lowest terms, if necessary.	Multiply $\frac{5}{8} \times \frac{2}{3}$ $\frac{5}{8} \times \frac{2}{3} = \frac{10}{24} = \frac{5}{12}$
Multiplying Fractions, Using Cancellation P/O 2-9, p. 51	Cancellation simplifies the numbers and leaves the answer in lowest terms. 1. Find a common factor that divides evenly into at least one of the denominators and one of the numerators. 2. Divide that common factor into the denominator and the numerator, thereby reducing it. 3. Repeat this process until there are no more common factors. 4. Multiply the fractions. The resulting product will be in lowest terms.	Use cancellation to solve the multiplication problem above: Cancellation Method: $\frac{5}{8} \times \frac{2}{3} = \frac{5}{\underset{4}{\cancel{8}}} \times \frac{\overset{1}{\cancel{2}}}{3} = \frac{5}{12}$.
Multiplying Mixed Numbers P/O 2-9, p. 52	1. Convert all mixed numbers to improper fractions. 2. Multiply, using cancellation wherever possible. 3. If the answer is an improper fraction, convert it to a whole or mixed number. 4. Reduce the answer to lowest terms, if necessary. *Note:* When multiplying fractions by whole numbers, change the whole numbers to fractions by placing them over 1.	Multiply $3\frac{1}{2} \times 2\frac{3}{8}$ $3\frac{1}{2} = \frac{7}{2} \qquad 2\frac{3}{8} = \frac{19}{8}$ $\frac{7}{2} \times \frac{19}{8} = \frac{133}{16} = 8\frac{5}{16}$

Section III: (continued)

Topic	Important Concepts	Illustrative Examples
Dividing Fractions and Mixed Numbers **P/O 2-10, p. 53**	Division of fractions requires that we invert the divisor, or turn it upside down. The inverted fraction is also known as a reciprocal. **Dividing fractions:** 1. Convert all mixed numbers to improper fractions. 2. Identify the fraction that is the divisor, and invert it. 3. Change ÷ to ×. 4. Multiply the fractions. 5. Reduce the answer to lowest terms, if necessary.	Divide $\frac{11}{12} \div \frac{2}{3}$ $\frac{11}{12}$ is the dividend $\frac{2}{3}$ is the divisor $\frac{11}{12} \div \frac{2}{3} = \frac{11}{12} \times \frac{3}{2}$ $\frac{11}{\cancel{12}_4} \times \frac{\cancel{3}^1}{2} = \frac{11}{8} = 1\frac{3}{8}$

TRY IT EXERCISE SOLUTIONS FOR CHAPTER 2

1a. Mixed fraction Seventy-six and three-fourths

1b. Common or proper fraction Three-fifths

1c. Improper fraction Eighteen-eighteenths

1d. Improper fraction Thirty-three-eighths

2a. $8 \div 3 = 2\frac{2}{3}$

2b. $25 \div 4 = 6\frac{1}{4}$

2c. $39 \div 3 = 13$

3a. $\frac{11}{4}$ $(2 \times 4 + 3 = 11)$

3b. $\frac{46}{5}$ $(9 \times 5 + 1 = 46)$

3c. $\frac{181}{8}$ $(22 \times 8 + 5 = 181)$

4a. $\frac{30 \div 5}{55 \div 5} = \frac{6}{11}$

4b. $\frac{72 \div 2}{148 \div 2} = \frac{36 \div 2}{74 \div 2} = \frac{18}{37}$

5a. $\frac{270 \div 270}{810 \div 270} = \frac{1}{3}$

$810 \div 270$: 270)810 = 3; 810; 0

5b. At lowest terms

175)232 = 1; 175; 57

57)175 = 3; 171; 4

4)57 = 14; 4; 17; 16; 1

6a. $\frac{7 \times 8}{8 \times 8} = \frac{56}{64}$ $(64 \div 8 = 8)$

6b. $\frac{3 \times 5}{7 \times 5} = \frac{15}{35}$ $(35 \div 7 = 5)$

7.

2	8	5	15	12
2	4	5	15	6
2	2	5	15	3
3	1	5	15	3
5	1	5	5	1
	1	1	1	1

$2 \times 2 \times 2 \times 3 \times 5 = 120 = \text{LCD}$

8. $\frac{3}{25} + \frac{9}{25} + \frac{8}{25} = \frac{3 + 9 + 8}{25} = \frac{20}{25} = \frac{4}{5}$

9.
$$\frac{1}{6} = \frac{5}{30}$$
$$\frac{3}{5} = \frac{18}{30}$$
$$+\frac{2}{3} = +\frac{20}{30}$$
$$\frac{43}{30} = \underline{\underline{1\frac{13}{30}}}$$

10.
$$45\frac{1}{4} = 45\frac{9}{36}$$
$$16\frac{5}{9} = 16\frac{20}{36}$$
$$+\frac{1}{3} = +\frac{12}{36}$$
$$61\frac{41}{36} = 61 + 1\frac{5}{36} = \underline{\underline{62\frac{5}{36}}}$$

11.
$$\frac{11}{25}$$
$$-\frac{6}{25}$$
$$\frac{5}{25} = \underline{\underline{\frac{1}{5}}}$$

12.
$$\frac{5}{12} = \frac{15}{36}$$
$$-\frac{2}{9} = -\frac{8}{36}$$
$$\underline{\underline{\frac{7}{36}}}$$

13a.
$$6\frac{3}{4} = 6\frac{9}{12}$$
$$-4\frac{2}{3} = -4\frac{8}{12}$$
$$\underline{\underline{2\frac{1}{12}}}$$

13b.
$$25\frac{2}{9} = 25\frac{4}{18} = 24\frac{18}{18} + \frac{4}{18} = 24\frac{22}{18}$$
$$-11\frac{5}{6} = -11\frac{15}{18} = -11\frac{15}{18}$$
$$\underline{\underline{13\frac{7}{18}}}$$

14. $\frac{\overset{\overset{1}{3}}{\cancel{12}}}{\underset{\underset{1}{3}}{\cancel{21}}} \times \frac{\overset{1}{\cancel{7}}}{\underset{2}{\cancel{8}}} = \underline{\underline{\frac{1}{2}}}$

15a. $8\frac{2}{5} \times 6\frac{1}{4} = \frac{\overset{21}{\cancel{42}}}{\underset{1}{\cancel{5}}} \times \frac{\overset{5}{\cancel{25}}}{\underset{2}{\cancel{4}}} = \frac{105}{2} = \underline{\underline{52\frac{1}{2}}}$

15b. $45 \times \frac{4}{9} \times 2\frac{1}{4} = \frac{45}{1} \times \frac{\overset{1}{\cancel{4}}}{\underset{1}{\cancel{9}}} \times \frac{\overset{1}{\cancel{9}}}{\underset{1}{\cancel{4}}} = \frac{45}{1} = \underline{\underline{45}}$

16a. $\frac{14}{25} \div \frac{4}{5} = \frac{\overset{7}{\cancel{14}}}{\underset{5}{\cancel{25}}} \times \frac{\overset{1}{\cancel{5}}}{\underset{2}{\cancel{4}}} = \underline{\underline{\frac{7}{10}}}$

16b. $11\frac{3}{16} \div 8\frac{2}{3} = \frac{179}{16} \div \frac{26}{3} = \frac{179}{16} \times \frac{3}{26} = \frac{537}{416} = \underline{\underline{1\frac{121}{416}}}$

16c. $18 \div 5\frac{3}{5} = \frac{18}{1} \div \frac{28}{5} = \frac{\overset{9}{\cancel{18}}}{1} \times \frac{5}{\underset{14}{\cancel{28}}} = \frac{45}{14} = \underline{\underline{3\frac{3}{14}}}$

CONCEPT REVIEW

1. In fractions, the number above the division line is the ____; the number below the division line is the ____. (2-1)
numerator, denominator

2. The numerator of a proper fraction is ____ than the denominator. (2-1)
less

3. To convert an improper fraction to a whole or mixed number, we ____ the numerator by the denominator. (2-2)
divide

4. To convert a mixed number to an improper fraction, we begin by multiplying the denominator by the ____ number. (2-3)
whole

5. A fraction can be reduced to lowest terms by inspection or by using the greatest common ____ method. (2-4)
divisor

6. Common multiples are whole numbers used to raise fractions to ____ terms. (2-5)
higher

7. In addition and subtraction of fractions, the most efficient common denominator is the ____ common denominator. It is abbreviated ____. (2-6)
least, LCD

8. A whole number divisible only by itself and 1 is a(n) ____ number. The first five of these numbers are ____, ____, ____, ____, and ____. (2-6)
prime, 2, 3, 5, 7, 11

9. Like fractions have the same ____. (2-7)
denominator

10. When adding unlike fractions, we begin by finding the ____ common denominator of those fractions. (2-7)
least

11. When subtracting like fractions, we subtract the numerators and place the difference over the original ____. (2-8)
denominator

12. When subtracting unlike fractions, we ____ each fraction to the denominator of the LCD. (2-8)
raise

13. When multiplying fractions, cancellation is the shortcut process of finding common factors that ____ evenly into at least one of the numerators and one of the denominators. (2-9)
divide

14. When dividing fractions, we ____ the fraction that is the divisor, and then ____ the fractions. (2-10)
invert, multiply

ASSESSMENT TEST

CHAPTER 2

Identify the type of fraction and write it in word form.

1. $\frac{18}{11}$ Improper fraction, Eighteen-elevenths

2. $4\frac{1}{6}$ Mixed fraction, Four and one-sixth

3. $\frac{13}{16}$ Proper fraction, Thirteen-sixteenths

Convert to whole or mixed numbers.

4. $\frac{57}{9} = 6\frac{3}{9} = 6\frac{1}{3}$

5. $\frac{125}{5} = 25$

Convert to improper fractions.

6. $12\frac{3}{4} = \frac{51}{4}$ $(12 \times 4 = 48 + 3 = 51)$

7. $9\frac{5}{9} = \frac{86}{9}$ $(9 \times 9 = 81 + 5 = 86)$

Reduce to lowest terms.

8. $\frac{96}{108} = \frac{96 \div 12}{108 \div 12} = \frac{8}{9}$

$108 \div 96 = 1$ R 12; $96 \div 12 = 8$ R 0

9. $\frac{26}{65} = \frac{26 \div 13}{65 \div 13} = \frac{2}{5}$

$65 \div 26 = 2$ R 13; $26 \div 13 = 2$ R 0

Convert to higher terms, as indicated.

10. $\frac{4}{5}$ to twenty-fifths $\frac{4}{5} = \frac{20}{25}$ $\left(\begin{matrix}25 \div 5 = 5\\ 5 \times 4 = 20\end{matrix}\right)$

11. $\frac{3}{13} = \frac{\quad}{78}$ $\frac{3}{13} = \frac{18}{78}$ $\left(\begin{matrix}78 \div 13 = 6\\ 3 \times 6 = 18\end{matrix}\right)$

Find the least common denominator for the following fractions.

12. $\frac{3}{4}, \frac{19}{20}, \frac{1}{6}, \frac{3}{5}, \frac{8}{15}$

$2 \times 2 \times 3 \times 5 = 60$ LCD

2	4	20	6	5	15
2	2	10	3	5	15
3	1	5	3	5	15
5	1	5	1	5	5
	1	1	1	1	1

Solve the following problems and reduce to lowest terms.

13. $\frac{3}{4} - \frac{1}{18}$ $\frac{27}{36} - \frac{2}{36} = \frac{25}{36}$

14. $\frac{2}{3} + \frac{1}{6} + \frac{11}{12}$ $\frac{8}{12} + \frac{2}{12} + \frac{11}{12} = \frac{21}{12} = 1\frac{9}{12} = 1\frac{3}{4}$

15. $\frac{2}{3} \div \frac{1}{8} = \frac{2}{3} \times \frac{8}{1} = \frac{16}{3} = 5\frac{1}{3}$

16. $\frac{5}{6} \times \frac{1}{4} = \frac{5}{24}$

17. $\frac{2}{5} \times 5\frac{3}{8} \times 2$

$\frac{2}{5} \times \frac{43}{8} \times \frac{2}{1} = \frac{43}{10}$ (cancel: 2 and 8 → 1 and 2; 2 and 2 → 1)

$\frac{43}{10} = 4\frac{3}{10}$

18. $6\frac{5}{6} - \frac{17}{18}$

$6\frac{15}{18} = 5\frac{18}{18} + \frac{15}{18} = 5\frac{33}{18}$

$-\frac{17}{18} = -\frac{17}{18} \qquad = -\frac{17}{18}$

$5\frac{16}{18} = 5\frac{8}{9}$

19. $4\frac{1}{2} + 5\frac{5}{6} + 3$

$4\frac{3}{6} + 5\frac{5}{6} + 3 = 12\frac{8}{6} = 13\frac{2}{6} = 13\frac{1}{3}$

20. $25\frac{1}{2} \div 1\frac{2}{3}$

$\frac{51}{2} \div \frac{5}{3} = \frac{51}{2} \times \frac{3}{5}$

$\frac{153}{10} = 15\frac{3}{10}$

Name

Class

Answers

1. Improper fraction, Eighteen-elevenths
2. Mixed fraction, Four and one-sixth
3. Proper fraction, Thirteen-sixteenths
4. $6\frac{1}{3}$
5. 25
6. $\frac{51}{4}$
7. $\frac{86}{9}$
8. $\frac{8}{9}$
9. $\frac{2}{5}$
10. $\frac{20}{25}$
11. $\frac{18}{78}$
12. 60
13. $\frac{25}{36}$
14. $1\frac{3}{4}$
15. $5\frac{1}{3}$
16. $\frac{5}{24}$
17. $4\frac{3}{10}$
18. $5\frac{8}{9}$
19. $13\frac{1}{3}$
20. $15\frac{3}{10}$

2 CHAPTER

Name

Class

Answers

21. 69 CPAs

22. $6\frac{1}{12}$ Tons remaining

23. $23\frac{5}{8}$ Feet

24. $37\frac{1}{2}$ Pounds of other materials

25. $10\frac{7}{16}$ inches

26. a. $180 Sale price

b. $144 Final selling price

27. a. $588,000

b. $49,000

21. The Number Crunchers, an accounting firm, has 161 employees. If $\frac{3}{7}$ of them are certified public accountants, how many CPAs are there?

$161 \times \frac{3}{7} = \frac{\overset{23}{\cancel{161}}}{1} \times \frac{3}{\underset{1}{\cancel{7}}} = \frac{69}{1} = \underline{\underline{69}}$ CPAs

22. Rockwell Coal mined $6\frac{2}{3}$ tons on Monday, $7\frac{3}{4}$ tons on Tuesday, and $4\frac{1}{2}$ tons on Wednesday. If the goal is to mine 25 tons this week, how many more tons must be mined?

$6\frac{2}{3} = 6\frac{8}{12}$

$7\frac{3}{4} = 7\frac{9}{12}$

$+4\frac{1}{2} = +4\frac{6}{12}$

$17\frac{23}{12} = 18\frac{11}{12}$ Tons mined

$25 = 24\frac{12}{12}$

$-18\frac{11}{12} = -18\frac{11}{12}$

$6\frac{1}{12}$ Tons remaining

23. A blueprint of a house has a scale of 1 inch equals $4\frac{1}{2}$ feet. If the living room wall measures $5\frac{1}{4}$ inches on the drawing, what is the actual length of the wall?

$4\frac{1}{2} \times 5\frac{1}{4} = \frac{9}{2} \times \frac{21}{4} = \frac{189}{8} = 23\frac{5}{8}$ Feet

24. If $\frac{3}{8}$ of a 60 pound bag of ready-mix concrete is Portland cement, how many pounds of other materials are in the bag?

$\frac{3}{8} \times 60 = 22\frac{1}{2}$ Pounds Portland cement $\qquad 60 - 22\frac{1}{2} = 37\frac{1}{2}$ Pounds of other materials

25. The total length of an extension cord measures $18\frac{9}{16}$ inches. The plug end measures $2\frac{3}{4}$ inches and the receptacle end measures $5\frac{3}{8}$ inches. What is the length of the wire portion of the extension cord?

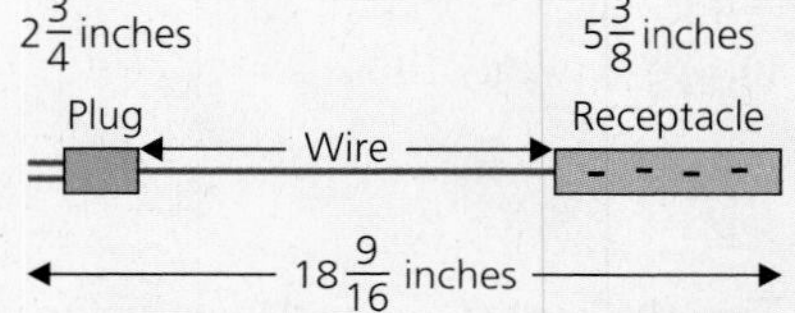

$2\frac{3}{4} + 5\frac{3}{8} = 8\frac{1}{8} \qquad 18\frac{9}{16} - 8\frac{1}{8} = 10\frac{7}{16}$ Inches

26. During a spring clearance sale, Sears advertises $\frac{1}{4}$ off the list price of Model II microwave ovens, and an additional $\frac{1}{5}$ off the sale price for ovens that are scratched or dented.

a. If the list price of a Model II is $240, what is the sale price?

$\frac{\overset{60}{\cancel{240}}}{1} \times \frac{1}{\underset{1}{\cancel{4}}} = \frac{60}{1} = \$60$ Off

240 List price
− 60 Discount
$180 Sale price

b. What is the price of a scratched one?

$180 \times \frac{1}{5} = \frac{\overset{36}{\cancel{180}}}{1} \times \frac{1}{\underset{1}{\cancel{5}}} = \frac{36}{1} = \$36$ Additional discount

180 Sale Price
− 36 Discount
$144 Final selling price

27. You are a sales representative for Sunshine Marine Equipment. Last year you sold $490,000 in marine products.

a. If this year you expect to sell $\frac{1}{5}$ more, how much will your sales be?

$\frac{1}{5} \times 490{,}000 = 98{,}000$

490,000
+ 98,000
$588,000

b. If you are paid a commission of $\frac{1}{12}$ of sales, how much will you earn this year?

$\frac{1}{12} \times \frac{588{,}000}{1} = \$49{,}000$

28. A developer owns three lots measuring $1\frac{2}{3}$ acres each, four lots measuring $2\frac{1}{2}$ acres each, and one lot measuring $3\frac{3}{8}$ acres.

a. What is the total acreage owned by the developer?

$3 \times 1\frac{2}{3} = 5 \quad 4 \times 2\frac{1}{2} = 10 \quad 1 \times 3\frac{3}{8} = 3\frac{3}{8}$

$5 + 10 + 3\frac{3}{8} = 18\frac{3}{8}$ Total acres

b. If each acre is worth $10,000, what is the total value of the properties?

$10{,}000 \times 18\frac{3}{8} = \frac{\overset{1,250}{\cancel{10{,}000}}}{1} \times \frac{147}{\underset{1}{\cancel{8}}} = \frac{183{,}750}{1} = \underline{\underline{\$183{,}750}}$ Total value

c. If the company plans to build 8 homes per acre, how many homes will they build?

$18\frac{3}{8} \times 8$

$\frac{147}{\underset{1}{\cancel{8}}} \times \frac{\overset{1}{\cancel{8}}}{1} = \frac{147}{1} = \underline{\underline{147 \text{ Homes}}}$

© Denis Poroy/Associated Press

The National Association of Home Builders is a Washington, DC-based trade association representing more than 215,000 residential home building and remodeling industry members. Known as "the voice of the housing industry," NAHB is affiliated with more than 800 state and local home builders associations around the country.

According to the NAHB, in 2006, 1,465,000 single family homes and 336,000 multi-family homes were started.

29. A house has 4,400 square feet. The bedrooms occupy $\frac{2}{5}$ of the space, the living and dining rooms occupy $\frac{1}{4}$ of the space, the garage represents $\frac{1}{10}$ of the space, and the balance is split evenly among three bathrooms and the kitchen.

a. How many square feet are in each bath and the kitchen?

$\frac{2}{5} = \frac{8}{20}$

$\frac{1}{4} = \frac{5}{20}$

$+\frac{1}{10} = +\frac{2}{20}$

$\frac{15}{20} = \frac{3}{4}$ Space for bedroom, living room, garage

$\frac{4}{4}$ Whole house

$-\frac{3}{4}$

$\frac{1}{4}$ Balance of space 3 baths and kitchen

$\frac{\overset{1,100}{\cancel{4{,}400}}}{1} \times \frac{1}{\underset{1}{\cancel{4}}} = \frac{1{,}100}{1} = $ 1,100 sq ft 3 baths and the kitchen

$\frac{1{,}100}{4} = \underline{\underline{275}}$ sq ft Each bath and the kitchen

b. If the owner wants to increase the size of the garage by $\frac{1}{8}$, how many total square feet will the new garage have?

$\frac{\overset{440}{\cancel{4{,}400}}}{1} \times \frac{1}{\underset{1}{\cancel{10}}} = 440$ sq ft garage

$\frac{\overset{55}{\cancel{440}}}{1} \times \frac{1}{\underset{1}{\cancel{8}}} = 55$ sq ft additional

440 sq ft
+ 55 sq ft
$\underline{\underline{495}}$ Total sq ft

30. Compact disks are $\frac{3}{32}$ inch thick.

a. How tall is a spindle of 50 CDs, plus a base of $\frac{1}{4}$ inch?

$50 \times \frac{3}{32} = \frac{150}{32} = 4\frac{22}{32}$

$4\frac{22}{32} = 4\frac{22}{32}$

$+\frac{1}{4} = +\frac{8}{32}$

$4\frac{30}{32} = \underline{\underline{4\frac{15}{16}}}$ Inches high

b. How tall is a spindle of 100 CDs, with the same $\frac{1}{4}$ inch base?

$4\frac{15}{16} = 4\frac{30}{32}$

$+4\frac{22}{32} = +4\frac{22}{32}$

$8\frac{52}{32} = 9\frac{20}{32} = \underline{\underline{9\frac{5}{8}}}$ Inches high

CHAPTER 2

Name ______________________

Class ______________________

Answers

28. a. $18\frac{3}{8}$ Total acres

b. $183,750 Total value

c. 147 homes

29. a. 275 sq ft Each bath and the kitchen

b. 495 Total sq ft

30. a. $4\frac{15}{16}$

b. $9\frac{5}{8}$

Chefs and cooks measure, mix, and cook ingredients according to recipes, using a variety of pots, pans, cutlery, and other kitchen equipment.

A working knowledge of fractions is one of the job requirements for people employed in the culinary arts. Most foods and other recipe ingredients are measured and combined using fractions.

31. Among other ingredients, a recipe for linguini with red sauce calls for the following: 24 ounces linguini pasta, $6\frac{2}{5}$ tablespoons minced garlic, 5 cups fresh tomatoes, and 10 tablespoons Parmesan cheese. If the recipe serves eight people, recalculate the quantities to serve five people.

Pasta:

$$\frac{\overset{3}{\cancel{24}}}{1} \times \frac{5}{\underset{1}{\cancel{8}}} = \frac{15}{1} = \underline{\underline{15}} \text{ Ounces}$$

Garlic:

$$6\frac{2}{5} \times \frac{5}{8} = \frac{\overset{4}{\cancel{32}}}{\underset{1}{\cancel{5}}} \times \frac{\overset{1}{\cancel{5}}}{\underset{1}{\cancel{8}}} = \frac{4}{1} = \underline{\underline{4}} \text{ Tablespoons}$$

Tomatoes:

$$\frac{5}{1} \times \frac{5}{8} = \frac{25}{8} = \underline{\underline{3\frac{1}{8}}} \text{ Cups}$$

Cheese:

$$\frac{\overset{5}{\cancel{10}}}{1} \times \frac{5}{\underset{4}{\cancel{8}}} = \frac{25}{4} = \underline{\underline{6\frac{1}{4}}} \text{ Tablespoons}$$

CHAPTER

Name

Class

Answers

31. Pasta: 15 Ounces

Garlic: 4 Tablespoons

Tomatoes: $3\frac{1}{8}$ Cups

Cheese: $6\frac{1}{4}$ Tablespoons

32. a. 99 Wheelbarrow loads of gravel

b. 22 Hours

c. $6,605 Total charge

BUSINESS DECISION DOWN IN THE DIRT

32. You are an engineer with Ace Foundations, Inc. Your company has been hired to build a 165-foot foundation wall for the construction of a house. You have calculated that the drainage line around the wall will take one cubic yard of gravel for every 5 feet of wall.

a. If a contractor's wheel barrow has a $\frac{1}{3}$ cubic yard capacity, how many wheelbarrow loads of gravel will be needed?

$$\frac{165}{5} \div \frac{1}{3} = 33 \times 3 = \underline{\underline{99}} \text{ Wheelbarrow loads of gravel}$$

b. If your company typically builds this type of a wall at an average rate of $7\frac{1}{2}$ feet per hour, how many hours will it take to build the foundation wall?

$$165 \div 7\frac{1}{2} = \underline{\underline{22}} \text{ Hours}$$

c. Each load of gravel costs $4. The wall materials cost $13 per foot, and labor costs $62 per hour. If $2,700 profit is to be added to the job, how much is the total charge to build the foundation wall?

4 × 99 =	$396	gravel
13 × 165 =	2,145	wall materials
62 × 22 =	1,364	labor charges
	+ 2,700	profit
	$6,605	Total charge

COLLABORATIVE LEARNING ACTIVITY

Knowing Fractions Is Half the Battle

As a team, investigate and share with the class how fractions are used in the following areas.

a. Cooking

b. Sports

c. Medicine or pharmacy

d. Architecture or building construction

e. Additional team choice ____________

f. Additional team choice ____________

Decimals

CHAPTER 3

PERFORMANCE OBJECTIVES

SECTION I UNDERSTANDING DECIMAL NUMBERS

In Chapter 1, we learned that the position of the digits in our number system affects their value. In whole numbers, we dealt with the positions or places to the left of the decimal point. In decimal numbers, we deal with the places to the right of the decimal point. These places express values that are less than whole numbers.

Just as with fractions, decimals are a way of expressing *parts* of a whole thing. Decimals are used extensively in business applications. In this chapter you learn to read, write, and work problems involving all types of decimal numbers.

3-1 READING AND WRITING DECIMAL NUMBERS IN NUMERICAL AND WORD FORM

decimal numbers, or decimals Amounts less than whole, or less than one. For example, .44 is a decimal number.

decimal point A dot written in a decimal number to indicate where the place values change from whole numbers to decimal numbers.

mixed decimals Decimals written in conjunction with whole numbers. For example, 2.44 is a mixed decimal.

By definition, **decimal numbers**, or **decimals**, are amounts less than whole, or less than one. They are preceded by a dot known as the **decimal point** and are written .31 or 0.31, for example. The zero is used to ensure that the decimal point is not missed. Often, decimals are written in conjunction with whole numbers. These are known as **mixed decimals**. In mixed decimals, the decimal point separates the whole numbers from the decimal, such as 4.31.

The place value chart, shown in Exhibit 3-1, expands the whole number chart from Chapter 1 to include the places representing decimals. In decimals, the value of each place, starting at the decimal point and moving from left to right, decreases by a factor of 10. The names of the places on the decimal side end in *ths*; they are tenths, hundredths, thousandths, ten-thousandths, hundred-thousandths, millionths, and so on.

To read or write decimal numbers in words, you must read or write the decimal part as if it were a whole number, then name the place value of the last digit on the right. For example, .0594 would be read as "five hundred ninety-four ten-thousandths."

Learning Tip

When reading numbers, remember that decimals start with the "tenths" place, whereas whole numbers start with the "ones" place.

Don't forget that the word "and" is used to represent the decimal point.

Decimals are used to express dollars and cents. The numbers to the left of the decimal point represent whole dollars; the numbers to the right represent parts of a dollar, or cents.

Exhibit 3-1
Decimal Numbers Place Value Chart

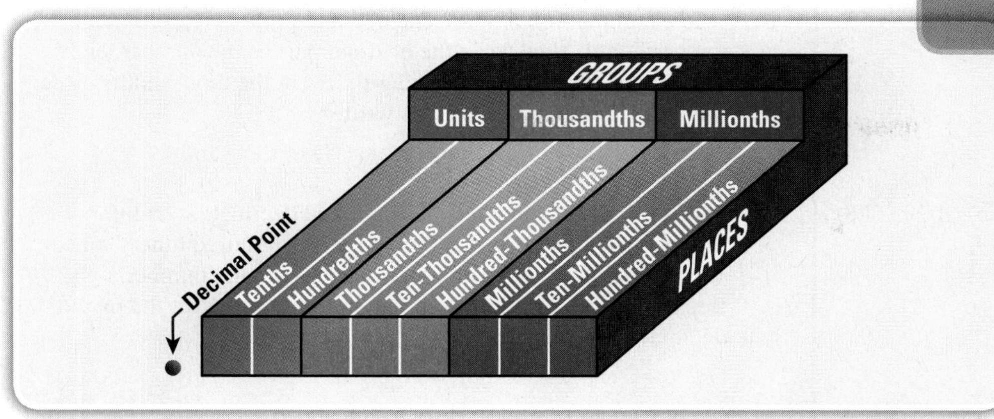

Teaching Transparency 3-1

In reading and writing mixed decimals, the decimal point should be read as "and." For example, 81.205 would be read as "eighty-one and two hundred five thousandths." If the decimal has a fraction at the end, simply read them together, using the place value of the last digit of the decimal. For example, $.12\frac{1}{2}$ would be read as "twelve and one-half hundredths."

When a dollar sign ($) precedes a number, the whole number value represents dollars and the decimal value represents cents. The decimal point is read as "and." For example, $146.79 would be read as "one hundred forty-six dollars and seventy-nine cents."

EXAMPLE 1 READING AND WRITING DECIMALS

Read and write the following numbers in word form.

a. .18 b. .0391 c. .00127 d. 34.892 e. 1,299.008 f. $.328\frac{2}{3}$

Read and write the following numbers in numerical form.

g. Three hundred seventy-two ten-thousandths
h. Sixteen thousand and forty-one hundredths
i. Twenty-five and sixty-three and one-half thousandths

SOLUTION STRATEGY

a. .18 — **Strategy:** In this example, write the number eighteen. Because the last digit, 8, is in the hundredths place, the decimal would be written:

Eighteen hundredths

b. .0391 — **Strategy:** Write the number three hundred ninety-one. The last digit, 1, is in the ten-thousandths place; therefore the decimal would be written:

Three hundred ninety-one ten-thousandths

c. .00127 — **Strategy:** Write the number one hundred twenty-seven. The last digit, 7, is in the hundred-thousandths place; therefore the decimal would be written:

One hundred twenty-seven hundred-thousandths

COLLABORATIVE LEARNING ACTIVITY

In business, numerical values are frequently given over the telephone. Have students choose a partner. Ask them to alternate, *verbally* communicating decimal numbers, while the other partner writes the number down.

Try this for practice:

You are driving to a new restaurant in an unfamiliar area. A highway billboard directs you to make a right turn at an intersection $4\frac{3}{5}$ miles ahead. If your odometer reads 16,237.8, at what mileage should you make the turn?

Solution:

$4\frac{3}{5} = 4.6$ 16,237.8 + 4.6 =
16,242.4 miles

© David J. Phillip/Associated Press

The Margin of Victory
Fractions and decimals are used in all forms of racing to express the time differences among the competitors.

d. 34.892

Strategy: This example is a mixed decimal. First, write the whole number, thirty-four. The decimal point is represented by the word *and*. Now write the decimal part as the number, eight hundred ninety-two. The last digit, 2, is in the thousandths place; therefore the mixed decimal is written:

Thirty-four and eight hundred ninety-two thousandths

e. 1,299.008

Strategy: This example is also a mixed decimal. Start by writing the whole number, one thousand, two hundred ninety-nine. Write "and" for the decimal point, and write the number eight. Because the last digit, 8, is in the thousandths place, the mixed decimal is written:

One thousand, two hundred ninety-nine and eight thousandths

f. $.328\frac{2}{3}$

Strategy: This decimal has a fraction at the end. Start by writing the number, three hundred twenty-eight. Write "and," then write the fraction, two-thirds. Because the last digit of the decimal, 8, is in the thousandths place, it is written:

Three hundred twenty-eight and two-thirds thousandths

g. Three hundred seventy-two ten-thousandths

Strategy: Write three hundred seventy-two in numerical form. Place the last digit, 2, in the ten-thousandths place. Because ten thousand has four zeros, this is four places to the right of the decimal point. Note that we have to add a zero in the tenths place for the last digit, 2, to be in the ten-thousandths place.

.0372

h. Sixteen thousand and forty-one hundredths

Strategy: Write the whole number sixteen thousand. Place the decimal point for the word *and*. Write the number forty-one, and place the last digit, 1, in the hundredths place. Note that hundred has two zeros; therefore the hundredths place is two places to the right of the decimal point.

16,000.41

i. Twenty-five and sixty-three and one-half thousandths

Strategy: Write the whole number twenty-five. Place the decimal point for the word *and*. Write the number sixty-three, and place the fraction one-half after it. Write the last digit, 3, in the thousandths place, three places to the right of the decimal point.

$25.063\frac{1}{2}$

TRY IT EXERCISE 1

Read and write the following numbers in word form.

a. .64 b. .492 c. .10019 d. 579.0004 e. 26.708 f. $.33\frac{1}{3}$

Write the following numbers in numerical form.

g. Twenty-one thousandths
h. Two hundred seventy-two and ninety-four hundred-thousandths
i. Eleven and three and one-quarter thousandths

CHECK YOUR ANSWERS WITH THE SOLUTIONS ON PAGE 90.

ROUNDING DECIMAL NUMBERS TO A SPECIFIED PLACE VALUE

Rounding decimals is important in business because frequently numbers contain many more decimal places than necessary. For monetary amounts, we round to the nearest cent, or hundredth place. For other business applications, we usually do not go beyond thousandths as a final answer.

STEPS TO ROUND DECIMALS TO A SPECIFIED PLACE VALUE

Step 1. Determine the place to which the decimal is to be rounded.

Step 2a. If the digit to the right of the one being rounded is 5 or more, increase the digit in the place being rounded by 1.

Step 2b. If the digit to the right of the one being rounded is 4 or less, do not change the digit in the place being rounded.

Step 3. Delete all digits to the right of the digit being rounded.

EXAMPLE 2 ROUNDING DECIMALS

Round the following numbers to the indicated place.

a. .0292 to hundredths b. .33945 to thousandths c. 36.798 to tenths

d. 177.0212782 to hundred-thousandths e. $46.976 to cents f. $66.622 to dollars

SOLUTION STRATEGY

Decimal Number	Indicated Place	Rounded Number
a. .0292	.0292	.03
b. .33945	.33945	.339
c. 36.798	36.798	36.8
d. 177.0212782	177.0212782	177.02128
e. $46.976	$46.976	$46.98
f. $66.622	$66.622	$67

TRY IT EXERCISE 2

Round the following numbers to the indicated place.

a. 5.78892 to thousandths b. .004522 to ten-thousandths c. $345.8791 to cents

d. 76.03324 to hundredths e. $766.43 to dollars f. 34,956.1229 to tenths

CHECK YOUR ANSWERS WITH THE SOLUTIONS ON PAGE 90.

SECTION I Review Exercises

Write the following numbers in word form.

1. .21
   Twenty-one hundredths
2. 3.76
   Three and seventy-six hundredths
3. .092
   Ninety-two thousandths
4. 14.659
   Fourteen and six hundred fifty-nine thousandths
5. 98,045.045
   Ninety-eight thousand, forty-five and forty-five thousandths
6. .000033
   Thirty-three millionths
7. .00938
   Nine hundred thirty-eight hundred-thousandths
8. $36.99\frac{2}{3}$
   Thirty-six and ninety-nine and two-thirds hundredths
9. $.00057\frac{1}{2}$
   Fifty-seven and one-half hundred-thousandths
10. $2,885.59
    Two-thousand, eight-hundred eighty-five dollars and fifty-nine cents

Write the following numbers in numerical form.

11. Eight tenths
    .8
12. Twenty-nine thousandths
    .029
13. Sixty-seven thousand, three hundred nine and four hundredths
    67,309.04
14. Eleven hundred fifty-four dollars and thirty-four cents
    $1,154.34
15. One hundred eighty-three thousand and one hundred eighty-three ten-thousandths
    183,000.0183

Round the following numbers to the indicated place.

16. .448557 to hundredths
    0.448557 = 0.45
17. 123.0069 to thousandths
    123.0069 = 123.007
18. .9229388 to ten-thousandths
    0.9229388 = 0.9229
19. .0100393 to hundred-thousandths
    0.0100393 = 0.01004
20. $688.75 to dollars
    $688.75 = $689
21. $14.59582 to cents
    $14.59582 = $14.60
22. 88.964 to tenths
    88.964 = 89.0
23. 43.0056 to hundredths
    43.0056 = 43.01
24. 1.344 to hundredths
    1.344 = 1.34
25. 45.80901 to whole numbers
    45.80901 = 46

BUSINESS DECISION TECH TALK

26. You are the assistant to the production manager for Imperial Industries. When you arrived at work, there was a message on your answering machine from an important client with a rush order. It stated the following:

Hi! This is Warren Jasper from Precision Fabricators. We need sixteen, three and three-quarter-inch widgets with a gap of fifty-seven thousandths; twenty, four and three-eighth-inch widgets with a gap of two hundred forty-nine ten-thousandths of an inch; and twenty-five widget connectors with clamps that adjust from one and twenty-three hundredths inches to five and three hundred seventy-six thousandths. Please bill and ship the order to the usual address. Thanks.

a. Write this order in numerals for the production department to process.

Imperial Industries—Production Order

Quantity	Description
16	$3\frac{3}{4}''$ Widgets —.057 Gap
20	$4\frac{3}{8}''$ Widgets —.0249 Gap
25	Connectors with Clamps—1.23″–5.376″

b. If widgets cost $4.80 per inch, regardless of gap size, and connectors cost $17.95 each, calculate the total cost of the order.

$3\frac{3}{4} \times 4.80 = \$18.00$ each

$4\frac{3}{8} \times 4.80 = \$21.00$ each

$16 \times 18.00 = 288.00$
$20 \times 21.00 = 420.00$
$25 \times 17.95 = 448.75$
$\$1,156.75$

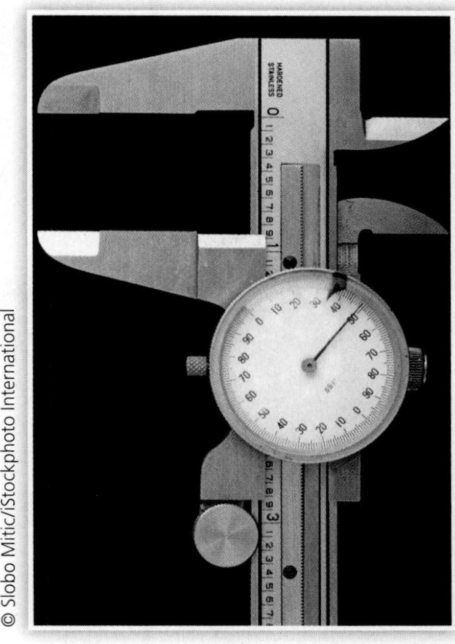

© Slobo Mitic/iStockphoto International

A *micrometer* is a device used in science and engineering for precisely measuring minute distances or thicknesses. The precision is often achieved by the rotation of a finely threaded screw mechanism.

A *micron* (also known as a *micrometer*) is a unit of length equal to one-millionth of a meter. The diameter of a human hair measures 80–100 microns.

DECIMAL NUMBERS AND THE FUNDAMENTAL PROCESSES

SECTION II 3

In business, working with decimals is an everyday occurrence. As you shall see, performing the fundamental processes of addition, subtraction, multiplication, and division on decimal numbers is very much like performing them on whole numbers. As before, the alignment of the numbers is very important. The difference is in the handling and placement of the decimal point.

ADDING AND SUBTRACTING DECIMALS

3-3

In adding and subtracting decimals we follow the same procedure as we did with whole numbers. As before, be sure that you line up all the place values, including the decimal points.

STEPS FOR ADDING AND SUBTRACTING DECIMALS

Step 1. Line up all the decimal points vertically.

Step 2. (Optional) Add zeros to the right of the decimal numbers that do not have enough places.

Step 3. Perform the addition or subtraction, working from right to left.

Step 4. Place the decimal point in the answer in the same position (column) as in the problem.

EXAMPLE 3 ADDING AND SUBTRACTING DECIMALS

a. Add 45.3922 + .0019 + 2.9 + 1,877.332
b. Add \$37.89 + \$2.76
c. Subtract 87.06 − 35.2
d. Subtract \$67.54 from \$5,400

In the Business World

Did you know the Romans called the total of addition problems *res summa*, the highest thing. Later this was shortened to *summa*, which is why we call addition answers *sums*.

When adding, the Romans always added a column of numbers starting from the bottom, putting the total at the top! This explains why we still say, "to add up."

SOLUTION STRATEGY

These examples are solved by lining up the decimal points, then performing the indicated operation as if they were whole numbers.

a.
```
    45.3922
      .0019
     2.9000
+ 1,877.3320
  1,925.6261
```

b.
```
 $37.89
 + 2.76
 $40.65
```

c.
```
  87.06
− 35.20
  51.86
```

d.
```
 $5,400.00
  − 67.54
 $5,332.46
```

TRY IT EXERCISE 3

Perform the indicated operation.

a. 35.7008 + 311.2 + 84,557.54
b. \$65.79 + \$154.33
c. Subtract 57.009 from 186.7
d. \$79.80 minus \$34.61

CHECK YOUR ANSWERS WITH THE SOLUTIONS ON PAGE 90.

3-4 MULTIPLYING DECIMALS

Decimals are multiplied in the same way as whole numbers, except we must now deal with placing the decimal point in the answer. The rule is that there must be as many decimal places in the product as there are total decimal places in the multiplier and the multiplicand. This may require adding zeros to the product.

Learning Tip

When adding, subtracting, multiplying, or dividing decimals, numbers should not be rounded until the final answer—unless you are estimating.

If the situation involves money, final answers should be rounded to the nearest cent.

STEPS FOR MULTIPLYING DECIMALS

Step 1. Multiply the numbers as if they are whole numbers. Disregard the decimal points.

Step 2. Total the number of decimal places in the multiplier and the multiplicand.

Step 3. Insert the decimal point in the product, giving it the same number of decimal places as the total from Step 2.

Step 4. If necessary, place zeros to the left of the product to provide the correct number of digits.

EXAMPLE 4 MULTIPLYING DECIMALS

a. **Multiply 125.4 by 3.12.**

SOLUTION STRATEGY

125.4	1 decimal place
× 3.12	2 decimal places
2 508	
12 54	
376 2	
391.248	3 decimal places

b. **Multiply .0004 by 6.3.**

SOLUTION STRATEGY

6.3	1 decimal place
× .0004	4 decimal places
.00252	5 decimal places

Here, we had to add 2 zeros to the left of the product to make five decimal places.

Multiplication Shortcut

3-2

Whenever you are multiplying a decimal by a power of 10, such as 10, 100, 1,000, 10,000, etc., count the number of zeros in the multiplier and move the decimal point in the multiplicand the same number of places to the right. If necessary, add zeros to the product to provide the required places.

c. **Multiply 138.57 by 10, 100, 1,000, and 10,000.**

SOLUTION STRATEGY

138.57 × 10 = 1,385.7	Decimal moved 1 place to the right
138.57 × 100 = 13,857	Decimal moved 2 places to the right
138.57 × 1,000 = 138,570	Decimal moved 3 places to the right—1 zero added
138.57 × 10,000 = 1,385,700	Decimal moved 4 places to the right—2 zeros added

TRY IT EXERCISE 4

Multiply the following numbers.

a. 876.66 × .045

b. 4,955.8 × 2.9

c. $65.79 × 558

d. .00232 by 1,000

CHECK YOUR ANSWERS WITH THE SOLUTIONS ON PAGE 90.

DIVIDING DECIMALS

In division of decimals, be aware of the decimal points. The basic rule is that you cannot divide with a decimal in the divisor. If there is a decimal, you must convert it to a whole number before dividing.

STEPS FOR DIVIDING DECIMALS IF THE DIVISOR IS A WHOLE NUMBER

Step 1. Place the decimal point in the quotient directly above the decimal point in the dividend.

Step 2. Divide the numbers.

EXAMPLE 5A DIVIDING DECIMALS

Divide: 8.50 ÷ 25.

SOLUTION STRATEGY

$$8.50 \div 25 = 25\overline{)8.50} = .34$$

```
                .34
8.50 ÷ 25 = 25)8.50
               7 5
               1 00
               1 00
                  0
```

In this example, the divisor, 25, is a whole number, so we place the decimal point in the quotient directly above the decimal point in the dividend, and then divide. The answer is .34.

STEPS FOR DIVIDING DECIMALS IF THE DIVISOR IS A DECIMAL NUMBER

TEACHING TIP
Be sure students understand that they cannot divide with a decimal in the divisor. It must be converted to a whole number.

Step 1. Move the decimal point in the divisor to the right until it becomes a whole number.

Step 2. Move the decimal point in the dividend the same number of places as you moved it in the divisor. It may be necessary to add zeros to the right of the dividend if there are not enough places.

Step 3. Place the decimal point in the quotient directly above the decimal point in the dividend.

Step 4. Divide the numbers.

Note: All answers involving money should be rounded to the nearest cent. This means dividing until the quotient has a thousandths place, and then rounding back to hundredths. For example, \$45.671 = \$45.67 or \$102.879 = \$102.88.

EXAMPLE 5B DIVIDING DECIMALS

Divide: 358.75 ÷ 17.5.

SOLUTION STRATEGY

358.75 ÷ 17.5 =

$17.5\overline{)358.75}$

In this example, the divisor, 17.5, is a decimal with one place. To make it a whole number, move the decimal point one place to the right.

$175\overline{)3587.5}$

Next move the decimal point in the dividend one place to the right and then place the decimal point in the quotient above the decimal point in the dividend.

```
      20.5
175)3587.5
    350
      87 5
      87 5
         0
```

Now divide the numbers. The answer is 20.5.

Division Shortcut

Whenever you divide a decimal by a power of 10, such as 10, 100, 1,000, 10,000, etc., count the number of zeros in the divisor and move the decimal point in the dividend the same number of places to the left. It may be necessary to add zeros to provide the required places.

3-3

EXAMPLE 5C DIVIDING DECIMALS BY A POWER OF 10

Divide 43.78 by 10, 100, 1,000, and 10,000.

SOLUTION STRATEGY

43.78 ÷ 10 = 4.378	Decimal moved 1 place to the left
43.78 ÷ 100 = .4378	Decimal moved 2 places to the left
43.78 ÷ 1,000 = .04378	Decimal moved 3 places to the left—1 zero added
43.78 ÷ 10,000 = .004378	Decimal moved 4 places to the left—2 zeros added

TRY IT EXERCISE 5

Divide the following decimals.

a. 716.8 ÷ 16 b. 21.336 ÷ .007 c. $3,191.18 ÷ 42.1 d. 2.03992 ÷ 1,000

CHECK YOUR ANSWERS WITH THE SOLUTIONS ON PAGE 90.

Review Exercises

SECTION II

Perform the indicated operation for the following.

1. 2.03 + 56.003
```
   2.030
+ 56.003
  58.033
```

2. .006 + 12.33
```
    .006
+ 12.330
  12.336
```

3. $24.66 + $19.72 + $.89
```
  $24.66
   19.72
+    .89
  $45.27
```

4. 54.669 + 121.3393 + 7.4
```
   54.6690
  121.3393
+   7.4000
  183.4083
```

5. .000494 + 45.776 + 16.008 + 91
```
   .000494
  45.776000
  16.008000
+ 91.000000
 152.784494
```

6. 495.09 − 51.05
```
  495.09
−  51.05
  444.04
```

7. 58.043 − 41.694

58.043
− 41.694
16.349

8. $70.55 − $12.79

$70.55
− 12.79
$57.76

9. $1.71 − $.84

$1.71
− .84
$87

10. 28.90922 − 16.41

28.90922
− 16.41000
12.49922

11. Meadow Brook Farms shipped 218 pounds of strawberries, 186.9 pounds of cherries, and 374.85 pounds of apples to the Ritz Hotel. What was the total weight of the order?

218.00 Strawberries
186.90 Cherries
+ 374.85 Apples
779.75 Pounds

12. While at the mall, Kimberly Adams spent $46.50 for a blouse, $39.88 for a skirt, and $51.99 for a pair of shoes. What was the total amount of Kimberly's purchases?

46.50 Blouse
39.88 Skirt
+ 51.99 Shoes
$138.37 Total purchase

13. On a recent trip, Carlos Mendez filled up his gas tank four times with the following quantities of gasoline: 23.4 gallons, 19.67 gallons, 21.008 gallons, and 16.404 gallons. How many gallons did Carlos buy?

23.400
19.670
21.008
+ 16.404
80.482 Gallons

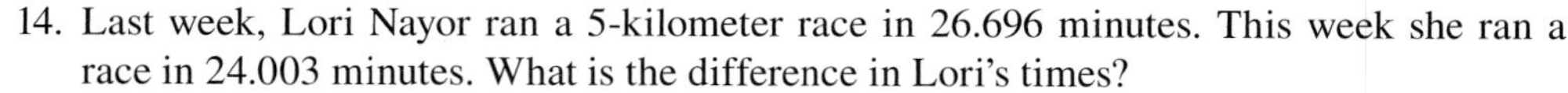

14. Last week, Lori Nayor ran a 5-kilometer race in 26.696 minutes. This week she ran a race in 24.003 minutes. What is the difference in Lori's times?

26.696
− 24.003
2.693 Minutes

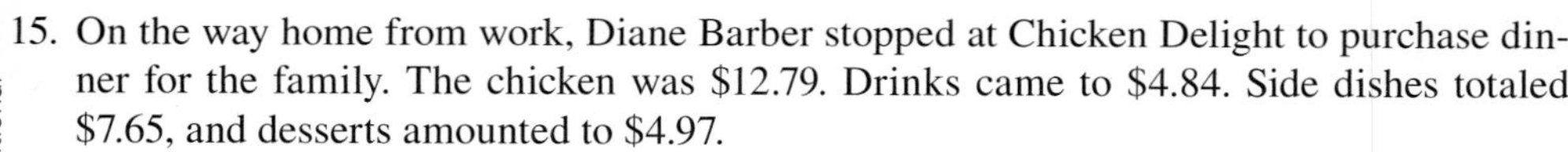

15. On the way home from work, Diane Barber stopped at Chicken Delight to purchase dinner for the family. The chicken was $12.79. Drinks came to $4.84. Side dishes totaled $7.65, and desserts amounted to $4.97.

a. What was the total cost of the food?

$12.79 Chicken
4.84 Drinks
7.65 Side dishes
+ 4.97 Desserts
$30.25 Total cost

b. If Diane had a coupon for "$2.50 off of any purchase over $15," how much did she pay?

$30.25 Total cost
− 2.50 Coupon discount
$27.75 Final cost

© Graham Heywood/iStockphoto International

A **kilometer** is a distance of one thousand meters. It is the equivalent of .62 miles. Running races are routinely measured in kilometers and miles. A 5-kilometer race distance is the equivalent of 3.1 miles. (5 × .62 = 3.1)

16. Before dieting, Gene Porter weighed 188.75 pounds. After three weeks, he weighed 179.46. How much weight did Gene lose?

188.75
− 179.46
9.29 Pounds

17. Rob Williamson needed a few groceries. At Quick-Stop Market he bought a loaf of cinnamon raisin bread for $2.29, a quart of milk for $1.78, a bunch of bananas for $1.83, and a pound of butter for $2.96. How much change did he receive from a $20 bill?

    $2.29 Bread
    1.78 Milk
    1.83 Bananas
    + 2.96 Butter
    $8.86 Total cost

    $20.00
    − 8.86
    $11.14 Change

18. Erica Gurley received her monthly pension check of $1,348.26. From that amount she transferred $180 to a savings account and paid the electricity bill for $156.33, the gas bill for $9.38, the water bill for $98.42, and the cable television bill for $48.54. How much remained of Erica's monthly pension?

    $180.00 Savings
    156.33 Electricity
    9.38 Gas
    98.42 Water
    + 48.54 Cable TV
    $492.67 Total

    $1,348.26
    − 492.67
    $855.59 Remained

19. A lab assistant at Dyno Tech weighed samples of a chemical compound. The samples weighed 6.12 grams, 6.102 grams, 6.122 grams, 6.0012 grams, and 6.0122 grams.

    a. Arrange the weights in ascending order.

    6.0012 grams, 6.0122 grams, 6.102 grams, 6.12 grams, 6.122 grams

    b. How much weight would need to be added to the lightest sample to make it weigh the same as the heaviest sample?

    6.1220
    −6.0012
    .1208 Grams

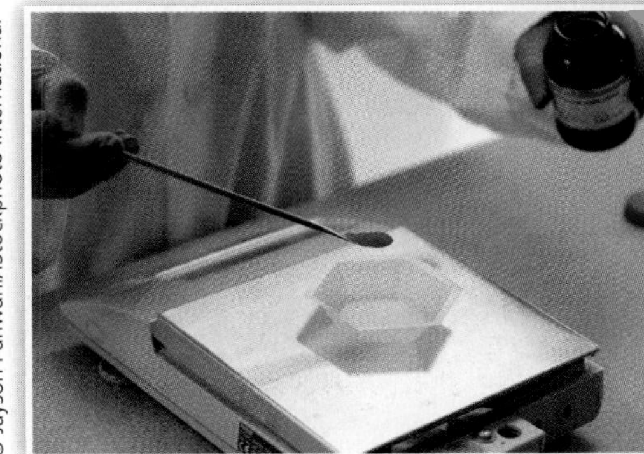

© Jayson Punwani/iStockphoto International

Decimals are used extensively in scientific and medical measurements. Today's electronic scales are able to measure extremely small quantities.

Multiply the following numbers.

20. 45.77 × 12 = 549.24

21. 494.09 × .81 = 400.2129

22. 2.311 × 3.2 = 7.3952

23. 112.005 × 10,000 = 1,120,050

24. .00202 × 24 = .04848

25. 15.032 × 1.008
    15.032
    × 1.008
    15.152256

26. 45.0079 × 1,000
    45.0079
    × 1,000
    45,007.9

27. .3309 × 100,000
    .3309
    × 100,000
    33,090

Divide the following numbers. Round to hundredths when necessary.

28. 24.6 ÷ 19
    1.294 = 1.29

29. .593 ÷ 8.6
    .068 = .07

30. 18.69 ÷ 1,000
    .018 = .02

31. $24.50 ÷ 9
    2.722 = $2.72

32. 72)266.4
    3.7
    72)266.4 = 3.7

33. 23.18)139.08
    6
    2318)13908 = 6

34. .04)62.2
    1555
    4)6220 = 1,555

35. 4.6)1000
    217.391
    46)10000.000 = 217.39

© Apple/PR Newswire Photo Service (Newscom)

iTunes is the world's most popular online music, TV and movie store, featuring a catalog of over five million songs, 550 television shows, and 500 movies. As of July 31, 2007, over three billion songs had been purchased and downloaded from the iTunes Stores, www.itunes.com.

36. Bruce Vaughn received a \$25 gift card to iTunes for his birthday. If he downloaded 14 songs at \$0.99 per song, how much credit remained on the gift card?

$$\begin{array}{r} 0.99 \\ \times\ \ 14 \\ \hline \$13.86 \end{array} \qquad \begin{array}{r} 25.00 \\ -\ 13.86 \\ \hline \underline{\underline{\$11.14}} \end{array} \text{ Remained}$$

37. Jim Bright bought a car at Auto Nation for \$14,566.90. The sticker price was \$17,047.88.

a. How much did Jim save from the sticker price?

$$\begin{array}{rl} 17,047.88 & \text{Sticker price} \\ -\ 14,566.90 & \text{Sale price} \\ \hline \underline{\underline{\$2,480.98}} & \text{Saved} \end{array}$$

b. The tax was \$957.70, and the registration and license plate cost \$65.40. What is the total cost of the car?

$$\begin{array}{rl} 14,566.90 & \text{Price of car} \\ 957.70 & \text{Tax} \\ +\ \ 65.40 & \text{Registration and license plate} \\ \hline \underline{\underline{\$15,590.00}} & \text{Total cost} \end{array}$$

c. If Jim makes a down payment of \$4,550 and gets an interest-free car loan from the dealer, what will the equal monthly payments be for 48 months?

$$\begin{array}{rl} 15,590 & \text{Total cost} \\ -\ \ 4,550 & \text{Down payment} \\ \hline \$11,040 & \text{Amount financed} \end{array} \qquad \frac{11,040}{48} = \underline{\underline{\$230}} \text{ Monthly payment}$$

38. Scott Willis needs parts to repair his electric stove. He buys a large cook top element for \$16.48, a shield for \$8.27, and a clip for \$2.96. Because Scott lacks experience, he decides to hire a repair person who charges \$65 an hour. If the hired repair person used the parts Scott bought and took an hour and a half to do the work, what is Scott's total outlay for repairing the stove?

$$\begin{array}{rl} 16.48 & \text{Cook top element} \\ 8.27 & \text{Shield} \\ 2.96 & \text{Clip} \\ +\ 97.50 & \text{Labor } (65 \times 1.5 \text{ hours}) \\ \hline \underline{\underline{\$125.21}} & \text{Total} \end{array}$$

39. A vegetable wholesaler sold 1,168.07 pounds of potatoes, 1,246.11 pounds of lettuce, and 1,217.82 pounds of onions on Monday.

    a. What is the total pounds the wholesaler sold?

    1,168.07 Potatoes
    1,246.11 Lettuce
    + 1,217.82 Onions
    3,632.00 Total pounds

    b. If the wholesaler had eight customers on Monday, what was the average pounds per sale?

    $\frac{3,632}{8} = \underline{\underline{454}}$ Average pounds per sale

TEACHING TIP

This may be a good time to introduce students to averages, a concept used extensively in business.

A numerical *average* is a number that is representative of a whole set of values.

$$\text{Average} = \frac{\text{Sum of values}}{\text{Number of values}}$$

To demonstrate, calculate the average age of the students in the class.

40. Last week you worked 18 hours and earned $256.50. What was your hourly rate?

    $\frac{256.50 \text{ Earnings}}{18 \text{ Hours}} = \underline{\underline{\$14.25}}$ Per hour

41. Danny Alioto purchased 153.6 square yards of carpeting on sale for $13.70 per yard.

    a. What was the cost of the carpet?

    153.6 Sq yd
    × 13.70 Price per yard
    $2,104.32 Cost of carpet

    b. Normally, this carpeting sells for $19.69 per yard. How much did Danny save by purchasing during the sale?

    19.69 Regular price
    − 13.70 Sale price
    $5.99 Savings per yard

    153.6 Sq yd
    × 5.99 Savings per yard
    $920.06 Total savings

42. Eric Wilson has room for 26 bedding plants in his garden. He can get pansies for $1.89 each, marigolds for $1.29 each, and zinnias for $0.84 each. He plans to buy 10 of one type and 8 each of the other two types of plants.

    a. What is the minimum Eric will have to spend?

    $(10 \times 0.84) + (8 \times 1.89) + (8 \times 1.29) = 8.40 + 15.12 + 10.32 = \underline{\underline{\$33.84}}$

    b. What is the maximum Eric could spend?

    $(10 \times 1.89) + (8 \times 1.29) + (8 \times 0.84) = 18.90 + 10.32 + 6.72 = \underline{\underline{\$35.94}}$

43. Southern Telecom is offering a prepaid phone card that contains 200 minutes of time for 8 cents per minute. What is the cost of the card?

    $200 \times 0.08 = \underline{\underline{\$16}}$ Cost of the phone card

44. A developer, Hidden Valley Homes, is building 13 townhouses at one time. Each roof measures 45.7 feet by 68.55 feet.

    a. What is the total square feet per roof? (Multiply length by width.)

    68.55
    × 45.7
    3,132.735 Sq ft per roof

    b. What is the total square feet of roof for the entire project?

    3,132.735
    × 13
    40,725.555 Total sq ft

    c. If the roofing company charges $4.15 per square foot, what is the total cost of the roofs?

    40,725.555 Total sq ft
    × 4.15 Cost per sq ft
    $169,011.05 Total cost

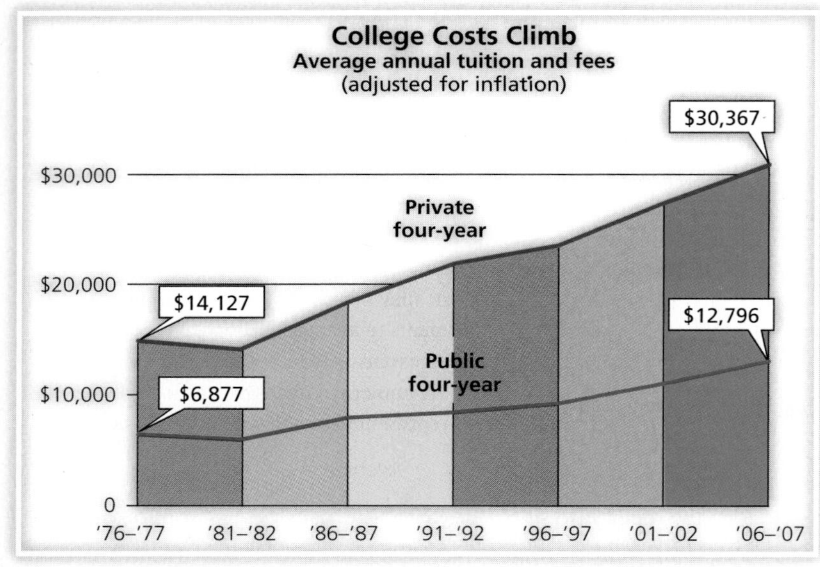

Source: *USA Today*, February 12, 2007, p. 2B. Reproduced with permission.

Use the chart, College Costs Climb, for Exercises 45–47.

45. How much did public four-year college costs increase from the '76–'77 school year to the '06–'07 school year?

    12,796 '06–'07
    − 6,877 '76–'77
    $5,919

46. How much did private four-year college costs increase from the '76–'77 school year to the '06–'07 school year?

    30,367 '06–'07
    − 14,127 '76–'77
    $16,240

47. Using the school year '06–'07 cost figures, how much more would 4 years at a private college cost?

    30,367 Private college
    − 12,796 Public college
    $17,571

    17,571
    × 4
    $70,284 More

BUSINESS DECISION PRICING FOR PROFIT

48. Brian Joyner owns a PepsiCo vending truck that holds 360 quarts of soda. Last Saturday at a carnival, Brian sold out completely. He sells a 10-ounce Pepsi for $1.25. There are 16 ounces in a pint and 2 pints in a quart.

    a. How many drinks did he serve?

    360 Quarts
    × 2
    720 Pints
    × 16
    11,520 Ounces

    $\frac{11{,}520 \text{ Total ounces}}{10 \text{ Ounces per drink}} = 1{,}152$ Drinks served

    b. How much revenue did he take in for the day?

    1,152 Drinks served
    × 1.25 Per drink
    $1,440 Revenue for the day

    c. For the next carnival, Brian is considering switching to either a 12-ounce drink for $1.65 or a 16-ounce drink for $1.95. As his business advisor, what size do you recommend, assuming each would be a sellout?

    $\frac{11{,}520 \text{ Total ounces}}{12 \text{ Ounces per drink}} =$ 960 Drinks
    × 1.65 Per drink
    $1,584 Revenue

    $\frac{11{,}520 \text{ Total ounces}}{16 \text{ Ounces per drink}} =$ 720 Drinks
    × 1.95 Per drink
    $1,404 Revenue

    12-ounce size Produces most revenue.

© Amy Etra/PhotoEdit, Inc.

Cola Wars!
According to Eurometer, in 2006, Coca-Cola had 44% and Pepsi had 31.2% of the $63 billion U.S. soft drink market.

CONVERSION OF DECIMALS TO FRACTIONS AND FRACTIONS TO DECIMALS

Changing a number from decimal form to its fractional equivalent, or changing a number in fractional form to its decimal equivalent, is common in the business world. For example, a builder or an architect may use fractions when dealing with the measurements of a project but convert to decimals when calculating the cost of materials.

CONVERTING DECIMALS TO FRACTIONS

3-6

Keep in mind that decimals are another way of writing fractions whose denominators are powers of 10 (10, 100, 1,000 . . .). When you are converting a mixed decimal, the whole number is added to the new fraction, resulting in a mixed fraction.

STEPS FOR CONVERTING DECIMALS TO THEIR FRACTIONAL EQUIVALENT

Step 1. Write the numerator of the fraction as the decimal number, without the decimal point.

Step 2. Write the denominator as 1 followed by as many zeros as there are decimal places in the original decimal number.

Step 3. Reduce the fraction to lowest terms.

EXAMPLE 6 CONVERTING DECIMALS TO FRACTIONS

Convert the following numbers to their reduced fractional equivalent.

a. .64 b. .125 c. .0457 d. 17.31

SOLUTION STRATEGY

a. $.64 = \frac{64}{100} = \frac{16}{25}$

In this example, 64 becomes the numerator. Because there are two decimal places, the denominator is 1 with two zeros. Then reduce the fraction.

b. $.125 = \frac{125}{1{,}000} = \frac{1}{8}$

Once again, the decimal becomes the numerator, 125. This decimal has three places; therefore, the denominator will be 1 followed by three zeros. The resulting fraction is then reduced to lowest terms.

c. $.0457 = \frac{457}{10{,}000}$

This fraction does not reduce.

d. $17.31 = 17 + \frac{31}{100} = 17\frac{31}{100}$

This mixed decimal results in a mixed fraction. It cannot be reduced.

Learning Tip

When converting decimals to fractions, verbally "say" the decimal and then write down what you said as a fraction. For example:

- .85 would be verbally stated as "eighty-five hundredths" and written as $\frac{85}{100}$.
- .655 would be verbally stated as "six hundred fifty-five thousandths" and written as $\frac{655}{1{,}000}$.

TRY IT EXERCISE 6

Convert the following decimals to their fractional equivalent, reducing where possible.

a. .875 b. 23.076 c. .0004 d. 84.75

CHECK YOUR ANSWERS WITH THE SOLUTIONS ON PAGE 90.

CONVERTING FRACTIONS TO DECIMALS

In Chapter 2, we learned that fractions are actually a way of expressing a division, with the line separating the numerator and the denominator representing "divided by."

$$\frac{\textbf{Numerator (dividend)}}{\textbf{Denominator (divisor)}} = \textbf{Denominator} \overline{)\textbf{Numerator}}$$

In business, decimal numbers are usually rounded to three places (thousandths) or less. When expressing money, round to the nearest hundredth, or cent.

STEPS FOR CONVERTING FRACTIONS TO DECIMALS

Step 1. Divide the numerator by the denominator.

Step 2. Add a decimal point and zeros, as necessary, to the numerator (dividend).

EXAMPLE 7 CONVERTING FRACTIONS TO DECIMALS

Convert the following fractions to their decimal equivalents, rounding to hundredths.

a. $\frac{3}{5}$ b. $\frac{1}{3}$ c. $\frac{23}{9}$ d. $15\frac{3}{8}$

SOLUTION STRATEGY

a. $\frac{3}{5} = 5\overline{)3.0}$ = .6 = $\underline{\underline{.6}}$

In this example, the numerator, 3, becomes the dividend, with a decimal point and zero added. The denominator, 5, becomes the divisor.

b. $\frac{1}{3} = 3\overline{)1.0000}$ = .3333 = $\underline{\underline{.33}}$

In this example, the division is uneven and goes on and on, so we round the quotient to hundredths.

c. $\frac{23}{9} = 9\overline{)23.00000}$ = 2.55555 = $\underline{\underline{2.56}}$

Improper fractions result in mixed decimals. Note that the quotient was rounded because of an endlessly repeating decimal.

d. $15\frac{3}{8} = 15 + 8\overline{)3.000}$ = .375 = $\underline{\underline{15.38}}$

This example contains a whole number. Remember to add it to the resulting decimal.

Learning Tip

When fractions such as $\frac{2}{3}$ are converted to decimals, the result is a *repeating decimal*. These may be written as .666, or for business applications, rounded to tenths or hundredths.

Others include: $\frac{1}{3}, \frac{1}{6}, \frac{5}{6}, \frac{1}{9}, \frac{4}{9}, \frac{23}{9}$.

TRY IT EXERCISE 7

Convert the following fractions to their decimal equivalents, rounding to hundredths where necessary.

a. $\frac{4}{5}$ b. $84\frac{2}{3}$ c. $\$6\frac{3}{4}$ d. $\frac{5}{2}$ e. $\frac{5}{8}$

CHECK YOUR ANSWERS WITH THE SOLUTIONS ON PAGE 91

Review Exercises

SECTION III 3

Convert the following decimals to fractions and reduce to lowest terms.

1. .125 $\frac{125}{1,000} = \frac{1}{8}$
2. 4.75 $4\frac{75}{100} = 4\frac{3}{4}$
3. .008 $\frac{8}{1,000} = \frac{1}{125}$
4. 93.0625 $93\frac{625}{10,000} = 93\frac{1}{16}$
5. 14.82 $14\frac{82}{100} = 14\frac{41}{50}$

Convert the following fractions to decimals. Round the quotients to hundredths when necessary.

6. $\frac{9}{16}$ .5625 = .56
7. $5\frac{2}{3}$ 5.666 = 5.67
8. $24\frac{1}{8}$ 24.125 = 24.13
9. $\frac{55}{45}$ $1\frac{10}{45}$ = 1.222 = 1.22
10. $\frac{3}{5}$ .6

For the following numbers, perform the indicated operation.

11. $34.55 + 14.08 + 9\frac{4}{5}$

$$\begin{array}{r} 34.55 \\ 14.08 \\ +\ 9.80 \\ \hline 58.43 \end{array}$$

12. $565.809 - 224\frac{3}{4}$

$$\begin{array}{r} 565.809 \\ -\ 224.750 \\ \hline 341.059 \end{array}$$

13. $12\frac{1}{2} \div 2.5$ 12.5 ÷ 2.5 = 5

14. $\$35.88 \times 21\frac{1}{4}$

$$\begin{array}{r} 35.88 \\ \times\ 21.25 \\ \hline \$762.45 \end{array}$$

15. a. How many eight-slice pizzas must you purchase to feed 24 women, who eat $2\frac{1}{8}$ slices each, and 20 men, who eat $3\frac{3}{4}$ slices each? Round to the nearest whole pizza.

Women 24 × 2.125 = 51 Slices
Men 20 × 3.75 = 75 Slices

$$\begin{array}{r} 51 \\ +\ 75 \\ \hline 126 \end{array}$$ Total slices

$\frac{126}{8} = 15.75 = 16$ Pizzas

b. If each pizza costs $11.89, what is the total cost?

$$\begin{array}{rl} 16 & \text{Pizzas} \\ \times\ 11.89 & \text{Cost per pizza} \\ \hline \$190.24 & \text{Total cost} \end{array}$$

16. Clare Davey buys $4\frac{3}{5}$ pounds of potatoes at $.75 per pound. What is the cost of the potatoes?

$4\frac{3}{5} \times .75 =$

$$\begin{array}{rl} 4.6 & \text{Pounds of potatoes} \\ \times\ .75 & \text{Price per pound} \\ \hline \$3.45 & \text{Total cost} \end{array}$$

17. a. What is the total cost of fuel for a 3,003 mile trip, if your vehicle gets 15.4 miles per gallon and the average cost of gasoline is $\$2.50\frac{9}{10}$? Round to the nearest cent.

$\frac{3,003}{15.4} = 195$ Gallons

$$\begin{array}{r} 195 \\ \times\ 2.509 \\ \hline 489.255 \end{array}$$ = $489.255 Cost of fuel

Pizza, Pizza!

According to the National Restaurant Association, pizza is a $30+ billion per year industry, with over 69,000 pizzerias in the United States.

Americans eat approximately 100 acres of pizza each day, or about 350 slices per second. That amounts to over 3 billion pizzas per year; an average of 46 slices (23 pounds) for each man, woman, and child.

b. While on the trip, you paid $368.50 for engine repairs and $37.80 for a new battery. In addition, tolls amounted to $45.75 and parking averaged $4.50 per day for nine days. What was the cost per mile for the trip? Round to the nearest tenth of a cent.

489.26 Fuel
368.50 Repairs
37.80 Battery
45.75 Tolls
+ 40.50 Parking (4.50 × 9)
$981.81

$\frac{981.81}{3{,}003} = .3269 = 32.7¢$ Per mile

18. You are the purchasing manager for Precision Graphics, a company that uses specially treated photo paper. The yellow paper costs $\$.07\frac{1}{5}$ per sheet and the blue paper costs $\$.05\frac{3}{8}$ per sheet. If you order 15,000 yellow sheets and 26,800 blue sheets, what is the total cost of the order?

Yellow
15,000 Sheets
× .072 Price per sheet
$1,080 Cost—yellow

Blue
26,800 Sheets
× .05375 Price per sheet
$1,440.50 Cost—blue

1,080.00 Cost—yellow
+ 1,440.50 Cost—blue
$2,520.50 Total cost

19. Magic City taxicabs charge $1.20 for the first $\frac{1}{4}$ of a mile, and $.35 for each additional $\frac{1}{4}$ of a mile. What is the cost of a trip from the airport to downtown, a distance of $8\frac{3}{4}$ miles?

.35 Cost per $\frac{1}{4}$ mile
× 4 $\frac{1}{4}$'s Per mile
$1.40 Cost per mile

1.40 Per mile
× 8.5 Miles left after first $\frac{1}{4}$
11.90
+ 1.20 First $\frac{1}{4}$ mile
$13.10 Cost from airport

BUSINESS DECISION QUALIFYING FOR A MORTGAGE

20. You are a loan officer at the Grand Luxe Savings and Loan. Mr. and Mrs. Winston are in your office to apply for a mortgage loan on a house they want to buy. The house has a market value of $180,000. Your bank requires $\frac{1}{5}$ of the market value as a down payment.

a. What is the amount of the down payment?

$\frac{1}{5} \times 180{,}000 = \$36{,}000$

b. What is the amount of the mortgage for which the Winstons are applying?

$180{,}000 - 36{,}000 = \$144{,}000$

c. The current annual interest rate for a 30-year mortgage is 9 percent. At that rate, the monthly payments for principal and interest on the loan will be $8.05 for every $1,000 financed. What is the amount of the principal and interest portion of the Winstons' monthly payment?

$\frac{144{,}000}{1{,}000} = 144 \quad 144 \times 8.05 = \$1{,}159.20$

d. What is the total amount of interest that will be paid over the life of the loan?

30 × 12 = 360 months
360 × 1,159.20 = $417,312
417,312 − 144,000 = $273,312

e. Your bank also requires that the monthly mortgage payments include property tax and homeowner's insurance payments. If the property tax is $1,710 per year and the property insurance is $1,458 per year, what is the total monthly payment for PITI (principal, interest, taxes, and insurance)?

$\frac{1{,}710 + 1{,}458}{12} = 264.00 \quad 1{,}159.20 + 264.00 = \$1{,}423.20$

f. To qualify for the loan, bank rules state that mortgage payments cannot exceed $\frac{1}{4}$ of the combined monthly income of the family. If the Winstons earn $5,350 per month, will they qualify for this loan?

$\frac{1}{4} \times 5{,}350 = \$1{,}337.50$ = Maximum payment allowed. Will not qualify.

g. What monthly income would be required to qualify for this size mortgage payment?

$1{,}423.20 \times 4 = \$5{,}692.80$

SUMMARY CHART

3

Section I: Understanding Decimal Numbers

Topic	Important Concepts	Illustrative Examples
Reading and Writing Decimal Numbers in Numerical and Word Form **P/O 3-1, p. 68**	In decimals, the value of each place, starting at the decimal point and moving from left to right, decreases by a factor of 10. The names of the places end in *ths;* they are tenths, hundredths, thousandths, ten-thousandths, hundred-thousandths, millionths and so on. 1. To write decimal numbers in words, write the decimal part as a whole number, then add the place value of the last digit on the right. 2. When writing mixed decimals, the decimal point should be read as "and." 3. If the decimal ends in a fraction, read them together, using the place value of the last digit of the decimal. 4. When a dollar sign ($) precedes a number, the whole number value represents dollars, the decimal value represents cents, and the decimal point is read as "and."	*Decimal Numbers* .0691 is six hundred ninety-one ten-thousandths Twenty-one ten-thousandths is .0021 *Mixed Decimals* 51.305 is fifty-one and three hundred five thousandths Eighteen and thirty-six thousandths is 18.036 *Decimals with Fractions* $.22\frac{1}{2}$ is twenty-two and one-half hundredths Seventeen and one-half hundredths is $.17\frac{1}{2}$ *Dollars and Cents* $946.73 is nine hundred forty-six dollars and seventy-three cents Six dollars and twelve cents is $6.12
Rounding Decimal Numbers to a Specified Place Value **P/O 3-2, p. 71**	1. Determine the place to which the decimal is to be rounded. 2a. If the digit to the right of the one being rounded is 5 or more, increase the digit in the place being rounded by 1. 2b. If the digit to the right of the one being rounded is 4 or less, do not change the digit in the place being rounded. 3. Delete all digits to the right of the one being rounded.	Round as indicated: .645 rounded to hundredths is .65 42.5596 rounded to tenths is 42.6 .00291 rounded to thousandths is .003 $75.888 rounded to cents is $75.89

Section II: Decimal Numbers and the Fundamental Processes

Topic	Important Concepts	Illustrative Examples
Adding and Subtracting Decimals **P/O 3-3, p. 73**	1. Line up all the place values, including the decimal points. 2. The decimal point in the answer will appear in the same position (column) as in the problem. 3. You may add zeros to the right of the decimal numbers that do not have enough places.	Addition: 2,821.049 12.500 + 143.008 2,976.557 Subtraction: 194.1207 − 45.3400 148.7807

Section II: (continued)

Topic	Important Concepts	Illustrative Examples
Multiplying Decimals **P/O 3-4, p. 74**	1. Multiply the numbers as if they are whole numbers, disregarding the decimal points. 2. Total the number of decimal places in the multiplier and the multiplicand. 3. Insert the decimal point in the product, giving it the same number of decimal places as the total from Step 2. 4. If necessary, place zeros to the left of the product to provide the correct number of digits. *Note:* If the situation involves money, answers should be rounded to the nearest cent.	Multiply 224.5 by 4.53 224.5 1 decimal place × 4.53 2 decimal places 6 735 112 25 898 0 1,016.985 3 decimal places
Multiplication Shortcut: Powers of 10 **P/O 3-4, p. 75**	When multiplying a decimal times a power of 10 (such as 10, 100, 1,000, 10,000, etc.): 1. Count the number of zeros in the multiplier and move the decimal point in the multiplicand the same number of places to the right. 2. If necessary, add zeros to the product to provide the required places.	Multiply .064 × 10 = .64 1 place .064 × 100 = 6.4 2 places .064 × 1,000 = 64 3 places .064 × 10,000 = 640 4 places .064 × 100,000 = 6,400 5 places
Dividing Decimals **P/O 3-5, p. 75**	*If the divisor is a whole number:* 1. Place the decimal point in the quotient directly above the decimal point in the dividend. 2. Divide the numbers. *If the divisor is a decimal number:* 1. Move the decimal point in the divisor to the right until it becomes a whole number. 2. Move the decimal point in the dividend the same number of places you moved it in the divisor. It may be necessary to add zeros to the right of the dividend if there are not enough places. 3. Place the decimal point in the quotient directly above the decimal point in the dividend. 4. Divide the numbers. *Note:* All answers involving money should be rounded to the nearest cent.	Divide: 9.5 ÷ 25 .38 25)9.50 7 5 2 00 2 00 0 Divide: 14.3 ÷ 2.2 2.2)14.3 6.5 22)143.0 132 11 0 11 0 0
Division Shortcut: Powers of 10 **P/O 3-5, p. 77**	When dividing a decimal by a power of 10 (10, 100, 1,000, 10,000, . . .): 1. Count the number of zeros in the divisor, and move the decimal point in the dividend the same number of places to the left. 2. It may be necessary to add zeros to provide the required number of decimal places.	Divide 21.69 ÷ 10 = 2.169 1 place 21.69 ÷ 100 = .2169 2 places 21.69 ÷ 1,000 = .02169 3 places 21.69 ÷ 10,000 = .002169 4 places
Converting Decimals to Fractions **P/O 3-6, p. 83**	1. Write the numerator of the fraction as the decimal number, without the decimal point. 2. Write the denominator as "1" followed by as many zeros as there are decimal places in the original decimal number. 3. Reduce the fraction to lowest terms.	$.88 = \frac{88}{100} = \frac{22}{25}$ $5.57 = 5 + \frac{57}{100} = 5\frac{57}{100}$
Converting Fractions to Decimals **P/O 3-7, p. 84**	1. Divide the numerator by the denominator. 2. Add a decimal point and zeros, as necessary, to the numerator.	$\frac{4}{5}$ = 5)4.0 = .8 $\frac{22}{4}$ = 4)22.0 = 5.5

TRY IT EXERCISE SOLUTIONS FOR CHAPTER 3

1a. Sixty-four hundredths

b. Four hundred ninety-two thousandths

c. Ten thousand nineteen hundred-thousandths

d. Five hundred seventy-nine and four ten-thousandths

e. Twenty-six and seven hundred eight thousandths

f. Thirty-three and one-third hundredths

g. .021

h. 272.00094

i. $11.003\frac{1}{4}$

2a. 5.78892 = 5.789

b. .004522 = .0045

c. \$345.8791 = \$345.88

d. 76.03324 = 76.03

e. \$766.43 = \$766

f. 34,956.1229 = 34,956.1

3a.
$$\begin{array}{r} 35.7008 \\ 311.2000 \\ +\ 84{,}557.5400 \\ \hline 84{,}904.4408 \end{array}$$

b.
$$\begin{array}{r} 65.79 \\ +154.33 \\ \hline \$220.12 \end{array}$$

c.
$$\begin{array}{r} 186.700 \\ -\ 57.009 \\ \hline 129.691 \end{array}$$

d.
$$\begin{array}{r} 79.80 \\ -\ 34.61 \\ \hline \$45.19 \end{array}$$

4a.
$$\begin{array}{r} 876.66 \\ \times\ .045 \\ \hline 4\ 38330 \\ 35\ 0664\ \ \\ \hline 39.44970 \end{array}$$

b.
$$\begin{array}{r} 4{,}955.8 \\ \times\ 2.9 \\ \hline 4\ 460\ 22 \\ 9\ 911\ 6\ \ \\ \hline 14{,}371.82 \end{array}$$

c.
$$\begin{array}{r} 65.79 \\ \times\ 558 \\ \hline 526\ 32 \\ 3\ 289\ 5\ \ \\ 32\ 895\ \ \ \ \\ \hline \$36{,}710.82 \end{array}$$

d. .00232 × 1,000 = 2.32

5a.
$$\begin{array}{r} 44.8 \\ 16\overline{)716.8} \\ 64 \\ \hline 76 \\ 64 \\ \hline 12\ 8 \\ 12\ 8 \\ \hline 0 \end{array}$$

b.
$$\begin{array}{r} 3048 \\ 7\overline{)21336} \\ 21 \\ \hline 33 \\ 28 \\ \hline 56 \\ 56 \\ \hline 0 \end{array}$$

c.
$$\begin{array}{r} 75.8 = \$75.80 \\ 421\overline{)31911.8} \\ +2947 \\ \hline 2441 \\ 2105 \\ \hline 336\ 8 \\ 336\ 8 \\ \hline 0 \end{array}$$

d. 2.03992 ÷ 1,000 = .00203992

6a. $\frac{875}{1,000} = \frac{7}{8}$

b. $23\frac{76}{1,000} = 23\frac{19}{250}$

c. $\frac{4}{10,000} = \frac{1}{2,500}$

d. $84\frac{75}{100} = 84\frac{3}{4}$

7a. $\frac{4}{5} = .8$

$$\begin{array}{r} .8 \\ 5\overline{)4.0} \\ 4\ 0 \\ \hline 0 \end{array}$$

b. $84\frac{2}{3} = 84.67$

$$\begin{array}{r} .666 \\ 84 + 3\overline{)2.000} \\ 1\ 8 \\ \hline 20 \\ 18 \\ \hline 20 \\ 18 \\ \hline 2 \end{array}$$

c. $\$6\frac{3}{4} = \$6.75$

$$\begin{array}{r} .75 \\ 6 + 4\overline{)3.00} \\ 2\ 8 \\ \hline 20 \\ 20 \\ \hline 0 \end{array}$$

d. $\frac{5}{2} = 2.5$

$$\begin{array}{r} 2.5 \\ 2\overline{)5.0} \\ 4 \\ \hline 1\ 0 \\ 1\ 0 \\ \hline 0 \end{array}$$

e. $\frac{5}{8} = .63$

$$\begin{array}{r} .625 \\ 8\overline{)5.000} \\ 4\ 8 \\ \hline 20 \\ 16 \\ \hline 40 \\ 40 \\ \hline 0 \end{array}$$

CONCEPT REVIEW

1. Just as with fractions, ____ are a way of expressing parts of a whole thing. (3-1)
decimals

2. The ____ ____ separates the whole number part from the decimal part of a mixed decimal. It is read as the word "____." (3-1)
decimal point, and

3. When rounding decimals, we delete all digits to the ____ of the digit being rounded. (3-2)
right

4. When rounding monetary amounts, we round to the nearest ____, or ____ place. (3-2)
cent, hundredths

5. When adding or subtracting decimals, we begin by lining up all the ____ ____ vertically. (3-3)
decimal points or place values

6. When adding or subtracting decimals, we work from ____ to ____. (3-3)
right, left

7. When multiplying decimals, the product has as many decimal places as the total number of decimal places in the two ____. (3-4)
factors

8. When multiplying a decimal by a power of 10, as a shortcut, move the decimal point to the right the same number of places as there are ____ in the power of 10. (3-4)
zeros

9. When dividing decimals, the basic rule is that you cannot divide with a decimal in the ____. (3-5)
divisor

10. When dividing a decimal by a power of 10, as a shortcut, move the decimal point in the dividend to the ____ the same number of places as there are zeros in the divisor. (3-5)
left

11. When converting a decimal to a fraction, we commonly ____ the fraction to lowest terms. (3-6)
reduce

12. To convert a fraction to a decimal, we divide the ____ by the ____. (3-7)
numerator, denominator

CHAPTER

ASSESSMENT TEST

Name ____________

Class ____________

Answers

1. Sixty-one hundredths
2. Thirty-four and five hundred eighty-one thousandths
3. One hundred nineteen dollars and eighty-five cents
4. Nine and three-sevenths hundredths
5. Four hundred ninety-five ten-thousandths
6. .0967
7. 5.014
8. 843.2
9. $16.57

Write the following numbers in word form.

1. .61
Sixty-one hundredths

2. 34.581
Thirty-four and five hundred eighty-one thousandths

3. $119.85
One hundred nineteen dollars and eighty-five cents

4. $.09\frac{3}{7}$
Nine and three-sevenths hundredths

5. .0495
Four hundred ninety-five ten-thousandths

Write the following numbers in numerical form.

6. Nine hundred sixty-seven ten-thousandths
.0967

7. Five and fourteen thousandths
5.014

8. Eight hundred forty-three and two tenths
843.2

9. Sixteen dollars and fifty-seven cents
$16.57

Round the following numbers to the indicated place.

10. .44857 to hundredths
.44857 = .45

11. 995.06966 to thousandths
995.06966 = 995.070

12. $127.94 to dollars
$127.94 = $128

13. 4.6935 to tenths
4.6935 = 4.7

Perform the indicated operation for the following.

14. 6.03 + 45.168

$$\begin{array}{r} 6.030 \\ +\ 45.168 \\ \hline 51.198 \end{array}$$

15. $1.58 + $15.63 + $19.81 + $.17

$$\begin{array}{r} \$\ 1.58 \\ 15.63 \\ 19.81 \\ +\ .17 \\ \hline \$37.19 \end{array}$$

16. .0031 + 69.271 + 193.55 + 211

$$\begin{array}{r} .0031 \\ 69.2710 \\ 193.5500 \\ +\ 211.0000 \\ \hline 473.8241 \end{array}$$

17. 23.0556 − 15.35

$$\begin{array}{r} 23.0556 \\ -15.3500 \\ \hline 7.7056 \end{array}$$

18. $95.67 − $2.84

$$\begin{array}{r} \$95.67 \\ -\ 2.84 \\ \hline \$92.83 \end{array}$$

19. .802 − .066

$$\begin{array}{r} .802 \\ -\ .066 \\ \hline .736 \end{array}$$

20.

$$\begin{array}{r} 14.74 \\ \times\ 15 \\ \hline 221.1 \end{array}$$

21.

$$\begin{array}{r} .008 \\ \times\ .024 \\ \hline .000192 \end{array}$$

22. .9912 × 100,000
99,120

23. .503 ÷ 1.2575 = .4

24. 79.3 ÷ 10,000 = .00793

25. $150.48 ÷ 7.5
= 20.064 = $20.06

Convert the following decimals to fractions and reduce to lowest terms.

26. $12.035 = 12\frac{35}{1{,}000} = 12\frac{7}{200}$

27. $.0441 = \frac{441}{10{,}000}$

Convert the following fractions to decimals. Round the quotients to hundredths.

28. $\frac{8}{29} = .275 = .28$

29. $3\frac{1}{9} = 3.111 = 3.11$

30. $\frac{95}{42} = 2.261 = 2.26$

31. Tony Kruessel can buy a box of 40 DVD/Rs for $18.99 and a box of 40 jewel cases for $9.98. Alternatively, he can purchase two boxes of 20 DVD/Rs already in jewel cases for $16.95 each. Which is the better buy, and by how much—the box of 40 DVD/Rs and a box of 40 cases, or the two boxes of 20 DVD/Rs with jewel cases included?

$$\begin{array}{r} 18.99 \\ +\ 9.98 \\ \hline \$28.97 \end{array} \quad \begin{array}{r} 16.95 \\ \times\ 2 \\ \hline \$33.90 \end{array} \quad \begin{array}{r} 33.90 \\ -\ 28.97 \\ \hline \$4.93 \end{array}$$

The box of 40 DVD/Rs and box of 40 jewel cases is the better buy, by $4.93

32. Mike's Bikes has a 22-inch off-road racer on sale this month for $239.95. If the original price of the bike was $315.10, how much would a customer save by purchasing it on sale?

315.10 Original price
−239.95 Sale price
$75.15 Savings

10. .45
11. 995.070
12. $128
13. 4.7
14. 51.198
15. $37.19
16. 473.8241
17. 7.7056
18. $92.83
19. .736
20. 221.1
21. .000192
22. 99,120
23. .4
24. .00793
25. $20.06
26. $12\frac{7}{200}$
27. $\frac{441}{10{,}000}$
28. .28
29. 3.11
30. 2.26
31. The box of 40 DVD/Rs and box of 40 cases by $4.93
32. $75.15

33. $19.89 Per hour

34. $.015

35. a. $.98

b. $.25

c. Sale price earns more revenue

36. $9.25 Savings

37. $2,161.19 Remains

38. a. $9.00 Per plant

33. The chief financial officer of Delta Corporation is setting up two production work shift pay schedules. Swing shift workers are to receive $\frac{1}{12}$ more pay than day shift workers. If his day shift workers are to receive average pay of $18.36 per hour, what is the average pay for the swing shift workers?

$\frac{1}{12} \times 18.36 = 1.53$

18.36
+ 1.53
$19.89 Per hour

34. A ream of paper contains 500 sheets and costs $7.50. What is the cost per sheet?

$\frac{7.50 \text{ Cost per ream}}{500 \text{ Sheets}} = \$.015$ Per sheet

35. At Mager's Market, a 24-bottle case of spring water is on sale for $5.99. If the regular price for the case is $6.97,

a. How much is saved if a customer buys the case at the sale price?

6.97
− 5.99
$.98

b. What is the sale price per bottle? Round to the nearest cent.

$\frac{5.99}{24} = .249 = \$.25$

c. Which sales strategy earns more revenue for Mager's Market, selling 400 cases of water per week at the sale price, or selling 300 cases per week at the regular price?

400 × 5.99 = $2,396
300 × 6.97 = $2,091

Sale price earns more revenue

36. Ashley Millinor has signed up for a one semester class that meets twice a week. The semester is 16 weeks long. She knows that she will miss three classes during her vacation. She has a choice of buying a semester parking pass for $41.50, or she can pay $1.75 daily for parking. How much will Ashley save if she buys the parking pass?

16
×2
32
−3
29 Classes

1.75
×29
50.75

50.75 Daily parking
−41.50 Parking pass
$9.25 Savings

37. Jill Quinn shares an apartment with a friend. They divide all expenses evenly. Jill's monthly take home pay is $2,792.15. The apartment expenses this month are $985.50 for rent, $192.00 for maintenance fees, $56.31 for electricity, and $28.11 for telephone. How much remains from Jill's check after she contributes to the paying of the monthly rent and expenses?

985.50 Rent
192.00 Maintenance
56.31 Electricity
+28.11 Telephone
$1,261.92 Total expenses

$\frac{1{,}261.92}{2} = \$630.96$ Jill's share

2,792.15
− 630.96
$2,161.19 Remains

38. Bill Walters wanted to make some money at a flea market. He purchased 55 small orchids from a nursery for a total of $233.75, three bags of potting soil for $2.75 each, and 55 ceramic pots at $4.60 each. After planting the orchids in the pots, Bill sold each plant for $15.50 at the next flea market.

a. What was his total cost per potted plant?

2.75 Per bag
× 3 Bags
$8.25 Total cost soil

4.60 Per pot
× 55 Pots
$253 Total cost pots

233.75 Plants
8.25 Soil
+ 253.00 Pots
$495.00 Total cost

$\frac{495 \text{ Total cost}}{55 \text{ Plants}} = \$9.00$ Per plant

b. How much profit did Bill make on this venture?

15.50	Selling price per plant	6.50	
− 9.00	Cost per plant	× 55	Plants
\$6.50	Profit per plant	\$357.50	Total profit

39. As the food manager for a local charity, you are planning a fund-raising pasta party. Spaghetti sells for \$1.79 per 16-ounce box.

a. If the average adult serving is $5\frac{3}{4}$ ounces, and the average child eats $3\frac{1}{2}$ ounces, how many boxes will you have to purchase to serve 36 adults and 46 children?

36	Adults	46	Children	207	
× 5.75	Ounces per adult	× 3.5	Ounces per child	+ 161	
207	Ounces	161	Ounces	368	Total ounces

$\frac{368}{16} = 23$ Boxes of pasta

b. What is the total cost of the spaghetti?

23	Boxes
× 1.79	Cost per box
\$41.17	Total cost

40. The Enchanted Island Theme Park took in \$663,750 in June on ticket sales.

a. If 35,400 people attended the park, what was the average price per ticket?

$\frac{663{,}750 \text{ Total revenue}}{35{,}400 \text{ People}} = \$18.75$ Average price per ticket

b. If, on the average, each person spent \$4.70 on food, how much did the park make on food?

35,400	Persons
× 4.70	Average food sales
\$166,380	Total food sales

c. What was the total revenue for the tickets and the food?

663,750	Total ticket sales
+ 166,380	Total food sales
\$830,130	Total revenue

38. b. \$357.50
39. a. 23
b. \$41.17
40. a. \$18.75
b. \$166,380
c. \$830,130
41. a. 1,033 Pounds
b. \$1,253 Canadian dollars
c. \$319 U.S. dollars

© Disneyland/PR Newswire Photo Service (Newscom)

Top 10 Theme Parks 2006 Attendance (millions)

1.	Disney's The Magic Kingdom	16.2
2.	Disneyland, Anaheim	14.5
3.	Disney's Epcot	9.9
4.	Disney-MGM Studios	8.6
5	Disney's Animal Kingdom	8.2
6.	Universal Studios	6.1
7.	Disney's California Adventure	5.8
8.	Universal Islands of Adventure	5.7
9.	SeaWorld Florida	5.6
10.	Universal Studios, Hollywood	4.7

BUSINESS DECISION THE INTERNATIONAL BUSINESS TRIP

41. U.S. dollars are legal currency only in the United States. International investment, travel, and trade require that dollars be exchanged for foreign currency. In today's global economy, a "floating exchange rate" system is used to value major currencies compared to each other. Because the values of these currencies vary continually, exchange rate tables are published daily by numerous business sources. The table below reflects the currency exchange rates on March 16, 2007.

Currency Exchange Rates – 3/16/07

Country – Currency	Dollar	Euro	Pound	SFranc	Peso	Yen	CdnDlr
Canada–Canadian dollar	1.1762	1.5569	2.2782	0.9658	0.1055	0.0100	....
Japan – Yen	117.56	155.62	227.71	96.532	10.547	....	99.953
Mexico – Peso	11.147	14.755	21.591	9.1528	....	0.0948	9.4772
Switzerland–Swiss Franc	1.2179	1.6121	2.3589	....	0.1093	0.0104	1.0354
Britain – Pound	0.5163	0.6834	....	0.4239	0.0463	0.0044	0.4389
Euro – Euro	0.7555	....	1.4632	0.6203	0.0678	0.0064	0.6423
U.S. – Dollar	....	1.3237	1.9369	0.8211	0.0897	0.0085	0.8502

For example, on that date, \$100 U.S. dollars was worth 75.5 euros.

$$\$100 \times 0.7555 = 75.5 \text{ euros}$$

STEPS TO CONVERT BETWEEN FOREIGN CURRENCIES

Step 1. Locate the *currency exchange rate* at the intersection of the column of the currency you are changing from (old currency) and the row of the currency you are changing to (new currency).

Step 2. Multiply the number of units you are changing from (old currency) by the currency exchange rate.

$$\text{New currency} = \text{Old currency} \times \text{Currency exchange rate}$$

You are the sales manager of Tundra, Inc., a company that sells motor parts in many countries. For the next two weeks, you are going on a selling trip to Canada and the United Kingdom. Your airline fare and hotel bill will be charged on company credit cards. Your boss has allotted an additional $2,000 for "out-of-pocket" expenses during the trip.

a. A few days before your trip, you exchange the $2,000 U.S. dollars for British pounds, to be used while you are in London. How many pounds will you have for the British portion of your trip? Round to the nearest pound.

British pounds = 2,000 × 0.5163 = 1,032.6 = 1,033 Pounds

b. When you finish your business in London, you have 550 pounds left. Your next stop is Toronto, Canada. How many Canadian dollars will those British pounds purchase? Round to the nearest Canadian dollar.

Canadian dollars = 550 × 2.2782 = 1,253.01 = $1,253 Canadian dollars

c. After completing your business in Canada, you have $375 Canadian dollars left. How many U.S. dollars will those Canadian dollars purchase? Round to the nearest U.S. dollar.

U.S. dollars = 375 × 0.8502 = 318.825 = $319 U.S. dollars

COLLABORATIVE LEARNING ACTIVITY

Sports Math

As a team, choose two sports.

a. Investigate how fractions and decimals are used in their record keeping and statistics.
b. Prepare a visual presentation of your findings to share with the class.

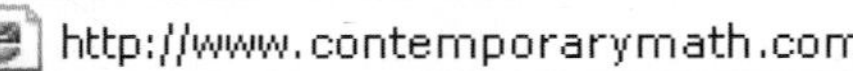

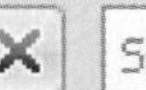

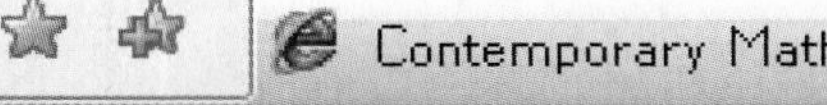

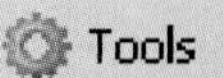

ContemporaryMath.com

All the Math That's Fit to Learn

Managing Your Personal Finances

Here are some personal financial planning tips from *The College Board*, an organization that provides students, parents, and educators with education-oriented information and services; www.collegeboard.com.

Budget

- Develop a realistic budget—Live with it!
- Review your expenses and personal balance sheet (page 15) periodically.
- Review your checking and savings account features every two to three years.
- Save 5 to 10 percent of your income each month.
- Set short-, medium-, and long-term financial goals. Monitor them.

Credit

- Pay bills on time.
- Check your credit rating annually.
- Don't allow your total debt to exceed 20% of your annual income.
- Reserve consumer credit for major purchases.
- Pay off credit card balances at the end of each month.

Taxes

- Consult with experts well before April 1 each year.
- Keep good records and a file system of tax-related items.
- If eligible, open an IRA/Keogh. Fund it annually.

Insurance

- Keep an inventory of all valuables.
- Protect yourself with the right types of insurance and coverage amounts.
- Review policy renewal contracts and beneficiaries.

Investments

- Establish an emergency fund of three to six months' income.
- Find an advisor you trust who understands your circumstances.
- Analyze your tolerance for risk, and don't exceed it.
- Don't invest in something you don't understand.
- If an investment sounds too good to be true, it almost certainly is!
- Don't put all your eggs in one basket. Keep a diversified portfolio.
- Track your investments.

Retirement and Estate Planning

- Keep good records.
- Check your social security and pension accounts periodically.
- Understand your employee benefits.
- Make a will and review it periodically.

Quote...UnQuote

- Why is there always so much month left at the end of the money? **–Sarah Lloyd**
- A goal is a dream with a deadline. **–Unknown**

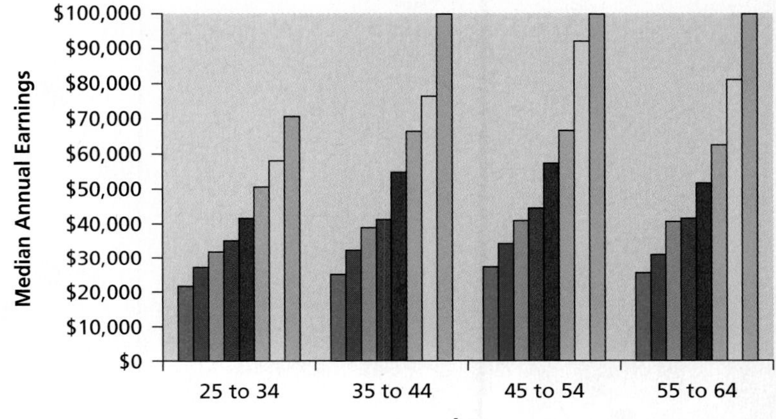

Source: U.S. Census Bureau data; from "Financial Planning Tips," copyright © 2005, the College Board, http://www.collegeboard.com. Reproduced with permission.

"Dear, your boss just called to tell you there was a slight mistake in your paycheck."

© Joe Kohl/www.CartoonStock.com

©Chuck Burton/ Associated Press

4

CHAPTER

Checking Accounts

PERFORMANCE OBJECTIVES

Section I Understanding and Using Checking Accounts

4-1: Opening a checking account and understanding how the various forms are used (p. 98)

4-2: Writing checks in proper form (p. 100)

4-3: Endorsing checks by using blank, restrictive, and full endorsements (p. 102)

4-4: Preparing deposit slips in proper form (p. 104)

4-5: Using check stubs or checkbook registers to record account transactions (p. 106)

Section II Bank Statement Reconciliation

4-6: Understanding the bank statement (p. 113)

4-7: Preparing a bank statement reconciliation (p. 113)

UNDERSTANDING AND USING CHECKING ACCOUNTS

SECTION I

Checking accounts are among the most useful and common banking services available today. They provide a detailed record of monetary transactions, and are used by most businesses and individuals to purchase goods and services and to pay bills. When a checking account is opened, banks often require an initial minimum deposit of $50 or $100. Certain types of accounts require a minimum *average monthly balance* in the account. If the balance falls below the minimum, the bank may charge a fee.

Checking account transactions are processed in our banking system using a combination of paper checks and electronic options such as automated teller machines (ATMs), debit cards, automatic bill paying, and electronic funds transfer (EFTs). Online banking uses today's technology to give account holders the option of bypassing some of the time consuming, paper-based aspects of traditional banking. When account holders use online banking, they connect to the bank through the Internet. This allows them to view their accounts, transfer money between accounts, view images of canceled checks, print copies of the check, and pay bills.

Statistics indicate that the use of paper money—both checks and cash—will continue to decline in the future, giving way in large part to a cashless economy using "virtual money." Today, over a quarter of Americans use debit cards at least once a week for all types of purchases. By 2010, it is predicted that over 60% of consumer payments will be made by credit card, debit card, or EFT. Exhibit 4-1 illustrates how our online banking will likely change in the coming years.

© Michael Blann/Digital Vision/Getty Images

With a **debit card**, you can shop without having to carry cash or remember your checkbook. The purchase amount is deducted directly from your checking or savings account. Debit cards are also used to get cash from ATMs.

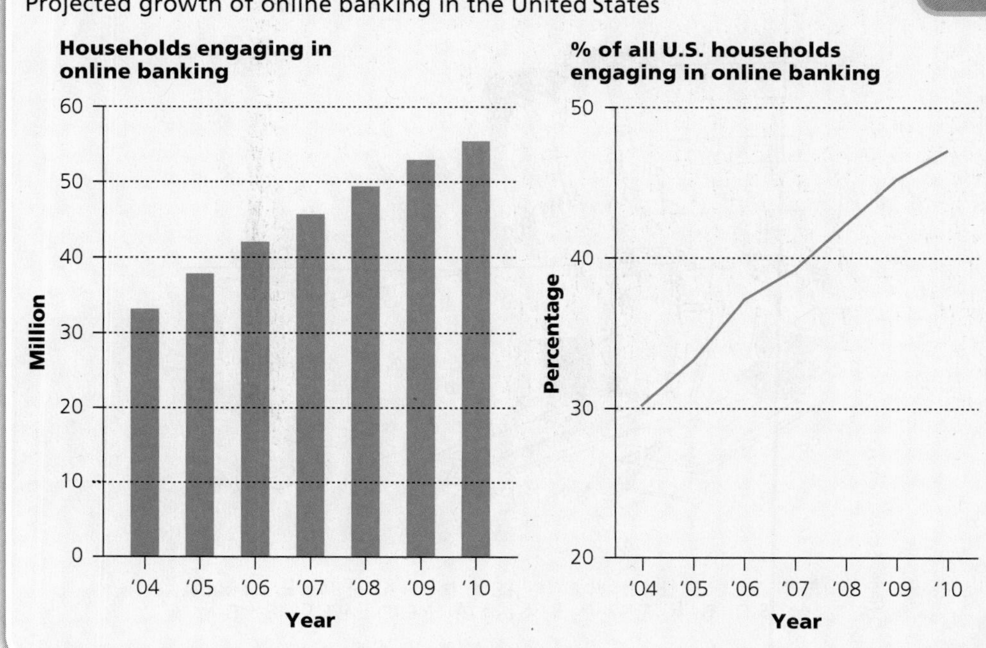

Exhibit 4-1
Paper or Plastic?

Source: *The Miami Herald*, February 26, 2006, p. 4E, Final Edition.
© The Miami Herald.

Teaching Transparency 4-1

4-1 OPENING A CHECKING ACCOUNT AND UNDERSTANDING HOW THE VARIOUS FORMS ARE USED

After you have chosen a bank, the account is usually opened by a new accounts officer or clerk. After the initial paperwork has been completed, the customer will place an amount of money into the account as an opening balance. Funds added to a checking account are known as **deposits**. The bank will then give the **depositor** a checkbook containing checks and deposit slips.

Checks, or **drafts**, are negotiable instruments ordering the bank to pay money from the checking account to the name written on the check. The person or business named on the check to receive the money is known as the **payee**. The person or business issuing the check is known as the **payor**.

Checks are available in many sizes, colors, and designs; however, they all contain the same fundamental elements. Exhibit 4-2 shows a check with the major parts labeled. Look at the illustration carefully, and familiarize yourself with the various parts of the check.

Deposit slips, or deposit tickets, are printed forms with the depositor's name, address, account number, and space for the details of the deposit. Deposit slips are used to record money, both cash and checks, being *added* to the checking account. They are presented to the bank teller along with the items to be deposited. When a deposit is completed, the depositor receives a copy of the deposit slip as a receipt, or proof of the transaction. The deposit should also be recorded by the depositor on the current check stub, or in the check register. Exhibit 4-3 is an example of a deposit slip.

Either **check stubs** or a **check register** can be used to keep track of the checks written, the deposits added, and the current account balance. It is very important to keep these records accurate and up to date. This will prevent the embarrassing error of writing checks with insufficient funds in the account.

Check stubs, with checks attached by perforation, are usually a bound part of the checkbook. A sample check stub with a check is shown in Exhibit 4-4. Note that the check number is preprinted on both the check and the attached stub. Each stub is used to record the issuing of its corresponding check and any deposits made on that date.

deposits Funds added to a checking account.

depositor A person who deposits money in a checking account.

check or draft A written order to a bank by a depositor to pay the amount specified on the check from funds on deposit in a checking account.

payee The person or business named on the check to receive the money.

payor The person or business issuing the check.

deposit slip Printed forms with the depositor's name, address, account number, and space for the details of the deposit. Used to record money, both cash and checks, being added to the checking account.

check stub A bound part of the checkbook, attached by perforation to checks. Used to keep track of the checks written, deposits, and current account balance of a checking account.

check register A separate booklet of blank forms used to keep track of all checking account activity. An alternative to the check stub.

"JASON FEELS INSECURE IF HE'S TOO FAR FROM HIS MONEY... BUT ELECTRONIC BANK STATEMENTS HAVE CURED THAT!"

Exhibit 4-2
Check

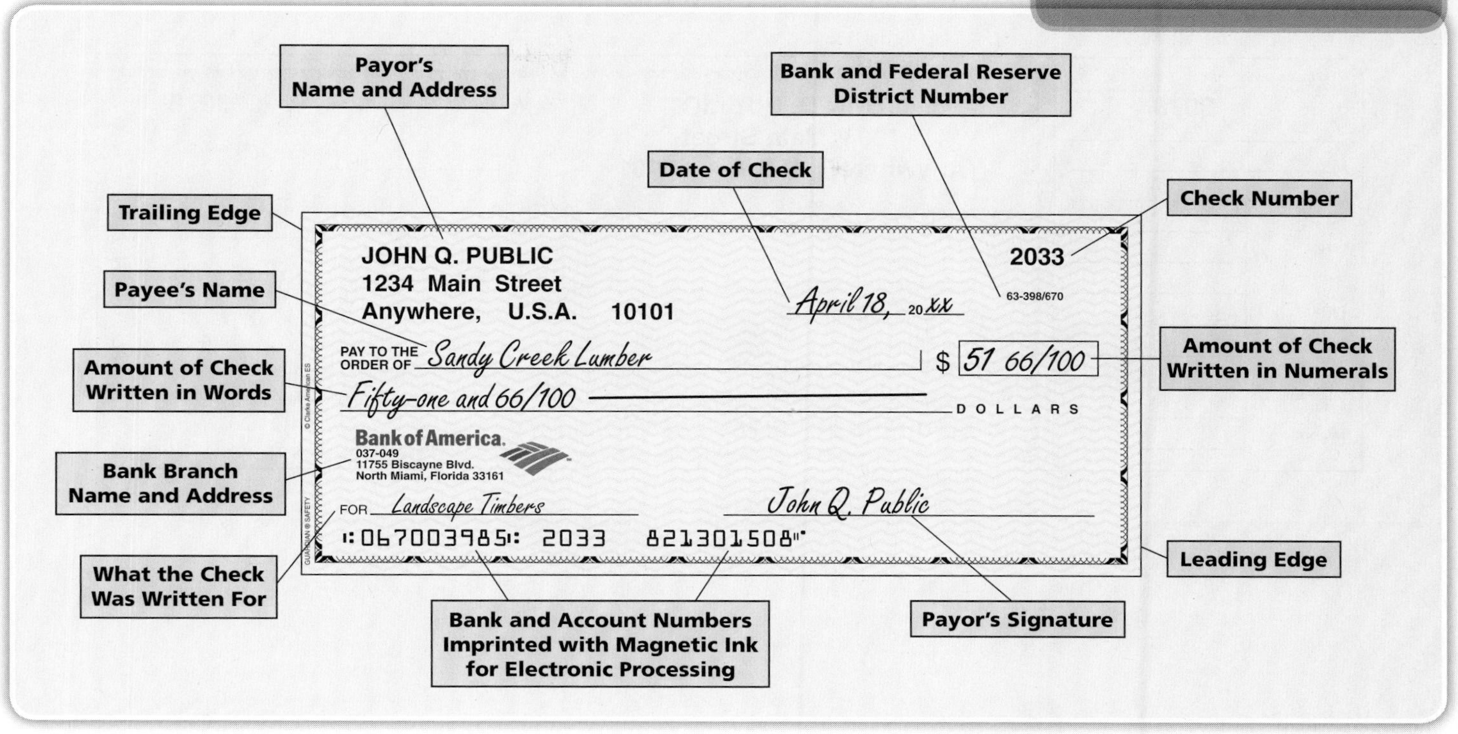

Payor's Name and Address
Bank and Federal Reserve District Number
Date of Check
Trailing Edge
Check Number
Payee's Name
Amount of Check Written in Words
Amount of Check Written in Numerals
Bank Branch Name and Address
What the Check Was Written For
Leading Edge
Bank and Account Numbers Imprinted with Magnetic Ink for Electronic Processing
Payor's Signature

JOHN Q. PUBLIC
1234 Main Street
Anywhere, U.S.A. 10101

2033
63-398/670

April 18, 20XX

PAY TO THE ORDER OF Sandy Creek Lumber $ 51 66/100

Fifty-one and 66/100 DOLLARS

Bank of America.
037-049
11755 Biscayne Blvd.
North Miami, Florida 33161

FOR Landscape Timbers

John Q. Public

⑆067003985⑆ 2033 821301508⑈

Exhibit 4-3
Deposit Slip

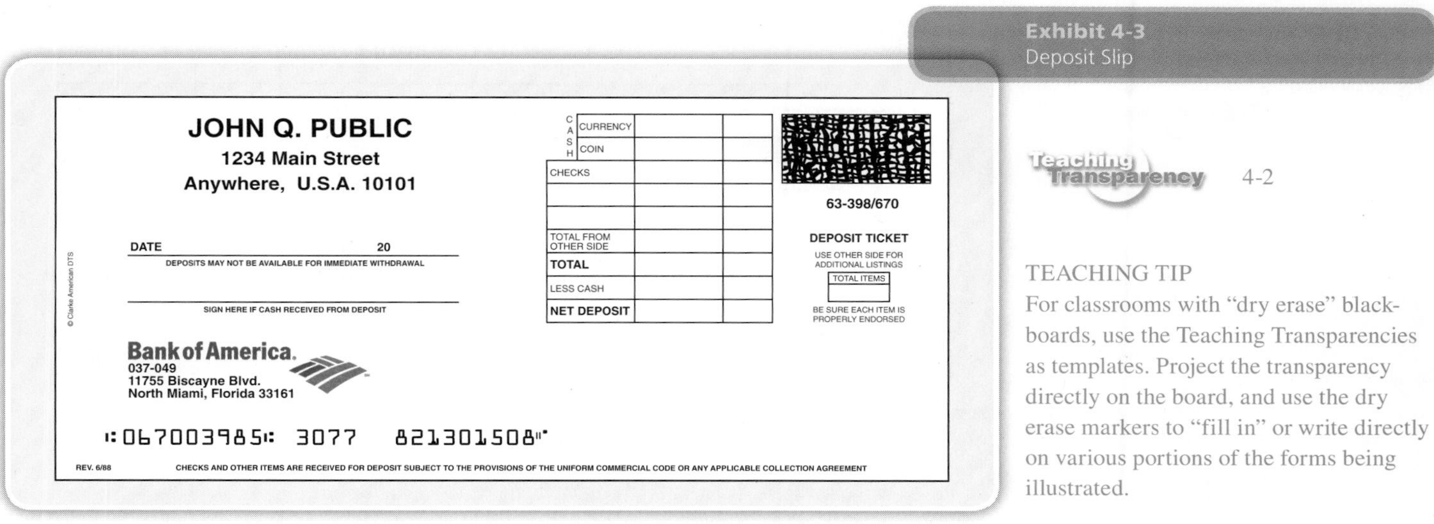

JOHN Q. PUBLIC
1234 Main Street
Anywhere, U.S.A. 10101

DATE 20
DEPOSITS MAY NOT BE AVAILABLE FOR IMMEDIATE WITHDRAWAL

SIGN HERE IF CASH RECEIVED FROM DEPOSIT

Bank of America.
037-049
11755 Biscayne Blvd.
North Miami, Florida 33161

CASH	CURRENCY		
	COIN		
CHECKS			
TOTAL FROM OTHER SIDE			
TOTAL			
LESS CASH			
NET DEPOSIT			

63-398/670

DEPOSIT TICKET
USE OTHER SIDE FOR ADDITIONAL LISTINGS
TOTAL ITEMS
BE SURE EACH ITEM IS PROPERLY ENDORSED

⑆067003985⑆ 3077 821301508⑈

REV. 6/88 CHECKS AND OTHER ITEMS ARE RECEIVED FOR DEPOSIT SUBJECT TO THE PROVISIONS OF THE UNIFORM COMMERCIAL CODE OR ANY APPLICABLE COLLECTION AGREEMENT

Teaching Transparency 4-2

TEACHING TIP
For classrooms with "dry erase" blackboards, use the Teaching Transparencies as templates. Project the transparency directly on the board, and use the dry erase markers to "fill in" or write directly on various portions of the forms being illustrated.

Check registers are the alternative method for keeping track of checking account activity. They are a separate booklet of forms, rather than stubs attached to each check. A sample check register is shown in Exhibit 4-5. Note that space is provided for all the pertinent information required to keep an accurate and up-to-date running balance of the account.

Exhibit 4-4
Check Stub with Check

IF TAX DEDUCTIBLE CHECK HERE ☐ $____

3078

____ 20____

TO ____

FOR ____

	DOLLARS	CENTS
BAL. FWD.		
DEPOSIT		
DEPOSIT		
TOTAL		
THIS ITEM		
SUB-TOTAL		
OTHER DEDUCT. (IF ANY)		
BAL. FWD.		

© Clarke American ES

GUARDIAN ® SAFETY

JOHN Q. PUBLIC
1234 Main Street
Anywhere, U.S.A. 10101

3078

63-398/670

____ 20____

PAY TO THE ORDER OF ____ $ ____

____ DOLLARS

Bank of America.
037-049
11755 Biscayne Blvd.
North Miami, Florida 33161

FOR ____ ____

⑆067003985⑆ 3078 821301508⑈

Exhibit 4-5
Check Register

Teaching Transparency 4-3

PLEASE BE SURE TO **DEDUCT** ANY BANK CHARGES THAT APPLY TO YOUR ACCOUNT.

CHECK NUMBER	DATE	DESCRIPTION OF TRANSACTION	AMOUNT OF PAYMENT OR WITHDRAWAL (-)		✓	AMOUNT OF DEPOSIT OR INTEREST (+)		BALANCE FORWARD		
		To								
		For						Bal.		
		To								
		For						Bal.		
		To								
		For						Bal.		
		To								
		For						Bal.		
		To								
		For						Bal.		
		To								
		For						Bal.		

4-2 WRITING CHECKS IN PROPER FORM

When a checking account is opened, you will choose the color and style of your checks. The bank will then order custom-printed checks with your name, address, and account number identifications. The bank will provide you with some blank checks and deposit slips to use until your printed ones arrive.

Checks should be typed or neatly written in ink. There are six parts to be filled in when writing a check.

STEPS FOR WRITING CHECKS IN PROPER FORM

Step 1. Enter the *date* of the check in the space provided.

Step 2. Enter the name of the person or business to whom the check is written, the payee, in the space labeled "*pay to the order of.*"

Step 3. Enter the amount of the check, in numerical form, in the space with the dollar sign, \$. The dollar amount should be written close to the \$ so additional digits cannot be added. The cents may be written as xx/100 or .xx.

Step 4. Enter the amount of the check, this time written in word form, on the next line down, labeled *dollars*. As before, the cents should be written as xx/100 or .xx. A horizontal, wavy line is then written to the end of the line.

Step 5. The space labeled *for* is used to write the purpose of the check. Although it is optional, it's a good idea to use this space so you will not forget why the check was written.

Step 6. The space in the lower right-hand portion of the check is for the signature.

When there is a discrepancy between the numerical and written word amount of a check, banks consider the *written word amount* as official.

EXAMPLE 1 WRITING A CHECK

Write a check for William H. Pearson to the Fifth Avenue Flower Shop, for a ceramic planter, in the amount of \$83.73, on June 7, 20xx.

SOLUTION STRATEGY

Here is the check for William H. Pearson, written in proper form. Note that the amount, \$83.73, is written \$83 73/100, and the name is signed as it is printed on the check.

Learning Tip

Don't forget, when writing the amount of a check in word form, that the word *and* represents the decimal point.

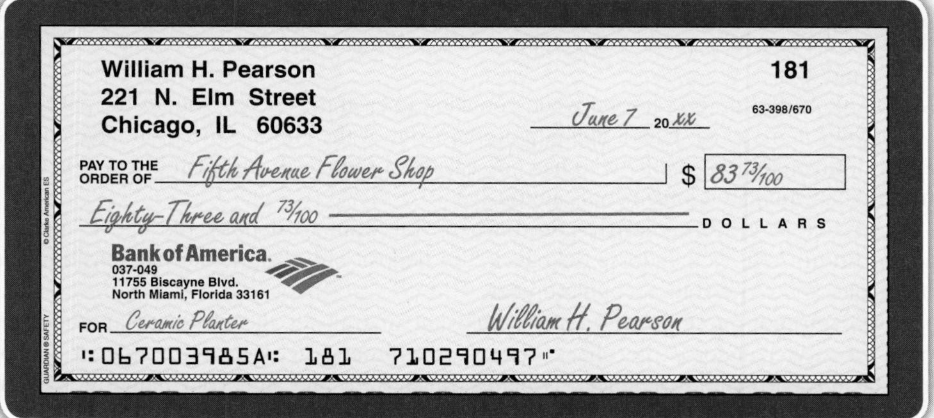

William H. Pearson
221 N. Elm Street
Chicago, IL 60633

181

63-398/670

June 7 20xx

PAY TO THE ORDER OF Fifth Avenue Flower Shop $ 83 73/100

Eighty-Three and 73/100 DOLLARS

Bank of America
037-049
11755 Biscayne Blvd.
North Miami, Florida 33161

FOR Ceramic Planter

William H. Pearson

⑆067003985A⑆ 181 7102904971⑈

TRY IT EXERCISE 1

1. Use the following blank to write a check for Sally Kerscher to Whole Foods for a party platter in the amount of $41.88 on April 27.

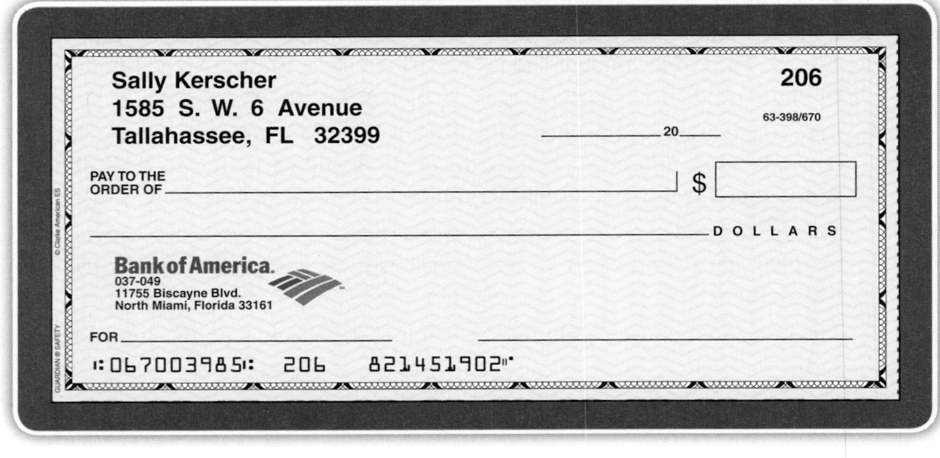

CHECK YOUR ANSWER WITH THE SOLUTION ON PAGE 124.

4-3 ENDORSING CHECKS BY USING BLANK, RESTRICTIVE, AND FULL ENDORSEMENTS

endorsement The signature and instructions on the back of a check instructing the bank on what to do with that check.

When you receive a check, you may either cash it, deposit it into your account, or transfer it to another party. The **endorsement** on the back of the check instructs the bank what to do. Federal regulations require that specific areas of the reverse side of checks be designated for the payee and bank endorsements. Your endorsement should be written within the $1\frac{1}{2}$-inch space at the trailing edge of the check, as shown in Exhibit 4-6. The space is usually labeled "ENDORSE HERE."

There are three types of endorsements with which you should become familiar: blank endorsements, restrictive endorsements, and full endorsements, which are shown in Exhibits 4-7, 4-8, and 4-9.

blank endorsement An endorsement used when the payee wants to cash a check.

A **blank endorsement** is used when you want to cash the check. You, as the payee, simply sign your name exactly as it appears on the front of the check. Once you have endorsed a check in this manner, anyone who has possession of the check can cash it. For this reason, you should use blank endorsements cautiously.

restrictive endorsement An endorsement used when the payee wants to deposit a check into his or her account.

A **restrictive endorsement** is used when you want to deposit the check into your account. In this case, you endorse the check "for deposit only," sign your name as it appears on the front, and write your account number.

full endorsement An endorsement used when the payee wants to transfer a check to another party.

A **full endorsement** is used when you want to transfer the check to another party. In this case, you endorse the check "pay to the order of," write the name of the person or business to whom the check is being transferred, and sign your name and account number.

Exhibit 4-6
Endorsement Space

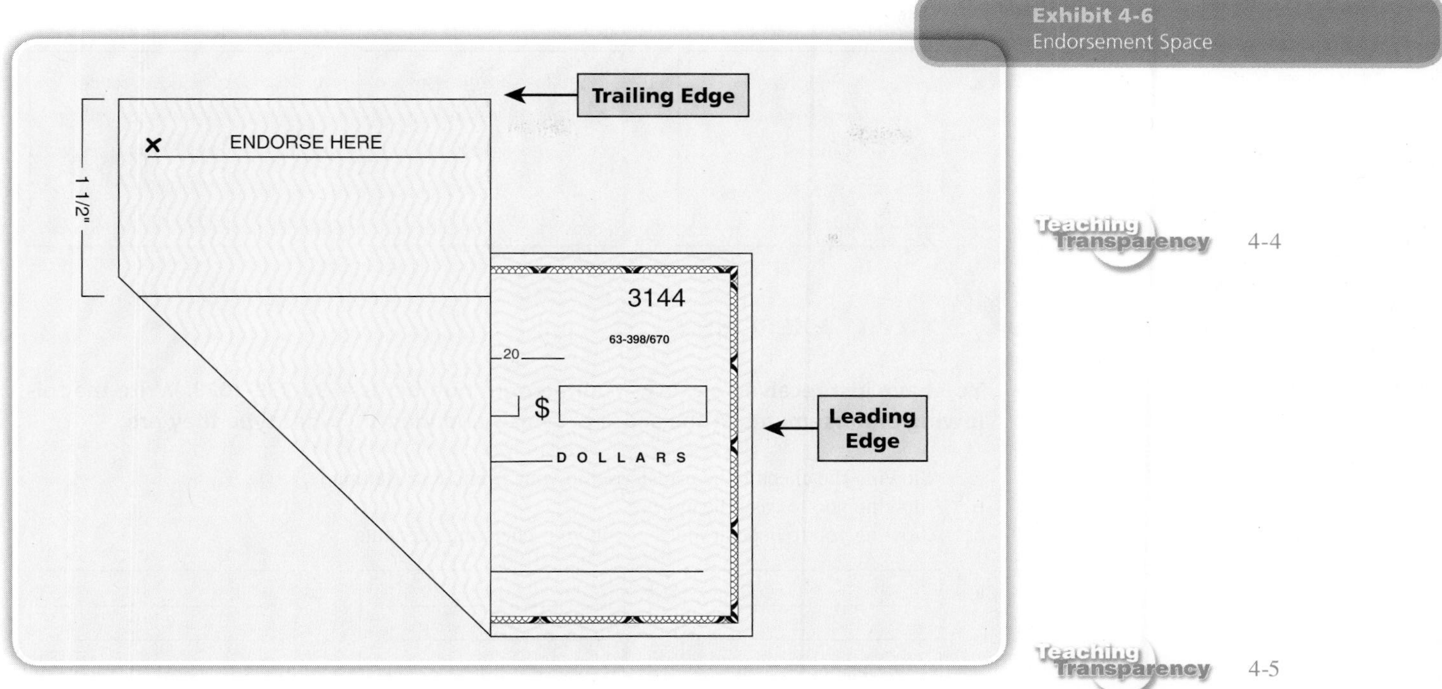

Teaching Transparency 4-4

Teaching Transparency 4-5

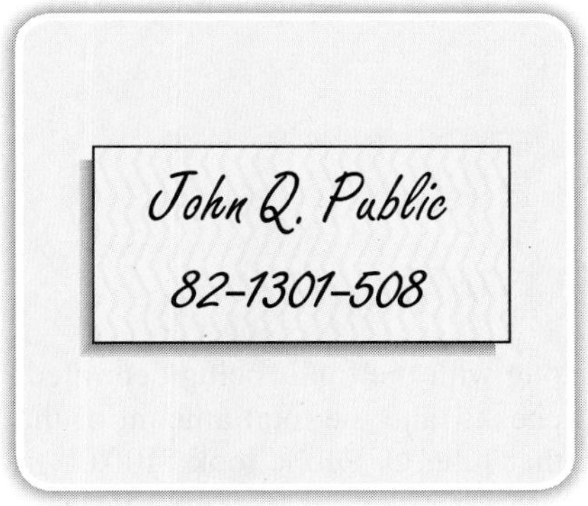

John Q. Public
82-1301-508

Exhibit 4-7
Blank Endorsement

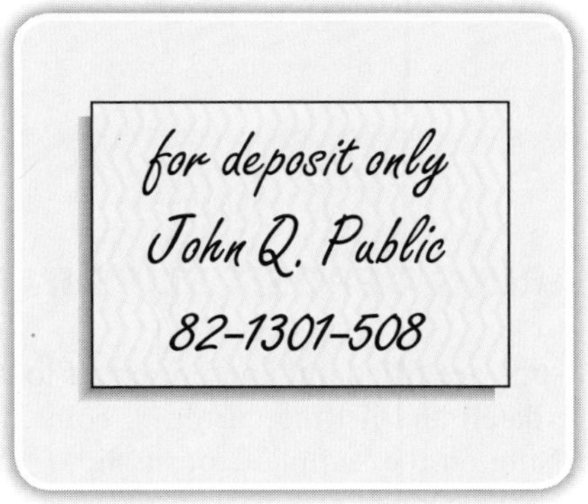

for deposit only
John Q. Public
82-1301-508

Exhibit 4-8
Restrictive Endorsement

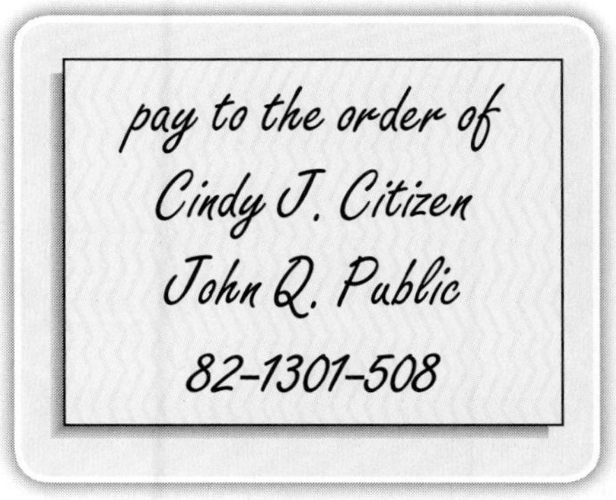

pay to the order of
Cindy J. Citizen
John Q. Public
82-1301-508

Exhibit 4-9
Full Endorsement

EXAMPLE 2 ENDORSING A CHECK

You have just received a check. Your account number is #2922-22-33-4. Write the following endorsements and identify what type they are.

a. Allowing you to cash the check.
b. Allowing you to deposit the check into your checking account.
c. Allowing the check to be transferred to your partner Sam Johnson.

TEACHING TIP
Remind students to be cautious when using the *blank endorsment.* Once a check is endorsed in that manner, it becomes a negotiable instrument. If lost or stolen, it can be cashed by anyone who has possession of it.

SOLUTION STRATEGY

a. **Blank Endorsement**
Your Signature
2922-22-33-4

b. **Restrictive Endorsement**
for deposit only
Your Signature
2922-22-33-4

c. **Full Endorsement**
pay to the order of
Sam Johnson
Your Signature
2922-22-33-4

TRY IT EXERCISE 2

You have just received a check. Your account number is #696-339-1028. Write the following endorsements in the space provided and identify what type they are.

a. Allowing the check to be transferred to your friend Roz Reitman.
b. Allowing you to cash the check.
c. Allowing you to deposit the check in your checking account.

a. ______

b. ______

c. 

CHECK YOUR ANSWERS WITH THE SOLUTIONS ON PAGE 124.

4-4 PREPARING DEPOSIT SLIPS IN PROPER FORM

Deposit slips are filled out and presented to the bank along with the funds being deposited. They are dated and list the currency, coins, individual checks, and the total amount of the deposit. Note on the sample deposit slip, Exhibit 4-10, that John Q. Public took $100.00 in cash out of the deposit, which required him to sign the deposit slip.

Teaching Transparency 4-6

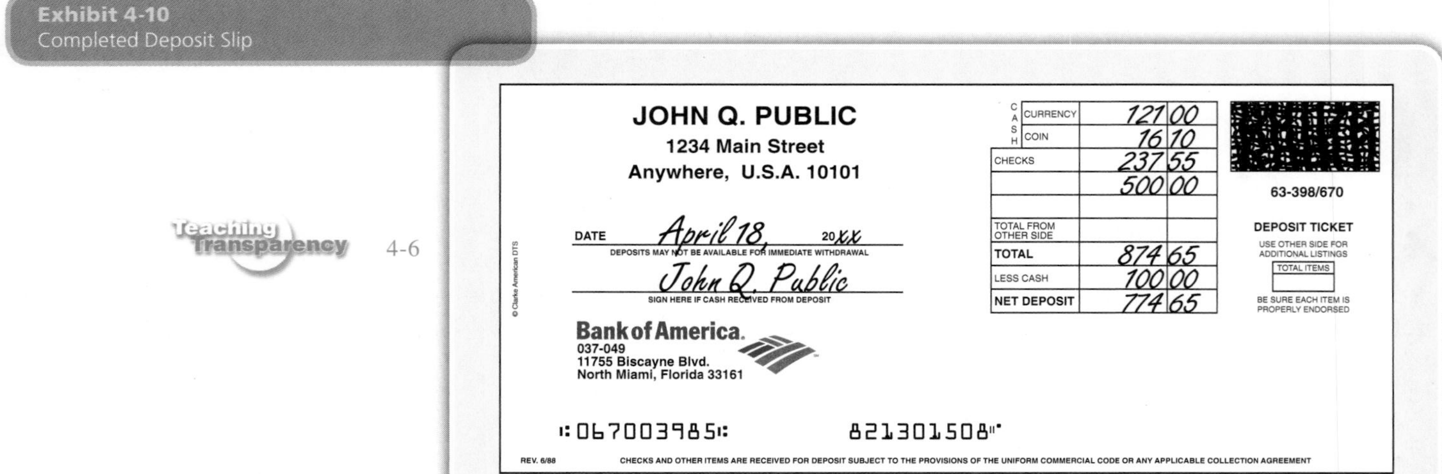

JOHN Q. PUBLIC
1234 Main Street
Anywhere, U.S.A. 10101

DATE *April 18*, 20*XX*
DEPOSITS MAY NOT BE AVAILABLE FOR IMMEDIATE WITHDRAWAL

John Q. Public
SIGN HERE IF CASH RECEIVED FROM DEPOSIT

Bank of America.
037-049
11755 Biscayne Blvd.
North Miami, Florida 33161

CASH CURRENCY	121 00
COIN	16 10
CHECKS	237 55
	500 00
TOTAL FROM OTHER SIDE	
TOTAL	874 65
LESS CASH	100 00
NET DEPOSIT	774 65

63-398/670

DEPOSIT TICKET
USE OTHER SIDE FOR ADDITIONAL LISTINGS
TOTAL ITEMS
BE SURE EACH ITEM IS PROPERLY ENDORSED

⑆067003985⑆ 821301508⑈

REV. 6/88 CHECKS AND OTHER ITEMS ARE RECEIVED FOR DEPOSIT SUBJECT TO THE PROVISIONS OF THE UNIFORM COMMERCIAL CODE OR ANY APPLICABLE COLLECTION AGREEMENT

© Clarke American DTS

Exhibit 4-10
Completed Deposit Slip

EXAMPLE 3 PREPARING A DEPOSIT SLIP

Prepare a deposit slip for Ben Qualls, based on the following information.

a. Date: June 4, 20xx
b. $127 in currency
c. $3.47 in coins
d. A check for $358.89 and a check for $121.68

SOLUTION STRATEGY

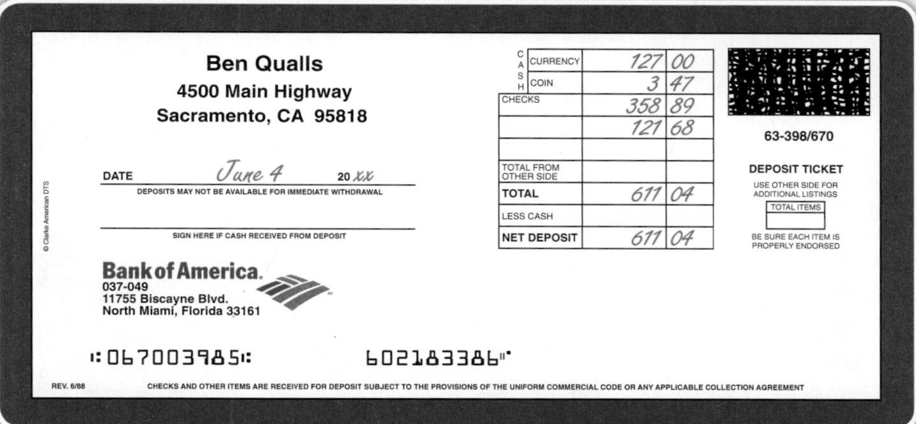

Ben Qualls
4500 Main Highway
Sacramento, CA 95818

DATE June 4 20 xx
DEPOSITS MAY NOT BE AVAILABLE FOR IMMEDIATE WITHDRAWAL

SIGN HERE IF CASH RECEIVED FROM DEPOSIT

Bank of America.
037-049
11755 Biscayne Blvd.
North Miami, Florida 33161

CASH CURRENCY	127	00
COIN	3	47
CHECKS	358	89
	121	68
TOTAL FROM OTHER SIDE		
TOTAL	611	04
LESS CASH		
NET DEPOSIT	611	04

63-398/670

DEPOSIT TICKET
USE OTHER SIDE FOR ADDITIONAL LISTINGS
TOTAL ITEMS
BE SURE EACH ITEM IS PROPERLY ENDORSED

⑆067003985⑆ 602183386⑈

REV. 6/88 CHECKS AND OTHER ITEMS ARE RECEIVED FOR DEPOSIT SUBJECT TO THE PROVISIONS OF THE UNIFORM COMMERCIAL CODE OR ANY APPLICABLE COLLECTION AGREEMENT

TRY IT EXERCISE 3

Fill out the deposit slip for Comdex Electronics, based on the following information.

a. Date: November 11, 20xx
b. $3,549 in currency
c. 67 quarters, 22 dimes, and 14 nickels
d. A check for $411.92, and a check for $2,119.56

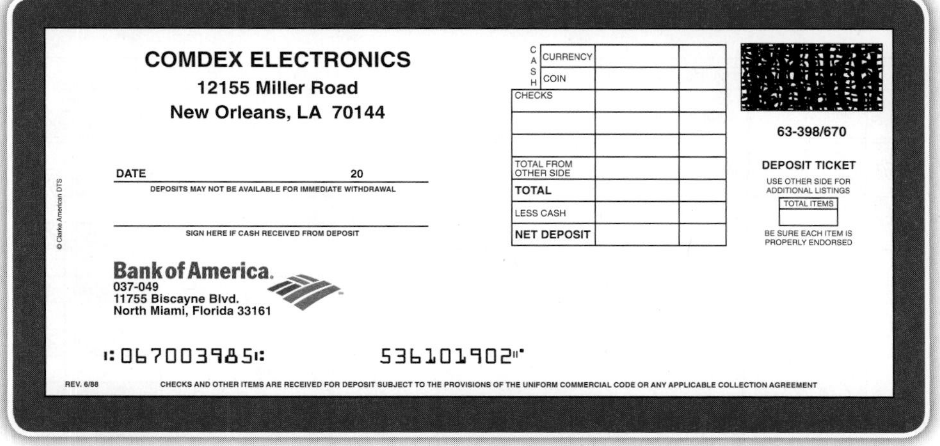

COMDEX ELECTRONICS
12155 Miller Road
New Orleans, LA 70144

DATE 20
DEPOSITS MAY NOT BE AVAILABLE FOR IMMEDIATE WITHDRAWAL

SIGN HERE IF CASH RECEIVED FROM DEPOSIT

Bank of America.
037-049
11755 Biscayne Blvd.
North Miami, Florida 33161

CASH CURRENCY		
COIN		
CHECKS		
TOTAL FROM OTHER SIDE		
TOTAL		
LESS CASH		
NET DEPOSIT		

63-398/670

DEPOSIT TICKET
USE OTHER SIDE FOR ADDITIONAL LISTINGS
TOTAL ITEMS
BE SURE EACH ITEM IS PROPERLY ENDORSED

⑆067003985⑆ 536101902⑈

REV. 6/88 CHECKS AND OTHER ITEMS ARE RECEIVED FOR DEPOSIT SUBJECT TO THE PROVISIONS OF THE UNIFORM COMMERCIAL CODE OR ANY APPLICABLE COLLECTION AGREEMENT

CHECK YOUR ANSWER WITH THE SOLUTION ON PAGE 124.

In the Business World

It is important to keep accurate checkbook records and reconcile the account balance each month. "It's your money." Banks can and do make mistakes!

Inaccurate record keeping on the part of the account holder can cause embarrassment due to incorrect balances, as well as service charges for "bounced" checks.

USING CHECK STUBS OR CHECKBOOK REGISTERS TO RECORD ACCOUNT TRANSACTIONS

In Part 4-1 we learned that some people use check stubs to keep records and some use check registers. Exhibit 4-11 shows a check and its corresponding stub properly filled out. Note that the check number is printed on the stub. The stub is used to record the amount of the check, the date, the payee, and the purpose of the check. In addition, the stub also records the balance forwarded from the last stub, deposits made since the previous check, and the new balance of the account, after deducting the current check and any other charges.

Check registers record the same information as the stub but in a different format. Exhibit 4-12 shows a check register properly filled out. The starting balance is located in the upper right-hand corner. In keeping a check register, it is your option to write it single spaced or double spaced. Remember, in reality you would use *either* the check stub or the checkbook register.

Exhibit 4-11
Check with Filled-Out Stub

IF TAX DEDUCTIBLE CHECK HERE ☐ $ 183.12

3078

May 26 20 xx

TO Circuit City

FOR Stereo

	DOLLARS	CENTS
BAL. FWD.	1,240	89
DEPOSIT	300	00
DEPOSIT		
TOTAL	1,540	89
THIS ITEM	183	12
SUB-TOTAL	1,357	77
OTHER DEDUCT. (IF ANY)		
BAL. FWD.	1,357	77

© Clarke American ES

GUARDIAN ® SAFETY

BARRY COOPER
299 Williams Road
Dallas, TX 75208

3078

63-398/670

May 26 20 xx

PAY TO THE ORDER OF Circuit City $ 183 12/100

One Hundred Eighty-Three and 12/100 DOLLARS

Bank of America.
037-049
11755 Biscayne Blvd.
North Miami, Florida 33161

FOR Stereo

Barry Cooper

⑆067003985⑆ 3078 53678792⑈

Exhibit 4-12
Filled-Out Check Register

PLEASE BE SURE TO **DEDUCT** ANY BANK CHARGES THAT APPLY TO YOUR ACCOUNT.

CHECK NUMBER	DATE	DESCRIPTION OF TRANSACTION	AMOUNT OF PAYMENT OR WITHDRAWAL (−)		✓	AMOUNT OF DEPOSIT OR INTEREST (+)			BALANCE FORWARD	
									560	00
450	1/6	To Mastercard	34	60						
		For						Bal.	525	40
451	1/8	To State Farm Insurance	166	25						
		For						Bal.	359	15
	1/12	To Electronic Payroll Deposit				340	00			
		For						Bal.	699	15
452	1/13	To Walgreens	15	50						
		For						Bal.	683	65
	1/15	To Deposit				88	62			
		For						Bal.	772	27
	1/17	To ATM-Withdrawal	100	00						
		For						Bal.	672	27
	1/21	To Debit Card—AMC Movie	24	15						
		For						Bal.	648	12

EXAMPLE 4 RECORDING ACCOUNT TRANSACTIONS

From the following information, complete the two check stubs and the check register in proper form.

a. Starting balance $1,454.21.
b. January 14, 20xx, check #056 in the amount of $69.97 issued to Paints & Pails Hardware for a ladder.
c. January 19, 20xx, deposit of $345.00.
d. February 1, 20xx, check #057, in the amount of $171.55 issued to Northern Power & Light for electricity bill.
e. February 1, 20xx, debit card purchase—groceries, $77.00.

SOLUTION STRATEGY

Below are the properly completed stubs and register. Note that the checks were subtracted from the balance and the deposits were added to the balance.

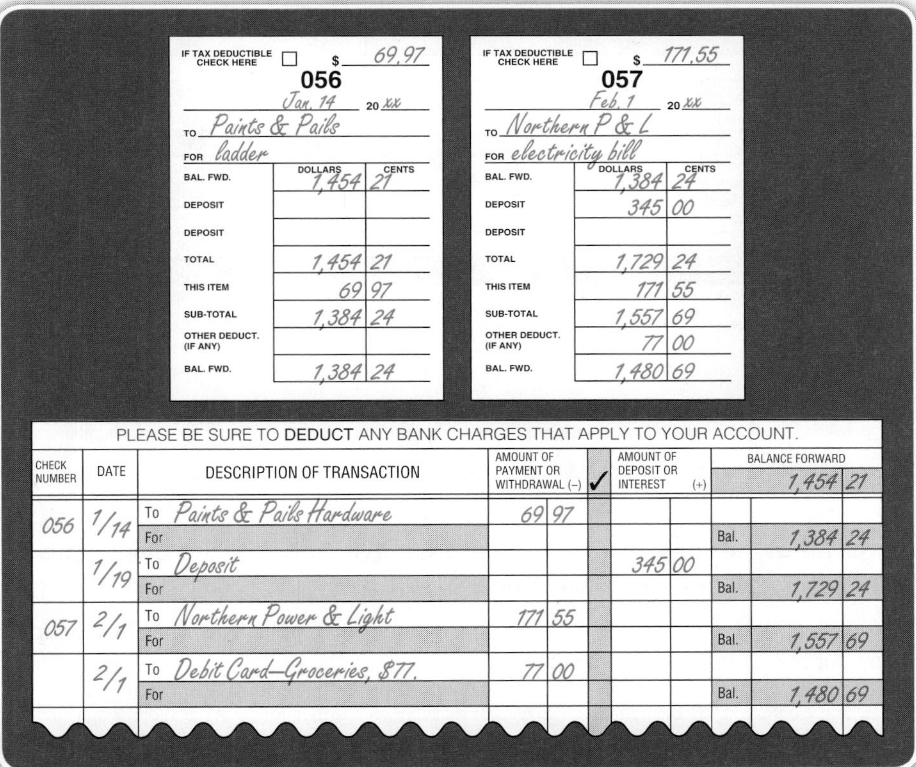

IF TAX DEDUCTIBLE CHECK HERE ☐ $ 69.97
056
Jan. 14 20 xx
TO Paints & Pails
FOR ladder

	DOLLARS	CENTS
BAL. FWD.	1,454	21
DEPOSIT		
DEPOSIT		
TOTAL	1,454	21
THIS ITEM	69	97
SUB-TOTAL	1,384	24
OTHER DEDUCT. (IF ANY)		
BAL. FWD.	1,384	24

IF TAX DEDUCTIBLE CHECK HERE ☐ $ 171.55
057
Feb. 1 20 xx
TO Northern P & L
FOR electricity bill

	DOLLARS	CENTS
BAL. FWD.	1,384	24
DEPOSIT	345	00
DEPOSIT		
TOTAL	1,729	24
THIS ITEM	171	55
SUB-TOTAL	1,557	69
OTHER DEDUCT. (IF ANY)	77	00
BAL. FWD.	1,480	69

PLEASE BE SURE TO **DEDUCT** ANY BANK CHARGES THAT APPLY TO YOUR ACCOUNT.

CHECK NUMBER	DATE	DESCRIPTION OF TRANSACTION	AMOUNT OF PAYMENT OR WITHDRAWAL (−)	✓	AMOUNT OF DEPOSIT OR INTEREST (+)	BALANCE FORWARD	
							1,454.21
056	1/14	To Paints & Pails Hardware	69.97				
		For				Bal.	1,384.24
	1/19	To Deposit			345.00		
		For				Bal.	1,729.24
057	2/1	To Northern Power & Light	171.55				
		For				Bal.	1,557.69
	2/1	To Debit Card—Groceries, $77.	77.00				
		For				Bal.	1,480.69

TRY IT EXERCISE 4

From the following information, complete the two check stubs and the check register on page 108, in proper form.

a. Starting balance $887.45.
b. March 12, 20xx, check #137 issued to Nathan & David Hair Stylists for a permanent and manicure in the amount of $55.75.
c. March 16, 20xx, deposits of $125.40 and $221.35.
d. March 19, 20xx, check #138 issued to Complete Auto Service for car repairs in the amount of $459.88.
e. March 20, 20xx, debit card purchase—post office, $53.00.

CLASSROOM ACTIVITY

Ask students to research and report to the class about

- Smart cards
- Bounce-proof checking
- Back office conversion

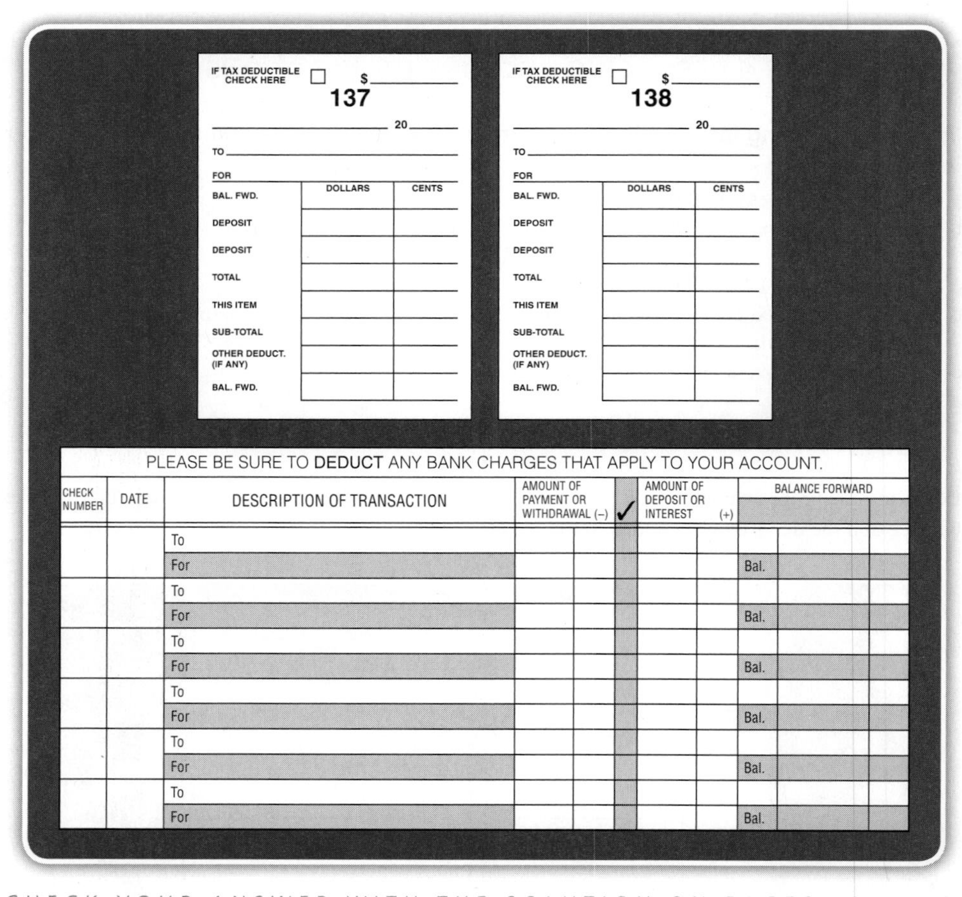

IF TAX DEDUCTIBLE CHECK HERE ☐ $ ______	
137	
______ 20____	
TO ______	
FOR ______	
	DOLLARS	CENTS
BAL. FWD.		
DEPOSIT		
DEPOSIT		
TOTAL		
THIS ITEM		
SUB-TOTAL		
OTHER DEDUCT. (IF ANY)		
BAL. FWD.		

IF TAX DEDUCTIBLE CHECK HERE ☐ $ ______	
138	
______ 20____	
TO ______	
FOR ______	
	DOLLARS	CENTS
BAL. FWD.		
DEPOSIT		
DEPOSIT		
TOTAL		
THIS ITEM		
SUB-TOTAL		
OTHER DEDUCT. (IF ANY)		
BAL. FWD.		

PLEASE BE SURE TO **DEDUCT** ANY BANK CHARGES THAT APPLY TO YOUR ACCOUNT.

CHECK NUMBER	DATE	DESCRIPTION OF TRANSACTION	AMOUNT OF PAYMENT OR WITHDRAWAL (–)	✓	AMOUNT OF DEPOSIT OR INTEREST (+)	BALANCE FORWARD
		To				
		For				Bal.
		To				
		For				Bal.
		To				
		For				Bal.
		To				
		For				Bal.
		To				
		For				Bal.
		To				
		For				Bal.

CHECK YOUR ANSWER WITH THE SOLUTION ON PAGES 124–125.

SECTION I Review Exercises

You are the owner of the Ultimate Care Car Wash. Using the blanks provided, write out the following checks, in proper form.

1. Check #2550, September 14, 20xx, in the amount of $345.54, to the Silky Soap Company, for 300 gallons of liquid soap.

ULTIMATE CARE CAR WASH
214 Collings Blvd.
Durham, NC 27704

2550

Sept. 14 20 *xx*

63-398/670

PAY TO THE ORDER OF *Silky Soap Company* $ *345 54/100*

Three Hundred Forty-Five and 54/100 DOLLARS

Bank of America.
037-049
11755 Biscayne Blvd.
North Miami, Florida 33161

FOR *300 gals. Soap* *Your Signature*

⑆067003985⑆ 2550 821301508⑈

© Clarke American ES

GUARDIAN ® SAFETY

2. Check #2551, September 20, 20xx, in the amount of $68.95, to the Tidy Towel Service, for six dozen wash rags.

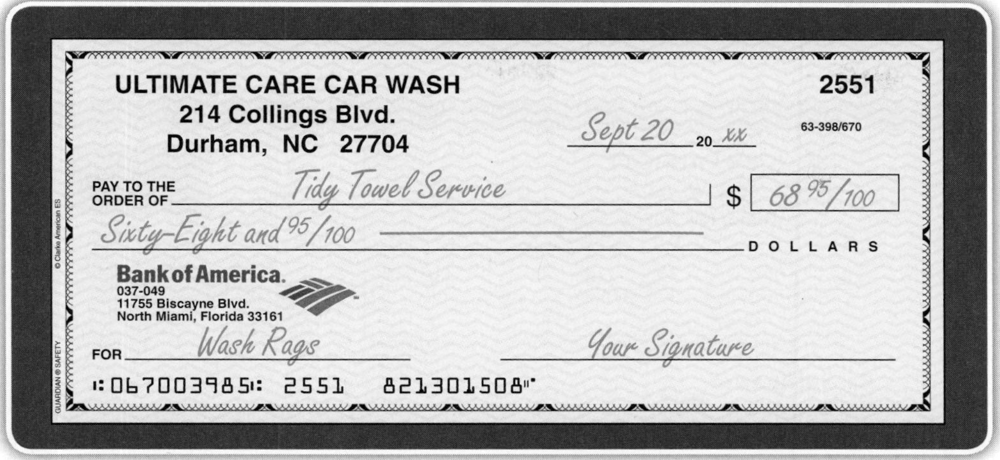
ULTIMATE CARE CAR WASH
214 Collings Blvd.
Durham, NC 27704
2551
Sept 20 20 xx
63-398/670
PAY TO THE ORDER OF Tidy Towel Service $ 68 95/100
Sixty-Eight and 95/100 DOLLARS
Bank of America.
037-049
11755 Biscayne Blvd.
North Miami, Florida 33161
FOR Wash Rags
Your Signature
⑆067003985⑆ 2551 821301508⑈

You have just received a check. Your account number is #099-506-8. Write the following endorsements in the space provided below, and identify what type they are.

3. Allowing you to deposit the check into your account.
4. Allowing you to cash the check.
5. Allowing you to transfer the check to your friend David Sporn.

3. 

Restrictive Endorsement

4. 

Blank Endorsement

5. 

Full Endorsement

6. Properly fill out the deposit slip for The Star Vista Corp., based on the following information:
   a. Date: July 9, 20xx.
   b. $1,680 in currency.
   c. $62.25 in coins.
   d. Checks in the amount of $2,455.94; $4,338.79; and $1,461.69.

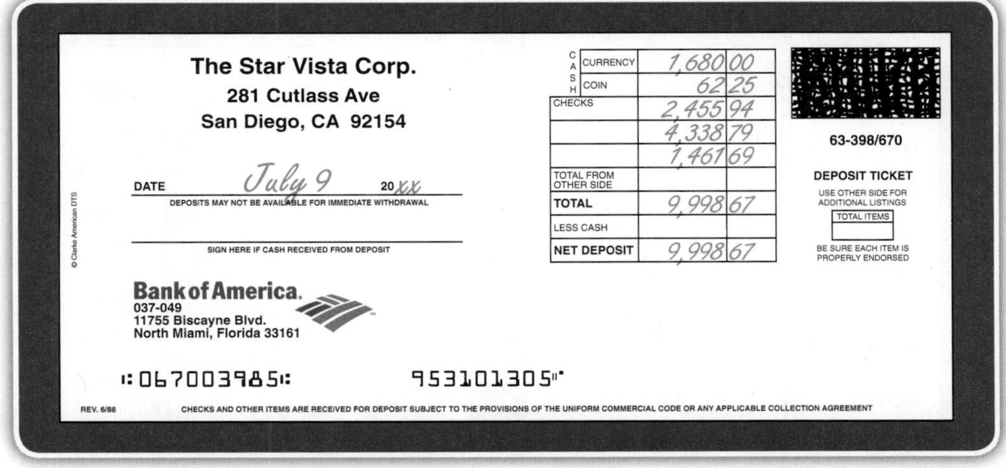
The Star Vista Corp.
281 Cutlass Ave
San Diego, CA 92154

DATE July 9 20 xx
DEPOSITS MAY NOT BE AVAILABLE FOR IMMEDIATE WITHDRAWAL

SIGN HERE IF CASH RECEIVED FROM DEPOSIT

CASH CURRENCY	1,680	00
CASH COIN	62	25
CHECKS	2,455	94
	4,338	79
	1,461	69
TOTAL FROM OTHER SIDE		
TOTAL	9,998	67
LESS CASH		
NET DEPOSIT	9,998	67

63-398/670
DEPOSIT TICKET
USE OTHER SIDE FOR ADDITIONAL LISTINGS
TOTAL ITEMS
BE SURE EACH ITEM IS PROPERLY ENDORSED

Bank of America.
037-049
11755 Biscayne Blvd.
North Miami, Florida 33161

⑆067003985⑆ 953101305⑈

REV. 6/88 CHECKS AND OTHER ITEMS ARE RECEIVED FOR DEPOSIT SUBJECT TO THE PROVISIONS OF THE UNIFORM COMMERCIAL CODE OR ANY APPLICABLE COLLECTION AGREEMENT

7. Properly fill out the deposit slip for Josh Parrott, based on the following information:
   a. Date: December 18, 20xx.
   b. A check for $651.03.
   c. $150 cash withdrawal.

JOSH PARROTT
5700 S. W. 4th St.
Reno, NV 89501

DATE *December 18* 20 *xx*
DEPOSITS MAY NOT BE AVAILABLE FOR IMMEDIATE WITHDRAWAL

Josh Parrott
SIGN HERE IF CASH RECEIVED FROM DEPOSIT

© Clarke American DTS

Bank of America.
037-049
11755 Biscayne Blvd.
North Miami, Florida 33161

CASH CURRENCY		
COIN		
CHECKS	651	03
TOTAL FROM OTHER SIDE		
TOTAL	651	03
LESS CASH	150	00
NET DEPOSIT	501	03

63-398/670
DEPOSIT TICKET
USE OTHER SIDE FOR ADDITIONAL LISTINGS
TOTAL ITEMS
BE SURE EACH ITEM IS PROPERLY ENDORSED

⑆067003985⑆ 450912507⑈

REV. 6/88 CHECKS AND OTHER ITEMS ARE RECEIVED FOR DEPOSIT SUBJECT TO THE PROVISIONS OF THE UNIFORM COMMERCIAL CODE OR ANY APPLICABLE COLLECTION AGREEMENT

8. From the following information, complete the three check stubs, in proper form:
   a. Starting balance $265.73.
   b. February 12, 20xx, check #439, in the amount of $175.05, to The Biloxie Bank, for a car payment.
   c. February 15, deposit of $377.10.
   d. February 18, check #440, in the amount of $149.88, to Fitness Equipment Co., for a set of dumbbells.
   e. February 22, deposit of $570.00.
   f. February 27, check #441, in the amount of $23.40, to Royalty Cleaners, for dry cleaning.
   g. March 3, debit card purchase—tires, $225.10.

IF TAX DEDUCTIBLE CHECK HERE ☐ $ *175.05*
439
February 12 20 *xx*
TO *Biloxie Bank*
FOR *Car Payment*

	DOLLARS	CENTS
BAL. FWD.	265	73
DEPOSIT		
DEPOSIT		
TOTAL	265	73
THIS ITEM	175	05
SUB-TOTAL	90	68
OTHER DEDUCT. (IF ANY)		
BAL. FWD.	90	68

IF TAX DEDUCTIBLE CHECK HERE ☐ $ *149.88*
440
February 18 20 *xx*
TO *Fitness Equipment Co.*
FOR *Dumbbells*

	DOLLARS	CENTS
BAL. FWD.	90	68
DEPOSIT *2/15*	377	10
DEPOSIT		
TOTAL	467	78
THIS ITEM	149	88
SUB-TOTAL	317	90
OTHER DEDUCT. (IF ANY)		
BAL. FWD.	317	90

IF TAX DEDUCTIBLE CHECK HERE ☐ $ *23.40*
441
February 27 20 *xx*
TO *Royalty Cleaners*
FOR *Dry Cleaning*

	DOLLARS	CENTS
BAL. FWD.	317	90
DEPOSIT *2/22*	570	00
DEPOSIT		
TOTAL	887	90
THIS ITEM	23	40
SUB-TOTAL	864	50
OTHER DEDUCT. (IF ANY)	225	10
BAL. FWD.	639	40

9. From the following information, complete the checkbook register:
   a. Starting balance $479.20.
   b. April 7, 20xx, deposit of $766.90.
   c. April 14, 20xx, debit card purchase, in the amount of $45.65, to Mario's Supermarket, for groceries.
   d. April 16, ATM withdrawal, $125.00.
   e. April 17, check #1208, in the amount of $870.00, to Howard Properties, Inc., for rent.
   f. April 21, 20xx, electronic payroll deposit of $1,350.00.
   g. April 27, check #1209, in the amount of $864.40, to Elegant Decor, for a dining room set.

PLEASE BE SURE TO **DEDUCT** ANY BANK CHARGES THAT APPLY TO YOUR ACCOUNT.

	DATE	DESCRIPTION OF TRANSACTION		✓		BALANCE FORWARD
						479.20
	4/7	To Deposit			766.90	
		For				Bal. 1,246.10
	4/14	To Mario's Market Debit Card	45.65			
		For				Bal. 1,200.45
	4/16	To ATM Withdrawal	125.00			
		For				Bal. 1,075.45
1208	4/17	To Howard Properties	870.00			
		For				Bal. 205.45
	4/21	To Electronic Payroll Deposit			1,350.00	
		For				Bal. 1,555.45
1209	4/27	To Elegant Decor	864.40			
		For				Bal. 691.05

10. From the following information, complete the checkbook register through October 10.

Casey McKee's account balance on September 26 was $1,196.19. On the first of October she received $3,023.11 by electronic payroll deposit. Also on the first of October, she wrote check #1804 to pay her rent in the amount of $1,175.00. Casey used her debit card to make purchases on September 28 for $37.79, on October 2 for $311.86, and on October 3 for $164.26. On October 8, she paid her electricity bill, gas bill, and phone bill using her bank's online bill-paying service. Her electricity bill was $142.87. Gas was $18.46, and phone amounted to $38.52. On October 9, she deposited a rebate check for $50.

PLEASE BE SURE TO **DEDUCT** ANY BANK CHARGES THAT APPLY TO YOUR ACCOUNT.

CHECK NUMBER	DATE	DESCRIPTION OF TRANSACTION	AMOUNT OF PAYMENT OR WITHDRAWAL (−)	✓	AMOUNT OF DEPOSIT OR INTEREST (+)	BALANCE FORWARD
						$1,196.19
	9/28	To Debit Card Purchase	37.79			
		For				Bal. 1,158.40
	10/1	To Payroll Deposit			3,023.11	
		For				Bal. 4,181.51
1804	10/1	To Rent Payment	1,175.00			
		For				Bal. 3,006.51
	10/2	To Debit Card Purchase	311.86			
		For				Bal. 2,694.65
	10/3	To Debit Card Purchase	164.26			
		For				Bal. 2,530.39
	10/8	To Online Bill-Payment Electricity	142.87			
		For				Bal. 2,387.52
	10/8	To Online Bill-Payment Gas	18.46			
		For				Bal. 2,369.06
	10/8	To Online Bill-Payment Phone	38.52			
		For				Bal. 2,330.54
	10/9	To Deposit			50.00	
		For				Bal. 2,380.54
	10/10	To				
		For				Bal. $2,380.54

BUSINESS DECISION TELLER TRAINING

Bank Teller

According to the U.S. Department of Labor, bank tellers make up approximately one-fourth of bank employees and conduct most of a bank's routine transactions.

In hiring tellers, banks seek people who enjoy public contact and have good numerical, clerical, and communication skills. Banks prefer applicants who have had courses in mathematics, accounting, bookkeeping, economics, and public speaking.

11. You are the training director for tellers at a large local bank. As part of a new training program that you are developing, you have decided to give teller trainees a "sample" deposit slip, check, and check register, with common errors on them. The trainees must find and correct the errors. Your task is to create the three documents.
    a. On a separate sheet of paper, list some "typical errors" that bank customers might make on a deposit slip, a check, and a check register.
    Answers will vary. Some might include addition or subtraction mistakes, wrong date, no signature, or missing information.
    b. Use the following blank deposit slip, check, and check register to create "filled-out" versions, each with one error you named for that document in part **a**. You make up all the details; names, dates, numbers, etc.
    c. After completing part **b.**, exchange documents with another student in the class, and try to find and correct the errors. (If this is a homework assignment, bring a copy of each document you created to class for the exchange. If this is an in-class assignment, temporarily trade texts with the other student, after completing part **b.**)

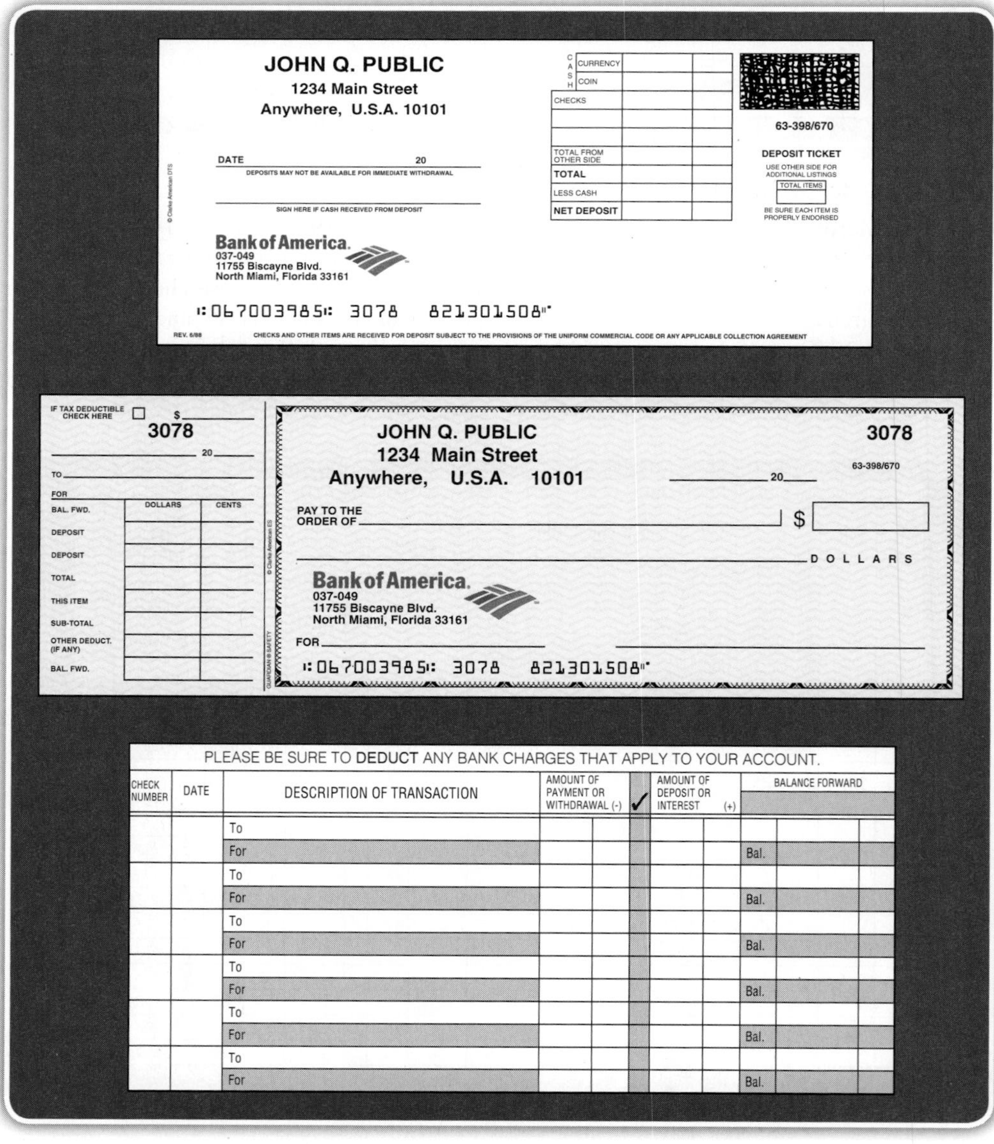

JOHN Q. PUBLIC
1234 Main Street
Anywhere, U.S.A. 10101

DATE ____________ 20 ____
DEPOSITS MAY NOT BE AVAILABLE FOR IMMEDIATE WITHDRAWAL

SIGN HERE IF CASH RECEIVED FROM DEPOSIT

CASH: CURRENCY / COIN
CHECKS
TOTAL FROM OTHER SIDE
TOTAL
LESS CASH
NET DEPOSIT

63-398/670

DEPOSIT TICKET
USE OTHER SIDE FOR ADDITIONAL LISTINGS
TOTAL ITEMS
BE SURE EACH ITEM IS PROPERLY ENDORSED

Bank of America.
037-049
11755 Biscayne Blvd.
North Miami, Florida 33161

⑆067003985⑆ 3078 821301508⑈

REV. 6/88 CHECKS AND OTHER ITEMS ARE RECEIVED FOR DEPOSIT SUBJECT TO THE PROVISIONS OF THE UNIFORM COMMERCIAL CODE OR ANY APPLICABLE COLLECTION AGREEMENT

IF TAX DEDUCTIBLE CHECK HERE ☐ $ ______
3078
____________ 20 ____
TO ______
FOR ______

	DOLLARS	CENTS
BAL. FWD.		
DEPOSIT		
DEPOSIT		
TOTAL		
THIS ITEM		
SUB-TOTAL		
OTHER DEDUCT. (IF ANY)		
BAL. FWD.		

JOHN Q. PUBLIC 3078
1234 Main Street
Anywhere, U.S.A. 10101 ____________ 20 ____
63-398/670

PAY TO THE ORDER OF ____________________ $ [ ]

____________________________________ DOLLARS

Bank of America.
037-049
11755 Biscayne Blvd.
North Miami, Florida 33161

FOR ____________ ____________

⑆067003985⑆ 3078 821301508⑈

PLEASE BE SURE TO **DEDUCT** ANY BANK CHARGES THAT APPLY TO YOUR ACCOUNT.

CHECK NUMBER	DATE	DESCRIPTION OF TRANSACTION	AMOUNT OF PAYMENT OR WITHDRAWAL (-)	✓	AMOUNT OF DEPOSIT OR INTEREST (+)	BALANCE FORWARD
		To				
		For				Bal.
		To				
		For				Bal.
		To				
		For				Bal.
		To				
		For				Bal.
		To				
		For				Bal.
		To				
		For				Bal.

BANK STATEMENT RECONCILIATION

Your monthly **bank statement** gives you a detailed review of the activity in your account for a specific period of time. It's your best opportunity to make sure your records match the bank's records. Be prepared to "match up" every activity (credits and debits) on the statement with your checkbook.

It is important that you review the bank statement in a timely fashion. If you find any discrepancies in ATM, debit card, or other electronic transactions, you must report them to the bank within 60 days of the date of the statement or the bank has no obligation to conduct an investigation. Another important reason to reconcile your checkbook with the statement is to look for debits you didn't make that might indicate that someone has access to your account.

bank statement A monthly summary of the activities in a checking account, including debits, credits, and beginning and ending balance. Sent by the bank to the account holder.

UNDERSTANDING THE BANK STATEMENT

Bank statements vary widely in style from bank to bank; however, most contain essentially the same information. Exhibit 4-13 illustrates typical online and printed bank statements. Note that it shows the balance brought forward from the last statement; the deposits and credits that have been added to the account during the month; the checks and debits that have been subtracted from the account during the month; any service charges assessed to the account; and the current or ending balance.

Credits are additions to the account, such as interest earned, notes collected, and electronic fund transfers of direct deposit payroll checks. **Debits** are subtractions from the account, such as automatic teller machine (ATM) withdrawals, debit card transactions, monthly service charges, check printing charges, nonsufficient fund (NSF) fees, and returned items. A **nonsufficient fund (NSF) fee** is a fee charged by the bank when a check is written without sufficient funds in the account to cover the amount of that check. **Returned items** are checks from others that you deposited into your account but were returned to your bank unpaid because the person or business issuing the check had insufficient funds in its account to cover the check. Banks usually charge a returned item fee when this occurs.

credits Additions to a checking account, such as deposits and interest earned.

debits Subtractions from a checking account, such as service charges.

nonsufficient fund (NSF) fees A fee charged by the bank when a check is written without sufficient funds in the account to cover the amount of that check.

returned item A check that you deposited but was returned to your bank unpaid because the person or business issuing the check had insufficient funds to cover the check.

PREPARING A BANK STATEMENT RECONCILIATION

When the statement arrives from the bank each month, the depositor must compare the bank balance with the balance shown in the checkbook. Usually, the balances are not the same because during the month some account activity has taken place without being recorded by the bank, and other activities have occurred without being recorded in the checkbook. The process of adjusting the bank and checkbook balances to reflect the actual current balance is known as **bank statement reconciliation**. When we use the word *checkbook* in this chapter, we are actually referring to the records kept by the depositor on the check stubs or in the checkbook register.

Before a statement can be reconciled, you must identify and total all the checks that have been written but have not yet reached the bank. These are known as **outstanding checks**. Outstanding checks are found by comparing and checking off each check in the checkbook with those shown on the statement. Any checks not appearing on the statement are outstanding checks.

Sometimes deposits are made close to the statement date, or by mail, and do not clear the bank in time to appear on the current statement. These are known as **deposits in transit**. Just like outstanding checks, deposits in transit must be identified and totaled. Once again, this is done by comparing and checking off the checkbook records with the deposits shown on the bank statement.

A bank statement is reconciled when the **adjusted checkbook balance** is equal to the **adjusted bank balance**. Most bank statements have a form on the back to use in reconciling the account. Exhibit 4-14 is an example of such a form and is used in this chapter.

bank statement reconciliation The process of adjusting the bank and checkbook balances to reflect the actual current balance of the checking account.

outstanding checks Checks that have been written but have not yet reached the bank and therefore do not appear on the current bank statement.

deposits in transit Deposits made close to the statement date, or by mail, which do not clear in time to appear on the current bank statement.

adjusted checkbook balance The checkbook balance minus service charges and other debits plus interest earned and other credits.

adjusted bank balance The bank balance minus outstanding checks plus deposits in transit.

Teaching Transparency 4-7

Exhibit 4-13
Paper and Electronic Bank Statements

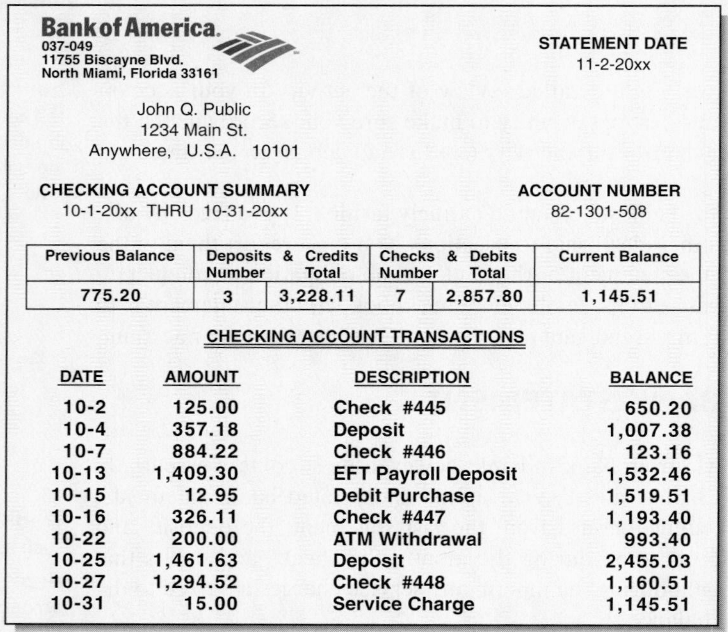

Bank of America
037-049
11755 Biscayne Blvd.
North Miami, Florida 33161

STATEMENT DATE
11-2-20xx

John Q. Public
1234 Main St.
Anywhere, U.S.A. 10101

CHECKING ACCOUNT SUMMARY
10-1-20xx THRU 10-31-20xx

ACCOUNT NUMBER
82-1301-508

Previous Balance	Deposits & Credits Number	Total	Checks & Debits Number	Total	Current Balance
775.20	3	3,228.11	7	2,857.80	1,145.51

CHECKING ACCOUNT TRANSACTIONS

DATE	AMOUNT	DESCRIPTION	BALANCE
10-2	125.00	Check #445	650.20
10-4	357.18	Deposit	1,007.38
10-7	884.22	Check #446	123.16
10-13	1,409.30	EFT Payroll Deposit	1,532.46
10-15	12.95	Debit Purchase	1,519.51
10-16	326.11	Check #447	1,193.40
10-22	200.00	ATM Withdrawal	993.40
10-25	1,461.63	Deposit	2,455.03
10-27	1,294.52	Check #448	1,160.51
10-31	15.00	Service Charge	1,145.51

Account Activity - Microsoft Internet Explorer

File Edit View Favorites Tools Help

Back Search Favorites Media

Log Out | ATM/Branch Locator | Calculators | Help Center | Contact Us | Privacy Policy

PA Central Bank

July 22, 2008

Home | Your Accounts | Bank One for You | Bank One for Your Business

Special Offers | Borrow Money | Reward Yourself

Account Summary > Account Activity

Account Activity

Print | Help With This Page

CHECKING | Current Balance | $8,404.67 | Select Action | GO

Displaying 41 transactions for account XXXXXXXXX1234.

This icon beside any transaction description means a copy of the cancelled check or deposit slip is available online. Click the icon to view the image. To sort your transactions by date, description, amount or type, just click the column heading.

Note: If a check image is no longer available online, you may order a paper copy. Deposit slip images are only available online at this time.

Date	Description	Amount	Type
07/12/2008	CHECK #1456 view	$-23.27	CHK
07/12/2008	CHECK #1457 view	$-179.00	CHK
07/12/2008	CHECK #1455 view	$-675.14	CHK
07/09/2008	ONLINE TRF FROM CHEC	$-563.00	W/D
07/09/2008	ATM WITHDRAWAL	$-360.00	W/D
07/08/2008	DEPOSIT view	$200.00	DEP
07/05/2008	AMOCO OIL 079104	$-41.00	W/D
07/02/2008	ATM WITHDRAWAL	$-20.00	W/D
07/02/2008	JUBILEE JUICE & FOOD	$-33.36	W/D
07/02/2008	CHICAGO SUN TIMES 70	$-99.00	W/D
07/01/2008	LEONA S HYDE PARK IL	$-25.94	W/D

Exhibit 4-14
Bank Statement Reconciliation Form

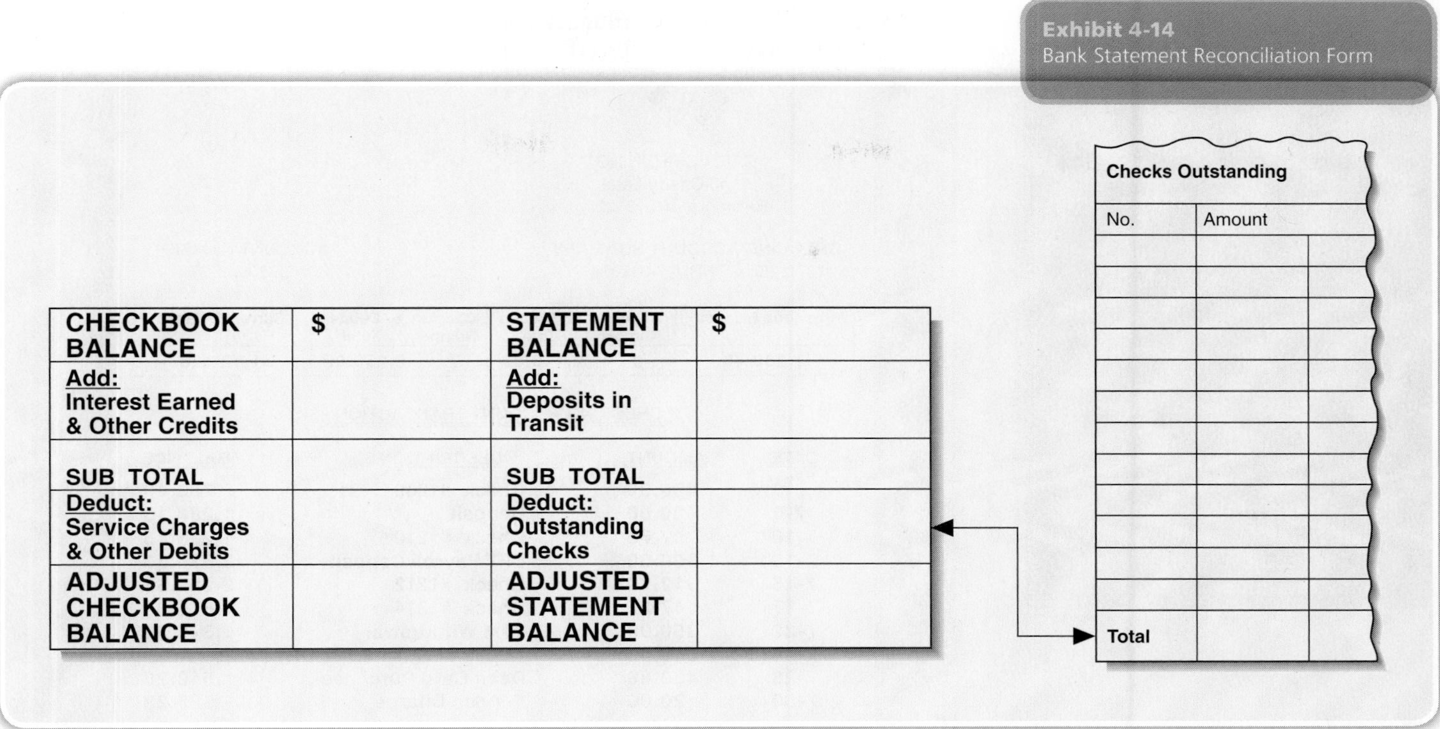

CHECKBOOK BALANCE	$	STATEMENT BALANCE	$
Add: Interest Earned & Other Credits		**Add:** Deposits in Transit	
SUB TOTAL		SUB TOTAL	
Deduct: Service Charges & Other Debits		**Deduct:** Outstanding Checks	
ADJUSTED CHECKBOOK BALANCE		ADJUSTED STATEMENT BALANCE	

Checks Outstanding		
No.	Amount	
Total		

Teaching Transparency 4-8

STEPS FOR PREPARING A BANK STATEMENT RECONCILIATION

Step 1. Calculate the adjusted checkbook balance:

a. Look over the bank statement and find any credits not recorded in the checkbook, such as interest earned or notes collected, and *add* them to the checkbook balance to get a subtotal.

b. From the bank statement, locate any charges or debits, such as service charges, NSF fees, or returned items, that have not been recorded in the checkbook, and *subtract* them from the subtotal from Step 1a.

Step 2. Calculate the adjusted bank balance:

a. Locate all of the deposits in transit and *add* them to the statement balance to get a subtotal.

b. Locate and total all outstanding checks and *subtract* them from the subtotal from Step 2a.

Step 3. Compare the adjusted balances:

a. If they are equal, the statement has been reconciled.

b. If they are not equal, an error exists that must be found and corrected. The error is either in the checkbook or on the bank statement.

EXAMPLE 5 RECONCILING A BANK STATEMENT

Prepare a bank reconciliation for Carrie Rushing from the bank statement and checkbook records on page 116.

Learning Tip

When a bank statement arrives, the balance on that statement will not agree with the checkbook balance until the account has been *reconciled*. Remember that ***both*** balances need to be adjusted.

To determine which balance, the checkbook or the bank, gets adjusted for various situations, ask, "Who didn't know?" For example,

- The bank *"didn't know"* about outstanding checks and deposits in transit; therefore these adjustments are made to the bank balance.
- The checkbook *"didn't know"* the amount of the service charges and other debits or credits. These adjustments are made to the checkbook.

Grove Isle Bank

STATEMENT DATE
8-2-20xx

CARRIE RUSHING
1190 Cherry Lane
Baltimore, Md. 21222

CHECKING ACCOUNT SUMMARY
7-1-20xx THRU 7-31-20xx

ACCOUNT NUMBER
82-1301-508

Previous Balance	Deposits & Credits Number	Total	Checks & Debits Number	Total	Current Balance
1,233.40	3	2,445.80	7	2,158.92	1,520.28

CHECKING ACCOUNT TRANSACTIONS

DATE	AMOUNT	DESCRIPTION	BALANCE
7-3	450.30	Check #1209	783.10
7-6	500.00	Deposit	1,283.10
7-10	47.75	Check #1210	1,235.35
7-13	1,300.00	EFT Payroll Deposit	2,535.35
7-15	312.79	Check #1212	2,222.56
7-17	547.22	Check #1214	1,675.34
7-22	350.00	ATM Withdrawal	1,325.34
7-24	645.80	Deposit	1,971.14
7-28	430.86	Debit Card Purchase	1,540.28
7-30	20.00	Service Charge	1,520.28

PLEASE BE SURE TO DEDUCT ANY BANK CHARGES THAT APPLY TO YOUR ACCOUNT

CHECK NUMBER	DATE	DESCRIPTION OF TRANSACTION	AMOUNT OF PAYMENT OR WITHDRAWAL (−)	✓	AMOUNT OF DEPOSIT OR INTEREST (+)	BALANCE FORWARD 1,233.40
1209	7/1	To Stillwell Supply Co.	450.30			
		For				Bal. 783.10
	7/6	To Deposit			500.00	
		For				Bal. 1,283.10
1210	7/8	To Food Spot	47.75			
		For				Bal. 1,235.35
1211	7/10	To Delta Air Lines	342.10			
		For				Bal. 893.25
	7/13	To Payroll Deposit			1,300.00	
		For				Bal. 2,193.25
1212	7/13	To Hyatt Hotel	312.79			
		For				Bal. 1,880.46
1213	7/15	To Wall Street Journal	75.00			
		For				Bal. 1,805.46
1214	7/15	To Builder's Depot	547.22			
		For				Bal. 1,258.24
	7/21	To ATM Withdrawal	350.00			
		For				Bal. 908.24
	7/24	To Deposit			645.80	
		For				Bal. 1,554.04
	7/28	To Williams Roofing—Debit Card	430.86			
		For				Bal. 1,123.18
	7/31	To Deposit			550.00	
		For				Bal. 1,673.18

SOLUTION STRATEGY

The properly completed reconciliation form is on page 117. Note that the adjusted checkbook balance equals the adjusted bank statement balance. The balances are now reconciled. After some practice, the format will become familiar to you, and you should no longer need the form.

CHECKBOOK BALANCE	$ 1,673.18	STATEMENT BALANCE	$ 1,520.28
Add: Interest Earned & Other Credits		**Add:** Deposits in Transit	550.00
SUB TOTAL	1,673.18	SUB TOTAL	2,070.28
Deduct: Service Charges & Other Debits	20.00	**Deduct:** Outstanding Checks	417.10
ADJUSTED CHECKBOOK BALANCE	1,653.18	ADJUSTED STATEMENT BALANCE	1,653.18

Reconciled Balances

Checks Outstanding

No.	Amount	
1211	342	10
1213	75	00
Total	417	10

TRY IT EXERCISE 5

Using the form provided, reconcile the following bank statement and checkbook records for John Monahan.

North Star Bank

STATEMENT DATE
4-3-20xx

JOHN MONAHAN
4121 Pinetree Rd.
Bangor, Maine 04401

CHECKING ACCOUNT SUMMARY
3-1-20xx THRU 3-31-20xx

ACCOUNT NUMBER
097440

Previous Balance	Deposits & Credits Number	Deposits & Credits Total	Checks & Debits Number	Checks & Debits Total	Current Balance
625.40	3	1,790.00	8	690.00	1,725.40

CHECKING ACCOUNT TRANSACTIONS

DATE	AMOUNT	DESCRIPTION	BALANCE
3-2	34.77	Debit Card Purchase	590.63
3-6	750.00	Payroll-EFT Deposit	1,340.63
3-10	247.05	Check #340	1,093.58
3-13	390.00	Deposit	1,483.58
3-15	66.30	Check #342	1,417.28
3-17	112.18	Check #343	1,305.10
3-22	150.00	ATM Withdrawal	1,155.10
3-24	650.00	Deposit	1,805.10
3-28	50.00	Check #345	1,755.10
3-30	17.70	Check printing charge	1,737.40
3-31	12.00	Service charge	1,725.40

PLEASE BE SURE TO **DEDUCT** ANY BANK CHARGES THAT APPLY TO YOUR ACCOUNT.

CHECK NUMBER	DATE	DESCRIPTION OF TRANSACTION	AMOUNT OF PAYMENT OR WITHDRAWAL (−)		✓	AMOUNT OF DEPOSIT OR INTEREST (+)			BALANCE FORWARD	
									625	40
	3/2	To *Naples Pet Shop — Debit Card*	34	77						
		For						Bal.	590	63
	3/5	To *Electronic Payroll Deposit*				750	00			
		For						Bal.	1,340	63
339	3/5	To *Alison Company*	19	83						
		For						Bal.	1,320	80
340	3/9	To *Silver Software*	247	05						
		For						Bal.	1,073	75
	3/12	To *Deposit*				390	00			
		For						Bal.	1,463	75
341	3/12	To *The Book Shelf*	57	50						
		For						Bal.	1,406	25
342	3/13	To *Wal-Mart*	66	30						
		For						Bal.	1,339	95
343	3/15	To *S.E. Office Supply*	112	18						
		For						Bal.	1,227	77
	3/22	To *ATM Withdrawal*	150	00						
		For						Bal.	1,077	77
	3/24	To *Deposit*				650	00			
		For						Bal.	1,727	77
344	3/24	To *Flower Decor, Inc.*	119	32						
		For						Bal.	1,608	45
345	3/28	To *Cablevision, Inc.*	50	00						
		For						Bal.	1,558	45
	3/30	To *Deposit*				240	23			
		For						Bal.	1,798	68

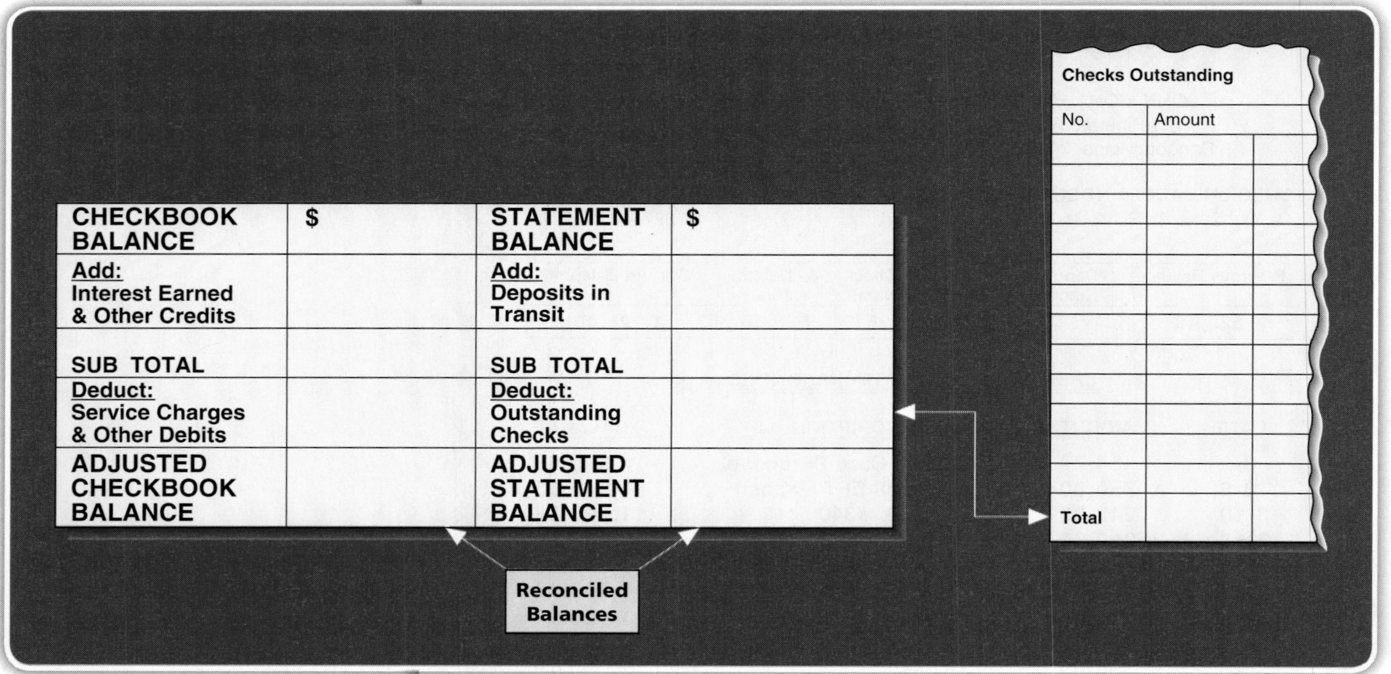

CHECK YOUR ANSWERS WITH THE SOLUTIONS ON PAGE 125.

Review Exercises

SECTION II 4

1. On April 3, Mikka Baker received her bank statement, showing a balance of $2,087.93. Her checkbook showed a balance of $1,493.90. Outstanding checks were $224.15, $327.80, $88.10, $122.42, and $202.67. There was an $8.00 service charge, and the deposits in transit amounted to $813.11. There was an electronic payroll deposit of $450.00. Use the form below to reconcile Mikka's account.

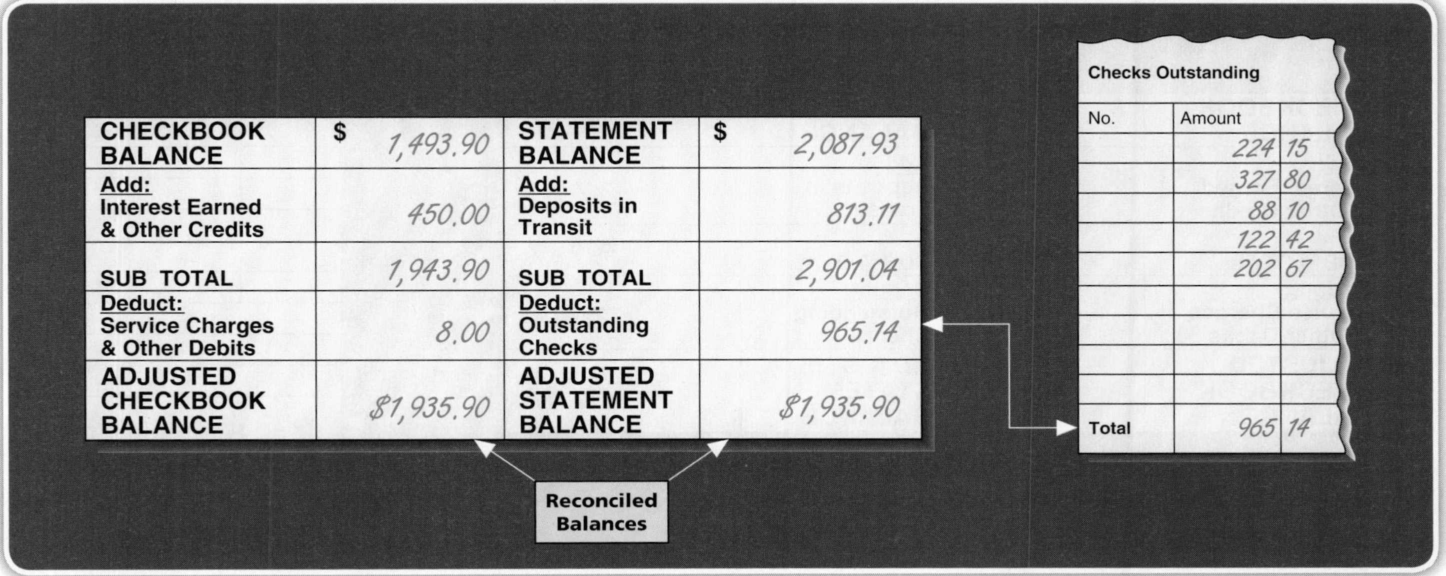

CHECKBOOK BALANCE	$ 1,493.90	STATEMENT BALANCE	$ 2,087.93
Add: Interest Earned & Other Credits	450.00	Add: Deposits in Transit	813.11
SUB TOTAL	1,943.90	SUB TOTAL	2,901.04
Deduct: Service Charges & Other Debits	8.00	Deduct: Outstanding Checks	965.14
ADJUSTED CHECKBOOK BALANCE	$1,935.90	ADJUSTED STATEMENT BALANCE	$1,935.90

Reconciled Balances

Checks Outstanding

No.	Amount	
	224	15
	327	80
	88	10
	122	42
	202	67
Total	965	14

2. Bob Albrecht received his bank statement on July 5, showing a balance of $2,663.31. His checkbook had a balance of $1,931.83. The statement showed a service charge of $15.80 and an electronic payroll deposit of $200.00. The deposits in transit totaled $314.12, and the outstanding checks were for $182.00, $261.40, and $418.00. Use the form below to reconcile Bob's account.

Teaching Transparency 4-9

CHECKBOOK BALANCE	$ 1,931.83	STATEMENT BALANCE	$ 2,663.31
Add: Interest Earned & Other Credits	200.00	Add: Deposits in Transit	314.12
SUB TOTAL	2,131.83	SUB TOTAL	2,977.43
Deduct: Service Charges & Other Debits	15.80	Deduct: Outstanding Checks	861.40
ADJUSTED CHECKBOOK BALANCE	2,116.03	ADJUSTED STATEMENT BALANCE	2,116.03

Reconciled Balances

Checks Outstanding

No.	Amount	
	182	00
	261	40
	418	00
Total	861	40

3. On December 2, Mike Strause received his bank statement showing a balance of $358.97. His checkbook showed a balance of $479.39. There was a check printing charge of $13.95, and interest earned was $6.40. The outstanding checks were for $22.97, $80.36, $19.80, and $4.50. The deposits in transit totaled $240.50. Use the form below to reconcile Mike's account.

CHECKBOOK BALANCE	$ 479.39	STATEMENT BALANCE	$ 358.97
Add: Interest Earned & Other Credits	6.40	Add: Deposits in Transit	240.50
SUB TOTAL	485.79	SUB TOTAL	599.47
Deduct: Service Charges & Other Debits	13.95	Deduct: Outstanding Checks	127.63
ADJUSTED CHECKBOOK BALANCE	471.84	ADJUSTED STATEMENT BALANCE	471.84

Reconciled Balances

Checks Outstanding

No.	Amount	
	22	97
	80	36
	19	80
	4	50
Total	127	63

BUSINESS DECISION CHOOSING A BANK

4. You are looking for a bank in which to open a checking account for your new part-time business. You estimate that in the first year you will be writing 30 checks per month and will make three debit transactions per month. Your average daily balance is estimated to be $900 for the first six months and $2,400 for the next six months.

   Use the following information to solve the problem.

Bank	Monthly Fees and Conditions
Intercontinental Bank	$15.00 with $1,000 min. daily balance -or- $25.00 under $1,000 min. daily balance
City National Bank	$4.50 plus $0.50 per check over 10 checks monthly $1.00 per debit transaction
Bank of America	$6 plus $0.25 per check $2.00 per debit transaction
First Union Bank	$9 plus $0.15 per check $1.50 per debit transaction

a. Calculate the cost of doing business with each bank for a year.

Intercontinental Bank:
6 Months at $25.00 = 150.00
6 Months at $15.00 = 90.00
$240.00

City National Bank:
Monthly service charge 4.50
20 Checks at \$0.50 = 10.00
3 Debit transactions at \$1.00 = 3.00
\$17.50
× 12 Months
\$210.00

Bank of America:
Monthly service charge 6.00
30 Checks at \$0.25 = 7.50
3 Debit transactions at \$2.00 = 6.00
\$19.50
× 12 Months
\$234.00

First Union Bank:
Monthly service charge 9.00
30 Checks at \$0.15 = 4.50
3 Debit transactions at \$1.50 = 4.50
\$18.00
× 12 Months
\$216.00

© Jon Freilich/Associated Press

SUPER ATM

ATMs have long been a staple in convenience stores, but now several major chains, including 7-Eleven, have installed transactional kiosks able to do a lot more. According to the New York Times, 7-Eleven has introduced custom-made terminals called Vcoms.

Often referred to as ATMs on steroids, the chain's more than 1,000 Vcoms dispense cash, sell Verizon services, and handle bill payments and money transfers. They can also cash checks to the penny and print digital check images on receipts.

Source: Adapted from *New York Times*, April 1, 2006. Page B1. The Convenience of an A.T. M., but So Much More. By Jennifer A. Kingson.

b. Which bank should you choose for your checking account?
City National Bank is the best choice.

SUMMARY CHART

Section I: Understanding and Using Checking Accounts

Topic	Important Concepts	Illustrative Examples
Checks **P/O 4-1, p. 98** **P/O 4-2, p. 100**	Checks, or drafts, are negotiable instruments ordering the bank to pay money from the checking account to the name written on the check. The person or business named on the check to receive the money is known as the payee. The person or business issuing the check is known as the payor.	See Check, with Parts Labeled Exhibit 4-2, p. 99 Payor's Name and Address; Bank and Federal Reserve District Number; Date of Check; Check Number; Trailing Edge; Payee's Name; Amount of Check Written in Words; Amount of Check Written in Numerals; Bank Branch Name and Address; What the Check Was Written For; Bank and Account Numbers Imprinted with Magnetic Ink for Electronic Processing; Payor's Signature; Leading Edge
Deposit Slips **P/O 4-1, p. 98** **P/O 4-4, p. 104**	Deposit slips, or deposit tickets are printed forms with the depositor's name, address, account number, and space for the details of the deposit. Deposit slips are used to record money, both cash and checks, being added to the checking account. They are presented to the bank teller along with the items to be deposited. When a deposit is completed, the depositor receives a copy of the deposit slip as a receipt, or proof of the transaction.	See Deposit Slip Exhibit 4-3, p. 99 JOHN Q. PUBLIC 1234 Main Street Anywhere, U.S.A. 10101 Bank of America See Completed Deposit Slip Exhibit 4-10, p. 104 JOHN Q. PUBLIC 1234 Main Street Anywhere U.S.A. 10101 DATE April 18, 20XX John Q. Public Currency 127.00; Coin 16.10; Checks 237.55, 500.00; Total 874.65; Less Cash 100.00; Net Deposit 774.65

(continued)

Section I: (continued)

Topic	Important Concepts	Illustrative Examples
Check Stubs **P/O 4-1, p. 98** **P/O 4-5, p. 106**	Check stubs, with checks attached by perforation, are a bound part of the checkbook. The check number is preprinted on both the check and the attached stub. Each stub is used to record the issuing of its corresponding check and any deposits made on that date.	See Check Stub with Check Exhibit 4-4, p. 100
Check Registers **P/O 4-1, p. 98** **P/O 4-5, p. 106**	Check registers are the alternative method for keeping track of checking account activities. They are a separate booklet of forms, rather than stubs attached to each check. Space is provided for all the pertinent information required to keep an accurate and up-to-date running balance of the account.	See Check Register Exhibit 4-5, p. 100
Endorsements **P/O 4-3, p. 102**	When you receive a check, you may either cash it, deposit it in your account, or transfer it to another party. The endorsement on the back of the check instructs the bank what to do. Your endorsement should be written within the $1\frac{1}{2}$-inch space at the trailing edge of the check.	See Endorsement Space Exhibit 4-6, p. 103
Blank Endorsement **P/O 4-3, p. 102**	A blank endorsement is used when you want to cash the check. You, as the payee, simply sign your name exactly as it appears on the front of the check. Once you have endorsed a check in this manner, anyone who has possession of the check can cash it.	See Blank Endorsement Exhibit 4-7, p. 103 *John Q. Public* *82-1301-508*
Restrictive Endorsement **P/O 4-3, p. 102**	A restrictive endorsement is used when you want to deposit the check into your account. In this case, you endorse the check "for deposit only," sign your name as it appears on the front, and write your account number.	See Restrictive Endorsement Exhibit 4-8, p. 103 *for deposit only* *John Q. Public* *82-1301-508*
Full Endorsement **P/O 4-3, p. 102**	A full endorsement is used when you want to transfer the check to another party. In this case, you endorse the check "pay to the order of," write the name of the person or business to whom the check is being transferred, and sign your name and account number.	See Full Endorsement Exhibit 4-9, p. 103 *pay to the order of* *Cindy J. Citizen* *John Q. Public* *82-1301-508*

Section II: Bank Statement Reconciliation

<table>
<tr><th>Topic</th><th>Important Concepts</th><th>Illustrative Examples</th></tr>
<tr>
<td>Bank Statements
P/O 4-6, p. 113</td>
<td>Bank statements are a recap of the checking account activity for the month. They show the balance brought forward from the last statement, the deposits and credits that have been added to the account during the month, the checks and debits that have been subtracted from the account during the month, service charges assessed to the account, and the current or ending balance.</td>
<td>See Bank Statement Exhibit 4-13, p. 114

Bank of America.
037-049
11755 Biscayne Blvd.
North Miami, Florida 33161

STATEMENT DATE
11-2-20xx

John Q. Public
1234 Main St.
Anywhere, U.S.A. 10101

CHECKING ACCOUNT SUMMARY
10-1-20xx THRU 10-31-20xx

ACCOUNT NUMBER
82-1301-508

<table>
<tr><th>Previous Balance</th><th>Deposits & Credits Number</th><th>Total</th><th>Checks & Debits Number</th><th>Total</th><th>Current Balance</th></tr>
<tr><td>775.20</td><td>3</td><td>3,228.11</td><td>7</td><td>2,857.80</td><td>1,145.51</td></tr>
</table>

CHECKING ACCOUNT TRANSACTIONS
<table>
<tr><th>DATE</th><th>AMOUNT</th><th>DESCRIPTION</th><th>BALANCE</th></tr>
<tr><td>10-2</td><td>125.00</td><td>Check #445</td><td>650.20</td></tr>
<tr><td>10-4</td><td>357.18</td><td>Deposit</td><td>1,007.38</td></tr>
<tr><td>10-7</td><td>884.22</td><td>Check #446</td><td>123.16</td></tr>
<tr><td>10-13</td><td>1,409.30</td><td>EFT Payroll Deposit</td><td>1,532.46</td></tr>
<tr><td>10-15</td><td>12.95</td><td>Debit Purchase</td><td>1,519.51</td></tr>
<tr><td>10-16</td><td>326.11</td><td>Check #447</td><td>1,193.40</td></tr>
<tr><td>10-22</td><td>200.00</td><td>ATM Withdrawal</td><td>993.40</td></tr>
<tr><td>10-25</td><td>1,461.63</td><td>Deposit</td><td>2,455.03</td></tr>
<tr><td>10-27</td><td>1,294.52</td><td>Check #448</td><td>1,160.51</td></tr>
<tr><td>10-31</td><td>15.00</td><td>Service Charge</td><td>1,145.51</td></tr>
</table>
</td>
</tr>
<tr>
<td>Bank Statement Reconciliation
P/O 4-7, p. 113</td>
<td>1. Calculate the adjusted checkbook balance:
a. Locate any credits on the statement not recorded in the checkbook, such as interest earned or notes collected, and add them to the checkbook balance to get a subtotal.
b. Subtract any debits or charges such as service charges, NSF fees, or returned items from the subtotal above.
2. Calculate the adjusted bank balance:
a. Locate all the deposits in transit and add them to the checkbook balance to get a subtotal.
b. Locate all outstanding checks and subtract them from the subtotal above.
3. Compare the adjusted balances:
a. If they are equal, the statement has been reconciled.
b. If they are not equal, an error exists that must be found and corrected. The error is either in the checkbook or on the bank statement.</td>
<td>See Blank Reconciliation Form Exhibit 4-14, p. 115

<table>
<tr><td>CHECKBOOK BALANCE</td><td>$</td><td>STATEMENT BALANCE</td><td>$</td></tr>
<tr><td>Add:
Interest Earned & Other Credits</td><td></td><td>Add:
Deposits in Transit</td><td></td></tr>
<tr><td>SUB TOTAL</td><td></td><td>SUB TOTAL</td><td></td></tr>
<tr><td>Deduct:
Service Charges & Other Debits</td><td></td><td>Deduct:
Outstanding Checks</td><td></td></tr>
<tr><td>ADJUSTED CHECKBOOK BALANCE</td><td></td><td>ADJUSTED STATEMENT BALANCE</td><td></td></tr>
</table>

<table>
<tr><th colspan="3">Checks Outstanding</th></tr>
<tr><td>No.</td><td>Amount</td><td></td></tr>
<tr><td>Total</td><td></td><td></td></tr>
</table>
</td>
</tr>
</table>

TRY IT EXERCISE SOLUTIONS FOR CHAPTER 4

1.

Sally Kerscher
1585 S. W. 6 Avenue
Tallahassee, FL 32399

206

April 27 20 xx

63-398/670

PAY TO THE ORDER OF Whole Foods $ 41 88/100

Forty-one and 88/100 DOLLARS

Bank of America
037-049
11755 Biscayne Blvd.
North Miami, Florida 33161

FOR Party Platter

Sally Kerscher

⑆067003985⑆ 3077 821451902⑈

2. a.

Pay to the order of
Roz Reitman
Your Signature
696-339-1028

Full Endorsement

b.

Your Signature
696-339-1028

Blank Endorsement

c.

for deposit only
Your Signature
696-339-1028

Restrictive Endorsement

3.

COMDEX ELECTRONICS
12155 Miller Road
New Orleans, LA 70144

DATE November 11 20xx

DEPOSITS MAY NOT BE AVAILABLE FOR IMMEDIATE WITHDRAWAL

SIGN HERE IF CASH RECEIVED FROM DEPOSIT

CASH CURRENCY	3,549	00
CASH COIN	19	65
CHECKS	411	92
	2,119	56
TOTAL FROM OTHER SIDE		
TOTAL	6,100	13
LESS CASH		
NET DEPOSIT	6,100	13

63-398/670

DEPOSIT TICKET

USE OTHER SIDE FOR ADDITIONAL LISTINGS

TOTAL ITEMS

BE SURE EACH ITEM IS PROPERLY ENDORSED

Bank of America
037-049
11755 Biscayne Blvd.
North Miami, Florida 33161

⑆067003985⑆ 536101902⑈

REV. 6/88 CHECKS AND OTHER ITEMS ARE RECEIVED FOR DEPOSIT SUBJECT TO THE PROVISIONS OF THE UNIFORM COMMERCIAL CODE OR ANY APPLICABLE COLLECTION AGREEMENT

4.

IF TAX DEDUCTIBLE CHECK HERE ☐ $ 55.75

137

March 12 20 xx

TO Nathan & David

FOR perm & manicure

	DOLLARS	CENTS
BAL. FWD.	887	45
DEPOSIT		
DEPOSIT		
TOTAL	887	45
THIS ITEM	55	75
SUB-TOTAL	831	70
OTHER DEDUCT. (IF ANY)		
BAL. FWD.	831	70

IF TAX DEDUCTIBLE CHECK HERE ☐ $ 459.88

138

March 19 20 xx

TO Complete Auto Service

FOR Car repair

	DOLLARS	CENTS
BAL. FWD.	831	70
DEPOSIT 3/16	125	40
DEPOSIT 3/16	221	35
TOTAL	1,178	45
THIS ITEM	459	88
SUB-TOTAL	718	57
OTHER DEDUCT. (IF ANY)	53	00
BAL. FWD.	665	57

PLEASE BE SURE TO **DEDUCT** ANY BANK CHARGES THAT APPLY TO YOUR ACCOUNT.

CHECK NUMBER	DATE	DESCRIPTION OF TRANSACTION	AMOUNT OF PAYMENT OR WITHDRAWAL (−)		✓	AMOUNT OF DEPOSIT OR INTEREST (+)			BALANCE FORWARD	
									887	45
137	3/12	To Nathan & David Hair Stylists	55	75						
		For						Bal.	831	70
	3/16	To Deposit				125	40			
		For						Bal.	957	10
	3/16	To Deposit				221	35			
		For						Bal.	1,178	45
138	3/19	To Complete Auto Service	459	88						
		For						Bal.	718	57
	3/20	To Debit Card—Post Office	53	00						
		For						Bal.	665	57

5.

CHECKBOOK BALANCE	$ 1,798.68	STATEMENT BALANCE	$ 1,725.40
Add: Interest Earned & Other Credits		Add: Deposits in Transit	240.23
SUB TOTAL	1,798.68	SUB TOTAL	1,965.63
Deduct: Service Charges & Other Debits	29.70	Deduct: Outstanding Checks	196.65
ADJUSTED CHECKBOOK BALANCE	1,768.98	ADJUSTED STATEMENT BALANCE	1,768.98

Reconciled Balances

Checks Outstanding

No.	Amount	
339	19	83
341	57	50
344	119	32
Total	196	65

CONCEPT REVIEW

1. A(n) ____ is a written order to a bank by a depositor to pay the amount specified from funds on deposit in a checking account. (4-1)
check

2. On a check, the ____ is the person or business issuing the check; the ____ is the person or business named on the check to receive the money. (4-1)
payor, payee

3. When a(n) ____ card is used, the amount of the transaction is deducted electronically from the checking account. (4-1)
debit

4. Write the word form of $52.45 as it would appear on a check.
fifty-two and 45/100

5. The signature and instructions on the back of a check are known as the ____. (4-3)
endorsement

6. There are three types of endorsements used on checks: the blank, the restrictive, and the ____ endorsement. (4-3)
full

7. The form used to record money being added to the checking account is a called a(n) ____ ____. (4-4)
deposit slip

8. When cash is being withdrawn at the time of a deposit, a(n) ____ is required on the deposit slip. (4-4)
signature

9. Attached by perforation to checks, check ____ are one method of tracking checking account activity. (4-5)
stubs

10. A check ____ is a separate booklet used to keep track of checking account activity. (4-5)
register

11. A bank ____ is a monthly summary of activities in a checking account. (4-6)
statement

12. Additions to a checking account are called ____; subtractions from a checking account are called ____. (4-6)
credits, debits

13. A bank statement is reconciled when the adjusted checkbook balance ____ the adjusted bank balance. (4-7)
equals

14. Checks that have not yet reached the bank are called ____ checks. Deposits that have not reached the bank are called deposits in ____. (4-7)
outstanding, transit

4 CHAPTER ASSESSMENT TEST

Name

Class

1. As the purchasing manager for Fuzzy Logic Industries, write a check dated April 29, 20xx, in the amount of $24,556.00, to Outback Electronics, Inc., for circuit boards.

FUZZY LOGIC INDUSTRIES
12221 Keystone Blvd
Greenville, SC 29610

206

April 29 20 xx

63-398/670

PAY TO THE ORDER OF Outback Electronics, Inc. $ 24,556 xx/100

Twenty-Four Thousand Five Hundred Fifty-Six and xx/100 DOLLARS

Bank of America.
037-049
11755 Biscayne Blvd.
North Miami, Florida 33161

FOR Circuit Boards Your Signature

⑆067003985⑆ 206 731021807⑈

© Clarke American ES

GUARDIAN ® SAFETY

2. You have just received a check. Your account number is #9299-144-006. Write the following endorsements in the space provided below, and identify what type they are.

a. Allowing the check to be transferred to Expo, Inc.
b. Allowing you to cash the check.
c. Allowing you to deposit the check into your account.

a.
Pay to the order of
Expo, Inc.
Your Signature
9299-144-006

Full Endorsement

b.
Your Signature
9299-144-006

Blank Endorsement

c.
for deposit only
Your Signature
9299-144-006

Restrictive Endorsement

Name

Class

3. As cashier for the Country Kitchen Cafe, it is your responsibility to make the daily deposits. Complete the deposit slip below, based on the following information.

a. Date: January 20, 20xx.
b. Checks totaling $344.20.
c. Currency of $547.00.
d. Coins: 125 quarters, 67 dimes, 88 nickels, and 224 pennies.

COUNTRY KITCHEN CAFE
1470 Fleetwood St.
Madison, WI 53704

DATE January 20 20 xx
DEPOSITS MAY NOT BE AVAILABLE FOR IMMEDIATE WITHDRAWAL

SIGN HERE IF CASH RECEIVED FROM DEPOSIT

CASH CURRENCY	547	00
CASH COIN	44	59
CHECKS	344	20
TOTAL FROM OTHER SIDE		
TOTAL	935	79
LESS CASH		
NET DEPOSIT	935	79

63-398/670

DEPOSIT TICKET
USE OTHER SIDE FOR ADDITIONAL LISTINGS
TOTAL ITEMS
BE SURE EACH ITEM IS PROPERLY ENDORSED

Grove Isle Bank

⑆067003985⑆ 730451408⑈

REV. 6/88 CHECKS AND OTHER ITEMS ARE RECEIVED FOR DEPOSIT SUBJECT TO THE PROVISIONS OF THE UNIFORM COMMERCIAL CODE OR ANY APPLICABLE COLLECTION AGREEMENT

© Clarke American DTS

4. Sherry Smith's account balance in the morning when she checked it online was $823.71. During the day, she used her debit card for the following purchases: groceries—$48.38, flowers—$13.86, prescription refill—$28.00, gasoline—$56.28. There was a $0.45 charge to use her debit card for the gas purchase. She also used her debit card to buy a roll of stamps for $41.00. In her mail was a birthday card with a $75 check from her uncle. Sherry took the check to the bank and deposited it. What should she expect her account balance to be the following morning?

$823.71 - 48.38 - 13.86 - 28.00 - 56.28 - 0.45 - 41.00 + 75.00 = \underline{\$710.74}$

5. From the following information, complete the two check stubs below and the check register on page 128.
   a. Starting balance: $463.30.
   b. April 15, 20xx, check #450, issued to the Keystone Market, for groceries, in the amount of $67.78.
   c. April 17, debit card purchase of $250.
   d. April 19, deposit of $125.45.
   e. April 20, deposit of $320.00.
   f. April 27, check #451, in the amount of $123.10, to Ace Appliance, Inc., for refrigerator repair.

IF TAX DEDUCTIBLE CHECK HERE ☐ $ 67.78
450
April 15 20 xx
TO Keystone Market
FOR Groceries

	DOLLARS	CENTS
BAL. FWD.	463	30
DEPOSIT		
DEPOSIT		
TOTAL	463	30
THIS ITEM	67	78
SUB-TOTAL	395	52
OTHER DEDUCT. (IF ANY) 4/17	250	00
BAL. FWD.	145	52

IF TAX DEDUCTIBLE CHECK HERE ☐ $ 123.10
451
April 27 20 xx
TO Ace Appliance
FOR Ref. Repair

	DOLLARS	CENTS
BAL. FWD.	145	52
DEPOSIT 4/19	125	45
DEPOSIT 4/20	320	00
TOTAL	590	97
THIS ITEM	123	10
SUB-TOTAL	467	87
OTHER DEDUCT. (IF ANY)		
BAL. FWD.	467	87

Name ______________________

Class ______________________

PLEASE BE SURE TO **DEDUCT** ANY BANK CHARGES THAT APPLY TO YOUR ACCOUNT.

CHECK NUMBER	DATE	DESCRIPTION OF TRANSACTION	AMOUNT OF PAYMENT OR WITHDRAWAL (−)	✓	AMOUNT OF DEPOSIT OR INTEREST (+)	BALANCE FORWARD 463.30
450	4/15	To *Keystone Market*	67.78			
		For				Bal. 395.52
	4/17	To *Debit Card Purchase*	250.00			
		For				Bal. 145.52
	4/19	To *Deposit*			125.45	
		For				Bal. 270.97
	4/20	To *Deposit*			320.00	
		For				Bal. 590.97
451	4/27	To *Ace Appliance*	123.10			
		For				Bal. 467.87
		To				
		For				Bal.

6. On October 1, Natalie King received her bank statement showing a balance of $374.52. Her checkbook records indicate a balance of $338.97. There was a service charge for the month of $4.40 on the statement. The outstanding checks were for $47.10, $110.15, $19.80, and $64.10. The deposits in transit totaled $125.50. There was a $75.70 debit for automatic payment of her telephone bill. Use the following form to reconcile Natalie's checking account.

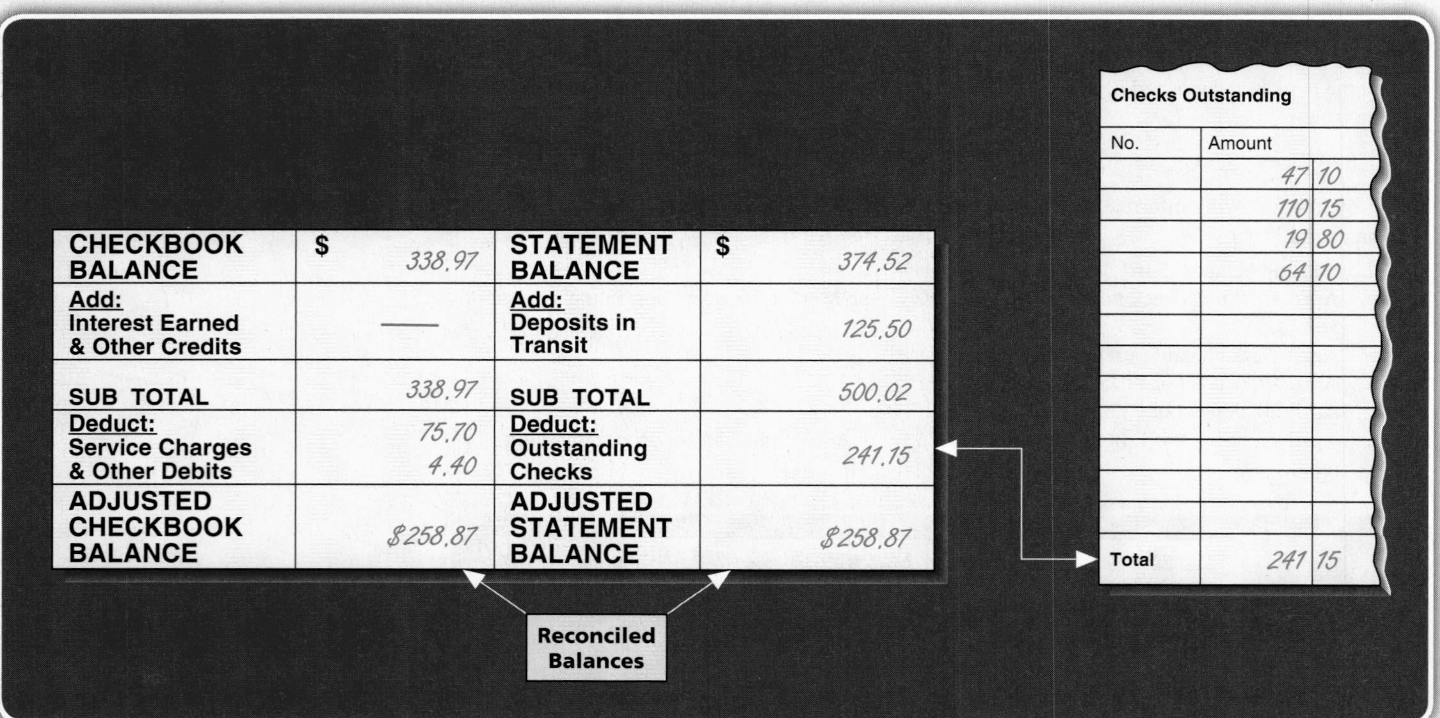

CHECKBOOK BALANCE	$ 338.97	STATEMENT BALANCE	$ 374.52
Add: Interest Earned & Other Credits	——	Add: Deposits in Transit	125.50
SUB TOTAL	338.97	SUB TOTAL	500.02
Deduct: Service Charges & Other Debits	75.70 4.40	Deduct: Outstanding Checks	241.15
ADJUSTED CHECKBOOK BALANCE	$258.87	ADJUSTED STATEMENT BALANCE	$258.87

Reconciled Balances

Checks Outstanding

No.	Amount
	47.10
	110.15
	19.80
	64.10
Total	241.15

Name

Class

7. Using the form on page 130, prepare a bank reconciliation for Avis Sohn from the following checkbook records and bank statement.

PLEASE BE SURE TO **DEDUCT** ANY BANK CHARGES THAT APPLY TO YOUR ACCOUNT.

CHECK NUMBER	DATE	DESCRIPTION OF TRANSACTION	AMOUNT OF PAYMENT OR WITHDRAWAL (–)	✓	AMOUNT OF DEPOSIT OR INTEREST (+)	BALANCE FORWARD
						879.36
801	10/1	To Technique Photo Lab	236.77			
		For				Bal. 642.59
	10/6	To Deposit			450.75	
		For				Bal. 1,093.34
802	10/8	To L.L. Bean	47.20			
		For				Bal. 1,046.14
803	10/10	To Sam Newman	75.89			
		For				Bal. 970.25
	10/13	To Deposit			880.34	
		For				Bal. 1,850.59
804	10/13	To Sheraton Hotel	109.00			
		For				Bal. 1,741.59
805	10/15	To American Express	507.82			
		For				Bal. 1,233.77
	10/20	To ATM Withdrawal	120.00			
		For				Bal. 1,113.77
	10/24	To Deposit			623.50	
		For				Bal. 1,737.27
	10/27	To Deposit			208.40	
		For				Bal. 1,945.67
	10/28	To K-Mart—Debit Card	48.25			
		For				Bal. 1,897.42

Aloha Bank

STATEMENT DATE
11-2-20xx

Avis Sohn
1127 Pineapple Place
Honolulu, HI 96825

CHECKING ACCOUNT SUMMARY
10-1-20xx THRU 10-31-20xx

ACCOUNT NUMBER
449-56-7792

Previous Balance	Deposits & Credits Number	Total	Checks & Debits Number	Total	Current Balance
879.36	3	1,954.59	7	1,347.83	1,486.12

CHECKING ACCOUNT TRANSACTIONS

DATE	AMOUNT	DESCRIPTION	BALANCE
10-3	236.77	Check #801	642.59
10-6	450.75	Deposit	1,093.34
10-10	324.70	Returned Item	768.64
10-13	880.34	EFT Payroll Deposit	1,648.98
10-15	75.89	Check #803	1,573.09
10-17	507.82	Check #805	1,065.27
10-22	120.00	ATM Withdrawal	945.27
10-24	623.50	Deposit	1,568.77
10-28	48.25	Debit Card Purchase	1,520.52
10-30	34.40	Check Printing Charge	1,486.12

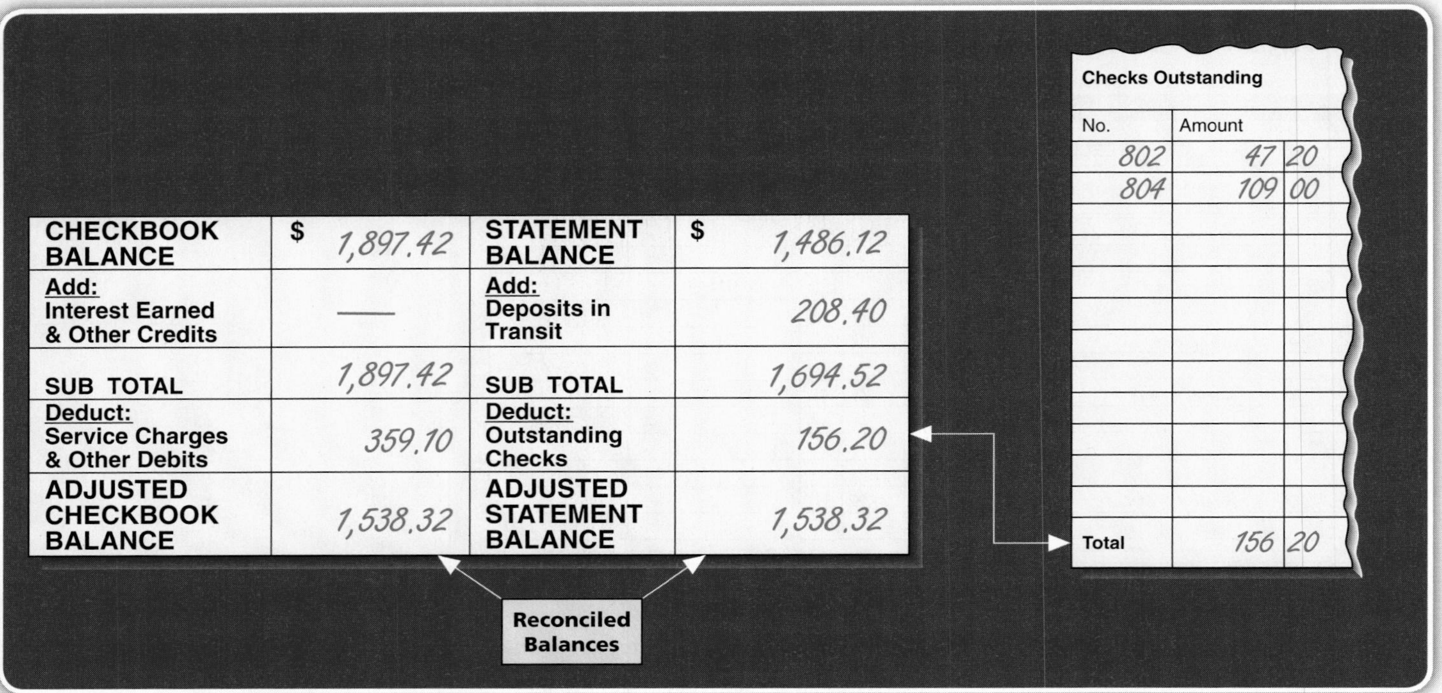

CHECKBOOK BALANCE	$ 1,897.42	STATEMENT BALANCE	$ 1,486.12
Add: Interest Earned & Other Credits	—	**Add:** Deposits in Transit	208.40
SUB TOTAL	1,897.42	SUB TOTAL	1,694.52
Deduct: Service Charges & Other Debits	359.10	**Deduct:** Outstanding Checks	156.20
ADJUSTED CHECKBOOK BALANCE	1,538.32	ADJUSTED STATEMENT BALANCE	1,538.32

Checks Outstanding

No.	Amount	
802	47	20
804	109	00
Total	156	20

CHAPTER

BUSINESS DECISION CHOOSING A BANK WITH INTEREST

Name

Class

8. Sometimes banks offer checking accounts that earn interest on the average daily balance of the account each month. This interest is calculated using a formula known as the simple interest formula. The formula is written as:

Interest = Principal × Rate × Time I = PRT

The formula states that the amount of **Interest** earned on the account is equal to the **Principal** (average daily balance) multiplied by the **Rate** (interest rate per year—expressed as a decimal) multiplied by the **Time** (expressed in years—use $\frac{1}{12}$ to represent one month of a year).

a. If you have not already done so, complete the Business Decision, Choosing a Bank, in Section II, page 120.

b. Use the simple interest formula to calculate the amount of interest you would earn per month if the Intercontinental Bank was offering 2 percent (.02) interest per year on checking accounts. (Note that your average daily balance changes from $900 to $2,400 in the last six months of the year.)

First 6 Months $I = 900 \times .02 \times \frac{1}{12} = \underline{\underline{\$1.50}}$ Per month

Last 6 Months $I = 2{,}400 \times .02 \times \frac{1}{12} = \underline{\underline{\$4.00}}$ Per month

In the Business World

Opportunity cost is the sacrifice of benefits from the next-best alternative when you make a financial or economic decision. To fully evaluate how much a checking account with a required minimum balance costs, calculate the opportunity cost.

Consider a bank that requires an average monthly balance of $1,500. If you can earn 3% a year in interest in a savings account, maintaining this checking account means giving up $45 in potential interest income.

Name

Class

c. How much interest would you earn per month at Bank of America if they were offering 1.5 percent (.015) interest per year on checking accounts? Round to the nearest cent, when necessary.

First 6 Months $\quad I = 900 \times .015 \times \frac{1}{12} = \$1.13$ Per month

Last 6 Months $\quad I = 2{,}400 \times .015 \times \frac{1}{12} = \$3.00$ Per month

d. Recalculate the cost of doing business with Intercontinental Bank and Bank of America for a year.

Intercontinental Bank		Bank of America	
240.00	Bank fees	234.00	Bank fees
− 33.00	Interest earned	− 24.78	Interest earned
$207.00	Cost for 1 year	$209.22	Cost for 1 year

e. Based on this new information, which of the four banks should you choose for your checking account?
Intercontinental Bank

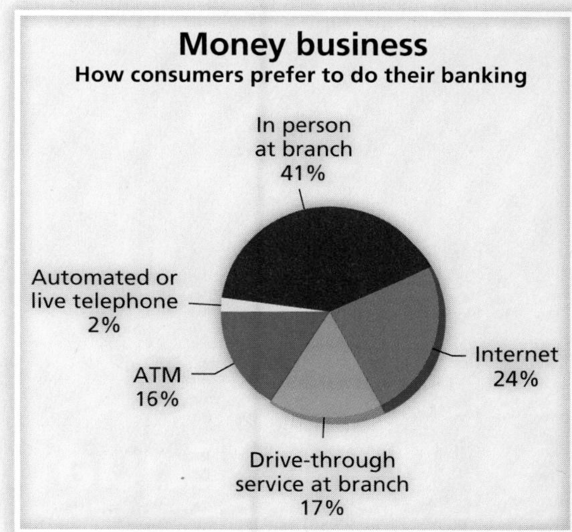

Source: *USA Today*, January 18, 2007, p. 1B. Reprinted with permission.

COLLABORATIVE LEARNING ACTIVITY

Choosing a Checking Account

Have each team member research a local bank, credit union, or other financial institution offering checking accounts to find the types of checking accounts that they have and other banking services they offer. As a team, look over the material and answer the following:

a. How do the accounts compare regarding monthly service charges, interest paid, account minimums, debit and ATM charges, and other rules and regulations?

b. Do the banks offer any incentives, such as a no-fee Visa or MasterCard, bounce-proof checking, or a line of credit?

c. Based on your team's research, which bank would you recommend for each of the following:

- College student. Why?
- Small business. Why?
- Family, with three teenagers. Why?

CHAPTER 5

Using Equations to Solve Business Problems

PERFORMANCE OBJECTIVES

Section I Solving Basic Equations

5-1: Understanding the concept, terminology, and rules of equations (p. 133)

5-2: Solving equations for the unknown and proving the solution (p. 134)

5-3: Writing expressions and equations from written statements (p. 141)

Section II Using Equations to Solve Business-Related Word Problems

5-4: Setting up and solving business-related word problems by using equations (p. 144)

5-5: Understanding and solving ratio and proportion problems (p. 149)

SOLVING BASIC EQUATIONS

SECTION I 5

One of the primary objectives of business mathematics is to describe business situations and solve business problems. Many business problems requiring a mathematical solution have been converted to formulas. A **formula** is a mathematical statement describing a real-world situation in which letters represent number quantities. A typical example of a formula follows:

Business Situation:	Revenue less expenses is profit
Mathematical Formula:	Revenue − Expenses = Profit

or

$$R - E = P$$

formula A mathematical statement describing a real-world situation in which letters represent number quantities. An example is the simple interest formula, $I = PRT$, where *interest* equals *principal* times *rate* times *time*.

By knowing the numerical value of any two of the three parts, we can use the formula to determine the unknown part. Formulas are a way of standardizing repetitive business situations. They are used in almost every aspect of business activity and are an essential tool for the businessperson. Later in the book, we see formulas applied to topics such as markup and markdown, percents, interest rates, financial ratios, inventory, and depreciation.

As valuable and widespread as formulas are, they cannot anticipate all business situations. Today, businesspeople must have the ability to analyze the facts of a situation and devise custom-made formulas to solve business problems. These formulas are actually mathematical **equations**.

In this important chapter, you learn to write and solve equations. At first, some of the concepts may seem a bit strange. Equations use letters of the alphabet as well as numbers. Do not be intimidated! After some practice, you will be able to write and solve equations comfortably.

equations Mathematical statements expressing a relationship of equality; usually written as a series of symbols that are separated into left and right sides and joined by an equal sign. $X + 7 = 10$ is an equation.

UNDERSTANDING THE CONCEPT, TERMINOLOGY, AND RULES OF EQUATIONS

In English, we write by using words to form complete thoughts known as sentences. Equations convert written sentences describing business situations into mathematical sentences. When the statement contains an equal sign (=) it is an equation. If it does not contain an equal sign, it is simply an **expression**. Equations express business problems in their simplest form. There are no adjectives or words of embellishment, just the facts.

$S + 12$ is an *expression* $\qquad$ $S + 12 = 20$ is an *equation*

An equation is a mathematical statement using numbers, letters, and symbols to express a relationship of equality. Equations have an expression on the left side and an expression on the right side, connected by an equal sign.

Letters of the alphabet are used to represent unknown quantities in equations and are called **variables**. In the equation above, S is the variable, or the **unknown**. The 12 and the 20 are the **constants**, or **knowns**. Variables and constants are also known as the **terms** of the equation. The plus sign and the equal sign separate the terms and describe the relationship between them.

To **solve an equation** means to find the numerical value of the unknown. From our equation $S + 12 = 20$, what value of S would make the equation true? Is it 6? No, 6 plus 12 is 18, and 18 does not equal 20. Is it 10? No, 10 plus 12 is 22, and 22 does not equal 20. How about 8? Yes, 8 plus 12 does equal 20.

$$S + 12 = 20$$
$$8 + 12 = 20$$
$$20 = 20$$

expression A mathematical operation or a quantity stated in symbolic form, not containing an equal sign. $X + 7$ is an expression.

variables (unknowns) The part of an equation that is not given. In equations, the unknowns are variables (letters of the alphabet), which are quantities having no fixed value. In the equation $X + 7 = 10$, X is the unknown or variable.

constants (knowns) The parts of an equation that are given. In equations, the knowns are constants (numbers), which are quantities having a fixed value. In the equation $X + 7 = 10$, 7 and 10 are the knowns or constants.

terms The knowns (constants) and unknowns (variables) of an equation. In the equation $X + 7 = 10$, the terms are X, 7, and 10.

solve an equation The process of finding the numerical value of the unknown in an equation.

By substituting 8 for the variable, S, we have found the value of the unknown that satisfies the equation and makes it true: 20 equals 20. The numerical value of the variable that makes the equation true, in this case, 8, is known as the **solution**, or **root**, of the equation.

solution, or root The numerical value of the unknown that makes the equation true. In the equation $X + 7 = 10$, for example, 3 is the solution, because $3 + 7 = 10$.

5-2 SOLVING EQUATIONS FOR THE UNKNOWN AND PROVING THE SOLUTION

© Digital Vision/Getty Images

Today, managers must have the ability to analyze the facts of a business problem and devise custom-made formulas to solve them.

In solving equations, we use the same basic operations we used in arithmetic: addition, subtraction, multiplication, and division. The meanings of the signs +, −, ×, and ÷ are still the same. Equations have a few new designations, however, that we must learn.

Multiplication of 5 times Y, for example, may be written as

$$5 \times Y$$

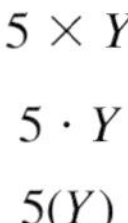

$$5 \cdot Y$$

$$5(Y)$$

$$5Y$$

The number 5 in the term $5Y$ is known as the **coefficient** of the term. In cases in which there is no numerical coefficient written, such as W, the coefficient is understood to be a 1. Therefore,

$$1W = W.$$

Division in equations is indicated by the fraction bar, just as in Chapter 2. For example, the term 5 divided by Y would be written as

$$\frac{5}{Y}$$

coefficient A number or quantity placed before another quantity, indicating multiplication. For example, 4 is the coefficient in the expression $4C$. This indicates 4 multiplied by C.

transpose To bring a term from one side of an equation to the other, with a corresponding change of sign.

It is important to remember that an equation is a statement of *equality*. The left side must always *equal* the right side. To solve equations, we must move or **transpose** all the unknowns to one side and all the knowns to the other side. It is customary for the unknowns to be on the left side and the knowns to be on the right side, such as $X = 7$.

Transposing involves the use of inverse or opposite operations. To transpose a term in an equation, (a) note the operation indicated and (b) apply the *opposite* operation to both sides of the equation, as follows:

Operation Indicated		Opposite Operation
Addition	⟶	Subtraction
Subtraction	⟶	Addition
Multiplication	⟶	Division
Division	⟶	Multiplication

STEPS FOR SOLVING EQUATIONS AND PROVING THE SOLUTION

Step 1. Transpose all the *unknowns* to the left side of the equation and all the *knowns* to the right side of the equation using the following "order of operations."

- *Parentheses,* if any, must be cleared before any other operations are performed. To clear parentheses, multiply the coefficient by each term inside the parentheses.

$$3(5C + 4) = 3(5C) + 3(4) = 15C + 12$$

- To solve equations with more than one operation, perform the *addition and subtraction* first, then the *multiplication and division.*

Step 2. Prove the solution by substituting your answer for the letter or letters in the original equation. If the left and right sides are *equal*, the equation is true, and your answer is correct.

EXAMPLE 1 SOLVING EQUATIONS

Solve the equation $X + 4 = 15$ and prove the solution.

SOLUTION STRATEGY

The equation $X + 4 = 15$ indicates addition (+4). To solve for X, apply the opposite operation, subtraction. Subtract 4 from each side.

$$\begin{array}{rcr} X + 4 & = & 15 \\ -\ 4 & & -\ 4 \\ \hline X & = & 11 \end{array}$$

$$\underline{\underline{X = 11}}$$

Proof: The solution can easily be proven by substituting our answer (11) for the letter or letters in the original equation. If the left and right sides are equal, the equation is true and the solution is correct.

$$X + 4 = 15$$

$$11 + 4 = 15$$

$$\underline{\underline{15 = 15}}$$

TRY IT EXERCISE 1

Solve the following equations for the unknown and prove your solutions.

a. $W + 10 = 25$ b. $Q + 30 = 100$

CHECK YOUR ANSWERS WITH THE SOLUTIONS ON PAGE 158.

Learning Tip

Remember, an equation is a statement of "equality." The left side must always equal the right side. The word *equation*, in fact, is derived from the word *equal*.

In the Business World

The equal sign, two parallel lines (=), was invented in the sixteenth century by Robert Recorde. He stated, "Nothing can be more equal than parallel lines!"

Other related mathematical symbols are:

- $\approx$ is approximately equal to
- $\neq$ is not equal to
- $\geq$ is greater than or equal to
- $\leq$ is less than or equal to

EXAMPLE 2 SOLVING EQUATIONS

Solve the equation $H - 20 = 44$ and prove the solution.

SOLUTION STRATEGY

The equation $H - 20 = 44$ indicates subtraction (−20). To solve for H, apply the opposite operation, addition. Add 20 to each side of the equation.

$$\begin{array}{rcr} H - 20 & = & 44 \\ +\ 20 & & +\ 20 \\ \hline H & = & 64 \end{array}$$

$$\underline{\underline{H = 64}}$$

Proof: Substitute 64 for H:

$$H - 20 = 44$$

$$64 - 20 = 44$$

$$\underline{\underline{44 = 44}}$$

TEACHING TIP

Remind students that they can "verify" the answer to an equation by subsituting the answer for each unknown in the original equation (yellow highlight):

For example: $8C + 4 = 20$

$$8C = 16$$

$$\underline{\underline{C = 2}}$$

Verify: $8C + 4 = 20$

$$8(2) + 4 = 20$$

$$16 + 4 = 20$$

$$\underline{\underline{20 = 20}}$$

TRY IT EXERCISE 2

Solve the following equations for the unknown and prove your solutions.

a. $A - 8 = 40$ b. $L - 3 = 7$

CHECK YOUR ANSWERS WITH THE SOLUTIONS ON PAGE 158.

EXAMPLE 3 SOLVING EQUATIONS

Solve the equation 9*T* = 36 and prove the solution.

SOLUTION STRATEGY

The equation $9T = 36$ indicates multiplication. $9T$ means 9 times T. To solve for T, apply the opposite operation. Divide both sides of the equation by 9.

$$9T = 36$$

$$\frac{\cancel{9}T}{\cancel{9}} = \frac{36}{9}$$

$$\underline{\underline{T = 4}}$$

Proof:

$$9T = 36$$

$$9(4) = 36$$

$$\underline{\underline{36 = 36}}$$

TRY IT EXERCISE 3

Solve the following equations for the unknown and prove your solutions.

a. $15L = 75$ b. $16F = 80$

CHECK YOUR ANSWERS WITH THE SOLUTIONS ON PAGE 158.

EXAMPLE 4 SOLVING EQUATIONS

Solve the equation $\frac{M}{5} = 4$ and prove the solution.

SOLUTION STRATEGY

The equation $\frac{M}{5} = 4$ indicates division. To solve for M, do the opposite operation. Multiply both sides of the equation by 5.

$$(\cancel{5})\frac{M}{\cancel{5}} = 4(5)$$

$$\underline{\underline{M = 20}}$$

Proof:

$$\frac{M}{5} = 4$$

$$\frac{20}{5} = 4$$

$$\underline{\underline{4 = 4}}$$

TRY IT EXERCISE 4

Solve the following equations for the unknown and prove your solutions.

a. $\frac{Z}{8} = 2$ b. $\frac{C}{9} = 9$

CHECK YOUR ANSWERS WITH THE SOLUTIONS ON PAGE 159.

EXAMPLE 5 SOLVING EQUATIONS CONTAINING MULTIPLE OPERATIONS

Solve the equation 7*R* − 5 = 51 and prove the solution.

SOLUTION STRATEGY

The equation $7R - 5 = 51$ indicates subtraction and multiplication. Following the rule for multiple operations, begin by adding 5 to each side of the equation.

$$\begin{array}{rcr} 7R - 5 & = & 51 \\ +5 & & +5 \\ \hline 7R & = & 56 \end{array}$$

$$7R = 56$$

Next, divide both sides of the equation by 7.

$$\frac{\not{7}R}{\not{7}} = \frac{56}{7}$$

$$\underline{\underline{R = 8}}$$

Proof:

$$7R - 5 = 51$$

$$7(8) - 5 = 51$$

$$56 - 5 = 51$$

$$\underline{\underline{51 = 51}}$$

TRY IT EXERCISE 5

Solve the following equations for the unknown and prove the solutions.

a. $12N + 14 = 50$ b. $3W - 4 = 26$

CHECK YOUR ANSWERS WITH THE SOLUTIONS ON PAGE 159.

Teaching Transparency 5-1

EXAMPLE 6 SOLVING EQUATIONS CONTAINING MULTIPLE OPERATIONS

Solve the equation $\frac{X}{2} + 20 = 34$ and prove the solution.

SOLUTION STRATEGY

The equation $\frac{X}{2} + 20 = 34$ indicates addition and division. Following the rule for multiple operations, begin by subtracting 20 from each side.

$$\begin{aligned} \frac{X}{2} + 20 &= \quad 34 \\ -20 &\quad -20 \\ \hline \frac{X}{2} \qquad &= \quad 14 \end{aligned}$$

$$\frac{X}{2} = 14$$

Next, multiply each side by 2.

$$(\not{2})\frac{X}{\not{2}} = 14(2)$$

$$\underline{\underline{X = 28}}$$

Proof:

$$\frac{X}{2} + 20 = 34$$

$$\frac{28}{2} + 20 = 34$$

$$14 + 20 = 34$$

$$\underline{\underline{34 = 34}}$$

TRY IT EXERCISE 6

Solve the following equations for the unknown and prove the solutions.

a. $\frac{F}{3} - 6 = 2$ b. $\frac{Z}{5} + 15 = 24$

CHECK YOUR ANSWERS WITH THE SOLUTIONS ON PAGE 159.

TEACHING TIP

When an equation contains parentheses, be sure students multiply the coefficient by "both" of the terms inside the parentheses.

Typical Error:
$4(2W + 8) = 8W + 8$,
instead of $8W + 32$

Parentheses

Sometimes, parentheses are used in equations. They contain a number just outside the left-hand parentheses known as the coefficient and two or more terms inside the parentheses. An example is $5(3X + 6)$.

Parentheses Rule

In solving equations, parentheses must be removed before any other operations are performed. To remove parentheses, multiply the coefficient by each term inside the parentheses.

To apply this rule to the example above,

$$5(3X + 6)$$

$$5(3X) + 5(6)$$

$$15X + 30$$

EXAMPLE 7 SOLVING EQUATIONS CONTAINING PARENTHESES

Solve the equation 8(2*K* − 4) = 48 and prove the solution.

SOLUTION STRATEGY

Because this equation contains parentheses, we must begin there. Following the rule for removing parentheses, multiply the coefficient, 8, by each term inside the parentheses.

$$8(2K - 4) = 48$$

$$8(2K) - 8(4) = 48$$

$$16K - 32 = 48$$

Now solve the equation as before, by isolating the unknown, *K,* on the left side of the equal sign. Remember, add and subtract first, then multiply and divide.

$$\begin{array}{rcr} 16K - 32 & = & 48 \\ +32 & & +32 \\ \hline 16K & = & 80 \end{array}$$

$$16K = 80$$

$$\frac{\cancel{16}K}{\cancel{16}} = \frac{80}{16}$$

$$\underline{\underline{K = 5}}$$

Proof:

$$8(2K - 4) = 48$$

$$8(2\{5\} - 4) = 48$$

$$8(10 - 4) = 48$$

$$8(6) = 48$$

$$\underline{\underline{48 = 48}}$$

TRY IT EXERCISE 7

Solve the following equations for the unknown and prove the solutions.

a. $4(5G + 6) = 64$ b. $6(3H - 5) = 42$

CHECK YOUR ANSWERS WITH THE SOLUTIONS ON PAGE 159.

Teaching Transparency 5-2

When equations contain unknowns that appear two or more times, they must be combined.

STEPS FOR COMBINING MULTIPLE UNKNOWNS

Step 1. To combine unknowns, they must be on the same side of the equation. If they are not, move them all to the same side.

$$5X = 12 + 2X$$

$$5X - 2X = 12$$

Step 2. Once the unknowns are on the same side of the equation, add or subtract their coefficients as indicated.

$$5X - 2X = 12$$

$$3X = 12$$

EXAMPLE 8 SOLVING EQUATIONS CONTAINING MULTIPLE UNKNOWNS

Solve the equation $4C + 7 - C = 25 - 6C$ and prove the solution.

SOLUTION STRATEGY

To solve this equation, we begin by combining the two terms on the left side that contain C: $4C - C = 3C$. This leaves

$$3C + 7 = 25 - 6C$$

Next move the $-6C$ to the left side by adding $+6C$ to both sides of the equation.

$$\begin{array}{r} 3C + 7 = 25 - 6C \\ \underline{+6C \qquad\qquad +6C} \\ 9C + 7 = 25 \end{array}$$

Now that all the terms containing the unknown, C, have been combined, we can solve the equation.

$$\begin{array}{r} 9C + 7 = \ 25 \\ \underline{-7 \quad -7} \\ 9C \qquad = \ 18 \end{array}$$

$$\frac{\not{9}C}{\not{9}} = \frac{18}{9}$$

$$\underline{\underline{C = 2}}$$

Proof:

$$4C + 7 - C = 25 - 6C$$

$$4(2) + 7 - 2 = 25 - 6(2)$$

$$8 + 7 - 2 = 25 - 12$$

$$\underline{\underline{13 = 13}}$$

TRY IT EXERCISE 8

Solve the following equations for the unknown and prove the solutions.

a. $X + 3 = 18 - 4X$ b. $9S + 8 - S = 2(2S + 8)$

CHECK YOUR ANSWERS WITH THE SOLUTIONS ON PAGE 159.

5-3

WRITING EXPRESSIONS AND EQUATIONS FROM WRITTEN STATEMENTS

Expressions and equations are created from written statements by identifying the unknowns and the knowns and then determining the mathematical relationship between them. The variables are assigned letters of the alphabet. The letter X is commonly used to represent the unknown. The relationship between the knowns and the unknowns involves either addition, subtraction, multiplication, or division, or a combination of two or more of these.

STEPS FOR WRITING EXPRESSIONS AND EQUATIONS

Step 1. Read the written statement carefully.
Step 2. Using the following list, identify and underline the key words and phrases.
Step 3. Convert the words to numbers and mathematical symbols.

5-4

Key Words and Phrases for Creating Equations

Equal Sign	Addition	Subtraction	Multiplication	Division	Parentheses
is	and	less	of	divide	times the quantity of
are	added to	less than	multiply	divided by	
was	totals	smaller than	times	average of	
equals	the sum of	minus	product of	divided into	
gives	plus	difference	multiplied by	quotient of	
giving	more than	decreased by	twice	ratio of	
leaves	larger than	reduced by	double		
results in	increased by	take away	triple		
produces	greater than	loss of	at		
yields	exceeds	fewer than	@		

When a written statement has no action word (verb), it is an expression. When there is a verb, such as "is," it represents an equal sign, and the statement is an equation.

EXAMPLE 9 WRITING EXPRESSIONS

For the following statements, underline the key words and translate into *expressions*.

a. A number increased by 18 b. 19 times W
c. 12 less than S d. $\frac{2}{3}$ of Y
e. 9 more than 2 times R f. 4 times the quantity of X and 8

TEACHING TIP

Using peer tutors can be an effective teaching strategy for "high-anxiety" material such as equations.

Have students work in small groups to write some equations. Next, have each group exchange and solve the equations of another group. When finished, ask them to compare answers and resolve any differences.

SOLUTION STRATEGY

Key Words	Expression
a. A number increased by 18	$N + 18$
b. 19 times W	$19W$
c. 12 less than S	$S - 12$
d. $\frac{2}{3}$ of Y	$\frac{2}{3}Y$
e. 9 more than 2 times R	$2R + 9$
f. 4 times the quantity of X and 8	$4(X + 8)$

TRY IT EXERCISE 9

For the following statements, underline the key words and translate into *expressions*.

a. The sum of twice E and 9

b. 6 times N divided by Z

c. 8 less than half of F

d. $45.75 more than the product of X and Y

e. The difference of Q and 44

f. R times A times B

CHECK YOUR ANSWERS WITH THE SOLUTIONS ON PAGE 159.

EXAMPLE 10 WRITING EQUATIONS

For the following statements, underline the key words and translate into *equations*.

a. A number decreased by 14 is 23
b. 8 less than 3D leaves 19
c. A number totals 4 times the quantity of V and N
d. The cost of X lbs at $3 per lb is $12
e. Cost is the product of price and quantity
f. The sum of liabilities and capital is assets

SOLUTION STRATEGY

Key Words	Equations
a. A number decreased by 14 is 23	$X - 14 = 23$
b. 8 less than 3D leaves 19	$3D - 8 = 19$
c. A number totals 4 times the quantity of V and N	$X = 4(V + N)$
d. The cost of X lbs at $3 per lb is $12	$3X = 12$
e. Cost is the product of price and quantity	$C = PQ$
f. The sum of liabilities and capital is assets	$L + C = A$

TRY IT EXERCISE 10

For the following statements, underline the key words and translate into *equations*.

a. What number increased by 32 yields 125?
b. 21 less than twice C gives 9.
c. 5 more than 6 times a number, plus 3 times that number, is 25.
d. The cost of G gallons at $1.33 per gallon equals $34.40.
e. The area of a rectangle is the length times the width.
f. (Challenge) What number less 12 is the average of A, B, and C?

CHECK YOUR ANSWERS WITH THE SOLUTIONS ON PAGE 159.

Review Exercises

SECTION I 5

Solve the following equations for the unknown and prove your solutions.

1. $B + 11 = 24$ — $B = 13$
2. $C - 16 = 5$ — $C = 21$
3. $S + 35 = 125$ — $S = 90$
4. $M - 58 = 12$ — $M = 70$
5. $21K = 63$ — $K = 3$
6. $\frac{Z}{3} = 45$ — $Z = 135$
7. $50Y = 375$ — $Y = 7\frac{1}{2}$
8. $\frac{L}{5} = 8$ — $L = 40$
9. $6G + 5 = 29$ — $G = 4$
10. $\frac{D}{3} - 5 = 15$ — $D = 60$
11. $25A - 11 = 64$ — $A = 3$
12. $\frac{R}{5} + 33 = 84$ — $R = 255$
13. $3(4X + 5) = 63$ — $X = 4$
14. $C + 5 = 26 - 2C$ — $C = 7$
15. $12(2D - 4) = 72$ — $D = 5$
16. $14V + 5 - 5V = 4(V + 5)$ — $V = 3$
17. $Q + 20 = 3(9 - 2Q)$ — $Q = 1$

Solution Transparencies

Complete worked-out solutions for Exercises 1–17 appear in Appendix B, following the index.

TEACHING TIP
For additional practice and understanding, have students write the equations in Exercises 1–17 in words.

For the following statements, underline the key words and translate into *expressions*.

18. 5 times G divided by R
    $\frac{5G}{R}$
19. The sum of 5 times F and 33
    $5F + 33$
20. 6 less than one-fourth of C
    $\frac{1}{4}C - 6$
21. 550 more than the product of H and P
    $HP + 550$
22. T times B times 9
    $9TB$
23. The difference of $8Y$ and 128
    $8Y - 128$
24. 7 times the quantity of X and 7
    $7(X + 7)$
25. 40 more than $\frac{3}{4}$ of B
    $\frac{3}{4}B + 40$

For the following statements, underline the key words and translate into *equations*.

26. A number increased by 24 is 35.
    $X + 24 = 35$
27. A number totals 5 times B and C.
    $X = 5B + C$
28. 12 less than $4G$ leaves 33.
    $4G - 12 = 33$
29. The cost of R at \$5.75 each is \$28.75.
    $\$5.75R = \$28.75$
30. Cost per person is the total cost divided by the number of persons.
    $C = \frac{T}{N}$
31. 4 more than 5 times a number, plus 2 times that number, is that number increased by 40.
    $5X + 4 + 2X = X + 40$

BUSINESS DECISION GROUPING SYMBOLS

32. Grouping symbols are used to arrange numbers, variables, and operations. In this chapter you learned to use the grouping symbols known as parentheses ( ). In addition to parentheses, other symbols used for grouping are brackets [ ] and braces { }. When solving equations with multiple grouping symbols, always start with the innermost symbols, and work to the outside.

In business, you may encounter situations that require you to set up equations with more than just parentheses. For practice, solve the following equation.

$$X = 6(2 + [3\{9 - 3\} + \{8 + 1\} - 4])$$
$$X = 6(2 + [3\{9 - 3\} + \{8 + 1\} - 4])$$
$$X = 6(2 + [3\{6\} + 9 - 4])$$
$$X = 6(2 + [18 + 9 - 4])$$
$$X = 6(2 + 23)$$
$$X = 6(25)$$
$$X = \underline{\underline{150}}$$

SECTION II USING EQUATIONS TO SOLVE BUSINESS-RELATED WORD PROBLEMS

Learning Tip

This is the real "bottom line" of equations: the ability to analyze a business situation, convert it to an equation, and solve it. Proficiency will come with practice.

In business, most of the math encountered is in the form of business-situation word problems. Variables such as profits, production units, inventory, employees, money, customers, and interest rates are constantly interacting mathematically. Your boss will not ask you simply to add, subtract, multiply, or divide but will ask for information requiring you to perform these functions in a business context. Business students must be able to analyze a business situation requiring math, set up the situation in a mathematical expression or equation, and work it out to a correct solution.

5-4 SETTING UP AND SOLVING BUSINESS-RELATED WORD PROBLEMS BY USING EQUATIONS

In Section I of this chapter we learned to create and solve equations from written statements. Let's see how to apply these skills in business situations. You will learn a logical procedure for setting up and solving business-related word problems. Some problems have more than one way to arrive at an answer. The key, once again, is not to be intimidated. Learning to solve word problems requires practice, and the more you do it, the easier it will become and the more comfortable you will feel with it.

STEPS FOR SETTING UP AND SOLVING WORD PROBLEMS

Step 1. **Understand the situation.** If the problem is written, read it carefully, perhaps a few times. If the problem is verbal, write down the facts of the situation.

Step 2. **Take inventory.** Identify all the parts of the situation. These parts can be any variables, such as dollars, people, boxes, tons, trucks, anything! Separate them into knowns and unknowns.

Step 3. **Make a plan—create an equation.** The object is to solve for the unknown. Ask yourself what math relationship exists between the knowns and the unknowns. Use the chart of key words and phrases on page 141 to help you write the equation.

Step 4. **Work out the plan—solve the equation.** To solve an equation you must move the unknowns to one side of the equal sign and the knowns to the other.

Step 5. **Check your solution.** Does your answer make sense? Is it exactly correct? It is a good idea to estimate an approximate answer by using rounded numbers. This will let you know if your answer is in the correct range. If it is not, either the equation is set up incorrectly or the solution is wrong. If this occurs, you must go back and start again.

"Just a darn minute — yesterday you said that X equals **two**!"

EXAMPLE 11 SOLVING BUSINESS-RELATED EQUATIONS

On Tuesday, the Jiffy Car Wash took in $360 less in wash business than in wax business. If the total sales for the day were $920, what were the sales for each service?

SOLUTION STRATEGY

Reasoning: Wax sales plus wash sales equal the total sales, $920.

Let X = $ amount of wax sales

Let $X - 360$ = $ amount of wash sales

$$\begin{array}{rcr} X + X - 360 & = & 920 \\ + 360 & & + 360 \\ \hline X + X & = & 1{,}280 \end{array}$$

$$2X = 1{,}280$$

$$\frac{\not{2}X}{\not{2}} = \frac{1{,}280}{2}$$

$$X = 640 \quad \underline{\underline{\text{Wax sales} = \$640}}$$

$$X - 360 = 640 - 360 = 280 \quad \underline{\underline{\text{Wash sales} = \$280}}$$

Proof:

$$X + X - 360 = 920$$

$$640 + 640 - 360 = 920$$

$$\underline{\underline{920 = 920}}$$

Frequently, the left side of an equation represents the "interaction" of the variables, and the right side shows the "result" of that interaction.

In this example, the left side is the interaction (in this case, addition) of the wax and wash sales. The right side is the result, or total.

$$\frac{\textbf{Interaction}}{X + X - 360} = \frac{\textbf{Result}}{920}$$

TRY IT EXERCISE 11

Don and Chuck are salesmen for Superior Alarms. Last week Don sold 12 fewer alarm systems than Chuck. Together they sold 44. How many did each sell?

CHECK YOUR ANSWERS WITH THE SOLUTIONS ON PAGE 160.

EXAMPLE 12 SOLVING BUSINESS-RELATED EQUATIONS

Regal Systems, Inc., spends $\frac{1}{4}$ of total revenue on employee payroll expenses. If last week's payroll amounted to $5,000, what was the revenue for the week?

SOLUTION STRATEGY

Reasoning: $\frac{1}{4}$ of revenue is the week's payroll, $5,000.

Let R = revenue for the week

$$\frac{1}{4}R = 5{,}000$$

$$(\not{4})\frac{1}{\not{4}}R = 5{,}000(4)$$

$$R = 20{,}000 \quad \underline{\underline{\text{Revenue for the week} = \$20{,}000}}$$

TEACHING TIP

Do not always use "X" to represent the unknown. Get students into the habit of recognizing any letter as the unknown variable.

In word problems, use the first letter of what you are solving for to represent the unknown, such as S for sales, C for cost, or P for profit.

Proof:

$$\frac{1}{4}R = 5{,}000$$

$$\frac{1}{4}(20{,}000) = 5{,}000$$

$$\underline{\underline{5{,}000 = 5{,}000}}$$

TRY IT EXERCISE 12

One-third of the checking accounts at the United Bank earn interest. If 2,500 accounts are this type, how many total checking accounts does the bank have?

CHECK YOUR ANSWER WITH THE SOLUTION ON PAGE 160.

EXAMPLE 13 SOLVING BUSINESS-RELATED EQUATIONS

Pinnacle Industries, Inc., has 25 shareholders. If management decides to split the $80,000 net profit equally among the shareholders, how much will each receive?

SOLUTION STRATEGY

Reasoning: Profit per shareholder is the net profit, $80,000, divided by the number of shareholders.

Let P = Profit per shareholder

$$P = \frac{80{,}000}{25}$$

$$P = 3{,}200 \quad \underline{\underline{\text{Profit per shareholder} = \$3{,}200}}$$

Proof:

$$P = \frac{80{,}000}{25}$$

$$3{,}200 = \frac{80{,}000}{25}$$

$$\underline{\underline{3{,}200 = 3{,}200}}$$

TRY IT EXERCISE 13

Pacific Trade and Export, Inc., fills an order for 58 cartons of merchandise weighing a total of 7,482 pounds. What is the weight per carton?

CHECK YOUR ANSWER WITH THE SOLUTION ON PAGE 160.

EXAMPLE 14 SOLVING BUSINESS-RELATED EQUATIONS

A local Circuit City store sold 144 TVs last week. If five times as many flat-screen models sold as compared to plasma models, how many of each were sold?

SOLUTION STRATEGY

Reasoning: Plasma models plus flat-screen models equals total TVs sold, 144.

Let X = plasma models

Let $5X$ = flat-screen models

$$X + 5X = 144$$

$$6X = 144$$

$$\frac{\not{6}X}{\not{6}} = \frac{144}{6}$$

$$X = 24$$ Plasma models sold = 24

$$5X = 5(24) = 120$$ Flat-screen models sold = 120

Proof:

$$X + 5X = 144$$

$$24 + 5(24) = 144$$

$$24 + 120 = 144$$

$$144 = 144$$

TRY IT EXERCISE 14

5-5

Dollar Discount Department Store sells three times as much in soft goods, such as clothing and linens, as it sells in hard goods, such as furniture and appliances. If total store sales on Saturday were $180,000, how much of each category was sold?

CHECK YOUR ANSWERS WITH THE SOLUTIONS ON PAGE 160.

EXAMPLE 15 SOLVING BUSINESS-RELATED EQUATIONS

Yesterday, the Bayside recycling van picked up a total of 4,500 pounds of material. If newspaper weighed three times as much as aluminum cans and aluminum weighed twice as much as glass, what was the weight of each material?

SOLUTION STRATEGY

Reasoning: Glass plus aluminum plus newspaper amounts to the total material, 4,500 pounds.

Municipal solid waste, MSW—more commonly known as trash or garbage—consists of everyday items we throw away.

According to the Environmental Protection Agency, in 2005, U.S. residents, businesses, and institutions produced more than 245 million tons of MSW. This amounts to approximately 4.5 pounds of waste per person per day, up from 2.7 pounds per person per day in 1960!

Hint: Let the least (smallest) element equal X. That way the larger ones will be multiples of X. By doing this, you avoid having fractions in your equation.

$$\text{Let } X = \text{pounds of glass}$$

$$\text{Let } 2X = \text{pounds of aluminum}$$

$$\text{Let } 3(2X) = \text{pounds of newspaper}$$

$$X + 2X + 3(2X) = 4{,}500$$

$$X + 2X + 6X = 4{,}500$$

$$9X = 4{,}500$$

$$\frac{\not{9}X}{\not{9}} = \frac{4{,}500}{9}$$

$$X = 500 \qquad \underline{\underline{\text{Glass collected} = 500 \text{ pounds}}}$$

$$2X = 2(500) = 1{,}000 \qquad \underline{\underline{\text{Aluminum collected} = 1{,}000 \text{ pounds}}}$$

$$3(2X) = 3(1{,}000) = 3{,}000 \qquad \underline{\underline{\text{Newspaper collected} = 3{,}000 \text{ pounds}}}$$

Proof:

$$X + 2X + 3(2X) = 4{,}500$$

$$500 + 2(500) + 3(2\{500\}) = 4{,}500$$

$$500 + 1{,}000 + 3{,}000 = 4{,}500$$

$$\underline{\underline{4{,}500 = 4{,}500}}$$

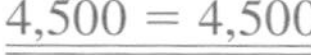

TRY IT EXERCISE 15

Last week a local Rooms To Go furniture store sold 520 items. They sold twice as many sofas as chairs and four times as many chairs as tables. How many were sold of each product?

CHECK YOUR ANSWER WITH THE SOLUTION ON PAGE 160.

EXAMPLE 16 SOLVING BUSINESS-RELATED EQUATIONS

Chicken Kitchen sells whole chicken dinners for \$12.00 and half chicken dinners for \$8.00. Yesterday they sold a total of 400 dinners and took in \$4,200. How many of each size dinner were sold? What were the dollar sales of each size dinner?

SOLUTION STRATEGY

Reasoning: The sum of the price multiplied by the quantity of each item is total sales, \$4,200.

Hint: This type of problem requires that we multiply the price of each item by the quantity. We know that a total of 400 dinners were sold, therefore,

$$\text{Let } X = \text{quantity of whole chicken dinners}$$

$$\text{Let } 400 - X = \text{quantity of half chicken dinners}$$

Note: By letting X equal the more expensive item, we avoid dealing with negative numbers.

$$\text{Price times quantity of whole chicken dinners} = \$12X$$

$$\text{Price times quantity of half chicken dinners} = \$8(400 - X)$$

$$12X + 8(400 - X) = 4{,}200$$
$$12X + 3{,}200 - 8X = 4{,}200$$
$$4X + 3{,}200 = 4{,}200$$
$$-3{,}200 \quad -3{,}200$$
$$4X = 1{,}000$$
$$\frac{4X}{4} = \frac{1{,}000}{4}$$
$$X = 250 \quad \underline{\text{Quantity of whole chicken dinners} = 250}$$
$$400 - X = 400 - 250 = 150 \quad \underline{\text{Quantity of half chicken dinners} = 150}$$

Proof:

$$12X + 8(400 - X) = 4{,}200$$
$$12(250) + 8(400 - 250) = 4{,}200$$
$$3{,}000 + 8(150) = 4{,}200$$
$$3{,}000 + 1{,}200 = 4{,}200$$
$$\underline{4{,}200 = 4{,}200}$$

Now that we have calculated the quantity sold of each size dinner, we can find the dollar sales.

Reasoning: Dollar sales are the price per dinner multiplied by the quantity sold.

Let S = dollar sales

Whole chicken dinners: $S = \$12(250) =$ $3,000 in sales

Half chicken dinners: $S = \$8(150) =$ $1,200 in sales

TRY IT EXERCISE 16

Auto Zone sells a regular car battery for $70 and a heavy-duty model for $110. If they sold 40 batteries yesterday for a total of $3,400, how many of each type battery were sold? What were the dollar sales of each type?

CHECK YOUR ANSWERS WITH THE SOLUTIONS ON PAGE 161.

UNDERSTANDING AND SOLVING RATIO AND PROPORTION PROBLEMS

5-5

Many business problems and situations are expressed as ratios. A **ratio** is a fraction that describes a comparison of two numbers or quantities. In business, numbers often take on much more meaning when compared with other numbers in the form of a ratio.

For example, a factory has an output of 40 units per hour. Is this good or bad? If we also know that the industry average is 20 units per hour, we can set up a ratio of our factory, 40, compared with the industry average, 20.

$$\frac{\text{Factory}}{\text{Industry}} = \frac{40}{20} = 40:20 \quad \text{Expressed verbally, we say, “40 to 20”}$$

Because ratios are fractions, we can reduce our fraction and state that our factory output is 2 to 1 over the industry average. If the industry average changed to 40, the ratio would be $\frac{40}{40}$, or 1 to 1. Had the industry average been 80, the ratio would be $\frac{40}{80}$, or 1 to 2.

ratio A fraction that describes a comparison of two numbers or quantities. For example, five cats for every three dogs would be a ratio of 5 to 3, written as 5:3.

5-6

Ratios can compare anything: money, weights, measures, output, or individuals. The units do not have to be the same. If we can buy 9 ounces of shampoo for \$2, this is actually a ratio of ounces to dollars, or 9:2.

proportion A mathematical statement showing that two ratios are equal. For example, 9 is to 3 as 3 is to 1, written 9:3 = 3:1.

A **proportion** is a statement showing that two ratios are equal. Proportions are equations, with "as" being the equal sign. For example, we could say, "9 is to 2 as 18 is to 4."

$$\frac{9}{2} = \frac{18}{4} \quad \text{or} \quad 9:2 = 18:4$$

This means that if we can buy 9 ounces for \$2, we can buy 18 ounces for \$4. Proportions with three knowns and one unknown become a very useful business tool. For example, if we can buy 9 ounces for \$2, how many ounces can we buy for \$7? This proportion, 9 is to 2 as X is to 7, would be written as

$$\frac{9 \text{ ounces}}{\$2} = \frac{X \text{ ounces}}{\$7} \quad \text{or} \quad 9:2 = X:7$$

STEPS FOR SOLVING PROPORTION PROBLEMS USING CROSS-MULTIPLICATION

Step 1. Assign a letter to represent the unknown quantity.

Step 2. Set up the proportion with one ratio (expressed as a fraction) on each side of the equal sign.

Step 3. Multiply the numerator of the first ratio by the denominator of the second and place the product to the left of the equal sign.

Step 4. Multiply the denominator of the first ratio by the numerator of the second and place the product to the right of the equal sign.

Step 5. Solve for the unknown.

EXAMPLE 17 SOLVING PROPORTIONS

On a recent trip, a car used 16 gallons of gasoline to travel 350 miles. At that rate, how many gallons of gasoline would be required to complete a trip of 875 miles?

Learning Tip

Remember, when setting up a proportion, the variables of both ratios must be in the same "order"—numerator to denominator. For example:

$$\frac{\text{dollars}}{\text{donuts}} = \frac{\text{dollars}}{\text{donuts}}$$

SOLUTION STRATEGY

This situation can be solved by setting up and solving a proportion. The proportion reads:

"16 gallons is to 350 miles as X gallons are to 875 miles"

$$\frac{16}{350} = \frac{X}{875}$$

Using cross-multiplication to solve the proportion,

$$\frac{16}{350} \times \frac{X}{875} \quad \rightarrow 350X \quad \rightarrow 16(875)$$

$$350X = 16(875)$$
$$350X = 14{,}000$$
$$X = \frac{14{,}000}{350}$$
$$\underline{\underline{X = 40 \text{ gallons}}}$$

TRY IT EXERCISE 17

If Steve earns \$87.50 for 7 hours of work, how much can he expect to earn in a 35-hour week?

CHECK YOUR ANSWER WITH THE SOLUTION ON PAGE 161.

Review Exercises

SECTION II

Set up and solve equations for the following business situations.

1. Kathy and Karen work in a boutique. During a sale, Kathy sold eight less dresses than Karen. If together they sold 86 dresses, how many did each sell?

   Karen = X
   Kathy = $X - 8$

   $$X + X - 8 = 86$$
   $$2X - 8 = 86$$
   $$+8 \quad +8$$
   $$2X = 94$$
   $$\frac{2X}{2} = \frac{94}{2}$$
   $$X = \underline{\underline{47}} \text{ Karen's sales}$$
   $$X - 8 = 47 - 8 = \underline{\underline{39}} \text{ Kathy's sales}$$

2. One-fifth of the employees of Niagara Industries, Inc. work in the Midwest region. If the company employs 252 workers in that region, what is the total number of employees working for the company?

   Total employees = X

   $$\frac{1}{5}X = 252$$
   $$(5)\frac{1}{5}X = 252(5)$$

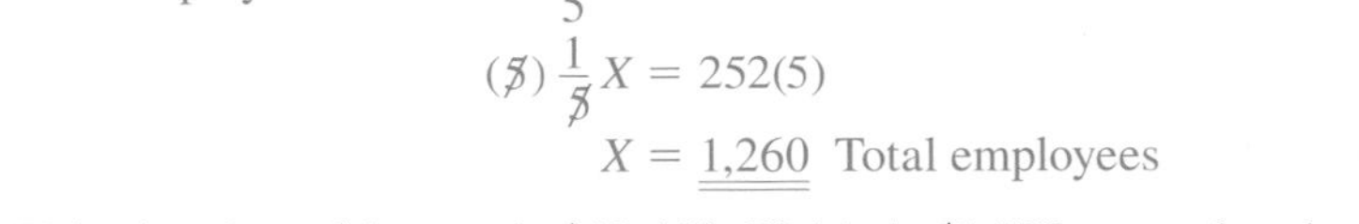

   $$X = \underline{\underline{1{,}260}} \text{ Total employees}$$

3. Walter's salary this year is \$23,400. If this is \$1,700 more than he made last year, what was his salary last year?

   S = Walter's salary last year
   $$S + \$1{,}700 = \$23{,}400$$
   $$S = \underline{\underline{\$21{,}700}} \text{ Last year's salary}$$

4. The Bookworm makes four times as much revenue on paperback books as on hardcover books. If last month's sales totaled \$124,300, how much was sold of each type book?

   Hardcover = X
   Paperback = $4X$

   $$X + 4X = 124{,}300$$
   $$5X = 124{,}300$$
   $$\frac{5X}{5} = \frac{124{,}300}{5}$$
   $$X = \underline{\underline{\$24{,}860}} \text{ Hardcover}$$
   $$4X = \underline{\underline{\$99{,}440}} \text{ Paperback}$$

5. Buystuff.com sells 4 gigabyte Apple iPod Nanos for \$190 and 1 gigabyte iPod Shuffles for \$80. Last week they sold three times as many Shuffles as Nanos. Combined sales totaled \$3,440. How many Nanos and Shuffles did they sell?

   Let N = number of iPod Nanos
   Let 3N = the number of iPod Shuffles

   $$190N + 80(3N) = 3{,}440$$
   $$190N + 240N = 3{,}440$$
   $$430N = 3{,}440$$
   $$N = \frac{3{,}440}{430} = \underline{\underline{8}} \text{ iPod Nanos}$$
   $$3N = 3(8) = \underline{\underline{24}} \text{ iPod Shuffles}$$

6. Jack's weekly salary is \$25 less than twice David's salary. If together their salaries total \$1,425, what is David's weekly salary?

Let D = David's weekly salary
$2D - 25$ = Jack's weekly salary

$$D + 2D - 25 = 1{,}425$$
$$3D - 25 = 1{,}425$$
$$3D = 1{,}425 + 25$$
$$3D = 1{,}450$$
$$\frac{3D}{3} = \frac{1{,}450}{3}$$
$$D = \underline{\underline{\$483.33}} \text{ David's weekly salary}$$

7. Kid's Kingdom a retail toy chain, placed a seasonal order for stuffed animals from a distributor. Large animals cost \$20, and small ones cost \$14.

a. If the total cost of the order was \$7,320 for 450 pieces, how many of each size were ordered?

Large size = X
Small size = $450 - X$

$$20X + 14(450 - X) = 7{,}320$$
$$20X + 6{,}300 - 14X = 7{,}320$$
$$6X = 1{,}020$$
$$X = \underline{\underline{170}} \text{ Large size}$$
$$450 - X = \underline{\underline{280}} \text{ Small size}$$

b. What was the dollar amount of each size ordered?

Large size = \$20(170) = $\underline{\underline{\$3,400}}$
Small size = \$14(280) = $\underline{\underline{\$3,920}}$

The Toy Industry
According to the Toy Industry Association, Inc. in 2006, total toy sales amounted to \$22.3 billion. Video games added another \$10.5 billion. The largest U.S. toy retailers are Wal-Mart, Toys"R"Us, Target, KB Toys, Kmart, Game Stop, and Electronics Boutique.

8. Jessy and Ashton invested \$89,600 in a business. If Ashton invested three times as much as Jessy, how much did each invest?

Jessy = X
Ashton = $3X$

$$X + 3X = 89{,}600$$
$$4X = 89{,}600$$
$$\frac{4X}{4} = \frac{89{,}600}{4}$$

$X = \underline{\underline{\$22{,}400}}$ Jessy's investment
$3X = \underline{\underline{\$67{,}200}}$ Ashton's investment

9. An estate is to be distributed among a wife, three children, and two grandchildren. The children will each receive three times as much as each grandchild, and the wife will receive four times as much as each child. If the estate amounted to \$115,000, how much will each person receive?

Grandchild = X
Child = $3X$
Wife = $4(3X)$

$$2X + 3(3X) + 4(3X) = 115{,}000$$
$$2X + 9X + 12X = 115{,}000$$
$$\frac{23X}{23} = \frac{115{,}000}{23}$$

$X = \underline{\underline{\$5{,}000}}$ = Each grandchild's share
$3X = \underline{\underline{\$15{,}000}}$ = Each child's share
$4(3X) = \underline{\underline{\$60{,}000}}$ = Wife's share

TEACHING TIP
Review Exercise #9 is a particularly challenging one, because it involves numerical relationships among three variables, not just two. Have students work in pairs to solve this one.

10. PC Solutions sells regular keyboards for \$84 and wireless keyboards for \$105. Last week the store sold three times as many regular keyboards as wireless. If total keyboard sales were \$4,998, how many of each type were sold?

Wireless keyboards = X
Regular keyboards = $3X$

$$105X + 84(3X) = 4{,}998$$
$$105X + 252X = 4{,}998$$
$$357X = 4{,}998$$
$$X = \underline{\underline{14}} \text{ Wireless keyboards}$$
$$3X = \underline{\underline{42}} \text{ Regular keyboards}$$

11. The deluxe model of a KitchenAid oven costs \$46 more than twice the cost of the standard model. If together they cost \$1,234, what is the cost of each model?

Standard oven = X
Deluxe oven = $2X + 46$

$$X + 2X + 46 = 1{,}234$$
$$3X + 46 = 1{,}234$$
$$3X = 1{,}188$$
$$X = \underline{\underline{\$396}} \text{ Cost of standard oven}$$
$$2X + 46 = \underline{\underline{\$838}} \text{ Cost of deluxe oven}$$

12. Yesterday, Castle Mountain Fashions had seven less than three-fourths of its sales transactions paid for by credit cards. If 209 transactions were charged, how many total transactions took place?

Total transactions $= X$ $\quad\quad \frac{3}{4}X - 7 = 209$

Charge cards $= \frac{3}{4}X - 7$ $\quad\quad \frac{3}{4}X = 216$

$X = \underline{\underline{288}}$ Total transactions

13. The Michigan plant of Titan Industries is four times as old as the Ohio plant. If the difference in the ages of the two plants is 9 years, what is the age of each?

Ohio plant $= X$ $\quad\quad 4X - X = 9$

Michigan plant $= 4X$ $\quad\quad 3X = 9$

$X = \underline{\underline{3}}$ Age of Ohio plant

$4X = \underline{\underline{12}}$ Age of Michigan plant

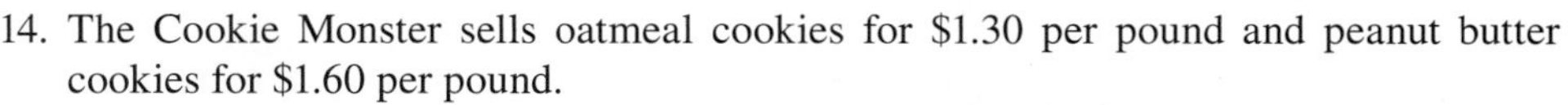

14. The Cookie Monster sells oatmeal cookies for \$1.30 per pound and peanut butter cookies for \$1.60 per pound.

a. If total cookie sales last week amounted to 530 pounds, valued at \$755, how many pounds of each type of cookie were sold?

Peanut butter $= X$ $\quad\quad 1.60X + 1.30(530 - X) = 755$ $\quad\quad X = \underline{\underline{220}}$ Pounds of peanut butter cookies

Oatmeal $= 530 - X$ $\quad\quad 1.60X + 689 - 1.30X = 755$ $\quad\quad 530 - X = \underline{\underline{310}}$ Pounds of oatmeal cookies

$.30X + 689 = 755$

$.30X = 66$

b. What dollar amount of each type was sold?

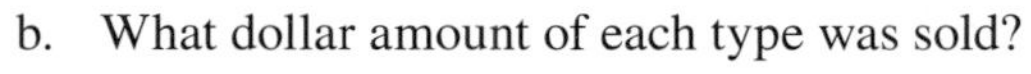

$1.60(220) = \underline{\underline{\$352}}$ Sales of peanut butter cookies

$1.30(310) = \underline{\underline{\$403}}$ Sales of oatmeal cookies

© Digital Vision/Getty Images

Credit Cards

According to a survey by CardTrak.com, in June of 2007, there were 88 million American households using credit cards with over \$2.1 trillion in outstanding debt. The average credit card debt load was nearly \$9,900 per household. Of cardholders carrying debt, over 64% had balances under \$10,000. However, 13% of the same group said they carry total credit card balances in excess of \$25,000.

15. One-ninth of Superior Plastics' sales are made in New England. If New England sales amount to \$600,000, what are the total sales of the company?

Total sales $= X$ $\quad\quad \frac{1}{9}X = 600{,}000$

New England sales $= \frac{1}{9}X$ $\quad\quad X = \underline{\underline{\$5{,}400{,}000}}$ Total sales

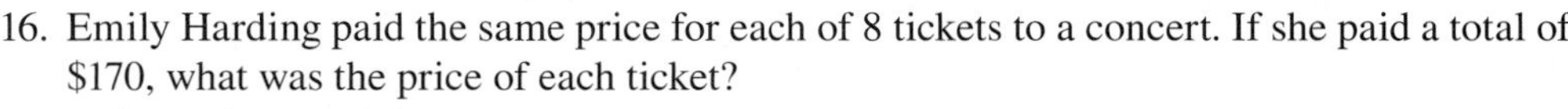

16. Emily Harding paid the same price for each of 8 tickets to a concert. If she paid a total of \$170, what was the price of each ticket?

$P =$ price per ticket

$8P = \$170$

$\frac{\cancel{8}P}{\cancel{8}} = \frac{170}{8}$

$P = \underline{\underline{\$21.25}}$ Per ticket

17. If a 48-piece set of stainless steel flatware costs \$124.80 at Bed, Bath, and Beyond, what is the cost per piece?

Cost per piece $= X$ $\quad\quad 48X = 124.80$ $\quad\quad X = \frac{124.80}{48}$

$\frac{\cancel{48}X}{\cancel{48}} = \frac{124.80}{48}$ $\quad\quad X = \underline{\underline{\$2.60}}$ Cost per piece

18. You are the shipping manager for World Imports. Calculate the total cost to ship an order of glassware weighing 1,860 pounds, if the breakdown is \$.04 per pound for packing, \$.02 per pound for insurance, \$.13 per pound for transportation, and \$132.40 for the crate.

Total cost $= X$ $\quad\quad X = .04(1{,}860) + .02(1{,}860) + .13(1{,}860) + 132.40$

$X = 74.40 + 37.20 + 241.80 + 132.40$

$X = \underline{\underline{\$485.80}}$ Total cost to ship order

19. Mike Taylor purchased a 4-unit apartment building as an investment before he retired. From the rent he collects each month, Mike pays out $600 for expenses. How much rent must he charge for each of the 4 apartments if he wants to make $500 profit each month? The amount of rent is the same for each of the apartments.

Let R = Amount of rent to charge each month

$$4R - 600 = 500$$
$$4R = 1{,}100$$
$$\frac{\cancel{4}R}{\cancel{4}} = \frac{1{,}100}{4}$$
$$R = \underline{\underline{\$275}} \text{ Rent for each apartment}$$

20. You are the facilities director of a local shopping mall. You have been asked to rope off a rectangular section of the parking lot for a car show next weekend. The area to be roped off is 250 feet long by 300 feet wide. Rubber traffic cones are to be placed every 25 feet around the lot. How many cones are needed?

The perimeter around the rectangular area is

$$(2 \times 250) + (2 \times 300) = 500 + 600 = 1{,}100 \text{ feet}$$

Let X = Number of cones needed

$$X = \frac{1{,}100}{25} = \underline{\underline{44}} \text{ Cones to be placed around the area}$$

Use ratio and proportion to solve the following business situations.

21. If the interest on a $4,600 loan is $370, what would be the interest on a loan of $9,660?

$$\frac{4{,}600}{370} = \frac{9{,}600}{X} \qquad 4{,}600X = 370(9{,}660)$$
$$4{,}600X = 3{,}574{,}200$$
$$X = \underline{\underline{\$777}} \text{ Interest on a \$9,660 loan}$$

22. At Carnival Fruit Distributors, Inc., the ratio of fruits to vegetables sold is 5 to 3. If 1,848 pounds of vegetables are sold, how many pounds of fruit are sold?

$$\frac{5}{3} = \frac{X}{1{,}848} \qquad 3X = 5(1{,}848)$$
$$3X = 9{,}240$$
$$X = \underline{\underline{3{,}080}} \text{ Pounds of fruit}$$

23. A local FedEx Kinko's has a press that can print 5,800 brochures per hour. How many can be printed during a $3\frac{1}{4}$-hour run?

$$\frac{5{,}800}{1} = \frac{X}{3\frac{1}{4}} \qquad X = 5{,}800\left(3\tfrac{1}{4}\right)$$
$$X = \underline{\underline{18{,}850}} \text{ Brochures printed in } 3\tfrac{1}{4} \text{ hours}$$

© R. Alcorn/South-Western Cengage Learning

FedEx Kinko's Office and Print Services is the world's leading provider of document solutions and business services. The Dallas-based company has a global network of more than 1,500 digitally connected locations in 11 countries, with revenue in 2007 of over $2.1 billion. More than 400 centers are open 24 hours a day, seven days a week.

24. A recipe for turkey stuffing calls for three eggs for every $12\frac{1}{2}$ ounces of corn bread. If a dinner party requires $87\frac{1}{2}$ ounces of corn bread for stuffing, how many eggs should be used?

$$\frac{3}{12\frac{1}{2}} = \frac{X}{87\frac{1}{2}} \qquad 12\tfrac{1}{2}X = 3\left(87\tfrac{1}{2}\right)$$
$$12\tfrac{1}{2}X = 262\tfrac{1}{2}$$
$$X = \underline{\underline{21}} \text{ Eggs needed for recipe}$$

25. An architect uses a scale of $\frac{3}{4}$ inch to represent 1 foot on a blueprint for a building. If the east wall of the building is 36 feet long, how long will the line be on the blueprint?

$$\frac{\frac{3}{4}}{1} = \frac{X}{36} \qquad X = \tfrac{3}{4}(36)$$
$$X = \underline{\underline{27}} \text{ Inches on the blueprint}$$

26. If a car goes 48 miles per hour at 3,300 rpm (revolutions per minute) of the engine, how fast will it go at 4,000 rpm in the same gear?

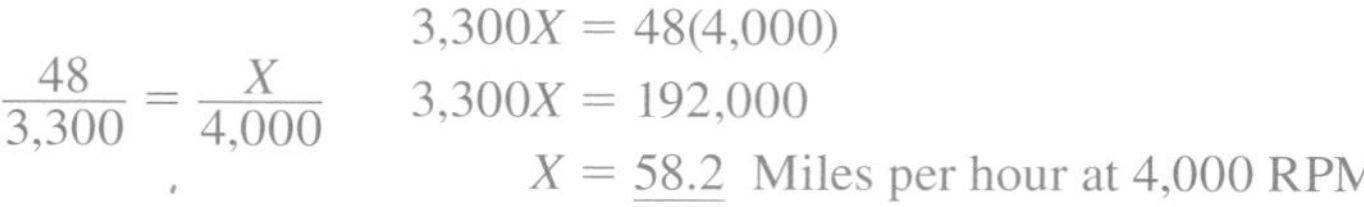

$$3{,}300X = 48(4{,}000)$$
$$\frac{48}{3{,}300} = \frac{X}{4{,}000} \qquad 3{,}300X = 192{,}000$$
$$X = \underline{\underline{58.2}} \text{ Miles per hour at 4,000 RPM}$$

27. If auto insurance costs \$6.52 per \$1,000 of coverage, what is the cost to insure a car valued at \$17,500?

$$\frac{6.52}{1{,}000} = \frac{X}{17{,}500} \qquad \begin{aligned} 1{,}000X &= 6.52(17{,}500) \\ 1{,}000X &= 114{,}100 \\ X &= \underline{\underline{\$114.10}} \text{ Cost of insurance} \end{aligned}$$

28. Marathon Airport handles passenger to cargo traffic in a ratio of 8 to 5. If 45 cargo planes landed yesterday, how many passenger flights came in?

$$\frac{8}{5} = \frac{X}{45} \qquad \begin{aligned} 5X &= 8(45) \\ 5X &= 360 \\ X &= \underline{\underline{72}} \text{ Passenger flights} \end{aligned}$$

29. Eighty ounces of Lazy Lawn fertilizer covers 1,250 square feet of lawn.
    a. How many ounces would be required to cover a 4,000-square-foot lawn?

$$\frac{80}{1{,}250} = \frac{X}{4{,}000} \qquad \begin{aligned} 1{,}250X &= 80(4{,}000) \\ 1{,}250X &= 320{,}000 \\ X &= \underline{\underline{256}} \text{ Ounces needed to cover 4,000 sq ft} \end{aligned}$$

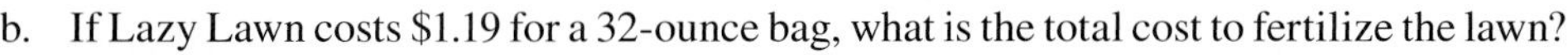

    b. If Lazy Lawn costs \$1.19 for a 32-ounce bag, what is the total cost to fertilize the lawn?

$$\frac{1.19}{32} = \frac{X}{256} \qquad \begin{aligned} 32X &= 1.19(256) \\ 32X &= 304.64 \\ X &= \underline{\underline{\$9.52}} \text{ Total cost} \end{aligned}$$

BUSINESS DECISION MANAGING *THE CHRONICLE*

30. You have just been hired as advertising manager of *The Daily Chronicle*, a not-very-successful newspaper. In the past, *The Chronicle* contained one-half advertising and one-half news stories. Current industry research indicates a newspaper must have three times as much advertising as news stories to make money. In addition, the advertising must be divided in the following ratio: 5 to 3 to 1, retail advertising to national advertising to classified advertising. *The Chronicle* is typically 48 pages in length.
    a. How many pages should be advertising and how many should be news stories?

$$\begin{aligned} X &= \text{News story pages} \\ 3X &= \text{Advertising pages} \\ X + 3X &= 48 \\ 4X &= 48 \\ X &= \underline{\underline{12}} \text{ Pages of news} \\ 3X &= \underline{\underline{36}} \text{ Pages of advertising} \end{aligned}$$

    b. Based on the industry ratios, how should the pages be divided among the three types of advertising?

$$\begin{aligned} \text{Let } 5X &= \text{Retail advertising pages} \\ 3X &= \text{National advertising pages} \\ X &= \text{Classified pages} \\ X + 3X + 5X &= 36 \\ 9X &= 36 \\ X &= \underline{\underline{4}} \text{ Pages classified} \\ 3X &= \underline{\underline{12}} \text{ Pages national} \\ 5X &= \underline{\underline{20}} \text{ Pages retail} \end{aligned}$$

    c. After you made the changes in the advertising distributions ratios, your newspaper began making a profit—for the first time in years. If last year's total advertising revenue was \$810,000, how much was earned by each type of advertising?

$$\text{Retail: } 810{,}000 \times \frac{20}{36} = \underline{\underline{\$450{,}000}}$$

$$\text{National: } 810{,}000 \times \frac{12}{36} = \underline{\underline{\$270{,}000}}$$

$$\text{Classified: } 810{,}000 \times \frac{4}{36} = \underline{\underline{\$90{,}000}}$$

© R. Alcorn/South-Western Cengage Learning

Top 10 Weekday Newspapers by Circulation in Thousands, 2007

	Newspaper	Circulation
1.	USA Today	2,282
2.	Wall Street Journal	2,070
3.	New York Times	1,122
4.	Los Angeles Times	908
5.	Washington Post	741
6.	New York Daily News	709
7.	Chicago Tribune	566
8.	New York Post	643
9.	Newsday	528
10.	Houston Chronicle	477

d. When you accepted the job of advertising manager, in addition to your salary, you were promised a $\frac{1}{50}$ share of each year's revenue from retail and classified advertising, and $\frac{1}{75}$ share for national. How much bonus will you receive for last year's sales?

Retail: $450{,}000 \times \frac{1}{50} = 9{,}000$

National: $270{,}000 \times \frac{1}{75} = 3{,}600$

Classified: $90{,}000 \times \frac{1}{50} = 1{,}800$

$14,400 Bonus

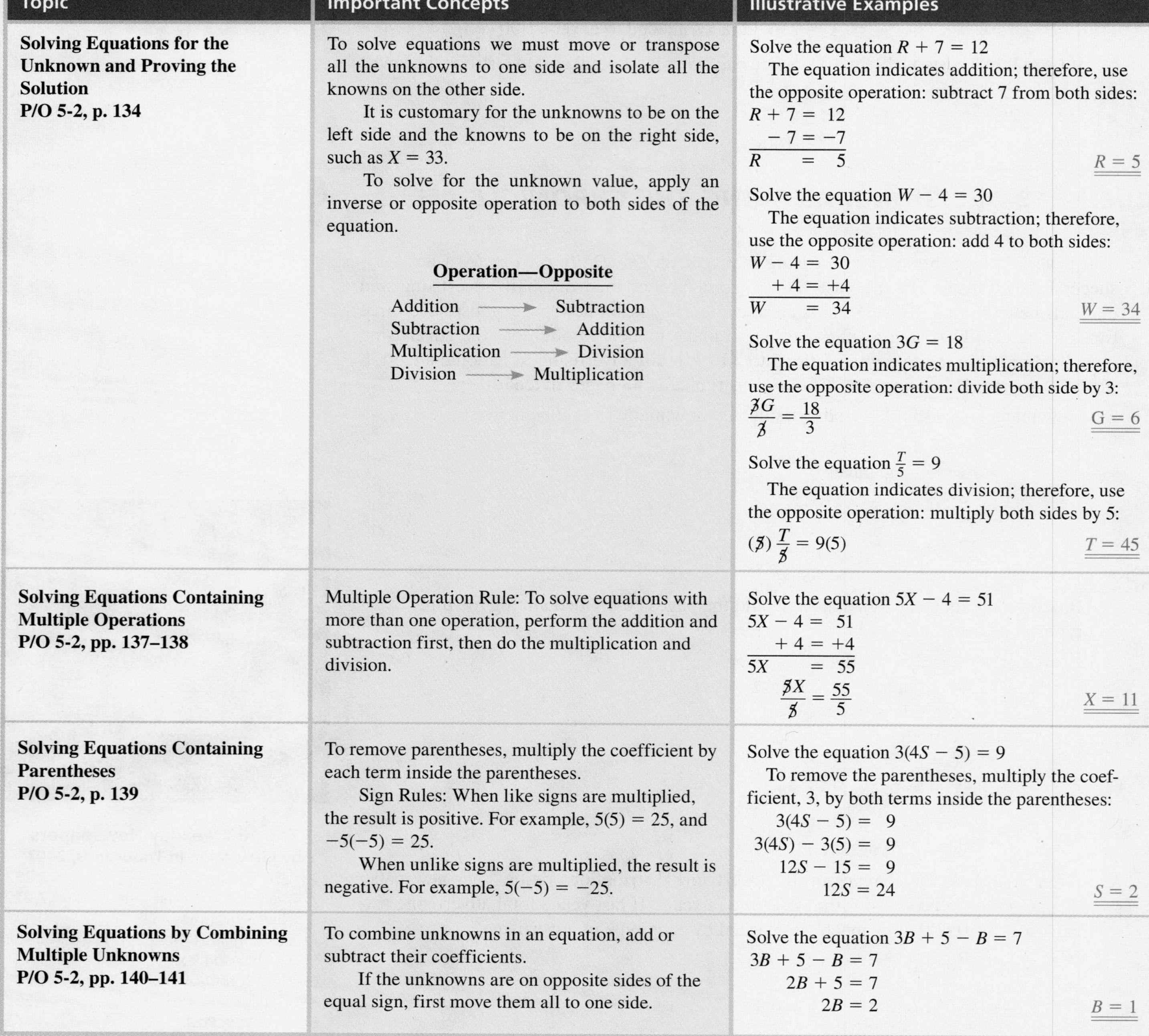

SUMMARY CHART

5

Section I: Solving Basic Equations

Topic	Important Concepts	Illustrative Examples
Solving Equations for the Unknown and Proving the Solution **P/O 5-2, p. 134**	To solve equations we must move or transpose all the unknowns to one side and isolate all the knowns on the other side. It is customary for the unknowns to be on the left side and the knowns to be on the right side, such as $X = 33$. To solve for the unknown value, apply an inverse or opposite operation to both sides of the equation. **Operation—Opposite** Addition → Subtraction Subtraction → Addition Multiplication → Division Division → Multiplication	Solve the equation $R + 7 = 12$ The equation indicates addition; therefore, use the opposite operation: subtract 7 from both sides: $R + 7 = 12$ $-7 = -7$ $R = 5$ $R = 5$ Solve the equation $W - 4 = 30$ The equation indicates subtraction; therefore, use the opposite operation: add 4 to both sides: $W - 4 = 30$ $+4 = +4$ $W = 34$ $W = 34$ Solve the equation $3G = 18$ The equation indicates multiplication; therefore, use the opposite operation: divide both side by 3: $\frac{\cancel{3}G}{\cancel{3}} = \frac{18}{3}$ $G = 6$ Solve the equation $\frac{T}{5} = 9$ The equation indicates division; therefore, use the opposite operation: multiply both sides by 5: $(\cancel{5})\frac{T}{\cancel{5}} = 9(5)$ $T = 45$
Solving Equations Containing Multiple Operations **P/O 5-2, pp. 137–138**	Multiple Operation Rule: To solve equations with more than one operation, perform the addition and subtraction first, then do the multiplication and division.	Solve the equation $5X - 4 = 51$ $5X - 4 = 51$ $+4 = +4$ $5X = 55$ $\frac{\cancel{5}X}{\cancel{5}} = \frac{55}{5}$ $X = 11$
Solving Equations Containing Parentheses **P/O 5-2, p. 139**	To remove parentheses, multiply the coefficient by each term inside the parentheses. Sign Rules: When like signs are multiplied, the result is positive. For example, $5(5) = 25$, and $-5(-5) = 25$. When unlike signs are multiplied, the result is negative. For example, $5(-5) = -25$.	Solve the equation $3(4S - 5) = 9$ To remove the parentheses, multiply the coefficient, 3, by both terms inside the parentheses: $3(4S - 5) = 9$ $3(4S) - 3(5) = 9$ $12S - 15 = 9$ $12S = 24$ $S = 2$
Solving Equations by Combining Multiple Unknowns **P/O 5-2, pp. 140–141**	To combine unknowns in an equation, add or subtract their coefficients. If the unknowns are on opposite sides of the equal sign, first move them all to one side.	Solve the equation $3B + 5 - B = 7$ $3B + 5 - B = 7$ $2B + 5 = 7$ $2B = 2$ $B = 1$

Section I: (continued)

Topic	Important Concepts	Illustrative Examples
Writing Expressions and Equations from Written Statements **P/O 5-3, p. 141**	Expressions and equations are created from written statements by identifying the unknowns and the knowns and determining the mathematical relationship between them. The variables are assigned letters of the alphabet. The relationship between the knowns and the unknowns involve addition, subtraction, multiplication, and division, or a combination of two or more. Key words indicate what relationship exists between the terms (see list, page 141). If the written statement has a verb, such as "is," the statement is an equation.	A number increased by 44 $X + 44$ 6 more than 3 times U $3U + 6$ 3 times the sum of C and 9 $3(C + 9)$ 7 less than 4 times M leaves 55 $4M - 7 = 55$ 2 less than 5 times a number, plus 9 times that number, is 88 $5X - 2 + 9X = 88$

Section II: Using Equations to Solve Business-Related Word Problems

Topic	Important Concepts	Illustrative Examples
Solving Business-Related Equations **P/O 5-4, pp. 144–148**	Example 1: Mary and Beth sell furniture at Futura Designs. Last week Mary sold eight less recliner chairs than Beth. Together they sold 30. How many chairs did each sell?	Solution: *Reasoning*: Beth's sales plus Mary's sales equal total sales, 30 Let X = Beth's sales Let $X - 8$ = Mary's sales $X + X - 8 = 30$ $2X - 8 = 30$ $2X = 38$ $X = 19$ Chairs—Beth's sales $X - 8 = 11$ Chairs—Mary's sales
Solving Business-Related Equations **P/O 5-4, pp. 144–148**	Example 2: One-fourth of the employees at Atlantic Distributors work in the accounting division. If there are 45 workers in this division, how many people work for Atlantic?	Solution: *Reasoning*: $\frac{1}{4}$ of the total employees are in accounting, 45. Let X = total employees Let $\frac{1}{4}X$ = accounting employees $\frac{1}{4}X = 45$ $(\not{4})\frac{1}{\not{4}}X = 45(4)$ $X = 180$ Total employees
Solving Business-Related Equations **P/O 5-4, pp. 144–148**	Example 3: Longhorn Industries, a small manufacturing company, made a profit of $315,000 last year. If the nine investors decide to evenly split this profit, how much will each receive?	Solution: *Reasoning*: Each investor's share is the total profit divided by the number of investors. Let X = each investor's share $X = \frac{315{,}000}{9}$ $X = \$35{,}000$ Investor's share
Solving Business-Related Equations **P/O 5-4, pp. 144–148**	Example 4: The Pet Carnival sells four times as much in cat supplies as in fish supplies. If total sales last week were $6,800, how much of each category was sold?	Solution: *Reasoning*: Fish supplies plus cat supplies equals total, $6,800. Let X = fish supplies Let $4X$ = cat supplies $X + 4X = 6{,}800$ $5X = 6{,}800$ $X = \$1{,}360$ Fish supplies $4X = \$5{,}440$ Cat supplies

Section II: (continued)

Topic	Important Concepts	Illustrative Examples
Solving Business-Related Equations **P/O 5-4, pp. 144–148**	Example 5: The Image, a men's clothing store, sells suits for \$275 and sport coats for \$180. Yesterday they made 20 sales, for a total of \$4,360. a. How many suits and how many sport coats were sold? b. What were the dollar sales of each?	Solution a: *Reasoning*: The sum of the price multiplied by the quantity of each item is the total sales, \$4,360. Let X = suit sales Let $20 - X$ = sport coat sales $275X + 180(20 - X) = 4{,}360$ $275X + 3{,}600 - 180X = 4{,}360$ $95X + 3{,}600 = 4{,}360$ $95X = 760$ $X = 8$ Number of suits sold $20 - X = 12$ Sports coats sold Solution b: 8 suits × \$275 each = \$2,200 Suits sales 12 coats × \$180 each = \$2,160 Coats sales
Understanding and Solving Ratio and Proportion Problems **P/O 5-5, pp. 149–151**	A ratio is a fraction that describes a comparison of two numbers or quantities. A proportion is a statement showing that two ratios are equal. Proportions are equations with "as" being the equal sign and "is to" being the division bar. Proportion problems are solved by cross-multiplication: 1. Let X represent the unknown quantity. 2. Set up the equation with one ratio on each side of the equal sign. 3. Multiply the numerator of the first ratio by the denominator of the second and place the product to the left of the equal sign. 4. Multiply the denominator of the first ratio by the numerator of the second and place the product to the right of the equal sign. 5. Solve the equation for X.	Example 1: 12 is to 42 as 6 is to X $\frac{12}{42} = \frac{6}{X}$ $12X = 42(6)$ $12X = 252$ $X = 21$ Example 2: If Larry works 6 hours for \$150, how much can he expect to earn in a 42-hour week? $\frac{6}{150} = \frac{42}{X}$ $6X = 150(42)$ $6X = 6{,}300$ $X = \$1{,}050$ Larry's salary for 42 hours work

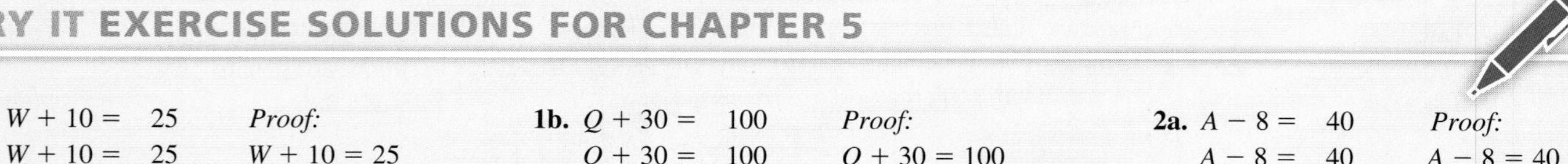

TRY IT EXERCISE SOLUTIONS FOR CHAPTER 5

1a. $W + 10 = 25$
$W + 10 = 25$
$-10 \quad -10$
$W = 15$
$W = 15$

Proof:
$W + 10 = 25$
$15 + 10 = 25$
$25 = 25$

1b. $Q + 30 = 100$
$Q + 30 = 100$
$-30 \quad -30$
$Q = 70$
$Q = 70$

Proof:
$Q + 30 = 100$
$70 + 30 = 100$
$100 = 100$

2a. $A - 8 = 40$
$A - 8 = 40$
$+8 \quad +8$
$A = 48$
$A = 48$

Proof:
$A - 8 = 40$
$48 - 8 = 40$
$40 = 40$

2b. $L - 3 = 7$
$L - 3 = 7$
$+3 \quad +3$
$L = 10$
$L = 10$

Proof:
$L - 3 = 7$
$10 - 3 = 7$
$7 = 7$

3a. $15L = 75$
$\frac{\cancel{15}L}{\cancel{15}} = \frac{75}{15}$
$L = 5$

Proof:
$15L = 75$
$15(5) = 75$
$75 = 75$

3b. $16F = 80$
$\frac{\cancel{16}F}{\cancel{16}} = \frac{80}{16}$
$F = 5$

Proof:
$16F = 80$
$16(5) = 80$
$80 = 80$

4a. $\frac{Z}{8} = 2$

$(\cancel{8})\frac{Z}{\cancel{8}} = 2(8)$

$Z = 16$

Proof:

$\frac{Z}{8} = 2$

$\frac{16}{8} = 2$

$2 = 2$

4b. $\frac{C}{9} = 9$

$(\cancel{9})\frac{C}{\cancel{9}} = 9(9)$

$C = 81$

Proof:

$\frac{C}{9} = 9$

$\frac{81}{9} = 9$

$9 = 9$

5a. $12N + 14 = 50$

$12N + 14 = 50$

$-14 \quad -14$

$12N = 36$

$\frac{\cancel{12}N}{\cancel{12}} = \frac{36}{12}$

$N = 3$

Proof:

$12N + 14 = 50$

$12(3) + 14 = 50$

$36 + 14 = 50$

$50 = 50$

5b. $3W - 4 = 26$

$3W - 4 = 26$

$+4 \quad +4$

$3W = 30$

$\frac{\cancel{3}W}{\cancel{3}} = \frac{30}{3}$

$W = 10$

Proof:

$3W - 4 = 26$

$3(10) - 4 = 26$

$30 - 4 = 26$

$26 = 26$

6a. $\frac{F}{3} - 6 = 2$

$\frac{F}{3} - 6 = 2$

$+6 \quad +6$

$\frac{F}{3} = 8$

$(\cancel{3})\frac{F}{\cancel{3}} = 8(3)$

$F = 24$

Proof:

$\frac{F}{3} - 6 = 2$

$\frac{24}{3} - 6 = 2$

$8 - 6 = 2$

$2 = 2$

6b. $\frac{Z}{5} + 15 = 24$

$\frac{Z}{5} + 15 = 24$

$-15 \quad -15$

$\frac{Z}{5} = 9$

$(\cancel{5})\frac{Z}{\cancel{5}} = 9(5)$

$Z = 45$

Proof:

$\frac{Z}{5} + 15 = 24$

$\frac{45}{5} + 15 = 24$

$9 + 15 = 24$

$24 = 24$

7a. $4(5G + 6) = 64$

$20G + 24 = 64$

$20G + 24 = 64$

$-24 \quad -24$

$20G = 40$

$\frac{\cancel{20}G}{\cancel{20}} = \frac{40}{20}$

$G = 2$

Proof:

$4(5G + 6) = 64$

$4(5\{2\} + 6) = 64$

$4(10 + 6) = 64$

$4(16) = 64$

$64 = 64$

7b. $6(3H - 5) = 42$

$18H - 30 = 42$

$18H - 30 = 42$

$+30 \quad +30$

$18H = 72$

$\frac{\cancel{18}H}{\cancel{18}} = \frac{72}{18}$

$H = 4$

Proof:

$6(3H - 5) = 42$

$6(3\{4\} - 5) = 42$

$6(12 - 5) = 42$

$6(7) = 42$

$42 = 42$

8a. $X + 3 = 18 - 4X$

$X + 3 = 18 - 4X$

$+4X \quad +4X$

$5X + 3 = 18$

$5X + 3 = 18$

$-3 \quad -3$

$5X = 15$

$\frac{\cancel{5}X}{\cancel{5}} = \frac{15}{5}$

$X = 3$

Proof:

$X + 3 = 18 - 4X$

$3 + 3 = 18 - 4(3)$

$6 = 18 - 12$

$6 = 6$

8b. $9S + 8 - S = 2(2S + 8)$

$9S + 8 - S = 4S + 16$

$8S + 8 = 4S + 16$

$8S + 8 = 4S + 16$

$-4S \quad -4S$

$4S + 8 = +16$

$4S + 8 = 16$

$-8 \quad -8$

$4S = 8$

$\frac{\cancel{4}S}{\cancel{4}} = \frac{8}{4}$

$S = 2$

Proof:

$9S + 8 - S = 2(2S + 8)$

$9(2) + 8 - 2 = 2(2\{2\} + 8)$

$18 + 8 - 2 = 2(4 + 8)$

$24 = 2(12)$

$24 = 24$

9a. The sum of twice E and 9

$2E + 9$

9b. 6 times N divided by Z

$\frac{6N}{Z}$

9c. 8 less than half of F

$\frac{1}{2}F - 8$

9d. \$45.75 more than the product of X and Y

$XY + \$45.75$

9e. The difference of Q and 44

$Q - 44$

9f. R times A times B

RAB

10a. What number increased by 32 yields 125?

$X + 32 = 125$

10b. 21 less than twice C gives 9.

$2C - 21 = 9$

10c. 5 more than 6 times a number, plus 3 times that number, is 25.

$6X + 5 + 3X = 25$

10d. The cost of G gallons at \$1.33 per gallon equals \$34.40.

$\$1.33G = \$34.40$

10e. The area of a rectangle is the length times the width.

$A = LW$

10f. What number less 12 is the average of A, B, and C?

$X - 12 = \frac{A + B + C}{3}$

11. *Reasoning:* Don's sales and Chuck's sales equal total sales, 44.

Let X = Chuck's sales

Let $X - 12$ = Don's sales

$$X + X - 12 = 44$$
$$2X - 12 = 44$$
$$2X = 56$$
$$\frac{2X}{2} = \frac{56}{2}$$
$$X = 28 \quad \text{Chuck's sales} = 28 \text{ Alarm systems}$$
$$X - 12 = 28 - 12 = 16 \quad \text{Don's sales} = 16 \text{ Alarm systems}$$

Proof:

$$X + X - 12 = 44$$
$$28 + 28 - 12 = 44$$
$$44 = 44$$

12. *Reasoning:* $\frac{1}{3}$ of the total checking accounts are interest-earning, 2,500.

Let C = total checking accounts

$$\frac{1}{3}C = 2{,}500$$
$$(3)\frac{1}{3}C = 2{,}500(3)$$
$$C = 7{,}500$$

Total checking accounts = 7,500

Proof:

$$\frac{1}{3}C = 2{,}500$$
$$\frac{1}{3}(7{,}500) = 2{,}500$$
$$2{,}500 = 2{,}500$$

13. *Reasoning:* Weight per carton equals the total weight divided by the number of cartons.

Let W = weight per carton

$$W = \frac{7{,}482}{58}$$
$$W = 129$$

Weight per carton = 129 pounds

Proof:

$$W = \frac{7{,}482}{58}$$
$$129 = \frac{7{,}482}{58}$$
$$129 = 129$$

14. *Reasoning:* Soft goods plus hard goods equals total store sales, $180,000.

Let X = hard goods

Let $3X$ = soft goods

$X + 3X = \$180{,}000$

$$4X = 180{,}000$$
$$\frac{4X}{4} = \frac{180{,}000}{4}$$
$$X = 45{,}000 \quad \text{Hard goods} = \$45{,}000$$
$$3X = 3(45{,}000) = 135{,}000 \quad \text{Soft goods} = \$135{,}000$$

Proof:

$$X + 3X = 180{,}000$$
$$45{,}000 + 3(45{,}000) = 180{,}000$$
$$45{,}000 + 135{,}000 = 180{,}000$$
$$180{,}000 = 180{,}000$$

15. *Reasoning:* Tables plus chairs plus sofas equals total items sold, 520.

Let X = tables

Let $4X$ = chairs

Let $2(4X)$ = sofas

$$X + 4X + 2(4X) = 520$$
$$X + 4X + 8X = 520$$
$$13X = 520$$
$$\frac{13X}{13} = \frac{520}{13}$$
$$X = 40 \quad \text{Tables sold} = 40$$
$$4X = 4(40) = 160 \quad \text{Chairs sold} = 160$$
$$2(4X) = 2(4\{40\}) = 2(160) = 320 \quad \text{Sofas sold} = 320$$

Proof:

$$X + 4X + 2(4X) = 520$$
$$40 + 4(40) + 2(4\{40\}) = 520$$
$$40 + 160 + 2(160) = 520$$
$$40 + 160 + 320 = 520$$
$$520 = 520$$

16. *Reasoning:* The sum of the price of each item multiplied by the quantity of each item is the total sales, $3,400.
Remember: Let X equal the more expensive item, thereby avoiding negative numbers.

Let $X =$ Quantity of heavy-duty batteries
Let $40 - X =$ Quantity of regular batteries
Price times quantity of heavy-duty batteries $= \$110X$
Price times quantity of regular batteries $= \$70(40 - X)$

$$110X + 70(40 - X) = 3{,}400$$
$$110X + 2{,}800 - 70X = 3{,}400$$
$$40X + 2{,}800 = 3{,}400$$
$$40X = 600$$
$$\frac{40X}{40} = \frac{600}{40}$$
$$X = 15$$ Quantity of heavy-duty batteries = 15
$$40 - X = 40 - 15 = 25$$ Quantity of regular batteries = 25

Proof:

$$110X + 70(40 - X) = 3{,}400$$
$$110(15) + 70(40 - 15) = 3{,}400$$
$$1{,}650 + 70(25) = 3{,}400$$
$$1{,}650 + 1{,}750 = 3{,}400$$
$$3{,}400 = 3{,}400$$

Now that we have calculated the quantity of each size battery, we can find the dollar sales:
Reasoning: Dollar sales are the price per battery multiplied by the quantity sold.

Let $S =$ dollar sales
Heavy-duty battery: $S = \$110(15) =$ $1,650 in sales
Regular battery: $S = \$70(25) =$ $1,750 in sales

17. $\frac{87.50}{7} = \frac{X}{35}$

$$7X = 87.50(35)$$
$$7X = 3{,}062.50$$
$$\frac{7X}{7} = \frac{3{,}062.50}{7}$$
$$X = 437.50$$ Steve would earn $437.50 for 35 hours of work.

Proof:

$$\frac{87.50}{7} = \frac{X}{35}$$
$$\frac{87.50}{7} = \frac{437.50}{35}$$
$$12.50 = 12.50$$

CONCEPT REVIEW

1. A(n) ____ is a mathematical statement describing a real-world situation in which letters represent number quantities. (5-1)
formula

2. A mathematical statement expressing a relationship of equality is known as a(n) ____. (5-1)
equation

3. The parts of an equation that are *given* are called the constants or ____. (5-1)
knowns

4. The variables or unknowns of an equation are represented by letters of the ____. (5-1)
alphabet

5. The numerical value of the unknown that makes an equation true is called the ____ or ____. (5-1)
solution, root

6. A coefficient is a number or quantity placed before another quantity, indicating ____. (5-2)
multiplication

7. To transpose means to bring a term from one side of an equation to the other, with a corresponding change of ____. (5-2)
sign

8. List the "order of operations" for solving equations. (5-2)
clear parentheses
addition and subtraction
multiplication and division

9. To prove the solution of an equation, we substitute the solution for the ____ in the original equation. (5-2)
unknown

10. When writing an equation from a written statement, the verb of the sentence represents the ____ ____ in the equation. (5-3)
equal sign

11. When writing an equation from a written statement, the word "difference" means ____, while the word "of" means ____. (5-3)
subtraction, multiplication

12. A comparison of two quantities by division is known as a(n) ____. (5-5)
ratio

13. A mathematical statement showing that two ratios are equal is known as a(n) ____. (5-5)
proportion

14. Proportions are solved using a process known as ____-multiplication. (5-5)
cross

CHAPTER

ASSESSMENT TEST

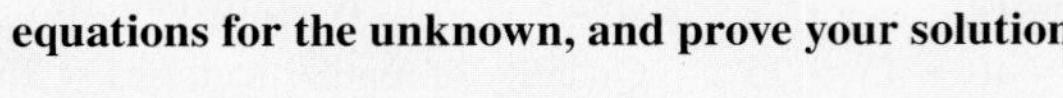

Name ______

Class ______

Answers

1. $T = 65$
2. $G = 99$
3. $K = 15$
4. $C = 10$
5. $X = 8$
6. $S = 84$
7. $B = 8$
8. $N = 60$
9. $X = 15$
10. $\frac{1}{9}P - 15$
11. $4R - 108$
12. $3(H - 233)$
13. $ZW + 24$
14. $X - 4 = 25$
15. $X = 4C + L$
16. $\$4.55Q = \$76.21$
17. $3F - 14 = 38$
18. $6X + 2 + 7X = X - 39$
19. Century Marine: 14 Boats
Marine Max: 19 Boats

Complete, worked-out solutions to Exercises 1–9 appear in Appendix B, following the index.

Solve the following equations for the unknown, and prove your solutions.

1. $T + 45 = 110$
$T = \underline{65}$

2. $G - 24 = 75$
$G = \underline{99}$

3. $11K = 165$
$K = \underline{15}$

4. $3(2C - 5) = 45$
$C = \underline{10}$

5. $8X - 15 = 49$
$X = \underline{8}$

6. $\frac{S}{7} = 12$
$S = \underline{84}$

7. $B + 5 = 61 - 6B$
$B = \underline{8}$

8. $\frac{N}{4} - 7 = 8$
$N = \underline{60}$

9. $4(3X + 8) = 212$
$X = \underline{15}$

For the following statements, underline the key words and translate into *expressions*.

10. 15 less than one-ninth of P
$\frac{1}{9}P - 15$

11. The difference of $4R$ and 108
$4R - 108$

12. 3 times the quantity of H less 233
$3(H - 233)$

13. 24 more than the product of Z and W
$ZW + 24$

For the following statements, underline the key words and translate into *equations*.

14. A number decreased by 4 is 25
$X - 4 = 25$

15. A number totals 4 times C and L
$X = 4C + L$

16. The cost of Q at \$4.55 each is \$76.21
$\$4.55Q = \$76.21$

17. 14 less than $3F$ leaves 38
$3F - 14 = 38$

18. 2 more than 6 times a number, and 7 times that number, is that number decreased by 39
$6X + 2 + 7X = X - 39$

Set up and solve equations for each of the following business situations.

19. At a recent boat show, Marine Max sold five more boats than Century Marine. If together they sold 33 boats, how many were sold by each company?

X = Century Marine
$X + 5$ = Marine Max

$X + X + 5 = 33$
$2X + 5 = 33$
$2X = 28$
$X = \underline{14}$ Boats sold by Century Marine
$X + 5 = \underline{19}$ Boats sold by Marine Max

CHAPTER 5

Name

Class

Answers

20. 1,015 Customers

21. $55

22. $8,000 Muffins

$36,000 Donuts

23. 95 Watts

24 a. 225 Long

150 Short

b. $6,412.50

$3,450.00

25. $1.15

26. $60,000 Beavin's share

$135,000 Gonzalez's share

20. One-seventh of the customers responding to a survey at Highland Department Store were not satisfied with the merchandise selection. If 145 customers were not satisfied, how many customers responded to the survey?

X = Customers responding

$\frac{1}{7}X = 145$

$(7)\frac{1}{7}X = 145(7)$

$X = \underline{\underline{1{,}015}}$ Customers responding

21. Fisher Island Electronics ordered three dozen cell phones from the manufacturer. If the total order amounted to $1,980, what was the cost of each phone?

X = Cost per phone

$36X = 1{,}980$ $\qquad X = \frac{1{,}980}{36}$

$\frac{36X}{36} = \frac{1{,}980}{36}$ $\qquad X = \underline{\underline{\$55}}$ Cost per phone

22. The Bon Appetit Bakery makes $4\frac{1}{2}$ times as much revenue on donuts as muffins. If total sales were $44,000 for May, what dollar amount of each was sold?

X = Muffins $\qquad X + 4\frac{1}{2}X = 44{,}000$ $\qquad X = \underline{\underline{\$8{,}000}}$ Muffin sales

$4\frac{1}{2}X$ = Donuts $\qquad 5\frac{1}{2}X = 44{,}000$ $\qquad 4\frac{1}{2}X = \underline{\underline{\$36{,}000}}$ Donut sales

23. A regular light bulb uses 20 watts less than twice the power of an energy-saver light bulb. If the regular bulb uses 170 watts, how much does the energy-saver bulb use?

X = Energy-saver bulb $\qquad 2X - 20 = 170$

$2X - 20$ = Regular bulb $\qquad 2X = 190$

$X = \underline{\underline{95}}$ Watts for energy-saver bulb

24. Royal Peacock menswear ordered short-sleeve shirts for $23 each and long-sleeve shirts for $28.50 each from Hugo Boss.

a. If the total order amounted to $9,862.50 for 375 shirts, how many of each were ordered?

X = Long-sleeve shirts $\qquad 28.50X + 23(375 - X) = 9{,}862.50$

$375 - X$ = Short-sleeve shirts $\qquad 28.50X + 8{,}625 - 23X = 9{,}862.50$

$5.50X + 8{,}625 = 9{,}862.50$

$5.50X = 1{,}237.50$

$X = \underline{\underline{225}}$ Long-sleeve shirts

$375 - X = \underline{\underline{150}}$ Short-sleeve shirts

b. What was the dollar amount of each type of shirt ordered?

$28.50(225) = \underline{\underline{\$6{,}412.50}}$ Long-sleeve shirts

$23(150) = \underline{\underline{\$3{,}450.00}}$ Short-sleeve shirts

25. Ace Hardware is offering a 140-piece mechanics tool set plus a $65 tool chest for $226. What is the cost per tool?

X = Cost per tool $\qquad 140X + 65 = 226$

$140X = 161$

$X = \underline{\underline{\$1.15}}$ Cost per tool

26. Beavin and Gonzalez invested $195,000 in a business venture. If Gonzalez invested $2\frac{1}{4}$ times as much as Beavin, how much did each invest?

X = Beavin $\qquad X + 2\frac{1}{4}X = 195{,}000$

$2\frac{1}{4}X$ = Gonzalez $\qquad 3\frac{1}{4}X = 195{,}000$

$X = \underline{\underline{\$60{,}000}}$ Beavin's share

$2\frac{1}{4}X = \underline{\underline{\$135{,}000}}$ Gonzalez's share

© Tom Gannam/Associated Press

Ace Hardware is a cooperative of 4,600 independently owned and operated hardware retailers throughout the U.S. and in about 70 other countries. Ace's $3.8 billion plus sales in 2006 make it the #1 hardware cooperative in the United States.

International Dairy Queen (IDQ), which is headquartered in Minneapolis, Minn., develops, licenses, and services a system of more than 5,600 Dairy Queen restaurants in the United States, Canada, and 22 other countries, offering dairy desserts, hamburgers, hot dogs, and beverages. IDQ is part of the Berkshire Hathaway family, a company owned by Warren Buffett, the legendary investor and CEO of Berkshire Hathaway.

CHAPTER

Name

Class

Answers

27. $430

28. a. Banana splits 200

Sundaes 800

b. Banana splits $850

Sundaes $2,880

29. $104,000

30. $150

31. $3\frac{1}{3}$ Quarts

32. a. 46 Bulbs

b. $40.71 Total cost

27. You are the shipping manager for Atlas Exports. Calculate the total cost to ship an order weighing 420 pounds if the breakdown is $.18 per pound for packing, $.12 per pound for insurance, $.37 per pound for transportation, and $148.60 for the shipping crate?

X = Total cost of shipping

$X = .18(420) + .12(420) + .37(420) + 148.60$

$X = 75.60 + 50.40 + 155.40 + 148.60$

$X = \underline{\underline{\$430}}$ Total shipping cost

28. A Dairy Queen ice cream shop sells sundaes for $3.60 and banana splits for $4.25. The shop sells four times as many sundaes as banana splits.

a. If total sales amount to $3,730 last weekend, how many of each dish were sold?

X = Banana splits
$4X$ = Sundaes

$4.25X + 3.60(4X) = 3{,}730$

$4.25X + 14.40X = 3{,}730$

$18.65X = 3{,}730$

$X = \underline{\underline{200}}$ Banana splits sold

$4X = \underline{\underline{800}}$ Sundaes sold

b. What were the dollar sales of each?

$4.25(200) = \underline{\underline{\$850}}$ Sales of banana splits

$3.60(800) = \underline{\underline{\$2{,}880}}$ Sales of sundaes

Use ratio and proportion to solve the following business situations.

29. At Premier Sports Center, the inventory ratio of equipment to clothing is 8 to 5. If the clothing inventory amounts to $65,000, what is the amount of the equipment inventory?

$\frac{8}{5} = \frac{X}{65{,}000}$

$5X = 8(65{,}000)$

$5X = 520{,}000$

$X = \underline{\underline{\$104{,}000}}$ Equipment inventory

30. If the interest on a $6,000 loan is $400, what would be the interest on a loan of $2,250?

$\frac{6{,}000}{400} = \frac{2{,}250}{X}$

$6{,}000X = 400(2{,}250)$

$6{,}000X = 900{,}000$

$X = \underline{\underline{\$150}}$ Interest

31. The directions on a bag of powdered driveway sealant call for the addition of 5 quarts of water for every 30 pounds of sealant. How much water should be added if only 20 pounds of sealant will be used?

X = Amount of water to be added

$\frac{5 \text{ quarts}}{30 \text{ pounds}} = \frac{X \text{ quarts}}{20 \text{ pounds}}$

$30X = 5(20)$

$30X = 100$

$X = \frac{100}{30} = \underline{\underline{3\frac{1}{3}}}$ Quarts of water

32. Courtney Sheldon is planting flower bulbs in her garden for this coming summer. She intends to plant 1 bulb for every 5 square inches of flower bed.

a. How many flower bulbs will she need for an area measuring 230 square inches?

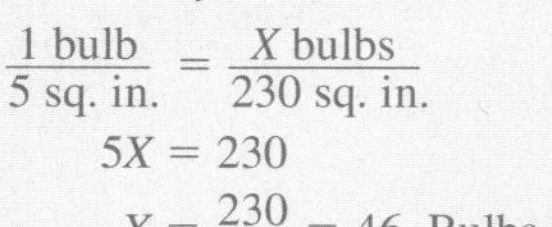

$\frac{1 \text{ bulb}}{5 \text{ sq. in.}} = \frac{X \text{ bulbs}}{230 \text{ sq. in.}}$

$5X = 230$

$X = \frac{230}{5} = \underline{\underline{46}}$ Bulbs

b. If the price is $1.77 for every 2 bulbs, how much will she spend on the flower bulbs?

$\frac{1.77}{2 \text{ bulbs}} = \frac{X}{46 \text{ bulbs}}$

$2X = 46(1.77)$

$2X = 81.42$

$X = \frac{81.42}{2} = \underline{\underline{\$40.71}}$ Total cost of flower bulbs

33. The Pizza Factory makes 30 pizzas every 2 hours to accommodate the lunch crowd.

a. If lunch lasts 3 hours, how many pizzas do they make?

$$\frac{30 \text{ pizzas}}{2 \text{ hours}} = \frac{X}{3 \text{ hours}}$$

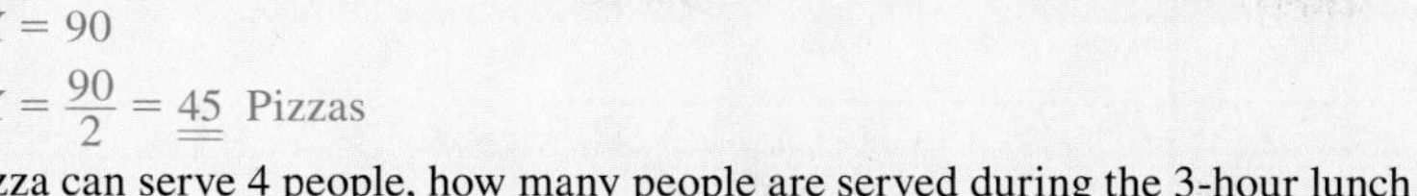

$$2X = 3(30)$$
$$2X = 90$$
$$X = \frac{90}{2} = \underline{\underline{45}} \text{ Pizzas}$$

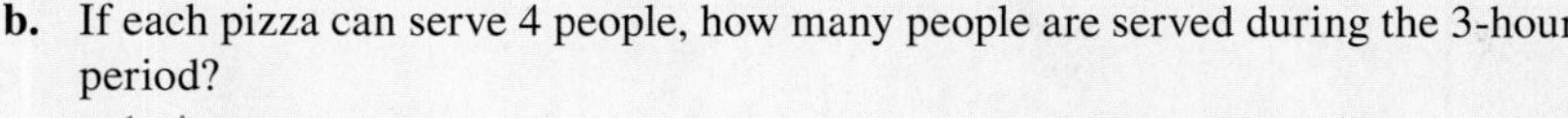

b. If each pizza can serve 4 people, how many people are served during the 3-hour lunch period?

$$\frac{1 \text{ pizza}}{4 \text{ people}} = \frac{45}{X \text{ people}}$$

$$X = 4(45) = \underline{\underline{180}} \text{ People served}$$

CHAPTER 5

Name ____________

Class ____________

Answers

33. a. 45 Pizzas

b. 180 People served

34. 20 pound bag at $1.93 per pound

BUSINESS DECISION DETERMINING THE "BEST BUY"

34. One special type of ratio is known as a *rate*. A rate is a ratio that compares two quantities that have different units such as miles per hour, calories per serving, pounds per square inch, or price per unit. In consumer economics, expressing prices as "price per unit" allows us to determine the "best buy" when comparing various shopping choices. All else being equal, the best buy is the choice with the *lowest* price per unit (unit price).

Donna Kelsch is comparing dry cat food brands for her cats Nicki and Nasty. If Nicki and Nasty's favorite, Funny Fish, comes in the three sizes as listed below, which size is the best buy? Hint: Determine the unit price for each size. Round to the nearest cent, if necessary.

Size	Price	Unit Price
5 pounds	$12.25	$2.45
10 pounds	$21.90	$2.19
20 pounds	$38.50	$1.93

Unit Prices: $\frac{12.25}{5} = \$2.45$

$\frac{21.90}{10} = \$2.19$

$\frac{38.50}{20} = 1.925 = \$1.93$

The best buy is the <u>20-pound bag at $1.93 per pound</u>

COLLABORATIVE LEARNING ACTIVITY

Using Formulas in Business

Have each member of the team speak with someone in one of the following professions to determine how they use standardized formulas in their business.

a. Store owner or manager

b. Real estate or insurance salesperson

c. Advertising or marketing manager

d. Production manager

e. Accountant

f. Banker

g. Additional choice: ____________

CHAPTER 6

Percents and Their Applications in Business

PERFORMANCE OBJECTIVES

Section I Understanding and Converting Percents

Section II Using the Percentage Formula to Solve Business Problems

Section III Solving Other Business Problems Involving Percents

UNDERSTANDING AND CONVERTING PERCENTS

SECTION I 6

Percents are commonly used in retailing to advertise discounts.

It takes only a glance at the business section of a newspaper or an annual report of a company to see how extensively percents are applied in business. Percents are the primary way of measuring change among business variables. For example, a business might report "revenue is up 6% this year" or "expenses have been cut by 2.3% this month." Interest rates, commissions, and many taxes are expressed in percent form. You may have heard phrases like these: "Sunnyside Bank charged 12% on the loan," "A real estate broker made 5% commission on the sale of the property," or "The state charges a $6\frac{1}{2}\%$ sales tax." Even price changes are frequently advertised as percents, "Sears Dishwasher Sale—All Models, 25% off!"

To this point, we have learned that fractions and decimals are ways of representing parts of a whole. Percents are another way of expressing quantity with relation to a whole. **Percent** means *per hundred or parts per hundred* and is represented by the **percent sign**, %.

Percents are numbers equal to a fraction with a denominator of 100. Five percent, for example, means five parts out of 100 and may be written in the following ways:

5 percent   5%   5 hundredths $\frac{5}{100}$ .05

percent A way of representing the parts of a whole. Percent means *per hundred* or *parts per hundred.*

percent sign The symbol, %, used to represent percents. For example, 1 percent would be written 1%.

Before performing any mathematical calculations with percents, they must be converted to either decimals or fractions. Although this function is performed automatically by the percent key on a calculator, Section I of this chapter covers the procedures for making these conversions manually. Sections II and III introduce you to some important applications of percents in business.

CONVERTING PERCENTS TO DECIMALS AND DECIMALS TO PERCENTS

6-1

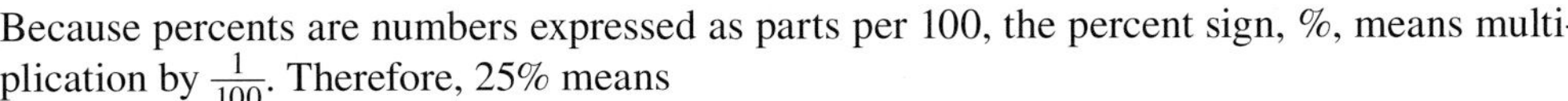

Because percents are numbers expressed as parts per 100, the percent sign, %, means multiplication by $\frac{1}{100}$. Therefore, 25% means

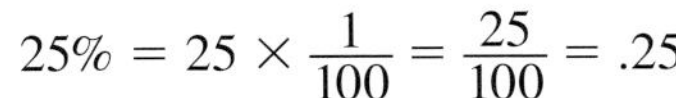

$$25\% = 25 \times \frac{1}{100} = \frac{25}{100} = .25$$

STEPS FOR CONVERTING A PERCENT TO A DECIMAL

Step 1. Remove the percent sign.

Step 2. Divide by 100.

Note: If the percent is a fraction, such as $\frac{3}{8}\%$, or a mixed number, such as $4\frac{3}{4}\%$, first change the fraction to a decimal, then follow Steps 1 and 2 above.

$$\frac{3}{8}\% = .375\% = .00375 \qquad 4\frac{3}{4}\% = 4.75\% = .0475$$

Note: If the percent is a fraction such as $\frac{2}{3}\%$, which converts to a repeating decimal, .66666, round the decimal to hundredths, .67, then follow Steps 1 and 2 above.

$$\frac{2}{3}\% = .67\% = .0067$$

Learning Tip

To divide a number by 100, move the decimal point two places to the left. Add zeros as needed.

Remember, if there is no decimal point, it is understood to be to the right of the digit in the ones place. (24 = 24.)

TEACHING TIP

Remind students that converting a percent that contains a fraction into a decimal is a **two-part process**. First the fraction must be changed to a decimal, then the percent should be converted.

Typically, students convert the fraction to a decimal, remove the percent sign, but forget to move the decimal point. For example, they would change $\frac{3}{8}\%$ to .375 instead of .00375.

EXAMPLE 1 CONVERTING PERCENTS TO DECIMALS

Convert the following percents to decimals.

a. 44% b. 233% c. 56.4% d. .68% e. $18\frac{1}{4}\%$ f. $\frac{1}{8}\%$ g. $9\frac{1}{3}\%$

SOLUTION STRATEGY

Remove the percent sign and move the decimal point two places to the left.

a. 44% = .44 b. 233% = 2.33 c. 56.4% = .564 d. .68% = .0068

e. $18\frac{1}{4}\%$ = 18.25% = .1825 f. $\frac{1}{8}\%$ = .125% = .00125 g. $9\frac{1}{3}\%$ = 9.33% = .0933

TRY IT EXERCISE 1

Convert the following percents to decimals.

a. 27% b. 472% c. 93.7% d. .81% e. $12\frac{3}{4}\%$ f. $\frac{7}{8}\%$

CHECK YOUR ANSWERS WITH THE SOLUTIONS ON PAGE 196.

STEPS FOR CONVERTING A DECIMAL OR WHOLE NUMBER TO A PERCENT

Step 1. Multiply by 100.

Step 2. Write a percent sign after the number.

Step 3. If there are fractions involved, such as $\frac{3}{4}$, convert them to decimals first, then proceed with Steps 1 and 2 above.

$$\frac{3}{4} = .75 = 75\%$$

Learning Tip

To multiply a number by 100, move the decimal point two places to the right. Add zeros as needed. As a "navigational aid" to the direction of the decimal point, consider the words *decimal* and *percent* as written alphabetically, with "decimal" preceding "percent."

- When converting from decimal to percent, the decimal moves **right**

  decimal ⟶ percent

- When converting from percent to decimal, the decimal moves **left**

  decimal ⟵ percent

EXAMPLE 2 CONVERTING DECIMALS TO PERCENTS

Convert the following decimals or whole numbers to percents.

a. .5 b. 3.7 c. .044 d. $.09\frac{3}{5}$ e. 7 f. $6\frac{1}{2}$

SOLUTION STRATEGY

Move the decimal point two places to the right and add a percent sign.

a. .5 = 50% b. 3.7 = 370% c. .044 = 4.4%

d. $.09\frac{3}{5}$ = .096 = 9.6% e. 7 = 700% f. $6\frac{1}{2}$ = 6.5 = 650%

TRY IT EXERCISE 2

Convert the following decimals or whole numbers to percents.

a. .8 b. 1.4 c. .0023 d. $.016\frac{2}{5}$ e. 19 f. $.57\frac{2}{3}$

CHECK YOUR ANSWERS WITH THE SOLUTIONS ON PAGE 196.

CONVERTING PERCENTS TO FRACTIONS AND FRACTIONS TO PERCENTS

STEPS FOR CONVERTING PERCENTS TO FRACTIONS

Step 1. Remove the percent sign.

Step 2. (*If the percent is a whole number*) Write a fraction with the percent as the numerator and 100 as the denominator. If that fraction is improper, change it to a mixed number. Reduce the fraction to lowest terms.

or

Step 2. (*If the percent is a fraction*) Multiply the number by $\frac{1}{100}$ and reduce to lowest terms.

or

Step 2. (*If the percent is a decimal*) Convert it to a fraction and multiply by $\frac{1}{100}$. Reduce to lowest terms.

TEACHING TIP
Remind students that multiplying a number by $\frac{1}{100}$ is the same as dividing by 100.

EXAMPLE 3 CONVERTING PERCENTS TO FRACTIONS

Convert the following percents to reduced fractions, mixed numbers, or whole numbers.

a. 3% b. 57% c. $2\frac{1}{2}\%$ d. 150% e. 4.5% f. 600%

SOLUTION STRATEGY

a. $3\% = \frac{3}{100}$

b. $57\% = \frac{57}{100}$

c. $2\frac{1}{2}\% = \frac{5}{2} \times \frac{1}{100} = \frac{5}{200} = \frac{1}{40}$

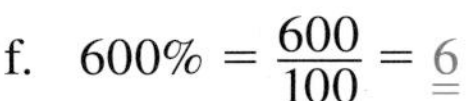

d. $150\% = \frac{150}{100} = 1\frac{50}{100} = 1\frac{1}{2}$

e. $4.5\% = 4\frac{1}{2}\% = \frac{9}{2} \times \frac{1}{100} = \frac{9}{200}$

f. $600\% = \frac{600}{100} = 6$

TRY IT EXERCISE 3

Convert the following percents to reduced fractions, mixed numbers, or whole numbers.

a. 9% b. 23% c. 75% d. 225% e. 8.7% f. 1,000%

CHECK YOUR ANSWERS WITH THE SOLUTIONS ON PAGE 196.

STEPS FOR CONVERTING FRACTIONS TO PERCENTS

Step 1. Change the fraction to a decimal by dividing the numerator by the denominator.

Step 2. Multiply by 100. (Move the decimal point two places to the right. Add zeros as needed.)

Step 3. Write a percent sign after the number.

Learning Tip

Use the % key on your calculator to save the step of multiplying by 100.

For example: $\frac{44}{50} = .88 = 88\%$.

Calculator sequence:

44 [÷] 50 [%] = 88

Note: Scientific and business calculators require pushing the [=] button after the % key; common arithmetic calculators do not.

EXAMPLE 4 CONVERTING FRACTIONS TO PERCENTS

Convert the following fractions or mixed numbers to percents.

a. $\frac{1}{10}$ b. $\frac{69}{100}$ c. $\frac{15}{4}$ d. $4\frac{3}{8}$ e. $\frac{18}{25}$ f. $13\frac{1}{2}$

SOLUTION STRATEGY

Change the fractions to decimals by dividing the denominator into the numerator, then move the decimal point two places to the right and add a percent sign.

a. $\frac{1}{10} = .10 = \underline{\underline{10\%}}$ b. $\frac{69}{100} = .69 = \underline{\underline{69\%}}$ c. $\frac{15}{4} = 3\frac{3}{4} = 3.75 = \underline{\underline{375\%}}$

d. $4\frac{3}{8} = 4.375 = \underline{\underline{437.5\%}}$ e. $\frac{18}{25} = .72 = \underline{\underline{72\%}}$ f. $13\frac{1}{2} = 13.5 = \underline{\underline{1350\%}}$

TEACHING TIP

As a quick review, have students complete the following chart:

Fraction	Decimal	Percent
$\frac{43}{800}$	*.05375*	$5\frac{3}{8}\%$
$2\frac{16}{25}$	**2.64**	*264%*
$\frac{9}{16}$	*.5625*	*56.25%*

TRY IT EXERCISE 4

Convert the following fractions or mixed numbers to percents.

a. $\frac{1}{5}$ b. $\frac{70}{200}$ c. $\frac{23}{5}$ d. $6\frac{9}{10}$ e. $\frac{45}{54}$ f. $140\frac{1}{8}$

CHECK YOUR ANSWERS WITH THE SOLUTIONS ON PAGES 196.

SECTION I Review Exercises

Convert the following percents to decimals.

1. 28% $\underline{\underline{.28}}$
2. 76% $\underline{\underline{.76}}$
3. 13.4% $\underline{\underline{.134}}$
4. 121% $\underline{\underline{1.21}}$
5. 42.68% $\underline{\underline{.4268}}$
6. $6\frac{1}{2}\%$ 6.5% = $\underline{\underline{.065}}$
7. .02% $\underline{\underline{.0002}}$
8. $\frac{3}{5}\%$ .6% = $\underline{\underline{.006}}$
9. $125\frac{1}{6}\%$ 125.17% = $\underline{\underline{1.2517}}$
10. 2,000% $\underline{\underline{20.0}}$

Convert the following decimals or whole numbers to percents.

11. 3.5

 350%

12. .11

 11%

13. 46

 4,600%

14. $.34\frac{1}{2}$

 $.345 = 34.5\%$

15. .00935

 .935%

16. $.9\frac{3}{4}$

 $.975 = 97.5\%$

17. 164

 16,400%

18. .04

 4%

19. 5.33

 533%

20. $1.15\frac{5}{8}$

 $1.15625 = 115.625\%$

CLASSROOM ACTIVITY

From the local newspaper, have students bring to class examples of advertisements and news stories that contain percents. Use these as the foundation for a discussion of percents and their variety of forms and uses.

Have students note how these percents are rounded in various situations. Point out that percents are rounded in the same way as whole numbers and decimals. For example, 47.486% rounded to tenths would be 47.5%.

Convert the following percents to reduced fractions, mixed numbers, or whole numbers.

21. 5%

 $\frac{5}{100} = \frac{1}{20}$

22. 75%

 $\frac{75}{100} = \frac{3}{4}$

23. 89%

 $\frac{89}{100}$

24. 230%

 $\frac{230}{100} = 2\frac{30}{100} = 2\frac{3}{10}$

25. 38%

 $\frac{38}{100} = \frac{19}{50}$

26. 37.5%

 $37\frac{1}{2} \times \frac{1}{100} = \frac{75}{2} \times \frac{1}{100} = \frac{75}{200} = \frac{3}{8}$

27. $62\frac{1}{2}\%$

 $62\frac{1}{2} \times \frac{1}{100} = \frac{125}{2} \times \frac{1}{100} = \frac{125}{200} = \frac{5}{8}$

28. 450%

 $\frac{450}{100} = 4\frac{50}{100} = 4\frac{1}{2}$

29. 125%

 $\frac{125}{100} = 1\frac{25}{100} = 1\frac{1}{4}$

30. .8%

 $\frac{8}{10} \times \frac{1}{100} = \frac{8}{1{,}000} = \frac{1}{125}$

Convert the following fractions or mixed numbers to percents.

31. $\frac{3}{4}$

 $.75 = 75\%$

32. $\frac{1}{8}$

 $.125 = 12.5\%$

33. $\frac{12}{5}$

 $2\frac{2}{5} = 2.4 = 240\%$

34. $6\frac{3}{10}$

 $6.3 = 630\%$

35. $\frac{125}{100}$

 $1\frac{1}{4} = 1.25 = 125\%$

36. $\frac{78}{24}$

 $3.25 = 325\%$

37. $\frac{3}{16}$

 $.1875 = 18.75\%$

38. $4\frac{1}{5}$

 $4.2 = 420\%$

39. $\frac{35}{100}$

 $.35 = 35\%$

40. $\frac{375}{1{,}000}$

 $.375 = 37.5\%$

Use the bar chart, U.S. Market Share of Pet Food and Treats, to find the decimal and reduced fraction equivalent for Exercises 41–45.

	Company	Decimal	Reduced fraction
41.	Nestle Purina	.32	$\frac{8}{25}$
42.	Mars	.12	$\frac{3}{25}$
43.	Iams	.11	$\frac{11}{100}$
44.	Hills	.10	$\frac{1}{10}$
45.	Del Monte	.09	$\frac{9}{100}$

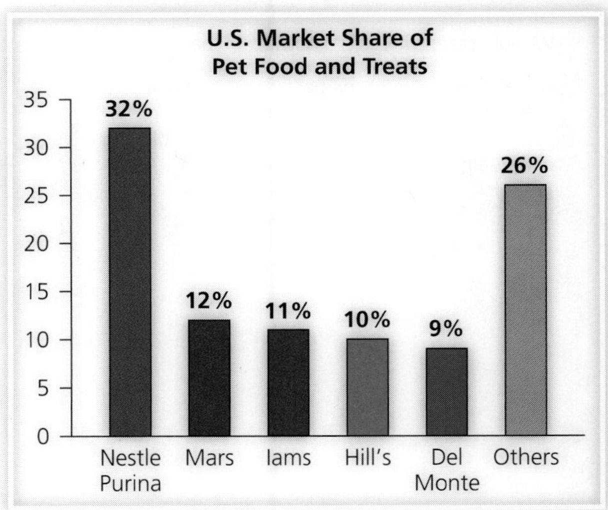

BUSINESS DECISION ENHANCING THE PIE

Disney Dollars

46. You have been asked to make a presentation about The Walt Disney Company. In your research, you locate the accompanying pie chart, which shows Disney revenue, by segment, expressed in billions of dollars.

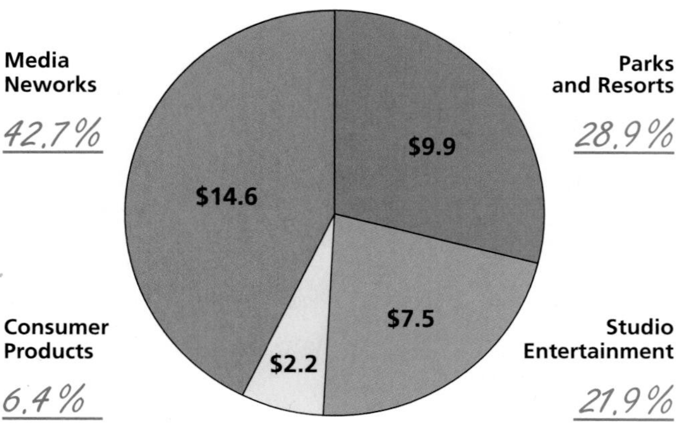

© Disney Enterprises, Inc.

To enhance your presentation, you have decided to convert the dollar amounts to percent, and display both numbers.

a. What is the total revenue?

$34.2 billion

b. For each category, write a fraction with the revenue from that category as the numerator and the total revenue as the denominator.

Media Networks $\frac{14.6}{34.2}$ Parks and Resorts $\frac{9.9}{34.2}$

Consumer Products $\frac{2.2}{34.2}$ Studio Entertainment $\frac{7.5}{34.2}$

c. Convert each fraction from part **b** to a percent, rounded to a tenth. Enter your answers on the red lines in the chart.

Media Networks	Parks and Resorts	Consumer Products	Studio Entertainment
42.7%	28.9%	6.4%	21.9%

SECTION II USING THE PERCENTAGE FORMULA TO SOLVE BUSINESS PROBLEMS

base The variable of the percentage formula that represents 100%, or the whole thing.

portion The variable of the percentage formula that represents a part of the base.

rate The variable of the percentage formula that defines how much or what part the portion is of the base. The rate is the variable with the percent sign.

Now that we have learned to manipulate percents, let's look at some of their practical applications in business. Percent problems involve the use of equations known as the percentage formulas. These formulas have three variables: the **base**, the **portion**, and the **rate**. In business situations, two of the variables will be given and are the *knowns*; one of the variables will be the *unknown*.

Once the variables have been properly identified, the equations are simple to solve. The variables have the following characteristics, which should be used to help identify them:

BASE: The base is the number that represents 100%, or the *whole thing*. It is the starting point, the beginning, or total value of something. The base is often preceded by the word *of* in the written statement of the situation because it is multiplied by the rate.

PORTION: The portion is the number that represents a *part* of the base. The portion is always in the same terms as the base. For example, if the base is dollars, the portion is dollars; if the base is people, the portion is people; if the base is production units, the portion will be production units. The portion often has a "unique characteristic" that is being measured or compared with the base. For example, if the base is the total number of cars in a parking lot, the portion could be the part of the total cars that are convertibles (the unique characteristic).

RATE: The rate is easily identified. It is the variable with the *percent sign* or the word *percent*. It defines what part the portion is of the base. If the rate is less than 100%, the portion is less than the base. If the rate is 100%, the portion is equal to the base. If the rate is more than 100%, the portion is greater than the base.

The following percentage formulas are used to solve percent problems:

Portion = Rate × Base	$P = R \times B$
Rate = $\dfrac{\textbf{Portion}}{\textbf{Base}}$	$R = \dfrac{P}{B}$
Base = $\dfrac{\textbf{Portion}}{\textbf{Rate}}$	$B = \dfrac{P}{R}$

STEPS FOR SOLVING PERCENTAGE PROBLEMS

Step 1. Identify the two knowns and the unknown.

Step 2. Choose the formula that solves for that unknown.

Step 3. Solve the equation by substituting the known values for the letters in the formula.

Hint: By remembering the one basic formula, $P = R \times B$, you can derive the other two by using your knowledge of solving equations from Chapter 5. Because multiplication is indicated, we isolate the unknown by performing the inverse or opposite operation, division.

To solve for rate, R, divide both sides of the equation by B:

$$P = R \times B \longrightarrow \frac{P}{B} = \frac{R \times \cancel{B}}{\cancel{B}} \longrightarrow \frac{P}{B} = R$$

To solve for base, B, divide both sides of the equation by R:

$$P = R \times B \longrightarrow \frac{P}{R} = \frac{\cancel{R} \times B}{\cancel{R}} \longrightarrow \frac{P}{R} = B$$

Another method for remembering the percentage formulas is by using the Magic Triangle.

The Magic Triangle

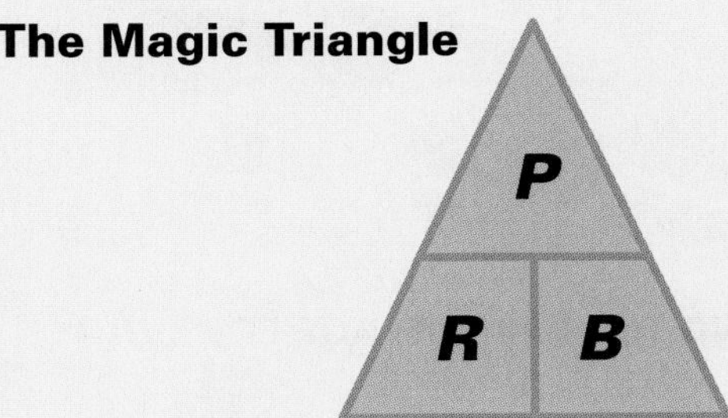

The triangle is divided into three sections, representing the portion, rate, and base. By circling or covering the letter in the triangle that corresponds to the *unknown* of the problem, the triangle will "magically" reveal the correct formula to use.

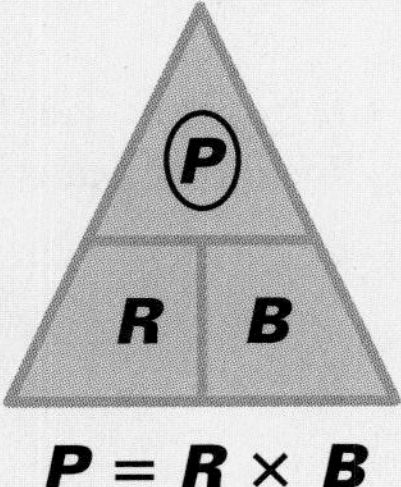

$P = R \times B$

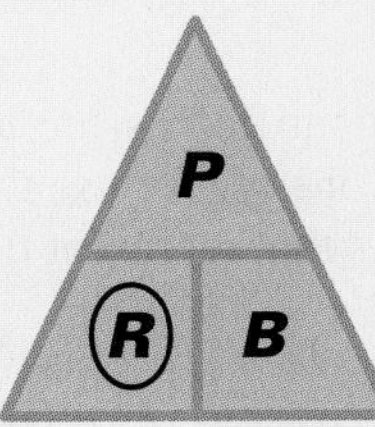

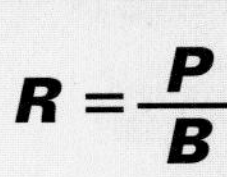

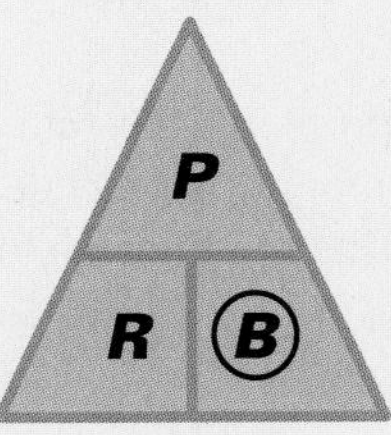

$B = \dfrac{P}{R}$

Don't confuse the word *percentage* with the percent, or rate. The *percentage* means the portion, not the rate.

6-1

SOLVING FOR THE PORTION

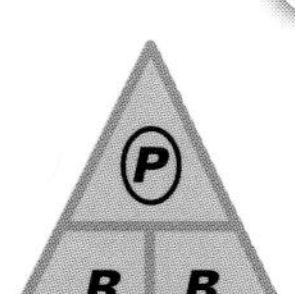
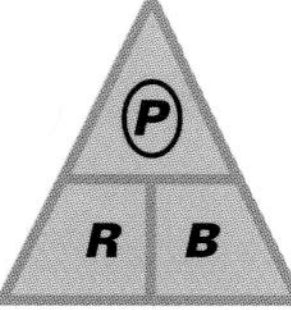

$P = R \times B$

Remember, the portion is a part of the whole and will always be in the same terms as the base. It is found by multiplying the rate times the base: $P = R \times B$. The following examples will demonstrate solving for the portion.

EXAMPLE 5 SOLVING FOR THE PORTION

What is the portion if the base is $400 and the rate is 12%?

SOLUTION STRATEGY

Substitute the knowns for the letters in the formula, Portion = Rate × Base. In this problem, 12% is the rate, and $400 is the base. Do not forget to convert the percent (rate) to a decimal by deleting the % sign and moving the decimal point two places to the left (12% = .12).

$$P = R \times B$$

$$P = 12\% \times 400 = .12 \times 400 = 48$$

Portion = $48

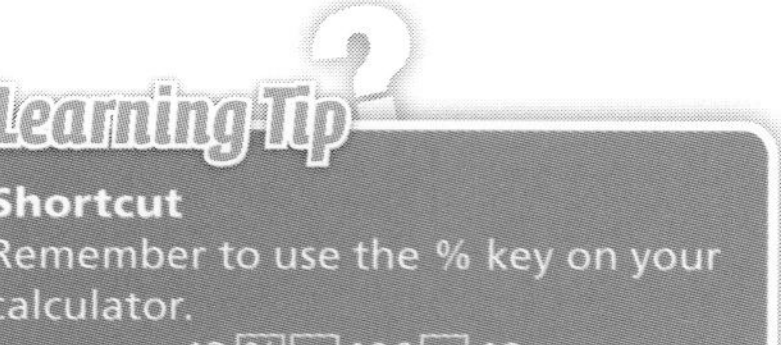

Learning Tip

Shortcut
Remember to use the % key on your calculator.
12 [%] [×] 400 [=] 48

TRY IT EXERCISE 5

Solve the following for the portion.

6-2

What is the portion if the base is 980 and the rate is 55%?

CHECK YOUR ANSWER WITH THE SOLUTION ON PAGE 196.

EXAMPLE 6 USING THE PERCENTAGE FORMULA

What number is 43.5% of 250?

SOLUTION STRATEGY

In this problem, the rate is easily identified as the term with the % sign. The base, or whole amount, is preceded by the word *of.* We use the formula Portion = Rate × Base, substituting the knowns for the letters that represent them.

$$P = R \times B$$

$$P = 43.5\% \times 250 = .435 \times 250 = 108.75$$

108.75

TRY IT EXERCISE 6

Solve the following for the portion.

What number is 72% of 3,200?

CHECK YOUR ANSWER WITH THE SOLUTION ON PAGE 196.

EXAMPLE 7 USING THE PERCENTAGE FORMULA

Grandville Industries produced 6,000 stoves last week. If 2% of them were defective, how many defective stoves were produced?

SOLUTION STRATEGY

To solve this problem, we must first identify the variables. Because 2% has the percent sign, it is the rate. The terms are stoves; the total number of stoves (6,000) is the base. The unique characteristic of the portion, the unknown, is that they were defective.

$$P = R \times B$$

$$P = 2\% \times 6{,}000 = .02 \times 6{,}000 = 120$$

$$\underline{\underline{120 = \text{Number of defective stoves last week}}}$$

TRY IT EXERCISE 7

Solve the following for the portion.

a. Gulf Stream Industries has 1,250 employees. 16% constitute the sales staff. How many employees are in sales?
b. If Sunshine Savings & Loan requires a 15% down payment on a mortgage loan, what is the down payment needed to finance a $148,500 home?

CHECK YOUR ANSWERS WITH THE SOLUTIONS ON PAGE 196.

SOLVING FOR THE RATE

The rate is the variable that describes what part of the base is represented by the portion. It is *always* the term with the percent sign. When solving for the rate, your answer will be a decimal. Be sure to convert the decimal to a percent by moving the decimal point two places to the right and adding a percent sign. We use the formula

$$\text{Rate} = \frac{\text{Portion}}{\text{Base}} \quad \text{or} \quad R = \frac{P}{B}$$

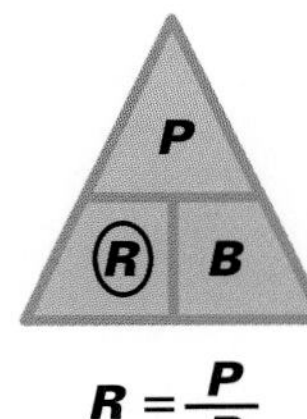

The following examples demonstrate solving for the rate.

Remember, the rate expresses "what part" the portion is of the base.

- When the rate is less than 100%, the portion is *less* than the base.
- When the rate is more than 100%, the portion is *more* than the base.
- When the rate is 100%, the portion *equals* the base.

EXAMPLE 8 SOLVING FOR THE RATE

What is the rate if the base is 160 and the portion is 40?

SOLUTION STRATEGY

Substitute the knowns for the letters in the formula.

$$\text{Rate} = \frac{\text{Portion}}{\text{Base}}$$

$$R = \frac{P}{B}$$

$$R = \frac{40}{160} = .25 = 25\%$$

$$\underline{\underline{\text{Rate} = 25\%}}$$

TRY IT EXERCISE 8

Solve the following for the rate. Round to the nearest tenth when necessary.

What is the rate if the base is 21 and the portion is 9?

CHECK YOUR ANSWER WITH THE SOLUTION ON PAGE 196.

EXAMPLE 9 USING THE PERCENTAGE FORMULA

What percent of 700 is 56?

SOLUTION STRATEGY

This problem asks what percent, indicating that the rate is the unknown. The 700 is preceded by the word *of* and is therefore the base. The 56 is part of the base and is therefore the portion. Once again we use the formula $R = P \div B$, substituting the knowns for the letters that represent them.

$$R = \frac{P}{B}$$

$$R = \frac{56}{700} = .08 = 8\%$$

$$\underline{\underline{8\%}}$$

TRY IT EXERCISE 9

Solve the following for the rate. Round to the nearest tenth when necessary.

67 is what percent of 142?

CHECK YOUR ANSWER WITH THE SOLUTION ON PAGE 196.

EXAMPLE 10 USING THE PERCENTAGE FORMULA

Pet Supermarket placed an order for 560 fish tanks. If only 490 tanks were delivered, what percent of the order was received?

SOLUTION STRATEGY

The first step in solving this problem is to identify the variables. The statement asks "what percent," therefore, the rate is the unknown. Because 560 is the total order, it is the base; 490 is a part of the total and is therefore the portion. Note that the base and the portion are in the same terms, fish tanks; the unique characteristic of the portion is that 490 tanks *were delivered.*

$$R = \frac{P}{B}$$

$$R = \frac{490}{560} = .875 = 87.5\%$$

87.5% = Percent of the order received

Note: Because 560 is the total order, it is the base, and therefore represents 100% of the order. If 87.5% of the tanks were received, then 12.5% of the tanks were *not* received.

$$100\% - 87.5\% = 12.5\% \text{ not received}$$

TRY IT EXERCISE 10

Solve the following for the rate. Round to the nearest tenth when necessary.

a. A contract called for 18,000 square feet of tile to be installed in a shopping mall. In the first week 5,400 feet of tile was completed.

   What percent of the job has been completed?

   What percent of the job remains?

b. During a recent sale, Image Makers, a boutique, sold $5,518 in men's business suits. If total sales amounted to $8,900, what percent of the sales were suits?

CHECK YOUR ANSWERS WITH THE SOLUTIONS ON PAGE 196.

CLASSROOM ACTIVITY

Have students list the names of between five and ten family members or friends. Next, have them calculate

- what percent are male and what percent are female—rounded to a whole percent.
- what percent are children and what percent are adults—rounded to a tenth percent.
- what percent live in-state and what percent live out of state—rounded to a hundredth percent.

To illustrate possible rounding error, have them add up the percents in each category. Note how many did not add up to exactly 100%.

TEACHING TIP

Remind students that by knowing what percent of the tanks *were* received, they can easily find what percent were *not* received using the "complement method"; subtracting from 100%. The alternate method is to solve for the rate using the percentage formula with the number of tanks *not* received as the portion.

6-3

SOLVING FOR THE BASE

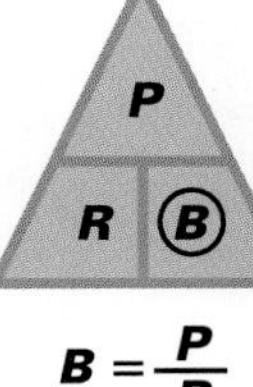

$$B = \frac{P}{R}$$

To solve business situations in which the whole or total amount is the unknown, we use the formula

$$\text{Base} = \frac{\text{Portion}}{\text{Rate}} \quad \text{or} \quad B = \frac{P}{R}$$

The following examples illustrate solving for the base.

EXAMPLE 11 SOLVING FOR THE BASE

What is the base if the rate is 21% and the portion is 58.8?

SOLUTION STRATEGY

In this basic problem, we simply substitute the known values for the letters in the formula. Remember, the rate must be converted from a percent to a decimal.

$$B = \frac{P}{R}$$

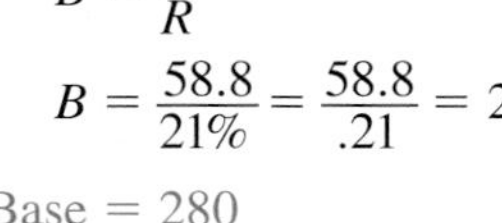

$$B = \frac{58.8}{21\%} = \frac{58.8}{.21} = 280$$

$$\underline{\underline{\text{Base} = 280}}$$

TRY IT EXERCISE 11

Solve the following for the base. Round to hundredths or the nearest cent when necessary.

What is the base if the rate is 40% and the portion is 690?

CHECK YOUR ANSWER WITH THE SOLUTION ON PAGE 196.

Learning Tip

Percentage problems can also be solved by using proportion. Set up the proportion

$$\frac{\text{Rate}}{100} = \frac{\text{Portion}}{\text{Base}}$$

and cross-multiply to solve for the unknown, For example:

At a Circuit City store last week, 70 televisions were sold with VCRs built in. If this represents 20% of all TVs sold, how many total TVs were sold?

$$\frac{20}{100} = \frac{70}{\text{base (total TVs)}}$$

$$20b = 100(70)$$

$$20b = 7{,}000$$

$$b = 350 \text{ Total TVs}$$

EXAMPLE 12 USING THE PERCENTAGE FORMULA

75 is 15% of what number?

SOLUTION STRATEGY

Remember, the base is usually identified as the value preceded by "of" in the statement. In this case, that value is the unknown. Because 15 has the percent sign, it is the rate and 75 is the part of the whole, or the portion.

$$B = \frac{P}{R}$$

$$B = \frac{75}{15\%} = \frac{75}{.15} = 500$$

$$\underline{\underline{500}}$$

TRY IT EXERCISE 12

Solve the following for the base. Round to hundredths or the nearest cent when necessary.

$550 is 88% of what amount?

CHECK YOUR ANSWER WITH THE SOLUTION ON PAGE 196.

EXAMPLE 13 USING THE PERCENTAGE FORMULA

Champs Sporting Goods reports that 28% of total shoe sales are from Nike products. If last week's Nike sales were $15,400, what was the total amount of sales for the week?

SOLUTION STRATEGY

In this problem, the total amount of sales, the base, is unknown. Because 28% has the percent sign, it is the rate, and $15,400 is the portion. Note again, the portion is in the same terms as the base, dollar sales; however, the unique characteristic is that the portion represents Nike sales.

$$B = \frac{P}{R}$$

$$B = \frac{15{,}400}{28\%} = \frac{15{,}400}{.28} = 55{,}000$$

$55,000 Total sales for the week

TRY IT EXERCISE 13

Solve the following for the base. Round to hundredths or the nearest cent when necessary.

a. In a machine shop, 35% of the motor repairs are for broken shafts. If 126 motors had broken shafts last month, how many total motors were repaired?

b. At Office Solutions, 75% of the copy paper sold is letter size. If 3,420 reams of letter size were sold, how many total reams of copy paper were sold?

CHECK YOUR ANSWERS WITH THE SOLUTIONS ON PAGE 197.

6-4

Review Exercises

SECTION II

Solve the following for the portion. Round to hundredths when necessary.

Solution Transparencies

1. 15% of 380 is ________
   $P = R \times B = .15 \times 380 = \underline{\underline{57}}$

2. 3.6% of 1,800 is ________
   $P = R \times B = .036 \times 1800 = \underline{\underline{64.8}}$

3. 200% of 45 is ________
   $P = R \times B = 2 \times 45 = \underline{\underline{90}}$

4. $5\frac{1}{2}\%$ of $600 is ________
   $P = R \times B = .055 \times 600 = \underline{\underline{33}}$

5. What is the portion if the base is 450 and the rate is 19%?
   $P = R \times B = .19 \times 450 = \underline{\underline{85.5}}$

6. What is the portion if the base is 1,650 and the rate is 150%?
   $P = R \times B = 1.5 \times 1{,}650 = \underline{\underline{2{,}475}}$

7. What number is 35.2% of 184?
   $P = R \times B = .352 \times 184 = \underline{\underline{64.77}}$

8. What number is .8% of 500?
   $P = R \times B = .008 \times 500 = \underline{\underline{4}}$

9. What number is $15\frac{4}{5}\%$ of 360?
   $P = R \times B = .158 \times 360 = \underline{\underline{56.88}}$

10. What number is 258% of 2,500?
   $P = R \times B = 2.58 \times 2{,}500 = \underline{\underline{6{,}450}}$

Solve the following for the rate. Round to the nearest tenth of a percent when necessary.

11. 40 is ______% of 125
    $R = \frac{P}{B} = \frac{40}{125} = .32 = \underline{\underline{32\%}}$

12. ______% of 50 is 23
    $R = \frac{P}{B} = \frac{23}{50} = .46 = \underline{\underline{46\%}}$

13. 600 is ______% of 240
    $R = \frac{P}{B} = \frac{600}{240} = 2.50 = \underline{\underline{250\%}}$

14. What is the rate if the base is 288 and the portion is 50?

$R = \frac{P}{B} = \frac{50}{288} = .1736 = \underline{\underline{17.4\%}}$

15. What is the rate if the portion is 21.6 and the base is 160?

$R = \frac{P}{B} = \frac{21.6}{160} = .135 = \underline{\underline{13.5\%}}$

16. What is the rate if the base is \$3,450 and the portion is \$290?

$R = \frac{P}{B} = \frac{290}{3{,}450} = .0840 = \underline{\underline{8.4\%}}$

17. What percent of 77 is 23?

$R = \frac{P}{B} = \frac{23}{77} = .2987 = \underline{\underline{29.9\%}}$

18. What percent of 1,600 is 1,900?

$R = \frac{P}{B} = \frac{1{,}900}{1{,}600} = 1.1875 = \underline{\underline{118.8\%}}$

19. 68 is what percent of 262?

$R = \frac{P}{B} = \frac{68}{262} = .2595 = \underline{\underline{26.0\%}}$

20. \$7.80 is what percent of \$58.60?

$R = \frac{P}{B} = \frac{7.80}{58.60} = .1331 = \underline{\underline{13.3\%}}$

Solve the following for the base. Round to hundredths when necessary.

21. 69 is 15% of ______

$B = \frac{P}{R} = \frac{69}{.15} = \underline{\underline{460}}$

22. 360 is 150% of ______

$B = \frac{P}{R} = \frac{360}{1.5} = \underline{\underline{240}}$

23. 6.45 is $18\frac{1}{2}\%$ of ______

$B = \frac{P}{R} = \frac{6.45}{.185} = \underline{\underline{34.86}}$

24. What is the base if the rate is 16.8% and the portion is 451?

$B = \frac{P}{R} = \frac{451}{.168} = \underline{\underline{2{,}684.52}}$

25. What is the base if the portion is 10 and the rate is $2\frac{3}{4}\%$?

$B = \frac{P}{R} = \frac{10}{.0275} = \underline{\underline{363.64}}$

26. What is the base if the portion is \$4,530 and the rate is 35%?

$B = \frac{P}{R} = \frac{4{,}530}{.35} = \underline{\underline{\$12{,}942.86}}$

27. 60 is 15% of what number?

$B = \frac{P}{R} = \frac{60}{.15} = \underline{\underline{400}}$

28. 160 is 130% of what number?

$B = \frac{P}{R} = \frac{160}{1.3} = \underline{\underline{123.08}}$

29. \$46.50 is $86\frac{2}{3}\%$ of what number?

$B = \frac{P}{R} = \frac{46.50}{.8667} = \underline{\underline{\$53.65}}$

30. .55 is 21.4% of what number?

$B = \frac{P}{R} = \frac{.55}{.214} = \underline{\underline{2.57}}$

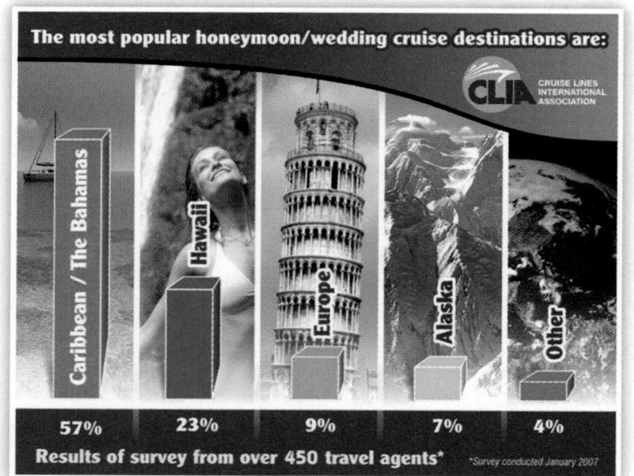

© CLIA/PR Newswire Photo Service/NewsCom

Travel Agent

According to the latest data from the U.S. Department of Labor, Bureau of Labor Statistics, travel agents held about 103,000 jobs in 2004 and are found in every part of the country. More than three out of five agents worked for travel agencies. Around 14 percent were self-employed.

Median annual earnings of travel agents were \$27,640. The middle 50 percent earned between \$21,600 and \$35,070. The top 10 percent earned more than \$44,090.

Solve the following word problems for the portion, rate, or base.

31. Claudia Monaco owns 37% of a travel agency.
    a. If the total worth of the business is \$160,000, how much is Claudia's share?

    $P = R \times B = .37 \times 160{,}000 = \underline{\underline{\$59{,}200}}$

    b. Last month Claudia's agency booked \$14,500 in airline fares on Orbit Airline. If Orbit pays agencies a commission of 4.1%, how much commission should the agency receive?

    $P = R \times B$

    $P = 4.1\% \times \$14{,}500$

    $P = 0.041 \times 14{,}500 = \underline{\underline{\$594.50}}$

32. What is the sales tax rate in a state where the tax on a purchase of \$464 is \$25.52?

$R = \frac{P}{B} = \frac{25.52}{464} = .055 = \underline{\underline{5.5\%}}$

33. *The Daily Times* reports that 28% of its advertising is for department stores. If department store advertising amounts to \$46,200, what is the total advertising revenue of the newspaper?

$B = \frac{P}{R} = \frac{46{,}200}{.28} = \underline{\underline{\$165{,}000}}$

34. Sam Pearl works part time for his father's landscaping service. He is paid 7.5% of the firm's profits each month. What will the firm's profits have to be in order for Sam to make $1,200 this month?

    $B = \frac{P}{R} = \frac{1{,}200}{0.075} = \underline{\underline{\$16{,}000}}$ Profit

35. If Rob Winter, a real estate agent, earned $6\frac{1}{2}\%$ commission on the sale of property valued at $210,000, how much was Rob's commission?

    $P = R \times B = .065 \times 210{,}000 = \underline{\underline{\$13{,}650}}$

Use the illustration, The Gas Spectrum, for Exercise 36.

36. a. What percent of the Lamborghini mileage does the Honda get? Round to the nearest whole percent.

    $\frac{66}{13} = 5.0769 = \underline{\underline{508\%}}$

    b. What percent of the Lamborghini price is the Honda price? Round to the nearest tenth of a percent.

    $\frac{19{,}330}{288{,}000} = .0671 = \underline{\underline{6.7\%}}$

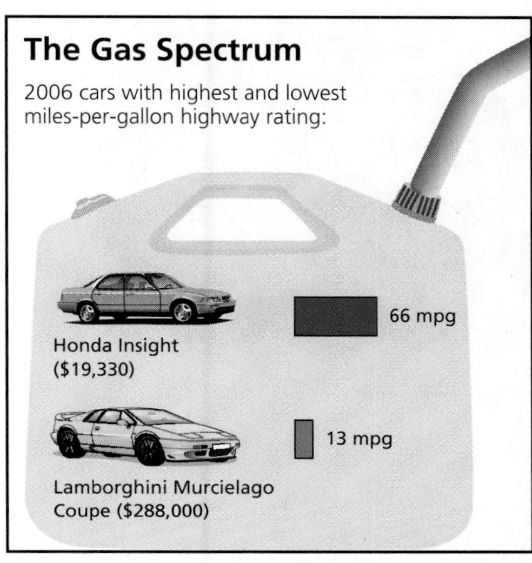

Source: *USA Today*, July 21–23, 2006, p. 1A. Reprinted with permission.

37. Thirty percent of the inventory of a Nine West shoe store is in high heels. If the store has 846 pairs of high heels in stock, how many total pairs of shoes are in the inventory?

    $B = \frac{P}{R} = \frac{846}{.3} = \underline{\underline{2{,}820}}$

38. Friendly Ford advertised a down payment of $1,200 on a Mustang valued at $14,700. What is the percent of the down payment? Round to the nearest tenth of a percent.

    $R = \frac{P}{B} = \frac{1{,}200}{14{,}700} = .0816 = \underline{\underline{8.2\%}}$

39. Lisa Walden, a sales associate for a large company, successfully makes the sale on 40% of her presentations. If she made 25 presentations last week, how many sales did she make?

    $P = R \times B = .4 \times 25 = \underline{\underline{10}}$

40. A quality control process finds 17.2 defects for every 8,600 units of production. What percent of the production is defective?

    $R = \frac{P}{B} = \frac{17.2}{8{,}600} = .002 = \underline{\underline{.2\%}}$

41. The Parker Company employs 68 part-time workers. If this represents 4% of the total work force, how many individuals work for the company?

    $B = \frac{P}{R} = \frac{68}{.04} = \underline{\underline{1{,}700}}$

42. A medical insurance policy requires Ana to pay the first $100 of her hospital expense. The insurance company will then pay 80% of the remaining expense. Ana is expecting a short surgical stay in the hospital, for which she estimates the total bill to be about $4,500. How much will Ana's portion of the bill amount to?

    Remaining expense: $4{,}500 - 100 = \$4{,}400$

    $P = R \times B = 0.8 \times 4{,}400 = \$3{,}520$

    Ana's portion of the bill: $4{,}500 - 3{,}520 = \underline{\underline{\$980}}$

43. A corporation earned $457,800 last year. If its tax rate is $13\frac{3}{8}\%$, how much tax was paid?

    $P = R \times B = .13375 \times 457{,}800 = \underline{\underline{\$61{,}230.75}}$

44. In June, the New York Yankees won 15 games and lost 9. What percent of the games did they win? (*Hint:* Use total games played as the base.)

    Total games = Base = 24 $R = \frac{P}{B} = \frac{15}{24} = .625 = \underline{\underline{62.5\%}}$

Use the pie chart, Cosmic Mutual Fund–Investments, for Exercises 45–46.

45. What is the total amount invested in the Cosmic Mutual Fund?

$5.2 + 3.4 + 8.1 + 15.6 = \underline{\$32.3 \text{ billion}}$

46. What percent does each investment category represent? Round your answers to the nearest tenth of a percent.

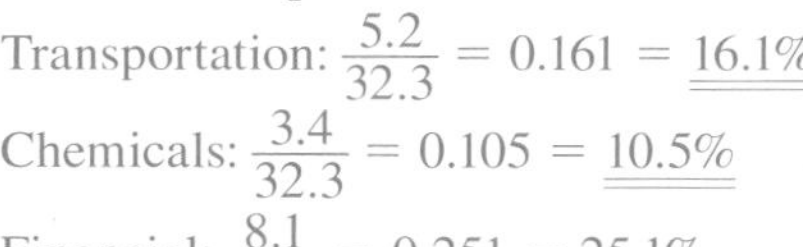

Transportation: $\frac{5.2}{32.3} = 0.161 = \underline{16.1\%}$

Chemicals: $\frac{3.4}{32.3} = 0.105 = \underline{10.5\%}$

Financial: $\frac{8.1}{32.3} = 0.251 = \underline{25.1\%}$

Manufacturing: $\frac{15.6}{32.3} = 0.483 = \underline{48.3\%}$

Cosmic Mutual Fund – Investments
($ billions)

Chemicals $3.4

Transportation $5.2

Financials $8.1

Manufacturing $15.6

47. The Bentley Bobcats have won 80% of their basketball games. If they lost 4 games, how many games have they played?

Won = 80% Lost = $\underline{20\%}$

$B = \frac{P}{R} = \frac{4}{0.2} = \underline{20 \text{ Games played}}$

48. Terry Forman attends a college that charges $1,400 tuition per semester for 12 credit hours of classes. If tuition is raised by 9% next year:

a. How much more will he pay for two semesters of classes, with the same course load?

$P = R \times B = 0.09 \times 1{,}400 = \$126 \times 2 = \underline{\$252 \text{ More}}$

b. If Terry works at a car wash earning $8 per hour and pays 15% in taxes, how many extra hours must he work to make up for the tuition increase? Round to the nearest whole hour.

$P = R \times B = 0.85 \times 8 = \$680$ After-tax earnings

$\frac{252}{6.80} = 37.05 = \underline{37 \text{ Hours}}$

BUSINESS DECISION THE PARTY PLANNER

© Buccina Studios/Photodisc/Getty Images

Nuptial Numbers

According to the Fairchild Bridal Group via Marriott International, Inc., in 2007, over $50 billion was spent in the United States on costs associated with wedding activity. The average cost for a wedding and reception was $22,360.

The average ages of wedding couples were 27 for the bride and 29 for the groom. Approximately 71 percent of all wedding receptions take place at a hotel, country club, or catering facility.

49. You are the catering manager for the Post Hotel. Last Saturday, your staff catered a wedding reception in the main ballroom, during which 152 chicken dinners, 133 steak dinners, and 95 fish dinners were served. All dinners are the same price. The hotel charges "per person" for catered events.

a. What percent of the total meals served was each type of dinner?

Total meals = Base = 380

Steak $R = \frac{P}{B} = \frac{133}{380} = \underline{35\%}$

Chicken $R = \frac{P}{B} = \frac{152}{380} = \underline{40\%}$

Fish $R = \frac{P}{B} = \frac{95}{380} = \underline{25\%}$

b. If $13,300 was charged for all the meals, how much revenue did each type produce?

$P = R \times B$

Chicken $.4 \times 13{,}300 = \underline{\$5{,}320}$

Steak $.35 \times 13{,}300 = \underline{\$4{,}655}$

Fish $.25 \times 13{,}300 = \underline{\$3{,}325}$

c. If a 20% price increase goes into effect next month, what will be the new price per meal?

Current price $= \frac{13{,}300}{380} = \$35$

Price increase $= 35 \times .20 = \$7$

New price $= 35 + 7 = \underline{\$42}$

d. When photographers, florists, DJs, bands, and other outside vendors are booked through your office for events at the hotel, a $5\frac{1}{2}\%$ "finder's fee" is charged. Last year, \$175,000 of such services were booked. How much did the hotel make on this service?

$P = R \times B$

Finder's fee $= .055 \times 175{,}000 = \underline{\underline{\$9{,}625}}$

e. If your boss is expecting \$11,000 in "finder's fee" revenue next year, what amount of these services must be booked?

$B = \frac{P}{R} = \frac{11{,}000}{.055} = \underline{\underline{\$200{,}000}}$

SOLVING OTHER BUSINESS PROBLEMS INVOLVING PERCENTS

In addition to the basic percentage formulas, percents are used in many other ways in business. Measuring increases and decreases, comparing results from one year with another, and reporting economic activity and trends are just a few of these applications.

The ability of managers to make correct decisions is fundamental to success in business. These decisions require accurate and up-to-date information. Measuring percent changes in business activity is an important source of this information. Percents often describe a situation in a more informative way than simply the raw data alone.

For example, a company reports a profit of \$50,000 for the year. Although the number \$50,000 is correct, it does not give a perspective of whether that amount of profit is good or bad. A comparison to last year's figures, using percents, might reveal that profits are up 45% over last year, or profits are down 66.8%. Significant news!

Learning Tip

It is important to remember, when solving percentage problems that involve "change" from an original number to a new number, the original number is always the *base* and represents 100%.

DETERMINING RATE OF INCREASE OR DECREASE

In calculating the rate of increase or decrease of something, we use the same percentage formula concepts as before. Rate of change means percent change, therefore the *rate* is the unknown. Once again we use the formula $R = P \div B$. Rate of change situations contain an original amount of something, which either increases or decreases to a new amount.

In solving these problems, the original amount is always the base. The amount of change is the portion. The unknown, which describes the percent change between the two amounts, is the rate.

$$\textbf{Rate of change (Rate)} = \frac{\textbf{Amount of change (Portion)}}{\textbf{Original amount (Base)}}$$

STEPS FOR DETERMINING THE RATE OF INCREASE OR DECREASE

Step 1. Identify the original and the new amounts, and find the *difference* between them.

Step 2. Using the rate formula, $R = P \div B$, substitute the difference from Step 1 for the portion, and the original amount for the base.

Step 3. Solve the equation for R. Remember, your answer will be in decimal form, which must be converted to a percent.

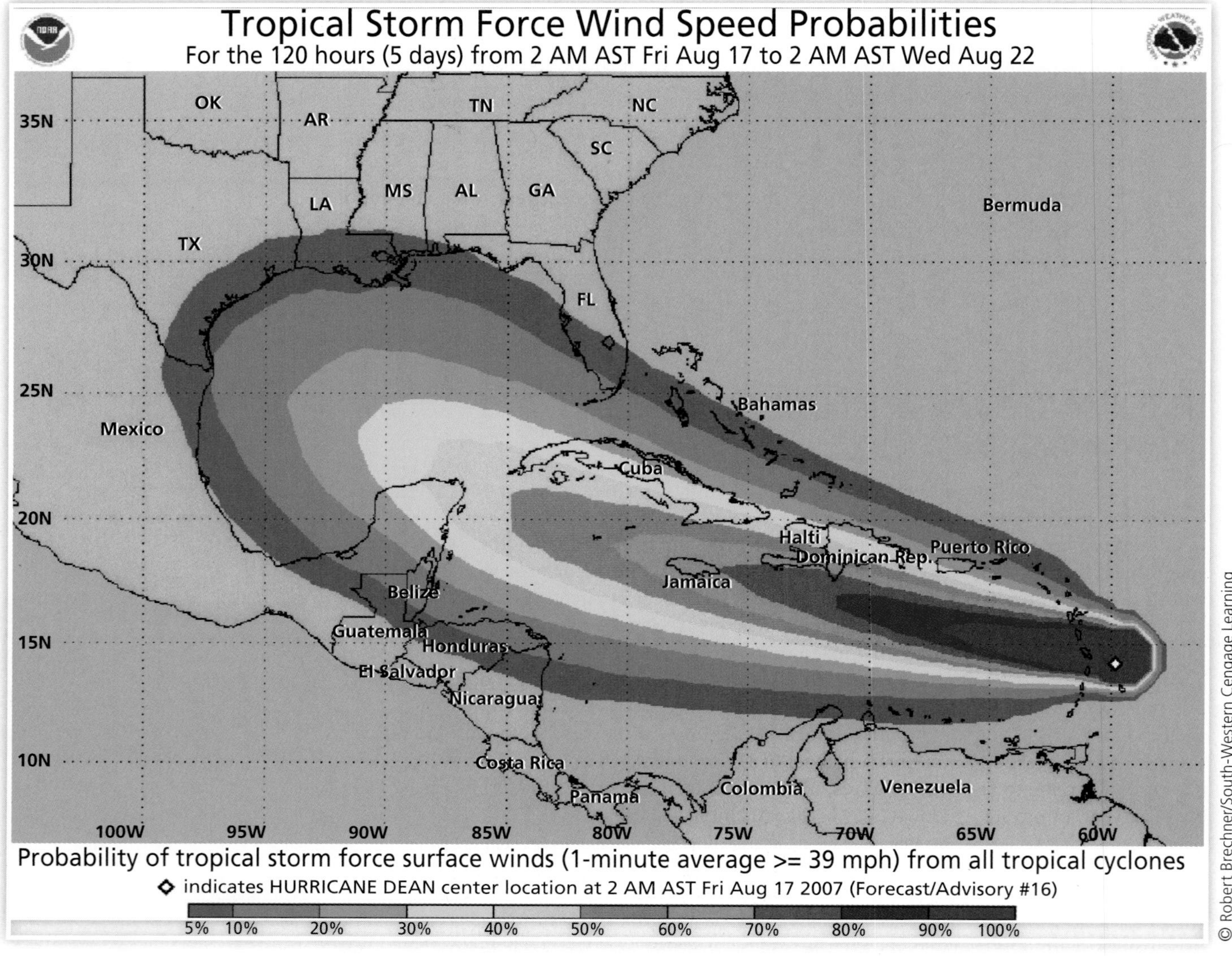

Predicting the probability of an event occurring is often expressed as a percent. This graphic illustrates the tropical storm force winds probabilities during Hurricane Dean in 2007.

TEACHING TIP

As a shortcut, remind students of the following calculator sequence:

75 [−] 60 [÷] 60 [%] = 25

Note: Scientific and business calculators require pushing the = button after the % key; common arithmetic calculators do not.

EXAMPLE 14 FINDING THE RATE OF INCREASE

If a number increases from 60 to 75, what is the rate of increase?

SOLUTION STRATEGY

In this basic situation, a number changes from 60 to 75, and we are looking for the percent change; in this case it is an increase. The original amount is 60; the new amount is 75.

The portion is the difference between the amounts, $75 - 60 = 15$, and the base is the original amount, 60. We now substitute these values into the formula,

$$R = \frac{P}{B} = \frac{15}{60} = .25 = 25\%$$

Rate of increase = 25%

TRY IT EXERCISE 14

Solve the following problem for the rate of increase or decrease. Round to the nearest tenth of a percent when necessary.

If a number increases from 650 to 948, what is the rate of increase?

CHECK YOUR ANSWER WITH THE SOLUTION ON PAGE 197.

EXAMPLE 15 FINDING THE RATE OF DECREASE

A number decreased from 120 to 80. What is the rate of decrease?

SOLUTION STRATEGY

This problem illustrates a number decreasing in value. The unknown is the rate of decrease. We identify the original amount as 120 and the new amount as 80.

The difference between them is the portion: 120 − 80 = 40. The original amount, 120, is the base. Now apply the rate formula.

$$R = \frac{P}{B} = \frac{40}{120} = .333 = 33.3\%$$

Rate of decrease = 33.3%

TRY IT EXERCISE 15

Solve the following problem for the rate of increase or decrease. Round to the nearest tenth of a percent when necessary.

If a number decreases from 21 to 15, what is the rate of decrease?

CHECK YOUR ANSWER WITH THE SOLUTION ON PAGE 197.

EXAMPLE 16 FINDING THE RATE OF CHANGE

Last year Continental Furniture had a work force of 360 employees. This year there are 504 employees. What is the rate of change in the number of employees?

SOLUTION STRATEGY

The key to solving this problem is to properly identify the variables. The problem asks "what is the rate"; therefore, the rate is the unknown. The original amount, 360 employees, is the base. The difference between the two amounts, 504 − 360 = 144, is the portion. Now apply the rate formula.

$$R = \frac{P}{B} = \frac{144}{360} = .4 = 40\%$$

40% Increase in employees

TRY IT EXERCISE 16

Solve the following problem for the rate of increase or decrease. Round to the nearest tenth of a percent when necessary.

When Leonardo Mendez was promoted from supervisor to manager, he received a salary increase from \$450 to \$540 per week. What was the percent change in his salary?

CHECK YOUR ANSWER WITH THE SOLUTION ON PAGE 197.

EXAMPLE 17 FINDING THE RATE OF CHANGE

Action Sporting Goods had revenue of \$122,300 in May and \$103,955 in June. What is the percent change in revenue from May to June?

SOLUTION STRATEGY

In this problem, the rate of change, the unknown, is a decrease. The original amount, \$122,300, is the base. The difference between the two amounts, \$122,300 − \$103,955 = \$18,345, is the portion. Now apply the rate formula.

$$R = \frac{P}{B} = \frac{18{,}345}{122{,}300} = .15 = 15\%$$

15% Decrease in revenue

TRY IT EXERCISE 17

Solve the following problem for the rate of increase or decrease. Round to the nearest tenth of a percent when necessary.

You are the production manager for the Keystone Corporation. After starting a quality control program on the production line, the number of defects per day dropped from 60 to 12. Top management was very pleased with your results but wanted to know what percent decrease this change represented. Calculate the percent change in the number of defects per day.

CHECK YOUR ANSWER WITH THE SOLUTION ON PAGE 197.

6-7 DETERMINING AMOUNTS IN INCREASE OR DECREASE SITUATIONS

Finding the New Amount after a Percent Change

Sometimes the original amount of something and the rate of change will be known and the new amount, after the change, will be the unknown. For example, if a store sold \$5,000 in merchandise on Tuesday and 8% more on Wednesday, what are Wednesday's sales?

Keep in mind that the original amount, or beginning point, is always the base and represents 100%. Because the new amount is the total of the original amount, 100%, and the amount of increase, 8%, the rate of the new amount is 108% (100% + 8%). If the rate of change had been a decrease instead of an increase, the rate would have been 8% less than the base, or 92% (100% − 8%).

The unknown in this situation, the new amount, is the portion; therefore, we use the formula Portion = Rate × Base.

Learning Tip

Remember

- If the rate of change is an increase, *add* that rate to 100%.
- If the rate of change is a decrease, *subtract* that rate from 100%.

STEPS FOR DETERMINING THE NEW AMOUNT AFTER A PERCENT CHANGE

Step 1. In the formula Portion = Rate × Base, substitute the original amount, or starting point, for the base.

Step 2a. If the rate of change is an increase, add that rate to 100% to get the rate.

Step 2b. If the rate of change is a decrease, subtract that rate from 100% to get the rate.

Step 3. Solve the equation for the portion.

EXAMPLE 18 FINDING THE NEW AMOUNT AFTER A PERCENT CHANGE

Progressive Insurance estimated that the number of claims on homeowner's insurance would increase by 15% this year. If the company received 1,240 claims last year, how many can it expect this year?

SOLUTION STRATEGY

Last year's claims, the original amount, is the base. Because the rate of change is an increase, we find the rate by adding that change to 100% (100% + 15% = 115%). Now substitute these values in the portion formula.

$$P = R \times B$$

$$P = 115\% \times 1{,}240 = 1.15 \times 1{,}240 = 1{,}426$$

1,426 Homeowners' claims expected this year

TRY IT EXERCISE 18

Solve the following business situation for the new amount, after a percent change.

Maxwell Imports had a computer with a 28 gigabyte hard drive. If it was replaced with a new model containing 60% more capacity, how many gigabytes would the new hard drive have?

CHECK YOUR ANSWER WITH THE SOLUTION ON PAGE 197.

EXAMPLE 19 FINDING THE NEW AMOUNT AFTER A PERCENT CHANGE

Scotty's Drive-in Restaurant sold 25% fewer milk shakes this week than last week. If they sold 380 shakes last week, how many did they sell this week?

SOLUTION STRATEGY

Because this situation represents a percent decrease, the rate is determined by subtracting the rate of decrease from 100% (100% − 25% = 75%). As usual, the base is the original amount.

$$P = R \times B$$

$$P = 75\% \times 380 = .75 \times 380 = 285$$

<u>285 Milk shakes sold this week</u>

TRY IT EXERCISE 19

Solve the following business situation for the new amount, after a percent change.

Rapid Transfer has delivery trucks that cover 20% fewer miles per week during the winter snow season. If the trucks average 650 miles per week during the summer, how many miles can be expected per week during the winter?

CHECK YOUR ANSWER WITH THE SOLUTION ON PAGE 197.

Finding the Original Amount before a Percent Change

In another business situation involving percent change, the new amount is known and the original amount, the base, is unknown. For example, a car dealer sold 42 cars today. If this represents a 20% increase from yesterday, how many cars were sold yesterday? Solving for the original amount is a base problem, therefore we use the formula:

$$\text{Base} = \frac{\text{Portion}}{\text{Rate}}$$

STEPS FOR DETERMINING THE ORIGINAL AMOUNT BEFORE A PERCENT CHANGE

Step 1. In the formula Base = Portion ÷ Rate, substitute the new amount for the portion.

Step 2a. If the rate of change is an increase, add that rate to 100% to get the rate.

Step 2b. If the rate of change is a decrease, subtract that rate from 100% to get the rate.

Step 3. Solve the equation for the base.

TEACHING TIP
Remind students

- If the rate of change is an increase, add that rate to 100%.
- If the rate of change is a decrease, subtract that rate from 100%.

EXAMPLE 20 FINDING THE ORIGINAL AMOUNT

Sunbelt Technologies found that after an advertising campaign, business in April increased 12% over March. If April sales were $53,760, how much were the sales in March?

SOLUTION STRATEGY

April's sales, the new amount, is the portion. Because the rate of change is an increase, we find the rate by adding that change to 100%. 100% + 12% = 112%.

$$B = \frac{P}{R}$$

$$B = \frac{53{,}760}{112\%} = \frac{53{,}760}{1.12} = 48{,}000$$

$48,000

TRY IT EXERCISE 20

Solve the following business situation for the original amount, before a percent change.

A harvester can cover 90 acres per day with a new direct-drive system. If this represents an increase of 20% over the conventional chain-drive system, how many acres per day were covered with the old chain-drive?

CHECK YOUR ANSWER WITH THE SOLUTION ON PAGE 197.

EXAMPLE 21 FINDING THE ORIGINAL AMOUNT

At Best Buy, the price of a Sony HD camcorder dropped by 15% to $425. What was the original price?

TEACHING TIP
As a review of Section III, have students break into groups to write and solve some business-related word problems that involve percentage change.

Next, have each group work the problems of another group, compare answers, and resolve any differences.

SOLUTION STRATEGY

Because this situation represents a percent decrease, the rate is determined by subtracting the rate of decrease from 100%. 100% − 15% = 85%. The portion is the new amount, $425. The original price, the base, is the unknown. Using the formula for the base,

$$B = \frac{P}{R}$$

$$B = \frac{425}{85\%} = \frac{425}{.85} = 500$$

$500

TRY IT EXERCISE 21

Solve the following business situation for the original amount, before a percent change.

The water level in a large holding tank decreased to 12 feet. If it is down 40% from last week, what was last week's level?

CHECK YOUR ANSWER WITH THE SOLUTION ON PAGE 197.

6-8 UNDERSTANDING AND SOLVING PROBLEMS INVOLVING PERCENTAGE POINTS

percentage points A way of expressing a change from an original amount to a new amount, without using a percent sign.

Percentage points are another way of expressing a change from an original amount to a new amount, without using a percent sign. When percentage points are used, it is assumed that the base amount, 100%, stays constant. For example, if a company's market share increased from 40 to 44 percent of a total market, this is expressed as an increase of 4 percentage points.

The actual percent change in business, however, is calculated by using the formula:

$$\textbf{Rate of change} = \frac{\textbf{Change in percentage points}}{\textbf{Original amount of percentage points}}$$

In this illustration, the change in percentage points is 4, and the original amount of percentage points is 40; therefore,

$$\text{Rate of change} = \frac{4}{40} = .10 = \underline{\underline{10\% \text{ increase in market share}}}$$

Calculating percentage points is an application of the rate formula, Rate = Portion ÷ Base, with the change in percentage points as the *portion* and the original percentage points as the *base*.

EXAMPLE 22 SOLVING A PERCENTAGE POINTS PROBLEM

When a competitor built a better mouse trap, a company's market share dropped from 55 to 44 percent of the total market, a drop of 11 percentage points. What percent decrease in market share did this represent?

SOLUTION STRATEGY

In this problem, the change in percentage points is 11, and the original market share is 55. Using the formula to find rate of change:

$$\text{Rate of change} = \frac{\text{Change in percentage points}}{\text{Original amount of percentage points}}$$

$$\text{Rate of change} = \frac{11}{55} = .2 = 20\%$$

$\underline{\underline{\text{20\% Decrease in market share}}}$

TRY IT EXERCISE 22

Prior to an election, a political research firm announced that a candidate for mayor had gained 8 percentage points in the polls that month, from 20 to 28 percent of the total registered voters. What is the candidate's actual percent increase in voters?

CHECK YOUR ANSWER WITH THE SOLUTION ON PAGE 197.

Review Exercises

SECTION III

Solve the following increase or decrease problems for the unknown. Round decimals to hundredths and percents to the nearest tenth.

1. If a number increases from 320 to 440, what is the rate of increase?

   Portion = Increase = 440 − 320 = 120
   Base = Original number = 320
   $R = \frac{P}{B} = \frac{120}{320} = .375 = \underline{\underline{37.5\%}}$

2. If a number decreases from 56 to 49, what is the rate of decrease?

   Portion = Decrease = 56 − 49 = 7
   Base = Original number = 56
   $R = \frac{P}{B} = \frac{7}{56} = .125 = \underline{\underline{12.5\%}}$

3. What is the rate of change if the price of an item rises from \$123.00 to \$154.00?

   Portion = Increase = 154 − 123 = 31
   Base = Original number = 123
   $R = \frac{P}{B} = \frac{31}{123} = .252 = \underline{\underline{25.2\%}}$

4. What is the rate of change if the number of employees in a company decreases from 133 to 89?

   Portion = Decrease = 133 − 89 = 44
   Base = Original number = 133
   $R = \frac{P}{B} = \frac{44}{133} = .3308 = \underline{\underline{33.1\%}}$

5. 50 increased by 20% = __________

   Rate = 100% + 20% = 120%
   Base = Original number = 50
   $P = R \times B = 1.2 \times 50 = \underline{\underline{60}}$

6. 750 increased by 60% = __________

   Rate = 100% + 60% = 160%
   Base = Original number = 750
   $P = R \times B = 1.6 \times 750 = \underline{\underline{1{,}200}}$

7. 25 decreased by 40% = __________

   Rate = 100% − 40% = 60%
   Base = Original number = 25
   $P = R \times B = .6 \times 25 = \underline{\underline{15}}$

8. 3,400 decreased by 18.2% = __________

   Rate = 100% − 18.2% = 81.8%
   Base = Original number = 3,400
   $P = R \times B = .818 \times 3{,}400 = \underline{\underline{2{,}781.2}}$

9. 2,500 increased by 300% = __________

   Rate = 100% + 300% = 400%
   Base = Original number = 2,500
   $P = R \times B = 4 \times 2{,}500 = \underline{\underline{10{,}000}}$

10. \$46 decreased by $10\frac{1}{2}\%$ = __________

    Rate = 100% − 10.5% = 89.5%
    Base = Original number = \$46
    $P = R \times B = .895 \times 46 = \underline{\underline{\$41.17}}$

11. Allied Plumbing sold 2,390 feet of $\frac{5}{8}$-inch galvanized pipe in July. If 2,558 feet were sold in August, what is the percent increase in pipe footage sales?

    Portion = Increase = 2,558 − 2,390 = 168
    Base = Original number = 2,390
    $R = \frac{P}{B} = \frac{168}{2{,}390} = .070 = \underline{\underline{7\%}}$

12. Sunshine Honda sold 112 cars this month. If that is 40% greater than last month, how many cars were sold last month?

    Rate = 100% + 40% = 140%
    Portion = 112
    $B = \frac{P}{R} = \frac{112}{1.4} = \underline{\underline{80}}$ Cars

Top U.S. Supermarkets—2006 Revenue ($billions)

1. Wal-Mart Supercenters
Bentonville, AR
$317.3
Stores—1,929

2. Kroger
Cincinnati, OH
$59.9
Stores—2,515

3. Costco
Issaquah, WA
$51.9
Stores—433

4. Albertson's
Boise, ID
$41.3
Stores—1,743

5. Safeway
Pleasanton, CA
$38.6
Stores—1,802

6. Ahold USA
Chantilly, VA
$22.6
Stores—1,048

Source: Supermarket News, 2006
Top 75 North American Food Retailers
www.supermarketnews.com

13. At a Sports King store, 850 tennis racquets were sold last season.

    a. If business is predicted to be 30% higher this season, how many racquets should be ordered from the distributor?

    Rate = 100% + 30% = 130%
    Base = Original number = 850
    $P = R \times B = 1.3 \times 850 =$ 1,105 Racquets

    b. If racquet sales break down into 40% metal alloy and 60% graphite, how many of each type should be ordered?

Metal Alloy	Graphite
Rate = 40%	Rate = 60%
Base = 1,105	Base = 1,105
$P = R \times B = .4 \times 1{,}105 =$ 442 Racquets	$P = R \times B = .6 \times 1{,}105 =$ 663 Racquets

14. At a Kroger Supermarket, the price of yellow onions dropped from $.59 per pound to $.45 per pound.

    a. What is the percent decrease in the price of onions?

    Portion = Decrease = .59 − .45 = $.14
    Base = Original number = $.59
    $R = \frac{P}{B} = \frac{.14}{.59} = .2372 =$ 23.7%

    b. Tomatoes are expected to undergo the same percent decrease in price. If they currently sell for $1.09 per pound, what will be the new price of tomatoes?

    Rate = 100% − 23.7% = 76.3%
    Base = Original number = $1.09
    $P = R \times B = .763 \times 1.09 =$ $.83 Per pound

15. The American Eagle Racing Team increased the horsepower of an engine from 340 to 440 by converting to fuel injection. What was the percent increase in horsepower?

    Portion = 440 − 340 = 100
    Base = Original number = 340
    $R = \frac{P}{B} = \frac{100}{340} = .2941 =$ 29.4%

16. Housing prices in San Marino County have increased 37.5% over the price of houses 5 years ago.

    a. If $80,000 was the average price of a house 5 years ago, what is the average price of a house today?

    Rate = 100% + 37.5% = 137.5%
    Base = $80,000
    $P = R \times B = 1.375 \times 80{,}000 =$ $110,000

    b. Economists predict that next year housing prices will drop by 4%. Based on your answer from part **a**, what will the average price of a house be next year?

    Rate = 100% − 4% = 96%
    Base = $110,000
    $P = R \times B = .96 \times 110{,}000 =$ $105,600

17. At Camper's Paradise, sales have increased 15%, 20%, and 10% respectively over the past 3 years. If sales this year are $1,000,000, how much were sales 3 years ago? Round each year's sales to the nearest dollar.

1 year ago:	2 years ago:	3 years ago:
Rate = 110%	Rate = 120%	Rate = 115%
Portion = $1,000,000	Portion = $909,091	Portion = $757,576
$B = \frac{1{,}000{,}000}{1.1} = \$909{,}091$	$B = \frac{909{,}091}{1.2} = \$757{,}576$	$B = \frac{757{,}576}{1.15} = \underline{\underline{\$658{,}762}}$

18. After a vigorous promotion campaign, Kellogg's Frosted Flakes increased its market share from 5.4% to 8.1%, a rise of 2.7 percentage points. What percent increase in sales does this represent?

Portion = 2.7
Base = 5.4
$R = \frac{P}{B} = \frac{2.7}{5.4} = .5 = \underline{\underline{50\%}}$

19. Recent economic reports indicate that unemployment in Winter Haven dropped from 8.8% to 6.8% in the past quarter, a decrease of 2 percentage points. What percent decrease does this represent?

Portion = 2
Base = 8.8
$R = \frac{P}{B} = \frac{2}{8.8} = .2272 = \underline{\underline{22.7\%}}$

BUSINESS DECISION TOP RETAIL ADVERTISERS

20. You are the editor of a newsletter about retailing. For the next edition, you have located the following chart listing the top retailers and the amount they spent on advertising in 2004 and 2005. Unfortunately, portions of the chart are missing.

Fill in the blank spaces to complete the chart for the newsletter. Round percents to the nearest tenth of a percent. Round amounts to the nearest hundred thousand dollars.

Top Retail Advertisers
Advertising Spending
($ millions)

Company	2005	2004	Percent Change
Sears	809.6	965.4	−16.1%
Target	602.0	527.6	+14.1%
Wal-Mart	578.7	598.2	−3.3%
Home Depot	551.3	592.2	−6.9%
Lowe's	423.7	366.6	+15.6%
Safeway	194.2	192.1	+1.1%
Kroger	150.9	158.5	−4.8%

Source: Advertising Age Data Center

CHAPTER FORMULAS

The Percentage Formula

Portion = Rate × Base

Rate = Portion ÷ Base

Base = Portion ÷ Rate

Rate of Change

$$\text{Rate of change (Rate)} = \frac{\text{Amount of change (Portion)}}{\text{Original amount (Base)}}$$

Percentage Points

$$\text{Rate of change} = \frac{\text{Change in percentage points}}{\text{Original amount of percentage point}}$$

SUMMARY CHART

Section I: Understanding and Converting Percents

Topic	Important Concepts	Illustrative Examples
Converting a Percent to a Decimal **P/O 6-1, p. 167**	1. Remove the percent sign. 2. Move the decimal point two places to the left. *Note:* If the percent is a fraction, such as $\frac{4}{5}$%, or a mixed number, such as $9\frac{1}{2}$%, first change the fraction part to a decimal, then follow Steps 1 and 2.	28% = .28 159% = 1.59 .37% = .0037 $\frac{4}{5}$% = .8% = .008 $9\frac{1}{2}$% = 9.5% = .095
Converting a Decimal or Whole Number to a Percent **P/O 6-1, p. 168**	1. Move the decimal point two places to the right. 2. Write a percent sign after the number. *Note:* If there are fractions involved, convert them to decimals first, then proceed with Steps 1 and 2.	.8 = 80% 2.9 = 290% .075 = 7.5% 3 = 300% $\frac{1}{2}$ = .5 = 50%
Converting a Percent to a Fraction **P/O 6-2, p. 169**	1. Remove the percent sign. 2. *(If the percent is a whole number)* Write a fraction with the percent as the numerator and 100 as the denominator. Reduce to lowest terms. or 2. *(If the percent is a fraction)* Multiply the number by $\frac{1}{100}$ and reduce to lowest terms. or 2. *(If the percent is a decimal)* Convert it to a fraction and multiply by $\frac{1}{100}$. Reduce to lowest terms.	$7\% = \frac{7}{100}$ $60\% = \frac{60}{100} = \frac{3}{5}$ $400\% = \frac{400}{100} = 4$ $2.1\% = 2\frac{1}{10}\% = \frac{21}{10} \times \frac{1}{100} = \frac{21}{1{,}000}$ $5\frac{3}{4}\% = \frac{23}{4} \times \frac{1}{100} = \frac{23}{400}$
Converting Fractions or Mixed Numbers to Percents **P/O 6-2, p. 170**	1. Change the fraction to a decimal by dividing the numerator by the denominator. 2. Move the decimal point two places to the right. 3. Write a percent sign after the number.	$\frac{1}{8}$ = .125 = 12.5% $\frac{16}{3}$ = 5.333 = 533.3% $12\frac{3}{4}$ = 12.75 = 1,275%

Section II: Using the Percentage Formula to Solve Business Problems

Topic	Important Concepts	Illustrative Examples
Solving for the Portion **P/O 6-3, p. 174**	The portion is the number that represents a part of the base. To solve for portion, use the formula Portion = Rate × Base 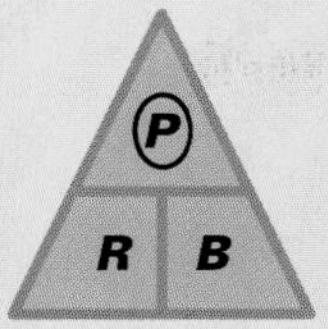 (P) R B	15% of Kwik-Mix Concrete employees got raises this year. If 1,800 individuals work for the company, how many got raises? $P = .15 \times 1{,}800 = 270$ 270 employees got raises this year
Solving for the Rate **P/O 6-4, p. 175**	The rate is the variable that describes what part of the base is represented by the portion. It is always the term with the percent sign. To solve for rate, use the formula $\text{Rate} = \dfrac{\text{Portion}}{\text{Base}}$ 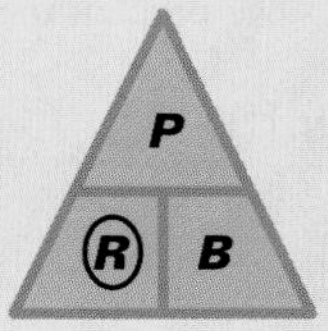 P (R) B	28 out of 32 warehouses owned by Metro Distributors passed safety inspection. What percent of the warehouses passed? $\text{Rate} = \dfrac{28}{32} = .875 = 87.5\%$ 87.5% passed inspection
Solving for the Base **P/O 6-5, p. 177**	Base is the variable that represents 100%, the starting point, or the whole thing. To solve for base, use the formula $\text{Base} = \dfrac{\text{Portion}}{\text{Rate}}$ 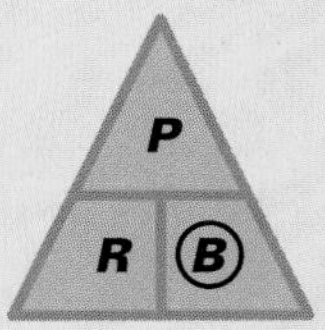 P R (B)	34.3% of Thrifty Tile's sales are from customers west of the Mississippi River. If those sales last year were $154,350, what are the company's total sales? $\text{Base} = \dfrac{154{,}350}{.343} = \$450{,}000$ Total sales = $450,000

Section III: Solving Other Business Problems Involving Percents

Topic	Important Concepts	Illustrative Examples
Determining Rate of Increase or Decrease **P/O 6-6, p. 183**	1. Identify the original and the new amounts, and find the difference between them. 2. Using the rate formula $R = P \div B$, substitute the difference from Step 1 for the portion and the original amount for the base. 3. Solve the equation for *R*. $\text{Rate of change (R)} = \dfrac{\text{Amount of change (P)}}{\text{Original amount (B)}}$	A price rises from $45 to $71. What is the rate of increase? Portion = 71 − 45 = 26 $\text{Rate} = \dfrac{P}{B} = \dfrac{26}{45} = .5778 = 57.8\%$ What is the rate of decrease from 152 to 34? Portion = 152 − 34 = 118 $\text{Rate} = \dfrac{P}{B} = \dfrac{118}{152} = .776 = 77.6\%$
Determining New Amount after a Percent Change **P/O 6-7, p. 186**	Solving for the new amount is a portion problem, therefore we use the formula Portion = Rate × Base 1. Substitute the original amount for the base. 2a. If the rate of change is an increase, add that rate to 100%. 2b. If the rate of change is a decrease, subtract that rate from 100%.	Prestige Plastics projects a 24% increase in sales for next year. If sales this year were $172,500, what sales can be expected next year? Rate = 100% + 24% = 124% $P = R \times B = 1.24 \times 172{,}500$ $P = 213{,}900$ Projected sales = $213,900

(continued)

Section III: (continued)

Topic	Important Concepts	Illustrative Examples
Determining Original Amount before a Percent Change P/O 6-7, p. 188	Solving for the original amount is a base problem, therefore we use the formula $$\text{Base} = \frac{\text{Portion}}{\text{Rate}}$$ 1. Substitute the new amount for the portion. 2a. If the rate of change is an increase, add that rate to 100%. 2b. If the rate of change is a decrease, subtract that rate from 100%.	If a DVD was marked down by 30% to \$16.80, what was the original price? $\text{Portion} = 100\% - 30\% = 70\%$ $\text{Base} = \frac{P}{R} = \frac{16.80}{.7} = 24$ Original price = \$24
Solving Problems Involving Percentage Points P/O 6-8, p. 190	Percentage points are another way of expressing a change from an original amount to a new amount, without using the percent sign. When percentage points are used, it is assumed that the base amount, 100%, stays constant. The actual percent change in business, however, is calculated by using the formula $$\text{Rate of change} = \frac{\text{Change in percentage points}}{\text{Original percentage points}}$$	After an intensive advertising campaign, General Industries' market share increased from 21 to 27%, an increase of 6 percentage points. What percent increase in business does this represent? $\%\text{ change} = \frac{6}{21} = .2857 = 28.6\%$ % increase in business = 28.6%

TRY IT EXERCISE SOLUTIONS FOR CHAPTER 6

1a. $27\% = .27$ **1b.** $472\% = 4.72$ **1c.** $93.7\% = .937$ **1d.** $.81\% = .0081$

1e. $12\frac{3}{4}\% = 12.75\% = .1275$ **1f.** $\frac{7}{8}\% = .875\% = .00875$ **2a.** $.8 = 80\%$ **2b.** $1.4 = 140\%$

2c. $.0023 = .23\%$ **2d.** $.016\frac{2}{5} = .0164 = 1.64\%$ **2e.** $19 = 1{,}900\%$ **2f.** $.57\frac{2}{3} = .5767 = 57.67\%$

3a. $9\% = \frac{9}{100}$ **3b.** $23\% = \frac{23}{100}$ **3c.** $75\% = \frac{75}{100} = \frac{3}{4}$ **3d.** $225\% = \frac{225}{100} = 2\frac{25}{100} = 2\frac{1}{4}$

3e. $8.7\% = 8\frac{7}{10}\% = \frac{87}{10} \times \frac{1}{100} = \frac{87}{1{,}000}$ **3f.** $1{,}000\% = \frac{1{,}000}{100} = 10$ **4a.** $\frac{1}{5} = .2 = 20\%$

4b. $\frac{70}{200} = .35 = 35\%$ **4c.** $\frac{23}{5} = 4\frac{3}{5} = 4.6 = 460\%$ **4d.** $6\frac{9}{10} = 6.9 = 690\%$ **4e.** $\frac{45}{54} = .8333 = 83.33\%$

4f. $140\frac{1}{8} = 140.125 = 14{,}012.5\%$ **5.** $P = R \times B = .55 \times 980 = 539$ **6.** $P = R \times B = .72 \times 3{,}200 = 2{,}304$

7a. $P = R \times B = .16 \times 1{,}250 = 200$ Salespeople **7b.** $P = R \times B = .15 \times 148{,}500 = \$22{,}275$ Down payment

8. $R = \frac{P}{B} = \frac{9}{21} = .4285 = 42.9\%$ **9.** $R = \frac{P}{B} = \frac{67}{142} = .4718 = 47.2\%$ **10a.** $R = \frac{P}{B} = \frac{5{,}400}{18{,}000} = .3 = 30\%$ Completed

$100\% - 30\% = 70\%$ Remains

10b. $R = \frac{P}{B} = \frac{5{,}518}{8{,}900} = .62 = 62\%$ Suits **11.** $B = \frac{P}{R} = \frac{690}{.4} = 1{,}725$ **12.** $B = \frac{P}{R} = \frac{550}{.88} = \$625$

13a. $B = \frac{P}{R} = \frac{126}{.35} = \underline{\underline{360}}$ Motors

13b. $B = \frac{P}{R} = \frac{3{,}420}{.75} = \underline{\underline{4{,}560}}$ Reams of paper

14. Portion = Increase = 948 − 650 = 298

Base = Original number = 650

$R = \frac{P}{B} = \frac{298}{650} = .45846 = \underline{\underline{45.8\%}}$ Increase

15. Portion = Decrease = 21 − 15 = 6

Base = Original number = 21

$R = \frac{P}{B} = \frac{6}{21} = .2857 = \underline{\underline{28.6\%}}$ Decrease

16. Portion = Increase = \$540 − \$450 = \$90

Base = Original number = \$450

$R = \frac{P}{B} = \frac{90}{450} = .2 = \underline{\underline{20\%}}$ Increase

17. Portion = Decrease = 60 − 12 = 48

Base = Original number = 60

$R = \frac{P}{B} = \frac{48}{60} = .8 = \underline{\underline{80\%}}$ Decrease

18. Rate = 100% + 60% = 160%

$P = R \times B = 1.6 \times 28 = \underline{\underline{44.8}}$ Gigabytes

19. Rate = 100% − 20% = 80%

$P = R \times B = .8 \times 650 = \underline{\underline{520}}$ Miles per week

20. Rate = 100% + 20% = 120%

$B = \frac{P}{R} = \frac{90}{1.2} = \underline{\underline{75}}$ Acres per day

21. Rate = 100% − 40% = 60%

$B = \frac{P}{R} = \frac{12}{.6} = \underline{\underline{20}}$ Feet

22. $R = \frac{P}{B} = \frac{8}{20} = .4 = \underline{\underline{40\%}}$ Increase in voters

CONCEPT REVIEW

1. A percent is a way of expressing a part of a(n) ____. (6-1)

whole

2. In previous chapters, we expressed these parts as ____ and ____. (6-1)

fractions, decimals

3. Percent means "part per ____." The percent sign is written as ____. (6-1)

hundred, %

4. To convert a percent to a decimal, we remove the percent sign and ____ by 100. (6-1)

divide

5. To convert a decimal to a percent, we multiply by 100 and write a(n) ____ sign after the number. (6-1)

percent

6. To convert a percent to a fraction, we remove the percent sign and place the number over ____. (6-2)

100

7. List the steps for converting a fraction to a percent. (6-2)

- Change the fraction to a decimal by dividing the numerator by the denominator.
- Multiply by 100. (Move the decimal point two places to the right. Add zeros as needed.)
- Write a percent sign after the number.

8. The three basic parts of the percentage formula are the ____, ____, and ____. (6-3)

portion, rate, base

9. The percentage formula is written as ____. (6-3)

Portion = Rate × Base

10. In the percentage formula, the ____ is the variable with the percent sign or the word "percent." (6-4)

rate

11. In the percentage formula, the ____ represents 100%, or the "whole thing." In a sentence, it follows the word ____. (6-5)

base, of

12. Write the formula for the rate of change. (6-6)

$$\text{Rate of change} = \frac{\text{Amount of change}}{\text{Original amount}}$$

13. When calculating amounts in percent change situations, the rate of change is added to 100% if the change is a(n) ____ and subtracted from 100% if the change is a(n) ____. (6-7)

increase, decrease

14. Percentage ____ are a way of expressing a change from an original amount to a new amount, without using a percent sign. (6-8)

points

ASSESSMENT TEST

Name

Class

Answers

1. .88
2. .0375
3. .5968
4. 4.22
5. .005625
6. 1,260%
7. 68.1%
8. 5,300%
9. 2,480%
10. 9.29%
11. $\frac{19}{100}$
12. $2\frac{17}{100}$
13. $\frac{93}{1,250}$
14. $1\frac{13}{50}$
15. $\frac{127}{500}$
16. 80%
17. 55.56%
18. 825%
19. 5,630%
20. 745%
21. 408
22. 44.8%
23. 103.41
24. 306
25. 180%
26. 250
27. 69
28. 50%
29. 2,960

Convert the following percents to decimals.

1. 88% — .88

2. $3\frac{3}{4}\%$ — 3.75% = .0375

3. 59.68% — .5968

4. 422% — 4.22

5. $\frac{9}{16}\%$ — .5625% = .005625

Convert the following decimals or whole numbers to percents.

6. 12.6 — 1,260%

7. .681 — 68.1%

8. 53 — 5,300%

9. $24\frac{4}{5}$ — 24.8 = 2,480%

10. .0929 — 9.29%

Convert the following percents to reduced fractions, mixed numbers, or whole numbers.

11. 19% — $\frac{19}{100}$

12. 217% — $\frac{217}{100} = 2\frac{17}{100}$

13. 7.44% — $7\frac{44}{100} \times \frac{1}{100} = \frac{744}{100} \times \frac{1}{100} = \frac{744}{10,000} = \frac{93}{1,250}$

14. 126% — $\frac{126}{100} = 1\frac{26}{100} = 1\frac{13}{50}$

15. $25\frac{2}{5}\%$ — $25\frac{2}{5} \times \frac{1}{100} = \frac{127}{5} \times \frac{1}{100} = \frac{127}{500}$

Convert each of the following fractions or mixed numbers to percents.

16. $\frac{4}{5}$ — .8 = 80%

17. $\frac{5}{9}$ — .5556 = 55.56%

18. $\frac{33}{4}$ — $8\frac{1}{4}$ = 8.25 = 825%

19. $56\frac{3}{10}$ — 56.3 = 5,630%

20. $\frac{745}{100}$ — $7\frac{45}{100}$ = 7.45 = 745%

Solve the following for the portion, rate, or base, rounding decimals to hundredths and percents to the nearest tenth when necessary.

21. 24% of 1,700 =

$P = R \times B = .24 \times 1,700 = 408$

22. 56 is ________ % of 125

$R = \frac{P}{B} = \frac{56}{125} = .448 = 44.8\%$

23. 91 is 88% of ________

$B = \frac{P}{R} = \frac{91}{.88} = 103.41$

24. What number is 45% of 680?

$P = R \times B = .45 \times 680 = 306$

25. \$233.91 is what percent of \$129.95?

$R = \frac{P}{B} = \frac{233.91}{129.95} = 1.8 = 180\%$

26. 315 is 126% of ________

$B = \frac{P}{R} = \frac{315}{1.26} = 250$

27. 60 increased by 15% = ________

$R = 100\% + 15\% = 115\%$

$P = R \times B = 1.15 \times 60 = 69$

28. If a number increases from 47 to 70.5, what is the rate of increase?

Portion = Increase = 70.5 − 47 = 23.5

$R = \frac{P}{B} = \frac{23.5}{47} = .5 = 50\%$

29. What is the base if the portion is 444 and the rate is 15%?

$B = \frac{P}{R} = \frac{444}{.15} = 2,960$

30. What is the portion if the base is 900 and the rate is $12\frac{3}{4}\%$?

$P = R \times B = .1275 \times 900 = 114.75$

31. What is 100% of 1,492?

$P = R \times B = 1.0 \times 1{,}492 = 1{,}492$

32. 7,000 decreased by 62% = __________

Rate = 100% − 62% = 38%

$P = R \times B = .38 \times 7{,}000 = 2{,}660$

Name

Class

Answers

30. 114.75

31. 1,492

32. 2,660

33. $122.48 Savings

34. 73.1% Finished the race

35. a. $72,000 Total cost

b. $.24 Per mile

c. 25% Savings per mile

36. a. 50% Increase

b. 189 Homes per hour

37. 21.0% Increase

Solve the following word problems for the unknown. Round decimals to hundredths and percents to the nearest tenth when necessary.

33. An ad for Target read, "This week only, all merchandise 35% off!" If a television set normally sells for $349.95, what is the amount of the savings?

$P = R \times B = .35 \times 349.95 = \$122.48$ Savings

34. If 453 runners out of 620 completed a marathon, what percent of the runners finished the race?

$R = \frac{P}{B} = \frac{453}{620} = 73.1\%$ Finished the race

35. Last year Bridgestone's corporate jet required $23,040 in maintenance and repairs.

a. If this represents 32% of the total operating costs of the airplane, what was the total cost to fly the plane for the year?

$B = \frac{P}{R} = \frac{23{,}040}{.32} = \$72{,}000$ Total cost

b. If the plane flew 300,000 miles last year, what is the cost per mile to operate the plane?

$\text{Cost per mile} = \frac{\text{Total cost}}{\text{Total miles}} = \frac{72{,}000}{300{,}000} = \$.24$ Per mile

c. Lakeside Leasing offered a deal whereby it would operate the plane for Bridgestone for only $.18 per mile. What is the percent decrease in operating expense per mile being offered by Lakeside?

Portion = Decrease = .24 − .18 = .06

$R = \frac{P}{B} = \frac{.06}{.24} = 25\%$ Savings per mile

36. A letter carrier can deliver mail to 112 homes per hour by walking and 168 homes per hour by driving.

a. By what percent is productivity increased by driving?

Portion = Increase = 168 − 112 = 56

$R = \frac{P}{B} = \frac{56}{112} = .5 = 50\%$ Increase in productivity

b. If a new zip code system improves driving productivity by 12.5%, what is the new number of homes per hour for driving?

$168 \times 1.125 = 189$ Homes per hour

37. Last year the Vanguard Corporation had sales of $343,500. If this year's sales are forecast to be $415,700, what is the percent increase in sales?

Portion = Increase = 415,700 − 343,500 = 72,200

$R = \frac{P}{B} = \frac{72{,}200}{343{,}500} = .210 = 21.0\%$ Increase

The **U.S. Postal Service** delivers to everyone, everywhere! With over 700,000 employees, the USPS handles and delivers 213 billion pieces of mail a year. That amounts to five pieces per address per day to over 146 million homes, businesses and P.O. boxes.

On average, the 300,000 carriers each deliver about 2,900 pieces of mail a day to about 500 addresses.

CHAPTER

Name

____

Class

____

Answers

38. $24,000

39. $3.4 Billion

40. 57.1%

41. 18.1% Increase

42. 66.7% Brighter

43. $33.3 Billion

44. a. $6.40 Increase

b. 11.7% Increase

45. $40,583.33

38. After a 15% pay raise, Raul Vargas now earns $27,600. What was his salary before the raise?

$$B = \frac{P}{R} = \frac{\$27{,}600}{115\%} = \frac{27{,}600}{1.15} = \underline{\underline{\$24{,}000}}$$

39. According to Beverage Digest, in 2006 sales of energy drinks were $4.9 billion, up 44% from 2005. How much were the energy drink sales in 2005?

$$B = \frac{P}{R} = \frac{4.9}{1.44} = 3.403 = \underline{\underline{\$3.4 \text{ Billion}}}$$

40. Three of every seven sales transactions at Dollar Discount are on credit cards. What percent of the transactions are *not* credit card sales?

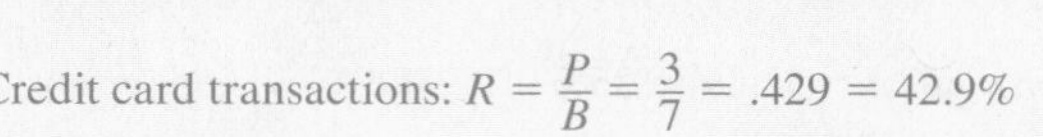

Credit card transactions: $R = \frac{P}{B} = \frac{3}{7} = .429 = 42.9\%$

Noncredit transactions: $100\% - 42.9\% = \underline{\underline{57.1\%}}$

41. A pre-election survey shows that an independent presidential candidate has increased his popularity from 26.5 percent to 31.3 percent of the electorate, an increase of 4.8 percentage points. What percent does this increase represent?

$$R = \frac{P}{B} = \frac{4.8}{26.5} = .181 = \underline{\underline{18.1\%}} \text{ Increase}$$

42. By what percent is a 100-watt light bulb brighter than a 60-watt bulb?

Portion = Increase = 100 − 60 = 40 Watts

$$R = \frac{P}{B} = \frac{40}{60} = .667 = \underline{\underline{66.7\%}} \text{ Brighter}$$

43. According to Organic Monitor, an industry trade group, global sales of organic foods amounted to $40 billion in 2006, up 20% from 2005. What was the amount of organic foods sales in 2005? Round to the nearest tenth of a billion dollars.

$$B = \frac{P}{R} = \frac{40}{1.2} = 33.33 = \underline{\underline{\$33.3 \text{ Billion}}}$$

44. Kelly Jordan, an ice cream vendor, pays $17.50 for a five-gallon container of premium ice cream. From this quantity, he sells 80 scoops at $.90 per scoop. If he sold smaller scoops, he could sell 98 scoops from the same container; however, he could only charge $.80 per scoop. As his accountant, you are asked the following questions.

a. If Kelly switches to the smaller scoops, by how much will his profit per container go up or down? (Profit = Sales − Expenses.)

Large		Small		
.90	72.00	.80	78.40	60.90
× 80	−17.50	× 98	−17.50	− 54.50
$72.00	$54.50 Profit	$78.40	$60.90 Profit	$6.40 Profit increase using small scoops

b. By what percent will the profit change? Round to the nearest tenth of a percent.

$$R = \frac{P}{B} = \frac{6.40}{54.50} = .1174$$

$$= \underline{\underline{11.7\%}} \text{ Increase}$$

45. An insurance adjuster for Kemper found that 12% of a shipment was damaged in transit. If the damaged goods amounted to $4,870, what was the total value of the shipment?

EXCEL

$$B = \frac{P}{R} = \frac{4{,}870}{.12} = \underline{\underline{\$40{,}583.33}} \text{ Total shipment}$$

46. Morley Fast, a contractor, built a warehouse complex for the following costs: land, \$12,000; concrete and steel, \$34,500; plumbing and electrical, \$48,990; general carpentry and roof, \$42,340; and other expenses, \$34,220.

a. What percent of the total cost is represented by each category of expenses?

Base = Total expenses = \$172,050

Land: $R = \frac{P}{B} = \frac{12,000}{172,050} = \underline{\underline{7.0\%}}$

Carpentry and roof: $R = \frac{P}{B} = \frac{42,340}{172,050} = \underline{\underline{24.6\%}}$

Concrete and steel: $R = \frac{P}{B} = \frac{34,500}{172,050} = \underline{\underline{20.1\%}}$

Other expenses: $R = \frac{P}{B} = \frac{34,220}{172,050} = \underline{\underline{19.9\%}}$

Plumbing and electrical: $R = \frac{P}{B} = \frac{48,990}{172,050} = \underline{\underline{28.5\%}}$ *Note: Total = 100.1% due to rounding

b. When the project was completed, Morley sold the entire complex for 185% of its cost. What was the selling price of the complex?

$P = R \times B = 1.85 \times 172,050 = \underline{\underline{\$318,292.50}}$ Selling price

Use the chart, Cell Phone TV Viewers, for Exercises 47–49.

47. What is the projected rate of change in cell phone TV viewers from 2007 to 2011? Round to the nearest whole persent.

$R = \frac{P}{B} = \frac{25.6 - 11.9}{11.9} = 1.1513 = \underline{\underline{115\%}}$

48. If the 2008 viewership was a 30% increase from 2007, how many viewers were there in 2008? Round to the nearest tenth of a million.

$R = 130\%$

$B = 11.9$

$P = 1.3 \times 11.9 = 15.47 = \underline{\underline{\$15.5 \text{ Million}}}$

49. If the 2011 projected figure represents a 10% increase from 2010, what is the projected viewership for 2010? Round to the nearest tenth of a million.

$P = 25.6$

$R = 110\%$

$B = \frac{P}{R} = \frac{25.6}{1.1} = 23.27 = \underline{\underline{\$23.3 \text{ Million}}}$

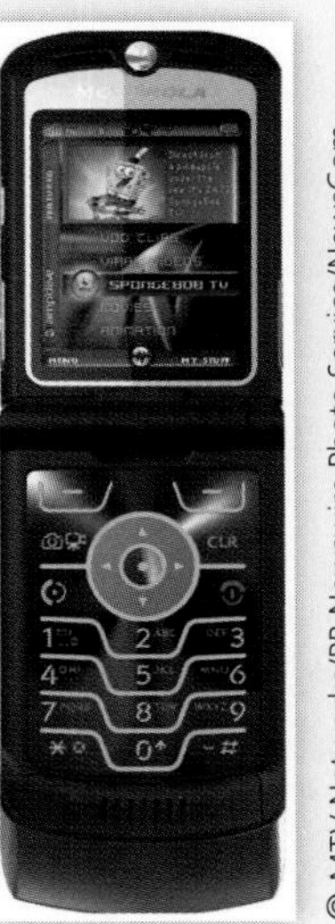

© MTV Networks/PR Newswire Photo Service/NewsCom

Name

Class

Answers

46. a. 7.0% land, 20.1% concrete and steel, 28.5% plumbing and electrical, 24.6% carpentry and roof, 19.9% other expenses

b. \$318,292.50 Selling price

47. 115%

48. \$15.5 Million

49. \$23.3 Million

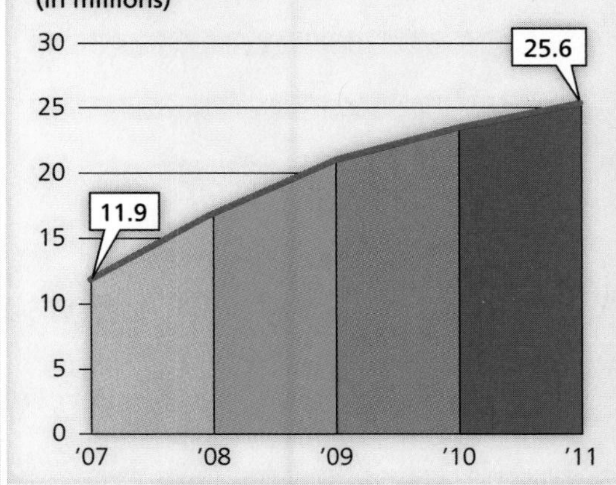

CHAPTER

BUSINESS DECISION ALLOCATING OVERHEAD EXPENSES

Name

Class

Answers

50. a. $7,536.00, $4,832.00, $3,632.00

b. $7,363.20, $4,720.00

$3,549.44, $3,247.36

c. Advertising and promotion;

administrative office

d. Square feet; number of employees

50. You are the owner of a chain of three successful restaurants, with the following number of seats in each location: airport, 340 seats; downtown, 218 seats; and suburban, 164 seats.

a. If the liability insurance premium is $16,000 per year, how much of that premium should be allocated to each of the restaurants, based on percent of total seating capacity? Round each percent to the nearest tenth.

$R = \frac{P}{B}$

Total seats = Base = 722

Airport = $\frac{340}{722}$ = 47.1% — .471 × 16,000 = $7,536.00

Downtown = $\frac{218}{722}$ = 30.2% — .302 × 16,000 = $4,832.00

Suburban = $\frac{164}{722}$ = 22.7% — .227 × 16,000 = $3,632.00

b. If you open a fourth location at the beach, with 150 seats, and the liability insurance premium increases by 18%, what is the new allocation of insurance premium among the four locations?

New Base = 722 + 150 = 872

New insurance premium = 16,000 × 1.18 = $18,880

Airport = $\frac{340}{872}$ = 39% — .39 × 18,880 = $7,363.20

Downtown = $\frac{218}{872}$ = 25% — .25 × 18,880 = $4,720.00

Suburban = $\frac{164}{872}$ = 18.8% — .188 × 18,880 = $3,549.44

Beach = $\frac{150}{872}$ = 17.2% — .172 × 18,880 = $3,247.36

c. (Optional) What other expenses could be allocated to the 4 restaurants?

Answers may vary. Some examples include advertising and promotion; administrative office

d. (Optional) What other ways, besides seating capacity, could you use to allocate expenses?

Answers may vary. Some examples include square feet; number of employees

COLLABORATIVE LEARNING ACTIVITY

Percents—The Language of Business

For emphasis and illustration, business percentage figures, when printed, are frequently presented in circle, bar, and line chart format. Charts add a compelling element to otherwise plain "numbers in the news."

As a team, search business publications, annual reports, and the Internet to find 10 interesting and varied examples of business percentage figures being presented in chart form. Share your findings with the class.

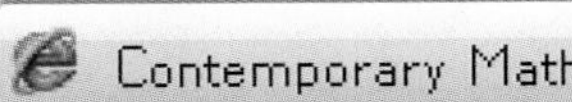

ContemporaryMath.com

All the Math That's Fit to Learn

No Bank Account? No Problem!

About 10 million U.S. households don't have a bank account, but that hasn't stopped the credit card industry from giving them plastic. An increasing number of these consumers use their paychecks to buy prepaid cards. The business has drawn the attention of hip-hop mogul Russell Simmons and pop artist Usher, who have attached their names to prepaid cards from Visa and MasterCard, respectively. Even former basketball star Earvin "Magic" Johnson has a prepaid card called MagicCash Visa.

Source: Wall Street Journal, www.collegejournal.com, February 9, 2007.

The table below illustrates how purchases made with branded prepaid cards nearly doubled from 2005 to 2006, and are expected to top $100 billion by 2010.

Prepaid Payment Cards Surging
($ billions)

2005	2006	2007	2008	2009	2010
$14	$25	$38	$54	$76	$103

Source: USA Today June 7, 2007 Page 1A, data from Aite Group. Reprinted with permission.

Bouncing Checks Can Be Expensive—Use Overdraft Protection

Anyone might bounce a check on a rare occasion, but some folks do it a tad more frequently. Bouncing checks can be expensive; it's not at all unusual to see non-sufficient funds, or NSF, fees of $35 per check. Compounding the problem is the way in which many financial institutions process checks.

Let's say, for example, that you had $300 in your checking account and you wrote six checks totaling $375. The six checks are for $200, $12, $50, $60, $23, and $30. If they all came back to the bank on the same day, the bank could clear the last five and just bounce the one check that's for $200. But, more than likely, the bank will clear the $200 check and the $60 check and bounce the rest since the next largest check ($50) won't clear. You'd have to pay four NSF fees. The banks say they clear checks in this manner because they assume the larger checks are more important, such as for a mortgage payment or car loan.

If you tend to bounce checks you can avoid this hassle by signing up for overdraft protection. You'll need another account with the bank like a savings account, a credit card, or a home equity line of credit. If you overdraw your checking account, the bank will pay the check and take the money from one of your other accounts. As long as you have funds in one of the other accounts to cover the check, the bank guarantees the check will be paid. You'll be charged a fee, but it will be far less than an NSF fee.

Source: Overdraft Protection Plans. http://aol1.bankrate.com/aol/green/chk/basics1-5a.asp?caret=6, 10-31-07.

Quote...UnQuote

- Banks will lend you money if you can prove you don't need it. **–Mark Twain**
- Now and then it's good to pause in the pursuit of happiness and just be happy. **–Guillaume Apollinaire**

United States' Largest Banks
(in millions of U.S. dollars)

Rank	Name (city, state)	Consolidated Assets
1	Citigroup (New York, N.Y.)	$2,220,866
2	Bank of America Corp. (Charlotte, N.C.)	1,535,684
3	J. P. Morgan Chase & Company (Columbus, Ohio)	1,458,042
4	Wachovia Corp. (Charlotte, N.C.)	719,922
5	Taunus Corp. (New York, N.Y.)	579,062
6	Wells Fargo & Company (San Fransisco, Calif.)	539,865
7	HSBC North America Inc. (Prospect Heights, Ill.)	483,630
8	U.S. Bancorp (Minneapolis, Minn.)	222,530
9	Suntrust Banks, Inc. (Atlanta, Ga.)	180,314
10	ABN Amro North America (Chicago, Ill.)	160,341

Source: Federal Reserve System National Information Center, September 30, 2007.

"How about that? Your premature withdrawal and your substantial penalty are exactly equal."

© Steve Allen/Brand X Pictures/Jupiter Images

CHAPTER 7

Invoices, Trade Discounts, and Cash Discounts

PERFORMANCE OBJECTIVES

THE INVOICE

SECTION I 7

In business, merchandise is bought and sold many times as it passes from the manufacturer through wholesalers and retailers to the final consumer. A bill of sale or an **invoice** is a business document used to keep track of these sales and purchases. From the seller's point of view, they are sales invoices; from the buyer's point of view, they are purchase invoices, or purchase orders.

invoice A document detailing a sales transaction, containing a list of goods shipped or services rendered, with an account of all costs.

Invoices are a comprehensive record of a sales transaction. They show what merchandise or services have been sold, to whom, in what quantities, at what price, and under what conditions and terms. They vary in style and format from company to company, but most contain essentially the same information. Invoices are used extensively in business, and it is important to be able to read and understand them. In this chapter, you will learn how businesses use invoices and the math applications that relate to them.

F.O.B. shipping point The buyer pays all transportation charges from the vendor's location.

READING AND UNDERSTANDING THE PARTS OF AN INVOICE

Exhibit 7-1 shows a typical format used in business for an invoice. The important parts have been labeled and are explained in Exhibit 7-2. Some of the terms have page references, which direct you to the sections in this chapter that further explain those terms and their business math applications. Exhibit 7-2 also presents some of the most commonly used invoice abbreviations. These pertain to merchandise quantities and measurements.

With some practice, these terms and abbreviations will become familiar to you. Take some time to look them over before you continue reading.

F.O.B. destination The seller pays all the shipping changes to the buyer's store or warehouse and then bills the buyer for these charges on the invoice.

F.O.B. Term used in quoting shipping charges meaning "free on board" or "freight on board."

Shipping Terms

Two frequently used shipping terms that you should become familiar with are **F.O.B. shipping point** and **F.O.B. destination. F.O.B.** means "free on board" or "freight on board." These terms define the shipping charges and when the title (ownership) of the goods is transferred from the seller to the buyer. Ownership becomes important when insurance claims must be filed due to problems in shipment.

F.O.B. Shipping Point When the terms are F.O.B. shipping point, the buyer pays the shipping company directly. The merchandise title is transferred to the buyer at the manufacturer's factory, or at a shipping point such as a railroad freight yard or air freight terminal. From this point, the buyer is responsible for the merchandise.

F.O.B. Destination When the shipping terms are F.O.B. destination, the seller is responsible for prepaying the shipping charges to the destination. The destination is usually the buyer's store or warehouse. Unless prices are quoted as "delivered," the seller then bills the buyer on the invoice for the shipping charges.

Sometimes the freight terms are stated as F.O.B. with the name of a city. For example, if the seller is in Ft. Worth and the buyer is in New York, F.O.B. Ft. Worth means the title is transferred in Ft. Worth, and the buyer pays the shipping charges from Ft. Worth to New York. If the terms are F.O.B. New York, the seller pays the shipping charges to New York and then bills the buyer for those charges on the invoice. Exhibit 7-3, Shipping Terms, on page 209, illustrates these transactions.

When companies ship and receive merchandise, invoices and purchase orders are used to record the details of the transaction.

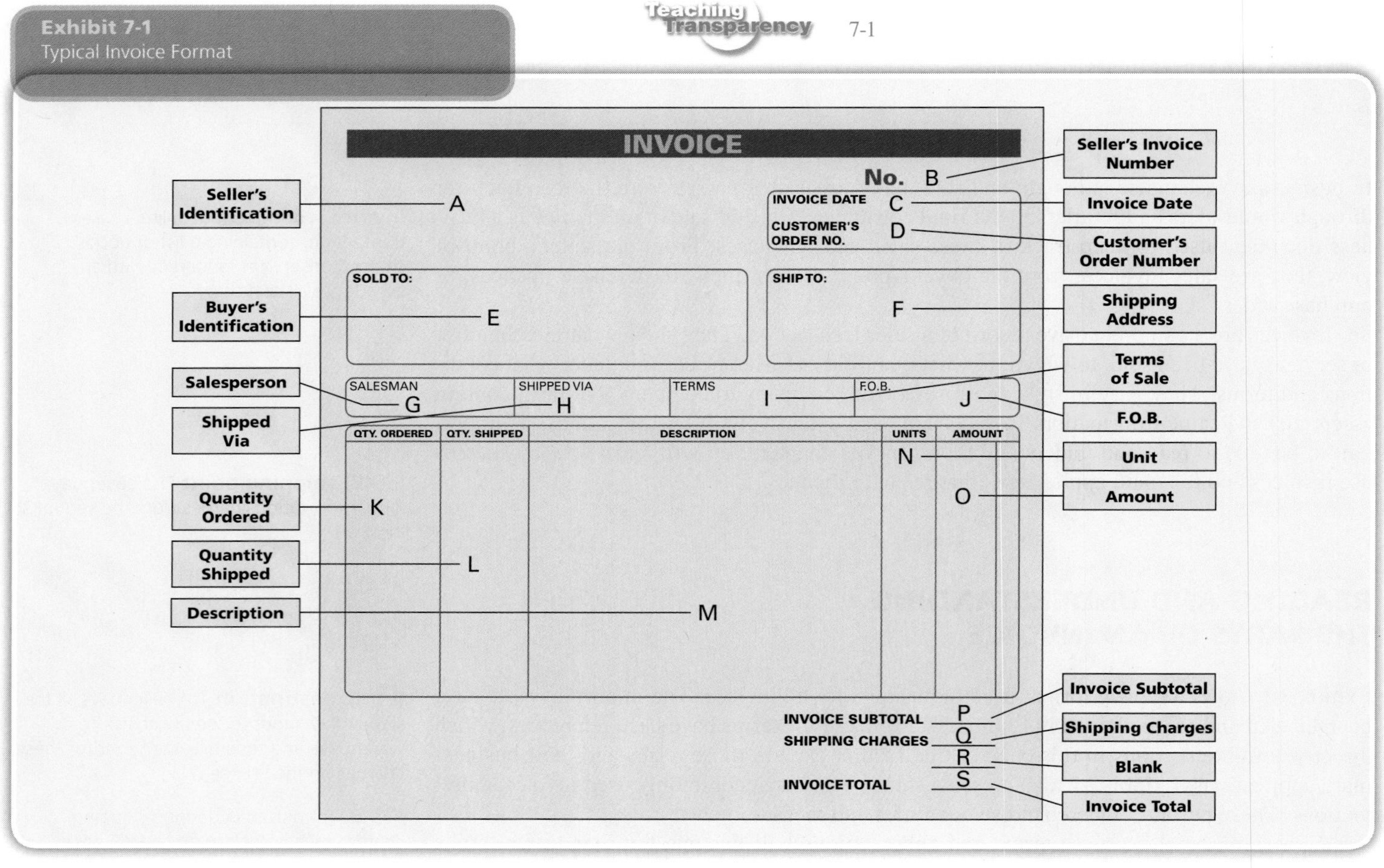

Exhibit 7-1
Typical Invoice Format

Exhibit 7-2
Invoice Terminology and Abbreviations

Invoice Terminology

A **Seller's Identification**—Name, address, and logo or corporate symbol of the seller

B **Seller's Invoice Number**—Seller's identification number of the transaction

C **Invoice Date**—Date the invoice was written

D **Customer's Order Number**—Buyer's identification number of the transaction

E **Buyer's Identification**—Name and mailing address of the buyer

F **Shipping Address**—Address where merchandise will be shipped

G **Salesperson**—Name of salesperson credited with the sale

H **Shipped Via**—Name of shipping company handling the shipment

I **Terms**—Terms of sale—Section detailing date of payment and cash discount (p. 225)

J **F.O.B.**—"Free on board"—Section detailing who pays the shipping company and when title is transferred. (p. 205)

K **Quantity Ordered**—Number of units ordered

L **Quantity Shipped**—Number of units shipped

M **Description**—Detailed description of the merchandise, including model numbers

N **Unit**—Price per unit of merchandise

O **Amount**—Extended total—Quantity in units times the unit price for each line (p. 209)

P **Invoice Subtotal**—Total of the "amount" column—Merchandise total (p. 208)

Q **Shipping Charges**—Cost to physically transport the merchandise from the seller to the buyer (p. 205)

R **Blank Line**—Line used for other charges, such as insurance or handling

S **Invoice Total**—Total amount of the invoice—Includes merchandise plus all other charges (p. 208)

Invoice Abbreviations

ea	**each**	**pr**	**pair**	**in.**	**inch**	**oz**	**ounce**
dz or **doz**	**dozen**	**dm** or **drm**	**drum**	**ft**	**foot**	**g** or **gr**	**gram**
gr or **gro**	**gross**	**bbl**	**barrel**	**yd**	**yard**	**kg**	**kilogram**
bx	**box**	**sk**	**sack**	**mm**	**millimeter**	**pt**	**pint**
cs	**case**	**@**	**at**	**cm**	**centimeter**	**qt**	**quart**
ct or **crt**	**crate**	**C**	**100 items**	**m**	**meter**	**gal**	**gallon**
ctn or **cart**	**carton**	**M**	**1,000 items**	**lb**	**pound**	**cwt**	**hundred weight**

EXAMPLE 1 IDENTIFYING PARTS OF AN INVOICE

From the following Whole Grain Cereal Co. invoice, identify the indicated parts.

a.	Seller	______	b.	Invoice number	______
c.	Invoice date	______	d.	Cust. order #	______
e.	Buyer	______	f.	Terms of sale	______
g.	Shipping address	______	h.	Salesperson	______
i.	Shipped via	______	j.	Insurance	______
k.	Shipping charges	______	l.	Invoice subtotal	______
m.	Unit price—Fruit and Nut Flakes	______	n.	Invoice total	______

SOLUTION STRATEGY

a.	Seller	Whole Grain Cereal Co.	b.	Invoice number	2112
c.	Invoice date	August 19, 20XX	d.	Cust. order #	B-1623
e.	Buyer	A & P Supermarkets	f.	Terms of sale	Net 45 days
g.	Shipping address	1424 Peachtree Rd	h.	Salesperson	H.L. Mager
i.	Shipped via	Terminal transport	j.	Insurance	$33.00
k.	Shipping charges	$67.45	l.	Invoice subtotal	$2,227.05
m.	Unit price—Fruit and Nut Flakes	$19.34	n.	Invoice total	$2,327.50

INVOICE

No. 2112

Whole Grain Cereal Co.
697 Canyon Road
Boulder, CO 80304

INVOICE DATE August 19, 20XX
CUSTOMER'S ORDER NO. B-1623

SOLD TO:
A & P SUPERMARKETS
565 North Avenue
Atlanta, Georgia 30348

SHIP TO:
DISTRIBUTION CENTER
1424 Peachtree Road
Atlanta, Georgia 30341

SALESMAN	SHIPPED VIA	TERMS	F.O.B.
H. L. Mager	Terminal Transport	Net - 45 Days	Boulder, CO

QTY. ORDERED	QTY. SHIPPED	DESCRIPTION		UNIT	AMOUNT
55 cs.	55 cs.	Corn Crunchies	24 ounce	22.19	$1220 45
28 cs.	28 cs.	Fruit and Nut Flakes	24 ounce	19.34	541 52
41 cs.	22 cs.	Rice and Wheat Flakes	16 ounce	21.14	465 08

INVOICE SUBTOTAL	2,227.05
SHIPPING CHARGES	67.45
INSURANCE	33.00
INVOICE TOTAL	$2,327.50

TEACHING TIP
Have students keep in mind that invoices may vary in style and format from company to company, but most contain essentially the same information.

TRY IT EXERCISE 1

From the following FotoFair invoice, identify the indicated parts:

a. Buyer	______	b. Invoice number	______
c. Invoice date	______	d. Amount—Pocket Pro 55	______
e. Seller	______	f. Terms of sale	______
g. Shipping address	______	h. Salesperson	______
i. Shipped via	______	j. F.O.B.	______
k. Shipping charges	______	l. Invoice subtotal	______
m. Unit price—Pocket Pro 75	______	n. Invoice total	______

Teaching Transparency 7-2

CHECK YOUR ANSWERS WITH THE SOLUTIONS ON PAGE 242.

INVOICE

No. 44929

FotoFair Distributors
3900 Crescent Way
Knoxville, TN 37996

INVOICE DATE November 27, 20XX
CUSTOMER'S ORDER NO. 09022

SOLD TO:
SHUTTERBUG CAMERA SHOPS
1518 N. W. 123rd. Street
Chicago, Illinois 60613

SHIP TO:
Warehouse
1864 N. W. 123rd. Street
Chicago, Illinois 60613

SALESMAN	SHIPPED VIA	TERMS	F.O.B.
J. Herman	Federal Express	Net - 30 Days	Knoxville, TN

QTY. ORDERED	QTY. SHIPPED	DESCRIPTION	UNIT	AMOUNT
12	12	Pocket Pro 55—digital camera	260.00	3,120 00
6	6	Pocket Pro 75—digital camera	345.00	2,070 00
15	15	Compact flash memory cards	24.40	366 00
8	8	Tripods	9.60	76 80

Invoice Subtotal	5,632.80
Shipping Charges	125.00
Invoice Total	$5,757.80

7-2 EXTENDING AND TOTALING AN INVOICE

invoice subtotal The amount of all merchandise or services on the invoice before adjustments.

invoice total The final amount due from the buyer to the seller.

Extending an invoice is the process of computing the value in the Total or Amount column for each line of the invoice. This number represents the total dollar amount of each type of merchandise or service being purchased. The **invoice subtotal** is the amount of all items on the invoice before shipping and handling charges, insurance, and other adjustments, such as discounts, returns, and credits. The **invoice total** is the final amount due from the buyer to the seller.

Exhibit 7-3
Shipping Terms

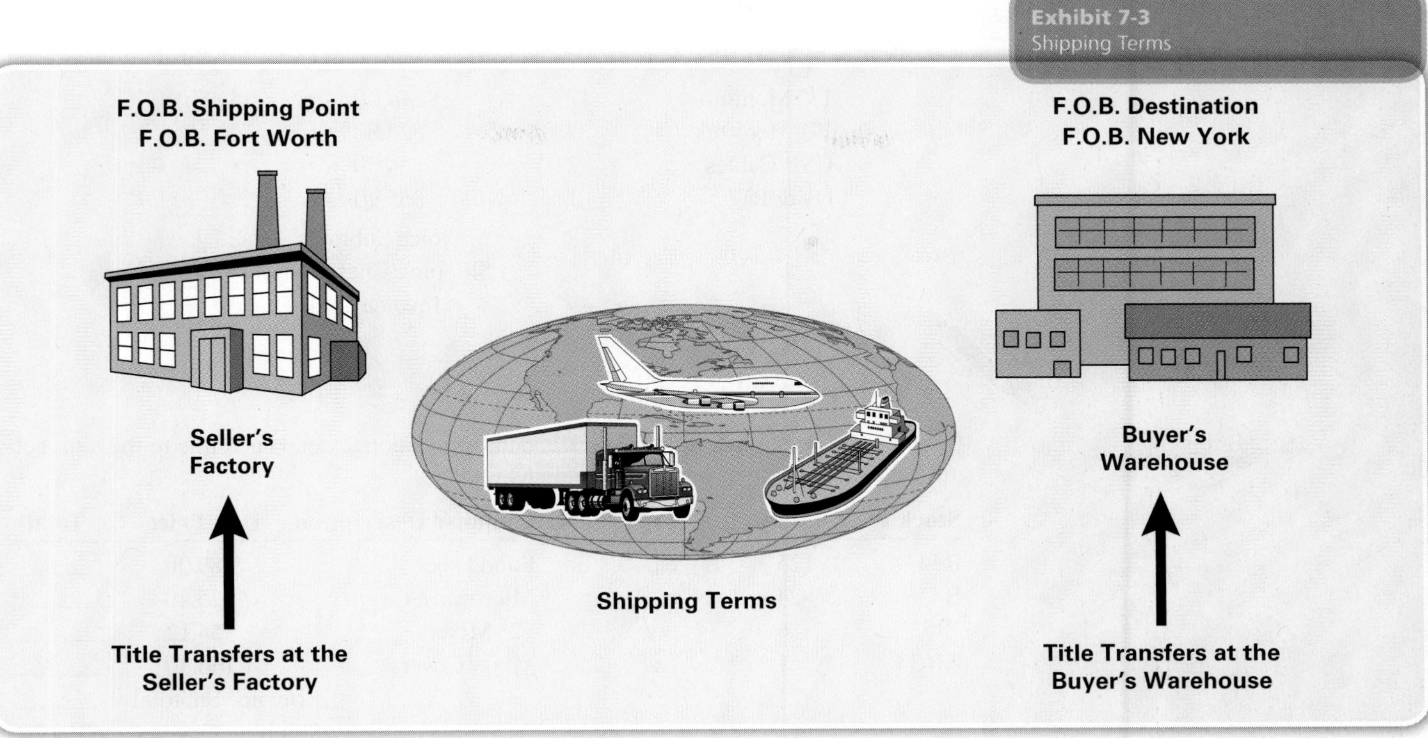

STEPS TO EXTEND AND TOTAL AN INVOICE

Step 1. For each line of the invoice, multiply the number of items by the cost per item.

$$\text{Extended total} = \text{Number of items} \times \text{Cost per item}$$

Step 2. Add all extended totals to get the invoice subtotal.

Step 3. Calculate the invoice total by adding the freight charges, insurance, and other charges, if any, to the subtotal.

EXAMPLE 2 EXTENDING AND TOTALING AN INVOICE

From the following invoice for Computer Mart, extend each line to the total column and calculate the invoice subtotal and total.

Stock #	Quantity	Unit	Merchandise Description	Unit Price	Total
4334	17	ea.	13" Monitors	$244.00	______
1217	8	ea.	17" Monitors	525.80	______
2192	2	doz.	USB Cables	24.50	______
5606	1	bx.	DVD-RW	365.90	______
				Invoice Subtotal	______
				Shipping Charges	$244.75
				Invoice Total	______

SOLUTION STRATEGY

					Total
13" Monitors	17	×	$244.00	=	$4,148.00
17" Monitors	8	×	525.80	=	4,206.40
USB Cables	2	×	24.50	=	49.00
DVD-RW	1	×	365.90	=	365.90
			Invoice Subtotal		$8,769.30
			Shipping Charges		+ 244.75
			Invoice Total		$9,014.05

TRY IT EXERCISE 2

Teaching Transparency 7-3

From the following invoice for The Kitchen Connection, extend each line to the total column and calculate the invoice subtotal and total.

Stock #	Quantity	Unit	Merchandise Description	Unit Price	Total
R443	125	ea.	Food Processors	$ 89.00	______
B776	24	ea.	Microwave Ovens	225.40	______
Z133	6	doz.	12" Mixers	54.12	______
Z163	1	bx.	Mixer Covers	166.30	______
				Invoice Subtotal	______
				Shipping Charges	$194.20
				Invoice Total	______

CHECK YOUR ANSWERS WITH THE SOLUTIONS ON PAGE 242.

SECTION I Review Exercises

What word is represented by each of the following abbreviations?

1. bx. Box
2. pt Pint
3. drm. Drum
4. kg Kilogram
5. gro. Gross
6. oz Ounce
7. M. Thousand
8. cwt Hundredweight

Using the Frasier invoice on page 211, extend each line to the amount column and calculate the subtotal and total. Then answer Questions 9–22. (*Note:* Although 26 boxes of 2-inch reflective tape were ordered, only 11 boxes were shipped. Charge only for the boxes shipped.)

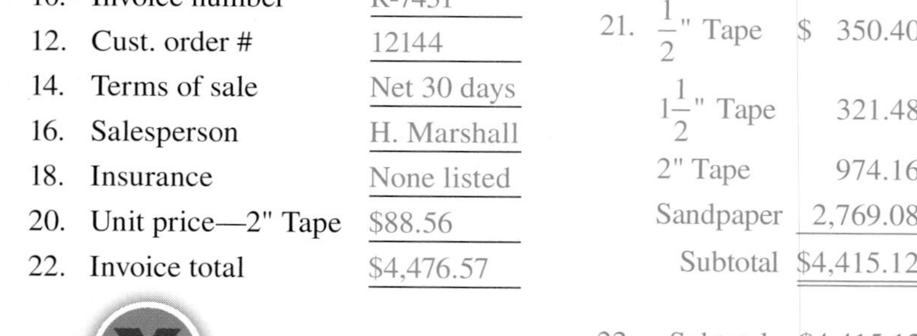

9. Seller: Frasier Manufacturing
10. Invoice number: R-7431
11. Invoice date: June 16, 20XX
12. Cust. order #: 12144
13. Buyer: J.M. Hardware Supply
14. Terms of sale: Net 30 days
15. Shipping address: 2051 W. Adams Blv d. Lansing, MI 48901
16. Salesperson: H. Marshall
17. Shipped via: Gilbert Trucking
18. Insurance: None listed
19. Shipping charges: $61.45
20. Unit price—2" Tape: $88.56
21. Invoice subtotal: $4,415.12
22. Invoice total: $4,476.57

21.

$\frac{1}{2}$" Tape	$ 350.40
$1\frac{1}{2}$" Tape	321.48
2" Tape	974.16
Sandpaper	2,769.08
Subtotal	$4,415.12

22.

Subtotal	$4,415.12
Shipping	61.45
Total	$4,476.57

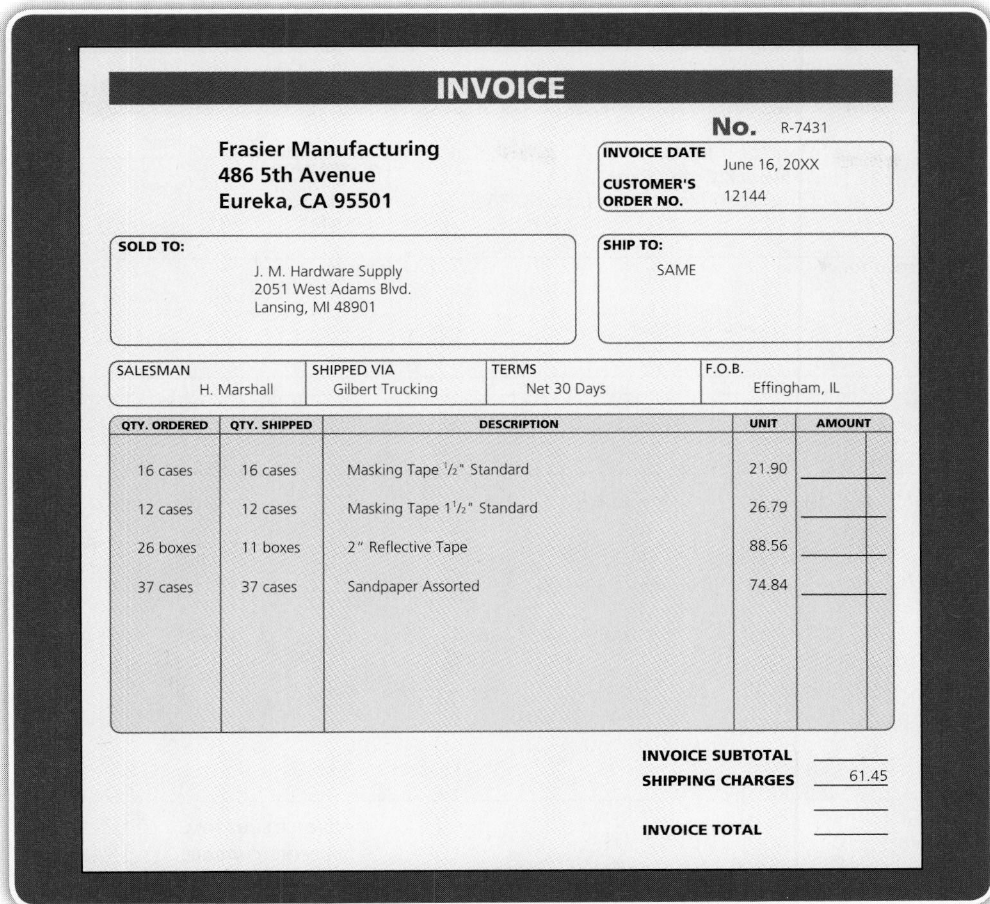

INVOICE

Frasier Manufacturing
486 5th Avenue
Eureka, CA 95501

No. R-7431

INVOICE DATE	June 16, 20XX
CUSTOMER'S ORDER NO.	12144

SOLD TO:
J. M. Hardware Supply
2051 West Adams Blvd.
Lansing, MI 48901

SHIP TO:
SAME

SALESMAN	SHIPPED VIA	TERMS	F.O.B.
H. Marshall	Gilbert Trucking	Net 30 Days	Effingham, IL

QTY. ORDERED	QTY. SHIPPED	DESCRIPTION	UNIT	AMOUNT
16 cases	16 cases	Masking Tape 1/2" Standard	21.90	
12 cases	12 cases	Masking Tape 1 1/2" Standard	26.79	
26 boxes	11 boxes	2" Reflective Tape	88.56	
37 cases	37 cases	Sandpaper Assorted	74.84	

INVOICE SUBTOTAL	
SHIPPING CHARGES	61.45
INVOICE TOTAL	

In the Business World

Frequently, merchandise that is ordered from vendors is "out of stock" and goes into back-order status.

As a general rule, companies charge only for the merchandise that is shipped.

BUSINESS DECISION MANAGING MERCHANDISE

23. You are the store manager for The Bedding Warehouse. The invoice on page 212 is due for payment to one of your vendors, Hamilton Mills.

a. Check the invoice for errors, and correct any you find.

Corrected figures: Shams • $266.00

Subtotal $5,857.55

Total due $6,011.20

b. Your warehouse manager reports that there were three king-size sheets and five queen-size sheets returned, along with four packages of queen pillow cases. Calculate the revised total due.

3 × 45.10 = $135.30 Total return = $394.70
5 × 37.60 = $188.00 Total due = $5,616.50
4 × 17.85 = $71.40

c. The vendor has offered a 4% early payment discount that applies only to the merchandise, not the shipping or insurance. What is the amount of the discount?

5,616.50 − 153.65 = 5,462.85
5,462.85 × .04 = $218.51

d. What is the new balance due after the discount?

5,616.50 − 218.51 = $5,397.99

Retail store managers manage stores that specialize in selling a specific line of merchandise, such as groceries, meat, liquor, apparel, furniture, automobile parts, electronic items or household appliances.

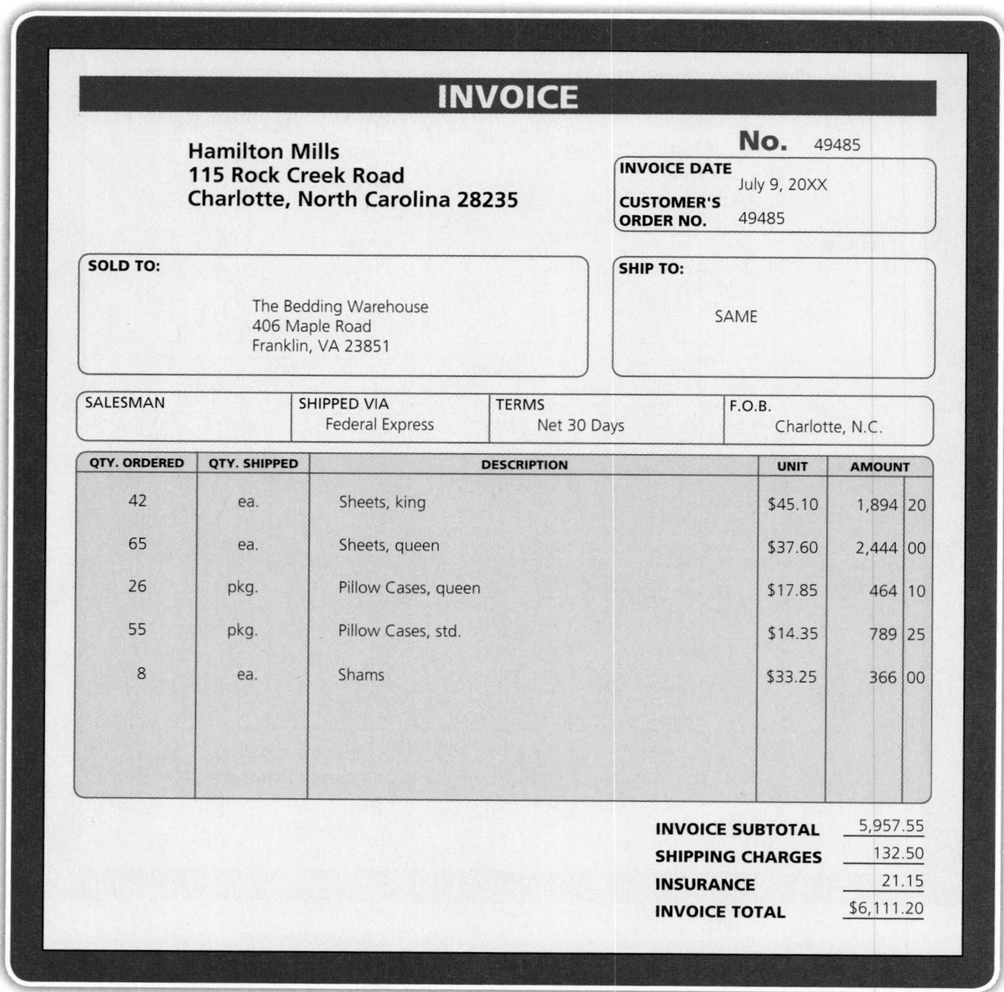

INVOICE

Hamilton Mills
115 Rock Creek Road
Charlotte, North Carolina 28235

No. 49485

INVOICE DATE July 9, 20XX
CUSTOMER'S ORDER NO. 49485

SOLD TO: The Bedding Warehouse, 406 Maple Road, Franklin, VA 23851

SHIP TO: SAME

SALESMAN	SHIPPED VIA	TERMS	F.O.B.
	Federal Express	Net 30 Days	Charlotte, N.C.

QTY. ORDERED	QTY. SHIPPED	DESCRIPTION	UNIT	AMOUNT
42	ea.	Sheets, king	$45.10	1,894 20
65	ea.	Sheets, queen	$37.60	2,444 00
26	pkg.	Pillow Cases, queen	$17.85	464 10
55	pkg.	Pillow Cases, std.	$14.35	789 25
8	ea.	Shams	$33.25	366 00

INVOICE SUBTOTAL	5,957.55
SHIPPING CHARGES	132.50
INSURANCE	21.15
INVOICE TOTAL	$6,111.20

SECTION II TRADE DISCOUNTS—SINGLE

The path merchandise travels as it moves from the manufacturer through wholesalers and retailers to the ultimate consumer is known as a channel of distribution or trade channel. The businesses that form these channels are said to be "in the trade." In today's complex economy, a number of different trade channels are used to move goods and services efficiently.

trade discount Reductions from the manufacturer's list price given to businesses that are "in the trade," for performance of marketing functions.

list price Suggested retail selling price of an item, set by the manufacturer or supplier. The original price from which discounts are taken.

Trade discounts are reductions from the manufacturer's suggested **list price**. They are given to businesses at various levels of the trade channel for the performance of marketing functions. These functions may include activities such as selling, advertising, storage, service, and display.

Manufacturers print catalogs showcasing their merchandise. Often, these catalogs contain the manufacturer's suggested list or retail prices. Businesses in the trade receive price sheets from the manufacturer listing the trade discounts, in percent form, associated with each item in the catalog. By issuing updated price sheets of trade discounts, manufacturers have the flexibility of changing the prices of their merchandise without the expense of reprinting the entire catalog.

Trade discounts are sometimes quoted as a single discount and sometimes as a series or chain of discounts. The number of discounts is dependent on the extent of the marketing services performed by the channel member.

CALCULATING THE AMOUNT OF A SINGLE TRADE DISCOUNT

The amount of a single trade discount is calculated by multiplying the list price by the trade discount rate.

TEACHING TIP
Point out that trade discounts are covered before cash discounts because that is the order in which they occur in sales transactions. The trade discount determines the price of the merchandise, whereas the cash discount relates to when the bill is paid.

Trade discount = List price × Trade discount rate

EXAMPLE 3 CALCULATING THE AMOUNT OF A SINGLE TRADE DISCOUNT

What is the amount of the trade discount on merchandise with a list price of $2,800 and a trade discount rate of 45%?

SOLUTION STRATEGY

Trade discount = List price × Trade discount rate

Trade discount = 2,800 × .45 = $1,260

TRY IT EXERCISE 3

Gifts Galore, a retail gift shop, buys merchandise with a list price of $7,600 from a wholesaler of novelty items and toys. The wholesaler extends a 30% trade discount rate to the retailer. What is the amount of the trade discount?

CHECK YOUR ANSWER WITH THE SOLUTION ON PAGE 242.

CALCULATING NET PRICE BY USING THE NET PRICE FACTOR, COMPLEMENT METHOD

The **net price** is the amount a business actually pays for the merchandise after the discount has been deducted. It may be calculated by subtracting the amount of the trade discount from the list price.

net price The amount a business actually pays for the merchandise after the discount has been deducted.

Net price = List price − Trade discount

Frequently, merchants are more interested in knowing the net price of an item than the amount of the trade discount. In that case, the net price can be calculated directly from the list price without first finding the amount of the discount.

The list price of an item is considered to be 100%. If, for example, the trade discount on an item is 40% of the list price, the net price will be 60%, because the two must equal 100%. This 60%, the complement of the trade discount rate (100% − 40%), is the portion of the list price that *is* paid. Known as the **net price factor**, it is usually written in decimal form.

net price factor The percent of the list price a business pays for merchandise. It is the multiplier used to calculate the net price.

STEPS TO CALCULATE NET PRICE BY USING THE NET PRICE FACTOR

Step 1. Calculate the net price factor, complement of the trade discount rate.

Net price factor = 100% − Trade discount rate

Step 2. Calculate the net price.

Net price = List price × Net price factor

Note: This procedure can be combined into one step by the formula.

Net price = List price(100% − Trade discount rate)

Learning Tip

Complements are two numbers that add up to 100%. The trade discount rate and the net price factor are complements of each other. This means that if we know one of them, the other can be found by subtracting from 100%.

EXAMPLE 4 CALCULATING THE NET PRICE

Calculate the net price of merchandise listing for $900 less a trade discount rate of 45%.

SOLUTION STRATEGY

Net price = List price(100% − Trade discount rate)
Net price = 900(100% − 45%)
Net price = 900(.55) = $495

TRY IT EXERCISE 4

Smitty's Hardware Store bought paint supplies listing for $2,100 with a single trade discount rate of 35%. What is the net price of the order?

CHECK YOUR ANSWER WITH THE SOLUTION ON PAGE 242.

7-5 CALCULATING TRADE DISCOUNT RATE WHEN LIST PRICE AND NET PRICE ARE KNOWN

The trade discount rate can be calculated by using the now-familiar percentage formula, Rate = Portion ÷ Base. For this application, the amount of the trade discount is the portion, or numerator, and the list price is the base, or denominator.

$$\textbf{Trade discount rate} = \frac{\textbf{Trade discount}}{\textbf{List price}}$$

STEPS FOR CALCULATING TRADE DISCOUNT RATE

Step 1. Calculate the amount of the trade discount.

Trade discount = List price − Net price

Step 2. Calculate the trade discount rate.

$$\textbf{Trade discount rate} = \frac{\textbf{Trade discount}}{\textbf{List price}}$$

EXAMPLE 5 CALCULATING THE SINGLE TRADE DISCOUNT AND RATE

Sterling Manufacturing sells tools to American Garden Supply. In a recent transaction, the list price of an order was $47,750, and the net price of the order was $32,100. Calculate the amount of the trade discount. What was the trade discount rate? Round your answer to the nearest tenth percent.

SOLUTION STRATEGY

Trade discount = List price − Net price

Trade discount = 47,750 − 32,100 = $15,650

$$\text{Trade discount rate} = \frac{\text{Trade discount}}{\text{List price}}$$

$$\text{Trade discount rate} = \frac{15{,}650}{47{,}750} = .3277 = 32.8\%$$

TRY IT EXERCISE 5

Wilson Sporting Goods recently sold tennis rackets listing for $109,500 to The Sports Authority. The net price of the order was $63,300. What was the amount of the trade discount? What was the trade discount rate? Round your answer to the nearest tenth percent.

CHECK YOUR ANSWER WITH THE SOLUTION ON PAGE 242.

Review Exercises

Calculate the following trade discounts. Round all answers to the nearest cent.

	List Price	Trade Discount Rate	Trade Discount
1.	$860.00	30%	$258.00
	Trade discount = 860.00 × .30 = $258.00		
2.	125.50	12%	$15.06
	Trade discount = 125.50 × .12 = $15.06		
3.	41.75	19%	$7.93
	Trade discount = 41.75 × .19 = $7.93		
4.	499.00	8%	$39.92
	Trade discount = 499.00 × .08 = $39.92		
5.	88.25	50%	$44.13
	Trade discount = 88.25 × .50 = $44.13		

Calculate the following trade discounts and net prices to the nearest cent.

	List Price	Trade Discount Rate	Trade Discount	Net Price	Net Price	Trade Discount
6.	$286.00	25%	$71.50	$214.50	286.00 − 71.50 = $214.50	286.00 × .25 = $71.50
7.	134.79	40%	$53.92	$80.87	134.79 − 53.92 = $80.87	134.79 × .4 = $53.92
8.	21.29	18%	$3.83	$17.46	21.29 − 3.83 = $17.46	21.29 × .18 = $3.83
9.	959.00	55%	$527.45	$431.55	959.00 − 527.45 = $431.55	959.00 × .55 = $527.45

Calculate the following net price factors and net prices by using the complement method. Round all answers to the nearest cent.

Complete, worked-out solutions for Exercises 10–16 appear in Appendix B, following the index.

	List Price	Trade Discount Rate	Net Price Factor	Net Price
10.	$3,499.00	37%	63%	$2,204.37
11.	565.33	24%	76%	$429.65
12.	1,244.25	45.8%	54.2%	$674.38
13.	4.60	$12\frac{3}{4}$%	87.25%	$4.01

Calculate the following trade discounts and trade discount rates. Round answers to the nearest tenth of a percent.

	List Price	Trade Discount	Trade Discount Rate	Net Price
14.	$4,500.00	$935.00	20.8%	$3,565.00
15.	345.50	$120.50	34.9%	225.00
16.	2.89	$.74	25.6%	2.15

17. Find the amount of the trade discount on a television set that has a list price of $799.95 less a trade discount of 30%.

Trade discount = List price × Trade discount rate
Trade discount = 799.95 × .30 = $239.99

18. Find the amount of the trade discount on a set of fine china that lists for $345.70 less 55%.

Trade discount = 345.70 × .55 = $190.14

19. What is the amount of the trade discount offered to a shoe store for merchandise purchased at a total list price of $7,800 less a trade discount of 25%?

Trade discount = 7,800 × .25 = $1,950

© Andrew Ward/Life File/Photodisc/ Getty Images

Food Marketing Facts and Figures

According to the Food Marketing Institute, U.S. supermarkets had $499.5 billion in sales during 2006. The United States has 34,052 supermarkets with annual sales of $2 million or more. More than three-quarters of those supermarkets, 25,890, belong to a chain. The remaining 8,162 are independent supermarkets. Grocery stores with less than $2 million in annual sales account for 13,047 stores.

In addition to supermarkets and independent grocery stores, the United States has 1,067 wholesale club stores that market groceries and 140,241 convenience stores.

20. Sunshine Market ordered twelve cases of soup with a list price of $18.90 per case, and eight cases of baked beans with a list price of $33.50 per case. The wholesaler offered a 39% trade discount to Sunshine Market.

a. What is the total extended list price of the order?

18.90 × 12 = 226.80
33.50 × 8 = +268.00
Total extended list price = $494.80

b. What is the total amount of the trade discount on this order?

Trade discount = 494.80 × .39 = $192.97

c. What is the total net amount Sunshine Market owes the wholesaler for the order?

Net amount = 494.80 − 192.97 = $301.83

21. Kalaidoscope for Kids, a chain of clothing stores, purchased merchandise with a total list price of $25,450 from Sandy Sport, a manufacturer. The order has a trade discount of 34%.

a. What is the amount of the trade discount?

Trade discount = 25,450 × .34 = $8,653

b. What is the net amount Kalaidoscope owes Sandy Sport for the merchandise?

Net price = 25,450 − 8,653 = $16,797

22. An item with a trade discount of 41% has a list price of $289.50. What is the net price?

Net price factor = 100 − 41 = 59%
Net price = 289.50 × .59 = $170.81

23. Nathan and David Beauty Salon places an order for beauty supplies from a wholesaler. The list price of the order is $2,800. If the vendor offers a trade discount of 46%, what is the net price of the order?

    Net price factor = 100% − 46% = 54%
    Net price = 2,800 × .54 = $1,512

24. A watch has a list price of $889 and can be bought by Sterling Jewelers for a net price of $545.75.

    a. What is the amount of the trade discount?

    Trade discount = 889 − 545.75 = $343.25

    b. What is the trade discount rate?

    $$\text{Trade discount rate} = \frac{343.25}{889} = .3861 = 38.6\%$$

25. You are the buyer for the housewares department of the Galleria Department Store. A number of vendors in your area carry similar lines of merchandise. On sets of microwavable serving bowls, Kitchen Magic offers a list price of $400 per dozen, less a 38% trade discount. Pro-Chef offers a similar set for a list price of $425, less a 45% trade discount.

    a. Which vendor is offering the lower net price?

Kitchen Magic	Pro-Chef
400 (100% − 38%)	425 (100% − 45%)
400 × .62 = 248	425 × .55 = 233.75
Net price per dozen = $248.00	Net price per dozen = $233.75
Pro-Chef has a lower price.	

    b. If you order 500 dozen sets of the bowls, how much money will be saved by using the lower-priced vendor?

    500 × 248.00 = 124,000
    500 × 233.75 = 116,875
    124,000 − 116,875 = $7,125 Savings

26. Nutrition Central pays $11.90 net price for a bottle of 60 multi-vitamins. The price represents a 30% trade discount from the manufacturer. What is the list price of the vitamins?

    Net price = List price (100% − Trade discount rate)
    11.90 = List price (100% − 30%)
    11.90 = List price × 70%

    $$\text{List price} = \frac{11.90}{.7} = \$17$$

BUSINESS DECISION QUANTITY DISCOUNT

27. You are the purchasing manager for Apex Electronics, a company that manufactures scanners and other computer peripherals. Your vendor for scanner motors, Enfield Industries, is now offering "quantity discounts" in the form of instant rebates and lower shipping charges, as follows:

Quantity	Net Price	Rebate	Shipping
1–500 motors	$16	none	$1.30
501–1,000 motors	16	$1.20	.90
1,001–2,000 motors	16	1.80	.60

(continued)

a. Calculate the cost of the motors, including shipping charges, for each category.

1–500 = $17.30

501–1,000 = $15.70

1,001–2,000 = $14.80

b. If you usually purchase 400 motors per month, what percent would be saved per motor by ordering 800 every two months? Round to the nearest tenth of a percent.

$17.30 - 15.70 = 1.60 \qquad \frac{1.60}{17.30} = 9.2\%$

c. What percent would be saved per motor by ordering 1,200 every three months? Round to the nearest tenth of a percent.

$17.30 - 14.80 = 2.50 \qquad \frac{2.50}{17.30} = 14.5\%$

d. How much money can be saved in a year by purchasing the motors every three months instead of every month?

400 × 12 = 4,800 motors per year

4,800 × 2.50 = $12,000 Savings

e. (Optional) What other factors, besides price, should be considered before changing your purchasing procedures?

Some typical answers may include cost of warehousing and insuring the extra motors; prices falling in the future; new models coming out; and the opportunity cost of the money.

SECTION III TRADE DISCOUNTS—SERIES

Chain, or series, trade discount Term used when a vendor offers a buyer more than one trade discount.

Trade discounts are frequently offered by manufacturers to wholesalers and retailers in a series of two or more, known as **chain** or **series trade discounts**. For example, a series of 25% and 10% is verbally stated as "25 and 10." It is written 25/10. A three-discount series is written 25/10/5. Multiple discounts are given for many reasons. Some of the more common ones follow:

Position or Level in the Channel of Distribution A manufacturer might sell to a retailer at 30% trade discount, whereas a wholesaler in the same channel might be quoted a 30% and a 15% trade discount.

Volume Buying Many manufacturers and wholesalers grant an extra discount for buying a large volume of merchandise. For example, any purchase more than 5,000 units at one time may earn an extra 7% trade discount. Retailers with many stores or those with large storage capacity can enjoy a considerable savings (additional trade discounts) by purchasing in large quantities.

Advertising and Display Additional discounts are often given to retailers and wholesalers who heavily advertise and aggressively promote a manufacturer's line of merchandise.

Competition Competitive pressures often cause extra trade discounts to be offered. In certain industries, such as household products and consumer electronics, price wars are not an uncommon occurrence.

Learning Tip

Remember, when calculating the net price by using a series of trade discounts, you *cannot* simply add the trade discounts together. Each discount must be applied to a successively lower base.

CALCULATING NET PRICE AND THE AMOUNT OF A TRADE DISCOUNT BY USING A SERIES OF TRADE DISCOUNTS

Finding net price with a series of trade discounts is accomplished by taking each trade discount, one at a time, from the previous net price until all discounts have been deducted. Note that you *cannot* simply add the trade discounts together. They must be calculated individually, unless we use the net price factor method—a handy shortcut. Trade discounts can be taken in any order, although they are usually listed and calculated in descending order.

For illustrative purposes, let's begin with an example of how to calculate a series of trade discounts one at a time; then we shall try the shortcut method.

EXAMPLE 6 CALCULATING NET PRICE AND THE AMOUNT OF A TRADE DISCOUNT

Calculate the net price and trade discount for merchandise with a list price of $2,000 less trade discounts of 30/20/15.

SOLUTION STRATEGY

$2,000	$2,000	$1,400	$1,400	$1,120	$1,120	
× .30	− 600	× .20	− 280	× .15	− 168	
$600	$1,400	$280	$1,120	$168	$952	= Net price

Trade discount = List price − Net price

Trade discount = 2,000 − 952 = $1,048

TRY IT EXERCISE 6

Northwest Publishers sold an order of books to The Bookworm, Inc., a chain of bookstores. The list price of the order was $25,000. The Bookworm buys in volume from Northwest. They also prominently display and heavily advertise Northwest's books. Northwest, in turn, gives The Bookworm a series of trade discounts, amounting to 35/20/10. Calculate the net price of the order and the amount of the trade discount.

CHECK YOUR ANSWERS WITH THE SOLUTIONS ON PAGE 242.

7-4

CALCULATING THE NET PRICE OF A SERIES OF TRADE DISCOUNTS BY USING THE NET PRICE FACTOR, COMPLEMENT METHOD

7-7

As a shortcut, the net price can be calculated directly from the list price, bypassing the trade discount, by using the net price factor as before. Remember, the net price factor is the complement of the trade discount rate. With a series of discounts, we must find the complement of each trade discount to calculate the net price factor of the series.

The net price factor indicates to buyers what percent of the list price they actually *do* pay. For example, if the net price factor of a series of discounts is calculated to be .665, this means that the buyer is paying 66.5% of the list price.

STEPS FOR CALCULATING NET PRICE BY USING THE NET PRICE FACTOR

Step 1. Find the complement of the trade discounts in the series by subtracting each from 100% and converting them to decimal form.

Step 2. Calculate the net price factor of the series by multiplying all the decimals together.

Step 3. Calculate the net price by multiplying the list price by the net price factor.

Net price = List price × Net price factor

EXAMPLE 7 CALCULATING NET PRICE FACTOR AND NET PRICE

The Crystal Gallery purchased merchandise from a manufacturer in Italy with a list price of $37,000 less trade discounts of 40/25/10. Calculate the net price factor and the net price of the order.

SOLUTION STRATEGY

Step 1. Subtract each trade discount from 100% and convert to decimals.

100%	100%	100%
− 40%	− 25%	− 10%
60% = .6	75% = .75	90% = .9

Step 2. Multiply all the complements together to get the net price factor.

Net price factor = .6 × .75 × .9

Net price factor = .405

Step 3.

Net price = List price × Net price factor

Net price = 37,000 × .405

Net price = $14,985

CLASSROOM ACTIVITY

Be sure students **do not round** the net price factor!

To illustrate how rounding can change the final result, have them solve the following problem by rounding to hundredths (incorrect) and not rounding (correct):

What is the net price of an order with a list price of $50,000 and trade discounts of 35/25/15?

Rounding to hundredths:
.65 × .75 × .85 = .414375
.41 × 50,000 = $20,500.00

Not rounding:
.65 × .75 × .85 = .414375
.414375 × 50,000 = $20,718.75

TRY IT EXERCISE 7

Something's Fishy, a pet shop, always gets a 30/20/12 series of trade discounts from the Clearview Fish Tank Company. In June, the shop ordered merchandise with a list price of $3,500. In September, the shop placed an additional order listing for $5,800.

a. What is the net price factor for the series of trade discounts?

b. What is the net price of the merchandise purchased in June?

c. What is the net price of the merchandise purchased in September?

CHECK YOUR ANSWERS WITH THE SOLUTIONS ON PAGE 242.

CALCULATING THE AMOUNT OF A TRADE DISCOUNT BY USING A SINGLE EQUIVALENT DISCOUNT

7-8

Sometimes retailers and wholesalers want to know the one single discount rate that equates to a series of trade discounts. This is known as the **single equivalent discount**. We have already learned that the trade discounts *cannot* simply be added together.

Here is the logic: The list price of the merchandise is 100%. If the net price factor is the part of the list price that is paid, then 100% minus the net price factor is the part of the list price that is the trade discount. The single equivalent discount, therefore, is the complement of the net price factor (100% − Net price factor percent).

single equivalent discount A single trade discount that equates to all the discounts in a series or chain.

STEPS TO CALCULATE THE SINGLE EQUIVALENT DISCOUNT AND THE AMOUNT OF A TRADE DISCOUNT

Step 1. Calculate the net price factor as before, by subtracting each trade discount from 100% and multiplying them all together in decimal form.

Step 2. Calculate the single equivalent discount by subtracting the net price factor in decimal form from 1.

Single equivalent discount = 1 − Net price factor

Step 3. Find the amount of the trade discount by multiplying the list price by the single equivalent discount.

Trade discount = List price × Single equivalent discount

EXAMPLE 8 CALCULATING THE SINGLE EQUIVALENT DISCOUNT AND THE AMOUNT OF A TRADE DISCOUNT

Calculate the single equivalent discount and amount of the trade discount on merchandise listing for $10,000, less trade discounts of 30/10/5.

SOLUTION STRATEGY

Step 1. Calculate the net price factor.

$$\begin{array}{r} 100\% \\ -\ 30\% \\ \hline .70 \end{array} \times \begin{array}{r} 100\% \\ -\ 10\% \\ \hline .90 \end{array} \times \begin{array}{r} 100\% \\ -\ 5\% \\ \hline .95 \end{array} = .5985 = \text{Net price factor}$$

Step 2. Calculate the single equivalent discount.

Single equivalent discount = 1 − Net price factor

Single equivalent discount = 1 − .5985 = .4015

Note: 40.15% is the single equivalent discount of the series 30%, 10%, and 5%.

Step 3. Calculate the amount of the trade discount.

Trade discount = List price × Single equivalent discount

Trade discount = 10,000 × .4015 = $4,015

CLASSROOM ACTIVITY

As a review of trade discounts, in groups, have students write and solve some word problems involving a series of trade discounts. Next, have each group work the problems of another group, compare answers, and resolve any differences.

TRY IT EXERCISE 8

The Rainbow Appliance Center purchased an order of dishwashers and ovens listing for $36,800. The manufacturer allows Rainbow a series of trade discounts of 25/15/10. What are the single equivalent discount and the amount of the trade discount?

CHECK YOUR ANSWERS WITH THE SOLUTIONS ON PAGE 242.

SECTION III Review Exercises

Calculate the following net price factors and net prices. For convenience, round net price factors to five decimal places when necessary.

The complete, worked-out solutions for Exercises 1–6 appear in Appendix B, following the index.

	List Price	Trade Discount Rates	Net Price Factor	Net Price
1.	$360.00	12/10	.792	$285.12
2.	425.80	18/15/5	.66215	$281.94
3.	81.75	20/10/10	.648	$52.97
4.	979.20	15/10/5	.72675	$711.63
5.	7.25	25/15/10$\frac{1}{2}$	.57056	$4.14
6.	.39	20/9/8	.66976	$.26

Calculate the following net price factors and single equivalent discounts. Round to five places when necessary.

	Trade Discount Rates	Net Price Factor	Single Equivalent Discount
7.	15/10	.765	.235
8.	20/15/12	.5984	.4016
9.	25/15/7	.59288	.40712
10.	30/5/5	.63175	.36825
11.	35/15/7.5	.51106	.48894

Net Price Factor	Single Equivalent Discount
$.85 \times .90 = .765$	$1.00 - .765 = .235$
$.80 \times .85 \times .88 = .5984$	$1.00 - .5984 = .4016$
$.75 \times .85 \times .93 = .59288$	$1.00 - .59288 = .40712$
$.70 \times .95 \times .95 = .63175$	$1.00 - .63175 = .36825$
$.65 \times .85 \times .925 = .51106$	$1.00 - .51106 = .48894$

Complete the following table. Round net price factors to five decimal places when necessary.

The complete, worked-out solution for Exercise 12 appears in Appendix B, following the index.

	List Price	Trade Discount Rates	Net Price Factor	Single Equivalent Discount	Trade Discount	Net Price
12.	$7,800.00	15/5/5	.76713	.23287	$1,816.39	$5,983.61
13.	1,200.00	20/15/7	.6324	.3676	$441.12	$758.88
14.	560.70	25/15/5	.60563	.39437	$221.12	$339.58
15.	883.50	18/12/9	.65666	.34334	$303.34	$580.16
16.	4.89	12/10/10	.7128	.2872	$1.40	$3.49
17.	2,874.95	30/20/5.5	.5292	.4708	$1,353.53	$1,521.42

18. What is the net price factor of a 25/10 series of trade discounts?

    25/10: .75 × .90

    Net price factor = 0.675

19. What is the net price factor of a 35/15/10 series of discounts?

    35/15/10: .65 × .85 × .90

    Net price factor = 0.49725

20. Kidzstuff.com ordered toys, games, and videos from a vendor. The order had a list price of $10,300 less trade discounts of 25/15/12.

    a. What is the net price factor?

       Net price factor = .75 × .85 × .88 = 0.561

    b. What is the net price of the order?

       Net price = 10,300 × .561 = $5,778.30

21. Legacy Designs places an order for furniture listing for $90,500 less trade discounts of 25/20.

    a. What is the net price factor?

       Net price factor = .75 × .80 = .6

    b. What is the net price of the order?

       Net price = 90,500 × .6 = $54,300

22. If a supplier offers you trade discounts with a net price factor of .5788, what is the single equivalent discount?

    Single equivalent discount = 1.00 − .5788 = .4212

23. A vendor offers trade discounts of 25/15/10.

    a. What is the net price factor?

       Net price factor = .75 × .85 × .90 = .57375

    b. What is the single equivalent discount?

       Single equivalent discount = 1.00 − .57375 = .42625

24. Audio Giant received an order of XM satellite radios listing for $9,500 with trade discounts of 25/13/8.

    a. What is the net price factor?

       Net price factor = .75 × .87 × .92 = .6003

    b. What is the single equivalent discount?

       Single equivalent discount = 1.00 − .6003 = .3997

    c. What is the amount of the trade discount?

       Trade discount = 9,500 × .3997 = $3,797.15

    d. What is the net price of the order?

       Net price = 9,500 × .6003 = $5,702.85

Satellite Radio

Satellite radio or subscription radio (SR) is a digital radio signal that is broadcast by a communications satellite, which covers a much wider geographical range than terrestrial radio signals. Satellite radio is currently at the forefront of the evolution of radio services in the United States.

There are currently two satellite radio companies dividing the pay-for-radio business in the United States.: XM Satellite Radio, Inc., and Sirius Satellite Radio, Inc. These two former rivals have announced their intention to merge, which, if approved would create a single satellite radio entity for the entire country. According to Orbitcast.com, as of September 2007, Sirius had 7,142,538 subscribers and XM had 8,250,000 subscribers.

25. Shari's Boutique is offered a line of blouses that list for $700 per dozen from a clothing manufacturer. They are offering trade discounts of 35/25/5.

    a. What is the net price per dozen Shari will pay for the blouses?

    $.65 \times .75 \times .95 = .46313 \times 700 = \underline{\underline{\$324.19}}$ Per dozen

    b. What is the single equivalent discount of this deal?

    Single equivalent discount $= 1.00 - .46313 = \underline{\underline{.53687}}$

26. The Speedy Auto Service Center can buy auto parts from Southeast Auto Supply at a series discount of 20/15/5 and from Northwest Auto Supply for 25/10/8.

    a. Which auto parts supplier offers a better discount to Speedy?

Southeast	Northwest
$.80 \times .85 \times .95 = .646$	$.75 \times .90 \times .92 = .621$
Single equivalent discount $= 1.00 - .646$	Single equivalent discount $= 1.00 - .621$
Single equivalent discount $= .354$	Single equivalent discount $= .379$

    Northwest offers a better discount.

    b. If Speedy orders $15,000 in parts at list price per month, how much will they save in a year by choosing the lower-priced supplier?

Southeast	Northwest	
$15{,}000 \times .646 = 9{,}690$	$15{,}000 \times .621 = 9{,}315$	$9{,}690 - 9{,}315$
		$375 \times 12 = \underline{\underline{\$4{,}500}}$ Savings per year

27. Samsung offers wholesalers a series discount of 35/20/20 and retailers a series discount of 35/20. A television set has a list price of $560.

    a. What is the price the wholesaler pays?

    $.65 \times .80 \times .80 = 0.416$ $\quad 560 \times .416 = \underline{\underline{\$232.96}}$

    b. What is the price to the retailer?

    $.65 \times .80 = .52$ $\quad 560 \times .52 = \underline{\underline{\$291.20}}$

© Thinkstock/Jupiter Images

The Pharmacy and Drug Store Industry in the U.S. retails a range of prescription and over-the-counter products. These include medicines, apothecaries, health and beauty items such as vitamin supplements, cosmetics and toiletries, as well as photo processing services.

According to the National Association of Chain Drug Stores, (NACDS), in 2006 the industry, with 694,000 employees, generated sales of $249.8 billion in over 55,000 drug stores. Major industry competitors include Walgreen's, CVS Pharmacy, Eckerd, Rite Aid, Brooks, and Long Drug Stores.

28. Midtown Pharmacy buys merchandise from B. G. Distributors with a series discount of 35/15/7.

    a. What is the single equivalent discount?

    $.65 \times .85 \times .93 = .51383$ $\quad 1.00 - .51383 = \underline{\underline{.48617}}$

    b. What is the amount of the trade discount on an order with a list price of $5,700?

    $5{,}700 \times .48617 = \underline{\underline{\$2{,}771.17}}$

29. La Fiesta Food Distributors received the following items at a discount of 25/20/10: 18 cases of canned peaches listing at $26.80 per case and 45 cases of canned pears listing at $22.50 per case.

    a. What is the total list price of this order?

    $26.80 \times 18 = 482.40$

    $22.50 \times 45 = 1{,}012.50$

    Total list price $\underline{\underline{\$1{,}494.90}}$

    b. What is the amount of the trade discount?

    $.75 \times .80 \times .90 = .54$ Net price factor

    $1.00 - .54 = .46$ Single equivalent discount

    $1{,}494.90 \times .46 = \underline{\underline{\$687.65}}$ Trade discount

c. What is the net price of the order?

Net price = 1,494.90 × .54 = $807.25

30. Shopper's Mart purchased the following items. Calculate the extended total after the trade discounts for each line, the invoice subtotal, and the invoice total.

Quantity	Unit	Merchandise	Unit List	Trade Discounts	Extended Total
150	ea.	Blenders	$ 59.95	20/15/15	$5,197.67
400	ea.	Toasters	39.88	20/10/10	10,336.90
18	doz.	Coffee Mills	244.30	30/9/7	2,605.06
12	doz.	Juicers	460.00	25/10/5	3,539.70
				Invoice subtotal	21,679.33
		Extra $5\frac{1}{2}$% volume discount on total order			−1,192.36
				Invoice total	$20,486.97

Blenders 150 × 59.95 × .578 = $5,197.67
Toasters 400 × 39.88 × .648 = $10,336.90
Coffee mills 18 × 244.30 × .59241 = $2,605.06
Juicers 12 × 460 × .64125 = $3,539.70

BUSINESS DECISION NEGOTIATE AND SAVE

31. Referring back to Exercise 30, you have just been hired as the buyer for the kitchen division of Shopper's Mart, a general merchandise retailer. After looking over the discounts offered to the previous buyer by the vendor, you decide to ask for better discounts.

After negotiating with the vendor's salesperson, you now can buy blenders at trade discounts of 20/20/15, and juicers at 25/15/10. In addition, the vendor has increased the volume discount to $6\frac{1}{2}$%.

a. How much would have been saved with your new discounts, based on the quantities of the previous order (Exercise 30)?

Blenders	4,891.92
Toasters	10,336.90
Coffee mills	2,605.06
Juicers	+3,167.10
	21,000.98
$-6\frac{1}{2}$%	1,365.06
	19,635.92

20,486.97	Original net
−19,635.92	New net
$851.05	Savings

b. As a result of your negotiations, the vendor has offered an additional discount of 2% of the total amount due if the invoice is paid within 15 days instead of the usual 30 days. What would be the amount of this discount?

19,635.92 × .02 = $392.72

CASH DISCOUNTS AND TERMS OF SALE

SECTION IV 7

As merchandise physically arrives at the buyer's back door, the invoice ordinarily arrives by mail through the front door. Today, more and more arrive by e-mail. What happens next? The invoice has a section entitled **terms of sale**. The terms of sale are the details of when the invoice must be paid and whether any additional discounts will be offered.

terms of sale The details of when an invoice must be paid, and if a cash discount is being offered.

Commonly, manufacturers allow wholesalers and retailers 30 days or even longer to pay the bill. In certain industries, the time period is as much as 60 or 90 days. This is known as the **credit period**. This gives the buyer time to unpack and check the order, and more important, begin selling the merchandise. This credit period clearly gives the wholesaler and retailer an advantage. They can generate revenue by selling merchandise that they have not paid for yet.

To encourage them to pay the bill earlier than the **net date**, or **due date**, sellers frequently offer buyers an optional extra discount, over and above the trade discounts. This is known as a **cash discount**. Cash discounts are an extra few percent offered as an incentive for early payment of the invoice, usually within 10 to 15 days after the **invoice date**. This is known as the **cash discount period**. The last date for a buyer to take advantage of a cash discount is known as the **discount date**.

credit period The time period that the seller allows the buyer to pay an invoice.

net date, due date The last day of the credit period.

cash discount An extra discount offered by the seller as an incentive for early payment of an invoice.

invoice date The date an invoice is written. The beginning of the discount and credit periods when ordinary dating is used.

cash discount period The time period in which a buyer can take advantage of the cash discount.

discount date The last day of the discount period.

The Importance of Cash Discounts

Both buyers and sellers benefit from cash discounts. Sellers get their money much sooner, which improves their cash flow, whereas buyers get an additional discount, which lowers their merchandise cost, thereby raising their margin or gross profit.

Cash discounts generally range from an extra 1% to 5% off the net price of the merchandise. A 1% to 5% discount may not seem significant, but it is. Let's say that an invoice is due in 30 days; however, a distributor would like payment sooner. They might offer the retailer a cash discount of 2% if the bill is paid within 10 days rather than 30 days. If the retailer chooses to take the cash discount, he or she must pay the bill by the 10th day after the date of the invoice. Note that this is *20 days* earlier than the due date. The retailer is therefore receiving a 2% discount for paying the bill 20 days early.

The logic: There are 18.25 twenty-day periods in a year (365 days divided by 20 days). By multiplying the 2% discount by the 18.25 periods, we see that on a yearly basis, 2% cash discounts can *theoretically* amount to 36.5%. Very significant!

In the Business World

Cash discounts are so important to wholesalers' and retailers' "profit picture" that frequently they borrow the money on a short-term basis to take advantage of the cash discount savings. This procedure is covered in Chapter 10, "Simple Interest."

CALCULATING CASH DISCOUNTS AND NET AMOUNT DUE

Cash discounts are offered in the terms of sale. A transaction with no cash discount would have terms of sale of net 30, for example. This means the **net amount** of the invoice is due in 30 days. If a cash discount is offered, the terms of sale would be written as 2/10, n/30. This means a 2% cash discount may be taken if the invoice is paid within 10 days; if not, the net amount is due in 30 days. See Exhibit 7-4.

net amount The amount of money due from the buyer to the seller.

Exhibit 7-4
Terms of Sale

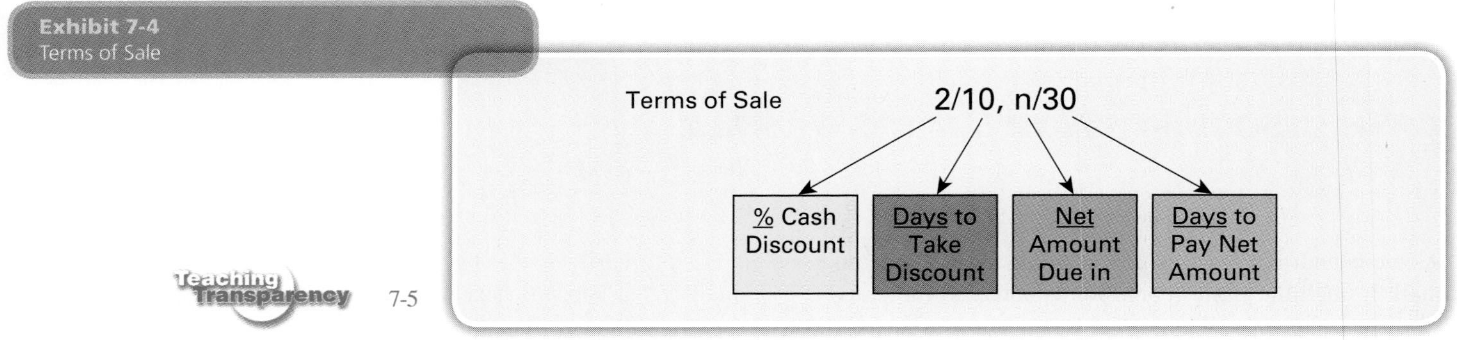

Teaching Transparency 7-5

Exhibit 7-5 shows a time line of the discount period and credit period on an invoice, dated October 15. The 2/10, n/30 terms of sale stipulate a cash discount if the bill is paid within 10 days. If not, the balance is due in 30 days. As you can see, the cash discount period runs for 10 days from the invoice date, October 15 to October 25. The credit period, 30 days, extends from the invoice date through November 14.

Sometimes, two cash discounts are offered, such as 3/15, 1/25, n/60. This means a 3% cash discount is offered if the invoice is paid within 15 days, a 1% cash discount if the invoice is paid within 25 days, with the net amount due in 60 days.

Cash discounts cannot be taken on shipping charges or returned goods, only on the net price of the merchandise. If shipping charges are included in the amount of an invoice, they must be subtracted before taking the cash discount. After the cash discount has been deducted, the shipping charges are added back to get the invoice total.

If arriving merchandise is damaged or is not what was ordered, those goods will be returned to the vendor. The amount of the returned goods must also be subtracted from the amount of the invoice. They are no longer a part of the transaction.

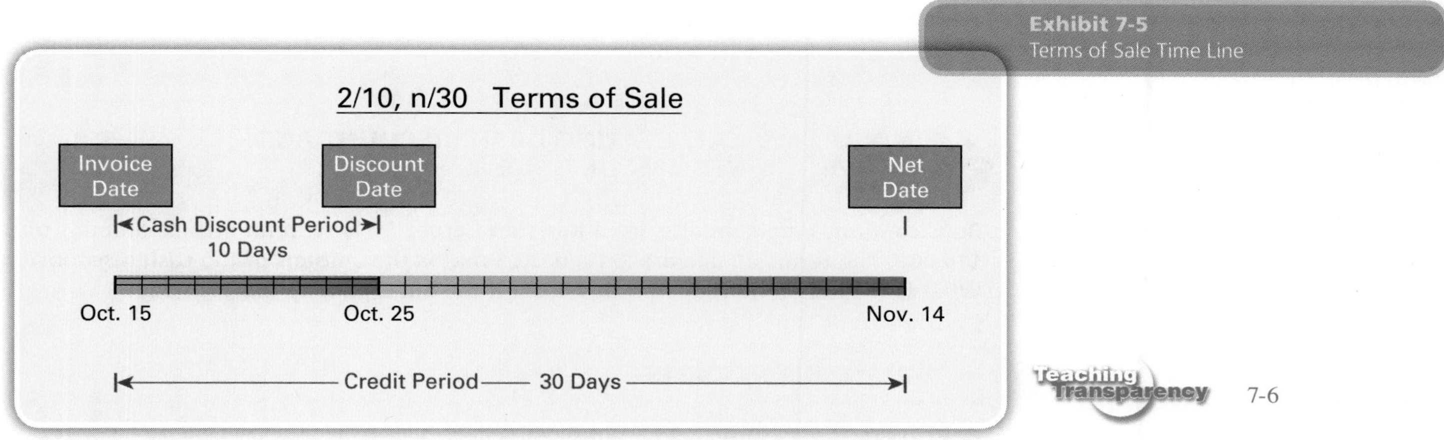

Exhibit 7-5
Terms of Sale Time Line

"If an invoice is due in 30 days, we pay it in 60 days. If it's due in 60 days, we pay it in 90 days. If it's due in 90 days, then they probably don't need the money anyway."

STEPS TO CALCULATE CASH DISCOUNT AND NET AMOUNT DUE

Step 1. Calculate the amount of the cash discount by multiplying the cash discount rate by the net price of the merchandise.

Cash discount = Net price × Cash discount rate

Step 2. Calculate the net amount due by subtracting the amount of the cash discount from the net price.

Net amount due = Net price − Cash discount

Note: As with trade discounts, buyers are frequently more interested in the net amount due than the amount of the discount. When that is the case, we can simplify the calculation by using the complement method to determine the net amount due.

Net amount due = Net price(100% − Cash discount rate)

Learning Tip

Remember, shipping charges or returned items are not subject to cash discounts. These must be deducted from the invoice before the cash discount is applied. After the discount is taken, shipping charges, if any, are added back to get the invoice total.

EXAMPLE 9 CALCULATING CASH DISCOUNT AND NET AMOUNT DUE

Rugs.com buys merchandise from Karistan Carpet Mills with an invoice amount of $16,000. The terms of sale are 2/10, n/30. What is the amount of the cash discount? What is the net amount due on this order if the bill is paid by the 10th day?

SOLUTION STRATEGY

Cash discount = Net price × Cash discount rate

Cash discount = 16,000 × .02 = $320

Net amount due = Net price − Cash discount

Net amount due = 16,000 − 320 = $15,680

TRY IT EXERCISE 9

7-7

All City Plumbing ordered sinks from a supplier with a net price of $8,300 and terms of sale of 3/15, n/45. What is the amount of the cash discount? What is the net amount due if the bill is paid by the 15th day?

CHECK YOUR ANSWERS WITH THE SOLUTIONS ON PAGE 243.

7-10 CALCULATING NET AMOUNT DUE, WITH CREDIT GIVEN FOR PARTIAL PAYMENT

partial payment When a portion of the invoice is paid within the discount period.

Sometimes buyers do not have all the money needed to take advantage of the cash discount. Manufacturers and suppliers usually allow them to pay part of the invoice by the discount date and the balance by the end of the credit period. These **partial payments** earn partial cash discount credit. In this situation, we must calculate how much **partial payment credit** is given.

partial payment credit The amount of the invoice paid off by the partial payment.

Here is how it works: Assume a cash discount of 4/15, n/45 is offered to a retailer. A 4% cash discount means that the retailer will pay 96% of the bill (100% − 4%) and receive 100% credit. Another way to look at it is that every \$.96 paid toward the invoice earns \$1.00 credit. We must determine how many \$.96s are in the partial payment. This will tell us how many \$1.00s of credit we receive.

STEPS TO CALCULATE PARTIAL PAYMENT CREDIT AND NET AMOUNT DUE

Step 1. Calculate the amount of credit given for a partial payment by dividing the partial payment by the complement of the cash discount rate.

$$\textbf{Partial payment credit} = \frac{\textbf{Partial payment}}{\textbf{100\%} - \textbf{Cash discount rate}}$$

Step 2. Calculate the net amount due by subtracting the partial payment credit from the net price.

$$\textbf{Net amount due} = \textbf{Net price} - \textbf{Partial payment credit}$$

The extension of partial payment credit by vendors is important to small retailers who don't always have the cash flow to take advantage of the full cash discount.

EXAMPLE 10 CALCULATING NET AMOUNT DUE AFTER A PARTIAL PAYMENT

Happy Feet, a chain of children's shoe stores, receives an invoice from a tennis shoe manufacturer on September 3, with terms of 3/20, n/60. The net price of the order is \$36,700. Happy Feet wants to send a partial payment of \$10,000 by the discount date and the balance on the net date. How much credit does Happy Feet get for the partial payment? What is the remaining net amount due to the manufacturer?

SOLUTION STRATEGY

$$\text{Partial payment credit} = \frac{\text{Partial payment}}{100\% - \text{Cash discount rate}}$$

$$\text{Partial payment credit} = \frac{10{,}000}{100\% - 3\%} = \frac{10{,}000}{.97} = \underline{\underline{\$10{,}309.28}}$$

$$\text{Net amount due} = \text{Net price} - \text{Partial payment credit}$$

$$\text{Net amount due} = \$36{,}700.00 - \$10{,}309.28 = \underline{\underline{\$26{,}390.72}}$$

TRY IT EXERCISE 10

All Pro Sports Center purchases \$45,300 in baseball gloves from Spaulding on May 5. Spaulding allows 4/15, n/45. If All Pro sends a partial payment of \$20,000 on the discount date, how much credit will be given for the partial payment? What is the net amount still due on the order?

7-8

CHECK YOUR ANSWERS WITH THE SOLUTIONS ON PAGE 243.

7-11 DETERMINING DISCOUNT DATE AND NET DATE BY USING VARIOUS DATING METHODS

To determine the discount date and net date of an invoice, you must know how many days are in each month, or use a calendar.

Following are two commonly used memory devices to help you remember how many days are in each month. Remember, in a leap year, February has 29 days. Leap years fall every 4 years. They are the only years evenly divisible by 4 and are the years of our presidential elections (2008, 2012).

7-9

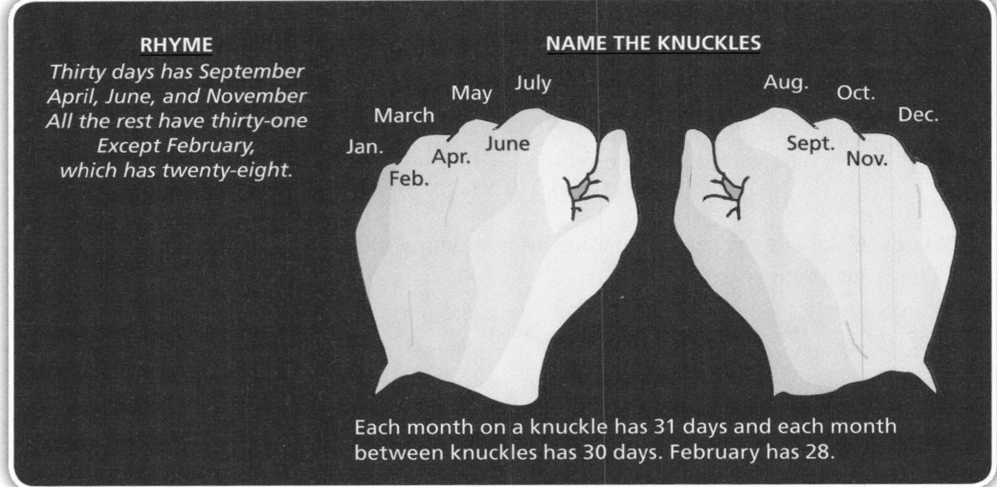

Another way to find these dates is to use the days-in-a-year calendar, shown in Exhibit 7-6. In Chapter 10, you will be able to use this calendar again to find future dates and calculate the number of days of a loan.

STEPS TO FINDING A FUTURE DATE USING A DAYS-IN-A-YEAR CALENDAR

Step 1. Find the "day number" of the starting date.

Note: In leap years, add 1 to the day numbers, beginning with March 1.

Step 2. Add the number of days of the discount or credit period to that day number.

Note: If the new day number is over 365, subtract 365. This means the future date is in the next year.

Step 3. Find the date by looking up the new day number from Step 2.

EXAMPLE 11 FINDING THE NET DATE

If an invoice dated April 14 is due in 75 days, what is the net date?

SOLUTION STRATEGY

Step 1. From the calendar, April 14 is day number 104.

Step 2. $104 + 75 = 179$

Step 3. From the calendar, day number 179 is June 28.

TRY IT EXERCISE 11

If an invoice dated September 12 is due in 60 days, what is the net date?

CHECK YOUR ANSWER WITH THE SOLUTION ON PAGE 243.

7-10

Exhibit 7-6
Days-In-A-Year Calendar

Day of month	Jan.	Feb.	Mar.	Apr.	May	June	July	Aug.	Sept.	Oct.	Nov.	Dec.
1	1	32	60	91	121	152	182	213	244	274	305	335
2	2	33	61	92	122	153	183	214	245	275	306	336
3	3	34	62	93	123	154	184	215	246	276	307	337
4	4	35	63	94	124	155	185	216	247	277	308	338
5	5	36	64	95	125	156	186	217	248	278	309	339
6	6	37	65	96	126	157	187	218	249	279	310	340
7	7	38	66	97	127	158	188	219	250	280	311	341
8	8	39	67	98	128	159	189	220	251	281	312	342
9	9	40	68	99	129	160	190	221	252	282	313	343
10	10	41	69	100	130	161	191	222	253	283	314	344
11	11	42	70	101	131	162	192	223	254	284	315	345
12	12	43	71	102	132	163	193	224	255	285	316	346
13	13	44	72	103	133	164	194	225	256	286	317	347
14	14	45	73	104	134	165	195	226	257	287	318	348
15	15	46	74	105	135	166	196	227	258	288	319	349
16	16	47	75	106	136	167	197	228	259	289	320	350
17	17	48	76	107	137	168	198	229	260	290	321	351
18	18	49	77	108	138	169	199	230	261	291	322	352
19	19	50	78	109	139	170	200	231	262	292	323	353
20	20	51	79	110	140	171	201	232	263	293	324	354
21	21	52	80	111	141	172	202	233	264	294	325	355
22	22	53	81	112	142	173	203	234	265	295	326	356
23	23	54	82	113	143	174	204	235	266	296	327	357
24	24	55	83	114	144	175	205	236	267	297	328	358
25	25	56	84	115	145	176	206	237	268	298	329	359
26	26	57	85	116	146	177	207	238	269	299	330	360
27	27	58	86	117	147	178	208	239	270	300	331	361
28	28	59	87	118	148	179	209	240	271	301	332	362
29	29		88	119	149	180	210	241	272	302	333	363
30	30		89	120	150	181	211	242	273	303	334	364
31	31		90		151		212	243		304		365

During leap years, 2008 or 2012, add 1 to the day numbers, beginning with March 1.

TERMS OF SALE—DATING METHODS

Ordinary Dating

ordinary dating When the discount period and credit period start on the invoice date.

When the discount period and the credit period start on the date of the invoice, this is known as **ordinary dating**. It is the most common method of dating the terms of sale. The last day to take advantage of the cash discount, the discount date, is found by adding the number of days in the discount period to the date of the invoice. For example, to receive a cash discount, an invoice dated November 8 with terms of 2/10, n/30 should be paid no later than November 18 (November 8 + 10 days). The last day to pay the invoice, the net date, is found by adding the number of days in the credit period to the invoice date. With terms of 2/10, n/30, the net date would be December 8 (November 8 + 30 days). If the buyer does not pay the bill by the net date, the seller may impose a penalty charge for late payment.

EXAMPLE 12 USING ORDINARY DATING

AccuCare Pharmacy receives an invoice from Sterling Drug Wholesalers for merchandise on August 19. The terms of sale are 3/10, n/45. If AccuCare elects to take the cash discount, what is the discount date? If AccuCare does not take the cash discount, what is the net date?

TEACHING TIP
Have students keep in mind when determining due dates that the last day is counted but *not* the first. For example, if the invoice date is June 3, counting begins with June 4.

Point out that when the due date falls on a weekend or a holiday, it is commonly advanced to the next regular business day.

SOLUTION STRATEGY

Find the discount date by adding the number of days in the discount period to the date of the invoice.

Discount date = August 19 + 10 days = <u>August 29</u>

If the discount is not taken, find the net date by adding the number of days in the credit period to the invoice date.

August 19 + 45 days = 12 days left in August (31 − 19)
+ 30 days in September
+ 3 days in October
45 days

The net date, the 45th day, is <u>October 3</u>

TRY IT EXERCISE 12

Great Impressions Printing buys ink and paper from a supplier with an invoice date of June 11. If the terms of sale are 4/10, n/60, what is the discount date and what is the net date of the invoice?

CHECK YOUR ANSWERS WITH THE SOLUTIONS ON PAGE 243.

EOM dating End-of-month dating. Depending on invoice date, terms of sale start at the end of the month of the invoice or the end of the following month.

proximo, or prox Another name for EOM dating. Means "in the following month."

EOM or Proximo Dating

EOM dating, or end-of-month dating, means that the terms of sale start *after* the end of the month of the invoice. Another name for this dating method is **proximo**, or **prox**. Proximo means "in the following month." For example, 2/10 EOM, or 2/10 proximo, means that a

2% cash discount will be allowed if the bill is paid 10 days after the *end of the month* of the invoice. This is the case for any invoice dated from the 1st to the 25th of a month. If an invoice is dated after the 25th of the month, the terms of sale begin *after* the end of the *following* month. Unless otherwise specified, the net amount is due *20 days* after the discount date.

EXAMPLE 13 USING EOM DATING

a. What are the discount date and the net date of an invoice dated March 3, with terms of 3/15 EOM?

b. What are the discount date and the net date of an invoice dated March 27, with terms of 3/15 EOM?

SOLUTION STRATEGY

a. Because the invoice date is between the 1st and the 25th of the month, March 3, the discount date on terms of 3/15 EOM would be 15 days *after* the end of the month of the invoice. The net date would be 20 days later.

Discount date = 15 days after the end of March = <u>April 15</u>

Net date = April 15 + 20 days = <u>May 5</u>

b. Because the invoice date is after the 25th of the month, March 27, the discount date on terms of 3/15 EOM would be 15 days *after* the end of the month *following* the invoice month. The net date would be 20 days later.

Discount date = 15 days after the end of April = <u>May 15</u>

Net date = May 15 + 20 days = <u>June 4</u>

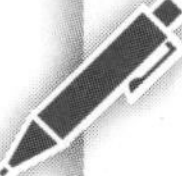

TRY IT EXERCISE 13

a. What are the discount date and the net date of an invoice dated November 18, with terms of 3/15 EOM?

b. What are the discount date and the net date of an invoice dated November 27, with terms of 3/15 EOM?

CHECK YOUR ANSWERS WITH THE SOLUTIONS ON PAGE 243.

ROG Dating

Receipt of goods or **ROG dating** is a common method used when shipping times are long, such as with special or custom orders. When ROG dating is used, the terms of sale begin the day the goods are received at the buyer's location. With this method, the buyer does not have to pay for the merchandise before it arrives. An example would be 2/10 ROG. As usual, the net date is 20 days after the discount date.

ROG dating Receipt of goods dating. Terms of sale begin on the date the goods are received by the buyer.

EXAMPLE 14 USING ROG DATING

What are the discount date and the net date for an invoice dated June 23 if the shipment arrives on August 16 and the terms are 3/15 ROG?

SOLUTION STRATEGY

In this case, the discount period starts on August 16, the date the shipment arrives. The net date will be 20 days after the discount date.

Discount date = August 16 + 15 days = August 31

Net date = August 31 + 20 days = September 20

TRY IT EXERCISE 14

What are the discount date and the net date of an invoice dated October 11 if the shipment arrives on December 29 and the terms are 2/20 ROG?

CHECK YOUR ANSWERS WITH THE SOLUTIONS ON PAGE 243.

Extra Dating

Extra, Ex, or X dating The buyer receives an extra discount period as an incentive to purchase slow-moving or out-of-season merchandise.

The last dating method commonly used in business today is called **Extra**, **Ex**, or **X dating**. With this dating method, the seller offers an extra discount period to the buyer as an incentive for purchasing slow-moving or out-of-season merchandise, such as Christmas goods in July or bathing suits in January. An example would be 3/10, 60 extra. This means the buyer gets a 3% cash discount in 10 days plus 60 *extra* days, or a total of 70 days. Once again, unless otherwise specified, the net date is 20 days after the discount date.

EXAMPLE 15 USING EXTRA DATING

What are the discount date and the net date of an invoice dated February 9, with terms of 3/15, 40 Extra?

Remember, when using extra dating, unless otherwise specified, the net date is 20 days after the discount date.

SOLUTION STRATEGY

These terms, 3/15, 40 Extra, give the retailer 55 days (15 + 40) from February 9 to take the cash discount. The net date will be 20 days after the discount date.

Discount date = February 9 + 55 days = April 5

Net date = April 5 + 20 days = April 25

TRY IT EXERCISE 15

What are the discount date and the net date of an invoice dated February 22, with terms of 4/20, 60 Extra?

CHECK YOUR ANSWERS WITH THE SOLUTIONS ON PAGE 243.

Review Exercises

Calculate the cash discount and the net amount due for each of the following transactions.

Complete, worked-out solutions for Exercises 1–9 appear in Appendix B, following the index.

	Amount of Invoice	Terms of Sale	Cash Discount	Net Amount Due
1.	$15,800.00	3/15, n/30	$474.00	$15,326.00
2.	12,660.00	2/10, n/45	$253.20	$12,406.80
3.	2,421.00	4/10, n/30	$96.84	$2,324.16
4.	6,940.20	2/10, n/30	$138.80	$6,801.40
5.	9,121.44	$3\frac{1}{2}$/15, n/60	$319.25	$8,802.19

For the following transactions, calculate the credit given for the partial payment and the net amount due on the invoice.

	Amount of Invoice	Terms of Sale	Partial Payment	Credit for Partial Payment	Net Amount Due
6.	$8,303.00	2/10, n/30	$2,500	$2,551.02	$5,751.98
7.	1,344.60	3/10, n/45	460	$474.23	$870.37
8.	5,998.20	4/15, n/60	3,200	$3,333.33	$2,664.87
9.	7,232.08	$4\frac{1}{2}$/20, n/45	5,500	$5,759.16	$1,472.92

Using the ordinary dating method, calculate the discount date and the net date for the following transactions.

	Date of Invoice	Terms of Sale	Discount Date(s)	Net Date
10.	November 4	2/10, n/45	Nov. 14	Dec. 19
11.	April 23	3/15, n/60	May 8	June 22
12.	August 11	3/20, n/45	Aug. 31	Sept. 25
13.	January 29	2/10, 1/20, n/60	2% Feb. 8, 1% Feb. 18	Mar. 30
14.	July 8	4/25, n/90	Aug. 2	Oct. 6

Using the EOM, ROG, and Extra dating methods, calculate the discount date and the net date for the following transactions. Unless otherwise specified, the net date is 20 days after the discount date.

	Date of Invoice	Terms of Sale	Discount Date	Net Date
15.	December 5	2/10, EOM	Jan. 10	Jan. 30
16.	June 27	3/15, EOM	Aug. 15	Sept. 4
17.	September 1	3/20, ROG		
		Rec'd Oct. 3	Oct. 23	Nov. 12
18.	February 11	2/10, 60 Extra	Apr. 22	May 12
19.	May 18	4/25, EOM	June 25	July 15
20.	October 26	2/10, ROG		
		Rec'd Nov. 27	Dec. 7	Dec. 27

21. The Apollo Company received an invoice from a vendor on April 12 in the amount of $1,420.00. The terms of sale were 2/15, n/45. The invoice included shipping charges of $108. The vendor sent $250 in merchandise that was not ordered. These goods will be returned by Apollo. (Remember, no discounts on shipping charges or returned goods.)

    a. What are the discount date and the net date?

    Discount date: April 12 + 15 days = April 27

    Net date: April 12 + 45 days = May 27

    b. What is the amount of the cash discount?

    Cash discount 1,420 − 108 − 250 = 1,062

    1,062 × .02 = $21.24

    c. What is the net amount due?

    1,062 − 21.24 = 1,040.76
    + 108.00 Shipping charges
    Net amount due $1,148.76

22. An invoice is dated August 29 with terms of 4/15 EOM.

    a. What is the discount date?

    October 15

    b. What is the net date?

    October 15 + 20 days = November 4

23. An invoice dated January 15 has terms of 3/20 ROG. The goods are delayed in shipment and arrive on March 2.

    a. What is the discount date?

    March 22

    b. What is the net date?

    March 22 + 20 days = April 11

24. What payment should be made on an invoice in the amount of $3,400 dated August 7 if the terms of sale are 3/15, 2/30, n/45 and the bill is paid on

    a. August 19?

    August 7 to August 19 = 12 days   This is within the 3% discount period.
    3,400 × .03 = 102
    3,400 − 102 = $3,298 on August 19

    b. September 3?

    August 7 to September 3 = 27 days   This is within the 2% discount period.
    3,400 × .02 = 68
    3,400 − 68 = $3,332 on September 3

25. Red Tag Furniture received a SeaLand container of sofas from Thailand on April 14. The invoice, dated March 2, was for $46,230 in merchandise and $2,165 in shipping charges. The terms of sale were 3/15 ROG. Red Tag Furniture made a partial payment of $15,000 on April 27.

    a. What is the net amount due?

    $$\text{Partial payment credit} = \frac{15{,}000}{0.97} = 15{,}463.92$$

    Invoice total = 46,230 + 2,165 = 48,395

    Net amount due = 48,395.00 − 15,463.92 = $32,931.08

    b. What is the net date?

    Discount date = April 14 + 15 = April 29

    Net date = April 29 + 20 days = May 19

26. City Cellular purchased $28,900 in cell phones on April 25. The terms of sale were 4/20, 3/30, n/60. Freight terms were F.O.B. destination. Returned goods amounted to $650.

    a. What is the net amount due if City Cellular sends the manufacturer a partial payment of $5,000 on May 20?

    April 25 to May 20 = 25 days This is within 3% discount period.
    28,900 − 650 = 28,250 Invoice less returns

    $$\text{Partial payment credit} = \frac{5{,}000}{.97} = 5{,}154.64$$

    28,250 − 5,154.64 = $23,095.36 Net due

    b. What is the net date?

    April 25 + 60 days = June 24

    c. If the manufacturer charges a $4\frac{1}{2}\%$ late fee, how much would City Cellular owe if they did not pay the balance by the net date?

    Net due on net date = $23,095.36
    23,095.36 × .045 = $1,039.29 Late fee
    $23,095.36
    + 1,039.29
    $24,134.65 Net due after net date

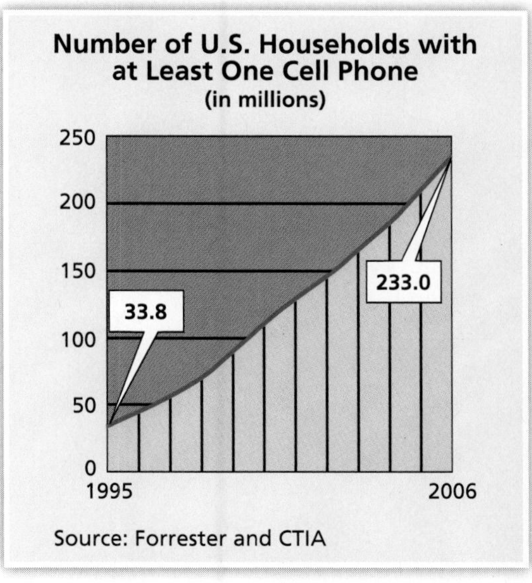

As wireless costs have dropped, consumer adoption rates have sky-rocketed. About 78% of all U.S. households currently have at least one cell phone.

BUSINESS DECISION THE EMPLOYMENT TEST

27. As part of the employment interview for an accounting job at StereoMaster Stores, you have been asked to answer the questions on page 238, based on an invoice from one of StereoMaster's vendors, Target Electronic Wholesalers.

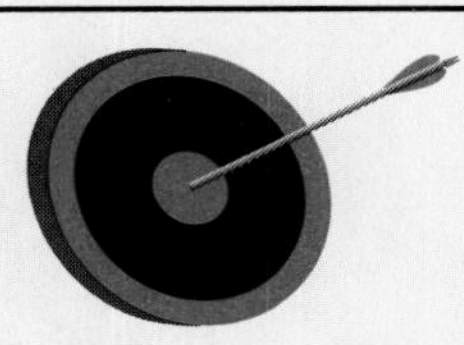

TARGET
ELECTRONIC WHOLESALERS
1979 N.E. 123 Street
Jacksonville, Florida 32204

Sold to: StereoMaster Stores
480 McDowell Rd.
Phoenix, AZ 85008

Invoice Date: June 28, 20XX

Terms of Sale: 3/15,n/30 ROG

Stock #	Description	Unit Price	Amount
4811V	Stereo Receivers	50 × $297.50 =	$14,875.00
511CX	DVD Players	25 × $132.28 =	3,307.00
6146M	Home Theater Systems	40 × $658.12 =	26,324.80
1031A	LCD TVs	20 × $591.00 =	11,820.00
		Merchandise Total	$56,326.80
		Insurance + Shipping	$1,150.00
		Invoice Total	$57,476.80

Stereo Receivers	50 × $297.50 =	$14,875.00
DVD Players	25 × $132.28 =	3,307.00
Home Theater Systems	40 × $658.12 =	26,324.80
LCD TVs	20 × $591.00 =	11,820.00
	Merchandise total	$56,326.80
	Insurance + Shipping	1,150.00
	Invoice total	$57,476.80

a. Extend each line and calculate the merchandise total and the total amount of the invoice, using the space provided on the invoice. See invoice on page 237.

b. What are the discount date and the net date if the shipment arrived on July 16?

Discount date = July 16 + 15 days = July 31

Net date = July 16 + 30 days = August 15

c. While in transit, five DVD players and four LCD TVs were damaged and will be returned. What is the amount of the returned merchandise? What is the revised merchandise total?

DVD Players $5 \times 132.28 =$ 661.40
LCD TVs $4 \times 591.00 =$ + 2,364.00
Returned merchandise = $3,025.40

Revised merchandise total = 56,326.80 − 3,025.40 = $53,301.40

d. What are the amount of the cash discount and the net amount due if the discount is taken?

$53{,}301.40 \times .03 =$ $1,599.04 Cash discount

$53,301.40	Merchandise total
− 1,599.04	Cash discount
+ 1,150.00	Insurance and shipping
$52,852.36	Net amount due

e. If StereoMaster sends in a partial payment of $20,000 within the discount period, what is the net balance still due?

$$\text{Partial payment credit} = \frac{20{,}000}{.97} = \$20{,}618.56$$

$53,301.40	Merchandise total
− 20,618.56	Partial payment credit
+ 1,150.00	Insurance and shipping
$33,832.84	Net balance

7

CHAPTER FORMULAS

The Invoice

Extended total = Number of items × Cost per item

Trade Discounts—Single

Trade discount = List price × Trade discount rate

Net price = List price − Trade discount

Net price = List price(100% − Trade discount rate)

$$\text{Trade discount rate} = \frac{\text{Trade discount}}{\text{List price}}$$

Trade Discounts—Series

Net price = List price × Net price factor

Single equivalent discount = 1 − Net price factor

Trade discount = List price × Single equivalent discount

Cash Discounts and Terms of Sale

Net amount due = Net price(100% − Cash discount rate)

$$\text{Partial payment credit} = \frac{\text{Partial payment}}{100\% - \text{Cash discount rate}}$$

Net amount due = Net price − Partial payment credit

CHAPTER SUMMARY

7

Section I: The Invoice

Topic	Important Concepts	Illustrative Examples
Reading and Understanding the Parts of an Invoice **P/O 7-1, p. 205**	Refer to Exhibits 7-1, 7-2, and 7-3.	
Extending and Totaling an Invoice **P/O 7-2, p. 208**	**Extended amount =** **Number of items × Cost per item** **Invoice subtotal =** **Total of extended amount column** **Invoice total =** **Invoice subtotal + Other charges**	The Great Subversion, a sandwich shop, ordered 25 lbs. of ham at $3.69 per pound, and 22 lbs. of cheese at $4.25 per pound. There is a $7.50 delivery charge. Extend each item and find the invoice subtotal and invoice total. 25 × 3.69 = 92.25 Ham 22 × 4.25 = 93.50 Cheese 185.75 Subtotal + 7.50 Delivery $193.25 Invoice total

Section II: Trade Discounts—Single

Topic	Important Concepts	Illustrative Examples
Calculating the Amount of a Single Trade Discount **P/O 7-3, p. 213**	Trade discounts are reductions from the manufacturer's list price given to businesses in the trade for the performance of various marketing functions. **Trade discount =** **List price × Trade discount rate**	The Sunglass King ordered merchandise from a manufacturer with a list price of $12,700. Because they are in the trade, Sunglass King gets a 35% trade discount. What is the amount of the trade discount? Trade discount = 12,700 × .35 = $4,445
Calculating Net Price by Using the Net Price Factor, Complement Method **P/O 7-4, p. 213**	**Net price factor = 100% − Trade discount rate** **Net price =** **List price(100% − Trade discount rate)**	From the previous problem, use the net price factor to find the net price of the order for Sunglass King. Net price = 12,700(100% − 35%) Net price = 12,700 × .65 = $8,255
Calculating Trade Discount Rate When List Price and Net Price Are Known **P/O 7-5, p. 214**	$\text{Trade discount rate} = \dfrac{\text{Trade discount}}{\text{List price}}$	Cycle World Bike Shop orders merchandise listing for $5,300 from Schwinn. The net price of the order is $3,200. What is the trade discount rate? Trade discount = 5,300 − 3,200 = $2,100 $\text{Trade discount rate} = \dfrac{2{,}100}{5{,}300} = 39.6\%$

Section III: Trade Discounts—Series

Topic	Important Concepts	Illustrative Examples
Calculating Net Price and the Amount of a Trade Discount by Using a Series of Trade Discounts P/O 7-6, p. 219	Net price is found by taking each trade discount in the series from the succeeding net price until all discounts have been deducted. **Trade discount = List price − Net price**	An invoice with merchandise listing for \$4,700 was entitled to trade discounts of 20% and 15%. What is the net price and the amount of the trade discount? 4,700 × .20 = 940 4,700 − 940 = 3,760 3,760 × .15 = 564 3,760 − 564 = \$3,196 Net price Trade discount = 4,700 − 3,196 = \$1,504
Calculating Net Price of a Series of Trade Discounts by Using the Net Price Factor, Complement Method P/O 7-7, p. 219	Net price factor is found by subtracting each trade discount from 100% (complement) and multiplying these complements together. **Net price = List price × Net price factor**	Use the net price factor method to verify your answer to the previous problem. 100% − 20% = .80 × 100% − 15% = .85 = .68 Net price factor Net price = 4,700 × .68 = \$3,196
Calculating the Amount of a Trade Discount by Using a Single Equivalent Discount P/O 7-8, p. 221	**Single equivalent discount = 1 − Net price factor** **Trade discount = List price × Single equivalent discount**	What is the single equivalent in the previous problem? Use this to verify your trade discount answer. Single equivalent discount = 1 − .68 = .32 Trade discount = 4,700 × .32 = \$1,504

Section IV: Cash Discounts and Terms of Sale

Topic	Important Concepts	Illustrative Examples
Calculating Cash Discounts and Net Amount Due P/O 7-9, p. 226	Terms of sale specify when an invoice must be paid and if a cash discount is offered. Cash discount is an extra discount offered by the seller as an incentive for early payment of an invoice. **Cash discount = Net price × Cash discount rate** **Net amount due = Net price − Cash discount**	Action Auto Parts orders merchandise for \$1,800 including \$100 in freight charges. Action gets a 3% cash discount. What is the amount of the cash discount and the net amount due? 1,800 − 100 = 1,700 Net price Cash discount = 1,700 × .03 = \$51 1,700 − 51 = 1,649 + 100 Shipping \$1,749 Net amount due
Calculating Net Amount Due, with Credit Given for Partial Payment P/O 7-10, p. 228	$\text{Partial Payment credit} = \dfrac{\text{Partial payment}}{100\% - \text{Cash discount rate}}$ **Net amount due = Net price − Partial payment credit**	Elite Fashions makes a partial payment of \$3,000 on an invoice of \$7,900. The terms of sale are 3/15, n/30. What is the amount of the partial payment credit, and how much does Elite Fashions still owe on the invoice? $\text{Part pmt credit} = \dfrac{3{,}000}{100\% - 3\%} = \$3{,}092.78$ Net amount due = 7,900.00 − 3,092.78 = \$4,807.22

Section IV: (continued)

Topic	Important Concepts	Illustrative Examples
Determining Discount Date and Net Date by Using Various Dating Methods **P/O 7-11, p. 230**	Discount date: last date to take advantage of a cash discount. Net date: last date to pay an invoice without incurring a penalty charge.	
Ordinary Dating **P/O 7-11, p. 232**	Ordinary dating: discount period and the credit period start on the date of the invoice.	Galaxy Jewelers receives an invoice for merchandise on March 12 with terms of 3/15, n/30. What are the discount date and the net date? Disc date = March 12 + 15 days = March 27 Net date = March 12 + 30 days = April 11
EOM or Proximo Dating Method **P/O 7-11, p. 232**	EOM means end of month. It is a dating method in which the terms of sale start *after* the end of the month of the invoice. If the invoice is dated after the 25th of the month, the terms of sale start *after* the end of the *following* month. Unless otherwise specified, the net date is *20 days* after the discount date. *Proximo* or prox. is another name for EOM dating. It means "in the following month."	Majestic Cleaning Service buys supplies with terms of sale of 2/10, EOM. What are the discount date and the net date if the invoice date is a. May 5? b. May 27? a. May 5 invoice terms start *after* the end of May: Discount date = June 10 Net date = June 10 + 20 days = June 30 b. May 27 invoice terms start *after* the end of the *following* month, June: Discount date = July 10 Net date = July 10 + 20 days = July 30
ROG Dating Method **P/O 7-11, p. 233**	ROG means receipt of goods. It is a dating method in which the terms of sale begin on the date the goods are received rather than the invoice date. This is used to accommodate long shipping times. Unless otherwise specified, the net date is *20 days* after the discount date.	An invoice dated August 24 has terms of 3/10 ROG. If the merchandise arrives on October 1, what are the discount date and the net date? Disc date = October 1 + 10 days = October 11 Net date = October 11 + 20 days = October 31
Extra Dating Method **P/O 7-11, p. 234**	Extra, Ex, or X is a dating method in which the buyer receives an extra period of time before the terms of sale begin. Vendors use extra dating as an incentive to entice buyers to purchase out-of-season or slow-moving merchandise. Unless otherwise specified, the net date is *20 days* after the discount date.	Sugar Pine Candy Company buys merchandise from a vendor with terms of 3/15, 60 Extra. The invoice is dated December 11. What are the discount date and the net date? Disc date = December 11 + 75 days = February 24 Net date = February 24 + 20 = March 16

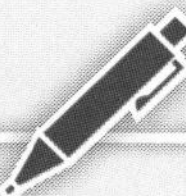

TRY IT EXERCISE SOLUTIONS FOR CHAPTER 7

1. **a.** Shutterbug Camera Shops **b.** 44929
c. November 27, 20XX **d.** $3,120.00
e. FotoFair Distributors **f.** Net—30 days
g. 1864 N.W. 123rd St., Chicago, IL 60613 **h.** J. Herman
i. Federal Express **j.** Knoxville, TN
k. $125.00 **l.** $5,632.80
m. $345.00 **n.** $5,757.80

2.

Stock #	Quantity	Unit	Merchandise Description	Unit Price	Total
R443	125	ea.	Food Processors	$ 89.00	$11,125.00
B776	24	ea.	Microwave Ovens	225.40	5,409.60
Z133	6	doz.	12" Mixers	54.12	324.72
Z163	1	bx.	Mixer Covers	166.30	166.30
				Invoice Subtotal	$17,025.62
				Shipping Charges	+ 194.20
				Invoice Total	$17,219.82

3. Trade discount = List price × Trade discount rate
Trade discount = 7,600 × .30 = $2,280

4. Net price = List price(100% − Trade discount rate)
Net price = 2,100(100% − 35%)
Net price = 2,100 × .65 = $1,365

5. Trade discount = List price − Net price
Trade discount = 109,500 − 63,300 = $46,200

$$\text{Trade discount rate} = \frac{\text{Trade discount}}{\text{List price}} = \frac{46{,}200}{109{,}500} = .4219 = \underline{\underline{42.2\%}}$$

6.

$$\begin{array}{r} 25{,}000 \\ \times\ .35 \\ \hline 8{,}750 \end{array} \quad \begin{array}{r} 25{,}000 \\ -\ 8{,}750 \\ \hline 16{,}250 \end{array} \quad \begin{array}{r} 16{,}250 \\ \times\ .20 \\ \hline 3{,}250 \end{array} \quad \begin{array}{r} 16{,}250 \\ -\ 3{,}250 \\ \hline 13{,}000 \end{array} \quad \begin{array}{r} 13{,}000 \\ \times\ .10 \\ \hline 1{,}300 \end{array} \quad \begin{array}{r} 13{,}000 \\ -\ 1{,}300 \\ \hline \$11{,}700 \end{array} = \text{Net price}$$

Trade discount = 25,000 − 11,700 = $13,300

7. **a.**

$$\begin{array}{r} 100\% \\ -\ 30\% \\ \hline .7 \end{array} \times \begin{array}{r} 100\% \\ -\ 20\% \\ \hline .8 \end{array} \times \begin{array}{r} 100\% \\ -\ 12\% \\ \hline .88 \end{array} = \underline{\underline{.4928}} = \text{Net price factor}$$

b. Net price = List price × Net price factor
Net price = 3,500 × .4928 = $1,724.80

c. Net price = List price × Net price factor
Net price = 5,800 × .4928 = $2,858.24

8.

$$\begin{array}{r} 100\% \\ -\ 25\% \\ \hline .75 \end{array} \times \begin{array}{r} 100\% \\ -\ 15\% \\ \hline .85 \end{array} \times \begin{array}{r} 100\% \\ -\ 10\% \\ \hline .9 \end{array} = .57375 = \text{Net price factor}$$

Single equivalent discount = 1 − Net price factor
Single equivalent discount = 1 − .57375 = .42625
Trade discount = List price × Single equivalent discount
Trade discount = 36,800 × .42625 = $15,686

9. Cash discount = Net price × Cash discount rate

Cash discount = 8,300 × .03 = $249

Net amount due = Net price − Cash discount

Net amount due = 8,300 − 249 = $8,051

10. $$\text{Partial payment credit} = \frac{\text{Partial payment}}{100\% - \text{Cash discount rate}}$$

$$\text{Partial payment credit} = \frac{20{,}000}{100\% - 4\%} = \frac{20{,}000}{.96} = \$20{,}833.33$$

Net amount due = Net price − Partial payment credit

Net amount due = 45,300.00 − 20,833.33 = $24,466.67

11. From the calendar, September 12 is day number 255

255 + 60 = 315

From the calendar, day number 315 is November 11

12. Discount date = June 11 + 10 days = June 21

Net date = June 11 + 60 days

30	Days in June
− 11	Discount date
19	June
31	July
+ 10	Aug → August 10
60	days

13. **a.** Discount date = 15 days after end of November = December 15

Net date = December 15 + 20 days = January 4

b. Discount date = 15 days after end of December = January 15

Net date = January 15 + 20 days = February 4

14. Discount date = December 29 + 20 days = January 18

Net date = January 18 + 20 days = February 7

15. Discount date = February 22 + 80 days = May 13

Net date = May 13 + 20 days = June 2

CONCEPT REVIEW

1. The document detailing a sales transaction is known as a(n) ____. (7-1)

invoice

2. F.O.B. shipping point and F.O.B. destination are shipping terms that specify where the merchandise ____ is transferred. (7-1)

title (ownership)

3. To extend an invoice, for each line, we multiply the number of items by the ____ per item. (7-2)

cost

4. To calculate the amount of a single trade discount, we multiply the ____ price by the trade discount rate. (7-3)

list

5. The ____ price is the amount a business actually pays for merchandise, after the discount has been deducted. (7-4)

net

6. To calculate the net price factor, we subtract the trade discount rate from ____. (7-4)

100%

7. Write the formula for the trade discount rate. (7-5)

$$\text{Trade discount rate} = \frac{\text{Trade discount}}{\text{List price}}$$

8. In a chain or ____ of trade discounts, we calculate the final net price by taking each discount one at a time from the previous net price. (7-6)

series

9. As a shortcut, we can use the net price ____ method to calculate the net price. (7-7)

factor

10. To calculate the net price factor, we subtract each trade discount from 100% and then ____ all the complements together. (7-7)

multiply

11. A single trade discount that equates to all the discounts in a series or chain is called a single ____ discount. (7-8)

equivalent

12. The "____ of sale" specify when an invoice must be paid and if a ____ discount is being offered. (7-9)

terms, cash

13. To calculate the credit given for a partial payment, we divide the amount of the partial payment by 100% ____ the cash discount rate. (7-10)

minus

14. The most common method for dating an invoice is when the discount period and the credit period start on the date of the invoice. This method is known as ____ dating. (7-11)

ordinary

7 CHAPTER ASSESSMENT TEST

Name

____

Class

____

Answers

1. Leisure Time Industries
2. November 2
3. 4387
4. dozen
5. $46.55
6. Raleigh, NC
7. $2,558
8. The buyer, Patio Magic Stores

Answer the following questions based on the Leisure Time Industries invoice on page 245.

1. Who is the vendor?

Leisure Time Industries

2. What is the date of the invoice?

November 2

3. What is the stock # of rockers?

4387

4. What does dz. mean?

dozen

5. What is the unit price of plastic lounge covers?

$46.55

6. What is the destination?

Raleigh, NC

7. What is the extended total for chaise lounges with no armrest?

$20 \times 127.90 = \$2{,}558$

8. Who pays the freight if the terms are F.O.B. shipping point?

The buyer, Patio Magic Stores

CHAPTER 7

Name

Class

Answers

9. $11,562.45

10. $12,164.95

11. $1,485

12. a. $203.99

b. $475.96

13. 33.76%

9. What is the invoice subtotal?

$40 \times 169.00 = \$\ 6,760.00$
$20 \times 127.90 = \ \ 2,558.00$
$24 \times \ \ 87.70 = \ \ 2,104.80$
$3 \times \ \ 46.55 = \ \ \ \ 139.65$
Invoice subtotal $11,562.45

10. What is the invoice total?

$11,562.45
125.00
+ 477.50
Invoice total $12,164.95

LEISURE TIME INDUSTRIES

Patio Furniture Manufacturers
1930 Main Street
Ft. Worth, Texas 76102

DATE: November 2, 20XX

SOLD TO: Patio Magic Stores
3386 Fifth Avenue
Raleigh, NC 27613

INVOICE # B-112743

TERMS OF SALE: Net 30 days

SHIPPING INFO: Fed-Ex Freight

STOCK #	QUANTITY	UNIT	MERCHANDISE DESCRIPTION	UNIT PRICE	TOTAL
1455	40	ea.	Chaise Lounges with armrest	$169.00	$6,760.00
1475	20	ea.	Chaise Lounges—no armrest	127.90	2,558.00
4387	24	ea.	Rocker Chairs	87.70	2,104.80
8100	3	dz.	Plastic Lounge Covers	46.55	139.65

INVOICE SUBTOTAL: $11,562.45
Packing and Handling: $125.00
Shipping Charges: 477.50

INVOICE TOTAL: $12,164.95

11. Penny Wise Art Supplies receives an invoice for the purchase of merchandise with a list price of $5,500. Because they are in the trade, they receive a 27% trade discount. What is the amount of the trade discount?

Trade discount $= 5,500 \times .27 =$ $1,485

12. Natureland Garden Center buys lawnmowers that list for $679.95 less a 30% trade discount.

a. What is the amount of the trade discount?

Trade discount $= 679.95 \times .30 =$ $203.99

b. What is the net price of each lawnmower?

Net price $= 679.95 - 203.99 =$ $475.96

13. Shorty's BBQ Restaurant places an order with a meat and poultry supplier listing for $1,250. They receive a trade discount of $422 on the order. What is the trade discount rate on this transaction?

$$\text{Trade discount rate} = \frac{422}{1,250} = .3376 = 33.76\%$$

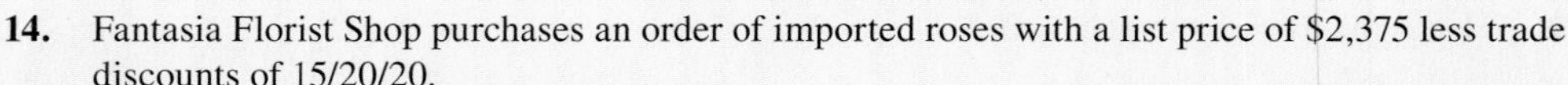

7 CHAPTER

Name

Class

Answers

14. a. $1,083

b. $1,292

15. Fancy Footwear

16. a. 0.57375

b. $459

17. a. 0.6052

b. .3948

18. a. June 5

b. $15,994.80

19. a. April 24

b. May 9

c. May 15

d. June 4

20. a. November 1

b. November 16

© Hill Street Studios/Brand X Pictures/ Jupiter Images

The U.S. Carpet Industry

According to the Carpet and Rug Institute, in 2005, the U.S. carpet industry production figure totaled 2.057 billion square yards of carpeting valued at over $12 billion. The United States supplies approximately 45% of the world's carpet.

14. Fantasia Florist Shop purchases an order of imported roses with a list price of $2,375 less trade discounts of 15/20/20.

a. What is the amount of the trade discount?

$.85 \times .80 \times .80 = 0.544 \quad 1.00 - 0.544 = .456$

Trade discount $= 2,375 \times .456 =$ $1,083

b. What is the net amount of the order?

Net price of order $= 2,375 - 1,083 =$ $1,292

15. All-American Sports can purchase sneakers for $450 per dozen less trade discounts of 14/12 from Ideal Shoes. Fancy Footwear is offering the same sneakers for $435 less trade discounts of 18/6. Which supplier offers a lower net price?

Ideal Shoes	Fancy Footwear
$.86 \times .88 = .7568$	$.82 \times .94 = .7708$
$450 \times .7568 = \$340.56$	$435 \times .7708 = \$335.30$

Fancy Footwear offers a lower price.

16. a. What is the net price factor for trade discounts of 25/15/10?

Net price factor $= .75 \times .85 \times .90 =$ 0.57375

b. Use that net price factor to find the net price of a couch listing for $800.

Net price of couch $= 800 \times .57375 =$ $459

17. a. What is the net price factor of the trade discount series 20/15/11?

Net price factor $= .80 \times .85 \times .89 =$ 0.6052

b. What is the single equivalent discount?

Single equivalent discount $= 1.00 - 0.6052 =$ .3948

18. The Kingston Carpet Company orders merchandise for $17,700, including $550 in shipping charges, from Mohawk Carpet Mills on May 4. Carpets valued at $1,390 will be returned because they are damaged. The terms of sale are 2/10, n/30 ROG. The shipment arrives on May 26, and Kingston wants to take advantage of the cash discount.

a. By what date must Kingston pay the invoice?

May 26 + 10 = June 5

b. As the bookkeeper for Kingston, how much will you send to Mohawk?

$17,700	
− 550	Shipping
− 1,390	Returns
$15,760	Amount subject to discount

15,760 × .98 =	$15,444.80	
+	550.00	Shipping
Total amount due	$15,994.80	

19. Super Suds Laundry receives an invoice for detergent dated April 9 with terms of 3/15, n/30.

a. What is the discount date?

April 9 + 15 = April 24

b. What is the net date?

April 9 + 30 = May 9

c. If the invoice terms are changed to 3/15 EOM, what is the new discount date?

May 15

d. What is the new net date?

May 15 + 20 = June 4

20. Ned's Sheds purchases building materials from Timbertown Lumber for $3,700 with terms of 4/15, n/30. The invoice is dated October 17. Ned's decides to send in a $2,000 partial payment.

a. By what date must the partial payment be sent to take advantage of the cash discount?

Discount date = October 17 + 15 = November 1

b. What is the net date?

Net date = October 17 + 30 = November 16

c. If partial payment was sent by the discount date, what is the balance still due on the order?

$$\text{Partial payment credit} = \frac{2,000}{.96} = \$2,083.33$$

$$\begin{array}{rr} & \$3,700.00 \\ & -\ 2,083.33 \\ \text{Balance due} & \$1,616.67 \end{array}$$

21. Club Z is in receipt of new electronics to control the lighting on their dance floor. The invoice, dated June 9, shows the total cost of the equipment as $14,350. Shipping charges amount to $428, and insurance is $72.80. Terms of sale are 2/10 prox. If the invoice is paid on July 9, what is the net amount due?

14,350.00 × .98 = $14,063.00	Merchandise
428.00	Shipping charges
+ 72.80	Insurance
$14,563.80	Net amount due

Name

Class

Answers

c. $1,616.67

21. $14,563.80

22. a. see invoice on page 248

b. April 19

c. $3,066.33 Balance due

d. May 19

e. $153.32 Late fee

BUSINESS DECISION THE BUSY EXECUTIVE

22. You are a salesperson for Victory Lane Wholesale Auto Parts. You have just taken a phone order from one of your best customers, Champion Motors. Because you were busy when the call came in, you recorded the details of the order on a notepad.

EXCEL

Phone Order Notes

- The invoice date is April 4, 20XX.
- The customer order no. is 443B.
- Champion Motors's warehouse is located at 7011 N.W. 4th Avenue, Columbus, Ohio 43205.
- Terms of sale—3/15, n/45.
- The order will be filled by D. Watson.
- The goods will be shipped by truck.
- Champion Motors's home office is located next to the warehouse at 7013 N.W. 4th Avenue.
- Champion ordered 44 car batteries, stock #394, listing for $69.95 each, and 24 truck batteries, stock #395, listing for $89.95 each. These items get trade discounts of 20/15.
- Champion also ordered 36 cases of 10W/30 motor oil, stock #838-W, listing for $11.97 per case, and 48 cases of 10W/40 super-oil, stock #1621-S, listing for $14.97 per case. These items get trade discounts of 20/20/12.
- The shipping charges for the order amount to $67.50.
- Insurance charges amount to $27.68.

AutoZone is the nation's leading retailer of automotive parts and accessories with over 3,900 stores. Net sales in 2006 were $5.948 billion.

Advance Auto Parts is in second place, with over 3,000 stores and $4.617 billion in sales in 2006. Other national and regional auto-parts chains include O'Reilly Automotive and The Pep Boys—Manny, Moe and Jack.

a. Transfer your notes to the invoice on page 248, extend each line, and calculate the total.

b. What is the discount date of the invoice?

April 19

c. If Champion sends a partial payment of $1,200 by the discount date, what is the balance due on the invoice?

$$\frac{1,200}{.97} = 1,237.11 \qquad \begin{array}{r} \$4,303.44 \\ -\ 1,237.11 \\ \$3,066.33 \end{array} \text{ Balance due}$$

d. What is the net date of the invoice?

May 19

e. Your company has a policy of charging a 5% late fee if invoice payments are more than five days late. What is the amount of the late fee that Champion will be charged if it fails to pay the balance due on time?

3,066.33 × .05 = $153.32 Late fee

INVOICE

Victory Lane
Wholesale Auto Parts
422 Riverfront Road
Cincinnati, Ohio 45244

Invoice #

Invoice Date: April 4, 20XX

Sold To: Champion Motors
7013 N.W. 4th Ave
Columbus, Ohio 43205

Ship To: Champion Motors
7011 N.W. 4th Ave
Columbus, Ohio 43205

Customer Order No.	Salesperson	Ship via	Terms of Sale	Filled By
443B		Truck	3/15,n/45	D.Watson

Quantity Ordered	Stock Number	Description	Unit List Price	Trade Discounts	Extended Amount
44	#394	Car Batteries	$69.95	20/15	$2,092.90
24	#395	Truck Batteries	$89.95	20/15	1,467.98
36 Cases	#838-W	10W/30 Motor Oil	$11.97	20/20/12	242.69
48 Cases	#1621-S	10W/40 Super Oil	$14.97	20/20/12	404.69

Invoice Subtotal	$4,208.26
Shipping Charges	67.50
Insurance	27.68
Invoice Total	$4,303.44

COLLABORATIVE LEARNING ACTIVITY

Comparing Invoices and Discounts

1. As a team, collect invoices from a number of businesses in different industries in your area.

- **a.** How are they similar?
- **b.** How are they different?

2. Have each member of the team speak with a wholesaler or a retailer in your area.

- **a.** What are the typical trade discounts in that industry?
- **b.** What are the typical terms of sale in that industry?

Markup and Markdown

CHAPTER 8

PERFORMANCE OBJECTIVES

SECTION I MARKUP BASED ON COST

Determining an appropriate selling price for a company's goods or services is an extremely important function in business. The price must be attractive to potential customers, yet sufficient to cover expenses and provide the company with a reasonable profit.

In business, expenses are separated into two major categories. The first is the **cost of goods sold**. To a manufacturer, this expense would be the cost of production; to a wholesaler or retailer, the expense is the price paid to a manufacturer or distributor for the merchandise. The second category includes all the other expenses required to operate the business, such as salaries, rent, utilities, taxes, insurance, advertising, and maintenance. These expenses are known as **operating expenses**, overhead expenses, or simply **overhead**.

The amount added to the cost of an item to cover the operating expenses and profit is known as the **markup, markon,** or **margin**. It is the difference between the cost and the selling price of an item. Markup is applied at all levels of the marketing channels of distribution. This chapter deals with the business math applications involved in the pricing of goods and services.

cost of goods sold The cost of the merchandise sold during an operating period. One of two major expense categories of a business.

operating expenses, or overhead All business expenses, other than cost of merchandise, required to operate a business, such as payroll, rent, utilities, and insurance.

markup, markon, margin The amount added to the cost of an item to cover the operating expenses and profit. It is the difference between the cost and the selling price.

8-1 UNDERSTANDING AND USING THE RETAILING EQUATION TO FIND COST, AMOUNT OF MARKUP, AND SELLING PRICE OF AN ITEM

The fundamental principle on which business operates is to sell goods and services for a price high enough to cover all expenses and provide the owners with a reasonable profit. The formula that describes this principle is known as the **retailing equation**. The equation states that the selling price of an item is equal to the cost plus the markup.

retailing equation The selling price of an item is equal to the cost plus the markup.

Selling price = Cost + Markup

Teaching Transparency 8-1

Using the abbreviations C for cost, M for markup, and SP for selling price, the formula is written as

$$SP = C + M$$

To illustrate, if a camera costs a retailer \$60 and a \$50 markup is added to cover operating expenses and profit, the selling price of the camera would be \$110.

\$60 (cost) + \$50 (markup) = \$110 (selling price)

© David Young-Wolff/PhotoEdit, Inc.

According to the retailing equation, the selling price of an item is equal to the cost plus the markup.

In Chapter 5, we learned that equations are solved by isolating the unknown on one side and the knowns on the other. Using this theory, when the amount of markup is the unknown, the equation can be rewritten as

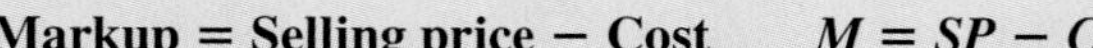

Markup = Selling price − Cost $\quad M = SP - C$

When the cost is the unknown, the equation becomes

Cost = Selling price − Markup $\quad C = SP - M$

The following examples illustrate how these formulas are used to determine the dollar amount of cost, markup, and selling price.

EXAMPLE 1 FINDING THE SELLING PRICE

Mementos Gift Shop pays $8.00 for a picture frame. If a markup of $6.50 is added, what is the selling price of the frame?

SOLUTION STRATEGY

Because selling price is the unknown variable, we use the formula $SP = C + M$ as follows:

$$SP = C + M$$

$$SP = 8.00 + 6.50 = 14.50$$

$$\text{Selling price} = \underline{\underline{\$14.50}}$$

TRY IT EXERCISE 1

For the following, use the basic retailing equation to solve for the unknown.

Ceramic planters cost the manufacturer $6.80 per unit to produce. If a markup of $9.40 each is added to the cost, what is the selling price per planter?

CHECK YOUR ANSWER WITH THE SOLUTION ON PAGE 278.

In the Business World

Real-World Connection
Many retailers use a psychological pricing strategy known as **odd pricing**, whereby prices are set to end in odd numbers such as $.79, $2.47, or $9.95.

Theoretically, customers perceive odd prices as being substantially below even prices, and therefore a bargain. For example, $299.95 is "perceived" as being much lower than $300.00.

Retailers, to psychologically project a prestigious image for their products, use **even pricing** such as $10.00 or $500.00.

CLASSROOM ACTIVITY
Have students bring to class examples of odd pricing and even pricing from local stores or newspaper advertisements. Have them discuss the effectiveness of this pricing policy in retailing.

EXAMPLE 2 FINDING THE AMOUNT OF MARKUP

Office Mart buys printing calculators from Taiwan for $22.50 each. If they are sold for $39.95, what is the amount of the markup?

SOLUTION STRATEGY

Because the markup is the unknown variable, we use the formula $M = SP - C$ as follows:

$$M = SP - C$$

$$M = 39.95 - 22.50 = 17.45$$

$$\text{Markup} = \underline{\underline{\$17.45}}$$

TRY IT EXERCISE 2

For the following, use the basic retailing equation to solve for the unknown.

Golfer's Paradise sells a dozen golf balls for $28.50. If the distributor was paid $16.75, what is the amount of the markup?

CHECK YOUR ANSWER WITH THE SOLUTION ON PAGE 278.

TEACHING TIP
Point out to students that the retailing equation can be expressed in dollar amounts or percents.

EXAMPLE 3 FINDING THE COST

Safeway Supermarkets sell Corn Crunchies for $3.29 per box. If the markup on this item is $2.12, how much did the store pay for the cereal?

SOLUTION STRATEGY

Because the cost is the unknown variable in this problem, we use the formula $C = SP - M$.

$$C = SP - M$$

$$C = 3.29 - 2.12 = 1.17$$

$$\text{Cost} = \underline{\underline{\$1.17}}$$

TRY IT EXERCISE 3

For the following, use the basic retailing equation to solve for the unknown.

After a wholesaler adds a markup of $75 to a television set, it is sold to a retail store for $290. What is the wholesaler's cost?

CHECK YOUR ANSWER WITH THE SOLUTION ON PAGE 278.

 8-2 

CALCULATING PERCENT MARKUP BASED ON COST

markup based on cost When cost is 100%, and the markup is expressed as a percent of that cost.

Learning Tip

A shortcut for calculating the factors of the retailing equation is to use the **markup table**. The cells represent cost, markup, and selling price, in both dollars and percents.

Markup Table

	$	%
C		
+ *MU*		
SP		

In addition to being expressed in dollar amounts, markup is frequently expressed as a percent. There are two ways of representing markup as a percent: based on cost and based on selling price. Manufacturers and most wholesalers use cost as the base in calculating the percent markup because cost figures are readily available to them. When markup is based on cost, the cost is 100%, and the markup is expressed as a percent of that cost. Retailers, however, use selling price figures as the base of most calculations, including percent markup. In retailing, the selling price represents 100%, and the markup is expressed as a percent of that selling price.

In Chapter 6, we used the percentage formula, Portion = Rate × Base. To review these variables, portion is a *part* of a whole amount, base is the *whole amount*, and the rate, as a percent, describes what part the portion is of the base. When we calculate markup as a percent, we are actually solving a rate problem, using the formula: Rate = Portion ÷ Base.

When the markup is based on cost, the percent markup is the rate, the dollar amount of markup is the portion, and the cost, representing 100%, is the base. The answer will describe what percent the markup is of the cost; therefore, it is called percent **markup based on cost**. We use the formula:

$$\textbf{Percent markup based on cost (rate)} = \frac{\textbf{Markup (portion)}}{\textbf{Cost (base)}} \quad \textbf{or} \quad \%M_{\text{COST}} = \frac{M}{C}$$

EXAMPLE 4 CALCULATING PERCENT MARKUP BASED ON COST

Blanco Industries produces stainless steel sinks at a cost of $56.00 each. If the sinks are sold to distributors for $89.60 each, what are the amount of the markup and the percent markup based on cost?

SOLUTION STRATEGY

$$M = SP - C$$

$$M = 89.60 - 56.00 = 33.60$$

$$\text{Markup} = \underline{\underline{\$33.60}}$$

$$\%M_{\text{COST}} = \frac{M}{C}$$

$$\%M_{\text{COST}} = \frac{33.60}{56.00} = .6$$

$$\text{Percent markup based on cost} = \underline{\underline{60\%}}$$

TRY IT EXERCISE 4

The Lighting Center buys lamps for $45 and sells them for $63. What is the amount of the markup and the percent markup based on cost?

CHECK YOUR ANSWERS WITH THE SOLUTIONS ON PAGE 278.

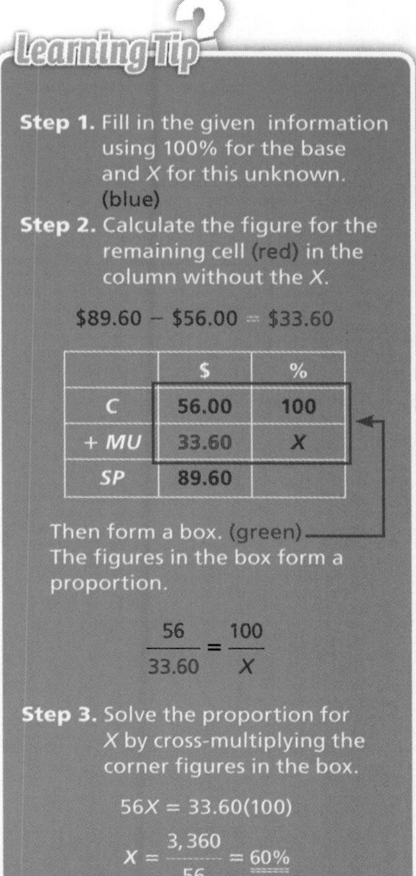

Learning Tip

Step 1. Fill in the given information using 100% for the base and *X* for this unknown. (blue)

Step 2. Calculate the figure for the remaining cell (red) in the column without the *X*.

$89.60 − $56.00 = $33.60

	$	%
C	56.00	100
+ *MU*	33.60	*X*
SP	89.60	

Then form a box. (green) The figures in the box form a proportion.

$$\frac{56}{33.60} = \frac{100}{X}$$

Step 3. Solve the proportion for *X* by cross-multiplying the corner figures in the box.

$$56X = 33.60(100)$$

$$X = \frac{3,360}{56} = \underline{\underline{60\%}}$$

CALCULATING SELLING PRICE WHEN COST AND PERCENT MARKUP BASED ON COST ARE KNOWN

From the basic retailing equation, we know that the selling price is equal to the cost plus the markup. When the markup is based on cost, the cost equals 100%, and the selling price equals 100% plus the percent markup. If, for example, the percent markup is 30%, then

Selling price = Cost + Markup

Selling price = 100% + 30%

Selling price = 130% *of* the cost

Because "of" means multiply, we multiply the cost by (100% plus the percent markup)

Selling price = Cost(100% + Percent markup based on cost)

$$SP = C(100\% + \%M_{\text{COST}})$$

TEACHING TIP

Emphasize that "based on . . ." denotes which element represents 100%, and therefore the *base* of the percentage formula.

Have students highlight or underline the "based on . . ." phrase of each problem. This will keep them from using the wrong base.

EXAMPLE 5 CALCULATING THE SELLING PRICE

A watch costs \$50 to produce. If the manufacturer wants a 70% markup based on cost, what should be the selling price of the watch?

SOLUTION STRATEGY

$$SP = C(100\% + \%M_{\text{COST}})$$

$$SP = 50(100\% + 70\%)$$

$$SP = 50(170\%) = 50(1.7) = 85$$

Selling price = $\underline{\underline{\$85}}$

	\$	%
C	50	100
+ MU		70
SP	*X*	170

Note: When the green box has six cells, use the four corner figures to form the proportion.

$100X = 50(170)$

$X = \underline{\underline{\$85}}$

TRY IT EXERCISE 5

Capital Appliances buys toasters for \$38. If a 65% markup based on cost is desired, what should be the selling price of the toaster?

CHECK YOUR ANSWER WITH THE SOLUTION ON PAGE 278.

8-3

CALCULATING COST WHEN SELLING PRICE AND PERCENT MARKUP BASED ON COST ARE KNOWN

To calculate cost when selling price and percent markup on cost are known, let's use our knowledge of solving equations from Chapter 5. Because we are dealing with the same three variables from the last section, simply solve the equation $SP = C(100\% + \%M_{\text{COST}})$ for the cost. Cost, the unknown, is isolated to one side of the equation by dividing both sides by (100% + Percent markup).

$$\textbf{Cost} = \frac{\textbf{Selling price}}{\textbf{100\% + Percent markup on cost}} \qquad C = \frac{SP}{100\% + \%M_{\text{COST}}}$$

EXAMPLE 6 CALCULATING COST

A Nose for Clothes sells a blouse for \$66. If a 50% markup based on cost is used, what is the cost of the blouse?

SOLUTION STRATEGY

$$\text{Cost} = \frac{\text{Selling price}}{100\% + \text{Percent markup on cost}}$$

$$\text{Cost} = \frac{66}{100\% + 50\%} = \frac{66}{150\%} = \frac{66}{1.5} = 44$$

Cost = $\underline{\underline{\$44}}$

	\$	%
C	*X*	100
+ MU		50
SP	66	150

$150X = 66(100)$

$X = \underline{\underline{\$44}}$

TRY IT EXERCISE 6

General Electric sells automatic coffee makers to distributors for $39. If a 30% markup based on cost is used, how much did it cost to manufacture the coffee maker?

CHECK YOUR ANSWER WITH THE SOLUTION ON PAGE 278.

Review Exercises

SECTION I

For the following items, calculate the missing information. Round dollars to the nearest cent and percents to the nearest tenth of a percent.

Item	Cost	Amount of Markup	Selling Price	Percent Markup Based on Cost
1. television set	$161.50	$138.45	$299.95	85.7%
2. bookcase	$32.40	$21.50	$53.90	66.4%
3. automobile	$6,944.80	$5,400.00	$12,344.80	77.8%
4. dress	$75.00	$60.00	$135.00	80%
5. vacuum cleaner	$156.22	$93.73	$249.95	60%
6. hat	$46.25	$50.00	$96.25	108.1%
7. computer	$1,350.00	$2,149.00	$3,499.00	159.2%
8. treadmill	$1,455.00	$880.00	$2,335.00	60.5%
9. 1 lb potatoes	$.58	$.75	$1.33	130%
10. wallet	$25.69	$19.26	$44.95	75%

Solution Transparencies

Complete, worked-out solutions for Exercises 1–10 appear in Appendix B, following the index.

TEACHING TIP
Students sometimes have difficulty at first understanding the concept of markup calculations. As a peer teaching strategy, have them work in pairs to solve Section I Review Exercises 1–10.

Solve the following word problems. Round dollars to the nearest cent and percents to the nearest tenth of a percent.

11. Alarm clocks cost the manufacturer $56.10 per unit to produce. If a markup of $29.80 is added to the cost, what is the selling price per clock?

$SP = C + M = 56.10 + 29.80 = \underline{\$85.90}$

12. En Vogue Boutique sells blouses for $22.88. If the cost per shirt is $15.50, what is the amount of the markup?

$M = SP - C = 22.88 - 15.50 = \underline{\$7.38}$

13. After a wholesaler adds a markup of $125 to a stereo, it is sold for $320. What is the cost of the stereo?

$C = SP - M = 320 - 125 = \underline{\$195}$

14. Best Buy purchases flat-screen computer monitors from H.P. for $275.59 and sells them for $449.99.

a. What is the amount of the markup?

$M = SP - C$

$M = 449.99 - 275.59 = \underline{\$174.40}$

b. What is the percent markup based on cost?

$$\%M_C = \frac{M}{C} = \frac{174.40}{275.59} = .6328 = \underline{63.3\%}$$

Best Buy Co., Inc., is a specialty retailer of consumer electronics, home-office products, entertainment software, appliances and related services. The company operates retail stores and Web sites under the brand names Best Buy, Five Star, Future Shop, Geek Squad, Magnolia Audio Video, and Pacific Sales Kitchen and Bath Centers.

In 2007, Best Buy's 140,000 employees generated sales of over $35.9 billion in 1,160 stores in the United States, Canada, and China.

15. The Holiday Card Shop purchased stationery for \$2.44 per box. A \$1.75 markup is added to the stationery.

    a. What is the selling price?

    $SP = C + M = 2.44 + 1.75 = \underline{\underline{\$4.19}}$

    b. What is the percent markup based on cost?

    $$\%M_C = \frac{M}{C} = \frac{1.75}{2.44} = .7172 = \underline{\underline{71.7\%}}$$

16. Staples adds a \$4.60 markup to calculators and sells them for \$9.95.

    a. What is the cost of the calculators?

    $C = SP - M = 9.95 - 4.60 = \underline{\underline{\$5.35}}$

    b. What is the percent markup based on cost?

    $$\%M_C = \frac{M}{C} = \frac{4.60}{5.35} = .8598 = \underline{\underline{86\%}}$$

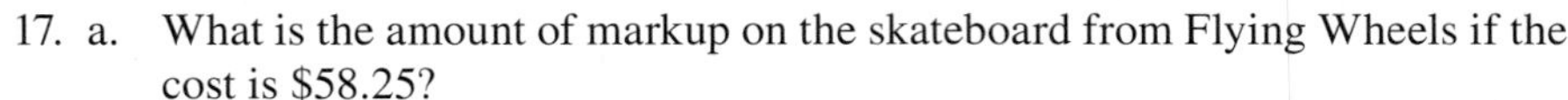

17. a. What is the amount of markup on the skateboard from Flying Wheels if the cost is \$58.25?

    $M = SP - C$

    $M = \$118.88 - 58.25 = \underline{\underline{\$60.63}}$

    b. What is the percent markup based on cost?

    $$\%M_C = \frac{M}{C} = \frac{60.63}{58.25} = 1.0408 = \underline{\underline{104.1\%}}$$

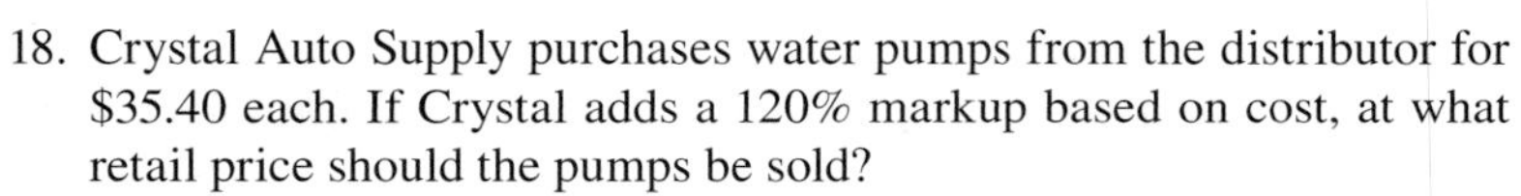

18. Crystal Auto Supply purchases water pumps from the distributor for \$35.40 each. If Crystal adds a 120% markup based on cost, at what retail price should the pumps be sold?

    $SP = C(100\% + \%M_C) = 35.40(100\% + 120\%) = 35.40(2.2) = \underline{\underline{\$77.88}}$

19. Broadway Carpets sells designer rugs at retail for \$875.88. If a 50% markup based on cost is added, what is the cost of the designer rugs?

    $$C = \frac{SP}{100\% + \%M_C} = \frac{875.88}{100\% + 50\%} = \frac{875.88}{1.5} = \underline{\underline{\$583.92}}$$

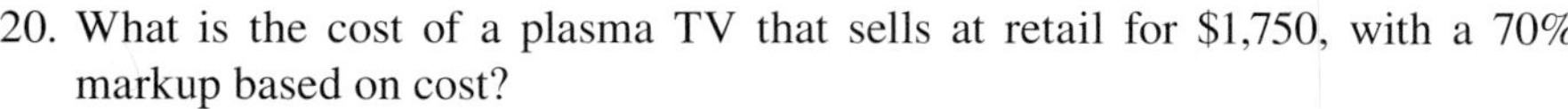

20. What is the cost of a plasma TV that sells at retail for \$1,750, with a 70% markup based on cost?

    $$C = \frac{SP}{100\% + \%M_C} = \frac{1,750}{100\% + 70\%} = \frac{1,750}{1.7} = \underline{\underline{\$1,029.41}}$$

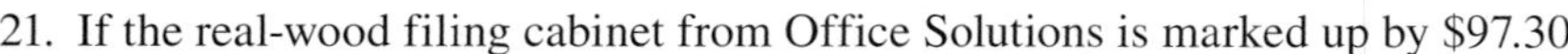

21. If the real-wood filing cabinet from Office Solutions is marked up by \$97.30,

    a. What is the cost?

    $C = SP - M$

    $C = 178.88 - 97.30 = \underline{\underline{\$81.58}}$

    b. What is the percent markup based on cost?

    $$\%M_C = \frac{M}{C} = \frac{97.30}{81.58} = 1.1926 = \underline{\underline{119.3\%}}$$

22. The Green Thumb Garden Shop purchases automatic lawn sprinklers for \$12.50 from the manufacturer. If a 75% markup based on cost is added, at what retail price should the sprinklers be marked?

    $SP = C(100\% + \%M_C) = 12.50(100\% + 75\%) = 12.50(1.75) = \underline{\underline{\$21.88}}$

23. a. What is the cost of the cheese and fruit platter from Party Central if the markup is 70% based on the cost?

    $$C = \frac{SP}{100\% + \%M_C} = \frac{19.99}{1.7} = \underline{\underline{\$11.76}}$$

    b. What is the amount of the markup?

    $M = SP - C$

    $M = 19.99 - 11.76 = \underline{\underline{\$8.23}}$

BUSINESS DECISION KEYSTONE MARKUP

24. In department and specialty store retailing, a common markup strategy is to double the cost of an item to arrive at a selling price. This strategy is known as **keystoning** the markup, and is widely used in apparel, cosmetics, fashion accessories, shoes, and other categories of merchandise.

    The reasoning for the high amount of markup is that these stores have particularly high operating expenses. In addition, they have a continuing need to update fixtures and remodel stores to attract customers.

    You are the buyer in the women's shoe department of the Roma Grande Department Store. You normally keystone your markups on certain shoes and handbags. This amount of markup allows you enough gross margin so that you can lower prices when "sales" occur and still have a profitable department.

© Jim Mone/Associated Press

According to the Department of Commerce, there were 48,695 shopping centers in the U.S. in 2005, employing over 17.5 million people.

Top U.S. Shopping Centers Gross Leasable Area (GLA) in sq. ft.

Shopping Center	GLA
King of Prussia Mall, King of Prussia, Pennsylvania	2,856,000
Mall of America, Bloomington, Minnesota	2,777,918
South Coast Plaza, Costa Mesa, California	2,700,000
Sawgrass Mills, Sunrise, Florida	2,503,035
Del Amo Fashion Center, Torrance, California	2,500,000
Grand Canyon Parkway, Las Vagas, Nevada	2,500,000
Aventura Mall, North Miami Beach, Florida	2,400,000
The Galleria, Houston, Texas	2,298,417

Source: www.directoryofmajormalls.com

a. If you are looking for a line of handbags that will retail for \$120, what is the most you can pay for the bags?

   \$60.00

b. At a women's wear trade show, you find a line of handbags that you like with a suggested retail price of \$130.00. The vendor has offered you trade discounts of 30/20/5. Will this series of trade discounts allow you to keystone the handbags?

   Need cost of \$65.00

   $130(.7)(.8)(.95) = \$69.16$

   No—Cost too high

c. (Challenge) The vendor tells you that the first two discounts, 30% and 20%, are fixed, but the 5% is negotiable. What trade discount, rounded to a whole percent, should you ask for, in order to keystone the markup?

   Reasoning: Solve for a third discount in the trade discount series that yields a single equivalent discount of 50% or more (Chapter 7, Performance Objective 7-8). This will allow the markup to be keystoned.

   Let X = Complement of discount needed

   $(.7)(.8)X = .5$

   $.56X = .5$

   $X = .893$ Discount needed $= 100\% - 89.3\% = 10.7\% = \underline{\underline{11\%}}$

SECTION II MARKUP BASED ON SELLING PRICE

In Section I, we calculated markup as a percentage of the cost of an item. The cost was the base and represented 100%. As noted, this method is primarily used by manufacturers and wholesalers. In this section, the markup is calculated as a percentage of the selling price; therefore, the selling price will be the base and represent 100%. This practice is used by most retailers because most retail records and statistics are kept in sales dollars.

8-5 CALCULATING PERCENT MARKUP BASED ON SELLING PRICE

markup based on selling price When selling price is 100%, and the markup is expressed as a percent of that selling price.

TEACHING TIP
Remind students to highlight or underline the "based on . . ." phrase of each problem to keep them from using the wrong base.

The calculation of percent **markup based on selling price** is the same as that for percent markup based on cost, except the base (the denominator) changes from cost to selling price. Remember, finding percent markup is a rate problem, using the now familiar percentage formula, Rate = Portion ÷ Base.

For this application of the formula, the percent markup based on selling price is the rate, the amount of the markup is the portion, and the selling price is the base. The formula is

$$\textbf{Percent markup based in selling price (rate)} = \frac{\textbf{Markup (portion)}}{\textbf{Selling price (base)}} \quad \textbf{or} \quad \%M_{SP} = \frac{M}{SP}$$

$125 − $60 = $65

	$	%
C	60	
+ *MU*	65	*X*
SP	125	100

$125X = 65(100)$

$X = \underline{\underline{52\%}}$

EXAMPLE 7 CALCULATING THE PERCENT MARKUP BASED ON SELLING PRICE

American Hardware & Garden Supply purchases electric drills for $60 each. If it sells the drills for $125, what is the amount of the markup, and what is the percent markup based on selling price?

SOLUTION STRATEGY

$$M = SP - C$$

$$M = 125 - 60 = 65$$

$$\text{Markup} = \underline{\underline{\$65}}$$

$$\%M_{SP} = \frac{M}{SP}$$

$$\%M_{SP} = \frac{65}{125} = .52$$

$$\text{Percent markup based on selling price} = \underline{\underline{52\%}}$$

TRY IT EXERCISE 7

Deals on Wheels buys bicycles from the distributor for $94.50 each. If the bikes sell for $157.50, what is the amount of the markup and what is the percent markup based on selling price?

CHECK YOUR ANSWERS WITH THE SOLUTIONS ON PAGE 279.

CALCULATING SELLING PRICE WHEN COST AND PERCENT MARKUP BASED ON SELLING PRICE ARE KNOWN

When the percent markup is based on selling price, remember that the selling price is the base and represents 100%. This means the percent cost plus the percent markup must equal 100%. If, for example, the markup is 25% of the selling price, the cost must be 75% of the selling price,

$$\text{Cost} + \text{Markup} = \text{Selling price}$$

$$75\% + 25\% = 100\%$$

Because the percent markup is known, the percent cost will always be the complement, or

$$\textbf{\% Cost} = \textbf{100\%} - \textbf{Percent markup based on selling price}$$

Because the selling price is the base, we can solve for the selling price by using the percentage formula Base = Portion ÷ Rate, where the cost is the portion and the percent cost or (100% − Percent markup on selling price) is the rate.

$$\textbf{Selling price} = \frac{\textbf{Cost}}{\textbf{100\%} - \textbf{Percent markup on selling price}} \quad \textbf{or } SP = \frac{C}{100\% - \%M_{SP}}$$

CLASSROOM ACTIVITIES

Some businesses operate on low markup with high volume, whereas others use high markup with low volume. Ask students for examples of each. Some typical responses might include supermarkets and drug stores for high volume and automobile dealerships, art galleries, and jewelry stores for low volume.

EXAMPLE 8 CALCULATING SELLING PRICE

Fairmont Furniture purchases wall units from the manufacturer for $550. If the store policy is to mark up all merchandise 60% based on the selling price, what is the retail selling price of the wall units?

SOLUTION STRATEGY

$$SP = \frac{C}{100\% - \%M_{SP}}$$

$$SP = \frac{550}{100\% - 60\%} = \frac{550}{40\%} = 1{,}375$$

$$\text{Selling price} = \underline{\underline{\$1{,}375}}$$

	$	%
C	550	40
+ MU		60
SP	*X*	100

$$40X = 550(100)$$

$$X = \underline{\underline{\$1{,}375}}$$

TRY IT EXERCISE 8

Grand Prix Menswear buys suits for $169 from the manufacturer. If a 35% markup based on selling price is the objective, what should be the selling price of the suit?

CHECK YOUR ANSWER WITH THE SOLUTION ON PAGE 279.

CALCULATING COST WHEN SELLING PRICE AND PERCENT MARKUP BASED ON SELLING PRICE ARE KNOWN

8-7

Often, retailers know how much their customers are willing to pay for an item. The following procedure is used to determine the most a retailer can pay for an item and still get the intended markup.

To calculate the cost of an item when the selling price and percent markup based on selling price are known, we use a variation of the formula used in the last section. To solve for cost, we must isolate cost on one side of the equation by multiplying both sides of the equation by (100% − Percent markup). This yields the equation for cost:

Cost = Selling price(100% − Percent markup on selling price)

$$C = SP(100\% - \%M_{SP})$$

100 − 40 = 60

	$	%
C	*X*	60
+ *MU*		40
SP	120	100

$100X = 120(60)$

$X = \$72$

EXAMPLE 9 CALCULATING COST

A buyer for a chain of boutiques is looking for a line of dresses to retail for $120. If a 40% markup based on selling price is the objective, what is the most the buyer can pay for these dresses and still get the intended markup?

SOLUTION STRATEGY

$C = SP(100\% - \%M_{SP})$

$C = 120(100\% - 40\%) = 120(.6) = 72$

Cost = $72

TRY IT EXERCISE 9

What is the most a gift shop buyer can pay for a clock if he wants a 55% markup based on selling price and expects to sell the clock for $79 at retail?

CHECK YOUR ANSWER WITH THE SOLUTION ON PAGE 279.

8-8 CONVERTING PERCENT MARKUP BASED ON COST TO PERCENT MARKUP BASED ON SELLING PRICE, AND VICE VERSA

Converting Percent Markup Based on Cost to Percent Markup Based on Selling Price

When percent markup is based on cost, it can be converted to percent markup based on selling price by using the following formula:

$$\textbf{Percent markup based on selling price} = \frac{\textbf{Percent markup based on cost}}{\textbf{100\% + Percent markup based on cost}}$$

EXAMPLE 10 CONVERTING BETWEEN MARKUP TYPES

If a calculator is marked up 60% based on cost, what is the corresponding percent markup based on selling price?

SOLUTION STRATEGY

$$\text{Percent markup based on selling price} = \frac{\text{Percent markup based on cost}}{100\% + \text{Percent markup based on cost}}$$

$$\text{Percent markup based on selling price} = \frac{60\%}{100\% + 60\%} = \frac{.6}{1.6} = .375$$

$$\text{Percent markup based on selling price} = \underline{\underline{37.5\%}}$$

Learning Tip

The percent markup on cost is always *greater* than the corresponding percent markup on selling price because markup on cost uses cost as the base, which is *less* than the selling price. In the percentage formula, the lower the base, the greater the rate.

TRY IT EXERCISE 10

A pillow is marked up 50% based on cost. What is the corresponding percent markup based on selling price?

8-4

CHECK YOUR ANSWER WITH THE SOLUTION ON PAGE 279.

Converting Percent Markup Based on Selling Price to Percent Markup Based on Cost

When percent markup is based on selling price, it can be converted to percent markup based on cost by the formula:

$$\textbf{Percent markup based on cost} = \frac{\textbf{Percent markup based on selling price}}{\textbf{100\% − Percent markup based on selling price}}$$

EXAMPLE 11 CONVERTING BETWEEN MARKUP TYPES

A Panasonic stereo is marked up 25% based on selling price at Circuit City. What is the corresponding percent markup based on cost? Round to the nearest tenth of a percent.

SOLUTION STRATEGY

$$\text{Percent markup based on cost} = \frac{\text{Percent markup based on selling price}}{100\% - \text{Percent markup based on selling price}}$$

$$\text{Percent markup based on cost} = \frac{25\%}{100\% - 25\%} = \frac{.25}{.75} = .3333$$

$$\text{Percent markup based on cost} = \underline{\underline{33.3\%}}$$

TRY IT EXERCISE 11

Teaching Transparency 8-5

A Nintendo video game is marked up 75% based on selling price at Video Mart. What is the corresponding percent markup based on cost? Round to the nearest tenth of a percent.

CHECK YOUR ANSWER WITH THE SOLUTION ON PAGE 279.

SECTION II Review Exercises

Solution Transparencies

Complete, worked-out solutions for Exercises 1–12 appear in Appendix B, following the index.

COLLABORATIVE LEARNING ACTIVITY
As a Section II review, have students work in pairs to solve Section II Review Exercises 1–12.

For the following items, calculate the missing information. Round dollars to the nearest cent and percents to the nearest tenth of a percent.

Item	Cost	Amount of Markup	Selling Price	Percent Markup Based on Cost	Percent Markup Based on Selling Price
1. sink	$65.00	$50.00	$115.00		43.5%
2. textbook	$34.44	$17.06	$51.50		33.1%
3. telephone	$75.00	$61.36	$136.36		45%
4. bicycle	$53.40	$80.10	$133.50		60%
5. magazine				60%	37.5%
6. flashlight				53.8%	35%
7. doll house	$71.25	$94.74	$165.99	133%	57.1%
8. 1 qt. milk	$1.18	$.79	$1.97	66.9%	40.1%
9. truck	$15,449.00	$9,468.74	$24,917.74	61.3%	38%
10. sofa	$584.55	$714.45	$1,299.00	122.2%	55%
11. fan				150%	60%
12. drill				88.7%	47%

Solve the following word problems. Round dollars to the nearest cent and percents to the nearest tenth of a percent.

13. If the Precision Computer has a cost of $544,

a. What is the amount of the markup?

$M = SP - C$

$M = 999.99 - 544.00$

$M = \$455.99$

b. What is the percent markup based on selling price?

$$\%M_{SP} = \frac{M}{SP}$$

$$\%M_{SP} = \frac{455.99}{999.99} = .4559 = 45.6\%$$

14. A distributor purchases tractors at a cost of \$6,500 and sells them for \$8,995.
    a. What is the amount of the markup?

    $M = SP - C = 8{,}995 - 6{,}500 = \underline{\underline{\$2{,}495}}$

    b. What is the percent markup based on selling price?

    $$\%M_{SP} = \frac{M}{SP} = \frac{2{,}495}{8{,}995} = .2773 = \underline{\underline{27.7\%}}$$

15. Waterbed City purchases beds from the manufacturer for \$212.35. If the store policy is to mark up all merchandise 42% based on selling price, what is the retail selling price of the beds?

$$SP = \frac{C}{100\% - \%M_{SP}} = \frac{212.35}{100\% - 42\%} = \frac{212.35}{.58} = \underline{\underline{\$366.12}}$$

16. Galaxy Tools manufactures an 18-volt drill at a cost of \$38.32. They import rechargeable battery packs for \$20.84 each. Galaxy offers its distributors a "package deal" that includes a drill and two battery packs. The markup is 36% based on selling price. What is the selling price of the package?

$$\text{Selling price} = \frac{\text{Cost}}{100\% - \%M_{SP}}$$

$$\frac{38.32 + 2(20.84)}{100\% - 36\%} = \underline{\underline{\$125}}$$

17. If the potted plants at Garden Center have a markup of 28% based on selling price,
    a. What is the cost?

    $C = SP(100\% - \%M_{SP})$

    $C = 3.99(.72) = \underline{\underline{\$2.87}}$

    b. What is the amount of the markup?

    $M = SP - C$

    $M = 3.99 - 2.87 = \underline{\underline{\$1.12}}$

    c. What is the percent markup based on cost?

    $$\%M_C = \frac{M}{C} = \frac{1.12}{2.87} = .3902 = \underline{\underline{39\%}}$$

18. You are the buyer for The Shoe Outlet. You are looking for a line of men's shoes to retail for \$79.95. If your objective is a 55% markup based on selling price, what is the most that you can pay for the shoes to still get the desired markup?

$C = SP(100\% - \%M_{SP}) = 79.95(100\% - 55\%) = 79.95(.45) = \underline{\underline{\$35.98}}$

19. If the markup on a washing machine is 43% based on selling price, what is the corresponding percent markup based on cost?

$$\%M_C = \frac{\%M_{SP}}{100\% - \%M_{SP}} = \frac{43\%}{100\% - 43\%} = \frac{.43}{.57} = .7543 = \underline{\underline{75.4\%}}$$

20. If the markup on an oven is 200% based on cost, what is the corresponding percent markup based on selling price?

$$\%M_{SP} = \frac{\%M_C}{100\% + \%M_C} = \frac{200\%}{100\% + 200\%} = \frac{2}{3} = .6666 = \underline{\underline{66.7\%}}$$

21. A purse has a cost of \$21.50 and a selling price of \$51.99.

    a. What is the amount of markup on the purse?

    $M = SP - C = 51.99 - 21.50 = \underline{\underline{\$30.49}}$

    b. What is the percent markup based on cost?

    $$\%M_C = \frac{M}{C} = \frac{30.49}{21.50} = 1.4181 = \underline{\underline{141.8\%}}$$

c. What is the corresponding percent markup based on selling price?

$$\%M_{SP} = \frac{M}{SP} = \frac{30.49}{51.99} = .5864 = \underline{\underline{58.6\%}}$$

22. If a cordless phone at Phones, etc., has a 45% markup based on selling price,

a. What is the cost?

$C = SP(100\% - \%M_{SP})$

$C = 49.99(.55) = \underline{\underline{\$27.49}}$

b. What is the amount of markup?

$M = SP - C$

$M = 49.99 - 27.49 = \underline{\underline{\$22.50}}$

c. If the store changed to a 90% markup based on cost, what would be the new selling price?

$SP = C(100\% + \%M_C)$

$SP = 27.49(1.9) = \underline{\underline{\$52.23}}$

BUSINESS DECISION INCREASING THE MARGIN

23. If Target pays $37.50 for the vacuum cleaner shown here,

a. What is the percent markup based on selling price?

$M = SP - C = 89.99 - 37.50 = \$52.49$

$$\%M_{SP} = \frac{M}{SP} = \frac{52.49}{89.99} = \underline{\underline{58.3\%}}$$

b. If Target pays $1.50 to the insurance company for each product replacement policy sold, what is the percent markup based on selling price of the vacuum cleaner and policy combination?

Markup on policy = 7.99 − 1.50 = $6.49

$$\%M_{SP} = \frac{M}{SP} = \frac{52.49 + 6.49}{89.99 + 7.99} = \frac{58.98}{97.98} = \underline{\underline{60.2\%}}$$

c. If 6,000 vacuum cleaners are sold in a season, and 40% are sold with the insurance policy, how many additional "markup dollars," or **gross margin**, was made by offering the policy?

$6{,}000 \times .4 = 2{,}400$ Policies sold

$2{,}400 \times 6.49 = \underline{\underline{\$15{,}576}}$

d. (Optional) As a housewares buyer for Target, what is your opinion of such insurance policies considering their effect on the "profit picture" of the department? How can you sell more policies?

Answers will vary: The policies are important to profit; department managers could offer sales staff an incentive for selling vacuum cleaners with policies.

SECTION III MARKDOWNS, MULTIPLE OPERATIONS, AND PERISHABLE GOODS

markdown A price reduction from the original selling price of merchandise.

The original selling price of merchandise usually represents only a temporary situation, based on customer and competitor reaction to that price. A price reduction from the original selling price of merchandise is known as a **markdown**. Markdowns are frequently used in retailing because of errors in initial pricing or merchandise selection. For example, the original price may have been set too high, or the buyer ordered the wrong styles, sizes, or quantities of merchandise.

Most markdowns should not be regarded as losses but as sales promotion opportunities used to increase sales and profits. When a sale has been concluded, raising prices back to the original selling price is known as a **markdown cancellation**. This section deals with the mathematics of markdowns, a series of markups and markdowns, and the pricing of perishable merchandise.

markdown cancellation Raising prices back to the original selling price after a sale is over.

DETERMINING THE AMOUNT OF MARKDOWN AND THE MARKDOWN PERCENT

A markdown is a reduction from the original selling price of an item to a new **sale price**. To determine the amount of a markdown, we use the formula:

sale price The promotional price of merchandise, after a markdown.

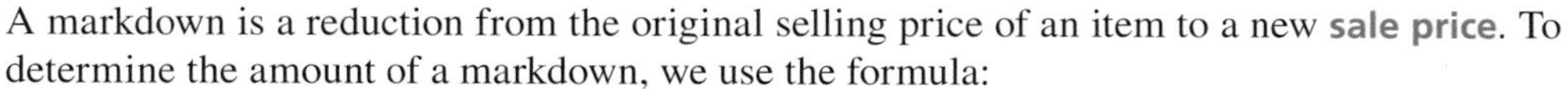

$$\textbf{Markdown} = \textbf{Original selling price} - \textbf{Sale price}$$

For example, if a sweater was originally marked at \$89.95 and then was sale priced at \$59.95, the amount of the markdown would be \$30.00 (\$89.95 − \$59.95 = \$30.00).

To find the markdown percent, we use the percentage formula once again, Rate = Portion ÷ Base, where the markdown percent is the rate, the amount of the markdown is the portion, and the original selling price is the base:

$$\textbf{Markdown percent} = \frac{\textbf{Markdown}}{\textbf{Original selling price}}$$

Prudent shoppers often spend time comparing products in order to make "informed" buying decisions.

EXAMPLE 12 DETERMINING THE MARKDOWN AND MARKDOWN PERCENT

A picture frame that originally sold for $60 was marked down and sold for $48. What is the amount of the markdown and the markdown percent?

Learning Tip

Note that *markdown percent* calculations are an application of *rate of decrease*, covered in Chapter 6.

In the percentage formula, the markdown (portion) represents the amount of the decrease, and the original selling price (base) represents the original amount.

SOLUTION STRATEGY

$$\text{Markdown} = \text{Original selling price} - \text{Sale price}$$

$$\text{Markdown} = 60 - 48 = 12$$

$$\text{Markdown} = \underline{\underline{\$12}}$$

$$\text{Markdown percent} = \frac{\text{Markdown}}{\text{Original selling price}} = \frac{12}{60} = .2$$

$$\text{Markdown percent} = \underline{\underline{20\%}}$$

TRY IT EXERCISE 12

Teaching Transparency 8-6

A briefcase that originally sold for $75 was marked down and sold for $56. What is the amount of the markdown and the markdown percent? Round your answer to the nearest tenth of a percent.

CHECK YOUR ANSWERS WITH THE SOLUTIONS ON PAGE 279.

8-10 DETERMINING THE SALE PRICE AFTER A MARKDOWN AND THE ORIGINAL PRICE BEFORE A MARKDOWN

Determining Sale Price after a Markdown

In markdown calculations, the original selling price is the base, or 100%. After a markdown is subtracted from that price, the new price represents (100% − Markdown percent) *of* the original price. For example, if a chair is marked down 30%, the sale price would be 70% (100% − 30%) of the original price.

To find the new sale price after a markdown, we use the familiar percentage formula, Portion = Rate × Base, where the sale price is the portion, the original price is the base, and (100% − Markdown percent) is the rate.

Sale price = Original selling price(100% − Markdown percent)

EXAMPLE 13 DETERMINING THE SALE PRICE

Fernando's Hideaway, a men's clothing store, originally sold a line of ties for $55 each. If the manager decides to mark them down 40% for a clearance sale, what is the sale price of a tie?

SOLUTION STRATEGY

Remember, if the markdown is 40%, the sale price must be 60% (100% − 40%) *of* the original price.

Sale price = Original selling price(100% − Markdown percent)

Sale price = $55(100% − 40%) = 55(.6) = 33

Sale price = $33

TRY IT EXERCISE 13

Craftsman's Village originally sold paneling for $27.50 per sheet. When the stock was almost depleted, the price was marked down 60% to make room for incoming merchandise. What was the sale price per sheet of paneling?

CHECK YOUR ANSWER WITH THE SOLUTION ON PAGE 279.

Finding the Original Price before a Markdown

To find the original selling price before a markdown, we use the sale price formula solved for the original selling price. The original selling price is isolated to one side by dividing both sides of the equation by (100% − Markdown percent). *Note*: This is actually the percentage formula Base = Portion ÷ Rate, with the original selling price as the base.

$$\textbf{Original selling price} = \frac{\textbf{Sale price}}{\textbf{100\% − Markdown percent}}$$

EXAMPLE 14 DETERMINING THE ORIGINAL SELLING PRICE

What was the original selling price of a backpack, currently on sale for $99 after a 25% markdown?

SOLUTION STRATEGY

Reasoning: $99 = 75% (100% − 25%) *of* the original price. Solve for the original price.

$$\text{Original selling price} = \frac{\text{Sale price}}{100\% - \text{Markdown percent}} = \frac{99}{100\% - 25\%} = \frac{99}{.75} = 132$$

Original selling price = $132

TRY IT EXERCISE 14

What was the original selling price of a lamp, currently on sale for $79 after a 35% markdown? Round your answer to the nearest cent.

CHECK YOUR ANSWER WITH THE SOLUTION ON PAGE 279.

8-11 COMPUTING THE FINAL SELLING PRICE AFTER A SERIES OF MARKUPS AND MARKDOWNS

staple goods Products, considered basic and routinely purchased, that do not undergo seasonal fluctuations in sales, such as food, tools, and furniture.

seasonal goods Products that undergo seasonal fluctuations in sales, such as fashion apparel and holiday merchandise.

Products that do not undergo seasonal fluctuations in sales, such as food, tools, tires, and furniture, are known as **staple goods**. These products are usually marked up once and perhaps marked down occasionally, on sale. **Seasonal goods**, such as men's and women's fashion items, snow shovels, bathing suits, and holiday merchandise, may undergo many markups and markdowns during their selling season. Merchants must continually adjust prices as the season progresses. Getting caught with an excessive amount of out-of-season inventory can ruin an otherwise bright profit picture. Christmas decorations in January or snow tires in June are virtually useless profit-wise!

EXAMPLE 15 COMPUTING A SERIES OF MARKUPS AND MARKDOWNS

Learning Tip

In a series of markups and markdowns, each calculation is based on the *previous* selling price.

In March, Swim and Sport purchased designer bathing suits for $50 each. The original markup was 60% based on the selling price. In May, the shop took a 25% markdown by having a sale. After three weeks, the sale was over and all merchandise was marked up 15%. By July, many of the bathing suits were still in stock, so the shop took a 30% markdown to stimulate sales. At the end of August, the balance of the bathing suits were put on clearance sale, with a final markdown of another 25%. Compute the intermediate prices and the final selling price of the bathing suits. Round to the nearest cent.

SOLUTION STRATEGY

When solving a series of markups and markdowns, remember that each should be based on the previous selling price. Use the formulas presented in this chapter, and take each step one at a time.

Step 1. Find the original selling price, with markup based on the selling price.

$$\text{Selling price} = \frac{\text{Cost}}{100\% - \text{Percent markup}} = \frac{50}{100\% - 60\%} = \frac{50}{.4} = 125$$

Original selling price = $\underline{\underline{\$125}}$

Step 2. Calculate the 25% markdown in May.

Sale price = Original selling price(100% − Markdown percent)

Sale price = 125(100% − 25%) = 125(.75) = 93.75

Sale price = $\underline{\underline{\$93.75}}$

Step 3. Calculate the after-sale 15% markup.
Remember, the base is the previous selling price, $93.75.

Selling price = Sale price(100% + Percent markup)

Selling price = 93.75(100% + 15%) = 93.75(1.15) = 107.81

Selling price = $107.81

Step 4. Calculate the July 30% markdown.

Sale price = Previous selling price(100% − Markdown percent)

Sale price = 107.81(100% − 30%) = 107.81(.7) = 75.47

Sale price = $75.47

Step 5. Calculate the final 25% markdown.

Sale price = Previous selling price(100% − Markdown percent)

Sale price = 75.47(100% − 25%) = 75.47(.75) = 56.60

Final sale price = $56.60

TRY IT EXERCISE 15

In September, Tire Depot in Chicago purchased snow tires from a distributor for $48.50 each. The original markup was 55% based on the selling price. In November, the tires were marked down 30% and put on sale. In December, they were marked up 20%. In February, the tires were again on sale at 30% off, and in March were cleared out with a final 25% markdown. What was the final selling price of the tires? Round to the nearest cent.

CHECK YOUR ANSWERS WITH THE SOLUTIONS ON PAGE 279.

8-12 CALCULATING THE SELLING PRICE OF PERISHABLE GOODS

perishable goods Products that have a certain shelf life and then no value at all, such as fruits, vegetables, flowers, and dairy products.

Out-of-season merchandise still has some value, whereas **perishable goods** (such as fruits, vegetables, flowers, and dairy products) have a certain shelf life and then no value at all. For sellers of this type of merchandise to achieve their intended markups, the selling price must be based on the quantity of products sold at the original price. The quantity sold is calculated as total items less spoilage. For example, if a tomato vendor anticipates a 20% spoilage rate, the selling price of the tomatoes should be calculated based on 80% of the original stock. To calculate the selling price of perishables, use the formula:

$$\textbf{Selling price of perishables} = \frac{\textbf{Total expected selling price}}{\textbf{Total quantity} - \textbf{Anticipated spoilage}}$$

EXAMPLE 16 CALCULATING THE SELLING PRICE OF PERISHABLE GOODS

The Farmer's Market buys 1,500 pounds of fresh peaches at a cost of \$.60 a pound. If a 15% spoilage rate is anticipated, at what price per pound should the peaches be sold to achieve a 50% markup based on selling price? Round to the nearest cent.

SOLUTION STRATEGY

Step 1. Find the total expected selling price: The total expected selling price is found by applying the selling price formula, $SP = C \div (100\% - \%M_{SP})$. The cost will be the total pounds times the price per pound, $1{,}500 \times \$.60 = \$900$

$$SP = \frac{\text{Cost}}{100\% - \%M_{SP}} = \frac{900}{100\% - 50\%} = \frac{900}{.5} = 1{,}800$$

Total expected selling price = \$1,800

Step 2. Find the anticipated spoilage: To find the amount of anticipated spoilage, use the formula,

Anticipated spoilage = Total quantity × Spoilage rate

Anticipated spoilage = 1,500 × 15% = 1,500(.15) = 225

Anticipated spoilage = 225 pounds

Step 3. Calculate the selling price of the perishables:

$$\text{Selling price of perishables} = \frac{\text{Total expected selling price}}{\text{Total quantity} - \text{Anticipated spoilage}}$$

$$\text{Selling price} = \frac{1{,}800}{1{,}500 - 225} = \frac{1{,}800}{1{,}275} = 1.411$$

Selling price of peaches = \$1.41 per pound

TRY IT EXERCISE 16

Enchanted Gardens, a chain of flower shops, purchases 800 dozen roses for Valentine's Day at a cost of \$6.50 per dozen. If a 10% spoilage rate is anticipated, at what price per dozen should the roses be sold to achieve a 60% markup based on selling price? Round to the nearest cent.

CHECK YOUR ANSWER WITH THE SOLUTION ON PAGE 279.

Review Exercises

SECTION III 8

For the following items, calculate the missing information. Round dollars to the nearest cent and percents to the nearest tenth of a percent.

Complete, worked-out solutions for Exercises 1–10 appear in Appendix B, following the index.

	Item	Original Selling Price	Amount of Markdown	Sale Price	Markdown Percent
1.	fish tank	$189.95	$28.50	$161.45	15%
2.	sneakers	$53.88	$16.38	$37.50	30.4%
3.	cantaloupe	$1.68	$.39	$1.29	23.2%
4.	CD player	$264.95	$79.48	$185.47	30%
5.	1 yd carpet	$41.10	$16.44	$24.66	40%
6.	suitcase	$68.00	$16.01	$51.99	23.5%
7.	chess set	$115.77	$35.50	$80.27	30.7%
8.	necklace	$390.00	$155.00	$235.00	39.7%
9.	copier	$1,599.88	$559.96	$1,039.92	35%
10.	pen	$21.20	$5.30	$15.90	25%

TEACHING TIP
As a Section III review, have students work in small groups to solve Section III Review Exercises 1–10.

Solve the following word problems, rounding dollars to the nearest cent and percents to the nearest tenth of a percent.

11. A motorcycle that originally sold for $9,700 was marked down and sold for $7,950.

    a. What is the amount of the markdown?

    $MD = \text{Original price} - \text{Sale price} = 9{,}700 - 7{,}950 = \underline{\underline{\$1{,}750}}$

    b. What is the markdown percent?

    $$MD\% = \frac{MD}{\text{Original price}} = \frac{1{,}750}{9{,}700} = .1804 = \underline{\underline{18.0\%}}$$

12. A DVD that originally sold for $34.88 was marked down by $12.11.

    a. What is the sale price?

    $\text{Sale price} = \text{Original price} - MD = 34.88 - 12.11 = \underline{\underline{\$22.77}}$

    b. What is the markdown percent?

    $$MD\% = \frac{MD}{\text{Original price}} = \frac{12.11}{34.88} = .3471 = \underline{\underline{34.7\%}}$$

13. a. A notebook that originally sold for $1.69 at Dollar General was marked down to $.99. What is the amount of the markdown on these notebooks?

    $MD = \text{Original price} - \text{Sale price}$

    $MD = 1.69 - .99 = \underline{\underline{\$.70}}$

    b. What is the markdown percent?

    $$MD\% = \frac{MD}{\text{Original price}} = \frac{.70}{1.69} = .4142 = \underline{\underline{41.4\%}}$$

    c. If the sale price is then marked up by 40%, what is the new selling price?

    $SP = .99(1.4) = \underline{\underline{\$1.39}}$

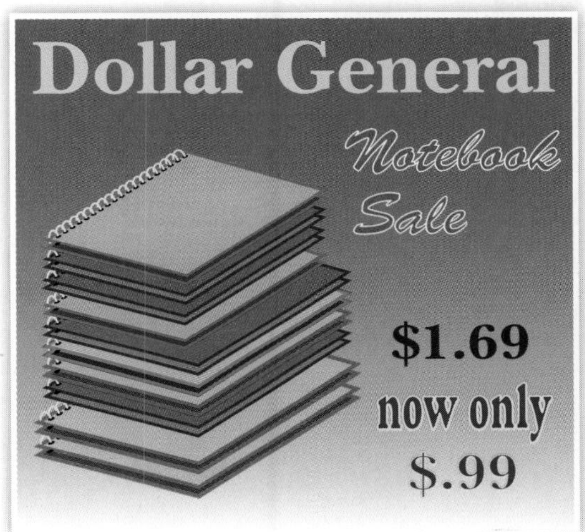

Video Games
Video gaming becomes more popular each year. In 2006, 62.7 million video games consoles were sold globally, with a market value of $12.4 billion. In 2011, the global games consoles market is forecast to sell 80.6 million units, with a value of $15.3 billion. Nintendo is the market leader, generating 41.9% of the market's volume.

Source: marketresearch.com

14. Video Warehouse sells both the Microsoft Xbox 360 and the Sony Playstation 3 video game hardware.

    a. If the Xbox 360 originally sold for $599.99 and was then reduced to $449.99, what is the markdown percent?

    $$\text{MD\%} = \frac{\text{MD}}{\text{Original price}} = \frac{150.00}{599.99} = \underline{\underline{25\%}}$$

    b. If the Playstation 3 originally sold for $449.99 and now sells for 10% off, what is the sale price?

    Sale price = Original price(100% − MD%)

    Sale price = 449.99(100% − 10%) = 449.99(0.9) = $\underline{\underline{\$404.99}}$

15. Readers Delight, a book store, sells atlases for $75. If they are put on clearance sale at 60% off, what is the sale price?

    Sale price = Original price(100% − *MD%*) = 75(100% − 60%) = 75(.4) = $\underline{\underline{\$30}}$

16. Carousel Toys has Romper Buckaroos, wooden rocking horses for toddlers, on a 30% markdown sale for $72.09. What was the original price before they were marked down? Round to the nearest cent.

    $$\text{Original price} = \frac{\text{Sale price}}{100\% - MD\%} = \frac{72.09}{100\% - 30\%} = 102.985 = \underline{\underline{\$102.99}}$$

17. Lawn and Garden Galleria is having a 20% off sale on riding lawn mowers. The XL Deluxe model is on sale for $4,815. What was the original price of the mower?

    $$\text{Original price} = \frac{\text{Sale price}}{100\% - MD\%} = \frac{4{,}815}{100\% - 20\%} = \underline{\underline{\$6{,}018.75}}$$

18. From the Office Depot coupon shown here,

    a. Calculate the markdown percent.

    $$MD\% = \frac{MD}{\text{Original price}} = \frac{8.99}{26.97} = \underline{\underline{33.3\%}}$$

    b. If the offer was changed to "Buy 3, Get 2 Free," what is the new markdown percent?

    $$MD\% = \frac{MD}{\text{Original price}} = \frac{17.98}{44.95} = \underline{\underline{40\%}}$$

    c. Which offer is more profitable for the store? Explain.

    "Buy 2, Get 1 Free" is more profitable. The lower the markdown, the higher the profit.

19. In February, Golf World, a retail shop, purchased golf clubs for $453.50 per set. The original markup was 35% based on selling price. In April, the shop took a 20% markdown by having a special sale. After two weeks, the sale was over and the clubs were marked up 10%. In June, the shop offered a storewide sale of 15% off all merchandise, and in September, a final 10% markdown was taken on the clubs. What was the final selling price of the golf clubs?

    $$SP = \frac{C}{100\% - \%M_{SP}} = \frac{453.50}{100\% - 35\%} = \frac{453.50}{.65} = \$697.69$$

    Markdown #1: Original price(100% − *MD%*) = 697.69(.8) = $558.15

    10% Markup: 558.15(1.10) = $613.97

    Markdown #2: 613.97(.85) = $521.87

    Final markdown: 521.87(.9) = $\underline{\underline{\$469.68}}$

20. Prestige Produce purchases 460 pounds of sweet potatoes at \$.76 per pound. If a 10% spoilage rate is anticipated, at what price per pound should the sweet potatoes be sold to achieve a 35% markup based on selling price?

Total cost = 460 pounds @ \$.76 = \$349.60

$$\text{Expected selling price} = \frac{C}{100\% - \%M_{SP}} = \frac{349.60}{.65} = \$537.85$$

$$SP \text{ perishable} = \frac{\text{Expected } SP}{\text{Total quantity} - \text{Spoilage}} = \frac{537.85}{460 - 46} = \frac{537.85}{414} = \underline{\underline{\$1.30 \text{ Per pound}}}$$

21. A microwave oven cost The Appliance Warehouse \$141.30 and was initially marked up by 55% based on selling price. In the next few months the item was marked down 20%, marked up 15%, marked down 10%, and marked down a final 10%. What was the final selling price of the microwave oven?

$$SP = \frac{C}{100\% - \%M_{SP}} = \frac{141.30}{100\% - 55\%} = \frac{141.30}{.45} = \$314$$

Markdown #1: Original price(100% − *MD*%) = 314(.8) = \$251.20
15% Markup: 251.20(1.15) = \$288.88
Markdown #2: 288.88(.9) = \$259.99
Final markdown: 259.99(.9) = $\underline{\underline{\$233.99}}$

22. The Flour Power Bakery makes 200 cherry cheesecakes at a cost of \$2.45 each. If a spoilage rate of 5% is anticipated, at what price should the cakes be sold to achieve a 40% markup based on cost?

Total cost = 200 Cheesecakes @ 2.45 = \$490.00

Expected selling price = $C(100\% + \%M_C) = 490(1.4) = \$686$

$$SP \text{ perishable} = \frac{\text{Expected } SP}{\text{Total quantity} - \text{Spoilage}} = \frac{686}{200 - 10} = \frac{686}{190} = \underline{\underline{\$3.61 \text{ Per cheesecake}}}$$

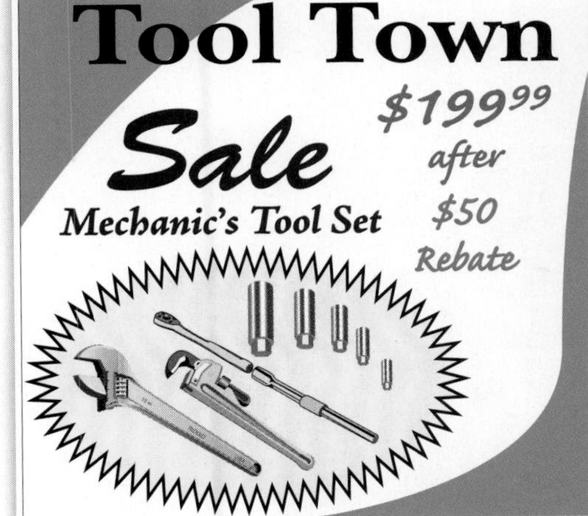

23. a. What is the markdown percent of the rebate offered by Tool Town on this mechanic's tool set?

$$MD\% = \frac{MD}{\text{Original price}} = \frac{50.00}{249.99} = \underline{\underline{20\%}}$$

b. If, during a sale, Tool Town offered an additional 20% off the "after rebate" price, what would be the new sale price of the tool set?

Sale price = Original price(100% − *MD*%)

Sale price = 199.99(.8) = $\underline{\underline{\$159.99}}$

BUSINESS DECISION THE PERMANENT MARKDOWN

24. You are the manager of World Wide Athlete, a chain of six sporting goods shops in your area. The shops sell 12 racing bikes per week at a retail price of \$679.99. Recently, you put the bikes on sale at \$599.99. At the sale price, 15 bikes were sold during the one-week sale.

a. What was your markdown percent on the bikes?

$MD = SP - C = 679.99 - 599.99 = \$80.00$

$$MD\% = \frac{MD}{\text{Original price}} = \frac{80.00}{679.99} = \underline{\underline{11.8\%}}$$

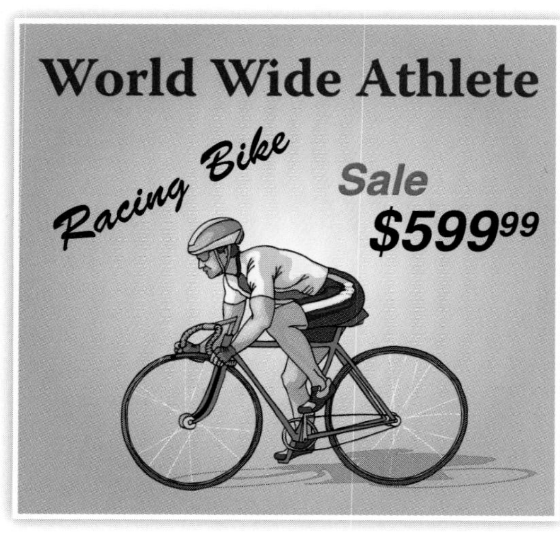

b. What is the percent increase in number of bikes sold during the sale?

Increase = 15 − 12 = 3

$$\% \text{ Increase} = \frac{3}{12} = \underline{\underline{25\%}}$$

c. How much more revenue would be earned in six months by permanently selling the bikes at the lower price, rather than having a one-week sale, each month? (6 sale weeks in 26 weeks)

6 weeks @ 599.99 × 15 =	53,999.10	233,996.10	
20 weeks @ 679.99 × 12 =	163,197.60	− 217,196.70	
Revenue	$217,196.70	$16,799.40	More revenue
26 weeks @ 599.99 × 15 =	$233,996.10		

d. (Optional) As manager of World Wide, would you recommend this permanent price reduction? Explain.

Yes, permanent markdown increases revenue significantly.

8 CHAPTER FORMULAS

Markup

Selling price = Cost + Markup

Cost = Selling price − Markup

Markup = Selling price − Cost

$$\text{Percent markup}_{\text{COST}} = \frac{\text{Markup}}{\text{Cost}}$$

$$\text{Percent markup}_{SP} = \frac{\text{Markup}}{\text{Selling price}}$$

$$\text{Selling price} = \text{Cost}(100\% + \%\text{Markup}_{\text{COST}})$$

$$\text{Cost} = \frac{\text{Selling price}}{100\% + \%\text{Markup}_{\text{COST}}}$$

$$\text{Selling price} = \frac{\text{Cost}}{100\% - \%\text{Markup}_{SP}}$$

$$\text{Cost} = \text{Selling price}(100\% - \%\text{Markup}_{SP})$$

$$\%\text{Markup}_{SP} = \frac{\%\text{Markup}_{\text{COST}}}{100\% + \%\text{Markup}_{\text{COST}}}$$

$$\%\text{Markup}_{\text{COST}} = \frac{\%\text{Markup}_{SP}}{100\% - \%\text{Markup}_{SP}}$$

Markdown

Markdown = Original selling price − Sale price

$$\text{Markdown}\% = \frac{\text{Markdown}}{\text{Original price}}$$

$$\text{Sale price} = \text{Original price}(100\% - \text{Markdown}\%)$$

$$\text{Original price} = \frac{\text{Sale price}}{100\% - \text{Markdown}\%}$$

Perishables

$$\text{Selling price}_{\text{Perishables}} = \frac{\text{Expected selling price}}{\text{Total quantity} - \text{Spoilage}}$$

SUMMARY CHART

8

Section I: Markup Based on Cost

Topic	Important Concepts	Illustrative Examples
Using the Basic Retailing Equation **P/O 8-1, p. 250**	The basic retailing equation is used to solve for selling price (*SP*), cost (*C*), and amount of markup (*M*). **Selling price = Cost + Markup** $SP = C + M$ **Cost = Selling price − Markup** $C = SP - M$ **Markup = Selling price − Cost** $M = SP - C$	1. What is the selling price of a blender that costs \$86.00 and has a \$55.99 markup? $SP = 86.00 + 55.99$ Selling price = \$141.99 2. What is the cost of a radio that sells for \$125.50 and has a \$37.29 markup? $C = 125.50 - 37.29$ Cost = \$88.21 3. What is the markup on a set of dishes costing \$53.54 and selling for \$89.95? $M = 89.95 - 53.54$ Markup = \$36.41
Calculating Percent Markup Based on Cost **P/O 8-2, p. 252**	$\%\text{Markup}_{\text{COST}} = \dfrac{\text{Markup}}{\text{Cost}}$ $\%M_{\text{COST}} = \dfrac{M}{C}$	A calculator costs \$25. If the markup is \$10, what is the percent markup based on cost? $\%M_{\text{COST}} = \dfrac{10}{25} = .4$ $\%M_{\text{COST}} = 40\%$
Calculating Selling Price **P/O 8-3, p. 253**	**Selling price = Cost(100% + %Markup$_{\text{COST}}$)** $SP = C(100\% + \%M_{\text{COST}})$	A desk costs \$260 to manufacture. What should be the selling price if a 60% markup based on cost is desired? $SP = 260(100\% + 60\%)$ $SP = 260(1.6) = 416$ Selling price = \$416
Calculating Cost **P/O 8-4, p. 254**	$\text{Cost} = \dfrac{\text{Selling price}}{100\% + \text{Markup}_{\text{COST}}}$ $C = \dfrac{SP}{100\% + \%M_{\text{COST}}}$	What is the cost of a leather chair with a selling price of \$250 and a 45% markup based on cost? $C = \dfrac{250}{100\% + 45\%} = \dfrac{250}{1.45}$ Cost = \$172.41

Section II: Markup Based on Selling Price

Topic	Important Concepts	Illustrative Examples
Calculating Percent Markup Based on Selling Price P/O 8-5, p. 258	$\%\text{Markup}_{SP} = \dfrac{\text{Markup}}{\text{Selling price}}$ $\%M_{SP} = \dfrac{M}{SP}$	What is the percent markup on the selling price of a Xerox copier with a selling price of \$400 and a markup of \$188? $\%M_{SP} = \dfrac{188}{400} = .47$ $\%M_{SP} = \underline{\underline{47\%}}$
Calculating Selling Price P/O 8-6, p. 259	$\text{Selling price} = \dfrac{\text{Cost}}{100\% - \%\text{Markup}_{SP}}$ $SP = \dfrac{C}{100\% - \%M_{SP}}$	What is the selling price of a quart of milk with a cost of \$1.19 and a 43% markup based on selling price? $SP = \dfrac{1.19}{100\% - 43\%} = \dfrac{1.19}{.57}$ $SP = \underline{\underline{\$2.09}}$
Calculating Cost P/O 8-7, p. 259	$\text{Cost} = \text{Selling price}(100\% - \%\text{Markup}_{SP})$ $C = SP(100\% - \%M_{SP})$	What is the most a hardware store can pay for a drill if it will have a selling price of \$65.50 and a 45% markup based on selling price? $C = 65.50(100\% - 45\%)$ $C = 65.50(.55)$ $\text{Cost} = \underline{\underline{\$36.03}}$
Converting Percent Markup Based on Cost to Percent Markup Based on Selling Price P/O 8-8, p. 260	$\%\text{Markup}_{SP} = \dfrac{\%\text{Markup}_{COST}}{100\% + \%\text{Markup}_{COST}}$ $\%M_{SP} = \dfrac{\%M_{COST}}{100\% + \%M_{COST}}$	If a hair dryer is marked up 70% based on cost, what is the corresponding percent markup based on selling price? $\%M_{SP} = \dfrac{70\%}{100\% + 70\%} = \dfrac{.7}{1.7}$ $\%M_{SP} = .4118 = \underline{\underline{41.2\%}}$
Converting Percent Markup Based on Selling Price to Percent Markup Based on Cost P/O 8-8, p. 261	$\%\text{Markup}_{COST} = \dfrac{\%\text{Markup}_{SP}}{100\% - \%\text{Markup}_{SP}}$ $\%M_{COST} = \dfrac{\%M_{SP}}{100\% - \%M_{SP}}$	If a toaster is marked up 35% based on selling price, what is the corresponding percent markup based on cost? $\%M_{COST} = \dfrac{35\%}{100\% - 35\%} = \dfrac{.35}{.65}$ $\%M_{COST} = .5384 = \underline{\underline{53.8\%}}$

Section III: Markdowns, Multiple Operations, and Perishable Goods

Topic	Important Concepts	Illustrative Examples
Calculating Markdown and Markdown Percent **P/O 8-9, p. 265**	**Markdown = Original price − Sale price** $MD = \text{Orig} - \text{Sale}$ $\text{Markdown \%} = \dfrac{\text{Markdown}}{\text{Original price}}$ $MD\% = \dfrac{MD}{\text{Orig}}$	Calculate the amount of markdown and the markdown percent of a television set that originally sold for \$425.00 and was then put on sale for \$299.95. $MD = 425.00 - 299.95$ Markdown = \$125.05 $MD\% = \dfrac{125.05}{425.00} = .2942$ Markdown % = 29.4%
Determining the Sale Price after a Markdown **P/O 8-10, p. 266**	**Sale price = Original price (100% − Markdown %)** $\text{Sale} = \text{Orig}(100\% - MD\%)$	What is the sale price of a computer that originally sold for \$2,500 and was then marked down by 35%? Sale = 2,500(100% − 35%) Sale = 2,500(.65) = 1,625 Sale price = \$1,625
Determining the Original Selling Price before a Markdown **P/O 8-10, p. 267**	$\text{Original price} = \dfrac{\text{Sale price}}{100\% - \text{Markdown \%}}$ $\text{Orig} = \dfrac{\text{Sale}}{100\% - MD\%}$	What is the original selling price of an exercise bicycle, currently on sale at Sears for \$235.88 after a 30% markdown? $\text{Orig} = \dfrac{235.88}{100\% - 30\%} = \dfrac{235.88}{.7}$ Original price = \$336.97
Computing the Final Selling Price after a Series of Markups and Markdowns **P/O 8-11, p. 268**	To solve for the final selling price after a series of markups and markdowns, calculate each step based on the previous selling price.	Compute the intermediate prices and the final selling price of an umbrella costing \$27.50, with the following seasonal activity: a. Initial markup, 40% on cost b. 20% markdown c. 15% markdown d. 10% markup e. Final clearance, 25% markdown a. Initial 40% markup: $SP = C(100\% + \%M_{COST})$ $SP = 27.50(100\% + 40\%)$ $SP = 27.50(1.4) = 38.50$ Original price = \$38.50 b. 20% markdown: Sale = Orig(100% − $MD\%$) Sale = 38.50(100% − 20%) Sale = 38.50(.8) Sale price = \$30.80

(continued)

Section III: (continued)

Topic	Important Concepts	Illustrative Examples
		c. 15% markdown: $\text{Sale} = \text{Orig}(100\% - MD\%)$ $\text{Sale} = 30.80(100\% - 15\%)$ $\text{Sale} = 30.80(.85)$ Sale price = $26.18 d. 10% markup: $SP = \text{sale price}(100\% + M\%)$ $SP = 26.18(100\% + 10\%)$ $SP = 26.18(1.10)$ Selling price = $28.80 e. Final 25% markdown: $\text{Sale} = \text{Orig}(100\% - MD\%)$ $\text{Sale} = 28.80(100\% - 25\%)$ $\text{Sale} = 28.80(.75)$ Final selling price = $21.60
Calculating the Selling Price of Perishable Goods **P/O 8-12, p. 270**	**Selling price$_{\text{Perishables}}$** $= \dfrac{\textbf{Total expected selling price}}{\textbf{Total quantity} - \textbf{Anticipated spoilage}}$ $SP_{\text{perish}} = \dfrac{\text{Exp } SP}{\text{Quan} - \text{Spoil}}$	A grocery store purchases 250 pounds of apples from a wholesaler for $.67 per pound. If a 10% spoilage rate is anticipated, what selling price per pound will yield a 45% markup based on cost? Total Cost = 250 lb @ .67 = $167.50 $\text{Exp } SP = C(100\% + M_{\text{COST}})$ $\text{Exp } SP = 167.50(100\% + 45\%)$ $\text{Exp } SP = 167.50(1.45) = \$242.88$ $SP_{\text{perish}} = \dfrac{242.88}{250 - 25} = \dfrac{242.88}{225}$ $SP_{\text{perish}} = \$1.08 \text{ per lb}$

TRY IT EXERCISE SOLUTIONS FOR CHAPTER 8

1. $SP = C + M = 6.80 + 9.40 = \underline{\underline{\$16.20}}$
2. $M = SP - C = 28.50 - 16.75 = \underline{\underline{\$11.75}}$
3. $C = SP - M = 290 - 75 = \underline{\underline{\$215}}$
4. $M = SP - C = 63 - 45 = \underline{\underline{\$18}}$

   $\%M_{\text{COST}} = \dfrac{M}{C} = \dfrac{18}{45} = .4 = 40\%$
5. $SP = C(100\% + \%M_{\text{COST}}) = 38.00(100\% + 65\%) = 38(1.65) = \underline{\underline{\$62.70}}$
6. $C = \dfrac{SP}{100\% + \%M_{\text{COST}}} = \dfrac{39}{100\% + 30\%} = \dfrac{39}{1.3} = \underline{\underline{\$30}}$

7. $M = SP - C = 157.50 - 94.50 = \underline{\underline{\$63}}$

$$\%M_{SP} = \frac{M}{SP} = \frac{63.00}{157.50} = .40 = \underline{\underline{40\%}}$$

8. $SP = \dfrac{C}{100\% - \%M_{SP}} = \dfrac{169}{100\% - 35\%} = \dfrac{169}{.65} = \underline{\underline{\$260}}$

9. $C = SP(100\% - \%M_{SP}) = 79(100\% - 55\%) = 79(.45) = \underline{\underline{\$35.55}}$

10. $\%M_{SP} = \dfrac{\%M_{COST}}{100\% + \%M_{COST}} = \dfrac{50\%}{100\% + 50\%} = \dfrac{.5}{1.5} = .333 = \underline{\underline{33.3\%}}$

11. $\%M_{COST} = \dfrac{\%M_{SP}}{100\% - \%M_{SP}} = \dfrac{75\%}{100\% - 75\%} = \dfrac{.75}{.25} = 3 = \underline{\underline{300\%}}$

12. $MD = \text{Original price} - \text{Sale price} = 75 - 56 = \underline{\underline{\$19}}$

$$MD\% = \frac{MD}{\text{Original price}} = \frac{19}{75} = .2533 = \underline{\underline{25.3\%}}$$

13. $\text{Sale price} = \text{Original price}(100\% - MD\%) = 27.50(100\% - 60\%) = 27.50(.4) = \underline{\underline{\$11}}$

14. $\text{Original price} = \dfrac{\text{Sale price}}{100\% - MD\%} = \dfrac{79}{100\% - 35\%} = \dfrac{79}{.65} = \underline{\underline{\$121.54}}$

15. $SP = \dfrac{C}{100\% - \%M_{SP}} = \dfrac{48.50}{100\% - 55\%} = \dfrac{48.50}{.45} = \$107.78$

Markdown #1: $\text{Original price}(100\% - MD\%) = 107.78(.7) = \$75.45$

20% markup: $75.45(100\% + 20\%) = 75.45(1.2) = \$90.54$

Markdown #2: $\text{Original price}(100\% - MD\%) = 90.54(.7) = \$63.38$

Final markdown: $\text{Original price}(100\% - MD\%) = 63.38(.75) = \underline{\underline{\$47.54}}$

16. Total cost = 800 dozen @ \$6.50 = \$5,200.00

$$\text{Expected selling price} = \frac{C}{100\% - \%M_{SP}} = \frac{5,200}{100\% - 60\%} = \frac{5,200}{.4} = \$13,000$$

$$\text{Selling price}_{\text{perishables}} = \frac{\text{Expected selling price}}{\text{Total quantity} - \text{Spoilage}} = \frac{13,000}{800 - 80} = \frac{13,000}{720} = \underline{\underline{\$18.06 \text{ per doz.}}}$$

CONCEPT REVIEW

1. The retailing equation states that the selling price is equal to the _____ plus the _____. (8-1)
cost, markup

2. In business, expenses are separated into two major categories. The cost of _____ sold and _____ expenses. (8-1)
goods, operating or overhead

3. There are two ways of expressing markup as a percent, based on _____ and based on _____ _____. (8-2)
cost, selling price

4. Write the formula for calculating the selling price when markup is based on cost. (8-3)
Selling price = Cost(100% + Percent markup on cost)

5. To calculate cost, we divide the _____ price by 100% plus the percent markup on cost. (8-4)
selling

6. The percent markup based on selling price is equal to the _____ divided by the selling price. (8-5)
markup

7. When markup is based on selling price, the _____ price is the base, and represents _____ percent. (8-6)
selling, 100

8. We use the formula for calculating _____ to find the most a retailer can pay for an item and still get their intended markup. (8-7)
cost

9. To convert percent markup based on cost to percent markup based on selling price, we divide percent markup based on cost by 100% ______ the percent markup based on cost. (8-8)
plus

10. To convert percent markup based on selling price to percent markup based on cost, we divide percent markup based on selling price by 100% ______ the percent markup based on selling price. (8-8)
minus

11. A price reduction from the original selling price of merchandise is called a(n) ______. (8-9)
markdown

12. Write the formula for calculating the sale price after a markdown. (8-10)
Sale price = Original selling price(100% − MD%)

13. In calculating a series of markups and markdowns, each calculation is based on the previous ______ price. (8-11)
selling

14. Products that have a certain shelf life and then no value at all such as fruit, vegetables, flowers, and dairy products are known as ______. (8-12)
perishable goods

CHAPTER 8

ASSESSMENT TEST

Name ______

Class ______

Answers

1. $152.60
2. $133.34
3. $18.58
4. a. $81.50
   b. 71.6%
   c. 41.7%
5. a. $66.99
   b. 44.2%
   c. 79.1%

Solve the following word problems. Round dollars to the nearest cent and percents to the nearest tenth of a percent.

1. Electric woks cost the manufacturer $83.22 to produce. If a markup of $69.38 is added to the cost, what is the selling price per unit?

$SP = C + M = 83.22 + 69.38 = \$152.60$

2. Castle Mountain Furniture sells desks for $346.00. If the desks cost $212.66, what is the amount of the markup?

$M = SP - C = 346.00 - 212.66 = \$133.34$

3. After Sunset Food Wholesalers adds a markup of $15.40 to a case of tomato sauce, it sells for $33.98. What is the wholesaler's cost per case?

$C = SP - M = 33.98 - 15.40 = \$18.58$

4. Wyatt's Western Wear purchases shirts for $47.50 each. A $34.00 markup is added to the shirts.

a. What is the selling price?

$SP = C + M = 47.50 + 34.00 = \$81.50$

b. What is the percent markup based on cost?

$$\%M_C = \frac{M}{C} = \frac{34.00}{47.50} = .7157 = 71.6\%$$

c. What is the percent markup based on selling price?

$$\%M_{SP} = \frac{M}{SP} = \frac{34.00}{81.50} = .4171 = 41.7\%$$

5. If Brand Central Station adds a $53 markup to each toaster shown here,

a. What is the cost?

$C = SP - M$

$C = 119.99 - 53.00 = \$66.99$

b. What is the percent markup based on selling price?

$$\%M_{SP} = \frac{M}{SP} = \frac{53.00}{119.99} = .4417 = 44.2\%$$

c. What is the percent markup based on cost?

$$\%M_C = \frac{M}{C} = \frac{53.00}{66.99} = .7911 = 79.1\%$$

Name

Class

Answers

6.	\$39.84
7.	\$15.95
8. a.	100%
b.	54.5%
9. a.	\$778
b.	21.3%
10. a.	63%
b.	\$84.98
11.	\$216.06
12.	\$3,105

6. Macy's purchases imported perfume for \$24.30 per ounce. If the store policy is to mark up all merchandise in that department 39% based on selling price, what is the retail selling price of the perfume?

$$SP = \frac{C}{100\% - \%M_{SP}} = \frac{24.30}{100\% - 39\%} = \frac{24.30}{.61} = \underline{\underline{\$39.84}}$$

7. The Carpet Gallery is looking for a new line of nylon carpeting to retail at \$39.88 per square yard. If management wants a 60% markup based on selling price, what is the most that can be paid for the carpeting to still get the desired markup?

$C = SP(100\% - \%M_{SP}) = 39.88(100\% - 60\%) = 39.88(.4) = \underline{\underline{\$15.95}}$

8. a. At The Luminary, the markup on a halogen light fixture is 50% based on selling price. What is the corresponding percent markup based on cost?

$$\%M_C = \frac{\%M_{SP}}{100\% - \%M_{SP}} = \frac{50\%}{100\% - 50\%} = \frac{.5}{.5} = \underline{\underline{100\%}}$$

b. If the markup on a flourescent light fixture rod is 120% based on cost, what is the corresponding percent markup based on selling price?

$$\%M_{SP} = \frac{\%M_C}{100\% + \%M_C} = \frac{120\%}{100\% + 120\%} = \frac{1.2}{2.2} = .5454 = \underline{\underline{54.5\%}}$$

9. A three-day cruise on the Island Queen originally selling for \$988 was marked down by \$210 at the end of the season.

a. What is the sale price of the cruise?

Sale price = Original price − MD = 988 − 210 = $\underline{\underline{\$778}}$

b. What is the markdown percent?

$$MD\% = \frac{MD}{\text{Original price}} = \frac{210}{988} = .2125 = \underline{\underline{21.3\%}}$$

10. a. What is the markdown percent of the advertised tennis racquets at Golf and Tennis Warehouse?

$MD = 269.99 - 99.98 = \$170.01$

$$MD\% = \frac{MD}{\text{Original price}} = \frac{170.01}{269.99} = .6296 = \underline{\underline{63\%}}$$

b. If the store offered an additional 15% off on all merchandise on "Sale Sunday," what is the new sale price of the racquet?

99.98(.85) = $\underline{\underline{\$84.98}}$

11. Music Mart originally sold MP3 players for \$277. If they are put on sale at a markdown of 22%, what is the sale price?

Sale price = Original price(100% − $MD\%$) = 277(100% − 22%) = 277(.78) = $\underline{\underline{\$216.06}}$

12. What was the original selling price of a treadmill, currently on sale for \$2,484 after a 20% markdown?

$$\text{Original price} = \frac{\text{Sale price}}{100\% - MD\%} = \frac{2{,}484}{100\% - 20\%} = \frac{2{,}484}{.8} = \underline{\underline{\$3{,}105}}$$

Name

Class

Answers

13. a. \$56.25

b. \$64.68

14. a. \$9.72

b. 10.3%

15. a. \$2,499.99

b. \$1,000

c. 60%

d. 36%

13. Sports Mania advertised a line of basketball hoops for the summer season. The store uses a 55% markup based on selling price.

a. If they were originally priced at \$124.99, what was the cost?

$C = SP(100\% - \%M_{SP})$

$C = 124.99(.45) = \underline{\underline{\$56.25}}$

b. As the summer progressed, they were marked down 25%, marked up 15%, marked down 20%, and cleared out in October at a final 25%-off sale. What was the final selling price of the hoops?

MD #1: 124.99(.75) = 93.74
15% MU: 93.74(1.15) = 107.80
MD #2: 107.80(.8) = 86.24
Final MD: 86.24(.75) = $\underline{\underline{\$64.68}}$

14. Epicure Market prepares fresh gourmet entrees each day. On Wednesday, 80 baked chicken dinners were made at a cost of \$3.50 each. A 10% spoilage rate is anticipated.

a. At what price should the dinners be sold to achieve a 60% markup based on selling price?

Total cost = 80 Dinners @ 3.50 = \$280

$$\text{Expected } SP = \frac{C}{100\% - \%M_{SP}} = \frac{280}{100\% - 60\%} = \frac{280}{.4} = \$700$$

$$SP_{\text{Perishables}} = \frac{\text{Expected } SP}{\text{Total quantity} - \text{Spoilage}} = \frac{700}{80 - 8} = \frac{700}{72} = \underline{\underline{\$9.72}}$$

b. If Epicure offers a \$1.00-off coupon in a newspaper advertisement, what markdown percent does the coupon represent?

$$MD\% = \frac{MD}{\text{Original price}} = \frac{1.00}{9.72} = .1028 = \underline{\underline{10.3\%}}$$

15. a. What is the original selling price of the guitar on sale at Musicland if the \$1,999.99 sale price represents 20% off?

$$\text{Original price} = \frac{\text{Sale price}}{100\% - MD\%} = \frac{1{,}999.99}{.8} = \underline{\underline{\$2{,}499.99}}$$

b. How much did the store pay for the guitar if the initial markup was 150% based on cost?

$$C = \frac{SP}{100\% + \%M_C} = \frac{2{,}499.99}{2.5} = \underline{\underline{1{,}000}}$$

c. What is the percent markup based on selling price?

$M = SP - C = 2{,}499.99 - 1{,}000.00 = \$1{,}499.99$

$$\%M_{SP} = \frac{M}{SP} = \frac{1{,}499.99}{2{,}499.99} = .5999 = \underline{\underline{60\%}}$$

d. If next month the guitar is scheduled to be on sale for \$1,599.99, what is the markdown percent?

$MD = \text{Original price} - \text{Sale price}$

$MD = 2{,}499.99 - 1{,}599.99 = \$900.00$

$$MD\% = \frac{MD}{\text{Original price}} = \frac{900.00}{2{,}499.99} = .36 = \underline{\underline{36\%}}$$

BUSINESS DECISION MAINTAINED MARKUP

CHAPTER 8

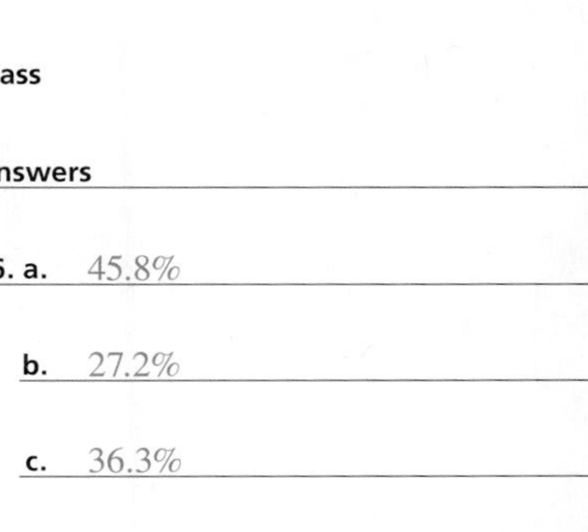

Name

Class

Answers

16. a. 45.8%

b. 27.2%

c. 36.3%

16. The markup that a retail store actually realizes on the sale of their goods is called **maintained markup**. It is what is achieved after "retail reductions" (markdowns) have been subtracted from the initial markup. Maintained markup is one of the "keys to profitability" in retailing. It is the difference between the actual selling price and the cost, and therefore has a direct effect on net profits.

$$\textbf{Maintained markup} = \frac{\textbf{Actual selling price} - \textbf{Cost}}{\textbf{Actual selling price}}$$

You are the buyer for Kingsley's, a chain of four men's clothing stores. For the spring season you purchased a line of men's casual shirts with a manufacturer's suggested retail price of \$29.50. Your cost was \$16.00 per shirt.

a. What is the initial percent markup based on selling price?

$M = SP - C = 29.50 - 16.00 = \$13.50$

$$\%M_{SP} = \frac{M}{SP} = \frac{13.50}{29.50} = \underline{\underline{45.8\%}}$$

b. The shirts did not sell as expected at the regular price, so you marked them down to \$21.99, and sold them out. What is the maintained markup on the shirts?

$$\text{Maintained markup} = \frac{21.99 - 16.00}{21.99} = \underline{\underline{27.2\%}}$$

c. When you complained to the manufacturer's sales representative about having to take excessive markdowns in order to sell their merchandise, they offered a \$2.00 rebate per shirt. What is your new maintained markup?

New cost = Cost − Rebate = 16.00 − 2.00 = \$14.00

$$\text{Maintained markup} = \frac{21.99 - 14.00}{21.99} = \underline{\underline{36.3\%}}$$

COLLABORATIVE LEARNING ACTIVITY

Comparative Shopping

1. As a team, collect newspaper advertisements for merchandise that is "on sale" at the following types of retail stores in your area. Calculate the amount of the markdown, the markdown percent, or the original price—whichever is not given in the ad.

- **a.** Supermarket
- **b.** Drugstore
- **c.** Department store
- **d.** Specialty shop
- **e.** Additional Choice: ____________________

2. How do the markdown percent figures compare among the categories?

3. How do in-store sale prices compare with prices for the same item on the Internet?

4. Have each member of the team visit one of the stores advertising "sale" merchandise in Question 1, and answer the following:

- **a.** Were the items on sale marked correctly with the advertised sale price?
- **b.** Were the items on sale featured with special displays, signs, or other "attention-getting" devices?
- **c.** How would you rate the store's coordination of their newspaper advertising with in-store efforts?

PAYDAY
ADVANCE

9

CHAPTER

Payroll

PERFORMANCE OBJECTIVES

Section I Employee's Gross Earnings and Incentive Pay Plans

9-1: Prorating annual salary on the basis of weekly, biweekly, semimonthly, and monthly pay periods (p. 285)

9-2: Calculating gross pay by hourly wages, including regular and overtime rates (p. 286)

9-3: Calculating gross pay by straight and differential piecework schedules (p. 287)

9-4: Calculating gross pay by straight and incremental commission, salary plus commission, and drawing accounts (p. 289)

Section II Employee's Payroll Deductions

9-5: Computing FICA taxes, both social security and Medicare, withheld from an employee's paycheck (p. 296)

9-6: Calculating an employee's federal income tax withholding (FIT) by the percentage method (p. 298)

9-7: Determining an employee's total withholding for federal income tax, social security, and Medicare using the combined wage bracket tables (p. 301)

Section III Employer's Payroll Expenses and Self-Employed Person's Tax Responsibility

9-8: Computing FICA tax for employers and self-employment tax for self-employed persons (p. 307)

9-9: Computing the amount of state unemployment taxes (SUTA) and federal unemployment taxes (FUTA) (p. 309)

9-10: Calculating employer's fringe benefit expenses (p. 310)

9-11: Calculating quarterly estimated tax for self-employed persons (p. 311)

EMPLOYEE'S GROSS EARNINGS AND INCENTIVE PAY PLANS

SECTION I

Because payroll is frequently a company's largest operating expense, efficient payroll preparation and record keeping are extremely important functions in any business operation. Although today most businesses computerize their payroll functions, it is important for businesspeople to understand the processes and procedures involved.

Employers are responsible for paying employees for services rendered to the company over a period of time. In addition, the company is responsible for withholding certain taxes and other deductions from an employee's paycheck and depositing those taxes with the Internal Revenue Service (IRS) through authorized financial institutions. Other deductions, such as insurance premiums and charitable contributions, are also disbursed by the employer to the appropriate place.

In business, the term **gross pay** or **gross earnings** means the *total* amount of earnings due an employee for work performed before payroll deductions are withheld. The **net pay**, **net earnings**, or **take-home pay** is the actual amount of the employee's paycheck after all payroll deductions have been withheld. This concept is easily visualized by the formula

Net pay = Gross pay − Total deductions

This chapter deals with the business math involved in payroll management: the computation of employee gross earnings, calculating withholding taxes and other deductions, and the associated governmental deposits, regulations, and record keeping requirements.

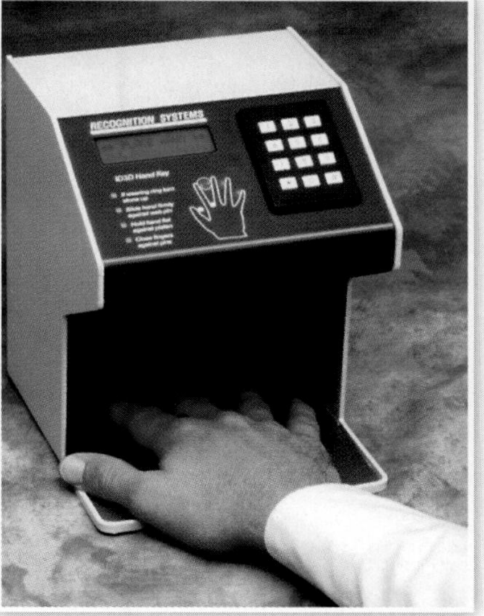

Today, hand recognition time clocks are commonly used by companies to keep track of employee attendance and work hours. Advanced models of these devices can be fully integrated through software to the company's payroll accounting system.

PRORATING ANNUAL SALARY ON THE BASIS OF WEEKLY, BIWEEKLY, SEMIMONTHLY, AND MONTHLY PAY PERIODS

Employee compensation takes on many forms in the business world. Employees who hold managerial, administrative, or professional positions are paid a salary. A **salary** is a fixed gross amount of pay, equally distributed over periodic payments, without regard to the number of hours worked. Salaries are usually expressed as an annual, or yearly, amount. For example, a corporate accountant might receive an annual salary of $50,000.

Although salaries may be stated as annual amounts, they are usually distributed to employees on a more timely basis. A once-a-year paycheck would be a real trick to manage! Employees are most commonly paid in one of the following ways:

Weekly	52 paychecks per year	Annual salary ÷ 52
Biweekly	26 paychecks per year	Annual salary ÷ 26
Semimonthly	24 paychecks per year	Annual salary ÷ 24
Monthly	12 paychecks per year	Annual salary ÷ 12

gross pay, or gross earnings Total amount of earnings due an employee for work performed before payroll deductions are withheld.

net pay, or net earnings, or take-home pay The actual amount of the employee's paycheck after all payroll deductions have been withheld.

salary A fixed gross amount of pay, equally distributed over periodic payments, without regard to the number of hours worked.

EXAMPLE 1 PRORATING ANNUAL SALARY

What is the weekly, biweekly, semimonthly, and monthly amount of gross pay for a corporate accountant with an annual salary of $50,000?

SOLUTION STRATEGY

The amount of gross pay per period is determined by dividing the annual salary by the number of pay periods per year.

TEACHING TIP
Students sometimes confuse biweekly, every 2 weeks, and semimonthly, every half month, or twice per month. Point out that

- *Bi* means two, such as in bicycle—two wheels
- *Semi* means half, such as in semicircle—half a circle

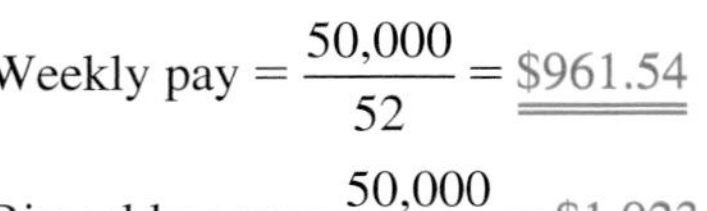

$$\text{Weekly pay} = \frac{50{,}000}{52} = \underline{\underline{\$961.54}}$$

$$\text{Biweekly pay} = \frac{50{,}000}{26} = \underline{\underline{\$1{,}923.08}}$$

$$\text{Semimonthly pay} = \frac{50{,}000}{24} = \underline{\underline{\$2{,}083.33}}$$

$$\text{Monthly pay} = \frac{50{,}000}{12} = \underline{\underline{\$4{,}166.67}}$$

TRY IT EXERCISE 1

An executive of a large manufacturing company earns a gross annual salary of $43,500. What is the weekly, biweekly, semimonthly, and monthly pay for this employee?

CHECK YOUR ANSWERS WITH THE SOLUTIONS ON PAGE 319.

9-2 CALCULATING GROSS PAY BY HOURLY WAGES, INCLUDING REGULAR AND OVERTIME RATES

wages Earnings for routine or manual work, usually based on the number of hours worked.

hourly wage, or hourly rate The amount an employee is paid for each hour worked.

overtime According to federal law, the amount an employee is paid for each hour worked over 40 hours per week.

Wages are earnings for routine or manual work, usually based on the number of hours worked. An **hourly wage** or **hourly rate** is the amount an employee is paid for each hour worked. The hourly wage is the most frequently used pay method and is designed to compensate employees for the amount of time spent on the job. The Fair Labor Standards Act of 1938, a federal law, specifies that a standard work week is 40 hours, and **overtime**, amounting to at least $1\frac{1}{2}$ times the hourly rate, must be paid for all hours worked over 40 hours per week. Paying an employee $1\frac{1}{2}$ times the hourly rate is known as time-and-a-half.

Many companies have taken overtime a step farther than required by compensating employees at time-and-a-half for all hours over 8 hours per day instead of 40 hours per week. Another common payroll benefit is when companies pay double time, twice the hourly rate, for holidays, midnight shifts, and weekend hours.

On May 25, 2007, an amendment to the Fair Labor Standards Act became law. The amendment provided for a three-stage increase to the federal minimum wage for the first time in a decade. The $5.15-an-hour minimum wage was mandated to rise to $7.25 an hour in $.70 increments, as follows: $5.85 an hour on July 24, 2007; $6.55 an hour on July 24, 2008; and $7.25 an hour on July 24, 2009.

In the Business World

Payroll is a very important business responsibility. Employees must be paid on a regular basis, and accurate records must be kept for government reporting.

- Payroll is usually one of the largest "expense" categories of a company.
- The department responsible for the payroll function may be called Payroll, Personnel, or Human Resources.
- In recent years, companies have evolved that specialize in doing payroll. When a business hires an outside firm to perform a function such as payroll, this is known as *outsourcing*.

STEPS TO CALCULATE AN EMPLOYEE'S GROSS PAY BY HOURLY WAGES

Step 1. Calculate an employee's regular gross pay for working 40 hours or less.

Regular pay = Hourly rate × Regular hours worked

Step 2. Calculate an employee's overtime pay by chain multiplying the hourly rate by the overtime factor by the number of overtime hours.

Overtime pay = Hourly rate × Overtime factor × Overtime hours worked

Step 3. Calculate total gross pay.

Total gross pay = Regular pay + Overtime pay

EXAMPLE 2 CALCULATING HOURLY PAY

Polly Richardson earns \$8 per hour as a checker on an assembly line. If her overtime rate is time-and-a-half, what is her total gross pay for working 46 hours last week?

SOLUTION STRATEGY

To find Polly's total gross pay, compute her regular pay plus overtime pay.

Regular pay = Hourly rate × Regular hours worked
Regular pay = 8 × 40 = \$320

Overtime pay = Hourly rate × Overtime factor × Overtime hours worked
Overtime pay = 8 × 1.5 × 6 = \$72

Total gross pay = Regular pay + Overtime pay
Total gross pay = 320 + 72 = \$392

TRY IT EXERCISE 2

John Miller works as a delivery truck driver for \$10.50 per hour, with time-and-a-half for overtime and double time on Sundays. What is his total gross pay for last week if he worked 45 hours on Monday through Saturday, plus a 4-hour shift on Sunday?

CHECK YOUR ANSWER WITH THE SOLUTION ON PAGE 319.

CLASSROOM ACTIVITY
Have students research companies that specialize in payroll preparation and report their findings to the class.
- What exactly do they do?
- What does it cost?
- What is the advantage of outsourcing the payroll function?

CALCULATING GROSS PAY BY STRAIGHT AND DIFFERENTIAL PIECEWORK SCHEDULES

9-3

A **piecework** pay rate schedule is not based on time but on production output. The incentive is that the more units the worker produces, the more money he or she makes. A **straight piecework plan** is when the worker receives a certain amount of pay per unit of output, regardless of output quantity. A **differential piecework plan** gives workers a greater incentive to increase output, because the rate per unit increases as output goes up. For example, a straight piecework plan might pay \$3.15 per unit, whereas a differential plan might pay \$3.05 for the first 50 units produced, \$3.45 for units 51–100, and \$3.90 for any units over 100.

piecework Pay rate schedule based on an employee's production output, not hours worked.

straight piecework plan Pay per unit of output, regardless of output quantity.

differential piecework plan Greater incentive method of compensation than straight piecework, where pay per unit increases as output goes up.

STEPS TO CALCULATE GROSS PAY BY PIECEWORK

Straight Piecework:

Step 1. Total gross pay under a straight piecework schedule is calculated by multiplying the number of pieces or output units by the rate per unit.

Total gross pay = Output quantity × Rate per unit

Differential Piecework:

Step 1. Multiply the number of output units at each level by the rate per unit at that level.

Step 2. Find the total gross pay by adding the total from each level.

EXAMPLE 3 CALCULATING PIECEWORK PAY

Erica Larsen works on a hat assembly line. Erica gets paid at a straight piecework rate of $.35 per hat. What is Erica's total gross pay for last week if she produced 1,655 hats?

SOLUTION STRATEGY

Total gross pay = Output quantity × Rate per unit

Total gross pay = 1,655 × .35 = $579.25

TRY IT EXERCISE 3

Jerry Kreshover works at a tire manufacturing plant. He is on a straight piecework rate of $.41 per tire. What is Jerry's total gross pay for last week if he produced 950 tires?

CHECK YOUR ANSWER WITH THE SOLUTION ON PAGE 319.

EXAMPLE 4 CALCULATING DIFFERENTIAL PIECEWORK PAY

Heather Gott assembled 190 watches last week. Calculate her total gross pay based on the following differential piecework schedule.

Pay Level	Watches Assembled	Rate per Watch
1	1–100	$2.45
2	101–150	$2.75
3	Over 150	$3.10

SOLUTION STRATEGY

To find Heather's total gross earnings, we calculate her earnings at each level of the pay schedule and add the totals. In this case, she will be paid for all of level 1, all of level 2, and for 40 watches at level 3 (190 − 150).

Level pay = Output × Rate per piece

Level 1 = 100 × 2.45 = $245

Level 2 = 50 × 2.75 = $137.50

Level 3 = 40 × 3.10 = $124

Total gross pay = Level 1 + Level 2 + Level 3

Total gross pay = 245 + 137.50 + 124 = $506.50

TEACHING TIP

Sometimes students incorrectly use the pay rate at the final level to calculate "all" the items produced, rather than using the "graduated" pay rates at each level.

- In groups, have students solve Try-It Exercise 4.
- Use Teaching Transparency 9-1 to illustrate the solution.

TRY IT EXERCISE 4

You are the payroll manager for Trendy Toys, Inc., a manufacturer of small plastic toys. Your production workers are on a differential piecework schedule as follows.

Pay Level	Toys Produced	Rate per Toy
1	1–300	$.68
2	301–500	$.79
3	501–750	$.86
4	Over 750	$.94

Calculate last week's total gross pay for the following employees.

Name	Toys Produced	Total Gross Pay
C. Gomez	515	______
L. Clifford	199	______
M. Maken	448	______
B. Nathan	804	______

CHECK YOUR ANSWERS WITH THE SOLUTIONS ON PAGE 319.

Teaching Transparency 9-1

CLASSROOM ACTIVITY
Invite a manager from a company's human resources department to class as a guest speaker to discuss "current happenings" regarding payroll and fringe benefits.

CALCULATING GROSS PAY BY STRAIGHT AND INCREMENTAL COMMISSION, SALARY PLUS COMMISSION, AND DRAWING ACCOUNTS

Straight and Incremental Commission

Commission is a method of compensation primarily used to pay employees who sell a company's goods or services. **Straight commission** is based on a single specified percentage of the sales volume attained. For example, Delta Distributors pays its sales staff a commission of 8% on all sales. **Incremental commission** is much like the differential piecework rate, whereby higher levels of sales earn increasing rates of commission. An example would be 5% commission on all sales up to $70,000; 6% on sales greater than $70,000 and up to $120,000; and 7% commission on any sales greater than $120,000.

commission Percentage method of compensation primarily used to pay employees who sell a company's goods and services.

straight commission Commission based on a specified percentage of the sales volume attained by an employee.

incremental commission Greater incentive method of compensation than straight commission, whereby higher levels of sales earn increasing rates of commission.

STEPS TO CALCULATE GROSS PAY BY COMMISSION

Straight Commission:

Step 1. Total gross pay under a straight commission schedule is calculated by multiplying the total sales by the commission rate.

Total gross pay = Total sales × Commission rate

Incremental Commission:

Step 1. Multiply the total sales at each level by the commission rate for that level.

Step 2. Find the total gross pay by adding the total from each level.

EXAMPLE 5 CALCULATING COMMISSIONS

West Coast Wholesalers pays its sales force a commission rate of 6% of all sales. What is the total gross pay for an employee who sold $113,500 last month?

SOLUTION STRATEGY

$$\text{Total gross pay} = \text{Total sales} \times \text{Commission rate}$$

$$\text{Total gross pay} = 113{,}500 \times .06 = \underline{\underline{\$6{,}810}}$$

TRY IT EXERCISE 5

Jami Minard sells for Supreme Designs, a manufacturer of women's clothing. Jami is paid a straight commission of 2.4%. If her sales volume last month was $233,760, what is her total gross pay?

CHECK YOUR ANSWER WITH THE SOLUTION ON PAGE 319.

EXAMPLE 6 CALCULATING INCREMENTAL COMMISSION

Telex Industries pays its sales representatives on the following incremental commission schedule.

Level	Sales Volume	Commission Rate (%)
1	$1–$50,000	4
2	$50,001–$150,000	5
3	Over $150,000	6.5

What is the total gross pay for a sales rep who sold $162,400 last month?

SOLUTION STRATEGY

Using an incremental commission schedule, we find the pay for each level and then add the totals from each level. In this problem, the sales rep will be paid for all of level 1, all of level 2, and for $12,400 of level 3 ($162,400 − $150,000).

$$\text{Level pay} = \text{Sales per level} \times \text{Commission rate}$$

$$\text{Level 1 pay} = 50{,}000 \times .04 = \underline{\$2{,}000}$$

$$\text{Level 2 pay} = 100{,}000 \times .05 = \underline{\$5{,}000}$$

$$\text{Level 3 pay} = 12{,}400 \times .065 = \underline{\$806}$$

$$\text{Total gross pay} = \text{Level 1} + \text{Level 2} + \text{Level 3}$$

$$\text{Total gross pay} = 2{,}000 + 5{,}000 + 806 = \underline{\underline{\$7{,}806}}$$

TRY IT EXERCISE 6

John Gray sells copiers for Sharp Business Products. He is on an incremental commission schedule of 1.7% of sales up to $100,000 and 2.5% on sales greater than $100,000. What is John's total gross pay for last month if his sales volume was $184,600?

CHECK YOUR ANSWER WITH THE SOLUTION ON PAGE 319.

In the Business World

Companies often give sales managers *override* commissions. This is a small commission on the total sales of the manager's sales force.

Example: Jim and Diane sell for Apex Electronics. They each receive 15% commission on their sales. John, their sales manager, receives a 3% override on their total sales. If Jim sells $20,000 and Diane sells $30,000 in June, how much commission does each person receive?

- Jim: $20,000 × 15% = $3,000
- Diane: $30,000 × 15% = $4,500
- John: $50,000 × 3% = $1,500

Salary Plus Commission

A variation of straight and incremental commission pay schedules is the **salary plus commission**, whereby the employee is paid a guaranteed salary plus a commission on sales over a certain specified amount. To calculate the total gross pay, find the amount of commission and add it to the salary.

salary plus commission A guaranteed salary plus a commission on sales over a certain specified amount.

EXAMPLE 7 CALCULATING SALARY PLUS COMMISSION

Brandi Lee works on a pay schedule of $1,500 per month salary plus a 3% commission on all sales greater than $40,000. If she sold $60,000 last month, what is her total gross pay?

SOLUTION STRATEGY

To solve for Brandi's total gross pay, add her monthly salary to her commission for the month.

Commission = Commission rate × Sales subject to commission

Commission = 3%(60,000 − 40,000)

Commission = .03 × 20,000 = $600

Total gross pay = Salary + Commission

Total gross pay = 1,500 + 600 = $2,100

TRY IT EXERCISE 7

Ed Diamond is a sales representative for Jersey Supply, Inc. He is paid a salary of $1,400 per month plus a commission of 4% on all sales greater than $20,000. If he sold $45,000 last month, what was his total gross earnings?

CHECK YOUR ANSWER WITH THE SOLUTION ON PAGE 319.

Draw against Commission

In certain industries and at certain times of the year, sales fluctuate significantly. To provide salespeople on commission with at least some income during slack periods of sales, a drawing account is used. A **drawing account**, or **draw against commission**, is a commission paid in advance of sales and later deducted from the commissions earned. If a period goes by when the salesperson does not earn enough commission to cover the draw, the unpaid balance carries over to the next period.

drawing account, or draw against commission Commission paid in advance of sales and later deducted from the commission earned.

EXAMPLE 8 CALCULATING DRAW AGAINST COMMISSION

Travis Wagner is a salesperson for Dynamo Corp. The company pays 8% commission on all sales, and gives Travis a $1,500 per month draw against commission. If he receives his draw at the beginning of the month and then sells $58,000 during the month, how much commission is owed to Travis?

SOLUTION STRATEGY

To find the amount of commission owed to Travis, find the total amount of commission he earned and subtract $1,500, the amount of his draw against commission.

Commission = Total sales × Commission rate

Commission = 58,000 × 8% = $4,640

Commission owed = Commission − Amount of draw

Commission owed = 4,640 − 1,500 = $3,140

TRY IT EXERCISE 8

Chris Manning sells for Panorama Products, Inc. He is on a 3.5% straight commission with a $2,000 drawing account. If he is paid the draw at the beginning of the month and then sells $120,000 during the month, how much commission is owed to Chris?

CHECK YOUR ANSWER WITH THE SOLUTION ON PAGE 319.

SECTION I Review Exercises

Calculate the gross earnings per pay period for the following pay schedules.

	Annual Salary	Monthly	Semimonthly	Biweekly	Weekly
1.	$15,000	1,250.00	625.00	576.92	288.46
2.	$44,200	3,683.33	1,841.67	1,700.00	850.00
3.	$100,000	8,333.33	4,166.67	3,846.15	1,923.08
4.	21,600	$1,800.00	900.00	830.77	415.38
5.	34,800	2,900.00	$1,450.00	1,338.46	669.23
6.	22,750	1,895.83	947.92	$875.00	437.50
7.	17,420	1,451.67	725.83	670.00	$335.00

TEACHING TIP
To solve Review Exercises 4–7, first have students calculate the annual salary, then prorate (divide) to determine the salary for the remaining pay periods.

8. Alice Kirk is an office manager who has gross earnings of $1,600 semimonthly. If her company switches pay schedules from semimonthly to biweekly, what are Alice's new gross earnings?

   1,600 × 24 = 38,400 Annual salary

   $\frac{38,400}{26} = \$1,476.92$ Biweekly salary

9. Susan Roberts is an accounting professional earning a salary of $58,000 at her firm. What is her equivalent weekly gross pay?

   Weekly pay $= \frac{58,000}{52} = \$1,115.38$

10. Roxanne McCorry works 40 hours per week as a chef's assistant. At the rate of $7.60 per hour, what are her gross weekly earnings?

    $7.60 \times 40 =$ $304

11. Bob Majors earns $22.34 per hour as a specialty chef at Le Bistro Restaurant. If he worked 53 hours last week, and was paid time-and-a-half for weekly hours over 40, what was his gross pay?

Regular pay:	$22.34 \times 40 =$	$893.60
Overtime pay:	$22.34 \times 1.5 \times 13 =$	435.63
	Total pay	$1,329.23

12. Rob Dolcini earns $8.25 per hour for regular time up to 40 hours, time-and-a-half for overtime, and double time for the midnight shift. Last week, Rob worked 58 hours, including 6 on the midnight shift. What are his gross earnings?

58 Total hours			
− 40 Regular hours	Regular pay:	$8.25 \times 40 =$	$330.00
18 Overtime hours	Time-and-a-half pay:	$8.25 \times 1.5 \times 12 =$	148.50
− 6 Double-time hours	Double time:	$8.25 \times 2 \times 6 =$	99.00
12 Time-and-half hours		Total pay	$577.50

As the payroll manager for Bentley Systems, Inc., it is your task to complete the following weekly payroll record. The company pays overtime for all hours worked over 40 at the rate of time-and-a-half. Round to the nearest cent, when necessary.

	Employee	M	T	W	T	F	S	S	Hourly Rate	Total Hours	Overtime Hours	Regular Pay	Overtime Pay	Total Pay
13.	Williams	7	8	5	8	8	0	0	$8.70	36	0	$313.20	0	$313.20
14.	Tanner	6	5	9	8	10	7	0	$9.50	45	5	$380.00	$71.25	$451.25
15.	Gomez	8	6	11	7	12	0	4	$7.25	48	8	$290.00	$87.00	$377.00
16.	Wells	9	7	7	7	9	0	8	$14.75	47	7	$590.00	$154.88	$744.88

EXCEL

EXCEL

17. Randy Branson gets paid a straight piecework rate of $3.15 for each alternator he assembles for Allied Mechanical Corp. If he assembled 226 units last week, what was his gross pay?

    $3.15 \times 226 =$ $711.90

You are the payroll manager for Glitzy Garments, a manufacturer of women's apparel. Your workers are paid per garment sewn on a differential piecework schedule as follows.

Pay Level	Garments Produced	Rate per Garment
1	1–50	$3.60
2	51–100	$4.25
3	101–150	$4.50
4	Over 150	$5.10

Calculate last week's total gross pay for each of the following employees.

Complete, worked-out solutions for Exercises 18–20 appear in Appendix B.

	Employee	Garments Produced	Total Gross Pay
18.	Johnston, C.	109	$433.00
19.	Barber, W.	83	$320.25
20.	Lynn, K.	174	$739.90

21. Elena Cabrera assembles motor mounts for C-207 executive planes. Her company has established a differential piecework scale as incentive to increase production due to backlogged orders. The pay scale is $11.50 for the first 40 mounts, $12.35 for the next 30 mounts, $13.00 for the next 20 mounts, and $13.40 for all remaining mounts assembled during the week. Elena assembled 96 mounts last week. What was her total gross pay?

$40 \times 11.50 =$ $460.00
$30 \times 12.35 =$ 370.50
$20 \times 13.00 =$ 260.00
$6 \times 13.40 =$ 80.40
96 $1,170.90 Total gross pay

22. Dave Bach works for a company that manufactures small appliances. Dave is paid $2.00 for each toaster, $4.60 for each microwave oven, and $1.55 for each food blender he assembles. If he produced 56 toasters, 31 microwave ovens, and 79 blenders, what were his total weekly gross earnings?

Toaster	$56 \times 2.00 =$	$112.00
Microwave	$31 \times 4.60 =$	142.60
Blender	$79 \times 1.55 =$	122.45
		$377.05

23. What is the total gross pay for a salesperson on a straight commission of 4.7% if his or her sales volume is $123,200?

$123,200 \times .047 =$ $5,790.40

24. Sheila Wilcox is paid on an incremental commission schedule. She is paid 2.6% on the first $60,000 and 3.4% on any sales over $60,000. If her weekly sales volume was $89,400, what was her total commission?

$60,000 × 2.6% = $1,560.00
29,400 × 3.4% = 999.60
$89,400 $2,559.60 Total commission

25. Adrianne Renata works for Imperial Imports. She is paid a weekly salary of $885 plus a 4% commission on sales over $45,000. If her sales were $62,000 last week, what was her total gross pay?

62,000 − 45,000 = $17,000

17,000 × 4% = $680 Commission
+885 Salary
$1,565 Total gross pay

26. Bill Lyon's company pays him a straight 6% commission with a $1,350 drawing account each month. If his sales last month totaled $152,480, how much commission is owed to Bill?

152,480 × 6% = $9,148.80 Total commission
−1,350.00 Draw against commission
$7,798.80 Commission owed

27. Lisa Goodrich works for Escapade selling clothing. She is on a salary of $140 per week plus a commission of 7% of her sales. Last week, she sold 19 dresses at $79.95 each, 26 skirts at $24.75 each, and 17 jackets at $51.50 each. What were her total gross earnings for the week?

19 × 79.95 =	$1,519.05	$3,038.05	
26 × 24.75 =	643.50	× .07	
17 × 51.50 =	875.50	$212.66	Commission
	$3,038.05 Total sales	+ 140.00	Salary
		$ 352.66	Total gross earnings

28. Steve Walker is a waiter in a restaurant that pays a salary of $22 per day. He also averages tips of 18% of his total gross food orders. Last week, he worked 6 days and had total food orders of $2,766.50. What was his total gross pay for the week?

6 × 22 =	$132.00	Salary
2,766.50 × .18 =	+497.97	Commission
	$629.97	Total gross earnings

BUSINESS DECISION THE MINIMUM WAGE HIKE

29. As we learned in Objective 9-2, on May 25, 2007, an amendment to the Fair Labor Standards Act became law. The amendment provided for a three-stage increase to the federal minimum wage; the first such increase since 1997. The $5.15-an-hour minimum wage was increased to $7.25 an hour in $.70 increments, as follows:

- $5.85 an hour on July 24, 2007
- $6.55 an hour on July 24, 2008
- $7.25 an hour on July 24, 2009

You are the accountant for a chain of 16 fast food restaurants. Each restaurant employs 35 workers, each averaging 20 hours per week, at minimum wage level.

a. How many total hours at minimum wage are paid out each week by the company?

16 × 35 × 20 = 11,200 hours

b. At $5.15 per hour, what was the amount of the weekly "minimum wage" portion of the restaurant's payroll?

11,200 × 5.15 = $57,680 Weekly payroll @ $5.15

c. Consider that a number of employees earning just above the minimum wage will have their hourly rate "bumped up" as a side effect of the minimum wage increase. At $7.25 per hour minimum wage, plus a 10% increase due to "bump up," what is the amount of the weekly payroll?

11,200 × 7.25 =	$81,200	Minimum wage payroll
81,200 × .10 =	8,120	Bump up
	$89,320	Weekly payroll

d. How much does each $.70 increment add to the payroll weekly? Annually? Total for all three stages?

11,200 × .70 =	$7,840	Weekly increment
7,840 × 52 =	$407,680	Annual increment
407,680 × 3 =	$1,223,040	Total increase in payroll

"And this is for keeping wages down."

e. (Optional) Suggest some ways that the restaurant chain, or other small businesses, can offset the increase in payroll and subsequent decrease in profit as a result of the minimum wage hike.

Answers may vary. Here are some possibilities for discussion:

Increase efficiency to cover more hours with fewer employees

Increase store traffic and revenue by increasing the advertising and promotion activities

Try to increase the amount of the average sale

SECTION II EMPLOYEE'S PAYROLL DEDUCTIONS

"Hey! What happened to my paycheck?" This is the typical reaction of employees on seeing their paychecks for the first time after a raise or a promotion. As we shall see, gross pay is by no means the amount of money that the employee takes home.

deductions, or withholdings Funds withheld from an employee's paycheck.

mandatory deductions Deductions withheld from an employee's paycheck by law: social security, Medicare, and federal income tax.

voluntary deductions Deductions withheld from an employee's paycheck by request of the employee, such as insurance premiums, dues, loan payments, and charitable contributions.

Employers, by federal law, are required to deduct or withhold certain funds, known as **deductions** or **withholdings**, from an employee's paychecks. Employee payroll deductions fall into two categories: mandatory and voluntary. The three major **mandatory deductions** most workers in the United States are subject to are social security, Medicare, and federal income tax. Other mandatory deductions, found only in some states, are state income tax and state disability insurance.

In addition to the mandatory deductions, employees may also choose to have **voluntary deductions** taken out of their paychecks. Some examples include payments for life or health insurance premiums, union or professional organization dues, credit union savings deposits or loan payments, stock or bond purchases, and charitable contributions.

After all the deductions have been subtracted from the employee's gross earnings, the remaining amount is known as net or take-home pay.

Net pay = Gross pay − Total deductions

9-5 COMPUTING FICA TAXES, BOTH SOCIAL SECURITY AND MEDICARE, WITHHELD FROM AN EMPLOYEE'S PAYCHECK

Federal Insurance Contribution Act (FICA) Federal legislation, enacted in 1937 during the Great Depression, to provide retirement funds and hospital insurance for retired and disabled workers. Today, FICA is divided into two categories, social security and Medicare.

wage base The amount of earnings up to which an employee must pay social security tax.

social security tax (OASDI) Old Age, Survivors, and Disability Insurance—a federal tax, based on a percentage of a worker's income up to a specified limit or wage base, for the purpose of providing monthly benefits to retired and disabled workers and to the families of deceased workers.

Medicare tax A federal tax used to provide health care benefits and hospital insurance to retired and disabled workers.

In 1937 during the Great Depression, Congress enacted legislation known as the **Federal Insurance Contribution Act (FICA)** with the purpose of providing monthly benefits to retired and disabled workers and to the families of deceased workers. This social security tax, which is assessed to virtually every worker in the United States, is based on a certain percent of the worker's income up to a specified limit or **wage base** per year. When the tax began in 1937, the tax rate was 1% up to a wage base of $3,000. At that time, the maximum a worker could be taxed per year for social security was $30.00 (3,000 × .01).

Today, the FICA tax is divided into two categories. **Social security tax** (OASDI, which stands for Old Age, Survivors, and Disability Insurance) is a retirement plan, and **Medicare** tax is for health care and hospital insurance. The social security wage base changes every year. For the most current information, consult the Internal Revenue Service, *Circular E: Employer's Tax Guide*. In 2007, the following rates and wage base were in effect for the FICA tax and should be used for all exercises in this chapter:

	Tax Rate	Wage Base
Social Security (OASDI)	6.2%	$97,500
Medicare	1.45%	no limit

When an employee reaches the wage base for the year, he or she is no longer subject to the tax. In 2007, the maximum social security tax per year was $6,045 (97,500 × .062). There is no limit on the amount of Medicare tax. The 1.45% is in effect regardless of how much an employee earns.

9-2

In the Business World

The current FICA deductions and wage base are listed in the IRS publication *Circular E, Employer's Tax Guide*.

This and other tax forms and publications can be obtained by calling the IRS at 1-800-TAX FORM or from their Web site, www.irs.gov.

EXAMPLE 9 CALCULATING SOCIAL SECURITY AND MEDICARE WITHHOLDINGS

What are the withholdings for social security and Medicare for an employee with gross earnings of $650 per week? Round to the nearest cent.

SOLUTION STRATEGY

To find the withholdings, we apply the tax rates for social security (6.2%) and Medicare (1.45%) to the gross earnings for the week:

Social security tax = Gross earnings × 6.2%

Social security tax = 650 × .062 = $40.30

Medicare tax = Gross earnings × 1.45%

Medicare tax = 650 × .0145 = 9.425 = $9.43

TRY IT EXERCISE 9

What are the withholdings for social security and Medicare for an employee with gross earnings of $5,000 per month?

CHECK YOUR ANSWERS WITH THE SOLUTIONS ON PAGE 319.

Mandatory payroll deductions enacted into law by Congress include social security, Medicare, and federal income tax.

Reaching the Wage Base Limit

In the pay period when an employee's year-to-date (YTD) earnings reach and surpass the wage base for social security, the tax is applied only to the portion of the earnings below the limit.

EXAMPLE 10 CALCULATING SOCIAL SECURITY WITH WAGE BASE LIMIT

Donna Starpointe has earned $94,900 so far this year. Her next paycheck, $5,000, will put her earnings over the wage base limit for social security. What is the amount of Donna's social security withholdings for that paycheck?

SOLUTION STRATEGY

To calculate Donna's social security deduction, first determine how much more she must earn to reach the wage base of $97,500.

Earnings subject to tax = Wage base − Year-to-date earnings

Earnings subject to tax = 97,500 − 94,900 = $2,600

Social security tax = Earnings subject to tax × 6.2%

Social security tax = 2,600 × .062 = $161.20

TRY IT EXERCISE 10

Harris Mones has year-to-date earnings of $92,300. If his next paycheck is for $6,000, what is the amount of his social security deduction?

CHECK YOUR ANSWER WITH THE SOLUTION ON PAGE 319.

9-6 CALCULATING AN EMPLOYEE'S FEDERAL INCOME TAX WITHHOLDING (FIT) BY THE PERCENTAGE METHOD

federal income tax (FIT) A graduated tax, based on gross earnings, marital status, and number of exemptions, that is paid by all workers earning over a certain amount of money in the United States.

withholding allowance, or exemption An amount that reduces an employee's taxable income. Employees are allowed one exemption for themselves, one for their spouse if the spouse does not work, and one for each dependent child or elderly parent living with the taxpayer but not working.

percentage method An alternative method to the wage bracket tables, used to calculate the amount of an employee's federal income tax withholding.

In addition to social security and Medicare tax withholdings, an employer is also responsible, by federal law, for withholding an appropriate amount of **federal income tax (FIT)** from each employee's paycheck. This graduated tax allows the government a steady flow of tax revenues throughout the year. Self-employed persons must send quarterly tax payments based on estimated earnings to the Internal Revenue Service.

The amount of income tax withheld from an employee's paycheck is determined by his or her amount of gross earnings, marital status, and the number of **withholding allowances** or **exemptions** claimed. Employees are allowed one exemption for themselves, one for their spouse if the spouse does not work, and one for each dependent child or elderly parent living with the taxpayer but not working.

Each employee is required to complete a form called W-4, Employee's Withholding Allowance Certificate, shown in Exhibit 9-1. The information provided on this form is used by the employer in calculating the amount of income tax withheld from the paycheck.

The **percentage method** for determining the amount of federal income tax withheld from an employee's paycheck is used by companies whose payroll processing is on a computerized system. The amount of tax withheld is based on the amount of gross earnings, the marital status of the employee, and the number of withholding allowances claimed.

Exhibit 9-1
Employee W-4 Form

Cut here and give Form W-4 to your employer. Keep the top part for your records.

Form **W-4** — Department of the Treasury, Internal Revenue Service

Employee's Withholding Allowance Certificate

▶ For Privacy Act and Paperwork Reduction Act Notice, see page 2.

OMB No. 1545-0010 — 20XX

1 Type or print your first name and middle initial | Last name | 2 Your social security number

Home address (number and street or rural route) | 3 ☐ Single ☐ Married ☐ Married, but withhold at higher Single rate.
Note: *If married, but legally separated, or spouse is a nonresident alien, check the "Single" box.*

City or town, state, and ZIP code | 4 **If your last name differs from that shown on your social security card, check here. You must call 1-800-772-1213 for a new card.** ▶ ☐

5 Total number of allowances you are claiming (from line **H** above **or** from the applicable worksheet on page 2) | 5

6 Additional amount, if any, you want withheld from each paycheck . . . . | 6 $

7 I claim exemption from withholding for 20XX, and I certify that I meet **both** of the following conditions for exemption:
- Last year I had a right to a refund of **all** Federal income tax withheld because I had **no** tax liability **and**
- This year I expect a refund of **all** Federal income tax withheld because I expect to have **no** tax liability.

If you meet both conditions, write "Exempt" here . . . . ▶ 7

Under penalties of perjury, I certify that I am entitled to the number of withholding allowances claimed on this certificate, or I am entitled to claim exempt status.

Employeeís signature
(Form is not valid unless you sign it.) ▶ **Date** ▶

8 Employerís name and address (Employer: Complete lines 8 and 10 only if sending to the IRS.) | 9 Office code (optional) | 10 Employer identification number (EIN)

Cat. No. 10220Q

The percentage method of calculating federal income tax requires the use of two tables. The first is the Percentage Method—Amount for One Withholding Allowance Table, Exhibit 9-2. This table shows the dollar amount of one withholding allowance, for the various payroll periods. The second, Exhibit 9-3, is the Rate Tables for Percentage Method of Withholding.

STEPS TO CALCULATE THE INCOME TAX WITHHELD BY THE PERCENTAGE METHOD

Step 1. Using the proper payroll period, multiply one withholding allowance, Exhibit 9-2, by the number of allowances claimed by the employee.

Step 2. Subtract that amount from the employee's gross earnings to find the wages subject to federal income tax.

Step 3. From Exhibit 9-3, locate the proper segment (Table 1, 2, 3, or 4) corresponding to the employee's payroll period. Within that segment, use the *left* side (a) for single employees and the *right* side (b) for married employees.

Step 4. Locate the "Over—" and "But not over—" brackets containing the employee's taxable wages from Step 2. The tax is listed to the right as a percent or a dollar amount and a percent.

EXAMPLE 11 CALCULATING INCOME TAX WITHHOLDING

Kim Johnson is a manager for Worldwide Travel. She is single and is paid $750 weekly. She claims two withholding allowances. Using the percentage method, calculate the amount of income tax that should be withheld from her paycheck each week.

SOLUTION STRATEGY

From Exhibit 9-2, the amount of one withholding allowance for an employee paid weekly is $65.38. Next, multiply this amount by the number of allowances claimed, two.

$$65.38 \times 2 = \$130.76$$

Subtract that amount from the gross earnings to get taxable income.

$$750.00 - 130.76 = \$619.24$$

TEACHING TIP

In groups, have students write some income tax withholding exercises and then calculate the solutions by using both the wage bracket tables method and the percentage method.

Next, have them compare the results of the two methods. The answers should be very close or exactly the same.

9-3

Exhibit 9-2
Percentage Method Amount for One Withholding Allowance

Payroll Period	One Withholding Allowance
Weekly	$ 65.38
Biweekly	130.77
Semimonthly	141.67
Monthly	283.33
Quarterly	850.00
Semiannually	1,700.00
Annually	3,400.00
Daily or miscellaneous (each day of the payroll period)	13.08

From Exhibit 9-3, find the tax withheld from Kim's paycheck in Table 1(a), Weekly payroll period, Single person. Kim's taxable wages of $619.24 fall in the category: "Over $195, but not over $645." The tax, therefore, is $14.40 plus 15% of the excess over $195.

Teaching Transparency 9-4

$$\text{Tax} = 14.40 + .15(619.24 - 195.00)$$
$$\text{Tax} = 14.40 + .15(424.24)$$
$$\text{Tax} = 14.40 + 63.64 = \underline{\underline{\$78.04}}$$

Exhibit 9-3
Tables for Percentage Method of Withholding

Tables for Percentage Method of Withholding

TABLE 1—WEEKLY Payroll Period

(a) SINGLE person (including head of household)—

If the amount of wages (after subtracting withholding allowances) is: Not over $51 . . . . . The amount of income tax to withhold is: $0

Over—	But not over—		of excess over—
$51	—$195	10%	—$51
$195	—$645	$14.40 plus 15%	—$195
$645	—$1,482	$81.90 plus 25%	—$645
$1,482	—$3,131	$291.15 plus 28%	—$1,482
$3,131	—$6,763	$752.87 plus 33%	—$3,131
$6,763	. . . . . .	$1,951.43 plus 35%	—$6,763

(b) MARRIED person—

If the amount of wages (after subtracting withholding allowances) is: Not over $154 . . . . . The amount of income tax to withhold is: $0

Over—	But not over—		of excess over—
$154	—$429	10%	—$154
$449	—$1,360	$29.50 plus 15%	—$449
$1,360	—$2,573	$166.15 plus 25%	—$1,360
$2,573	—$3,907	$469.40 plus 28%	—$2,573
$3,907	—$6,865	$842.92 plus 33%	—$3,907
$6,865	. . . . . .	$1,819.06 plus 35%	—$6,865

TABLE 2—BIWEEKLY Payroll Period

(a) SINGLE person (including head of household)—

If the amount of wages (after subtracting withholding allowances) is: Not over $102 . . . . . The amount of income tax to withhold is: $0

Over—	But not over—		of excess over—
$102	—$389	10%	—$102
$389	—$1,289	$28.70 plus 15%	—$389
$1,289	—$2,964	$163.70 plus 25%	—$1,289
$2,964	—$6,262	$582.45 plus 28%	—$2,964
$6,262	—$13,525	$1,505.89 plus 33%	—$6,262
$13,525	. . . . . .	$3,902.68 plus 35%	—$13,525

(b) MARRIED person—

If the amount of wages (after subtracting withholding allowances) is: Not over $308 . . . . . The amount of income tax to withhold is: $0

Over—	But not over—		of excess over—
$308	—$858	10%	—$308
$898	—$2,490	$59.00 plus 15%	—$898
$2,719	—$4,540	$332.15 plus 25%	—$2,719
$5,146	—$7,813	$938.90 plus 28%	—$5,146
$7,813	—$13,731	$1,685.66 plus 33%	—$7,813
$13,731	. . . . . .	$3,638.60 plus 35%	—$13,731

TABLE 3—SEMIMONTHLY Payroll Period

(a) SINGLE person (including head of household)—

If the amount of wages (after subtracting withholding allowances) is: Not over $110 . . . . . The amount of income tax to withhold is: $0

Over—	But not over—		of excess over—
$110	—$422	10%	—$110
$422	—$1,397	$31.20 plus 15%	—$422
$1,397	—$3,211	$177.45 plus 25%	—$1,397
$3,211	—$6,783	$630.95 plus 28%	—$3,211
$6,783	—$14,652	$1,631.11 plus 33%	—$6,783
$14,652	. . . . . .	$4,227.88 plus 35%	—$14,652

(b) MARRIED person—

If the amount of wages (after subtracting withholding allowances) is: Not over $333 . . . . . The amount of income tax to withhold is: $0

Over—	But not over—		of excess over—
$333	—$973	10%	—$333
$973	—$2,946	$64.00 plus 15%	—$973
$2,946	—$5,575	$359.95 plus 25%	—$2,946
$5,575	—$8,465	$1,017.20 plus 28%	—$5,575
$8,465	—$14,875	$1,826.40 plus 33%	—$8,465
$14,875	. . . . . .	$3,941.70 plus 35%	—$14,875

TABLE 4—MONTHLY Payroll Period

(a) SINGLE person (including head of household)—

If the amount of wages (after subtracting withholding allowances) is: Not over $221 . . . . . The amount of income tax to withhold is: $0

Over—	But not over—		of excess over—
$221	—$843	10%	—$221
$843	—$2,793	$62.20 plus 15%	—$843
$2,793	—$6,423	$354.70 plus 25%	—$2,793
$6,423	—$13,567	$1,262.20 plus 28%	—$6,423
$13,567	—$29,304	$3,262.52 plus 33%	—$13,567
$29,304	. . . . . .	$8,455.73 plus 35%	—$29,304

(b) MARRIED person—

If the amount of wages (after subtracting withholding allowances) is: Not over $667 . . . . . The amount of income tax to withhold is: $0

Over—	But not over—		of excess over—
$667	—$1,946	10%	—$667
$1,946	—$5,892	$127.90 plus 15%	—$1,946
$5,892	—$11,150	$719.80 plus 25%	—$5,892
$11,150	—$16,929	$2,034.30 plus 28%	—$11,150
$16,929	—$29,750	$3,652.42 plus 33%	—$16,929
$29,750	. . . . . .	$7,883.35 plus 35%	—$29,750

TRY IT EXERCISE 11

Megan Curry is married, claims five exemptions, and earns $3,670 per month. As the payroll manager of Megan's company, use the percentage method to calculate the amount of income tax that must be withheld from her paycheck.

CHECK YOUR ANSWER WITH THE SOLUTION ON PAGE 319.

9-5

DETERMINING AN EMPLOYEE'S TOTAL WITHHOLDING FOR FEDERAL INCOME TAX, SOCIAL SECURITY, AND MEDICARE USING THE COMBINED WAGE BRACKET TABLES

In 2001, the IRS introduced **combined wage bracket tables** that can be used to determine the combined amount of income tax, social security, and Medicare that must be withheld from an employee's gross earnings each pay period. These tables are found in *Publication 15-A: Employer's Supplemental Tax Guide*. This publication contains a complete set of tables for both single and married people, covering weekly, biweekly, semimonthly, monthly, and even daily pay periods.

Exhibit 9-4 shows a portion of the wage bracket tables for Married Persons—Weekly Payroll Period and Exhibit 9-5 shows a portion of the wage bracket table for Single Persons—Monthly Payroll Period. Use these tables to solve wage bracket problems in this chapter.

combined wage bracket tables
IRS tables used to determine the combined amount of income tax, social security, and Medicare that must be withheld from an employee's gross earnings each pay period.

STEPS TO FIND THE TOTAL INCOME TAX, SOCIAL SECURITY, AND MEDICARE WITHHELD USING THE COMBINED WAGE BRACKET TABLE

Step 1. Based on the employee's marital status and period of payment, find the corresponding table (Exhibit 9-4 or 9-5).

Step 2. Note that the two left-hand columns, labeled "At least" and "But less than," are the wage brackets. Scan down these columns until you find the bracket containing the gross pay of the employee.

Step 3. Scan across the row of that wage bracket to the intersection of the column containing the number of withholding allowances claimed by the employee.

Step 4. The number in that column, on the wage bracket row, is the amount of combined tax withheld.

In the Business World

All employees must have a Social Security number. Applications are available at all U.S. post offices.

Social Security numbers are used by the IRS as a taxpayer identification number as well as by banks, credit unions, and other financial institutions for reporting income from savings and other investments.

Information about an individual's Social Security account can be obtained by filing a Form 7004-SM—*Request for Earnings and Benefit Estimate Statement*. These can be obtained by calling the Social Security Administration at 1-800-772-1213.

EXAMPLE 12 USING THE COMBINED WAGE BRACKET TABLES

Use the combined wage bracket tables to determine the amount of income tax, social security, and Medicare withheld from the monthly paycheck of Alice Fox, a single employee, claiming three withholding allowances and earning $2,675 per month.

SOLUTION STRATEGY

To find Alice Fox's monthly income tax withholding, choose the table for Single Persons—Monthly Payroll Period, Exhibit 9-5. Scanning down the "At least" and "But less than" columns, we find the wage bracket containing Alice's earnings: "At least 2,640—But less than 2,680."

Exhibit 9-4
Payroll Deductions—Married, Paid Weekly

9-6

MARRIED Persons—WEEKLY Payroll Period

And the wages are—		And the number of withholding allowances claimed is—										
At least	But less than	0	1	2	3	4	5	6	7	8	9	10
		The amount of income, social security, and Medicare taxes to be withheld is—										
$740	$750	$130.99	$120.99	$110.99	$100.99	$91.99	$82.99	$76.99	$69.99	$63.99	$56.99	$56.99
750	760	132.76	123.76	113.76	103.76	93.76	84.76	78.76	71.76	65.76	58.76	57.76
760	770	135.52	125.52	115.52	105.52	96.52	86.52	80.52	73.52	67.52	60.52	58.52
770	780	137.29	128.29	118.29	108.29	98.29	88.29	82.29	75.29	69.29	62.29	59.29
780	790	140.05	130.05	120.05	110.05	101.05	91.05	84.05	77.05	71.05	64.05	60.05
790	800	141.82	132.82	122.82	112.82	102.82	92.82	85.82	78.82	72.82	65.82	60.82
800	810	144.58	134.58	124.58	114.58	105.58	95.58	87.58	80.58	74.58	67.58	61.58
810	820	146.35	137.35	127.35	117.35	107.35	97.35	89.35	82.35	76.35	69.35	63.35
820	830	149.11	139.11	129.11	119.11	110.11	100.11	91.11	84.11	78.11	71.11	65.11
830	840	150.88	141.88	131.88	121.88	111.88	101.88	92.88	85.88	79.88	72.88	66.88
840	850	153.64	143.64	133.64	123.64	114.64	104.64	94.64	87.64	81.64	74.64	68.64
850	860	155.41	146.41	136.41	126.41	116.41	106.41	97.41	89.41	83.41	76.41	70.41
860	870	158.17	148.17	138.17	128.17	119.17	109.17	99.17	91.17	85.17	78.17	72.17
870	880	159.94	150.94	140.94	130.94	120.94	110.94	101.94	92.94	86.94	79.94	73.94
880	890	162.70	152.70	142.70	132.70	123.70	113.70	103.70	94.70	88.70	81.70	75.70
890	900	164.47	155.47	145.47	135.47	125.47	115.47	106.47	96.47	90.47	83.47	77.47
900	910	167.23	157.23	147.23	137.23	128.23	118.23	108.23	98.23	92.23	85.23	79.23
910	920	169.00	160.00	150.00	140.00	130.00	120.00	111.00	101.00	94.00	87.00	81.00
920	930	171.76	161.76	151.76	141.76	132.76	122.76	112.76	102.76	95.76	88.76	82.76
930	940	173.53	164.53	154.53	144.53	134.53	124.53	115.53	105.53	97.53	90.53	84.53
940	950	176.29	166.29	156.29	146.29	137.29	127.29	117.29	107.29	99.29	92.29	86.29
950	960	178.06	169.06	159.06	149.06	139.06	129.06	120.06	110.06	101.06	94.06	88.06
960	970	180.82	170.82	160.82	150.82	141.82	131.82	121.82	111.82	102.82	95.82	89.82
970	980	182.59	173.59	163.59	153.59	143.59	133.59	124.59	114.59	104.59	97.59	91.59
980	990	185.35	175.35	165.35	155.35	146.35	136.35	126.35	116.35	106.35	99.35	93.35
990	1,000	187.12	178.12	168.12	158.12	148.12	138.12	129.12	119.12	109.12	101.12	95.12
1,000	1,010	189.88	179.88	169.88	159.88	150.88	140.88	130.88	120.88	110.88	102.88	96.88
1,010	1,020	191.65	182.65	172.65	162.65	152.65	142.65	133.65	123.65	113.65	104.65	98.65
1,020	1,030	194.41	184.41	174.41	164.41	155.41	145.41	135.41	125.41	115.41	106.41	100.41
1,030	1,040	196.18	187.18	177.18	167.18	157.18	147.18	138.18	128.18	118.18	108.18	102.18
1,040	1,050	198.94	188.94	178.94	168.94	159.94	149.94	139.94	129.94	119.94	110.94	103.94
1,050	1,060	200.71	191.71	181.71	171.71	161.71	151.71	142.71	132.71	122.71	112.71	105.71
1,060	1,070	203.47	193.47	183.47	173.47	164.47	154.47	144.47	134.47	124.47	115.47	107.47
1,070	1,080	205.24	196.24	186.24	176.24	166.24	156.24	147.24	137.24	127.24	117.24	109.24
1,080	1,090	208.00	198.00	188.00	178.00	169.00	159.00	149.00	139.00	129.00	120.00	111.00
1,090	1,100	209.77	200.77	190.77	180.77	170.77	160.77	151.77	141.77	131.77	121.77	112.77
1,100	1,110	212.53	202.53	192.53	182.53	173.53	163.53	153.53	143.53	133.53	124.53	114.53
1,110	1,120	214.30	205.30	195.30	185.30	175.30	165.30	156.30	146.30	136.30	126.30	116.30
1,120	1,130	217.06	207.06	197.06	187.06	178.06	168.06	158.06	148.06	138.06	129.06	119.06
1,130	1,140	218.83	209.83	199.83	189.83	179.83	169.83	160.83	150.83	140.83	130.83	120.83
1,140	1,150	221.59	211.59	201.59	191.59	182.59	172.59	162.59	152.59	142.59	133.59	123.59
1,150	1,160	223.36	214.36	204.36	194.36	184.36	174.36	165.36	155.36	145.36	135.36	125.36
1,160	1,170	226.12	216.12	206.12	196.12	187.12	177.12	167.12	157.12	147.12	138.12	128.12
1,170	1,180	227.89	218.89	208.89	198.89	188.89	178.89	169.89	159.89	149.89	139.89	129.89
1,180	1,190	230.65	220.65	210.65	200.65	191.65	181.65	171.65	161.65	151.65	142.65	132.65
1,190	1,200	232.42	223.42	213.42	203.42	193.42	183.42	174.42	164.42	154.42	144.42	134.42
1,200	1,210	235.18	225.18	215.18	205.18	196.18	186.18	176.18	166.18	156.18	147.18	137.18
1,210	1,220	236.95	227.95	217.95	207.95	197.95	187.95	178.95	168.95	158.95	148.95	138.95
1,220	1,230	239.71	229.71	219.71	209.71	200.71	190.71	180.71	170.71	160.71	151.71	141.71
1,230	1,240	241.48	232.48	222.48	212.48	202.48	192.48	183.48	173.48	163.48	153.48	143.48
1,240	1,250	244.24	234.24	224.24	214.24	205.24	195.24	185.24	175.24	165.24	156.24	146.24
1,250	1,260	246.01	237.01	227.01	217.01	207.01	197.01	188.01	178.01	168.01	158.01	148.01
1,260	1,270	248.77	238.77	228.77	218.77	209.77	199.77	189.77	179.77	169.77	160.77	150.77
1,270	1,280	250.54	241.54	231.54	221.54	211.54	201.54	192.54	182.54	172.54	162.54	152.54
1,280	1,290	253.30	243.30	233.30	223.30	214.30	204.30	194.30	184.30	174.30	165.30	155.30
1,290	1,300	255.07	246.07	236.07	226.07	216.07	206.07	197.07	187.07	177.07	167.07	157.07
1,300	1,310	257.83	247.83	237.83	227.83	218.83	208.83	198.83	188.83	178.83	169.83	159.83
1,310	1,320	259.60	250.60	240.60	230.60	220.60	210.60	201.60	191.60	181.60	171.60	161.60
1,320	1,330	262.36	252.36	242.36	232.36	223.36	213.36	203.36	193.36	183.36	174.36	164.36
1,330	1,340	264.13	255.13	245.13	235.13	225.13	215.13	206.13	196.13	186.13	176.13	166.13
1,340	1,350	266.89	256.89	246.89	236.89	227.89	217.89	207.89	197.89	187.89	178.89	168.89
1,350	1,360	268.66	259.66	249.66	239.66	229.66	219.66	210.66	200.66	190.66	180.66	170.66
1,360	1,370	271.42	261.42	251.42	241.42	232.42	222.42	212.42	202.42	192.42	183.42	173.42
1,370	1,380	275.19	264.19	254.19	244.19	234.19	224.19	215.19	205.19	195.19	185.19	175.19
1,380	1,390	277.95	265.95	255.95	245.95	236.95	226.95	216.95	206.95	196.95	187.95	177.95

9-7

Exhibit 9-5
Payroll Deductions—Single, Paid Monthly

SINGLE Persons—**MONTHLY** Payroll Period

And the wages are–		And the number of withholding allowances claimed is—										
At least	But less than	0	1	2	3	4	5	6	7	8	9	10
		The amount of income, social security, and Medicare taxes to be withheld is—										
$2,440	$2,480	$493.19	$450.19	$408.19	$365.19	$323.19	$280.19	$242.19	$214.19	$188.19	$188.19	$188.19
2,480	2,520	502.25	459.25	417.25	374.25	332.25	289.25	249.25	221.25	192.25	191.25	191.25
2,520	2,560	511.31	468.31	426.31	383.31	341.31	298.31	256.31	228.31	199.31	194.31	194.31
2,560	2,600	520.37	477.37	435.37	392.37	350.37	307.37	265.37	235.37	206.37	197.37	197.37
2,600	2,640	529.43	486.43	444.43	401.43	359.43	316.43	274.43	242.43	213.43	200.43	200.43
2,640	2,680	538.49	495.49	453.49	410.49	368.49	325.49	283.49	249.49	220.49	203.49	203.49
2,680	2,720	547.55	504.55	462.55	419.55	377.55	334.55	292.55	256.55	227.55	206.55	206.55
2,720	2,760	556.61	513.61	471.61	428.61	386.61	343.61	301.61	263.61	234.61	209.61	209.61
2,760	2,800	565.67	522.67	480.67	437.67	395.67	352.67	310.67	270.67	241.67	213.67	212.67
2,800	2,840	576.73	531.73	489.73	446.73	404.73	361.73	319.73	277.73	248.73	220.73	215.73
2,840	2,880	589.79	540.79	498.79	455.79	413.79	370.79	328.79	285.79	255.79	227.79	218.79
2,880	2,920	602.85	549.85	507.85	464.85	422.85	379.85	337.85	294.85	262.85	234.85	221.85
2,920	2,960	615.91	558.91	516.91	473.91	431.91	388.91	346.91	303.91	269.91	241.91	224.91
2,960	3,000	628.97	567.97	525.97	482.97	440.97	397.97	355.97	312.97	276.97	248.97	227.97
3,000	3,040	642.03	577.03	535.03	492.03	450.03	407.03	365.03	322.03	284.03	256.03	231.03
3,040	3,080	655.09	586.09	544.09	501.09	459.09	416.09	374.09	331.09	291.09	263.09	235.09
3,080	3,120	668.15	598.15	553.15	510.15	468.15	425.15	383.15	340.15	298.15	270.15	242.15
3,120	3,160	681.21	611.21	562.21	519.21	477.21	434.21	392.21	349.21	307.21	277.21	249.21
3,160	3,200	694.27	624.27	571.27	528.27	486.27	443.27	401.27	358.27	316.27	284.27	256.27
3,200	3,240	707.33	637.33	580.33	537.33	495.33	452.33	410.33	367.33	325.33	291.33	263.33
3,240	3,280	720.39	650.39	589.39	546.39	504.39	461.39	419.39	376.39	334.39	298.39	270.39
3,280	3,320	733.45	663.45	598.45	555.45	513.45	470.45	428.45	385.45	343.45	305.45	277.45
3,320	3,360	746.51	676.51	607.51	564.51	522.51	479.51	437.51	394.51	352.51	312.51	284.51
3,360	3,400	759.57	689.57	618.57	573.57	531.57	488.57	446.57	403.57	361.57	319.57	291.57
3,400	3,440	772.63	702.63	631.63	582.63	540.63	497.63	455.63	412.63	370.63	327.63	298.63
3,440	3,480	785.69	715.69	644.69	591.69	549.69	506.69	464.69	421.69	379.69	336.69	305.69
3,480	3,520	798.75	728.75	657.75	600.75	558.75	515.75	473.75	430.75	388.75	345.75	312.75
3,520	3,560	811.81	741.81	670.81	609.81	567.81	524.81	482.81	439.81	397.81	354.81	319.81
3,560	3,600	824.87	754.87	683.87	618.87	576.87	533.87	491.87	448.87	406.87	363.87	326.87
3,600	3,640	837.93	767.93	696.93	627.93	585.93	542.93	500.93	457.93	415.93	372.93	333.93
3,640	3,680	850.99	780.99	709.99	638.99	594.99	551.99	509.99	466.99	424.99	381.99	340.99
3,680	3,720	864.05	794.05	723.05	652.05	604.05	561.05	519.05	476.05	434.05	391.05	349.05
3,720	3,760	877.11	807.11	736.11	665.11	613.11	570.11	528.11	485.11	443.11	400.11	358.11
3,760	3,800	890.17	820.17	749.17	678.17	622.17	579.17	537.17	494.17	452.17	409.17	367.17
3,800	3,840	903.23	833.23	762.23	691.23	631.23	588.23	546.23	503.23	461.23	418.23	376.23
3,840	3,880	916.29	846.29	775.29	704.29	640.29	597.29	555.29	512.29	470.29	427.29	385.29
3,880	3,920	929.35	859.35	788.35	717.35	649.35	606.35	564.35	521.35	479.35	436.35	394.35
3,920	3,960	942.41	872.41	801.41	730.41	659.41	615.41	573.41	530.41	488.41	445.41	403.41
3,960	4,000	955.47	885.47	814.47	743.47	672.47	624.47	582.47	539.47	497.47	454.47	412.47
4,000	4,040	968.53	898.53	827.53	756.53	685.53	633.53	591.53	548.53	506.53	463.53	421.53
4,040	4,080	981.59	911.59	840.59	769.59	698.59	642.59	600.59	557.59	515.59	472.59	430.59
4,080	4,120	994.65	924.65	853.65	782.65	711.65	651.65	609.65	566.65	524.65	481.65	439.65
4,120	4,160	1,007.71	937.71	866.71	795.71	724.71	660.71	618.71	575.71	533.71	490.71	448.71
4,160	4,200	1,020.77	950.77	879.77	808.77	737.77	669.77	627.77	584.77	542.77	499.77	457.77
4,200	4,240	1,033.83	963.83	892.83	821.83	750.83	679.83	636.83	593.83	551.83	508.83	466.83
4,240	4,280	1,046.89	976.89	905.89	834.89	763.89	692.89	645.89	602.89	560.89	517.89	475.89
4,280	4,320	1,059.95	989.95	918.95	847.95	776.95	705.95	654.95	611.95	569.95	526.95	484.95
4,320	4,360	1,073.01	1,003.01	932.01	861.01	790.01	719.01	664.01	621.01	579.01	536.01	494.01
4,360	4,400	1,086.07	1,016.07	945.07	874.07	803.07	732.07	673.07	630.07	588.07	545.07	503.07
4,400	4,440	1,099.13	1,029.13	958.13	887.13	816.13	745.13	682.13	639.13	597.13	554.13	512.13
4,440	4,480	1,112.19	1,042.19	971.19	900.19	829.19	758.19	691.19	648.19	606.19	563.19	521.19
4,480	4,520	1,125.25	1,055.25	984.25	913.25	842.25	771.25	700.25	657.25	615.25	572.25	530.25
4,520	4,560	1,138.31	1,068.31	997.31	926.31	855.31	784.31	713.31	666.31	624.31	581.31	539.31
4,560	4,600	1,151.37	1,081.37	1,010.37	939.37	868.37	797.37	726.37	675.37	633.37	590.37	548.37
4,600	4,640	1,164.43	1,094.43	1,023.43	952.43	881.43	810.43	739.43	684.43	642.43	599.43	557.43
4,640	4,680	1,177.49	1,107.49	1,036.49	965.49	894.49	823.49	752.49	693.49	651.49	608.49	566.49
4,680	4,720	1,190.55	1,120.55	1,049.55	978.55	907.55	836.55	765.55	702.55	660.55	617.55	575.55
4,720	4,760	1,203.61	1,133.61	1,062.61	991.61	920.61	849.61	778.61	711.61	669.61	626.61	584.61
4,760	4,800	1,216.67	1,146.67	1,075.67	1,004.67	933.67	862.67	791.67	721.67	678.67	635.67	593.67
4,800	4,840	1,229.73	1,159.73	1,088.73	1,017.73	946.73	875.73	804.73	734.73	687.73	644.73	602.73
4,840	4,880	1,242.79	1,172.79	1,101.79	1,030.79	959.79	888.79	817.79	747.79	696.79	653.79	611.79
4,880	4,920	1,255.85	1,185.85	1,114.85	1,043.85	972.85	901.85	830.85	760.85	705.85	662.85	620.85
4,920	4,960	1,268.91	1,198.91	1,127.91	1,056.91	985.91	914.91	843.91	773.91	714.91	671.91	629.91
4,960	5,000	1,281.97	1,211.97	1,140.97	1,069.97	998.97	927.97	856.97	786.97	723.97	680.97	638.97
5,000	5,040	1,295.03	1,225.03	1,154.03	1,083.03	1,012.03	941.03	870.03	800.03	733.03	690.03	648.03

Next, scan across that row from left to right to the "3" withholding allowances column. The number at that intersection, $410.49, is the total combined tax to be withheld from Alice's paycheck.

TRY IT EXERCISE 12

Using the combined wage bracket tables, what is the total amount of income tax, social security, and Medicare that should be withheld from Justin Baker's weekly paycheck of $835 if he is married and claims two withholding allowances?

CHECK YOUR ANSWER WITH THE SOLUTION ON PAGE 319.

SECTION II Review Exercises

Solve the following problems using 6.2%, up to $97,500, for social security tax, and 1.45%, no wage limit, for Medicare tax.

1. What are the withholdings for social security and Medicare for an employee with gross earnings of $825 per week?

   825 × .062 = $51.15 Social security

   825 × .0145 = $11.96 Medicare

2. What are the Social Security and Medicare withholdings for an executive whose annual gross earnings are $98,430?

   97,500 × .062 = $6,045.00 Social security

   98,430 × .0145 = $1,427.24 Medicare

3. William Logan is an executive with Federal Distributors. His gross earnings are $8,800 per month.

   a. What are the withholdings for social security and Medicare for William in his January paycheck?

      8,800 × .062 = $545.60 Social security (January)

      8,800 × .0145 = $127.60 Medicare (January)

   b. In what month will William's salary reach the social security wage base limit?

      $\frac{97,500}{8,800} = 11.08$ 11 Full months, plus a portion of the 12th month, December

   c. What are the social security and Medicare tax withholdings for William in the month named in part **b**?

      $97,500 Wage base limit for social security
      − 96,800 (8,800 × 11) Salary reached in November
      $700 Wages subject to social security in December

      700 × .062 = $43.40 Social security in December

      8,800 × .0145 = $127.60 Medicare in December

4. Sandra Webber has biweekly gross earnings of $1,750. What are her total social security and Medicare tax withholdings for a whole year?

   1,750 × 26 = $45,500 Annual salary

   45,500 × .062 = $2,821 Annual social security deduction

   45,500 × .0145 = $659.75 Annual Medicare deduction

Medicare expenditures are expected to rise dramatically in the next few years.

As payroll manager for Andretti Enterprises, it is your task to calculate the monthly social security and Medicare withholdings for the following employees.

Employee	Year-to-Date Earnings	Current Month	Social Security	Medicare
5. Chad, J.	$23,446	$3,422	$212.16	$49.62
6. Graham, C.	$14,800	$1,540	$95.48	$22.33
7. Potter, R.	$95,200	$4,700	$142.60	$68.15
8. Andretti, K.	$145,000	$12,450	0	$180.53

Use the percentage method of income tax calculation to complete the following payroll roster.

Complete, worked-out solutions to Exercises 9–12 appear in Appendix B, following the index.

Employee	Marital Status	Withholding Allowances	Pay Period	Gross Earnings	Income Tax Withholding
9. Needle, B.	M	2	Weekly	$594	$31.64
10. White, W.	S	0	Semimonthly	$1,227	$151.95
11. Benator, B.	S	1	Monthly	$4,150	$623.12
12. Ismart, D.	M	4	Biweekly	$1,849	$123.19

Use the combined wage bracket tables, Exhibits 9-4 and 9-5, to solve Exercises 13–19.

13. How much combined tax should be withheld from the paycheck of a married employee earning $1,075 per week and claiming four withholding allowances?

    $166.24

14. How much combined tax should be withheld from the paycheck of a single employee earning $3,185 per month and claiming zero withholding allowances?

    $694.27

15. Josh McClary is single, claims one withholding allowance, and earns $2,670 per month. Calculate the amount of Josh's paycheck after his employer withholds social security, Medicare, and federal income tax.

    2,670.00 − 495.49 = $2,174.51 Paycheck

Employee	Marital Status	Withholding Allowances	Pay Period	Gross Earnings	Combined Withholding
16. Milton, A.	S	3	Monthly	$4,633	$952.43
17. Wallace, P.	M	5	Weekly	$937	$124.53
18. Blount, S.	M	4	Weekly	$1,172	$188.89
19. Cairns, K.	S	1	Monthly	$3,128	$611.21

BUSINESS DECISION TAKE HOME PAY

20. You are the payroll manager for the Canyon Ridge Resort. Mark Kelsch, the marketing director, earns a salary of $43,200 per year, payable monthly. He is married and claims four withholding allowances. His social security number is 444-44-4444.

    In addition to federal income tax, social security, and Medicare, Mark pays 2.3% state income tax, $\frac{1}{2}$% for state disability insurance (both based on gross earnings), $23.74 for term life insurance, $122.14 to the credit union, and $40 to the United Way.

    Fill out the payroll voucher below for Mark for the month of April:

Canyon Ridge Resort

Payroll Voucher

Employee: Mark Kelsch Tax Filing Status: Married
SSN: 444-44-4444 Withholding Allowances: 4

Full-time Pay Period From April 1 To April 30

Primary Withholdings:		Additional Withholdings:	
Federal income tax	$206.00	Term Life	$23.74
Social security	223.20	Credit Union	122.14
Medicare	52.20	United Way	40.00
State income tax	82.80		
State disability	18.00		

Gross Earnings:	$3,600.00
– Total withholdings:	768.08
NET PAY	$2,831.92

EMPLOYER'S PAYROLL EXPENSES AND SELF-EMPLOYED PERSON'S TAX RESPONSIBILITY

To this point we have discussed payroll deductions from the employee's point of view. Now let's take a look at the payroll expenses of the employer. According to the Fair Labor Standards Act, employers are required to maintain complete and up-to-date earnings records for each employee.

Employers are responsible for the payment of four payroll taxes: social security, Medicare, state unemployment tax (SUTA), and federal unemployment tax (FUTA). In addition, most employers are responsible for a variety of **fringe benefits** that are offered to their employees. These are benefits over and above an employee's normal earnings and can be a significant expense to the employer. Some typical examples are retirement plans, stock option plans, holiday leave, sick days, health and dental insurance, and tuition reimbursement. This section deals with the calculation of these employer taxes as well as the tax responsibility of self-employed persons.

fringe benefits Employer-provided benefits and service packages, over and above an employee's paycheck, such as pension funds, paid vacations, sick leave, and health insurance.

COMPUTING FICA TAX FOR EMPLOYERS AND SELF-EMPLOYMENT TAX FOR SELF-EMPLOYED PERSONS

FICA Tax for Employers

Employers are required to *match* all FICA tax payments, both social security and Medicare, made by each employee. For example, if a company withheld a total of $23,000 in FICA taxes from its employee paychecks this month, the company would be responsible for a matching share of $23,000.

EXAMPLE 13 COMPUTING FICA TAX FOR EMPLOYEES AND THE EMPLOYER

Precision Engineering has 25 employees, each with gross earnings of $250 per week. What are the total social security and Medicare taxes that should be withheld from the employee paychecks, and what is the employer's share of FICA for the first quarter of the year?

SOLUTION STRATEGY

To solve for the total FICA tax due quarterly from the employees and the employer, first calculate the tax due per employee per week, multiply by 25 to find the total weekly FICA for all employees, then multiply by 13 weeks to find the total quarterly amount withheld from all employees. The employer's share will be an equal amount.

Social security tax = Gross earnings × 6.2% = 250 × .062 = $15.50
Medicare tax = Gross earnings × 1.45% = 250 × .0145 = $3.63
Total FICA tax per employee per week = 15.50 + 3.63 = $19.13

Total FICA tax per week = FICA tax per employee × 25 employees
Total FICA tax per week = 19.13 × 25 = $478.25

Total FICA tax per quarter = Total FICA tax per week × 13 weeks
Total FICA tax per quarter = 478.25 × 13 = 6,217.25

Total FICA tax per quarter—Employee's share = $\underline{\underline{\$6,217.25}}$
Total FICA tax per quarter—Employer's share = $\underline{\underline{\$6,217.25}}$

TEACHING TIP
Remind students that there are 13 weeks in a quarter of a year.

$$\frac{52 \text{ weeks}}{4} = 13 \text{ weeks}$$

TRY IT EXERCISE 13

Big Pine Tree Service has 18 employees, 12 with gross earnings of $350 per week and six with gross earnings of $425 per week. What are the employee's share and the employer's share of the social security and Medicare tax for the first quarter of the year?

CHECK YOUR ANSWER WITH THE SOLUTION ON PAGE 319.

Self-Employment Tax

The self-employment tax, officially known as the Self-Employment Contributions Act tax (SECA), is the self-employed person's version of the FICA tax. It is due on the net earnings from self-employment.

Self-employed persons are responsible for social security and Medicare taxes at twice the rate deducted for employees. Technically, they are the employee and the employer and therefore must pay both shares. For a self-employed person, the social security and Medicare tax rates are twice the normal rates, as follows:

9-8

	Tax Rate	Wage Base
Social Security	12.4% (6.2% × 2)	$97,500
Medicare	2.9% (1.45% × 2)	No limit

EXAMPLE 14 CALCULATING SELF-EMPLOYMENT TAX

What are the social security and Medicare taxes of a self-employed landscaper with net earnings of $43,800 per year?

SOLUTION STRATEGY

To find the amount of self-employment tax due, we apply the self-employed tax rates, 12.4% for social security and 2.9% for Medicare, to the net earnings.

Social security tax = Net earnings × Tax rate

Social security tax = 43,800 × .124 = $5,431.20

Medicare tax = Net earnings × Tax rate

Medicare tax = 43,800 × .029 = $1,270.20

TRY IT EXERCISE 14

Arnold Barker, a self-employed commercial artist, had total net earnings of $60,000 last year. What is the amount of the social security and Medicare taxes that Arnold was required to send the IRS last year?

CHECK YOUR ANSWERS WITH THE SOLUTIONS ON PAGE 320.

COMPUTING THE AMOUNT OF STATE UNEMPLOYMENT TAXES (SUTA) AND FEDERAL UNEMPLOYMENT TAXES (FUTA)

The **Federal Unemployment Tax Act (FUTA)**, together with state unemployment systems, provides for payments of unemployment compensation to workers who have lost their jobs. Most employers are responsible for both a federal and a state unemployment tax.

In 2007, the FUTA tax was 6.2% of the first $7,000 of wages paid to each employee during the year. Generally, an employer can take a credit against the FUTA tax for amounts paid into state unemployment funds. These state taxes are commonly known as the **State Unemployment Tax Act (SUTA)**. This credit cannot be more than 5.4% of the first $7,000 of employees' taxable wages.

SUTA tax rates vary from state to state according to the employment record of the company. These merit-rating systems, found in many states, provide significant SUTA tax savings to companies with good employment records.

For companies with full and timely payments to the state unemployment system, the FUTA tax rate is .8% (6.2% FUTA rate − 5.4% SUTA credit).

Federal Unemployment Tax Act (FUTA) A federal tax that is paid by employers for each employee, to provide unemployment compensation to workers who have lost their jobs.

State Unemployment Tax Act (SUTA) A state tax that is paid by employers for each employee, to provide unemployment compensation to workers who have lost their jobs.

TEACHING TIP

Be sure students understand that FUTA and SUTA are paid by the employer, *not* the employee, and only on the first $7,000 of wages paid to each employee during the year.

EXAMPLE 15 CALCULATING SUTA AND FUTA TAXES

Panorama Industries, Inc., had a total payroll of $50,000 last month. Panorama pays a SUTA tax rate of 5.4% and a FUTA rate of 6.2% less the SUTA credit. If none of the employees had reached the $7,000 wage base, what is the amount of SUTA and FUTA tax the company must pay?

SOLUTION STRATEGY

To calculate the SUTA and FUTA taxes, apply the appropriate tax rates to the gross earnings subject to the tax, in this case, all the gross earnings.

SUTA tax = Gross earnings × 5.4%
SUTA tax = 50,000 × .054 = $2,700

The FUTA tax rate will be .8%. Remember, it is actually 6.2% less the 5.4% credit.

FUTA tax = Gross earnings × .8%
FUTA tax = 50,000 × .008 = $400

TRY IT EXERCISE 15

Master Host Catering had a total payroll of $10,000 last month. Master Host pays a SUTA tax rate of 5.4% and a FUTA rate of 6.2% less the SUTA credit. If none of the employees had reached the $7,000 wage base, what is the amount of SUTA and FUTA tax the company must pay?

CHECK YOUR ANSWERS WITH THE SOLUTIONS ON PAGE 320.

CLASSROOM ACTIVITY

FUTA and SUTA tax rates can be reduced if the employer has a good employment record. This means relatively few unemployment claims due to firings and layoffs.

Have students research and report to the class the SUTA tax rates and laws in your state.

CALCULATING EMPLOYER'S FRINGE BENEFIT EXPENSES

In addition to compensating employees with a paycheck, most companies today offer employee fringe benefit and services packages. These packages include a wide variety of benefits such as pension plans, paid vacations and sick leave, day-care centers, tuition assistance, and health insurance. Corporate executives may receive benefits such as company cars, first-class airline travel, and country club memberships. At the executive level of business, these benefits are known as **perquisites** or **perks**.

Over the past decade, employee benefits have become increasingly important to workers. They have grown in size to the point where today total benefits may cost a company as much as 40% to 50% of payroll. Frequently, employees are given a *menu* of fringe benefits to choose from, up to a specified dollar amount. These plans are known as **cafeteria-style**, or **flexible benefit programs**.

perquisites, or perks Executive-level fringe benefits such as first-class airline travel, company cars, and country club membership

cafeteria-style, or flexible benefit program A plan whereby employees are given a menu of fringe benefits to choose from, up to a specified dollar amount.

Although paid vacations and health insurance are still the most popular among company-sponsored benefits, there is a trend today toward more "work-life initiatives." These are benefits that help employees balance their professional and personal lives such as child-care assistance and flexible work hours.

STEPS TO CALCULATE EMPLOYER'S FRINGE BENEFITS EXPENSE

Step 1. If the fringe benefit is a percent of gross payroll, multiply that percent by the amount of the gross payroll. If the fringe benefit is a dollar amount per employee, multiply that amount by the number of employees.

Step 2. Find the total fringe benefits by adding all the individual fringe benefit amounts.

Step 3. Calculate the fringe benefit percent by using the percentage formula, Rate = Portion ÷ Base, with total fringe benefits as the portion and gross payroll as the base (remember to convert your answer to a percent).

$$\textbf{Fringe benefit percent} = \frac{\textbf{Total fringe benefits}}{\textbf{Gross payroll}}$$

EXAMPLE 16 CALCULATING FRINGE BENEFITS

In addition to its gross payroll of $150,000 per month, All City Distributors, Inc., with 75 employees, pays 7% of payroll to a retirement fund, 9% for health insurance, and $25 per employee for a stock purchase plan.

a. What are the company's monthly fringe benefit expenses?

b. What percent of payroll does this represent?

SOLUTION STRATEGY

a. To solve for monthly fringe benefits, compute the amount of each benefit, then add them to find the total.

Retirement fund expense = Gross payroll × 7%
Retirement fund expense = 150,000 × .07 = $10,500

Health insurance expense = Gross payroll × 9%
Health insurance expense = 150,000 × .09 = $13,500

Stock plan expense = Number of employees × $25
Stock plan expense = 75 × 25 = $1,875

Total fringe benefits = Retirement + Health + Stock
Total fringe benefits = 10,500 + 13,500 + 1,875 = $\underline{\underline{\$25,875}}$

b. $$\text{Fringe benefit percent} = \frac{\text{Total fringe benefits}}{\text{Gross payroll}} = \frac{25,875}{150,000} = .1725 = \underline{\underline{17.25\%}}$$

Paid vacation time is one of the many fringe benefits offered by employers today.

TRY IT EXERCISE 16

Metro Enterprises employs 250 workers with a gross payroll of $123,400 per week. Fringe benefits are 5% of gross payroll for sick days and holiday leave, 8% for health insurance, and $12.40 per employee for dental insurance.

a. What is the total weekly cost of fringe benefits for Metro?
b. What percent of payroll does this represent?
c. What is the cost of these fringe benefits to the company for a year?

CHECK YOUR ANSWERS WITH THE SOLUTIONS ON PAGE 320.

CLASSROOM ACTIVITY

Ask students who are working what fringe benefits their companies offer. Have them estimate how much each benefit might cost the employers.

Have students research and report to the class what type of fringe benefits companies in your area offer their employees.

CALCULATING QUARTERLY ESTIMATED TAX FOR SELF-EMPLOYED PERSONS

9-11

By IRS rules, you must pay Self-Employment tax if you had net earning of $400 or more as a self-employed person. This is income that is not subject to withholding tax. Quarterly estimated tax is the method used to pay tax on these earnings. You may pay all of your estimated tax by April, or in four equal amounts: in April, June, September, and January of the following year.

To calculate the quarterly estimated tax of a self-employed person, we divide the total of social security, Medicare, and income tax by 4. (There are 4 quarters in a year.) Internal Revenue Service form 1040 ES, Quarterly Estimated Tax Payment Voucher, Exhibit 9-6, is used to file this tax with the IRS each quarter.

$$\textbf{Quarterly estimated tax} = \frac{\textbf{Social security + Medicare + Income tax}}{\textbf{4}}$$

In the Business World

You may use your American Express Card, Discover Card, or MasterCard to make estimated tax payments. Call toll free or access by Internet one of the service providers listed below and follow the instructions of the provider. Each provider will charge a convenience fee based on the amount you are paying.

- Official Payments Corporation 1-800-2PAY-TAX (1-800-272-9829) www.officialpayments.com
- Link2Gov Corporation 1-888-PAY1040 (1-888-729-1040) www.pay1040.com

Exhibit 9-6
Quarterly Estimated Tax Payment Voucher

Form **1040-ES** Department of the Treasury Internal Revenue Service | **20XX** Payment Voucher **4** | OMB No. 1545-0087

File only if you are making a payment of estimated tax by check or money order. Mail this voucher with your check or money order payable to the **"United States Treasury."** Write your social security number and "20XX Form 1040-ES" on your check or money order. Do not send cash. Enclose, but do not staple or attach, your payment with this voucher.

Calendar year—Due Jan. 15,
Amount of estimated tax you are paying by check or money order. $

Type or print

Your first name and initial	Your last name	Your social security number
If joint payment, complete for spouse		
Spouse's first name and initial	Spouse's last name	Spouse's social security number
Address (number, street, and apt. no.)		
City, state, and ZIP code (If a foreign address, enter city, province or state, postal code, and country.)		

For Privacy Act and Paperwork Reduction Act Notice, see instructions on page 5.
Page 6

EXAMPLE 17 CALCULATING QUARTERLY ESTIMATED TAX FOR SELF-EMPLOYED PERSONS

Larry Qualls is a self-employed marketing consultant. His estimated annual earnings this year are $100,000. His social security tax rate is 12.4% up to the wage base, Medicare is 2.9%, and his estimated federal income tax rate is 18%. How much estimated tax must he send to the IRS each quarter?

SOLUTION STRATEGY

Note that Larry's salary is above the social security wage base limit.

$$\text{Social security} = 97{,}500 \times .124 = \$12{,}090$$

$$\text{Medicare} = 100{,}000 \times .029 = \$2{,}900$$

$$\text{Income tax} = 100{,}000 \times .18 = \$18{,}000$$

$$\text{Quarterly estimated tax} = \frac{\text{Social security} + \text{Medicare} + \text{Income tax}}{4}$$

$$\text{Quarterly estimated tax} = \frac{12{,}090 + 2{,}900 + 18{,}000}{4} = \frac{32{,}990}{4} = \underline{\underline{\$8{,}247.50}}$$

TRY IT EXERCISE 17

John Black is a self-employed freelance editor and project director for a large publishing company. His annual salary this year is estimated to be $120,000, with a federal income tax rate of 20%. What is the amount of estimated tax that John must send to the IRS each quarter?

CHECK YOUR ANSWER WITH THE SOLUTION ON PAGE 320.

SECTION III Review Exercises

1. Avanti Systems, Inc., has 40 employees on the assembly line, each with gross earnings of $325 per week.

   a. What is the total social security and Medicare taxes that should be withheld from the employee paychecks each week?

   325 × 40 = 13,000 Gross per week
   13,000 × .062 = $806.00 Total social security
   13,000 × .0145 = $188.50 Total Medicare

   b. What is the employer's share of these taxes for the first quarter of the year?

   806.00 × 13 = $10,478.00 Social security for 1st quarter
   188.50 × 13 = $2,450.50 Medicare for 1st quarter

2. All-Star Industries has 24 employees, 15 with gross earnings of \$345 per week and nine with gross earnings of \$385 per week. What is the total social security and Medicare tax that the company must send to the Internal Revenue Service for the first quarter of the year?

   $345 \times 15 = 5{,}175$
   $385 \times 9 = \underline{3{,}465}$
   \$8,640 Total gross weekly earnings

   $8{,}640 \times .062 \times 2 = 1{,}071.36$
   $8{,}640 \times .0145 \times 2 = \underline{250.56}$
   \$1,321.92

   $1{,}321.92 \times 13 = \underline{\$17{,}184.96}$ Total social security plus Medicare sent to the IRS in 1st quarter

3. What are the social security and Medicare taxes due on gross earnings of \$42,600 per year for a self-employed person?

   $42{,}600 \times .124 = \underline{\$5{,}282.40}$ Social security
   $42{,}600 \times .029 = \underline{\$1{,}235.40}$ Medicare

4. Luis Portillo is a self-employed electrical consultant. He estimates his annual net earnings at \$38,700. How much social security and Medicare must he pay this year?

   $38{,}700 \times .124 = \underline{\$4{,}798.80}$ Social security
   $38{,}700 \times .029 = \underline{\$1{,}122.30}$ Medicare

Average Employee Health Care Costs

2000 1500 1000 500 0
2000 2001 2002 2003 2004 2005 2006
Year
Average employee contribution
Average out-of-pocket costs
Source: Hewitt Associates

5. Bill Lisowski earns \$41,450 annually as a line supervisor for Blossom Manufacturers.

   a. If the SUTA tax rate is 5.4% of the first \$7,000 earned in a year, how much SUTA tax must Blossom pay each year for Bill?

      $7{,}000 \times .054 = \underline{\$378}$ SUTA annually

   b. If the FUTA tax rate is 6.2% of the first \$7,000 earned in a year minus the SUTA tax paid, how much FUTA tax must the company pay each year for Bill?

      $7{,}000 \times .008 = \underline{\$56}$ FUTA annually

6. Kathy Opach worked part time last year as a cashier in a Safeway Supermarket. Her total gross earnings were \$6,443.

   a. How much SUTA tax must the supermarket pay to the state for Kathy?

      $6{,}443 \times .054 = \underline{\$347.92}$ SUTA annually

   b. How much FUTA tax must be paid for her?

      $6{,}443 \times .008 = \underline{\$51.54}$ FUTA annually

7. Superior Roofing Company has three installers. Larry earns \$355 per week, Curly earns \$460 per week, and Moe earns \$585 per week. The company's SUTA rate is 5.4%, and the FUTA rate is 6.2% minus the SUTA. As usual, these taxes are paid on the first \$7,000 of each employee's earnings.

   a. How much SUTA and FUTA tax does Superior owe for the first quarter of the year?

Larry = 355 × 13 = \$4,615	Larry = 4,615 × .054 = \$249.21 SUTA	Larry = 4,615 × .008 = \$ 36.92 FUTA
Curly = 460 × 13 = \$5,980	Curly = 5,980 × .054 = 322.92 SUTA	Curly = 5,980 × .008 = 47.84 FUTA
Moe = 585 × 13 = \$7,605	Moe = 7,000 × .054 = 378.00 SUTA	Moe = 7,000 × .008 = 56.00 FUTA
	limit → \$950.13 Total SUTA	limit → \$140.76 Total FUTA

   b. How much SUTA and FUTA tax does Superior owe for the second quarter of the year?

Larry = 7,000 − 4,615 = 2,385	2,385 × .054 = \$128.79	2,385 × .008 = \$19.08
Curly = 7,000 − 5,980 = 1,020	1,020 × .054 = 55.08	1,020 × .008 = 8.16
Moe = 0	\$183.87 Total SUTA	\$27.24 FUTA

8. Ocean Drive Limousine Service employs 166 workers and has a gross payroll of $154,330 per week. Fringe benefits are $4\frac{1}{2}\%$ of gross payroll for sick days and maternity leave, 7.4% for health insurance, 3.1% for the retirement fund, and $26.70 per employee for a stock purchase plan.

   a. What is the total weekly cost of fringe benefits for the company?

154,330 × .045 =	6,944.85	Sick days
154,330 × .074 =	11,420.42	Insurance
154,330 × .031 =	4,784.23	Retirement
26.70 × 166 =	4,432.20	Stock purchase
	$27,581.70	Total fringe benefit costs per week

   b. What percent of payroll does this represent? Round to the nearest tenth of a percent.

$$R = \frac{P}{B} = R = \frac{27,581.70}{154,330} = 0.1787$$
$$= \underline{\underline{17.9\%}}$$

   c. What is the company's annual cost of fringe benefits?

   27,581.70 × 52 = $1,434,248.40 Annual cost of fringe benefits

9. Pasquale Giordano, a self-employed sales consultant, has estimated annual earnings of $300,000 this year. His social security tax rate is 12.4% up to the wage base, Medicare is 2.9%, and his federal income tax rate is 24%.

"It contains quarterly estimated tax forms from the I.R.S."

   a. How much estimated tax must Pasquale send to the IRS each quarter?

   97,500 × .124 = $12,090 Social security
   300,000 × .029 = $8,700 Medicare
   300,000 × .24 = $72,000 Income tax

$$\text{Quarterly estimated tax} = \frac{\text{Social security} + \text{Medicare} + \text{Income tax}}{4}$$

$$\text{Quarterly estimated tax} = \frac{12,090 + 8,700 + 72,000}{4} = \frac{92,790}{4} = \underline{\underline{\$23,197.50}}$$

   b. What form should he use?

   Form 1040-ES, *Quarterly Estimated Tax Voucher for Self-Employed Persons*

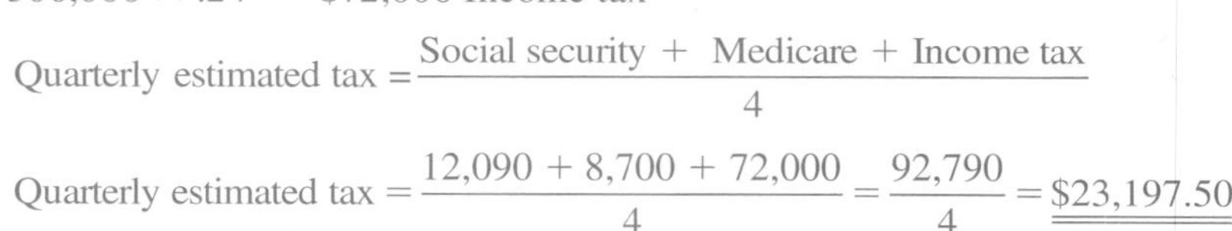

BUSINESS DECISION NEW FRINGE BENEFITS

CLASSROOM ACTIVITY
Have students research and report to the class about "cafeteria" plans and popular fringe benefits being offered by companies today.

10. You are the Human Resource Manager for Telcom International, a cellular phone company with 800 employees. Top management has asked you to implement three additional fringe benefits that were negotiated with employee representatives and agreed upon by a majority of the employees. These include group term life insurance, a group legal services plan, and a "wellness center."

    The life insurance is estimated to cost $260 per employee per quarter. The legal plan will cost $156 semiannually per employee. The company will contribute 40% to the life insurance premium and 75% to the cost of the legal services plan. The employees will pay the balance through payroll deductions from their biweekly paychecks. In addition, they will be charged $\frac{1}{4}\%$ of their gross earnings per paycheck for maintaining the wellness center. The company will pay the initial cost of $500,000 to build the center. This expense will be spread over 5 years.

a. What total amount should be deducted *per paycheck* for these new fringe benefits, for an employee earning $41,600 per year?

Term life: $\frac{260 \times 4 \times .6}{26} = \$24$

Legal services: $\frac{156 \times 2 \times .25}{26} = \$3$

Wellness center: $\frac{41,600 \times .0025}{26} = \$4$

Total deductions: $24 + 3 + 4 = \underline{\underline{\$31}}$

b. What is the total *annual* cost of the new fringe benefits to the company?

Term life:

$260 \times 4 \times .4 \times 800 = \$332,800$

Legal services:

$156 \times 2 \times .75 \times 800 = \$187,200$

Wellness center:

$\frac{500,000}{5} = \$100,000$

Total annual cost:

$332,800 + 187,200 + 100,000 = \underline{\underline{\$620,000}}$

© Digital Vision/Getty Images

Human Resource managers handle or oversee all aspects of human resources work. Typical responsibilities include unemployment compensation fringe benefits, training, and employee relations. They held about 820,000 jobs in 2004, with median annual earnings of $66,530. The middle 50% earned between $49,970 and $89,340.

CHAPTER FORMULAS 9

Hourly Wages

Regular pay = Hourly rate × Regular hours worked

Overtime pay = Hourly rate × Overtime factor × Overtime hours worked

Total gross pay = Regular pay + Overtime pay

Piecework

Total gross pay = Output quantity × Rate per unit

Commission

Total gross pay = Total sales × Commission rate

Payroll Deductions

Total deductions = Social security + Medicare + Income tax + Voluntary deductions

Net pay = Gross pay − Total deductions

Fringe Benefits

$$\text{Fringe benefit percent} = \frac{\text{Total fringe benefits}}{\text{Gross payroll}}$$

Quarterly Estimated Tax

$$\text{Quarterly estimated tax} = \frac{\text{Social security} + \text{Medicare} + \text{Income tax}}{4}$$

SUMMARY CHART

Section I: Employee's Gross Earnings and Incentive Pay Plans

Topic	Important Concepts	Illustrative Examples
Prorating Annual Salary to Various Pay Periods **P/O 9-1, p. 285**	Salaried employees are most commonly paid based on one of the following pay schedules: *Weekly:* 52 paychecks per year Annual salary ÷ 52 *Biweekly:* 26 paychecks per year Annual salary ÷ 26 *Semimonthly:* 24 paychecks per year Annual salary ÷ 24 *Monthly:* 12 paychecks per year Annual salary ÷ 12	What are the gross earnings of an employee with an annual salary of $40,000 based on weekly, biweekly, semimonthly, and monthly pay schedules? $\text{Weekly} = \frac{40{,}000}{52} = \underline{\underline{\$769.23}}$ $\text{Biweekly} = \frac{40{,}000}{26} = \underline{\underline{\$1{,}538.46}}$ $\text{Semimonthly} = \frac{40{,}000}{24} = \underline{\underline{\$1{,}666.67}}$ $\text{Monthly} = \frac{40{,}000}{12} = \underline{\underline{\$3{,}333.33}}$
Calculating Gross Pay by Regular Hourly Wages and Overtime **P/O 9-2, p. 286**	An hourly wage is the amount an employee is paid for each hour worked. Regular time specifies that a standard work week is 40 hours. Overtime amounting to at least time-and-a-half must be paid for all hours over 40. Some employers pay double time for weekend, holiday, and midnight shifts. **Regular pay = Hourly rate × Hours worked** **Overtime pay = Hourly rate × Overtime factor × Hours worked** **Total gross pay = Regular pay + Overtime pay**	Lindsay Haslam earns $9.50 per hour as a supervisor in a plant. If her overtime rate is time-and-a-half and holidays are double time, what is Lindsay's total gross pay for working 49 hours last week, including 4 holiday hours? Regular pay = 9.50 × 40 = $380.00 Time-and-a-half pay = 9.50 × 1.5 × 5 = $71.25 Double-time pay = 9.50 × 2 × 4 = $76.00 Total gross pay = 380.00 + 71.25 + 76.00 = $527.25
Calculating Gross Pay by Straight and Differential Piecework Schedules **P/O 9-3, p. 287**	A piecework pay rate schedule is based on production output, not time. Straight piecework pays the worker a certain amount of pay per unit, regardless of quantity. In differential piecework, the rate per unit increases as output quantity goes up. **Total gross pay = Output quantity × Rate per unit**	A factory pays its workers $2.50 per unit of production. What is the gross pay of a worker producing 233 units? Gross pay = 233 × 2.50 = $582.50 A factory pays its production workers $.54 per unit up to 5,000 units and $.67 per unit above 5,000 units. What is the gross pay of an employee who produces 6,500 units? 5,000 × .54 = 2,700 1,500 × .67 = 1,005 Total gross pay $3,705
Calculating Gross Pay by Straight and Incremental Commission **P/O 9-4, p. 289**	Commission is a method of compensation primarily used to pay employees selling goods and services. Straight commission is based on a single specified percentage of the sales volume attained. Incremental commission, like differential piecework, is when various levels of sales earn increasing rates of commission. **Total gross pay = Total sales × Commission rate**	A company pays 4% straight commission on all sales. What is the gross pay of an employee who sells $135,000? Gross pay = 135,000 × .04 = $5,400 A company pays incremental commissions of 3.5% on sales up to $100,000 and 4.5% on all sales greater than $100,000. What is the gross pay of an employee selling $164,000? 100,000 × .035 = 3,500 64,000 × .045 = 2,880 Gross pay $6,380

Section I: (continued)

Topic	Important Concepts	Illustrative Examples
Calculating Gross Pay by Salary Plus Commission P/O 9-4, p. 289	Salary plus commission is a pay schedule whereby the employee receives a guaranteed salary in addition to a commission on sales over a certain specified amount.	An employee is paid a salary of $350 per week plus a 2% commission on sales greater than $8,000. If he sold $13,400 last week, how much did he earn? 350 + 2%(13,400 − 8,000) 350 + .02 × 5,400 350 + 108 = $458
Calculating Gross Pay with Drawing Accounts P/O 9-4, p. 289	A drawing account, or draw against commission, is a commission paid in advance of sales and later deducted from the commission earned.	Scott Walker sells for a company that pays $6\frac{1}{2}$ % commission with a $600 per month drawing account. If Scott takes the draw and then sells $16,400 in goods, how much commission is he owed? (16,400 × .065) − 600 1,066 − 600 = $466

Section II: Employee's Payroll Deductions

Topic	Important Concepts	Illustrative Examples
Computing FICA Taxes, Both Social Security and Medicare P/O 9-5, p. 296	FICA taxes are divided into two categories: social security and Medicare. When employees reach the wage base for the year, they are no longer subject to the tax. **Tax Rate** / **Wage Base** **Social Security** 6.2% $97,500 **Medicare** 1.45% no limit	What are the FICA tax withholdings for social security and Medicare for an employee with gross earnings of $760 per week? Social security = $760 × 6.2% = $47.12 Medicare = $760 × 1.45% = $11.02
Calculating Federal Income Tax Using Percentage Method P/O 9-6, p. 298	1. Multiply one withholding allowance, in Exhibit 9-2, by the number of allowances the employee claims. 2. Subtract that amount from the employee's gross earnings to find the income subject to income tax. 3. Determine the amount of tax withheld from the appropriate section of Exhibit 9-3.	Holly Hewitt is single, earns $1,800 per week as a loan officer for Bank of America, and claims three withholding allowances. Calculate the amount of federal income tax withheld from Holly's weekly paycheck. From Exhibit 9-2: 65.38 × 3 = $196.14 Taxable income = 1,800 − 196.14 = $1,603.86 From Exhibit 9-3: Withholding tax = 291.15 + 28%(1,603.86 − 1,482) 291.15 + .28(121.86) 291.15 + 34.12 = $325.27
Determining an Employee's Total Withholding for Federal Income Tax, Social Security, and Medicare Using the Combined Wage Bracket Tables P/O 9-7, p. 301	1. Based on marital status and payroll period, choose either Exhibit 9-4 or 9-5. 2. Scan down the left-hand columns until you find the bracket containing the gross pay of the employee. 3. Scan across the row of that wage bracket to the intersection of that employee's "withholding allowances claimed" column. 4. The number in that column, on the wage bracket row, is the amount of combined withholding tax.	What amount of combined tax should be withheld from the monthly paycheck of a single employee claiming two withholding allowances and earning $3,495 per month? Use Exhibit 9-5. Scan down the wage brackets to $3,480–$3,520. Scan across to "2" withholding allowances to find the tax, $657.75

Section III: Employer's Payroll Expenses and Self-Employed Person's Tax Responsibility

Topic	Important Concepts	Illustrative Examples
Computing FICA Tax for Employers **P/O 9-8, p. 307**	Employers are required to match all FICA tax payments made by each employee.	Last month, a company withheld a total of $3,400 in FICA taxes from employee paychecks. What is the company's FICA liability? The company is responsible for a matching amount withheld from the employees, $3,400
Computing Self-Employment Tax **P/O 9-8, p. 307**	Self-employed persons are responsible for social security and Medicare taxes at twice the rate deducted for employees. Technically, they are the employee and the employer; therefore they must pay both shares, as follows: *Social Security* **12.4% (6.2% × 2), wage base $97,500** *Medicare* **2.9% (1.45% × 2), no limit**	What are the social security and Medicare taxes due on gross earnings of $4,260 per month for a self-employed person? *Social security* Gross earnings × 12.4% = 4,260 × .124 = $528.24 *Medicare* Gross earnings × 2.9% = 4,260 × .029 = 123.54
Calculating the Amount of State Unemployment Tax (SUTA) and Federal Unemployment Tax (FUTA) **P/O 9-9, p. 309**	SUTA and FUTA taxes provide for unemployment compensation to workers who have lost their jobs. These taxes are paid by the employer. The SUTA tax rate is 5.4% of the first $7,000 of earnings per year by each employee. The FUTA tax rate is 6.2% of the first $7,000 minus the SUTA tax paid (6.2% − 5.4% = .8%).	Gold Coast Enterprises had a total payroll of $40,000 last month. If none of the employees have reached the $7,000 wage base, what is the amount of SUTA and FUTA tax due? SUTA = 40,000 × 5.4% = $2,160 FUTA = 40,000 × .8% = $320
Calculating Employer's Fringe Benefit Expenses **P/O 9-10, p. 310**	In addition to compensating employees with a paycheck, most companies offer benefit packages that may include pensions, paid sick days, tuition assistance, and health insurance. Fringe benefits represent a significant expense to employers. $\text{Fringe benefit percent} = \frac{\text{Total fringe benefits}}{\text{Gross payroll}}$	Northern Industries employs 48 workers and has a monthly gross payroll of $120,000. In addition, the company pays 6.8% to a pension fund, 8.7% for health insurance, and $30 per employee for a stock purchase plan. What are Northern's monthly fringe benefit expenses? What percent of payroll does this represent? 120,000 × 6.8% = 8,160 120,000 × 8.7% = 10,440 48 × $30 = +1,440 Total fringe benefits $20,040 $\text{Fringe ben. \%} = \frac{20{,}040}{120{,}000} = 16.7\%$
Calculating Quarterly Estimated Tax for Self-Employed Persons **P/O 9-11, p. 311**	Each quarter, self-employed persons must send to the IRS Form 1040-ES along with a tax payment for social security, Medicare, and income tax. Quarterly estimated tax $= \frac{\text{Social security} + \text{Medicare} + \text{income tax}}{4}$	Sylvia Kendrick is a self-employed decorator. She estimates her annual net earnings at $44,000 for the year. Her income tax rate is 10%. What is the amount of her quarterly estimated tax? 44,000 × .124 = $5,456 Social security 44,000 × .029 = $1,276 Medicare 44,000 × .10 = $4,400 Income tax $\text{Quarterly estimated tax} = \frac{5{,}456 + 1{,}276 + 4{,}400}{4}$ $= \frac{11{,}132}{4} = \$2{,}783$

TRY IT EXERCISE SOLUTIONS FOR CHAPTER 9

1. $\text{Weekly pay} = \frac{\text{Annual salary}}{52} = \frac{43{,}500}{52} = \underline{\underline{\$836.54}}$

$\text{Biweekly pay} = \frac{\text{Annual salary}}{26} = \frac{43{,}500}{26} = \underline{\underline{\$1{,}673.08}}$

$\text{Semimonthly pay} = \frac{\text{Annual salary}}{24} = \frac{43{,}500}{24} = \underline{\underline{\$1{,}812.50}}$

$\text{Monthly pay} = \frac{\text{Annual salary}}{12} = \frac{43{,}500}{12} = \underline{\underline{\$3{,}625.00}}$

2. Regular pay = Hourly rate × Regular hours worked
Regular pay = 10.50 × 40 = $\underline{\underline{\$420}}$

Time-and-a-half pay
= Hourly rate × Overtime factor × Hours worked

Time-and-a-half pay = 10.50 ×1.5 × 5 = $\underline{\underline{\$78.75}}$

Double time pay
= Hourly rate × Overtime factor × Hours worked
Double time pay = 10.50 × 2 × 4 = $\underline{\underline{\$84}}$

Total gross pay = Regular pay + Overtime pay
Total gross pay = 420.00 + 78.75 + 84.00 = $\underline{\underline{\$582.75}}$

3. Total gross pay = Output quantity × Rate per unit
Total gross pay = 950 × .41 = $\underline{\underline{\$389.50}}$

4. Level pay = Output × Rate per piece

Gomez:
300 × .68 = $204.00
200 × .79 = 158.00
15 × .86 = + 12.90
$\underline{\underline{\$374.90}}$ Total gross pay

Clifford: 199 × .68 = $\underline{\underline{\$135.32}}$ Total gross pay

Maken:
300 × .68 = $204.00
148 × .79 = +116.92
$\underline{\underline{\$320.92}}$ Total gross pay

Nathan:
300 × .68 = $204.00
200 × .79 = 158.00
250 × .86 = 215.00
54 × .94 = + 50.76
$\underline{\underline{\$627.76}}$ Total gross pay

5. Total gross pay = Total sales × Commission rate
Total gross pay = 233,760 × .024 = $\underline{\underline{\$5{,}610.24}}$

6. Level pay = Sales per level × Commission rate
Level pay = 100,000 × .017 = $1,700
84,600 × .025 = +2,115
$\underline{\underline{\$3{,}815}}$

7. Commission = Commission rate × Sales subject to commission
Commission = 4%(45,000 − 20,000)
Commission = .04 × 25,000 = $1,000

Total gross pay = Salary + Commission
Total gross pay = 1,400 + 1,000 = $\underline{\underline{\$2{,}400}}$

8. Commission = Total sales × Commission rate
Commission = 120,000 × 3.5% = $4,200

Commission owed = Commission − Amount of draw
Commission owed = 4,200 − 2,000 = $\underline{\underline{\$2{,}200}}$

9. Social security tax = Gross earnings × 6.2%
Social security tax = 5,000 × .062 = $\underline{\underline{\$310}}$

Medicare tax = Gross earnings × 1.45%
Medicare tax = 5,000 × .0145 = $\underline{\underline{\$72.50}}$

10. Earnings subject to tax = Wage base − Year-to-date earnings
Earnings subject to tax = 97,500 − 92,300 = $5,200

Social security tax = Earnings subject to tax × 6.2%
Social security tax = 5,200 × .062 = $\underline{\underline{\$322.40}}$

11. From Exhibit 9-2
Withholding allowance = 1 allowance × Exemptions
Withholding allowance = $283.33 × 5 = $\underline{\underline{\$1{,}416.65}}$

Taxable income = Gross pay − Withholding allowance
Taxable income = 3,670.00 − 1,416.65 = $\underline{\underline{\$2{,}253.35}}$

From Exhibit 9-3, Table 4(b):
Category $1,946 to $5,892
Withholding Tax = 127.90 + 15% of amount greater than $1,946
Withholding Tax = 127.90 + .15(2,253.35 − 1,946)
Withholding Tax = 127.90 + .15(307.35)
Withholding Tax = 127.90 + 46.10 = $\underline{\underline{\$174.00}}$

12. From Exhibit 9-4
$835 Weekly, married, 2 Allowances = $\underline{\underline{\$131.88}}$

13. *12 employees @ $350*
Social security = 350 × .062 = 21.70
Medicare = 350 × .0145 = 5.08

Total FICA per employee = 21.70 + 5.08 = $26.78
Total FICA per week = 26.78 × 12 employees = $321.36
Total FICA per quarter = 321.36 × 13 weeks = $\underline{\underline{\$4{,}177.68}}$

6 employees @ $425
Social security = 425 × .062 = 26.35
Medicare = 425 × .0145 = 6.16

Total FICA per employee = 26.35 + 6.16 = $32.51
Total FICA per week = 32.51 × 6 employees = $195.06
Total FICA per quarter = 195.06 × 13 weeks = $\underline{\underline{\$2{,}535.78}}$

Total FICA per quarter:

Employees' share = 4,177.68 + 2,535.78 = $6,713.46

Employer's share = 4,177.68 + 2,535.78 = $6,713.46

14. Social security = 60,000 × .124 = $7,440

Medicare = 60,000 × .029 = $1,740

15. SUTA tax = Gross earnings × 5.4%

SUTA tax = 10,000 × .054 = $540

FUTA tax = Gross earnings × .8%

FUTA tax = 10,000 × .008 = $80

16. a. Fringe benefits

Sick days = Gross payroll × 5%

Sick days = 123,400 × .05 = $6,170

Health ins = Gross payroll × 8%

Health ins = 123,400 × .08 = $9,872

Dental ins = Number of employees × 12.40

Dental ins = 250 × 12.40 = $3,100

Total fringe benefits = 6,170 + 9,872 + 3,100 = $19,142

b. $\text{Fringe benefit percent} = \frac{\text{Total fringe benefits}}{\text{Gross payroll}}$

$\text{Fringe benefit percent} = \frac{19{,}142}{123{,}400} = .155 = 15.5\%$

c. Yearly fringe benefits = Weekly total × 52

Yearly fringe benefits = 19,142 × 52 = $995,384

17. Social security = 97,500 × .124 = $12,090

Medicare = 120,000 × .029 = $3,480

Income tax = 120,000 × .2 = $24,000

$\text{Quarterly estimated tax} = \frac{\text{Social security} + \text{Medicare} + \text{Income tax}}{4}$

$\text{Quarterly estimated tax} = \frac{12{,}090 + 3{,}480 + 24{,}000}{4} = \frac{39{,}570}{4} = \$9{,}892.50$

CONCEPT REVIEW

1. Gross pay is the amount of earnings before payroll ____ are withheld; net pay is the actual amount of the ____. (9.1)
deductions, paycheck

2. Annual salaries are commonly prorated to be paid weekly, biweekly, ____ and ____. (9-1)
semimonthly, monthly

3. Total gross pay includes regular pay and ____ pay, which according to federal law is for hours worked over ____ hours per week. (9-2)
overtime, 40

4. When employees are paid on their production output, not hours worked, this is called ____. (9-3)
piecework

5. To calculate total gross pay for an employee paid on commission, we multiply the total ____ by the commission rate. (9-4)
sales

6. A draw against commission is commission paid in ____ of sales and later ____ from the commission earned. (9-4)
advance, deducted

7. The current employee tax rate for social security is ____ percent of gross earnings; the current tax rate for Medicare is ____ percent of gross earnings. (9-5)
6.2, 1.45

8. The 2007 wage base limit for social security was ____. (9-5)
$97,500

9. In addition to social security and Medicare tax withholdings, an employer is also responsible, by federal law, for withholding an appropriate amount of federal ____ tax from each employee's paycheck. (9-6)
income

10. The combined wage bracket table is based on the ____ status of the employee and the ____ period used. The columns list the combined taxes to be withheld based on the number of withholding ____ claimed. (9-7)
marital, payroll, allowances

11. Self-employed persons are responsible for social security and Medicare taxes at ____ the rate deducted for employees. This amounts to ____ percent for social security and ____ percent for Medicare. (9-8)
twice, 12.4, 2.9

12. For companies with full and timely payments to the state unemployment system, the SUTA tax rate is ____ percent of gross earnings and the FUTA tax rate is ____ percent of gross earnings. (9-9)
5.4, 0.8

13. A plan whereby employees are given a menu of fringe benefits to choose from is known as the ____ style, or ____ benefit program. (9-10)
cafeteria, flexible

14. Write the formula for quarterly estimated tax for self-employed persons. (9-11)

$\text{Quarterly estimated tax} = \frac{\text{Social security} + \text{Medicare} + \text{Income tax}}{4}$

ASSESSMENT TEST

Name

Class

Answers

1. a. $67,200
   b. $2,584.62
2. $322
3. $898.70
4. $491.70
5. $656.25
6. a. $305.40
   b. $209.30
   c. $602.40

1. Bob Johnson earns $2,800 semimonthly as a congressional aide for a senator in the state legislature.

a. How much are his annual gross earnings?

2,800 × 24 = $67,200

b. If the senator switches pay schedules from semimonthly to biweekly, what will Bob's new gross earnings be per payroll period?

67,200 ÷ 26 = $2,584.62 Biweekly

2. Gigi LeBlanc works 40 hours per week as a bookkeeper. At the rate of $8.05 per hour, what are her gross weekly earnings?

8.05 × 40 = $322 Per week

3. Howard Lockwood's company pays him $18.92 per hour for regular time up to 40 hours and time-and-a-half for overtime. His time card for Monday through Friday last week had 8.3, 8.8, 7.9, 9.4 and 10.6 hours. What was Howard's total gross pay?

Total hours: 8.3 + 8.8 + 7.9 + 9.4 + 10.6 = 45.0

18.92 × 40 = $756.80 Regular pay
18.92 × 1.5 × 5 = 141.90 Overtime pay
$898.70 Total gross pay

4. Bill Kingman is a security guard. He earns $7.45 per hour for regular time up to 40 hours, time-and-a-half for overtime, and double time for the midnight shift. If Bill worked 56 hours last week, including 4 on the midnight shift, how much are his gross earnings?

Regular pay:	7.45 × 40 =	$298.00
Time-and-a-half pay:	7.45 × 1.5 × 12 =	134.10
Double-time pay:	7.45 × 2 × 4 =	59.60
	Total gross earnings	$491.70

5. Tracy Alvarez assembles toasters for the Breville Corporation. She is paid on a differential piecework rate of $2.70 per toaster for the first 160 toasters and $3.25 for each toaster over 160. If she assembled 229 units last week, how much were her gross earnings?

160 × $2.70 = $432.00
69 × $3.25 = 224.25
229 $656.25

6. You work in the payroll department of Reliable Manufacturing. The following piece rate schedule is used for computing earnings for assembly line workers. As an overtime bonus, on Saturdays, each unit produced counts as $1\frac{1}{2}$% units.

1–100	$2.30
101–150	2.60
151–200	2.80
over 200	3.20

Calculate the gross earnings for the following employees.

	Employee	Mon.	Tues.	Wed.	Thurs.	Fri.	Sat.	Total Units	Gross Earnings
a.	Anderson	0	32	16	36	27	12	129	$305.40
b.	Cavalcante	18	26	24	10	13	0	91	$209.30
c.	West	26	42	49	51	34	20	232	$602.40

a. Anderson: 100 × 2.30 = $230.00
29 × 2.60 = 75.40
$305.40

b. Cavalcante: 91 × 2.30 = $209.30

c. West: 100 × 2.30 = $230.00
50 × 2.60 = 130.00
50 × 2.80 = 140.00
32 × 3.20 = 102.40
$602.40

CHAPTER

Name

Class

Answers

7. $1,011.71

8. $1,341.00

9. $6,963.00

10. $1,799.00

11. $2,284.10

12. $2,134.00

13. $44.95 Social security

$10.51 Medicare

© Flying Colors, Ltd./Photodisc/Getty Images

Regardless of what they sell, telemarketers are responsible for initiating telephone sales calls to potential clients, using a prepared selling script. They are usually paid on a commission, based on the amount of their sales volume or number of new "leads" they generate.

7. Sabrina Pascal's company pays differential piecework for electronic product manufacturing. Production pay rates for a particular circuit board assembly and soldering are $18.20 per board for the first 14 boards, $19.55 each for boards 15–30, $20.05 each for boards 31–45, and $20.48 each for boards 46 and up. If Sabrina assembled and soldered 52 boards last week, what was her total gross pay

14 × $18.20 = $254.80
16 × 19.55 = 312.80
15 × 20.05 = 300.75
7 × 20.48 = 143.36
52 $1,011.71 Total gross pay

8. Pike Place Fish Market pays a straight commission of 18% on gross sales, divided equally among the three employees working the counter. If Pike Place sold $22,350 in seafood last week, how much was each counter employee's total gross pay?

22,350 × 18% = 4,023 Total commission

$\frac{4.023}{3}$ = $1,341 Per employee

9. Keith Walcheck booked $431,000 in new sales last month. Commission rates are 1% for the first $150,000; 1.8% for the next $200,000; and 2.3% for amounts over $350,000. What was Keith's total gross pay?

$150,000 × 1.0% = $1,500
200,000 × 1.8% = 3,600
81,000 × 2.3% = 1,863
$431,000 $6,963

10. Sam Best works in the telemarketing division for a company that pays a salary of $735 per month plus a commission of $3\frac{1}{2}$% of all sales greater than $15,500. If he sold $45,900 last month, what was his total gross pay?

$45,900 30,400 × .035 = $1,064
−15,500 1,064 + 735 = $1,799 Total gross pay
$30,400

11. Peggy Estes is on a 2.1% straight commission with a $700 drawing account. If she is paid the draw at the beginning of the month and then sells $142,100 during the month, how much commission is owed to Peggy?

142,100 × .021 = $2,984.10 Commission
−700.00 Drawing account
$2,284.10 Commission owed

12. Antonio Muina is the first mate on a charter fishing boat. He is paid a salary of $40 per day. He also averages tips amounting to 12% of the $475 daily charter rate. Last month during a fishing tournament, Antonio worked 22 days. What were his total gross earnings for the month?

$475 10,450 × .12 = $1,254 Tips
× 22 40 × 22 = 880 Salary
$10,450 $2,134 Total gross pay

Solve the following problems, using 6.2% up to $97,500 for social security withholding and 1.45% for Medicare.

13. What are the withholdings for social security and Medicare for an employee with gross earnings of $725 per week?

725 × .062 = $44.95 Social security
725 × .0145 = $10.51 Medicare

14. David Mayes is an executive with Ace Distributors. His gross earnings are $9,850 per month.

a. What are the withholdings for social security and Medicare for David's January paycheck?

9,850 × .062 = $610.70 Social security
9,850 × .0145 = $142.83 Medicare

b. In what month will his salary reach the social security wage base limit?

$\frac{97,500}{9,850} = 9.9$ 9 full months, plus a portion of the 10th month, October

c. What are the social security and Medicare tax withholdings for David in the month named in part **b**?

9 × 9,850 = $88,650 Year-to-date earnings
97,500 − 88,650 = 8,850 Subject to social security tax
8,850 × .062 = $548.70 Social security (October)
9,850 × .0145 = $142.83 Medicare (October)

Use the *percentage method* to solve the following.

15. Larry Alison is single, claims one withholding allowance, and earns $2,450 per month.

a. What is the amount of Larry's paycheck after his employer withholds social security, Medicare, and income tax?

2,450.00 − 283.33 = 2,166.67
2,166.67 − 843.00 = 1,323.67 →

62.20 + 15%(1,323.67) = $260.75 Income tax
2,450.00 × 6.2% = 151.90 Social security
2,450.00 × 1.45 = 35.53 Medicare
$448.18 Total deductions

2,450.00 − 448.18 = $2,001.82 Net pay

b. If Larry gets married and changes to two withholding allowances, what will be the new amount of his paycheck?

283.33 × 2 = 566.66
2,450.00 − 566.66 = 1,833.34
1,833.34 − 667.00 = 1,216.34 →

1,216.34 × 10% = $121.63 Income tax
2,450.00 × 6.2% = 151.90 Social security
2,450.00 × 1.45 = 35.53 Medicare
$309.06 Total deductions

2,450.00 − 309.06 = $2,140.94 Net pay

c. If he then gets a 15% raise, what is the new amount of his paycheck?

2,450.00 × 115% = 2,817.50 New salary
283.33 × 2 = 566.66
2,817.50 − 566.66 = 2,250.84
2,250.84 − 1,946.00 = 304.84 →

127.90 + 15%(304.84) = $173.63 Income tax
2,817.50 × 6.2% = 174.69 Social security
2,817.50 × 1.45% = 40.85 Medicare
$389.17 Total deductions

2,817.50 − 389.17 = $2,428.33 Net pay

Use the *combined wage bracket tables*, Exhibits 9-4 and 9-5, for Exercises 16 and 17.

16. How much combined tax should be withheld from the paycheck of a married employee earning $910 per week and claiming three withholding allowances?

$140

17. How much combined tax should be withheld from the paycheck of a single employee earning $4,458 per month and claiming zero withholding allowances?

$1,112.19

CHAPTER 9

Name

Class

Answers

14. a. $610.70 Social security
$142.83 Medicare
b. October
c. $548.70, $142.83

15. a. $2,001.82
b. $2,140.94
c. $2,428.33

16. $140

17. $1,112.19

In the Business World

Consider the tax implications of a pay raise. In part c., Larry got a 15% raise, but his total deductions increased by 25.9%! His net pay raise, after taxes, was 13.4%.

TEACHING TIP

Have students verify these percentages:

Percent increase in total deductions

$= \frac{389.17 - 309.06}{309.06} = 25.9\%$

Percent increase in net pay

$= \frac{2,428.33 - 2,140.94}{2,140.94} = 13.4\%$

CHAPTER

Name

Class

Answers

18. $2,877.34

19. a. $1,693.03 Social security

$395.95 Medicare

b. $44,018.78 Social security

$10,294.70 Medicare

20. $1,372.06 Social security

$320.89 Medicare

21. a. $378.00

b. $56.00

22. a. $1,032.26 SUTA

$152.93 FUTA

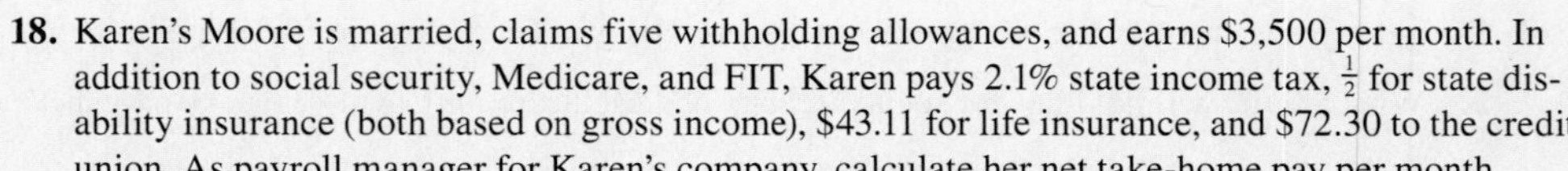

18. Karen's Moore is married, claims five withholding allowances, and earns $3,500 per month. In addition to social security, Medicare, and FIT, Karen pays 2.1% state income tax, $\frac{1}{2}$ for state disability insurance (both based on gross income), $43.11 for life insurance, and $72.30 to the credit union. As payroll manager for Karen's company, calculate her net take-home pay per month.

283.33 × 5 = 1,416.65
3,500.00 − 1,416.65 = 2,083.35
2,083.35 − 1,946.00 = 137.35

127.90 + 15%(137.35)	=	$148.50	Income tax
3,500 × .062	=	217.00	Social security
3,500 × .0145	=	50.75	Medicare
3,500 × .021	=	73.50	State income tax
3,500 × .005	=	17.50	Disability insurance
		43.11	Life insurance
		72.30	Credit union
		$622.66	Total deductions

3,500.00 − 622.66 = $2,877.34 Net pay

19. The Zeta Corporation has 83 employees on the assembly line, each with gross earnings of $329 per week.

a. What are the total social security and Medicare taxes that should be withheld from the employee paychecks each week?

329 × 83 = 27,307

27,307 × .062 = $1,693.03 Social security
27,307 × .0145 = $395.95 Medicare

b. What is the total social security and Medicare that Zeta should send to the IRS for the first quarter of the year?

1,693.03 × 13 × 2 = $44,018.78 Social security
395.95 × 13 × 2 = $10,294.70 Medicare

20. Ben Rakusin is a self-employed mechanic. Last year, he had total gross earnings of $44,260. What are Ben's quarterly social security and Medicare payments due the IRS?

$\frac{44,260}{4} = 11,065$ Quarterly earnings

11,065 × .124 = $1,372.06 Social security
11,065 × .029 = $320.89 Medicare

21. Luke Samson earns $48,320 annually as a supervisor for the International Bank.

a. If the SUTA tax rate is 5.4% of the first $7,000 earned in a year, how much SUTA tax must the bank pay each year for Luke?

7,000 × .054 = $378 SUTA per year

b. If the FUTA tax rate is 6.2% of the first $7,000 earned in a year minus the SUTA tax paid, how much FUTA tax must the bank pay each year for Luke?

7,000 × .008 = $56

EXCEL

22. Striker Exporting has three warehouse employees: John Abner earns $422 per week, Anne Clark earns $510 per week, and Todd Corbin earns $695 per week. The company's SUTA tax rate is 5.4%, and the FUTA rate is 6.2% minus the SUTA. As usual, these taxes are paid on the first $7,000 of each employee's earnings.

a. How much SUTA and FUTA tax does the company owe on these employees for the first quarter of the year?

422 × 13 = 5,486
510 × 13 = 6,630
695 × 13 = 9,035

Abner	$5,486	
Clark	6,630	
Corbin	7,000	(Limit)
	$19,116	

19,116 × .054 = $1,032.26 SUTA
19,116 × .008 = $152.93 FUTA

Name

Class

Answers

22. b. $101.74 SUTA

$15.07 FUTA

23. a. $58,589.20

b. 20.8% of payroll

c. $3,046,638.40

24. a. $6,592.50

b. Form 1040-ES

b. How much SUTA and FUTA tax does Striker owe for the second quarter of the year?

7,000 − 5,486 = $1.514
7,000 − 6,630 = 370
$1,884 Taxable amount
1,884 × .054 = $101.74 SUTA
1,884 × .008 = $15.07 FUTA

23. Flamingo Developers employs 150 workers and has a gross payroll of $282,100 per week. Fringe benefits are $6\frac{1}{2}$% of gross payroll for sick days and holiday leave, 9.1% for health and hospital insurance, 4.6% for the retirement fund, and $10.70 per employee for a stock purchase plan.

a. What is the total weekly cost of fringe benefits for the company?

282,100 × .065 = $18,336.50 Sick days
282,100 × .091 = 25,671.10 Health plan
282,100 × .046 = 12,976.60 Retirement
150 × 10.70 = 1,605.00 Stock purchase
$58,589.20 Total cost of benefits per week

b. What percent of payroll does this represent?

$$R = \frac{P}{B} = R = \frac{58,589.20}{282,100} = .2076 = 20.8\% \text{ of payroll}$$

c. What is the company's annual cost of fringe benefits?

58,589.20 × 52 = $3,046,638.40 Cost of benefits per year

24. Bobby Tutor is self-employed with estimated annual earnings of $90,000. His social security tax rate is 12.4%, Medicare is 2.9%, and his federal income tax rate is 14%.

a. How much estimated tax must Bobby send to the IRS each quarter?

90,000 × .124 = $11,160 Social security
90,000 × .029 = $2,610 Medicare
90,000 × .14 = $12,600 Income tax

$$\text{Quarterly estimated tax} = \frac{\text{Social security + Medicare + Income tax}}{4}$$

$$\text{Quarterly estimated tax} = \frac{11,160 + 2,610 + 12,600}{4} = \frac{26,370}{4} = \$6,592.50$$

b. What form should he use?

Form 1040-ES, *Quarterly Estimated Tax Voucher for Self-Employed Persons*

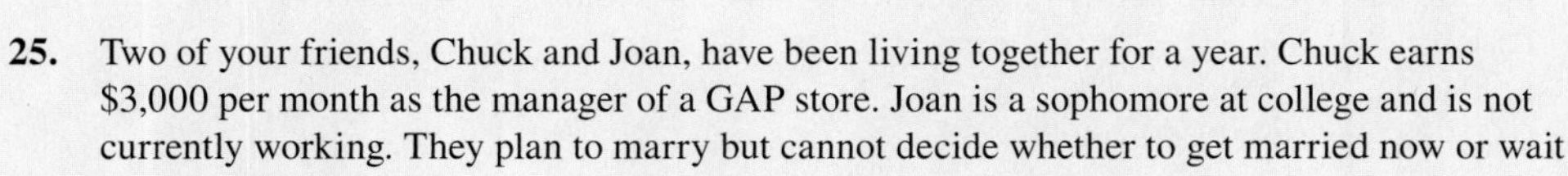

BUSINESS DECISION THE BRIDE, THE GROOM, AND THE TAXMAN

25. Two of your friends, Chuck and Joan, have been living together for a year. Chuck earns $3,000 per month as the manager of a GAP store. Joan is a sophomore at college and is not currently working. They plan to marry but cannot decide whether to get married now or wait a year or two.

After studying the payroll chapter in your business math class, you inform Chuck that married couples generally pay less income taxes and that if they got married now instead of waiting he would have less income tax withheld from his paychecks. Chuck's current tax filing status is single, one exemption. If he and Joan got married, he could file as married, two exemptions. Use the percentage method and Exhibits 9-2 and 9-3 to calculate the following:

CHAPTER

Name

Class

Answers

25. a. $343.25

b. $201.00

c. $6,251.88

a. How much income tax is withheld from Chuck's paycheck each month now?

Single

3,000.00 − 283.33 = 2,716.67
2,716.67 − 843.00 = 1,873.67
62.20 + .15(1.873.67) = $343.25 Income tax withheld

b. How much income tax would be withheld from Chuck's check if he and Joan got married?

Married

283.33 × 2 = 566.66
3,000.00 − 566.66 = 2,433.34
2,433.34 − 1,946.00 = 487.34
127.90 + .15(487.34) = $201.00 Income tax withheld

c. Assuming Joan has 3 more years of full-time college before going to work and Chuck expects a 10% raise in 1 year and a 15% raise the year after, what is the total 3-year tax advantage of their getting married now?

Year 2 10% Raise: 3,000 × 110% = 3,300 New salary

Single	Married
3,300.00 − 283.33 = 3,016.67	283.33 × 2 = 566.66
3,016.67 − 2,793.00 = 223.67	3,300.00 − 566.66 = 2,733.34
354.70 + .25(223.67) = $410.62 Income tax withheld	2,733.34 − 1,946.00 = 787.34
	127.90 + .15(787.34) = $246.00 Income tax withhe

Year 3 15% Raise: 3,300 × 1.15% = $3,795 New salary

Single	Married
3,795.00 − 283.33 = 3,511.67	283.33 × 2 = 566.66
3,511.67 − 2,793.00 = 718.67	3,795.00 − 566.66 = 3,228.34
354.70 + .25(718.67) = $534.37 Income tax withheld	3,228.34 − 1,946.00 = 1,282.34
	127.90 + .15(1,282.34) = $320.25 Income tax with

Total 3-year withholding

Single			Married		
Year 1	343.25 × 12 =	4,119.00	Year 1	201.00 × 12 =	2,412.00
Year 2	410.62 × 12 =	4,927.44	Year 2	246.00 × 12 =	2,952.00
Year 3	534.37 × 12 =	6,412.44	Year 3	320.25 × 12 =	3,843.00
		$15,458.88			$9,207.00

15,458.88 − 9,207.00 = $6,251.88 – Total 3-year tax savings if married.

COLLABORATIVE LEARNING ACTIVITY

Researching the Job Market

1. As a team, collect "Help Wanted" ads from the classified section of your local newspaper. (Note: Weekend editions are usually the most comprehensive.) Find examples of various jobs that are paid by salary, hourly rate, piece rate, and commission. Answer the following, for similar jobs.
   a. How much do they pay?
   b. What pay periods are used?
   c. What fringe benefits are being offered?
2. As a team, research the Internet or library for the following payroll information.
   a. Starting salaries of employees in various industries and in government occupations.
   b. Personal and household income by area of the country or by state. How does your area or state compare?
   c. Starting salaries by amount of education for various professions.
   d. List your sources for the answers in parts a., b., and c.

http://www.contemporarymath.com

Contemporary Math

ContemporaryMath.com

All the Math That's Fit to Learn

Retail Giants

Retailing is big business in the United States. In addition to the "stand alone" stores, in 2005, there were 48,695 shopping centers with over 6 billion square feet of leasable space. According to industry research, each month over 190 million adults visit shopping centers.

In 2006, the U.S. retail industry generated over $3.9 trillion in sales; $4.3 trillion if food service sales are included. That amounts to approximately $12,000 per person. The retail industry employs 15.3 million people. That accounts for about 11.6 percent of all U.S. employment.

Retail trade accounts for about 12.4 percent of all business establishments in the United States. Single-store businesses account for over 95 percent of all U.S. retailers, but generate less than 50% of all retail store sales.

Wal-Mart is the world's largest retailer and the world's largest company with more than $348 billion in sales annually. Wal-Mart employs 1.3 million associates in the United States and more than 400,000 internationally.

Source: retailindustry.about.com, www.plunkettresearch.com

Top U.S. Retailers

Rank	Company	Sales (000)	Income (000)	Stores
1	Wal-Mart	$348,650,000	$11,284,000	6,779
2	Home Depot	90,837,000	5,761,000	2,147
3	Kroger	66,111,200	1,114,900	3,659
4	Costco	60,151,227	1,103,215	488
5	Target	59,490,000	2,787,000	1,487
6	Sears	53,012,000	858,000	3,835
7	Walgreen	47,409,000	1,750,600	5,461
8	Lowe's	46,927,000	3,105,000	1,375
9	CVS	43,813,800	1,354,800	6,202
10	Safeway	40,185,000	870,600	1,761

Source: www.stores.org, 2006.

Apparel Outsells Computers Online

Online sales continue to grow at a record pace. In 2007, online sales represented over 6% of all retail sales. As an indication of a shift in consumer buying behavior, in 2006, for the first time, consumers spent more money online for apparel, accessories, and footwear than for computers.

Online apparel, accessories, and footwear sales are projected to increase dramatically in the next few years. Many retailers have made online clothing shopping easier by offering free and/or in-store returns along with high-tech imaging that offers a more realistic look at the merchandise. Top online apparel retailers include Victoria's Secret, L.L. Bean, Gap, Redcats USA, and Zappos.com.

Quote...UnQuote

- A business's flexibility in adapting to change and market dynamics will mark the winners and losers in this fast-changing Internet Age. –**Michael Dell**
- Vision is the art of seeing things invisible. –**Jonathan Swift**

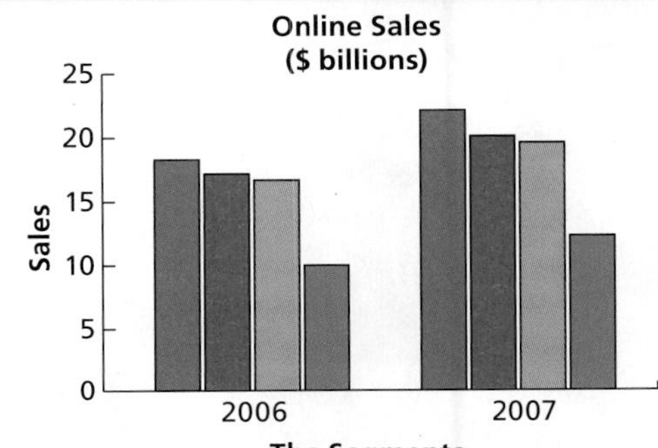

Source: Jayne O'Donnell "Computers bumped from top of online sales," *USA Today* (May 14, 2007) p. 1B. Reprinted with permission.

It was a good chance to get together and talk shop.

Internet 100%

Simple Interest and Promissory Notes

PERFORMANCE OBJECTIVES

UNDERSTANDING AND COMPUTING SIMPLE INTEREST

SECTION I 10

The practice of borrowing and lending money dates back in history for thousands of years. Today, institutions such as banks, savings and loans, and credit unions are specifically in business to borrow and lend money. They constitute a significant portion of the service sector of the American economy.

Interest is the rental fee charged by a lender to a business or individual for the use of money. The amount of interest charged is determined by three factors: the amount of money being borrowed or invested, known as the **principal**; the percent of interest charged on the money per year, known as the **rate**; and the length of time of the loan, known as **time**. The manner in which the interest is computed is an additional factor that influences the amount of interest. The two most commonly used methods in business today for computing interest are simple and compound.

Simple interest means that the interest is calculated *only once* for the entire time period of the loan. At the end of the time period, the borrower repays the principal plus the interest. Simple interest loans are usually made for short periods of time, such as a few days, weeks, or months. **Compound interest** means that the interest is calculated *more than once* during the time period of the loan. When compound interest is applied to a loan, each succeeding time period accumulates interest on the previous interest, in addition to interest on the principal. Compound interest loans are generally for time periods of a year or longer.

This chapter discusses the concepts of simple interest; simple discount, which is a variation of a simple interest loan; and promissory notes. Chapter 11 covers the concepts and calculations related to compound interest and present value.

interest The price or rental fee charged by a lender to a borrower for the use of money.

principal A sum of money, either invested or borrowed, on which interest is calculated.

rate The percent that is charged or earned for the use of money per year.

time Length of time, expressed in days, months, or years, of an investment or loan.

simple interest Interest calculated solely on the principal amount borrowed or invested. It is calculated only once for the entire time period of the loan.

compound interest Interest calculated at regular intervals on the principal and previously earned interest. Covered in Chapter 11.

COMPUTING SIMPLE INTEREST FOR LOANS WITH TERMS OF YEARS OR MONTHS

Simple interest is calculated by using a formula known as the simple interest formula. It is stated as

Interest = Principal × Rate × Time

$$I = PRT$$

When using the simple interest formula, the time factor, T, must be expressed in years or a fraction of a year.

Simple Interest Formula—Years or Months

Years

When the time period of a loan is a year or longer, use the number of years as the time factor, converting fractional parts to decimals. For example, the time factor for a 2-year loan is 2, 3 years is 3, $1\frac{1}{2}$ years is 1.5, $4\frac{3}{4}$ years is 4.75, and so on.

Months

When the time period of a loan is for a specified number of months, express the time factor as a fraction of a year. The number of months is the numerator, and 12 months (1 year) is the denominator. A loan for 1 month would have a time factor of $\frac{1}{12}$, a loan for 2 months would have a factor of $\frac{2}{12}$ or $\frac{1}{6}$, a 5-month loan would use $\frac{5}{12}$ as the factor, a loan for 18 months would use $\frac{18}{12}$ or $1\frac{1}{2}$, written as 1.5.

Banking institutions all over the world are in business specifically to borrow and lend money, at a profitable rate of interest.

TEACHING TIP
Remind students, when using $I = PRT$, the time variable, T, is expressed in years, or a portion of a year.
- Months are divided by 12
- Weeks are divided by 52
- Days are divided by 360 or 365

Be sure that students do not round the time fraction when using the percentage formula.

EXAMPLE 1 CALCULATING SIMPLE INTEREST

a. What is the amount of interest for a loan of \$8,000, at 9% interest, for 1 year?

SOLUTION STRATEGY

To solve this problem, we apply the simple interest formula,

$$\text{Interest} = \text{Principal} \times \text{Rate} \times \text{Time}$$
$$\text{Interest} = 8{,}000 \times 9\% \times 1$$
$$\text{Interest} = 8{,}000 \times .09 \times 1$$
$$\text{Interest} = \underline{\underline{\$720}}$$

b. What is the amount of interest for a loan of \$16,500, at $12\frac{1}{2}$% interest, for 7 months?

SOLUTION STRATEGY

In this example, the rate is converted to .125, and the time factor is expressed as a fraction of a year, $\frac{7}{12}$.

$$\text{Interest} = \text{Principal} \times \text{Rate} \times \text{Time}$$
$$\text{Interest} = 16{,}500 \times .125 \times \frac{7}{12}$$
$$\text{Interest} = \underline{\underline{\$1{,}203.13}}$$

Calculator Sequence: 16500 × .125 × 7 ÷ 12 = $\underline{\underline{\$1{,}203.13}}$

TRY IT EXERCISE 1

Find the amount of interest on each of the following loans.

	Principal	Rate (%)	Time
a.	\$4,000	7	$2\frac{1}{4}$ years
b.	\$45,000	$9\frac{3}{4}$	3 months
c.	\$130,000	10.4	42 months

CHECK YOUR ANSWERS WITH THE SOLUTIONS ON PAGE 362.

10-2 CALCULATING SIMPLE INTEREST FOR LOANS WITH TERMS OF DAYS BY USING THE EXACT INTEREST AND ORDINARY INTEREST METHODS

There are two methods for calculating the time factor, T, when applying the simple interest formula using days. Because time must be expressed in years, loans whose terms are given in days must be made into a fractional part of a year. This is done by dividing the days of a loan by the number of days in a year.

Simple Interest Formula—Days

Exact Interest

The first method for calculating the time factor is known as **exact interest**. Exact interest uses *365 days* as the time factor denominator. This method is used by government agencies, the Federal Reserve Bank, and most credit unions.

exact interest Interest calculation method using 365 days (366 in leap year) as the time factor denominator.

$$\textbf{Time} = \frac{\textbf{Number of days of a loan}}{\textbf{365}}$$

Teaching Transparency 10-1

Ordinary Intxerest

The second method for calculating the time factor is known as **ordinary interest**. Ordinary interest uses *360 days* as the denominator of the time factor. This method dates back to the time before electronic calculators and computers. In the past, when calculating the time factor manually, a denominator of 360 was easier to use than 365.

Regardless of today's electronic sophistication, banks and most other lending institutions still use ordinary interest because it yields a somewhat higher amount of interest than the exact interest method. Over the years, ordinary interest has become known as the **banker's rule**.

ordinary interest, or banker's rule Interest calculation method using 360 days as the time factor denominator.

$$\textbf{Time} = \frac{\textbf{Number of days of a loan}}{\textbf{360}}$$

EXAMPLE 2 CALCULATING EXACT INTEREST

Using the exact interest method, what is the amount of interest on a loan of $4,000, at 7% interest, for 88 days?

SOLUTION STRATEGY

Because we are looking for exact interest, we will use 365 days as the denominator of the time factor in the simple interest formula:

$$\text{Interest} = \text{Principal} \times \text{Rate} \times \text{Time}$$

$$\text{Interest} = 4{,}000 \times .07 \times \frac{88}{365}$$

$$\text{Interest} = 67.506849$$

$$\text{Interest} = \underline{\underline{\$67.51}}$$

Calculator Sequence: 4000 × .07 × 88 ÷ 365 = $67.51

CLASSROOM ACTIVITY

Have students calculate the difference in interest paid on a loan of $50,000 at 12% interest for 300 days using ordinary and exact.

Answer: Ordinary = $5,000.00
− Exact = $4,931.51
Difference = $68.49

To demonstrate why ordinary interest, 360 days, became popular, have students work this problem without a calculator.

TRY IT EXERCISE 2

Tim Lopez goes to a credit union and borrows $23,000, at 8%, for 119 days. If the credit union calculates interest by the exact interest method, what is the amount of interest on the loan?

CHECK YOUR ANSWER WITH THE SOLUTION ON PAGE 362.

10-2

EXAMPLE 3 CALCULATING ORDINARY INTEREST

Using the ordinary interest method, what is the amount of interest on a loan of $19,500, at 12% interest, for 160 days?

SOLUTION STRATEGY

Because we are looking for ordinary interest, we will use 360 days as the denominator of the time factor in the simple interest formula:

$$\text{Interest} = \text{Principal} \times \text{Rate} \times \text{Time}$$

$$\text{Interest} = 19{,}500 \times .12 \times \frac{160}{360}$$

$$\text{Interest} = \underline{\underline{\$1{,}040}}$$

Calculator Sequence: 19500 × .12 × 160 ÷ 360 = $1,040

TRY IT EXERCISE 3

Gisela Malek goes to the bank and borrows $15,000, at $9\frac{1}{2}$%, for 250 days. If the bank uses the ordinary interest method, how much interest will Gisela have to pay?

CHECK YOUR ANSWER WITH THE SOLUTION ON PAGE 362.

10-3 CALCULATING THE MATURITY VALUE OF A LOAN

maturity value The total payback of principal and interest of an investment or loan.

When the time period of a loan is over, the loan is said to mature. At that time, the borrower repays the original principal plus the interest. The total payback of principal and interest is known as the **maturity value** of a loan. Once the interest has been calculated, the maturity value can be found by using the formula:

Maturity value = Principal + Interest

$$MV = P + I$$

Learning Tip

When using the maturity value formula, $MV = P(1 + RT)$, the order of operation is

- Multiply Rate by Time
- Add the 1
- Multiply by the Principal

For example, if a loan for $50,000 had interest of $8,600, the maturity value would be found by adding the principal and the interest: 50,000 + 8,600 = $58,600.

Maturity value can also be calculated directly, without first calculating the interest, by using the following formula:

Maturity value = Principal(1 + Rate × Time)

$$MV = P(1 + RT)$$

EXAMPLE 4 CALCULATING MATURITY VALUE

What is the maturity value of a loan for \$25,000, at 11%, for $2\frac{1}{2}$ years?

SOLUTION STRATEGY

Because this example asks for the maturity value, not the amount of interest, we shall use the formula for finding maturity value directly, $MV = P(1 + RT)$. Remember to multiply the rate and time first, then add the 1. Note that the time, $2\frac{1}{2}$ years, should be converted to the decimal equivalent 2.5 for ease in calculation.

$$\text{Maturity value} = \text{Principal}(1 + \text{Rate} \times \text{Time})$$

$$\text{Maturity value} = 25{,}000(1 + .11 \times 2.5)$$

$$\text{Maturity value} = 25{,}000(1 + .275)$$

$$\text{Maturity value} = 25{,}000(1.275)$$

$$\text{Maturity value} = \underline{\underline{\$31{,}875}}$$

TRY IT EXERCISE 4

a. What is the amount of interest and the maturity value of a loan for \$15,400, at $6\frac{1}{2}\%$ simple interest, for 24 months? (Use the formula $MV = P + I$.)

b. Blue Sky Air Taxi Service borrowed \$450,000, at 8% simple interest, for 9 months, to purchase a new airplane. Use the formula $MV = P(1 + RT)$ to find the maturity value of the loan.

CHECK YOUR ANSWERS WITH THE SOLUTIONS ON PAGES 362 & 363.

CALCULATING THE NUMBER OF DAYS OF A LOAN

The first day of a loan is known as the **loan date** and the last day is known as the **due date** or **maturity date**. When these dates are known, the number of days of the loan can be calculated by using the days in each month chart and the steps that follow:

loan date The first day of a loan.

due date, or maturity date The last day of a loan.

10-3

Days in Each Month

28 Days	30 Days	31 Days
February (29 leap year)	April	January
	June	March
	September	May
	November	July
		August
		October
		December

STEPS FOR DETERMINING THE NUMBER OF DAYS OF A LOAN

Step 1. Determine the number of days remaining in the first month by subtracting the loan date from the number of days in that month.

Step 2. List the number of days for each succeeding whole month.

Step 3. List the number of loan days in the last month.

Step 4. Add the days from Steps 1, 2, and 3.

EXAMPLE 5 CALCULATING DAYS OF A LOAN

Jamie Baker borrowed money from the Central Bank on August 18 and repaid the loan on November 27. What was the number of days of the loan?

SOLUTION STRATEGY

The number of days from August 18 to November 27 would be calculated as follows:

Step 1.	Days remaining in first month	Aug. 31 Aug. −18 13 →	August	13 days
Step 2.	Days in succeeding whole months	→	September	30 days
		→	October	31 days
Step 3.	Days of loan in last month	→	November	+27 days
Step 4.	Add the days		Total	101 days

Learning Tip

An alternate method for calculating the number of days of a loan is to use the Days-in-a-Year Calendar, Exhibit 7-6, page 231.

- Subtract the "day number" of the loan date from the "day number" of the maturity date.
- If the maturity date is in the next year, add 365 to that day number, then subtract. *Note:* In leap years, add 1 to the day numbers, beginning with March 1.

TRY IT EXERCISE 5

a. A loan was made on April 4 and had a due date of July 18. What is the number of days of the loan?

b. Bobby Reynolds borrowed $3,500 on June 15, at 11% interest. If the loan was due on October 9, what was the amount of interest on Bobby's loan using the exact interest method?

CHECK YOUR ANSWERS WITH THE SOLUTIONS ON PAGE 363.

10-5 DETERMINING THE MATURITY DATE OF A LOAN

When the loan date and number of days of the loan are known, the maturity date can be found as follows:

STEPS FOR DETERMINING THE MATURITY DATE OF A LOAN

Step 1. Find the number of days remaining in the first month by subtracting the loan date from the number of days in that month.

Step 2. Subtract the days remaining in the first month (Step 1) from the number of days of the loan.

Step 3. Continue subtracting days in each succeeding whole month, until you reach a month with a difference less than the total days in that month. At that point, the maturity date will be the day that corresponds to the difference.

EXAMPLE 6 DETERMINING MATURITY DATE OF A LOAN

What is the maturity date of a loan that was taken out on April 14 for 85 days?

SOLUTION STRATEGY

Step 1. Days remaining in first month

	30	Days in April
	−14	Loan date April 14
Days remaining in April	16	

Step 2. Subtract remaining days in first month from days of the loan

	85	Days of the loan
	−16	Days remaining in April
Difference	69	

Step 3. Subtract succeeding whole months

	69	Difference
	−31	Days in May
Difference	38	
	38	Difference
	−30	Days in June
Difference	8	

At this point, the difference, 8, is less than the number of days in the next month, July, therefore the maturity date is July 8.

TRY IT EXERCISE 6

a. What is the maturity date of a loan taken out on September 9 for 125 days?

b. On October 21, Natalie Williams went to the Lincoln National Bank and took out a loan for $9,000, at 10% ordinary interest, for 80 days. What is the maturity value and maturity date of this loan?

CHECK YOUR ANSWERS WITH THE SOLUTIONS ON PAGE 363.

Learning Tip

An alternate method for calculating the maturity date of a loan is to use the Days-in-a-Year Calendar, Exhibit 7-6, page 231. Follow the steps for finding a future date, page 230.

In the Business World

In business, due dates that fall on weekends or holidays are commonly advanced to the next business day.

SECTION I Review Exercises

Complete, worked-out solutions to Exercises 1–24 appear in Appendix B, following the index.

Find the amount of interest on each of the following loans.

	Principal	Rate (%)	Time	Interest
1.	$5,000	8	2 years	$800.00
2.	$75,000	$10\frac{3}{4}$	6 months	$4,031.25
3.	$100,000	12.7	18 months	$19,050.00
4.	$80,000	15	$3\frac{1}{2}$ years	$42,000.00
5.	$6,440	$5\frac{1}{2}$	7 months	$206.62
6.	$13,200	9.2	$4\frac{3}{4}$ years	$5,768.40

Use the exact interest method (365 days) and the ordinary interest method (360 days) to compare the amount of interest for the following loans.

	Principal	Rate (%)	Time (days)	Exact Interest	Ordinary Interest
7.	$45,000	13	100	$1,602.74	$1,625.00
8.	$184,500	$15\frac{1}{2}$	58	$4,544.26	$4,607.38
9.	$32,400	8.6	241	$1,839.79	$1,865.34
10.	$7,230	9	18	$32.09	$32.54
11.	$900	$10\frac{1}{4}$	60	$15.16	$15.38
12.	$100,000	10	1	$27.40	$27.78
13.	$2,500	12	74	$60.82	$61.67
14.	$350	14.1	230	$31.10	$31.53
15.	$50,490	$9\frac{1}{4}$	69	$882.88	$895.15
16.	$486,000	$13\frac{1}{2}$	127	$22,828.68	$23,145.75

Find the amount of interest and the maturity value of the following loans. Use the formula $MV = P + I$ to find the maturity values.

	Principal	Rate (%)	Time	Interest	Maturity Value
17.	$54,000	11.9	2 years	$12,852.00	$66,852.00
18.	$125,000	$12\frac{1}{2}$	5 months	$6,510.42	$131,510.42
19.	$33,750	8.4	10 months	$2,362.50	$36,112.50
20.	$91,000	$9\frac{1}{4}$	$2\frac{1}{2}$ years	$21,043.75	$112,043.75

Find the maturity value of the following loans. Use $MV = P(1 + RT)$ to find the maturity values.

	Principal	Rate (%)	Time	Maturity Value
21.	$1,500	9	2 years	$1,770.00
22.	$18,620	$10\frac{1}{2}$	30 months	$23,507.75
23.	$1,000,000	11	3 years	$1,330,000.00
24.	$750,000	13.35	11 months	$841,781.25

From the following information, determine the number of days of each loan.

Complete, worked-out solutions for Exercises 25–33 appear in Appendix B, following the index.

	Loan Date	Due Date	Number of Days
25.	September 5	December 12	98
26.	June 27	October 15	110
27.	January 23	November 8	289
28.	March 9	July 30	143

From the following information, determine the maturity date of each loan.

	Loan Date	Time of Loan (days)	Maturity Date
29.	October 19	45	December 3
30.	February 5	110	May 26
31.	May 26	29	June 24
32.	July 21	200	February 6
33.	December 6	79	February 23

Solve the following word problems. Round to the nearest cent, when necessary.

34. On April 12, Ruth Odom borrowed \$5,000 from her credit union at 9% for 80 days. The credit union uses the ordinary interest method.

a. What is the amount of interest on the loan?

$$I = PRT = 5{,}000 \times .09 \times \frac{80}{360} = \$100$$

b. What is the maturity value of the loan?

$$MV = P + I = 5{,}000 + 100 = \$5{,}100$$

c. What is the maturity date of the loan?

30
−12
18 Days

18 Apr.
61 May–June
+1 July → July 1
80 Days

35. What is the maturity value of a \$60,000 loan, for 100 days, at 12.2% interest, using the exact interest method?

$$MV = P(1 + RT) = 60{,}000\left(1 + .122 \times \frac{100}{365}\right) = \$62{,}005.48$$

© R. Alcorn/Cengage Learning

Credit unions are like banks; however, they are owned and controlled by the members who use their services. Credit unions serve groups that share something in common, such as where they work, or where they live.

In 2006 there were more than 8,500 federal and state-chartered credit unions nationwide with over 89 million members. As with banks, deposits are insured up to \$100,000 per account.

36. Reliable Auto Parts borrowed \$350,000 at 9% interest on July 19 for 120 days.

a. If the bank uses the ordinary interest method, what is the amount of interest on the loan?

$$I = PRT = 350{,}000 \times .09 \times \frac{120}{360} = \$10{,}500$$

b. What is the maturity date?

31
−19
12 Days

12 July
92 Aug.–Oct.
+16 Nov. → November 16
120 Days

37. Tommy Blake missed an income tax payment of \$9,000. The Internal Revenue Service charges a 13% simple interest penalty calculated by the exact interest method. If the tax was due on April 15 but was paid on August 19, what is the amount of the penalty charge?

30	15 Apr.
−15	92 May–July
15 Days	+19 Aug.
	126 Days

$$I = PRT = 9{,}000 \times .13 \times \frac{126}{365} = \$403.89$$

38. At the Pacific National Credit Union, a 7%, \$8,000 loan for 180 days had interest charges of \$276.16. What type of interest did Pacific National use, ordinary or exact?

$I = PRT$

$$I = 8{,}000 \times .07 \times \frac{180}{365} = \$276.16 \text{ Exact interest}$$

39. Jim McDermott borrowed \$1,080 on June 16 at 9.2% exact interest from the Cromwell Bank. On August 10, Jim repaid the loan. How much interest did he pay?

30	14 June
−16	31 July
14 Days	+10 Aug.
	55 Days

$I = PRT$

$$I = 1{,}080 \times 0.092 \times \frac{55}{365} = \$14.97 \text{ Interest}$$

BUSINESS DECISION COMPETING BANKS

40. You are the accounting manager for Kool Ragz, Inc., a manufacturer of men's and women's clothing. The company needs to borrow \$1,800,000 for 90 days in order to purchase a large quantity of material at "closeout" prices. The interest rate for such loans at your bank, Coastal Bank, is 11%, using ordinary interest.

a. What is the amount of interest on this loan?

$I = PRT$

$$I = 1{,}800{,}000 \times .11 \times \frac{90}{360} = \$49{,}500$$

Banks are financial institutions that accept deposits and channel the money into lending activities. Major banks in the U.S. include: Bank of America, Citicorp, JP Morgan Chase, Wells Fargo, Wachovia, BankOne, Washington Mutual, U.S. Bancore, and SunTrust.

b. After making a few "shopping" calls, you find that City National Bank will lend at 11%, using exact interest. What is the amount of interest on this offer?

$I = PRT$

$$I = 1{,}800{,}000 \times .11 \times \frac{90}{365} = \$48{,}821.92$$

c. In order to keep your business, Coastal Bank has now offered a loan at 10.5%, using ordinary interest. What is the amount of interest on this offer?

$I = PRT$

$$I = 1{,}800{,}000 \times .105 \times \frac{90}{360} = \$47{,}250$$

d. (Challenge) If City National wants to beat Coastal's last offer (part c) by charging $1,250 less interest, what rate, rounded to the nearest hundredths of a percent, must they quote, using exact interest?

$I = PRT$

$$46{,}000 = 1{,}800{,}000 \times R \times \frac{90}{365}$$

$$R = \frac{46{,}000}{1{,}800{,}000 \times \frac{90}{365}} = .10364 = \underline{\underline{10.36\%}}$$

USING THE SIMPLE INTEREST FORMULA

SECTION II 10

In Section I, we used the simple interest formula, $I = PRT$, to solve for the interest. Frequently in business, however, the principal, rate, or time might be the unknown factor. Remember from Chapter 5 that an equation can be solved for any of the variables by isolating that variable to one side of the equation. In this section, we convert the simple interest formula to equations that solve for each of the other variable factors.

If you find this procedure difficult or hard to remember, use the magic triangle, as we did in Chapter 6, to calculate the portion, rate, and base. Remember, to use the Magic Triangle, cover the variable you are solving for and the new formula will "magically" appear!

10-4

Magic Triangle
Simple Interest Formula

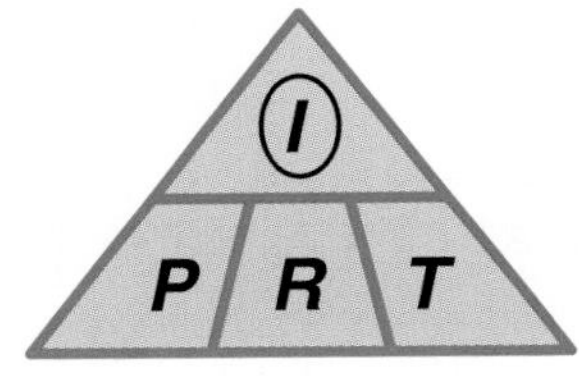

I = PRT

SOLVING FOR THE PRINCIPAL

When using the simple interest formula to solve for principal, P, we isolate the P on one side of the equation by dividing both sides of the equation by RT. This yields the new equation:

$$\textbf{Principal} = \frac{\textbf{Interest}}{\textbf{Rate} \times \textbf{Time}} \qquad P = \frac{I}{RT}$$

TEACHING TIP
When solving for principal, rate, and time, be sure students remember to calculate the product in the denominator first (no rounding), then divide the numerator by this product.

We can also find the formula in the Magic Triangle by covering the unknown variable, P, as follows:

10-5

Magic Triangle
Solving for Principal

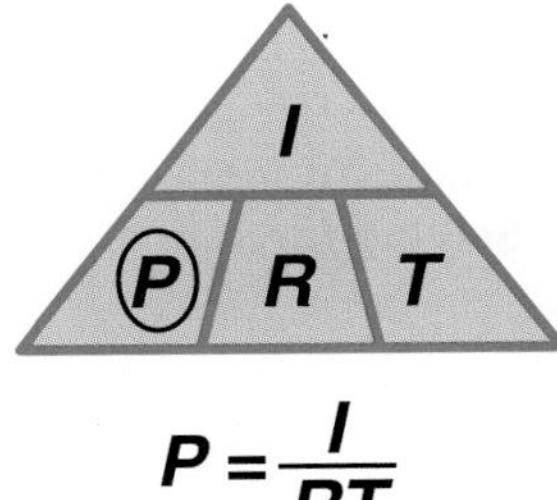

$$P = \frac{I}{RT}$$

EXAMPLE 7 FINDING THE PRINCIPAL OF A LOAN

Learning Tip

This formula provides a good opportunity to use your calculator's memory keys. Use M+ to store a number in memory, and MR to retrieve it.

Some financial and scientific calculators use STO (store) and RCL (recall) keys for the memory function.

A bank loaned a business money at 8% interest for 90 days. If the amount of interest was $4,000, use the ordinary interest method to find the amount of principal borrowed.

SOLUTION STRATEGY

To solve for the principal, we use the formula $P = \frac{I}{RT}$.

$P = \frac{I}{RT}$ Substitute the known variables into the equation.

$P = \frac{4{,}000}{.08 \times \frac{90}{360}}$ Calculate the denominator first.
Calculator sequence: .08 × 90 ÷ 360 = M+

$P = \frac{4{,}000}{.02}$ Next, divide the numerator by the denominator.
Calculator sequence: 4000 ÷ MR = 200,000

Principal = $200,000 The company borrowed $200,000 from the bank.

TRY IT EXERCISE 7

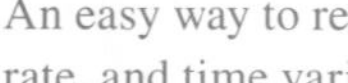

Teaching Transparency 10-6

Gold Coast Industries borrowed money at 9% interest for 125 days. If the interest charge was $560, use the ordinary interest method to calculate the amount of principal of the loan.

CHECK YOUR ANSWER WITH THE SOLUTION ON PAGE 363.

10-7 SOLVING FOR THE RATE

TEACHING TIP
An easy way to remember the principal, rate, and time variations of the percentage formula is that interest, I, is always the numerator.

When solving the simple formula for rate, the answer will be a decimal that must be converted to a percent. In business, interest rates are always expressed as a percent.

When the rate is the unknown variable, we isolate the R on one side of the equation by dividing both sides of the equation by PT. This yields the new equation:

$$\text{Rate} = \frac{\text{Interest}}{\text{Principal} \times \text{Time}} \qquad R = \frac{I}{PT}$$

We can also find the formula in the Magic Triangle by covering the unknown variable, R, as follows:

Teaching Transparency 10-7

Magic Triangle
Solving for Rate

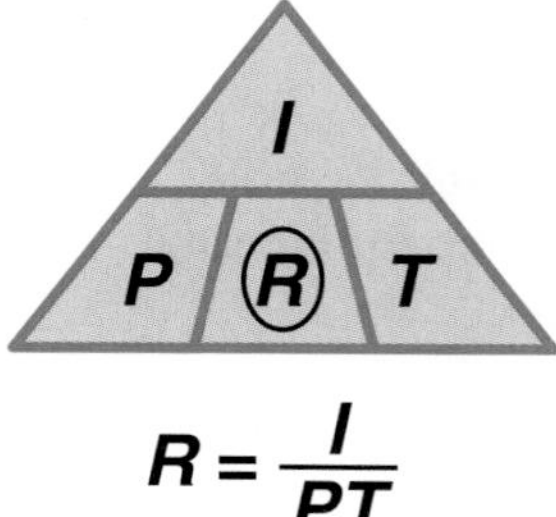

$$R = \frac{I}{PT}$$

EXAMPLE 8 FINDING THE RATE OF A LOAN

What is the rate of interest on a loan of $5,000, for 125 days, if the amount of interest is $166, using the ordinary interest method? Round your answer to the nearest hundredth of a percent.

SOLUTION STRATEGY

To solve for the rate, we use the formula $R = \frac{I}{PT}$.

$R = \frac{I}{PT}$ Substitute the known variables into the equation.

$R = \frac{166}{5{,}000 \times \frac{125}{360}}$ Calculate the denominator first.

Calculator sequence: 5000 × 125 ÷ 360 = M+

$R = \frac{166}{1{,}736.111111}$ Next, divide the numerator by the denominator.
Note: Don't round the denominator
Calculator sequence: 166 ÷ MR = .095616

$R = .095616$ Round the answer to the nearest hundredth percent.

Rate = <u>9.56%</u> The bank charged <u>9.56%</u> interest.

TRY IT EXERCISE 8

What is the rate of interest on a loan of $25,000, for 245 days, if the amount of interest is $1,960, using the ordinary interest method? Round your answer to the nearest hundredth of a percent.

10-8

CHECK YOUR ANSWER WITH THE SOLUTION ON PAGE 363.

SOLVING FOR THE TIME

When solving the simple interest formula for time, a whole number in the answer represents years and a decimal represents a portion of a year. The decimal should be converted to days by multiplying it by 360 for ordinary interest or by 365 for exact interest.

For example, an answer of 3 means 3 years. An answer of 3.23 means 3 years and .23 of the next year. Assuming ordinary interest, multiply the decimal portion of the answer, .23, by 360. This gives 82.8, which represents the number of days. The total time of the loan would be 3 years and 83 days.

When using the simple interest formula to solve for time, *T*, we isolate the *T* on one side of the equation by dividing both sides of the equation by *PR*. This yields the new equation:

$$\textbf{Time} = \frac{\textbf{Interest}}{\textbf{Principal} \times \textbf{Rate}} \qquad T = \frac{I}{PR}$$

Lending institutions consider any part of a day to be a full day. When calculating time, *T*, any fraction of a day is rounded up to the next higher day, even if it is less than .5.

For example, 25.1 days would round up to 26 days.

We can also find the formula in the Magic Triangle by covering the unknown variable, *T*, as follows:

10-9

Magic Triangle
Solving for Time

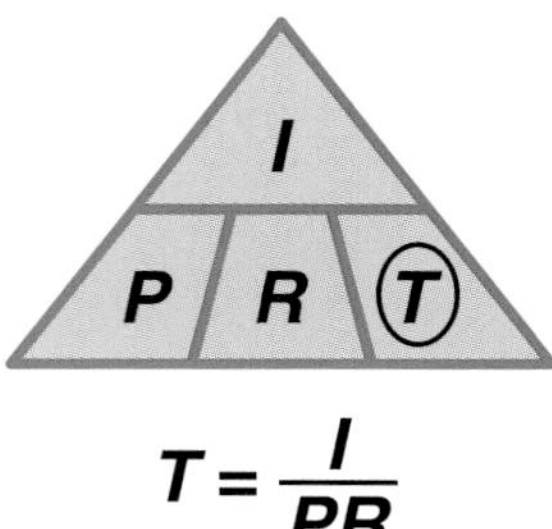

$$T = \frac{I}{PR}$$

EXAMPLE 9 FINDING THE TIME PERIOD OF A LOAN

What would be the time period of a loan for $7,600, at 11% ordinary interest, if the amount of interest is $290?

SOLUTION STRATEGY

To solve for the time, we use the formula $T = \frac{I}{PR}$.

$T = \frac{I}{PR}$	Substitute the known variables into the equation.
$T = \frac{290}{7{,}600 \times .11}$	Calculate the denominator first. Calculator sequence: 7600 [×] .11 [=] [M+]
$T = \frac{290}{836}$	Next, divide the numerator by the denominator. Calculator sequence: 290 [÷] [MR] [=] .3468899
$T = .3468899$ years	Because the answer is a decimal, the time is less than 1 year. Using ordinary interest, we multiply the entire decimal by 360 to find the number of days of the loan.
$T = .3468899 \times 360$	Calculator Sequence: .3468899 [×] 360 [=] 124.8 or 125 days

Time = 124.8 or 125 days

TRY IT EXERCISE 9

10-10

What is the time period of a loan for $15,000, at 9.5% ordinary interest, if the amount of interest is $650?

CHECK YOUR ANSWER WITH THE SOLUTION ON PAGE 363.

CALCULATING LOANS INVOLVING PARTIAL PAYMENTS BEFORE MATURITY

Frequently, businesses and individuals who have borrowed money for a specified length of time find that they want to save some interest by making one or more partial payments on the loan before the maturity date. The most commonly used method for this calculation is known as the **U.S. rule**. The rule states that when a partial payment is made on a loan, the payment is first used to pay off the accumulated interest to date, and the balance is used to reduce the principal. In this application, the ordinary interest method (360 days) will be used for all calculations.

U.S. rule Method for distributing early partial payments of a loan, whereby the payment is first used to pay off the accumulated interest to date, with the balance used to reduce the principal.

STEPS FOR CALCULATING MATURITY VALUE OF A LOAN AFTER ONE OR MORE PARTIAL PAYMENTS

Step 1. Using the simple interest formula, with *ordinary* interest, compute the amount of interest due from the date of the loan to the date of the partial payment.

Step 2. Subtract the interest from Step 1 from the partial payment. This pays the interest to date.

Step 3. Subtract the balance of the partial payment, after Step 2, from the original principal of the loan. This gives the adjusted principal.

Step 4. If another partial payment is made, repeat Steps 1, 2, and 3, using the adjusted principal and the number of days since the last partial payment.

Step 5. The maturity value is computed by adding the interest since the last partial payment to the adjusted principal.

Remember to use *ordinary interest*, 360 days, for all calculations involving partial payments.

EXAMPLE 10 CALCULATING LOANS INVOLVING PARTIAL PAYMENTS

Ben Becker borrowed $10,000 at 9% interest for 120 days. On day 30, Ben made a partial payment of $2,000. On day 70, he made a second partial payment of $3,000. What is the maturity value of the loan after the partial payments?

SOLUTION STRATEGY

To help you visualize the details of a loan with partial payments, construct a time line such as the one illustrated in Exhibit 10-1.

Exhibit 10-1
Partial Payment Time Line

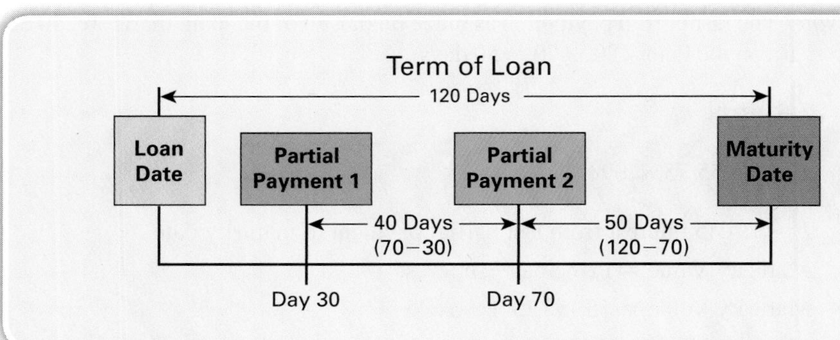

Teaching Transparency 10-11

Step 1. Compute the interest from the date of the loan to the partial payment. In this problem, the first partial payment was made on day 30.

$$I = PRT$$

$$I = 10{,}000 \times .09 \times \frac{30}{360} = 75$$

$$I = \$75$$

Step 2. Subtract the interest from the partial payment.

$2,000	Partial payment
− 75	Accumulated interest
$1,925	Amount of partial payment left to reduce the principal

Step 3. Reduce the principal.

$10,000	Original principal
− 1,925	Amount of partial payment used to reduce principal
$8,075	Adjusted principal

Step 4. A second partial payment of $3,000 was made on day 70. We now repeat Steps 1, 2, and 3 to properly credit the second partial payment. Remember, use the adjusted principal and 40 days (70 − 30 = 40) for this calculation.

Step 1.

$$I = PRT$$

$$I = \$8{,}075 \times .09 \times \frac{40}{360}$$

$I = \$80.75$ accumulated interest since last partial payment

Step 2.

$3,000.00	Partial payment
− 80.75	Accumulated interest
$2,919.25	Amount of partial payment left to reduce the principal

Step 3.

$8,075.00	Principal
−2,919.25	Amount of partial payment used to reduce principal
$5,155.75	Adjusted principal

Step 5. Once all partial payments have been credited, we find the maturity value of the loan by calculating the interest due from the last partial payment to the maturity date and adding it to the last adjusted principal.

Note: The last partial payment was made on day 70 of the loan, therefore, 50 days remain on the loan (120 − 70 = 50 days).

$$I = PRT$$

$$I = \$5{,}155.75 \times .09 \times \frac{50}{360}$$

$I = \$64.45$ interest from last partial payment to maturity date

Maturity Value = Principal + Interest

Maturity Value = $5,155.75 + $64.45

Maturity Value = $5,220.20

TRY IT EXERCISE 10

Fran Weaver borrowed $15,000 at 12% ordinary interest for 100 days. On day 20 of the loan, she made a partial payment of $4,000. On day 60, she made another partial payment of $5,000. What is the maturity value of the loan after the partial payments?

CHECK YOUR ANSWER WITH THE SOLUTION ON PAGE 363.

Review Exercises

SECTION II 10

Compute the principal for the following loans. Use ordinary interest when time is stated in days.

	Principal	Rate (%)	Time	Interest
1.	$1,250	12	2 years	$300
2.	$5,000	9	$1\frac{1}{2}$ years	$675
3.	$50,000	8	9 months	$3,000
4.	$200,000	10.7	90 days	$5,350
5.	$12,000	13.1	210 days	$917

Compute the rate for the following loans. Round answers to the nearest tenth of a percent; use ordinary interest when time is stated in days.

	Principal	Rate (%)	Time	Interest
6.	$5,000	8	3 years	$1,200
7.	$1,800	14	5 months	$105
8.	$48,000	9.1	60 days	$728
9.	$4,600	12.8	168 days	$275
10.	$125,000	7.5	2 years	$18,750

Solution Transparencies

Complete, worked-out solutions to Exercises 1–10 appear in Appendix B, following the index.

"A high-five isn't binding, sir. You still have to sign a loan agreement."

Use the ordinary interest method to compute the time for the following loans. Round answers to the next higher day, when necessary.

Complete, worked-out solutions to Exercises 11–20 appear in Appendix B, following the index.

	Principal	Rate (%)	Time	Interest
11.	$18,000	12	158 days	$948
12.	$7,900	10.4	100 days	$228
13.	$4,500	$9\frac{3}{4}$	308 days	$375
14.	$25,000	8.9	2 years	$4,450
15.	$680	15	180 days	$51

Calculate the missing information for the following loans. Round percents to the nearest tenth and days to the next higher day, when necessary.

CLASSROOM ACTIVITY
As a quick review, have students work in pairs to solve Section II Review Exercises 16–20.

	Principal	Rate (%)	Time (days)	Interest Method	Interest	Maturity Value
16.	$16,000	13	132	Ordinary	$760	$16,760.00
17.	$13,063.16	9.5	100	Exact	$340	$13,403.16
18.	$3,600	14.3	160	Exact	$225	$3,825.00
19.	$25,500	$11\frac{1}{4}$	300	Ordinary	$2,390.63	$27,890.63
20.	$55,000	10.4	256	Exact	$4,000	$59,000

Solve the following word problems. Round answers to the nearest cent, when necessary.

21. Midway Motors, a Toyota dealership, borrowed $225,000 on April 16 to purchase a shipment of new cars. The interest rate was 9.3% using the ordinary interest method. The amount of interest was $9,600.

a. For how many days was the loan?

$$T = \frac{I}{PR} = \frac{9{,}600}{225{,}000 \times .093} = .4587814$$

$$\times\ 360$$

$$\underline{\underline{166 \text{ Days}}}$$

b. What was the maturity date of the loan?

30
−16
14 Apr.
123 May–Aug.
+ 29 Sept. ⟶ September 29
166 Days

22. Tim O'Leary took out a loan for $3,500 at the Community Bank for 270 days. If the bank uses the ordinary interest method, what rate of interest was charged if the amount of interest was $269? Round your answer to the nearest tenth of a percent.

$$R = \frac{I}{PT} = \frac{269}{3{,}500 \times \frac{270}{360}} = \underline{\underline{10.2\%}}$$

23. Jennifer Stemberg borrowed money to buy a car at 13.5% simple interest from her credit union. If the loan was repaid in 2 years and the amount of interest was $2,700, how much did Jennifer borrow?

$$P = \frac{I}{RT} = \frac{2{,}700}{.135 \times 2} = \underline{\underline{\$10{,}000}}$$

24. What is the maturity date of a loan for $5,000, at 15% exact interest, taken out on June 3? The amount of interest on the loan was $150.

$$T = \frac{I}{PR} = \frac{150}{5{,}000 \times .15} = .2$$

$$\begin{array}{r} .2 \\ \times 365 \\ \hline 73 \text{ Days} \end{array}$$

June 3 + 73 days = August 15

25. What rate of interest was charged on an ordinary interest loan for $135,000, if the interest was $4,400 and the time period was from January 16 to April 27? Round your answer to the nearest tenth of a percent.

$$\begin{array}{r} 31 \\ -16 \\ \hline 15 \text{ Days} \end{array} \qquad \begin{array}{rl} 15 & \text{Jan.} \\ 59 & \text{Feb.–Mar.} \\ +27 & \text{Apr.} \\ \hline 101 & \text{Days} \end{array}$$

$$R = \frac{I}{PT} = \frac{4{,}400}{135{,}000 \times \frac{101}{360}} = 11.6\%$$

26. Portia Kabler deposited $8,000 in a savings account paying 6.25% simple interest. How long will it take for her investment to amount to $10,000?

$$T = \frac{I}{PR} = \frac{2{,}000}{8{,}000 \times .0625} = 4 \text{ Years}$$

27. Mike Lamb borrowed $10,000 at 12% ordinary interest for 60 days. On day 20 of the loan, Mike made a partial payment of $4,000. What is the new maturity value of the loan?

$$I = PRT = 10{,}000 \times .12 \times \frac{20}{360} = \$66.67$$

$$\begin{array}{rl} \$4{,}000.00 & \text{Pd} \\ -\ 66.67 & \text{Int} \\ \hline \$3{,}933.33 & \end{array} \qquad \begin{array}{rl} \$10{,}000.00 & \\ -3{,}933.33 & \\ \hline \$6{,}066.67 & \text{Adjusted Principal} \end{array}$$

$$MV = P(1 + RT) = 6{,}066.67\left(1 + .12 \times \frac{40}{360}\right) = \$6{,}147.56$$

28. Jasmine Hirsh borrowed $20,000 at 6.5% ordinary interest for 150 days. On day 30 of the loan, she made a partial payment of $8,000. What is the new maturity value of the loan?

$$I = PRT = 20{,}000 \times .065 \times \frac{30}{360} = \$108.33$$

$$\begin{array}{rl} \$8{,}000.00 & \text{Pd} \\ -\ 108.33 & \text{Int} \\ \hline \$7{,}891.67 & \end{array} \qquad \begin{array}{rl} \$20{,}000.00 & \\ -\ 7{,}891.67 & \\ \hline \$12{,}108.33 & \text{Adjusted Principal} \end{array}$$

$$MV = P(1 + RT) = 12{,}108.33\left(1 + .065 \times \frac{120}{360}\right) = \$12{,}370.68$$

29. United Plumbing Supplies borrowed $60,000 on March 15 for 90 days. The rate was 13% using the ordinary interest method. On day 25 of the loan, United made a partial payment of $16,000, and on day 55 of the loan United made a second partial payment of $12,000.

a. What is the new maturity value of the loan?

$$I = PRT = 60{,}000 \times .13 \times \frac{25}{360} = \$541.67$$

$$\begin{array}{rl} \$16{,}000.00 & \text{Pd} \\ -\ 541.67 & \text{Int} \\ \hline \$\ 15{,}458.33 & \end{array} \qquad \begin{array}{rl} \$60{,}000.00 & \text{Pd} \\ -15{,}458.33 & \\ \hline \$44{,}541.67 & \text{Adj. Prin.} \end{array} \qquad \begin{array}{rl} 55 & \\ -\ 25 & \\ \hline 30 & \text{Days} \end{array}$$

$$I = PRT = 44{,}541.67 \times .13 \times \frac{30}{360} = \$482.53$$

$$\begin{array}{rl} \$12{,}000.00 & \text{Pd} \\ -\ 482.53 & \text{Int} \\ \hline \$11{,}517.47 & \end{array} \qquad \begin{array}{rl} \$44{,}541.67 & \\ -11{,}517.47 & \\ \hline \$33{,}024.20 & \text{Adj. Prin.} \end{array} \qquad \begin{array}{rl} 90 & \\ -\ 55 & \\ \hline 35 & \text{Days left} \end{array}$$

$$MV = P(1 + RT) = 33{,}024.20\left(1 + .13 \times \frac{35}{360}\right) = \$33{,}441.59$$

b. What is the maturity date of the loan?

31		16	Mar.
− 15		61	Apr.–May
16 Days		+ 13	June ⟶ June 13
		90	Days

30. a. How many years will it take \$5,000 invested at 8% simple interest to double to \$10,000?

$$T = \frac{I}{PR} = \frac{5{,}000}{5{,}000 \times .08} = \underline{\underline{12.5 \text{ Years}}}$$

b. How long will it take if the interest rate is increased to 10%?

$$T = \frac{I}{PR} = \frac{5{,}000}{5{,}000 \times .1} = \underline{\underline{10 \text{ Years}}}$$

BUSINESS DECISION THE OPPORTUNITY COST

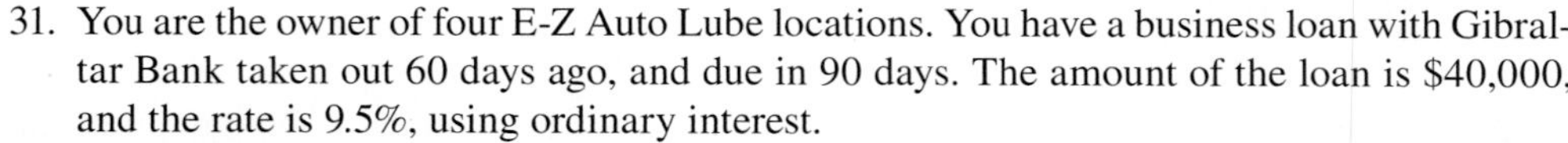

31. You are the owner of four E-Z Auto Lube locations. You have a business loan with Gibraltar Bank taken out 60 days ago, and due in 90 days. The amount of the loan is \$40,000, and the rate is 9.5%, using ordinary interest.

You currently have some excess cash. You have the choice of sending Gibraltar \$25,000 now as a partial payment on your loan, or purchasing \$25,000 of motor oil and filters for your inventory at a special discount price that is "10% off" your normal cost of these items.

© LM Otero/Jiffy Lube

Jiffy Lube International, a wholly owned subsidiary of Pennzoil-Quaker State Co., has the largest system of franchised and company-operated service centers in the rapidly expanding fast lube industry.

The company started in 1979 as an association of seven service centers in the Rocky Mountain States. Today, there are over 2,200 locations nationwide and in Canada servicing over 27.5 million customers per year.

a. How much interest will you save on this loan if you make the partial payment and don't buy the merchandise?

Interest—No Partial Payment

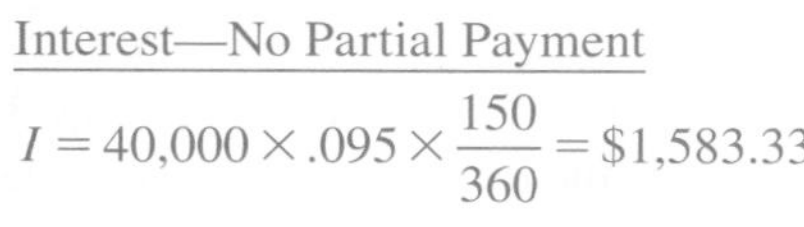

$$I = 40{,}000 \times .095 \times \frac{150}{360} = \$1{,}583.33$$

Interest—With Partial Payment

First 60 Days:

$$I = 40{,}000 \times .095 \times \frac{60}{360} = \$633.33$$

\$25,000.00	\$40,000.00	
− 633.33	− 24,366.67	
\$24,366.67	\$15,633.33	Adj. Prin.

Last 90 Days:

$$I = 15{,}633.33 \times .095 \times \frac{90}{360} = \$371.29$$

\$633.33	\$1,583.33	
+ 371.29	−1,004.62	
\$1,004.62	\$578.71	Savings

b. How much will you save by purchasing the discounted merchandise and not making the partial payment?

Merchandise discount = 25,000 × .10	=	\$2,500.00
Additional interest expense	=	− 578.71
Net savings		\$1,921.29

c. (Optional) What other factors should you consider before making this decision?

Answers will vary:

- Will there be enough cash to pay off the loan at maturity?
- Is it wise to use borrowed money to buy inventory?
- Do you have storage space for that much additional merchandise?

UNDERSTANDING PROMISSORY NOTES AND DISCOUNTING

Technically, the document that states the details of a loan, and is signed by the borrower, is known as a **promissory note**. *Promissory* means it is a promise to pay the principal back to the lender on a certain date. *Note* means that the document is a negotiable instrument and can be transferred or sold to others not involved in the original loan. Much like a check, with proper endorsement by the payee, the note can be transferred to another person, company, or lending institution.

promissory note A debt instrument in which one party agrees to repay money to another, within a specified period of time. Promissory notes may be noninterest-bearing, at no interest, or interest-bearing, at a specified rate of interest.

Promissory notes are either noninterest-bearing or interest-bearing. When a note is noninterest-bearing, the maturity value equals the principal, because there is no interest being charged. With interest-bearing notes, the maturity value equals the principal plus the interest.

Exhibit 10-2 is an example of a typical promissory note with its parts labeled. Notice the similarity between a note and a check. A list explaining the labels follows.

Maker: The person or company borrowing the money and issuing the note.

Payee: The person or institution lending the money and receiving the payment.

Term: The time period of the note, usually stated in days. (Use ordinary interest.)

Date: The date that the note is issued.

Face Value or Principal: The amount of money borrowed.

Interest Rate: The annual rate of interest being charged.

Maturity Date or Due Date: The date when maturity value is due the payee.

10-12

Exhibit 10-2
Interest-Bearing Promissory Note

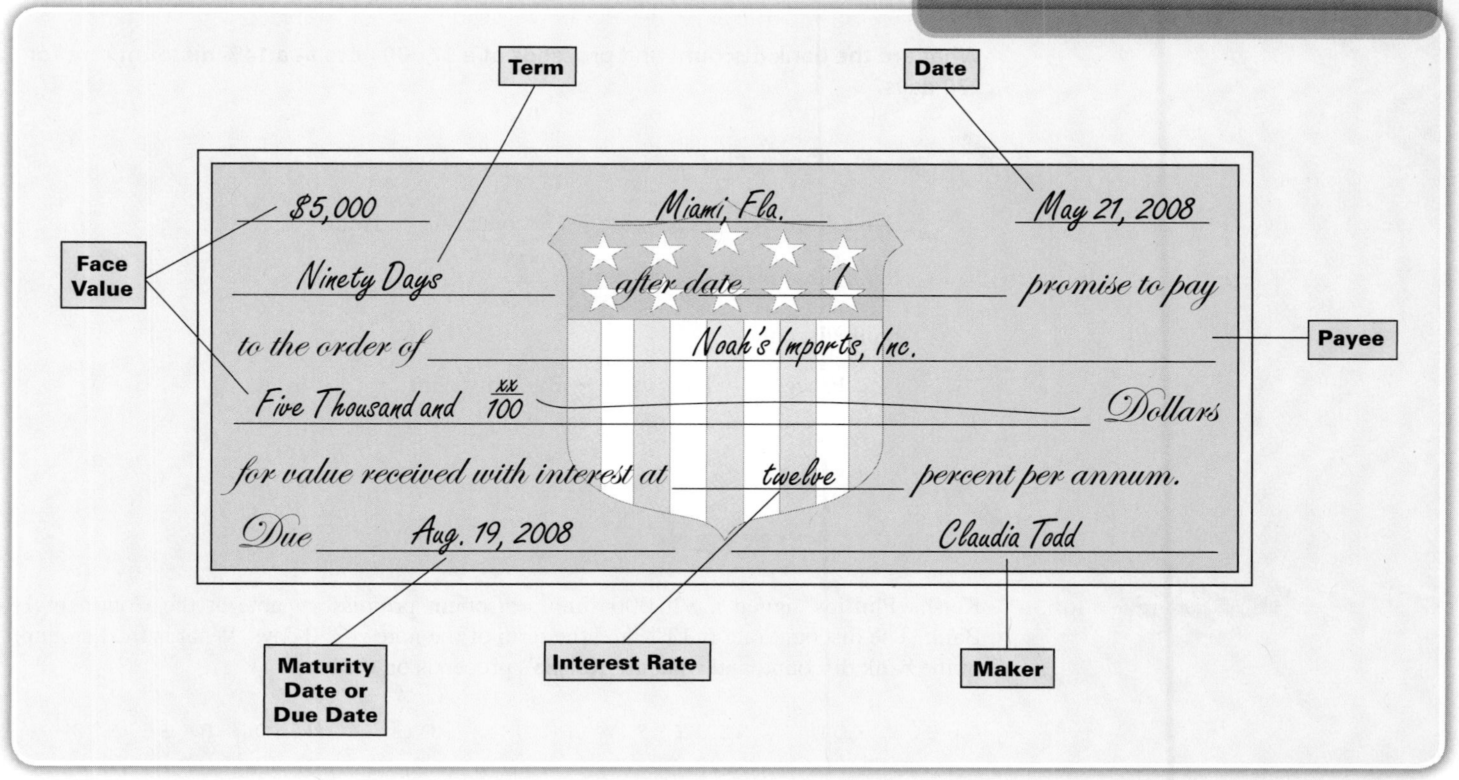

$5,000 | Miami, Fla. | May 21, 2008

Ninety Days after date I promise to pay

to the order of Noah's Imports, Inc.

Five Thousand and xx/100 Dollars

for value received with interest at twelve percent per annum.

Due Aug. 19, 2008 | Claudia Todd

Labels: Term; Date; Face Value; Payee; Maturity Date or Due Date; Interest Rate; Maker

10-10 CALCULATING BANK DISCOUNT AND PROCEEDS FOR SIMPLE DISCOUNT NOTES

simple discount note Promissory note in which the interest is deducted from the principal at the beginning of the loan.

bank discount The amount of interest charged (deducted from principal) on a discounted promissory note.

proceeds The amount of money that the borrower receives at the time a discounted note is made.

To this point, we have been dealing with simple interest notes in which the interest was added to the principal to determine the maturity value. Another way of lending money is to deduct the interest from the principal at the beginning of the loan and give the borrower the difference. These are known as **simple discount notes**. When this method is used, the amount of interest charged is known as the **bank discount**, and the amount that the borrower receives is known as the **proceeds**. When the term of the note is over, the borrower will repay the entire principal or face value of the note as the maturity value.

For example, Julie goes to a bank and signs a simple interest note for $5,000. If the interest charge amounts to $500, she will receive $5,000 at the beginning of the note and repay $5,500 on maturity of the note. If the bank used a simple discount note for Julie's loan, the bank discount (interest) would be deducted from the face value (principal). Julie's proceeds on the loan would be $4,500, and on maturity she would pay $5,000.

Bank Discount

Because bank discount is the same as interest, we use the formula $I = PRT$ as before, substituting bank discount for interest, face value for principal, and discount rate for interest rate. *Note:* Use ordinary interest, 360 days, for simple discount notes whose terms are stated in days.

Bank discount = Face value × Discount rate × Time

Proceeds

The proceeds of a note are calculated using the following formula:

Proceeds = Face value − Bank discount

EXAMPLE 11 CALCULATING BANK DISCOUNT AND PROCEEDS

What are the bank discount and proceeds of a $7,000 note at a 14% discount rate for 270 days?

SOLUTION STRATEGY

$$\text{Bank discount} = \text{Face value} \times \text{Discount rate} \times \text{Time}$$

$$\text{Bank discount} = \$7{,}000 \times .14 \times \frac{270}{360}$$

$$\text{Bank discount} = \underline{\underline{\$735}}$$

$$\text{Proceeds} = \text{Face value} - \text{Bank discount}$$

$$\text{Proceeds} = \$7{,}000 - \$735$$

$$\text{Proceeds} = \underline{\underline{\$6{,}265}}$$

TRY IT EXERCISE 11

10-13

Keisha Phillips signed a $20,000 simple discount promissory note at the Continental Bank. The discount rate is 13%, and the term of the note is 330 days. What is the amount of the bank discount, and what are Keisha's proceeds on the loan?

CHECK YOUR ANSWERS WITH THE SOLUTIONS ON PAGE 363.

CALCULATING TRUE OR EFFECTIVE RATE OF INTEREST FOR A SIMPLE DISCOUNT NOTE

10-11

In a simple interest note, the borrower receives the full face value, whereas with a simple discount note, the borrower receives only the proceeds. Because the proceeds are less than the face value, the stated discount rate is not the true or actual interest rate of the note.

To protect the consumer, the U.S. Congress has passed legislation requiring all lending institutions to quote the **true** or **effective interest rate** for all loans. Effective interest rate is calculated by substituting the bank discount for interest, and the proceeds for principal, in the rate formula,

true, or effective interest rate The actual interest rate charged on a discounted note. Takes into account the fact that the borrower does not receive the full amount of the principal.

$$\textbf{Effective interest rate} = \frac{\textbf{Bank discount}}{\textbf{Proceeds} \times \textbf{Time}}$$

EXAMPLE 12 CALCULATING EFFECTIVE INTEREST RATE

What is the effective interest rate of a simple discount note for $10,000, at a bank discount rate of 14%, for a period of 90 days? Round to the nearest tenth of a percent.

TEACHING TIP
Be sure students understand that the *true* or *effective* interest rate of a simple discount note is higher than the stated *discount* rate because the proceeds are less than the face value of the note.

SOLUTION STRATEGY

To find the effective interest rate, we must first calculate the amount of the bank discount and the proceeds of the note, then substitute these numbers in the effective interest rate formula.

Step 1. Bank Discount

$$\text{Bank discount} = \text{Face value} \times \text{Discount rate} \times \text{Time}$$

$$\text{Bank discount} = 10{,}000 \times .14 \times \frac{90}{360}$$

$$\text{Bank discount} = \$350$$

Step 2. Proceeds

$$\text{Proceeds} = \text{Face value} - \text{Bank discount}$$

$$\text{Proceeds} = 10{,}000 - 350$$

$$\text{Proceeds} = \$9{,}650$$

Step 3. Effective Interest Rate

$$\text{Effective interest rate} = \frac{\text{Bank discount}}{\text{Proceeds} \times \text{Time}}$$

$$\text{Effective interest rate} = \frac{350}{9{,}650 \times \frac{90}{360}}$$

$$\text{Effective interest rate} = \frac{350}{2{,}412.50}$$

$$\text{Effective interest rate} = .14507 \text{ or } \underline{\underline{14.5\%}}$$

TRY IT EXERCISE 12

What is the effective interest rate of a simple discount note for $40,000, at a bank discount rate of 11%, for a period of 270 days? Round your answer to the nearest hundredth of a percent.

CHECK YOUR ANSWER WITH THE SOLUTION ON PAGE 363.

10-12 DISCOUNTING NOTES BEFORE MATURITY

discounting a note A process whereby a company or individual can cash in or sell a promissory note, at a discount, at any time before maturity.

discount period The time period between the date a note is discounted and the maturity date. Used to calculate the proceeds of a discounted note.

Frequently in business, companies extend credit to their customers by accepting short-term promissory notes as payment for goods or services. These notes are simple interest and are usually for less than 1 year. Prior to the maturity date of these notes, the payee (lender) may take the note to a bank and sell it. This is a convenient way for a company or individual to *cash in* a note at any time before maturity. This process is known as **discounting a note**.

When a note is discounted at a bank, the original payee receives the proceeds of the discounted note, and the bank (the new payee) receives the maturity value of the note when it matures. The time period used to calculate the proceeds is from the date the note is discounted to the maturity date. This is known as the **discount period**.

Exhibit 10-3 illustrates the time line for a 90-day simple interest note discounted on the 60th day.

Exhibit 10-3
Time Line for Discounted Note

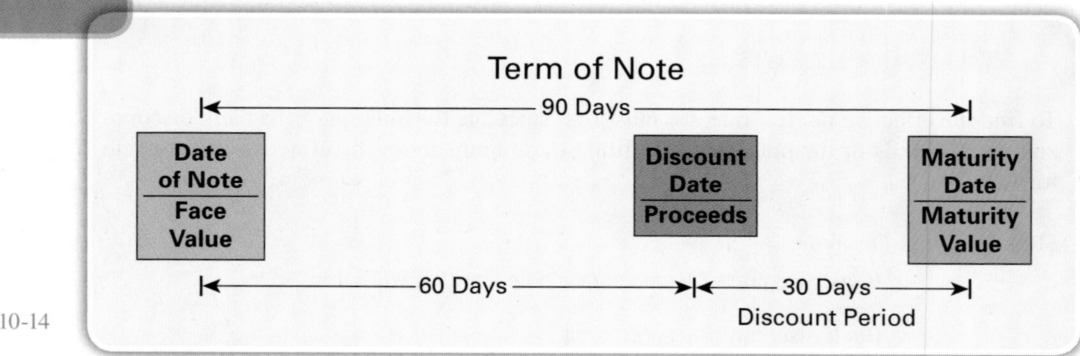

10-14

STEPS FOR DISCOUNTING A NOTE BEFORE MATURITY

Step 1. Calculate the maturity value of the note. If the original note was noninterest-bearing, the maturity value will be the same as the face value. If the original note was interest-bearing, the maturity value should be calculated as usual:

$$\text{Maturity value} = \text{Principal}(1 + \text{Rate} \times \text{Time})$$

Step 2. Determine the number of days or months of the discount period. The discount period is used as the numerator of the time in Step 3.

Step 3. Calculate the amount of the bank discount by using the following formula. *Note*: Use ordinary interest, 360 days, for discounting a note before maturity, when the terms are stated in days.

$$\text{Bank discount} = \text{Maturity value} \times \text{Discount rate} \times \text{Time}$$

Step 4. Calculate the proceeds of the note by using the formula:

$$\text{Proceeds} = \text{Maturity value} - \text{Bank discount}$$

EXAMPLE 13 CALCULATING PROCEEDS OF A DISCOUNTED NOTE

Satellite Industries received a $15,000 promissory note for 150 days at 12% simple interest from one of its customers. After 90 days, Satellite needed cash so it discounted the note at the InterAmerican Bank at a discount rate of 14%. What are the proceeds Satellite will receive from the discounted note?

SOLUTION STRATEGY

Step 1. Calculate the maturity value of the original note:

$$\text{Maturity value} = \text{Principal}(1 + \text{Rate} \times \text{Time})$$

$$\text{Maturity value} = 15{,}000\left(1 + .12 \times \frac{150}{360}\right)$$

$$\text{Maturity value} = 15{,}000\,(1 + .05) = 15{,}000(1.05)$$

$$\text{Maturity value} = \$15{,}750$$

Step 2. Find the number of days of the discount period: In this example, the note was discounted after 90 days of a 150-day note, therefore the discount period is 60 days (150 − 90 = 60).

Step 3. Calculate the amount of the bank discount:

$$\text{Bank discount} = \text{Maturity value} \times \text{Discount rate} \times \text{Time}$$

$$\text{Bank discount} = \$15{,}750 \times .14 \times \frac{60}{360}$$

$$\text{Bank discount} = \$367.50$$

Step 4. Calculate the proceeds of the discounted note:

$$\text{Proceeds} = \text{Maturity value} - \text{Bank discount}$$

$$\text{Proceeds} = \$15{,}750.00 - \$367.50$$

$$\text{Proceeds} = \underline{\underline{\$15{,}382.50}}$$

TRY IT EXERCISE 13

Pacific Lumber received a $35,000 promissory note at 10% simple interest for 6 months from one of its customers. After 4 months, the note was discounted at the Keystone Bank at a discount rate of 14%. What are the proceeds Pacific will receive from the discounted note?

CHECK YOUR ANSWER WITH THE SOLUTION ON PAGE 364.

CLASSROOM ACTIVITY

In groups, have students write and solve some word problems involving promissory notes and discounting. Next, have the groups exchange and solve the problems of another group, compare answers, and resolve any differences.

PURCHASING U.S. TREASURY BILLS

10-13

U.S. Treasury bills, or **T-bills**, are short-term government securities with maturities of 4 weeks, 13 weeks, and 26 weeks. Sold by banks, brokers, and dealers in increments of $1,000, these securities represent loans to the U.S. government and are considered to be among the safest of investments. Just like discounted bank notes, T-bills are sold at a discount from their face value.

U.S. Treasury bills, or T-bills, are short-term government securities that represent loans to the U.S. government.

For example, you might pay $970 for a T-bill with a face value of $1,000. When the bill matures, you would be paid its face value, $1,000. Your interest is the difference between the face value and the purchase price—in this example, \$30. The interest is determined by the discount rate, which is set when the bills are initially auctioned by the U.S. Treasury.

When comparing T-bills to discounted bank notes, the interest of a T-bill is the equivalent of the bank discount of a note; the face value of a T-bill is the equivalent of the proceeds of a note. Use the following formulas for T-bill calculations:

$$\textbf{Interest} = \textbf{Face value} \times \textbf{Discount rate} \times \textbf{Time}$$

$$\textbf{Purchase price} = \textbf{Face value} - \textbf{Interest}$$

$$\textbf{Effective interest rate} = \frac{\textbf{Interest}}{\textbf{Purchase price} \times \textbf{Time}}$$

EXAMPLE 14 PURCHASING U.S. TREASURY BILLS

Sandra Jackson purchased \$5,000 in U.S. Treasury bills with a discount rate of 4% for a period of 13 weeks.

a. How much interest did Sandra earn on the T-bill investment?
b. How much was the purchase price of Sandra's T-bills?
c. What was the effective interest rate of Sandra's T-bill investment? Round to the nearest hundredth of a percent.

SOLUTION STRATEGY

a. Interest = Face value × Discount rate × Time

$$\text{Interest} = 5{,}000 \times .04 \times \frac{13}{52} = \underline{\underline{\$50}}$$

b. Purchase price = Face value − Interest

Purchase price = 5,000 − 50 = $\underline{\underline{\$4{,}950}}$

c. $$\text{Effective interest rate} = \frac{\text{Interest}}{\text{Purchase price} \times \text{Time}}$$

$$\text{Effective interest rate} = \frac{50}{4{,}950 \times \frac{13}{52}} = .040404 = \underline{\underline{4.04\%}}$$

TRY IT EXERCISE 14

John Sanders purchased \$10,000 in U.S. Treasury bills with a discount rate of 4.6% for a period of 26 weeks.

a. How much interest did John earn on the T-bill investment?

b. How much was the purchase price of John's T-bills?

c. What was the effective interest rate of John's T-bill investment? Round to the nearest hundredth of a percent.

CHECK YOUR ANSWERS WITH THE SOLUTIONS ON PAGE 364.

Review Exercises

Solution Transparencies

Complete, worked-out solutions to Exercises 1–18 appear in Appendix B, following the index.

Calculate the bank discount and proceeds for the following simple discount notes. Use the ordinary interest method, 360 days, when applicable.

	Face Value	Discount Rate (%)	Term	Bank Discount	Proceeds
1.	$4,500	13	6 months	$292.50	$4,207.50
2.	$235	11.3	50 days	$3.69	$231.31
3.	$1,850	$12\frac{1}{2}$	1 year	$231.25	$1,618.75
4.	$35,000	9.65	11 months	$3,096.04	$31,903.96
5.	$7,800	$8\frac{1}{4}$	130 days	$232.38	$7,567.62

Using ordinary interest, 360 days, calculate the missing information for the following simple discount notes.

	Face Value	Discount Rate (%)	Date of Note	Term (days)	Maturity Date	Bank Discount	Proceeds
6.	$16,800	10	June 3	80	Aug. 22	$373.33	$16,426.67
7.	$5,000	14.7	April 16	84	July 9	$171.50	$4,828.50
8.	$800	12.1	Sept. 3	109	Dec. 21	$29.31	$770.69
9.	$1,300	$9\frac{1}{2}$	Aug. 19	100	Nov. 27	$34.31	$1,265.69
10.	$75,000	15	May 7	53	June 29	$1,656.25	$73,343.75

Using ordinary interest, 360 days, calculate the bank discount, proceeds, and effective rate for the following simple discount notes. Round effective rate to the nearest hundredth of a percent.

	Face Value	Discount Rate (%)	Term (days)	Bank Discount	Proceeds	Effective Rate (%)
11.	$2,700	14	126	$132.30	$2,567.70	14.72
12.	$6,505	10.39	73	$137.05	$6,367.95	10.61
13.	$3,800	$14\frac{1}{2}$	140	$214.28	$3,585.72	15.37
14.	$95,000	9.7	45	$1,151.88	$93,848.12	9.82
15.	$57,500	$12\frac{3}{4}$	230	$4,683.85	$52,816.15	13.88

The following interest-bearing promissory notes were discounted at a bank by the payee before maturity. Use the ordinary interest method, 360 days, to calculate the missing information.

	Face Value	Interest Rate (%)	Date of Note	Term of Note (days)	Maturity Date	Maturity Value	Date of Discount	Discount Period (days)	Discount Rate (%)	Proceeds
16.	$2,500	12	Mar. 4	70	May 13	$2,558.33	Apr. 15	28	13	$2,532.46
17.	$4,000	10.4	Dec. 12	50	Jan. 31	$4,057.78	Jan. 19	12	15	$4,037.49
18.	$850	$13\frac{1}{2}$	June 7	125	Oct. 10	$889.84	Sept. 3	37	16.5	$874.75

Calculate the interest, purchase price, and effective interest rate of the following Treasury bill (T-bill) purchases. Round effective interest rate to the nearest hundredth of a percent.

Complete, worked-out solutions to Exercises 19–21 appear in Appendix B, following the index.

	Face Value	Discount Rate (%)	Term (weeks)	Interest	Purchase Price	Effective Rate(%)
19.	$15,000	5.20	13	$195	$14,805	5.27
20.	$50,000	4.40	26	$1,100	$48,900	4.50
21.	$80,000	4.82	13	$964	$79,036	4.88

Use the ordinary interest method, 360 days, to solve the following word problems. Round to the nearest cent, when necessary.

22. Lisa Lozano signed a $24,000 simple discount promissory note at the Washington National Bank. The discount rate was 14%, and the note was made on February 19 for 50 days.

    a. What proceeds will Lisa receive on the note?

    $$\text{Bank discount} = FV \times R \times T = 24{,}000 \times .14 \times \frac{50}{360} = \$466.67$$

    $$\text{Proceeds} = FV - \text{Bank discount} = 24{,}000.00 - 466.67 = \underline{\underline{\$23{,}533.33}}$$

    b. What is the maturity date of the note?

    28
    −19
    9 Days → 9 Feb.
    31 Mar.
    + 10 Apr. → April 10
    50 Days

23. Bill Beck signed a $10,000 simple discount promissory note at a bank discount rate of 13%. If the term of the note was 125 days, what was the effective interest rate of the note? Round your answer to the nearest hundredth of a percent.

    $$\text{Bank discount} = FV \times R \times T = 10{,}000 \times .13 \times \frac{125}{360} = \$451.39$$

    $$\text{Proceeds} = FV - \text{Bank discount} = 10{,}000.00 - 451.39 = 9{,}548.61$$

    $$\text{Effective interest rate} = \frac{\text{Bank discount}}{\text{Proceeds} \times \text{Time}} = \frac{451.39}{9{,}548.61 \times \frac{125}{360}} = \underline{\underline{13.61\%}}$$

24. Meridian Manufacturing received a $40,000 promissory note at 12% simple interest for 95 days from one of its customers. On day 70, Meridian discounted the note at the North Shore Bank at a discount rate of 15%. The note was made on September 12.

    a. What was the maturity date of the note?

    30
    −12
    18 Days → 18 Sept.
    61 Oct.–Nov.
    + 16 Dec. → December 16
    95 Days

    b. What was the maturity value of the note?

    $$MV = P(1 + RT) = 40{,}000\left(1 + .12 \times \frac{95}{360}\right) = \underline{\underline{\$41{,}266.67}}$$

    c. What was the discount date of the note?

    30
    −12
    18 Days → 18 Sept.
    31 Oct.
    + 21 Nov. → November 21
    70 Days

d. What proceeds did Meridian receive after discounting the note?

$$\text{Bank discount} = MV \times R \times T = 41{,}266.67 \times .15 \times \frac{25}{360} = \$429.86$$

$$\text{Proceeds} = MV - \text{Bank discount} = 41{,}266.67 - 429.86 = \underline{\underline{\$40{,}836.81}}$$

25. Emerson Sweet purchased $150,000 in U.S. Treasury bills with a discount rate of 4.2% for a period of 4 weeks.

a. How much interest did Emerson earn on the T-bill investment?

$$\text{Interest} = \text{Face value} \times \text{Discount rate} \times \text{Time}$$

$$\text{Interest} = 150{,}000 \times .042 \times \frac{4}{52} = \underline{\underline{\$484.62}}$$

b. How much was the purchase price of Emerson's T-bills?

Purchase price = Face value − Interest

Purchase price = 150,000.00 − 484.62 = $\underline{\underline{\$149{,}515.38}}$

c. What was the effective interest rate of Emerson's T-bill investment? Round to the nearest hundredth of a percent.

$$\text{Effective interest rate} = \frac{\text{Interest}}{\text{Purchase price} \times \text{Time}}$$

$$\text{Effective interest rate} = \frac{484.62}{149{,}515.38 \times \frac{4}{52}} = .04213 = \underline{\underline{4.21\%}}$$

BUSINESS DECISION TIMING THE DISCOUNT?

26. Jim Reilly is the accounting manager for Aqua King, Inc., a manufacturer of custom fishing boats. As part payment for an order from Champion Marine, Jim has just accepted a 90-day, 9.5% promissory note for $600,000.

You are a manager for Atlantic Bank, and Jim is one of your clients. Atlantic's discount rate is currently 16%. Jim's goal is to discount the note as soon as possible, but not until the proceeds are at least equal to the face value of the note, $600,000.

a. As his banker, Jim has asked you to "run the numbers" at 10-day intervals, starting with day 20, and advise him when he can discount the note and still receive his $600,000.

$$MV = 600{,}000\left(1 + .095 \times \frac{90}{360}\right) = \$614.250$$

Strategy: Find the day when the bank discount is less than $14,250.

$$\text{Day 20: } 614{,}250 \times .16 \times \frac{70}{360} = \$19{,}110\text{—Too high}$$

$$\text{Day 30: } 614{,}250 \times .16 \times \frac{60}{360} = \$16{,}380\text{—Too high}$$

$$\underline{\underline{\text{Day 40:}}}\ 614{,}250 \times .16 \times \frac{50}{360} = \underline{\underline{\$13{,}650}}\text{—}\underline{\underline{\text{OK}}}$$

© John Zoiner/Workbook Stock/ Jupiter Images

Boat Builders

According to the National Marine Manufacturers Association, there are 1,486 active boat builders in the United States employing over 116,000 people. Top manufacturers include Sea Ray, Bayliner, Wellcraft, Cobalt, MasterCraft and Skier's Choice. In 2006, sales and service expenditures topped $39.5 billion.

With over 18 million boats in use, 72.6 million people, or 32.1% of the U.S. population over 18 years old, participate in boating activities each year.

b. (Challenge) Calculate the exact day the note should be discounted to meet Jim's goal.

Let X = days of discount period needed

$$614{,}250 \times .16 \times \frac{X}{360} = 14{,}250$$

$$273X = 14{,}250$$

$$X = 52.2 = 52 \text{ days}$$

$$\begin{array}{r} 90 \\ -52 \\ \hline 38 \end{array}$$ Discount note on Day 38

10 CHAPTER FORMULAS

Simple Interest

Interest = Principal × Rate × Time

$$\text{Time (exact interest)} = \frac{\text{Number of days of a loan}}{365}$$

$$\text{Time (ordinary interest)} = \frac{\text{Number of days of a loan}}{360}$$

Maturity value = Principal + Interest

Maturity value = Principal(1 + Rate × Time)

The Simple Interest Formula

$$\text{Principal} = \frac{\text{Interest}}{\text{Rate} \times \text{Time}}$$

$$\text{Rate} = \frac{\text{Interest}}{\text{Principal} \times \text{Time}}$$

$$\text{Time} = \frac{\text{Interest}}{\text{Principal} \times \text{Rate}}$$

Simple Discount Notes

Bank discount = Face value × Discount rate × Time

Proceeds = Face value − Bank discount

$$\text{Effective interest rate} = \frac{\text{Bank discount}}{\text{Proceeds} \times \text{Time}}$$

Discounting a Note before Maturity

Bank discount = Maturity value × Discount rate × Time

Proceeds = Maturity value − Bank discount

Purchasing U.S. Treasury Bills

Interest = Face value × Discount rate × Time

Purchase price = Face value − Interest

$$\text{Effective interest rate} = \frac{\text{Interest}}{\text{Purchase price} \times \text{Time}}$$

SUMMARY CHART

10

Section I: Understanding and Computing Simple Interest

Topic	Important Concepts	Illustrative Examples
Computing Simple Interest for Loans With Terms of Years or Months **P/O 10-1, p. 329**	Simple interest is calculated by using the formula $I = PRT$. **Interest = Principal × Rate × Time** *Note*: Time is always expressed in years or fractions of a year.	What is the amount of interest for a loan of \$20,000, at 12% simple interest, for 9 months? $I = 20{,}000 \times .12 \times \frac{9}{12}$ Interest = \$1,800
Calculating Interest for Loans with Terms of Days by the Exact Interest Method **P/O 10-2, p. 331**	Exact interest uses *365 days* as the time factor denominator. $\text{Time (exact)} = \frac{\text{Number of days of a loan}}{365}$	Using the exact interest method, what is the amount of interest on a loan of \$5,000, at 8%, for 95 days? $I = PRT$ $I = 5{,}000 \times .08 \times \frac{95}{365}$ Interest = \$104.11
Calculating Interest for Loans with Terms of Days by the Ordinary Interest Method **P/O 10-2, p. 331**	Ordinary interest uses *360 days* as the time factor denominator. $\text{Time (ordinary)} = \frac{\text{Number of days of a loan}}{360}$	Using the ordinary interest method, what is the amount of interest on a loan of \$8,000, at 9%, for 120 days? $I = PRT$ $I = 8{,}000 \times .09 \times \frac{120}{360}$ Interest = \$240
Calculating the Maturity Value of a Loan **P/O 10-3, p. 332**	When the time period of a loan is over, the loan is said to mature. The total payback of principal and interest is known as the maturity value of a loan. **Maturity value = Principal + Interest** **Maturity value = Principal(1 + Rate × Time)**	What is the maturity value of a loan for \$50,000, at 12% interest, for 3 years? $MV = 50{,}000(1 + .12 \times 3)$ $MV = 50{,}000(1.36)$ Maturity value = \$68,000
Calculating the Number of Days of a Loan **P/O 10-4, p. 333**	1. Determine the number of days remaining in the first month by subtracting the loan date from the number of days in that month. 2. List the number of days for each succeeding whole month. 3. List the number of loan days in the last month. 4. Add the days from Steps 1, 2, and 3.	Bob Delucia borrowed money from the Republic Bank on May 5 and repaid the loan on August 19. For how many days was this loan? May 31 −May 5 26 Days in May 61 June–July +19 August 106 Days

Section I: (continued)

Topic	Important Concepts	Illustrative Examples
Determining the Maturity Date of a Loan **P/O 10-5, p. 334**	1. Determine the number of days remaining in the first month. 2. Subtract days from Step 1 from number of days in the loan. 3. Subtract days in each succeeding whole month until you reach a month in which the difference is less than the days in that month. The maturity date will be the day of that month that corresponds to the difference.	What is the maturity date of a loan taken out on June 9 for 100 days? June 30 June − 9 21 Days in June 100 Days of the loan − 21 Days in June 79 − 31 Days in July 48 − 31 Days in August 17 At this point, the difference, 17, is less than the days in September; therefore the maturity date is September 17.

Section II: Using the Simple Interest Formula

Topic	Important Concepts	Illustrative Examples
Solving for the Principal **P/O 10-6, p. 339**	$\text{Principal} = \frac{\text{Interest}}{\text{Rate} \times \text{Time}}$ I (P) R T	Theresa Hayes borrowed money at 10% interest for 2 years. If the interest charge was $800, how much principal did Theresa borrow? $\text{Principal} = \frac{800}{.10 \times 2} = \frac{800}{.2}$ Principal = $4,000
Solving for the Rate **P/O 10-7, p. 340**	$\text{Rate} = \frac{\text{Interest}}{\text{Principal} \times \text{Time}}$ I P (R) T	Ed Williams borrowed $3,000 for 75 days. If the interest was $90 using ordinary interest, what was the rate on Ed's loan? $\text{Rate} = \frac{90}{3{,}000 \times \frac{75}{360}} = \frac{90}{625}$ Rate = .144 = 14.4%
Solving for the Time **P/O 10-8, p. 341**	When solving for time, whole numbers are years, and decimals are multiplied by 360 or 365 to get days. Any fraction of a day should be rounded up to the next higher day, because lending institutions consider any portion of a day to be another day. $\text{Time} = \frac{\text{Interest}}{\text{Principal} \times \text{Rate}}$ I P R (T)	What is the time period of a loan for $20,000 at 9% ordinary interest if the amount of interest is $1,000? $\text{Time} = \frac{1{,}000}{20{,}000 \times .09} = \frac{1{,}000}{1{,}800} = .555555$ Time = .555555 × 360 = 199.99 = 200 Days

Section II: (continued)

Topic	Important Concepts	Illustrative Examples
Calculating Loans Involving Partial Payments before Maturity **P/O 10-9, p. 343**	1. Compute the interest due from the date of loan to the date of partial payment. 2. Subtract the interest (Step 1) from the partial payment. 3. The balance of the partial payment is used to reduce the principal. 4. Maturity value is computed by adding the interest since the last partial payment to the adjusted principal.	Betty Price borrowed \$7,000 at 10% ordinary interest for 120 days. On day 90, Betty made a partial payment of \$3,000. What is the new maturity value of the loan? $I = PRT$ $I = 7{,}000 \times .10 \times \frac{90}{360} = \$175$ \$3,000 Partial payment − 175 Accumulated interest \$2,825 Reduces principal \$7,000 Original principal − 2,825 \$4,175 Adjusted principal Days remaining = 120 − 90 = 30 $I = PRT$ $I = 4{,}175 \times .10 \times \frac{30}{360} = \$34.79$ Maturity value = $P + I$ $MV = 4{,}175 + 34.79$ Maturity value = \$4,209.79

Section III: Understanding Promissory Notes and Discounting

Topic	Important Concepts	Illustrative Examples
Calculating Bank Discount and Proceeds for a Simple Discount Note **P/O 10-10, p. 350**	With discounting, the interest, known as the bank discount, is deducted from the face value of the loan. The borrower gets the difference, known as the proceeds. **Bank discount = Face value × Discount rate × Time** **Proceeds = Face value − Bank discount**	What are the bank discount and proceeds of a \$10,000 note discounted at 12% for 6 months? Bank discount $= 10{,}000 \times .12 \times \frac{6}{12}$ Bank discount = \$600 Proceeds = 10,000 − 600 = \$9,400
Calculating True or Effective Rate of Interest for a Simple Discount Note **P/O 10-11, p. 351**	Because the proceeds are less than the face value of a loan, the true or effective interest rate is higher than the stated bank discount rate. $\textbf{Effective interest rate} = \frac{\textbf{Bank discount}}{\textbf{Proceeds} \times \textbf{Time}}$	What is the effective rate of a simple discount note for \$20,000, at a bank discount of 15%, for a period of 9 months? Bank discount = $FV \times R \times T$ Bank discount $= 20{,}000 \times .15 \times \frac{9}{12}$ Bank discount = \$2,250 Proceeds = Face value − Bank discount Proceeds = 20,000 − 2,250 Proceeds = \$17,750 Effective interest rate $= \frac{2{,}250}{17{,}750 \times \frac{9}{12}}$ Effective interest rate = 16.9%

Section III: (continued)

Topic	Important Concepts	Illustrative Examples
Discounting Notes before Maturity **P/O 10-12, p. 352**	Frequently companies extend credit to their customers by accepting short-term promissory notes as payment for goods or services. These notes can be cashed in early by discounting them at a bank and receiving the proceeds. 1. Calculate the maturity value. $MV = P(1 + RT)$ 2. Determine the discount period. 3. Calculate the bank discount. **Bank discount = $MV \times R \times T$** 4. Calculate the proceeds. **Proceeds = MV − Bank discount**	East Coast Food Wholesalers received a $100,000 promissory note for 6 months, at 11% interest, from SuperSaver Supermarkets. If East Coast discounts the note after 4 months at a discount rate of 15%, what proceeds will they receive? $MV = 100{,}000\left(1 + .11 \times \frac{6}{12}\right)$ $MV = \$105{,}500$ Discount period = 2 months (6 − 4) $\text{Bank discount} = 105{,}500 \times .15 \times \frac{2}{12}$ Bank discount = $2,637.50 Proceeds = 105,500.00 − 2,637.50 Proceeds = $102,862.50
Purchasing U.S. Treasury Bills **P/O 10-13, p. 353**	U.S. Treasury bills, or T-bills, are short-term government securities with maturities of 4 weeks, 13 weeks, and 26 weeks. Sold by banks, brokers, and dealers in increments of $1,000, these securities represent loans to the U.S. government. Just like discounted bank notes, T-bills are sold at a discount from their face value. **Interest = Face value × Discount rate × Time** **Purchase price = Face value − Interest** $\textbf{Effective interest rate} = \frac{\textbf{Interest}}{\textbf{Purchase price} \times \textbf{Time}}$	Shauna Dixon purchased $3,000 in U.S. Treasury bills with a discount rate of 5% for a period of 26 weeks. a. How much interest did Shauna earn on the T-bill investment? $\text{Interest} = 3{,}000 \times .05 \times \frac{26}{52} = \$75$ b. How much was the purchase price of Shauna's T-bills? Purchase price = 3,000 − 75 = $2,925 c. What was the effective interest rate of Shauna's T-bill investment? Round to the nearest hundredth of a percent. $\text{Effective interest rate} = \frac{75}{2{,}925 \times \frac{26}{52}} = .05128 = 5.13\%$

TRY IT EXERCISE SOLUTIONS FOR CHAPTER 10

1a. $I = PRT = 4{,}000 \times .07 \times 2.25 = \$630$

1b. $I = PRT = 45{,}000 \times .0975 \times \frac{3}{12} = \$1{,}096.88$

1c. $I = PRT = 130{,}000 \times .104 \times \frac{42}{12} = \$47{,}320$

2. $I = PRT = 23{,}000 \times .08 \times \frac{119}{365} = \$599.89$

3. $I = PRT = 15{,}000 \times .095 \times \frac{250}{360} = \$989.58$

4a. $I = PRT = 15{,}400 \times .065 \times \frac{24}{12} = \$2{,}002$

$MV = P + I = 15{,}400 + 2{,}002 = \$17{,}402$

4b. $MV = P(1 + RT) = 450{,}000\left(1 + .08 \times \frac{9}{12}\right) = \underline{\underline{\$477{,}000}}$

5a.

$$\begin{array}{rl} 30 & 26 \text{ April} \\ -4 & 61 \text{ May–June} \\ \hline 26 \text{ Days} & +18 \text{ July} \\ & \underline{\underline{105 \text{ Days}}} \end{array}$$

5b.

$$\begin{array}{rl} 30 & 15 \text{ June} \\ -15 & 92 \text{ July–Sept.} \\ \hline 15 \text{ Days} & +9 \text{ Oct.} \\ & \underline{\underline{116 \text{ Days}}} \end{array}$$

$I = PRT = 3{,}500 \times .11 \times \frac{116}{365} = \underline{\underline{\$122.36}}$

6a.

$$\begin{array}{lr} \text{Days in Sept.} & 30 \\ \text{Loan date} & -\ 9 \\ \hline \text{Days of Sept.} & 21 \end{array} \qquad \begin{array}{rl} 125 & \text{Days of loan} \\ -\ 21 & \text{Days of Sept.} \\ \hline 104 & \\ -\ 31 & \text{October} \\ \hline 73 & \\ -\ 30 & \text{November} \\ \hline 43 & \\ -\ 31 & \text{December} \\ \hline 12 & \rightarrow \underline{\underline{\text{January 12}}} \end{array}$$

6b. $MV = P(1 + RT) = 9{,}000\left(1 + .10 \times \frac{80}{360}\right) = \underline{\underline{\$9{,}200}}$

$$\begin{array}{rll} 31 & 10 \text{ Oct.} & \\ -21 & 61 \text{ Nov.–Dec.} & \\ \hline 10 \text{ Days} & +\ 9 \text{ Jan.} & \rightarrow \underline{\underline{\text{January 9}}} \\ & 80 \text{ Days} & \end{array}$$

7. $P = \frac{I}{RT} = \frac{560}{.09 \times \frac{125}{360}} = \underline{\underline{\$17{,}920}}$

8. $R = \frac{I}{PT} = \frac{1{,}960}{25{,}000 \times \frac{245}{360}} = .1152 = \underline{\underline{11.52\%}}$

9. $T = \frac{I}{PR} = \frac{650}{15{,}000 \times .095} = .4561404$

$$\begin{array}{r} .4561404 \\ \times\ 360 \\ \hline 164.2 = \underline{\underline{165 \text{ Days}}} \end{array}$$

10. $I = PRT = 15{,}000 \times .12 \times \frac{20}{360} = \$100$ 1st Part pay = 20 days

$$\begin{array}{rrl} 4{,}000 \text{ Pmt} & 15{,}000 & \\ -\ 100 \text{ Int} & -3{,}900 & \\ \hline 3{,}900 & 11{,}100 & \text{Adjustment Principal} \end{array}$$

$I = PRT = 11{,}100 \times .12 \times \frac{40}{360} = \$148$ 2nd Part pay = 40 days (60 − 20)

$$\begin{array}{rrl} 5{,}000 \text{ Pmt} & 11{,}100 & \\ -\ 148 \text{ Int} & -4{,}852 & \\ \hline 4{,}852 & 6{,}248 & \text{Adjustment Principal} \end{array}$$

Days remaining = 40 (100 − 60)

$I = PRT = 6{,}248 \times .12 \times \frac{40}{360} = \$83.31$

Final due = $P + I$ = 6,248.00 + 83.31 = $\underline{\underline{\$6{,}331.31}}$

11. Bank discount $= FV \times R \times T = 20{,}000 \times .13 \times \frac{330}{360} = \underline{\underline{\$2{,}383.33}}$

Proceeds = Face value − Bank discount = 20,000.00 − 2,383.33 = $\underline{\underline{\$17{,}616.67}}$

12. Bank discount $= FV \times R \times T = 40{,}000 \times .11 \times \frac{270}{360} = \$3{,}300$

Proceeds = Face value − Bank discount = 40,000 − 3,300 = \$36,700

$\text{Effective interest rate} = \frac{\text{Bank discount}}{\text{Proceeds} \times \text{Time}} = \frac{3{,}300}{36{,}700 \times \frac{270}{360}} = \underline{\underline{11.99\%}}$

13. $MV = P(1+RT) = 35{,}000\left(1 + .10 \times \frac{6}{12}\right) = \$36{,}750$

$$\begin{array}{rr} & 6 \text{ months} \\ & -4 \text{ months} \\ \hline \text{Discount period} = & 2 \text{ months} \end{array}$$

Bank discount $= MV \times R \times T = 36{,}750 \times .14 \times \frac{2}{12} = \$857.50$

Proceeds = Maturity value − Bank discount = \$36,750.00 − 857.50 = $\underline{\underline{\$35{,}892.50}}$

14. a. Interest = Face value × Discount rate × Time $= 10{,}000 \times .046 \times \frac{26}{52} = \underline{\underline{\$230}}$

b. Purchase price = Face value − Interest = 10,000 − 230 = $\underline{\underline{\$9{,}770}}$

c. Effective interest rate $= \dfrac{\text{Interest}}{\text{Purchase price} \times \text{Time}} = \dfrac{230}{9{,}770 \times \frac{26}{52}} = .04708 = \underline{\underline{4.71\%}}$

CONCEPT REVIEW

1. The price or rental fee charged by a lender to a borrower for the use of money is known as ____. (10.1)
interest

2. List the three factors that determine the amount of interest charged on a loan. (10-1)
   - principal (amount borrowed)
   - rate (percent of interest)
   - time (length of time of the loan)

3. Interest calculated solely on the principal amount borrowed is known as ____ interest, while interest calculated at regular intervals on the principal and previously earned interest is known as ____ interest. (10-1)
simple, compound

4. The interest calculation method that uses 365 days (366 in leap year) as the time factor denominator is known as ____ interest. (10-2)
exact

5. The interest calculation method that uses 360 days as the time factor denominator is known as ____ interest. (10-2)
ordinary

6. Maturity value is the total payback of principal and interest of a loan. List the two formulas for calculating maturity value. (10-3)
Maturity value = Principal + Interest
Maturity value = Principal(1 + Rate × Time)

7. The first day of a loan is known as the ____ date; the last day of a loan is known as the ____ date. (10-4, 10-5)
loan, due or maturity

8. Write the formula for calculating simple interest. (10-6)
Simple interest = Principal × Rate × Time

9. When solving the simple interest formula for principal, rate, or time, the ____ is always the numerator. (10-6, 10-7, 10-8)
interest

10. The U.S. rule states that when a partial payment is made on a loan, the payment is first used to pay off the accumulated ____ to date, and the balance is used to reduce the ____. (10-9)
interest, principal

11. The amount of money that the borrower receives at the time a discounted note is made is known as the ____. (10-10)
proceeds

12. The actual interest rate charged on a discounted note is known as the ____, or ____ interest rate. (10-11)
true, effective

13. When discounting a note before maturity, the proceeds are calculated by substracting the amount of the bank discount from the ____ value of the loan. (10-12)
maturity

14. Discounted short term loans made to the U.S. government are known as U.S. Treasury ____. (10-13)
bills

ASSESSMENT TEST

CHAPTER 10

Name

Class

Using the exact interest method (365 days), find the amount of interest on the following loans.

	Principal	Rate (%)	Time (days)	Exact Interest
1.	$15,000	13	120	$641.10
2.	$1,700	$12\frac{1}{2}$	33	$19.21

Using the ordinary interest method (360 days), find the amount of interest on the following loans.

	Principal	Rate (%)	Time (days)	Ordinary Interest
3.	$20,600	12	98	$672.93
4.	$286,000	$13\frac{1}{2}$	224	$24,024.00

What is the maturity value of the following loans? Use $MV = P(1 + RT)$ to find the maturity values.

	Principal	Rate (%)	Time	Maturity Value
5.	$15,800	14	4 years	$24,648.00
6.	$120,740	$11\frac{3}{4}$	7 months	$129,015.72

From the following information, determine the number of days of each loan.

	Loan Date	Due Date	Number of Days
7.	April 16	August 1	107
8.	October 20	December 18	59

From the following information, determine the maturity date of each loan.

	Loan Date	Time Loan (days)	Maturity Date
9.	November 30	55	Jan. 24
10.	May 15	111	Sept. 3

Compute the principal for the following loans. Round answers to the nearest cent.

	Principal	Rate (%)	Time	Interest
11.	$11,666.67	12	2 years	$2,800
12.	$67,428.57	$10\frac{1}{2}$	10 months	$5,900

Compute the rate for the following loans. Round answers to the nearest tenth of a percent.

	Principal	Rate (%)	Time	Interest
13.	$2,200	9.1	4 years	$800
14.	$50,000	12	9 months	$4,500

Use the ordinary interest method to compute the time for the following loans. Round answers to the next higher day, when necessary.

	Principal	Rate (%)	Time (days)	Interest
15.	$13,500	13	72	$350
16.	$7,900	10.4	274	$625

Answers

1. $641.10
2. $19.21
3. $672.93
4. $24,024.00
5. $24,648.00
6. $129,015.72
7. 107
8. 59
9. Jan. 24
10. Sept. 3
11. $11,666.67
12. $67,428.57
13. 9.1%
14. 12%
15. 72 days
16. 274 days

Complete, worked-out solutions to Questions 1–16 appear in Appendix B, following the index.

CHAPTER 10

Name

Class

Answers

17. 190 days

$13,960.00

18. $40,265.62

$42,055.62

19. 15.2%

$2,795.00

20. 131 days

$2,365.28

$47,634.72

21. Jan. 20

$20,088.54

$854,911.46

22. $393.75

$22,106.25

10.69%

23. $10,544.72

$279,455.28

12.35%

24. Apr. 5

$8,202.89

35 days

$8,083.26

25. Aug. 25

$5,642.31

34 days

$5,569.30

26. $297.12

$74,702.88

5.17%

27. $686.00

$27,314.00

5.02%

28. a. $227.95

b. $4,227.95

c. Oct. 30

Calculate the missing information for the following loans. Round percents to the nearest tenth, and days to the next higher day, when necessary.

	Principal	Rate (%)	Time (days)	Interest Method	Interest	Maturity Value
17.	$13,000	14	190	Ordinary	$960	$13,960.00
18.	$40,265.62	12.2	133	Exact	$1,790	$42,055.62
19.	$2,500	15.2	280	Ordinary	$295	$2,795.00

Using ordinary interest, calculate the missing information for the following simple discount notes.

	Face Value	Discount Rate (%)	Date of Note	Term (days)	Maturity Date	Bank Discount	Proceeds
20.	$50,000	13	Apr. 5	131	Aug. 14	$2,365.28	$47,634.72
21.	$875,000	$9\frac{1}{2}$	Oct. 25	87	Jan. 20	$20,088.54	$854,911.46

Using ordinary interest (360 days), calculate the bank discount, proceeds, and effective rate for the following simple discount notes. Round effective rate to the nearest hundredth of a percent.

	Face Value	Discount Rate (%)	Term (days)	Bank Discount	Proceeds	Effective Rate (%)
22.	$22,500	$10\frac{1}{2}$	60	$393.75	$22,106.25	10.69
23.	$290,000	11.9	110	$10,544.72	$279,455.28	12.35

The following interest-bearing promissory notes were discounted at a bank by the payee before maturity. Use the ordinary interest method (360 days) to solve for the missing information.

	Face Value	Interest Rate (%)	Date of Note	Term of Note (days)	Maturity Date	Maturity Value	Date Note Discounted	Discount Period (days)	Discount Rate (%)	Proceeds
24.	$8,000	11	Jan. 12	83	Apr. 5	$8,202.89	Mar. 1	35	15	$8,083.26
25.	$5,500	$13\frac{1}{2}$	June 17	69	Aug. 25	$5,642.31	July 22	34	13.7	$5,569.30

Calculate the interest, purchase price, and effective interest rate of the following Treasury bill (T-bill) purchases. Round effective interest rate to the nearest hundredth of a percent.

	Face Value	Discount Rate (%)	Term (weeks)	Interest	Purchase Price	Effective Rate (%)
26.	$75,000	5.15	4	$297.12	$74,702.88	5.17
27.	$28,000	4.90	26	$686.00	$27,314.00	5.02

Solve the following word problems. Round to the nearest cent, when necessary.

28. On May 23, Karen Bryant borrowed $4,000 from the Northeast Credit Union at 13% for 160 days. The credit union uses the exact interest method.

a. What was the amount of interest on the loan?

$$I = PRT = 4{,}000 \times .13 \times \frac{160}{365} = \$227.95$$

b. What was the maturity value of the loan?

$MV = P + I = 4{,}000.00 + 227.95 = \$4{,}227.95$

c. What is the maturity date of the loan?

31
− 23
8 Days

8 May
122 June – Sept.
+ 30 Oct. → October 30
160 Days

Complete, worked-out solutions to Questions 17–27 appear in Appendix B, following the index.

29. Randy Moya missed an income tax payment of $2,600. The Internal Revenue Service charges a 15% simple interest penalty calculated by the exact interest method. If the tax was due on April 15 but was paid on July 17, what is the amount of the penalty charge?

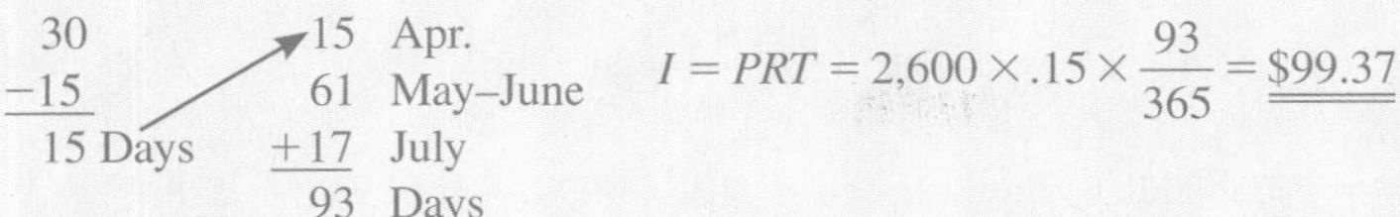

30	15	Apr.
−15	61	May–June
15 Days	+17	July
	93	Days

$$I = PRT = 2{,}600 \times .15 \times \frac{93}{365} = \$99.37$$

30. Teresa Hayes borrowed money to buy furniture from her credit union at 13.2% simple interest. If the loan was repaid in $2\frac{1}{2}$ years and the amount of interest was $1,320, how much did Teresa borrow?

$$P = \frac{I}{RT} = \frac{1{,}320}{.132 \times 2.5} = \$4{,}000$$

31. George Stone took out a loan for $5,880 at the Linville Ridge Bank for 110 days. The bank uses the ordinary method for calculating interest. What rate of interest was charged if the amount of interest was $275? Round to the nearest tenth of a percent.

$$R = \frac{I}{PT} = \frac{275}{5{,}880 \times \frac{110}{360}} = 15.3\%$$

32. Michelle Lockard deposited $2,000 in a savings account paying 6% ordinary interest. How long will it take for her investment to amount to $2,600?

$$T = \frac{I}{PR} = \frac{600}{2{,}000 \times .06} = 5 \text{ Years}$$

33. Karen Streeter borrowed $16,000 at 14% ordinary interest, for 88 days. On day 30 of the loan, she made a partial payment of $7,000. What is the new maturity value of the loan?

$$I = PRT = 16{,}000 \times .14 \times \frac{30}{360} = \$186.67 \qquad I = PRT = 9{,}186.67 \times .14 \times \frac{58}{360} = \$207.21$$

$$MV = P + I = 9{,}186.67 + 207.21 = \$9{,}393.88$$

$7,000.00 Paid	$16,000.00	88
− 186.67 Interest	− 6,813.33	− 30
$6,813.33	$9,186.67 Adjusted principal	58 Days remaining

34. Iberia Tile Company borrowed $40,000 on April 6 for 66 days. The rate was 14% using the ordinary interest method. On day 25 of the loan Iberia made a partial payment of $15,000, and on day 45 of the loan Iberia made a second partial payment of $10,000.

a. What is the new maturity value of the loan?

$$I = PRT = 40{,}000 \times .14 \times \frac{25}{360} = \$388.89 \qquad I = PRT = 25{,}388.89 \times .14 \times \frac{20}{360} = \$197.47 \qquad I = PRT = 15{,}586.36 \times .14 \times \frac{21}{360} = \$127.29$$

$$MV = P + I = 15{,}586.36 + 127.29 = \$15{,}713.65$$

$15,000.00 Paid	$40,000.00	$10,000.00 Paid	$25,388.89
− 388.89 Interest	−14,611.11	− 197.47 Interest	− 9,802.53
$14,611.11	$25,388.89 Adjusted principal	$9,802.53	$15,586.36 Adjusted principal

b. What is the maturity date of the loan?

30	24	Apr.
− 6	31	May
24 Days	+11	June → June 11
	66	Days

CHAPTER 10

Name

Class

Answers

29. $99.37

30. $4,000

31. 15.3%

32. 5 Years

33. $9,393.88

34. a. $15,713.65

b. June 11

Name

Class

Answers

35. a. $28,970.83

b. Nov. 12

c. 13.46%

36. a. May 20

b. $71,400

c. Apr. 10

d. $70,249.67

35. Alicia Morrow signed a $30,000 simple discount promissory note at the Grove Park Bank. The discount rate was 13%, ordinary interest, and the note was made on August 9 for 95 days.

a. What proceeds did Alicia receive on the note?

$$\text{Bank discount} = FV \times R \times T = 30{,}000 \times .13 \times \frac{95}{360} = \$1{,}029.17$$

$$\text{Proceeds} = \text{Face value} - \text{Bank discount} = 30{,}000.00 - 1{,}029.17 = \underline{\underline{\$28{,}970.83}}$$

b. What was the maturity date of the note?

31	22	Aug.
− 9	61	Sept.–Oct.
22 Days	+ 12	Nov. ⟶ November 12
	95	Days

c. What was the effective interest rate of the note? Round the answer to the nearest hundredth of a percent.

$$\text{Effective interest rate} = \frac{\text{Bank discount}}{\text{Proceeds} \times \text{Time}} = \frac{1{,}029.17}{28{,}970.83 \times \frac{95}{360}} = \underline{\underline{13.46\%}}$$

36. First Impressions, Inc., a publisher of college textbooks, received a $70,000 promissory note at 12% ordinary interest for 60 days from one of its customers, Reader's Choice Bookstores. After 20 days, First Impressions discounted the note at the Hemisphere Bank at a discount rate of 14.5%. The note was made on March 21.

a. What was the maturity date of the note?

31	10	Mar.
−21	30	Apr.
10 Days	+20	May ⟶ May 20
	60	Days

b. What was the maturity value of the note?

$$MV = P(1 + RT) = 70{,}000\left(1 + .12 \times \frac{60}{360}\right) = \underline{\underline{\$71{,}400}}$$

c. What was the discount date of the note?

31	10	Mar.
−21	+10	Apr. ⟶ April 10
10 Days	20	Days

d. What proceeds did First Impressions receive after discounting the note?

$$\text{Bank discount} = MV \times R \times T = 71{,}400 \times .145 \times \frac{40}{360} = \$1{,}150.33$$

$$\text{Proceeds} = \text{Maturity value} - \text{Bank discount} = 71{,}400.00 - 1{,}150.33 = \underline{\underline{\$70{,}249.67}}$$

On-campus and online bookstores are the main sources of textbooks for college students.

CHAPTER 10

Name

Class

Answers

37. a. $752

b. $63,248

c. 4.76%

38. a. $4,483.08

b. Borrow the money

37. Fernando Rodriguez purchased $64,000 in U.S. Treasury bills with a discount rate of 4.7% for a period of 13 weeks.

a. How much interest did Fernando earn on the T-bill investment?

Interest = Face value × Discount rate × Time

$$\text{Interest} = 64{,}000 \times .047 \times \frac{13}{52} = \$752$$

b. How much was the purchase price of Fernando's T-bills?

Purchase price = Face value − Interest

Purchase price = 64,000 − 752 = $63,248

c. What was the effective interest rate of Fernando's T-bill investment? Round to the nearest hundredth of a percent.

$$\text{Effective interest rate} = \frac{\text{Interest}}{\text{Purchase price} \times \text{Time}}$$

$$\text{Effective interest rate} = \frac{752}{63{,}248 \times \frac{13}{52}} = .04755 = 4.76\%$$

BUSINESS DECISION BORROWING TO TAKE ADVANTAGE OF A CASH DISCOUNT

38. You are the accountant for New Wave Designs, a retail furniture store. Recently, an order of sofas and chairs was received from a manufacturer with terms of 3/15, n/45. The order amounted to $230,000, and New Wave can borrow money at 13% ordinary interest.

a. How much can be saved by borrowing the funds for 30 days to take advantage of the cash discount? (Remember, New Wave only has to borrow the net amount due, after the cash discount is taken.)

Cash discount = 230,000 × .03 = $6,900

Amount needed = 230,000 − 6,900 = $223,100

$$I = PRT = 223{,}100 \times .13 \times \frac{30}{360} = \$2{,}416.92$$

Savings = Cash discount − Interest = 6,900.00 − 2,416.92 = $4,483.08

b. What would you recommend?

Recommendation: Savings of almost $4,500 is significant—Borrow the money

In the Business World

This Business Decision illustrates an important business concept, borrowing money to take advantage of a cash discount.

Note how much can be saved by taking the cash discount, even if the money is borrowed.

For a review of cash discounts, see Section IV, Chapter 7.

COLLABORATIVE LEARNING ACTIVITY

The Automobile Loan

As a team, choose a particular type of automobile category that you want to research (such as sport utility vehicle, sports car, hybrid, or luxury sedan). Then have each member of the team choose a different manufacturer's model within that category.

For example, if the team picked sport utility vehicle, then individual choices might include Nissan Murano, Mitsubishi Endeavor, Chrysler Pacifica, or Chevy Tahoe.

a. From your local newspaper and the Internet, collect advertisments and offers for the purchase of the model you have chosen.

b. Visit or call a dealership for the vehicle you picked. Speak with a salesperson about the types of "deals" currently being offered on that model.
- What loan rates and terms are available from the dealer?
- Who is the actual lender?

c. Contact various lending institutions (banks, finance companies, credit unions) and inquire about vehicle loans.
- What loan rates and terms are being offered?
- Which one is offering the best deal? Why?
- How do these rates and terms compare with those from the dealership?

CHAPTER 11

Compound Interest and Present Value

PERFORMANCE OBJECTIVES

Section I Compound Interest—The Time Value of Money

11-1: Manually calculating compound amount (future value) and compound interest (p. 374)

11-2: Computing compound amount (future value) and compound interest by using compound interest tables (p. 375)

11-3: Creating compound interest table factors for periods beyond the table (p. 378)

11-4: Calculating annual percentage yield (APY) or effective interest rate (p. 379)

11-5: (Optional) Calculating compound amount (future value) by using the compound interest formula (p. 380)

Section II Present Value

11-6: Calculating the present value of a future amount by using present value tables (p. 386)

11-7: Creating present value table factors for periods beyond the table (p. 388)

11-8: (Optional) Calculating present value of a future amount by using the present value formula (p. 389)

SECTION I COMPOUND INTEREST—THE TIME VALUE OF MONEY

compound interest Interest that is applied a number of times during the term of a loan or investment. Interest paid on principal and previously earned interest.

In Chapter 10 we studied simple interest, in which the formula $I = PRT$ was applied once during the term of a loan or investment to find the amount of interest. In business, another common way of calculating interest is by a method known as *compounding*, or **compound interest**, in which the interest calculation is applied a number of times during the term of the loan or investment.

Compound interest yields considerably higher interest than simple interest because the investor is earning interest on the interest. With compound interest, the interest earned for each period is reinvested or added to the previous principal before the next calculation or compounding. The previous principal plus interest then becomes the new principal for the next period. For example, $100 invested at 8% interest is worth $108 after the first year ($100 principal + $8 interest). If the interest is not withdrawn, the interest for the next period will be calculated based on $108 principal.

11-1

As this compounding process repeats itself each period, the principal keeps growing by the amount of the previous interest. As the number of compounding periods increases, the amount of interest earned grows dramatically, especially when compared with simple interest, as illustrated in Exhibit 11-1.

Exhibit 11-1
The Time Value of Money

THE VALUE OF COMPOUND INTEREST

Simple Interest

The value of $1,000 invested at a 10% annual interest rate varies greatly depending on the accumulation of simple or compound interest.

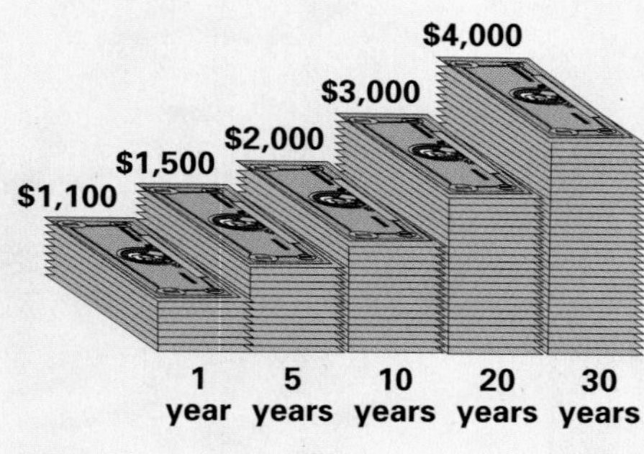

Compound Interest

Compound interest yields more than four times the investment that simple interest yields after 30 years.

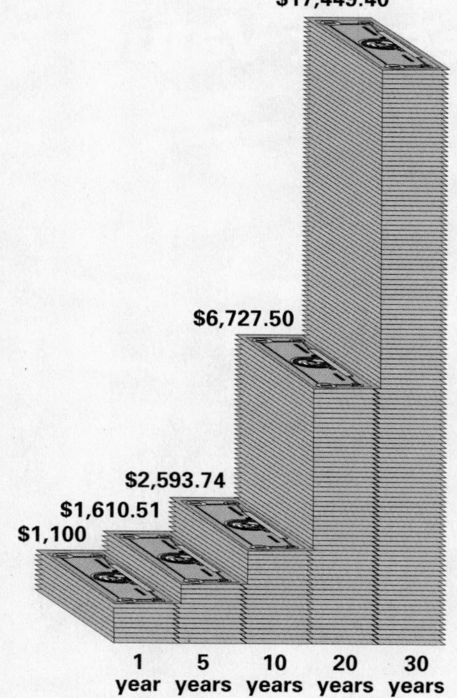

This chapter introduces you to an all-important business concept, the **time value of money**. Consider this: If you were owed $1,000, would you rather have it now or one year from now? If you answered "now," you already have a feeling for the concept. Money "now," or in the *present*, is more desirable than the same amount of money in the *future*, because it can be invested and earn interest as time goes by.

In this chapter you learn to calculate the **compound amount (future value)** of an investment at compound interest, when the **present amount (present value)** is known. You also learn to calculate the present value that must be deposited now, at compound interest, to yield a known future amount. See Exhibit 11-2.

time value of money The idea that money "now," or in the present, is more desirable than the same amount of money in the future, because it can be invested and earn interest as time goes by.

compound amount, or future value (FV) The total amount of principal and accumulated interest at the end of a loan or investment.

present amount, or present value (PV) An amount of money that must be deposited today, at compound interest, to provide a specified lump sum of money in the future.

5.39% APY* One Year CD

Great rates, more interest!

Certificates of Deposit

Term	Interest Rate	APY*
1 month	4.20%	4.29%
6 month	4.48%	4.58%
1 year	5.25%	5.39%
2 year	5.65%	5.81%
5 year	5.80%	5.97%

Ocean Vista Bank www.oceanvistabank.com

*Annual Percentage Yield
Interest compounded daily

In the Business World

Today, most banks, savings and loan institutions, and credit unions pay compound interest on depositor's money. The U.S. government also uses compounding for savings bonds.

Teaching Transparency 11-2

Exhibit 11-2
Present Value and Future Value at Compound Interest

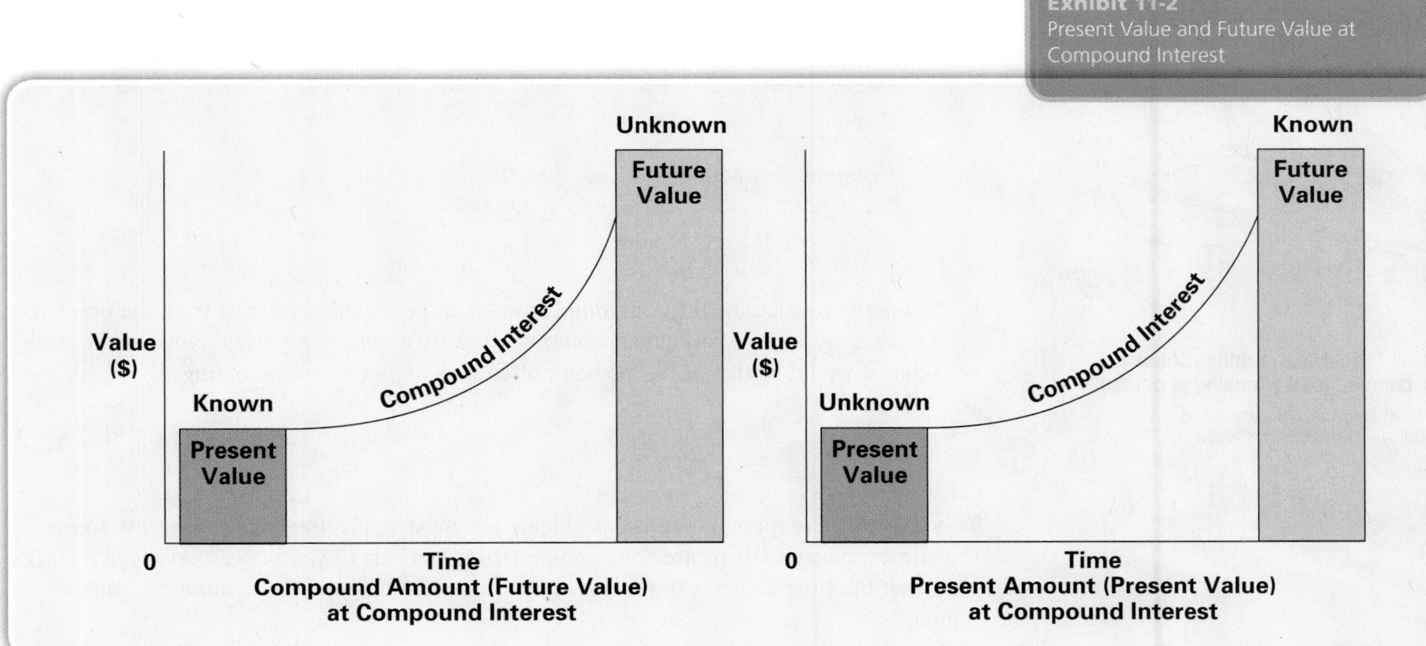

MANUALLY CALCULATING COMPOUND AMOUNT (FUTURE VALUE) AND COMPOUND INTEREST

Compounding divides the time of a loan or investment into compounding periods or simply periods. To manually calculate the compound amount or future value of an investment, we must compound or calculate the interest as many times as there are compounding periods, at the interest rate per period.

For example, an investment made for 5 years at 12% compounded annually (once per year) would have five compounding periods (5 years × 1 period per year), each at 12%. If the same investment was compounded semiannually (two times per year), there would be 10 compounding periods (5 years × 2 periods per year), each at 6% (12% annual rate ÷ 2 periods per year).

The amount of compound interest is calculated by subtracting the principal from the compound amount.

Compound interest = Compound amount − Principal

TEACHING TIP

Be sure students understand that compound interest is actually the simple interest formula, $I = PRT$, applied a number of times, with each time the interest added to the previous principal.

EXAMPLE 1 MANUALLY CALCULATING COMPOUND INTEREST

a. Katie Yanos invested $5,000 in a passbook savings account at 10% interest, compounded annually, for 2 years. Manually calculate the compound amount of the investment and the total amount of compound interest Katie earned.

SOLUTION STRATEGY

To solve this compound interest problem manually, we must apply the simple interest formula twice, because there are two compounding periods (2 years × 1 period per year). Note how the interest from the first period is reinvested or added to the original principal to earn interest in the second period.

Original principal	$5,000.00	
Interest—period 1	+ 500.00	($I = PRT = 5{,}000.00 \times .10 \times 1$)
Principal—period 2	5,500.00	
Interest—period 2	+ 550.00	($I = PRT = 5{,}500.00 \times .10 \times 1$)
Compound Amount	$6,050.00	

Compound Amount	$6,050.00
Principal	− 5,000.00
Compound Interest Earned	$1,050.00

"I feel like a million bucks, compounded annually, of course."

b. Manually recalculate the compound amount and compound interest from the previous example by using semiannual compounding (two times per year). How much more interest would Katie earn if the bank offered semiannual compounding?

SOLUTION STRATEGY

To solve this compound interest problem, we must apply the simple interest formula four times, because there are four compounding periods (2 years × 2 periods per year). Note that the time factor is now $\frac{6}{12}$ or $\frac{1}{2}$, because semiannual compounding means every 6 months.

Original principal	\$5,000.00	
Interest—period 1	+ 250.00	($I = PRT = 5{,}000.00 \times .10 \times \frac{1}{2}$)
Principal—period 2	5,250.00	
Interest—period 2	+ 262.50	($I = PRT = 5{,}250.00 \times .10 \times \frac{1}{2}$)
Principal—period 3	5,512.50	
Interest—period 3	+ 275.63	($I = PRT = 5{,}512.50 \times .10 \times \frac{1}{2}$)
Principal—period 4	5,788.13	
Interest—period 4	+ 289.41	($I = PRT = 5{,}788.13 \times .10 \times \frac{1}{2}$)
Compound Amount	\$6,077.54	

Compound Amount	\$6,077.54
Principal	− 5,000.00
Compound Interest	\$1,077.54

For the same investment variables, semiannual compounding yields \$27.54 more than annual compounding:

Interest with semiannual compounding	\$1,077.54
Interest with annual compounding	−1,050.00
	\$27.54

TRY IT EXERCISE 1

Gail Parker invested \$10,000 at 12% interest, compounded semiannually, for 3 years. Manually calculate the compound amount and the compound interest of Gail's investment.

CHECK YOUR ANSWERS WITH THE SOLUTIONS ON PAGE 395.

In the Business World

The Rule of 72
There is an easy method for calculating how long it takes an amount of money to double in value at compound interest. Simply divide the number 72 by the interest rate. The result is the number of years it takes to double in value.

$$\text{Years to double} = \frac{72}{\text{Compound interest rate}}$$

- For example, if you invested money at 6% compound interest, it would take 12 years ($\frac{72}{6} = 12$) to double your money.
- If you were able to find an investment that paid 9% interest, you could double your money in 8 years ($\frac{72}{9} = 8$).

COMPUTING COMPOUND AMOUNT (FUTURE VALUE) AND COMPOUND INTEREST BY USING COMPOUND INTEREST TABLES

You do not have to work many compound interest problems manually, particularly those with numerous compounding periods, before you start wishing for an easier way! In actuality, there are two other methods for solving compound interest problems. The first uses a compound interest formula, and the second uses compound interest tables.

The compound interest formula, $A = P(1 + i)^n$, contains an exponent and therefore requires the use of a calculator with an exponential function key. The use of the compound interest formula is covered in Performance Objective 11-5.

A compound interest table, such as Table 11-1 on page 376, is a useful set of factors that represents the future value of \$1.00 at various interest rates for a number of compounding periods. Because these factors are based on \$1.00, the future values of other principal amounts are found by multiplying the appropriate table factor by the number of dollars of principal.

Compound amount (future value) = Table factor × Principal

To use the compound interest tables, we must know the number of compounding periods and the interest rate per period. Exhibit 11-3, on page 377, shows the various compounding options and the corresponding number of periods per year. *Note:* The greater the number of compounding periods per year, the higher the interest earned on the investment. Today, interest can actually be calculated on a continuous basis—that is, up to the minute. In competitive markets, many banks offer continuous compounding as an incentive to attract new deposits.

11-3

Table 11-1
Compound Interest Table (Future Value of $1 at Compound Interest)

Periods	$\frac{1}{2}$%	1%	$1\frac{1}{2}$%	2%	3%	4%	5%	6%	7%	8%	Periods
1	1.00500	1.01000	1.01500	1.02000	1.03000	1.04000	1.05000	1.06000	1.07000	1.08000	1
2	1.01003	1.02010	1.03023	1.04040	1.06090	1.08160	1.10250	1.12360	1.14490	1.16640	2
3	1.01508	1.03030	1.04568	1.06121	1.09273	1.12486	1.15763	1.19102	1.22504	1.25971	3
4	1.02015	1.04060	1.06136	1.08243	1.12551	1.16986	1.21551	1.26248	1.31080	1.36049	4
5	1.02525	1.05101	1.07728	1.10408	1.15927	1.21665	1.27628	1.33823	1.40255	1.46933	5
6	1.03038	1.06152	1.09344	1.12616	1.19405	1.26532	1.34010	1.41852	1.50073	1.58687	6
7	1.03553	1.07214	1.10984	1.14869	1.22987	1.31593	1.40710	1.50363	1.60578	1.71382	7
8	1.04071	1.08286	1.12649	1.17166	1.26677	1.36857	1.47746	1.59385	1.71819	1.85093	8
9	1.04591	1.09369	1.14339	1.19509	1.30477	1.42331	1.55133	1.68948	1.83846	1.99900	9
10	1.05114	1.10462	1.16054	1.21899	1.34392	1.48024	1.62889	1.79085	1.96715	2.15892	10
11	1.05640	1.11567	1.17795	1.24337	1.38423	1.53945	1.71034	1.89830	2.10485	2.33164	11
12	1.06168	1.12683	1.19562	1.26824	1.42576	1.60103	1.79586	2.01220	2.25219	2.51817	12
13	1.06699	1.13809	1.21355	1.29361	1.46853	1.66507	1.88565	2.13293	2.40985	2.71962	13
14	1.07232	1.14947	1.23176	1.31948	1.51259	1.73168	1.97993	2.26090	2.57853	2.93719	14
15	1.07768	1.16097	1.25023	1.34587	1.55797	1.80094	2.07893	2.39656	2.75903	3.17217	15
16	1.08307	1.17258	1.26899	1.37279	1.60471	1.87298	2.18287	2.54035	2.95216	3.42594	16
17	1.08849	1.18430	1.28802	1.40024	1.65285	1.94790	2.29202	2.69277	3.15882	3.70002	17
18	1.09393	1.19615	1.30734	1.42825	1.70243	2.02582	2.40662	2.85434	3.37993	3.99602	18
19	1.09940	1.20811	1.32695	1.45681	1.75351	2.10685	2.52695	3.02560	3.61653	4.31570	19
20	1.10490	1.22019	1.34686	1.48595	1.80611	2.19112	2.65330	3.20714	3.86968	4.66096	20
21	1.11042	1.23239	1.36706	1.51567	1.86029	2.27877	2.78596	3.39956	4.14056	5.03383	21
22	1.11597	1.24472	1.38756	1.54598	1.91610	2.36992	2.92526	3.60354	4.43040	5.43654	22
23	1.12155	1.25716	1.40838	1.57690	1.97359	2.46472	3.07152	3.81975	4.74053	5.87146	23
24	1.12716	1.26973	1.42950	1.60844	2.03279	2.56330	3.22510	4.04893	5.07237	6.34118	24
25	1.13280	1.28243	1.45095	1.64061	2.09378	2.66584	3.38635	4.29187	5.42743	6.84848	25

Periods	9%	10%	11%	12%	13%	14%	15%	16%	17%	18%	Periods
1	1.09000	1.10000	1.11000	1.12000	1.13000	1.14000	1.15000	1.16000	1.17000	1.18000	1
2	1.18810	1.21000	1.23210	1.25440	1.27690	1.29960	1.32250	1.34560	1.36890	1.39240	2
3	1.29503	1.33100	1.36763	1.40493	1.44290	1.48154	1.52088	1.56090	1.60161	1.64303	3
4	1.41158	1.46410	1.51807	1.57352	1.63047	1.68896	1.74901	1.81064	1.87389	1.93878	4
5	1.53862	1.61051	1.68506	1.76234	1.84244	1.92541	2.01136	2.10034	2.19245	2.28776	5
6	1.67710	1.77156	1.87041	1.97382	2.08195	2.19497	2.31306	2.43640	2.56516	2.69955	6
7	1.82804	1.94872	2.07616	2.21068	2.35261	2.50227	2.66002	2.82622	3.00124	3.18547	7
8	1.99256	2.14359	2.30454	2.47596	2.65844	2.85259	3.05902	3.27841	3.51145	3.75886	8
9	2.17189	2.35795	2.55804	2.77308	3.00404	3.25195	3.51788	3.80296	4.10840	4.43545	9
10	2736	2.59374	2.83942	3.10585	3.39457	3.70722	4.04556	4.41144	4.80683	5.23384	10
11	2.58043	2.85312	3.15176	3.47855	3.83586	4.22623	4.65239	5.11726	5.62399	6.17593	11
12	2.81266	3.13843	3.49845	3.89598	4.33452	4.81790	5.35025	5.93603	6.58007	7.28759	12
13	3.06580	3.45227	3.88328	4.36349	4.89801	5.49241	6.15279	6.88579	7.69868	8.59936	13
14	3.34173	3.79750	4.31044	4.88711	5.53475	6.26135	7.07571	7.98752	9.00745	10.14724	14
15	3.64248	4.17725	4.78459	5.47357	6.25427	7.13794	8.13706	9.26552	10.53872	11.97375	15
16	3.97031	4.59497	5.31089	6.13039	7.06733	8.13725	9.35762	10.74800	12.33030	14.12902	16
17	4.32763	5.05447	5.89509	6.86604	7.98608	9.27646	10.76126	12.46768	14.42646	16.67225	17
18	4.71712	5.55992	6.54355	7.68997	9.02427	10.57517	12.37545	14.46251	16.87895	19.67325	18
19	5.14166	6.11591	7.26334	8.61276	10.19742	12.05569	14.23177	16.77652	19.74838	23.21444	19
20	5.60441	6.72750	8.06231	9.64629	11.52309	13.74349	16.36654	19.46076	23.10560	27.39303	20
21	6.10881	7.40025	8.94917	10.80385	13.02109	15.66758	18.82152	22.57448	27.03355	32.32378	21
22	6.65860	8.14027	9.93357	12.10031	14.71383	17.86104	21.64475	26.18640	31.62925	38.14206	22
23	7.25787	8.95430	11.02627	13.55235	16.62663	20.36158	24.89146	30.37622	37.00623	45.00763	23
24	7.91108	9.84973	12.23916	15.17863	18.78809	23.21221	28.62518	35.23642	43.29729	53.10901	24
25	8.62308	10.83471	13.58546	17.00006	21.23054	26.46192	32.91895	40.87424	50.65783	62.66863	25

Exhibit 11-3
Compounding Periods per Year

Interest Compounded		Compounding Periods per Year
Annually	Every year	1
Semiannually	Every 6 months	2
Quarterly	Every 3 months	4
Monthly	Every month	12
Daily	Every day	365
Continuously		Infinite

Teaching Transparency 11-4

To find the number of compounding periods of an investment, multiply the number of years by the number of periods per year.

Compounding periods = Years × Periods per year

To find the interest rate per period, divide the annual or nominal rate by the number of periods per year.

$$\textbf{Interest rate per period} = \frac{\textbf{Nominal rate}}{\textbf{Periods per year}}$$

STEPS FOR USING COMPOUND INTEREST TABLES

Step 1. Scan across the top row to find the interest rate per period.

Step 2. Look down that column to the row corresponding to the number of periods.

Step 3. The table factor at the intersection of the rate per period column and the number of periods row is the future value of $1.00 at compound interest. Multiply the table factor by the principal to determine the compound amount.

Compound amount = Table factor × Principal

EXAMPLE 2 USING COMPOUND INTEREST TABLES

Tom Wilson invested $1,200, at 8% interest compounded quarterly, for 5 years. Use Table 11-1 to find the compound amount of Tom's investment. What is the amount of the compound interest?

SOLUTION STRATEGY

To solve this compound interest problem, we must first find the interest rate per period and the number of compounding periods.

$$\text{Interest rate per period} = \frac{\text{Nominal rate}}{\text{Periods per year}}$$

$$\text{Interest rate per period} = \frac{8\%}{4} = 2\%$$

$$\text{Compounding periods} = \text{Years} \times \text{Periods per year}$$

$$\text{Compounding periods} = 5 \times 4 = 20$$

The Time Value of Money

Now find the table factor by scanning across the top row of the compound interest table to 2% and down the 2% column to 20 periods. The table factor at that intersection is 1.48595. The compound amount is found by multiplying the table factor by the principal:

Compound amount = Table factor × Principal
Compound amount = 1.48595 × 1,200 = $1,783.14

The amount of interest is found by subtracting the principal from the compound amount.

Compound interest = Compound amount − Principal
Compound interest = 1,783.14 − 1,200.00 = $583.14

TRY IT EXERCISE 2

11-5

Marcy Perman invested $20,000, at 14% interest compounded semiannually, for 8 years. Use Table 11-1 to find the compound amount of her investment. What is the amount of compound interest Marcy earned?

CHECK YOUR ANSWERS WITH THE SOLUTIONS ON PAGE 395.

CREATING COMPOUND INTEREST TABLE FACTORS FOR PERIODS BEYOND THE TABLE

When the number of periods of an investment is greater than the number of periods provided by the compound interest table, you can compute a new table factor by multiplying the factors for any two periods that add up to the number of periods required. For answer consistency in this chapter, use the two table factors that represent *half* of the periods required. For example,

STEPS FOR CREATING NEW COMPOUND INTEREST TABLE FACTORS

Step 1. For the stated interest rate per period, find the two table factors that represent *half* of the periods required.

Step 2. Multiply the two table factors from Step 1 to form the new factor.

Step 3. Round the new factor to five decimal places.

EXAMPLE 3 CALCULATING COMPOUND AMOUNT FOR PERIODS BEYOND THE TABLE

Calculate a new table factor and find the compound amount of $10,000, invested at 12% compounded monthly, for 3 years.

SOLUTION STRATEGY

This investment requires a table factor for 36 periods (12 periods per year for 3 years). Because Table 11-1 only provides factors up to 25 periods, we must create one using the steps above.

Step 1. At 12% interest compounded monthly, the rate per period is 1%. Because we are looking for 36 periods, we shall use the factors for 18 and 18 periods, at 1%.

Table factor for 18 periods, 1% = 1.19615

Table factor for 18 periods, 1% = 1.19615

Step 2. Multiply the factors for 18 and 18 periods.

$$1.19615 \times 1.19615 = 1.4307748$$

Step 3. Round to five decimal places.

The new table factor for 36 periods is 1.43077

The compound amount of the \$10,000 investment is

Compound amount = Table factor × Principal

Compound amount = 1.43077 × 10,000 = \$14,307.70

TRY IT EXERCISE 3

Jeremy Dunn invests \$3,500, at 16% interest compounded quarterly, for 7 years. Calculate a new table factor and find the compound amount of Jeremy's investment.

CHECK YOUR ANSWERS WITH THE SOLUTIONS ON PAGE 395.

CALCULATING ANNUAL PERCENTAGE YIELD (APY) OR EFFECTIVE INTEREST RATE

11-4

In describing investments and loans, the advertised or stated interest rate is known as the **annual** or **nominal rate**. It is also the rate used to calculate the compound interest. Consider, however, what happens to an investment of \$100 at 12% nominal interest.

annual or nominal rate The advertised or stated interest rate of an investment or loan. The rate used to calculate the compound interest.

As we learned in Performance Objective 11-2, the greater the number of compounding periods per year, the higher the amount of interest earned. See Exhibit 11-4. Although the nominal interest rate is 12%, with monthly compounding the \$100 earns more than 12%. This is why many investment offers today advertise daily or continuous compounding. How much are these investments really earning?

The **annual percentage yield (APY)** or **effective rate** reflects the real rate of return on an investment. APY is calculated by finding the total compound interest earned in 1 year and dividing by the principal. *Note*: This is actually the simple interest formula (from Chapter 10) solved for rate $R = I \div PT$, where T is equal to 1.

annual percentage yield (APY) or effective rate The real or true rate of return on an investment. It is the total compound interest earned in 1 year divided by the principal. The more compounding periods per year, the higher the APY.

$$\textbf{Annual percentage yield (APY)} = \frac{\textbf{Total compound interest earned in 1 year}}{\textbf{Principal}}$$

Exhibit 11-4
Compound Interest Earned on \$100 at 12%

Compounding	Interest Earned
Annually	\$12.00
Semiannually	\$12.36
Quarterly	\$12.55
Monthly	\$12.68

From Exhibit 11-4, on page 379, we can see that the annual percentage yield is the same as the nominal rate when interest is compounded annually; however, it jumps to 12.36% ($12.36) when the compounding is changed to semiannually and to 12.68% ($12.68) when compounded monthly.

In the Business World

Regulation DD of the Truth in Savings Law, enacted by Congress in 1993, requires banks and other depository institutions to fully disclose the terms of deposit accounts to consumers. The major provisions of the regulation require institutions to:

- Provide consumer account holders with written information about important terms of an account, including the **annual percentage yield**.
- Provide fee and other information on any periodic statement sent to consumers.
- Use prescribed methods to determine the balance on which interest is calculated.
- Comply with special requirements when advertising deposit accounts.

EXAMPLE 4 CALCULATING APY

What is the compound amount, compound interest, and annual percentage yield of $4,000, invested for 1 year at 8%, compounded semiannually?

SOLUTION STRATEGY

First we must find the total compound interest earned in 1 year. We can find the compound amount using the factor for 4%, two periods, from Table 11-1.

Compound amount = Table factor × Principal

Compound amount = 1.08160 × 4,000 = $4,326.40

Compound interest = Compound amount − Principal

Compound interest = 4,326.40 − 4,000 = $326.40

$$\text{Annual percentage yield} = \frac{\text{Total compound interest earned in 1 year}}{\text{Principal}}$$

$$\text{Annual percentage yield} = \frac{326.40}{4{,}000.00} = 8.16\%$$

TRY IT EXERCISE 4

Jan North invested $7,000 in a certificate of deposit for 1 year, at 6% interest, compounded quarterly. What is the compound amount, compound interest, and annual percentage yield of Jan's investment? Round the APY to the nearest hundredth of a percent.

CHECK YOUR ANSWERS WITH THE SOLUTIONS ON PAGE 395.

CLASSROOM ACTIVITY

Have students bring to class examples of advertisements from the local newspaper showing the nominal and annual percentage yield of interest being offered on various savings plans, investments, and loans.

11-5 (OPTIONAL) CALCULATING COMPOUND AMOUNT (FUTURE VALUE) BY USING THE COMPOUND INTEREST FORMULA

If your calculator has an exponential function key, y^x, you can calculate the compound amount of an investment by using the compound interest formula.

The compound interest formula states:

$$A = P(1 + i)^n$$

where:

A = **Compound amount**
P = **Principal**
i = **Interest rate per period (expressed as a decimal)**
n = **Total compounding periods (years × periods per year)**

STEPS FOR SOLVING THE COMPOUND INTEREST FORMULA

Step 1. Add the 1 and the interest rate per period, i.

Step 2. Raise the sum from Step 1 to the nth power, using the y^x key on your calculator.

Step 3. Multiply the principal, P, by the answer from Step 2.

Calculator Sequence: 1 [+] i [y^x] n [×] P [=] A

EXAMPLE 5 USING THE COMPOUND INTEREST FORMULA

Use the compound interest formula to calculate the compound amount of $5,000 invested, at 10% interest compounded semiannually, for 3 years.

SOLUTION STRATEGY

This problem is solved by substituting the investment information into the compound interest formula. It is important to solve the formula in the sequence of steps as outlined above. Note that the rate per period, i, is 5% (10% ÷ 2 periods per year). The total number of periods, the exponent n, is 6 (3 years × 2 periods per year).

$$A = P(1 + i)^n$$

$$A = 5{,}000(1 + .05)^6$$

$$A = 5{,}000(1.05)^6$$

$$A = 5{,}000(1.3400956) = 6{,}700.4782 = \underline{\underline{\$6{,}700.48}}$$

Calculator Sequence: 1 [+] .05 [y^x] 6 [×] 5000 [=] $6,700.4782 = $6,700.48

TRY IT EXERCISE 5

Use the compound interest formula to calculate the compound amount of $3,000, invested at 8% interest compounded quarterly, for 5 years.

CHECK YOUR ANSWER WITH THE SOLUTION ON PAGE 395.

Review Exercises

SECTION I 11

For the following investments, find the total number of compounding periods and the interest rate per period.

	Term of Investment	Nominal (Annual) Rate (%)	Interest Compounded	Compounding Periods	Rate per Period (%)
1.	3 years	13	annually	3	13
2.	5 years	16	quarterly	20	4
3.	12 years	8	semiannually	24	4

Complete, worked-out solutions to Exercises 1–3 appear in Appendix B, following the index.

Complete, worked-out solutions to Exercises 4–26 appear in Appendix B, following the index.

	Term of Investment	Nominal (Annual) Rate (%)	Interest Compounded	Compounding Periods	Rate per Period (%)
4.	6 years	18	monthly	72	1.5
5.	4 years	14	quarterly	16	3.5
6.	9 years	10.5	semiannually	18	5.25
7.	9 months	12	quarterly	3	3

Manually calculate the compound amount and compound interest for the following investments.

TEACHING TIP
Remind students to round to the nearest cent, when necessary.

	Principal	Term of Investment (years)	Nominal Rate (%)	Interest Compounded	Compound Amount	Compound Interest
8.	$4,000	2	10	annually	$4,840.00	$840.00
9.	$10,000	1	12	quarterly	$11,255.09	$1,255.09
10.	$8,000	3	8	semiannually	$10,122.55	$2,122.55

Using Table 11-1, calculate the compound amount and compound interest for the following investments.

	Principal	Term of Investment (years)	Nominal Rate (%)	Interest Compounded	Compound Amount	Compound Interest
11.	$7,000	4	13	annually	$11,413.29	$4,413.29
EXCEL 12.	$11,000	6	14	semiannually	$24,774.09	$13,774.09
13.	$5,300	3	8	quarterly	$6,721.67	$1,421.67
14.	$67,000	2	18	monthly	$95,776.50	$28,776.50
EXCEL 15.	$25,000	15	11	annually	$119,614.75	$94,614.75
16.	$400	2	6	monthly	$450.86	$50.86
17.	$8,800	$12\frac{1}{2}$	10	semiannually	$29,799.88	$20,999.88

The following investments require table factors for periods beyond the table. Create the new table factor, rounded to five places, and calculate the compound amount for each.

	Principal	Term of Investment (years)	Nominal Rate (%)	Interest Compounded	New Table Factor	Compound Amount
18.	$13,000	3	12	monthly	1.43077	$18,600.01
19.	$19,000	29	9	annually	12.17218	$231,271.42
20.	$34,700	11	16	quarterly	5.61652	$194,893.24
21.	$10,000	40	13	annually	132.78160	$1,327,816.00
22.	$1,000	16	14	semiannually	8.71525	$8,715.25

For the following investments, compute the amount of compound interest earned in 1 year and the annual percentage yield (APY).

	Principal	Nominal Rate (%)	Interest Compounded	Compound Interest Earned in 1 Year	Annual Percentage Yield (APY)
23.	$5,000	10	semiannually	$512.50	10.25%
24.	$2,000	13	annually	$260.00	13.00%
25.	$36,000	12	monthly	$4,565.88	12.68%
26.	$1,000	8	quarterly	$82.43	8.24%

Solve the following word problems by using either Table 11-1 or the optional compound interest formula, $A = P(1 + i)^n$.

27. Katie O'Brien invested $3,000 at the Galaxy Bank, at 6% interest compounded quarterly.

    a. What is the annual percentage yield of this investment?

    $1\frac{1}{2}\%$, 4 Periods

    Compound amount = 1.06136 × 3,000 = $3,184.08

    Compound amount = 3,184.08 − 3,000.00 = $184.08

    $$\text{Annual percentage yield} = \frac{184.08}{3{,}000.00} = \underline{\underline{6.14\%}}$$

    b. What will Katie's investment be worth after 6 years?

    $1\frac{1}{2}\%$, 24 Periods

    Compound amount = 1.42950 × 3,000 = $\underline{\underline{\$4{,}288.50}}$

28. As a savings plan for college, the Polands deposited $10,000 in an account paying 8% compounded annually when their son Nathan was born. How much will the account be worth when Nathan is 18 years old?

    8%, 18 Periods

    Compound amount = 3.99602 × 10,000 = $\underline{\underline{\$39{,}960.20}}$

29. All American Supply, Inc., deposited $500,000 in an account earning 12% compounded monthly. This account is intended to pay for the construction of a new warehouse. How much will be available for the project in $2\frac{1}{2}$ years?

    Table factor required = 1%, 30 periods
    1%, 15 Periods: 1.16097
    1%, 15 Periods: × 1.16097
    30 Periods 1.3478513 = 1.34785 "New" factor

    Compound amount = 1.34785 × 500,000 = $\underline{\underline{\$673{,}925}}$

30. The First National Bank is offering a 6-year certificate of deposit (CD) at 4% interest, compounded quarterly; Second National Bank is offering a 6-year CD at 5% interest, compounded annually.

    a. If you were interested in investing $8,000 in one of these CDs, calculate the compound amount of each offer.

    First National: 1%, 24 periods
    Compound amount = 1.26973 × 8,000 = $\underline{\underline{\$10{,}157.84}}$

    Second National: 5%, 6 periods
    Compound amount = 1.34010 × 8,000 = $\underline{\underline{\$10{,}720.80}}$

    b. What is the annual percentage yield of each CD?

    First National: 1%, 4 periods

    $$\text{APY} = \frac{324.80}{8{,}000.00} = \underline{\underline{4.06\%}}$$

    Second National: 5%, 1 period

    $$\text{APY} = \frac{400.00}{8{,}000.00} = \underline{\underline{5.0\%}}$$

TEACHING TIP

Point out to students how this exercise demonstrates that higher rates have a more significant effect on interest earned than increased compounding periods.

c. (Optional) If Third National Bank has a 6-year CD at 4.5% interest compounded monthly, use the compound interest formula to calculate the compound amount of this offer.

Third National: Rate per period $= \frac{.045}{12} = .00375$

Periods $= 6 \times 12 = 72$

$A = 8{,}000(1 + .00375)^{72} = \underline{\underline{\$10{,}474.42}}$

Compounding Sheep!
The concept of compounding may also be used to compound "other variables" besides money. Use the compound interest table for Exercises 31 and 32.

31. A certain animal husbandry program has a flock of sheep which increases in size by 15% every year. If there are currently 48 sheep, how many sheep are expected to be in the flock in 5 years? Round to the nearest whole sheep.

15%, 5 Periods

Compound amount = 2.01136 × 48 = 96.5 = <u>97 sheep</u>

32. The rate of bacteria growth in a laboratory experiment was measured at 16% per hour. If this experiment is repeated, and begins with 5 grams of bacteria, how much bacteria should be expected after 12 hours? Round to the nearest tenth of a gram.

16%, 12 Periods

Compound amount = 5.93603 × 5 grams = 29.68 = <u>29.7 grams</u>

BUSINESS DECISION DAILY COMPOUNDING

33. As an incentive to attract savings deposits, most financial institutions today offer **daily** or even **continuous compounding**. This means that savings or passbook accounts, as well as CDs, earn interest compounded each day, or even more frequently—continuously, such as every hour or even every minute. Let's take a look at daily compounding.

To calculate the compound amount, A, of an investment with daily compounding, use the compound interest formula, modified as follows:

- Rate per period (daily) $= \frac{i}{365}$ (nominal interest rate, i, divided by 365)
- Number of periods (days), n, = number of days of the investment.

$$A = P\left(1 + \frac{i}{365}\right)^n$$

Calculator Sequence: 1 [+] [(] i [÷] 365 [)] [y^x] n [×] P [=] A

a. On April 19, Roger Hartfield deposited $2,700 in a passbook savings account at 3.5% interest compounded daily. What is the compound amount of his account on August 5?

April 19 to August 5 = 108 days.

$$A = 2{,}700\left(1 + \frac{.035}{365}\right)^{108} = \underline{\underline{\$2{,}728.11}}$$

b. Using daily compounding, recalculate the compound amount for each of the three certificates of deposit in Exercise 30.

$365 \times 6 = 2{,}190$ days

$$\text{First National Bank: } A = 8{,}000\left(1+\frac{.04}{365}\right)^{2190} = \underline{\underline{\$10{,}169.86}}$$

$$\text{Second National Bank: } A = 8{,}000\left(1+\frac{.05}{365}\right)^{2190} = \underline{\underline{\$10{,}798.65}}$$

$$\text{Third National Bank: } A = 8{,}000\left(1+\frac{.045}{365}\right)^{2190} = \underline{\underline{\$10{,}479.54}}$$

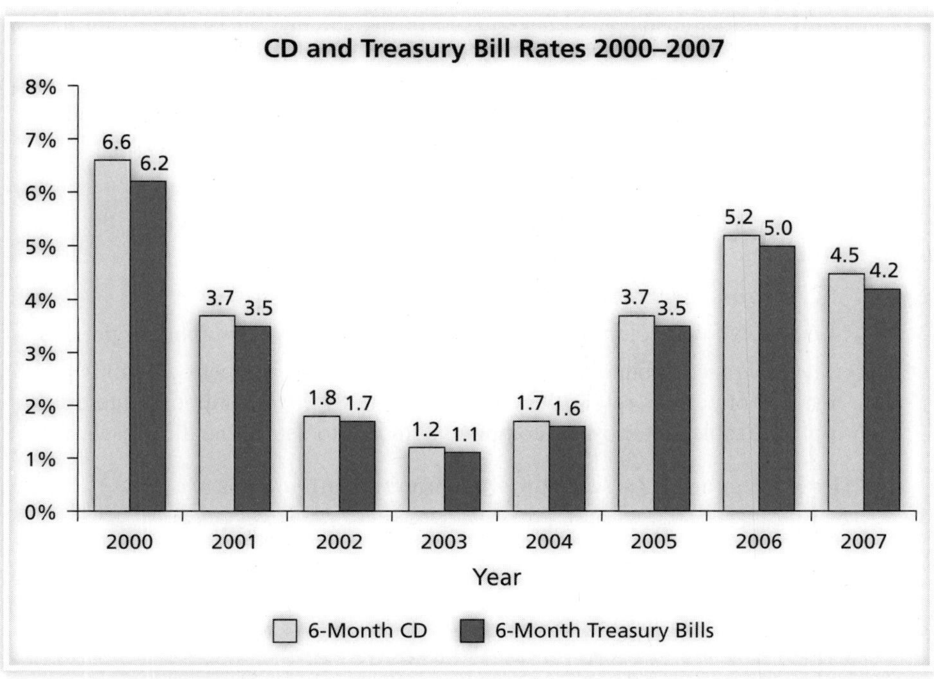

Source: Federal Reserve Board

PRESENT VALUE

In Section I we learned how to find a future value when the present value was known. Let's take a look at the reverse situation, also commonly found in business. When a future value (an amount needed in the future) is known, the present value is the amount that must be invested today to accumulate with compound interest to that future value. For example, if a corporation wants $100,000 in 5 years (future value—known) to replace its fleet of trucks, what amount must be invested today (present value—unknown) at 8% compounded quarterly to achieve this goal? See Exhibit 11-5.

Exhibit 11-5
Present Value to Future Value

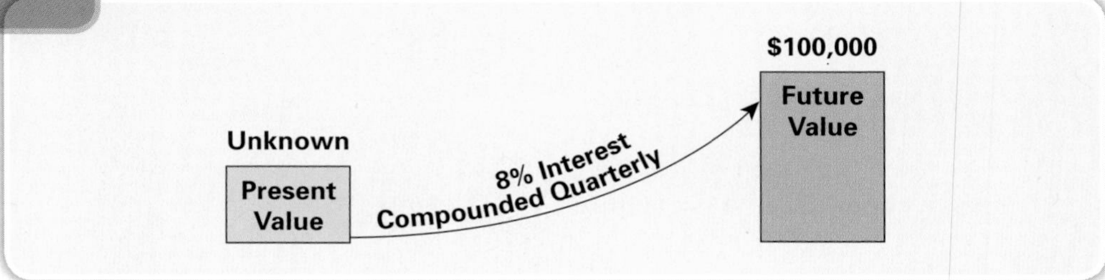

11-6 CALCULATING THE PRESENT VALUE OF A FUTURE AMOUNT BY USING PRESENT VALUE TABLES

Just as there are compound interest tables to aid in the calculation of compound amounts, present value tables help calculate the present value of a known future amount. Table 11-2 is such a table. Note that this table is similar to the compound interest table in that the table factors are based on the interest rate per period and the number of compounding periods.

TEACHING TIP
Demonstrate the relationship between Tables 11-1 and 11-2 by introducing the concept of reciprocals. Point out that each table factor, at a given rate and period, is the reciprocal of the other table factor.

$$\text{Table 11-1 factor} = \frac{1}{\text{Table 11-2 factor}}$$

and

$$\text{Table 11-2 factor} = \frac{1}{\text{Table 11-1 factor}}$$

For students who have a financial or scientific calculator, demonstrate how this calculation can be done by using the reciprocal key, $\frac{1}{X}$.

STEPS FOR USING PRESENT VALUE TABLES

Step 1. Scan across the top row to find the interest rate per period.

Step 2. Look down that column to the row corresponding to the number of periods.

Step 3. The table factor found at the intersection of the rate per period column and the number of periods row is the present value of $1.00 at compound interest. Multiply the table factor by the compound amount to determine the present value.

Present value = Table factor × Compound amount (future value)

EXAMPLE 6 CALCULATING PRESENT VALUE

Juan Ignacio will need $5,000 in 8 years. Use Table 11-2 to find how much he must invest now at 6% interest compounded semiannually to have $5,000, 8 years from now.

SOLUTION STRATEGY

To solve this present value problem, we shall use 3% per period (6% nominal rate ÷ 2 periods per year) and 16 periods (8 years × 2 periods per year).

Step 1. Scan across the top row of the present value table to 3%.

Step 2. Look down that column to the row corresponding to 16 periods.

Step 3. Find the table factor at the intersection of Steps 1 and 2, and multiply it by the compound amount to find the present value. Table factor = .62317.

Present value = Table factor × Compound amount

Present value = .62317 × 5,000 = $3,115.85

Teaching Transparency 11-6

Table 11-2
Present Value Table (Present Value of $1 at Compound Interest)

Periods	$\frac{1}{2}$%	1%	$1\frac{1}{2}$%	2%	3%	4%	5%	6%	7%	8%	Periods
1	0.99502	0.99010	0.98522	0.98039	0.97087	0.96154	0.95238	0.94340	0.93458	0.92593	1
2	0.99007	0.98030	0.97066	0.96117	0.94260	0.92456	0.90703	0.89000	0.87344	0.85734	2
3	0.98515	0.97059	0.95632	0.94232	0.91514	0.88900	0.86384	0.83962	0.81630	0.79383	3
4	0.98025	0.96098	0.94218	0.92385	0.88849	0.85480	0.82270	0.79209	0.76290	0.73503	4
5	0.97537	0.95147	0.92826	0.90573	0.86261	0.82193	0.78353	0.74726	0.71299	0.68058	5
6	0.97052	0.94205	0.91454	0.88797	0.83748	0.79031	0.74622	0.70496	0.66634	0.63017	6
7	0.96569	0.93272	0.90103	0.87056	0.81309	0.75992	0.71068	0.66506	0.62275	0.58349	7
8	0.96089	0.92348	0.88771	0.85349	0.78941	0.73069	0.67684	0.62741	0.58201	0.54027	8
9	0.95610	0.91434	0.87459	0.83676	0.76642	0.70259	0.64461	0.59190	0.54393	0.50025	9
10	0.95135	0.90529	0.86167	0.82035	0.74409	0.67556	0.61391	0.55839	0.50835	0.46319	10
11	0.94661	0.89632	0.84893	0.80426	0.72242	0.64958	0.58468	0.52679	0.47509	0.42888	11
12	0.94191	0.88745	0.83639	0.78849	0.70138	0.62460	0.55684	0.49697	0.44401	0.39711	12
13	0.93722	0.87866	0.82403	0.77303	0.68095	0.60057	0.53032	0.46884	0.41496	0.36770	13
14	0.93256	0.86996	0.81185	0.75788	0.66112	0.57748	0.50507	0.44230	0.38782	0.34046	14
15	0.92792	0.86135	0.79985	0.74301	0.64186	0.55526	0.48102	0.41727	0.36245	0.31524	15
16	0.92330	0.85282	0.78803	0.72845	0.62317	0.53391	0.45811	0.39365	0.33873	0.29189	16
17	0.91871	0.84438	0.77639	0.71416	0.60502	0.51337	0.43630	0.37136	0.31657	0.27027	17
18	0.91414	0.83602	0.76491	0.70016	0.58739	0.49363	0.41552	0.35034	0.29586	0.25025	18
19	0.90959	0.82774	0.75361	0.68643	0.57029	0.47464	0.39573	0.33051	0.27651	0.23171	19
20	0.90506	0.81954	0.74247	0.67297	0.55368	0.45639	0.37689	0.31180	0.25842	0.21455	20
21	0.90056	0.81143	0.73150	0.65978	0.53755	0.43883	0.35894	0.29416	0.24151	0.19866	21
22	0.89608	0.80340	0.72069	0.64684	0.52189	0.42196	0.34185	0.27751	0.22571	0.18394	22
23	0.89162	0.79544	0.71004	0.63416	0.50669	0.40573	0.32557	0.26180	0.21095	0.17032	23
24	0.88719	0.78757	0.69954	0.62172	0.49193	0.39012	0.31007	0.24698	0.19715	0.15770	24
25	0.88277	0.77977	0.68921	0.60953	0.47761	0.37512	0.29530	0.23300	0.18425	0.14602	25

Periods	9%	10%	11%	12%	13%	14%	15%	16%	17%	18%	Periods
1	0.91743	0.90909	0.90090	0.89286	0.88496	0.87719	0.86957	0.86207	0.85470	0.84746	1
2	0.84168	0.82645	0.81162	0.79719	0.78315	0.76947	0.75614	0.74316	0.73051	0.71818	2
3	0.77218	0.75131	0.73119	0.71178	0.69305	0.67497	0.65752	0.64066	0.62437	0.60863	3
4	0.70843	0.68301	0.65873	0.63552	0.61332	0.59208	0.57175	0.55229	0.53365	0.51579	4
5	0.64993	0.62092	0.59345	0.56743	0.54276	0.51937	0.49718	0.47611	0.45611	0.43711	5
6	0.59627	0.56447	0.53464	0.50663	0.48032	0.45559	0.43233	0.41044	0.38984	0.37043	6
7	0.54703	0.51316	0.48166	0.45235	0.42506	0.39964	0.37594	0.35383	0.33320	0.31393	7
8	0.50187	0.46651	0.43393	0.40388	0.37616	0.35056	0.32690	0.30503	0.28478	0.26604	8
9	0.46043	0.42410	0.39092	0.36061	0.33288	0.30751	0.28426	0.26295	0.24340	0.22546	9
10	0.42241	0.38554	0.35218	0.32197	0.29459	0.26974	0.24718	0.22668	0.20804	0.19106	10
11	0.38753	0.35049	0.31728	0.28748	0.26070	0.23662	0.21494	0.19542	0.17781	0.16192	11
12	0.35553	0.31863	0.28584	0.25668	0.23071	0.20756	0.18691	0.16846	0.15197	0.13722	12
13	0.32618	0.28966	0.25751	0.22917	0.20416	0.18207	0.16253	0.14523	0.12989	0.11629	13
14	0.29925	0.26333	0.23199	0.20462	0.18068	0.15971	0.14133	0.12520	0.11102	0.09855	14
15	0.27454	0.23939	0.20900	0.18270	0.15989	0.14010	0.12289	0.10793	0.09489	0.08352	15
16	0.25187	0.21763	0.18829	0.16312	0.14150	0.12289	0.10686	0.09304	0.08110	0.07078	16
17	0.23107	0.19784	0.16963	0.14564	0.12522	0.10780	0.09293	0.08021	0.06932	0.05998	17
18	0.21199	0.17986	0.15282	0.13004	0.11081	0.09456	0.08081	0.06914	0.05925	0.05083	18
19	0.19449	0.16351	0.13768	0.11611	0.09806	0.08295	0.07027	0.05961	0.05064	0.04308	19
20	0.17843	0.14864	0.12403	0.10367	0.08678	0.07276	0.06110	0.05139	0.04328	0.03651	20
21	0.16370	0.13513	0.11174	0.09256	0.07680	0.06383	0.05313	0.04430	0.03699	0.03094	21
22	0.15018	0.12285	0.10067	0.08264	0.06796	0.05599	0.04620	0.03819	0.03162	0.02622	22
23	0.13778	0.11168	0.09069	0.07379	0.06014	0.04911	0.04017	0.03292	0.02702	0.02222	23
24	0.12640	0.10153	0.08170	0.06588	0.05323	0.04308	0.03493	0.02838	0.02310	0.01883	24
25	0.11597	0.09230	0.07361	0.05882	0.04710	0.03779	0.03038	0.02447	0.01974	0.01596	25

TRY IT EXERCISE 6

11-7

Baron von Munster wants to renovate his castle in Bavaria in 3 years. He estimates the cost to be $3,000,000. Use Table 11-2 to find how much the Baron must invest now at 8% interest compounded quarterly to have $3,000,000, 3 years from now.

CHECK YOUR ANSWER WITH THE SOLUTION ON PAGE 396.

11-7 CREATING PRESENT VALUE TABLE FACTORS FOR PERIODS BEYOND THE TABLE

Just as with the compound interest tables, there may be times when the number of periods of an investment or loan is greater than the number of periods provided by the present value tables. When this occurs, you can create a new table factor by multiplying the table factors for any two periods that add up to the number of periods required.

For answer consistency in this chapter, use the two table factors that represent *half* of the periods required. For example,

20 periods + 20 periods → 40 periods

20 periods + 21 periods → 41 periods

STEPS FOR CREATING NEW TABLE FACTORS

Step 1. For the stated interest rate per period, find the two table factors that represent *half* of the periods required.

Step 2. Multiply the two table factors from Step 1 to form the new factor.

Step 3. Round the new factor to five decimal places.

EXAMPLE 7 CREATING PRESENT VALUE TABLE FACTORS

Calculate a new table factor and find the present value of $2,000, if the interest rate is 12% compounded quarterly, for 8 years.

SOLUTION STRATEGY

This investment requires a table factor for 32 periods, four periods per year for 8 years. Because Table 11-2 only provides factors up to 25 periods, we must create one by using the steps above.

Step 1. At 12% interest compounded quarterly, the rate per period is 3%. Because we are looking for 32 periods, we shall use the factors for 16 and 16 periods, at 3%.

Table factor for 16 periods, 3% = .62317

Table factor for 16 periods, 3% = .62317

Step 2. Multiply the factors for 16 and 16 periods:

$.62317 \times .62317 = .3883408$

Learning Tip

Which table to use—Compound Interest (Table 11-1) or Present Value (Table 11-2)?

Note that the Compound Interest Table factors are all *greater* than 1, whereas the Present Value Table factors are all less than 1.

- When solving for compound amount, a future amount greater than the present value, use the table with factors *greater* than 1—Compound Interest Table.
- When solving for present value, a present amount *less* than the future value, use the table with factors *less* than 1—Present Value Table.

Step 3. Rounding to five decimal places, the new table factor for 32 periods is .38834. The present value of the \$2,000 investment is

Present value = Table factor × Compound amount

Present value = .38834 × 2,000 = \$776.68

TRY IT EXERCISE 7

Calculate a new table factor and find the present value of \$8,500, if the interest rate is 6% compounded quarterly, for 10 years.

CHECK YOUR ANSWERS WITH THE SOLUTIONS ON PAGE 396.

(OPTIONAL) CALCULATING PRESENT VALUE OF A FUTURE AMOUNT BY USING THE PRESENT VALUE FORMULA

If your calculator has an exponential function key, y^x, you can calculate the present value of an investment by using the present value formula.

The present value formula states:

$$PV = \frac{A}{(1+i)^n}$$

where:

PV = Present value
A = Compound amount
i = Interest rate per period (expressed as a decimal)
n = Total compounding periods (years × periods per year)

STEPS FOR SOLVING THE PRESENT VALUE FORMULA

Step 1. Add the 1 and the interest rate per period, i.

Step 2. Raise the sum from Step 1 to the nth power, using the y^x key on your calculator.

Step 3. Divide the compound amount, A, by the answer from Step 2.

Calculator sequence: 1 [+] i [y^x] n [=] [M+] A [÷] [MR] [=] PV

EXAMPLE 8 USING THE PRESENT VALUE FORMULA

Use the present value formula to calculate the present value of \$3,000, if the interest rate is 16% compounded quarterly, for 6 years.

SOLUTION STRATEGY

CLASSROOM ACTIVITY
As a chapter review, have students break into groups to write and solve some word problems involving compound interest and present value. Next, have each group work the problems of another group, compare answers, and resolve differences.

This problem is solved by substituting the investment information into the present value formula. It is important to solve the formula in the sequence of steps as outlined. Note the rate per period, i, is 4% (16% ÷ 4 periods per year). The total number of periods, the exponent n, is 24 (6 years × 4 periods per year).

$$\text{Present value} = \frac{A}{(1+i)^n}$$

$$\text{Present value} = \frac{3{,}000}{(1+.04)^{24}}$$

$$\text{Present value} = \frac{3{,}000}{(1.04)^{24}}$$

$$\text{Present value} = \frac{3{,}000}{2.5633041} = \underline{\underline{\$1{,}170.36}}$$

Calculator Sequence: 1 [+] .04 [y^x] 24 [=] [M+] 3000 [÷] [MR] [=] $1,170.36

TRY IT EXERCISE 8

Ernie and Roni Sanchez want to accumulate $30,000, 17 years from now, as a college fund for their baby son, Michael. Use the present value formula to calculate how much they must invest now, at an interest rate of 8% compounded semiannually, to have $30,000 in 17 years.

CHECK YOUR ANSWER WITH THE SOLUTION ON PAGE 396.

SECTION II Review Exercises

Complete, worked-out solutions to Exercises 1–10 appear in Appendix B, following the index.

For the following investments, calculate the present value (principal) and the compound interest. Use Table 11-2. Round your answers to the nearest cent.

	Compound Amount	Term of Investment	Nominal Rate (%)	Interest Compounded	Present Value	Compound Interest
1.	$6,000	3 years	9	annually	$4,633.08	$1,366.92
2.	$24,000	6 years	14	semiannually	$10,656.24	$13,343.76
3.	$650	5 years	8	quarterly	$437.43	$212.57
4.	$2,000	12 years	6	semiannually	$983.86	$1,016.14
EXCEL → 5.	$50,000	25 years	11	annually	$3,680.50	$46,319.50
6.	$14,500	18 months	10	semiannually	$12,525.68	$1,974.32
EXCEL → 7.	$9,800	4 years	12	quarterly	$6,107.07	$3,692.93
8.	$100,000	10 years	9	annually	$42,241.00	$57,759.00
9.	$250	1 year	18	monthly	$209.10	$40.90
10.	$4,000	27 months	8	quarterly	$3,347.04	$652.96

The following investments require table factors for periods beyond the table. Create the new table factor, rounded to five places, and calculate the present value for each.

Complete, worked-out solutions to Exercises 11–15 appear in Appendix B, following the index.

	Compound Amount	Term of Investment (years)	Nominal Rate (%)	Interest Compounded	New Table Factor	Present Value
11.	$12,000	10	16	quarterly	.20829	$2,499.48
12.	$33,000	38	7	annually	.07646	$2,523.18
13.	$1,400	12	12	quarterly	.24200	$338.80
14.	$1,000	45	13	annually	.00409	$4.09
15.	$110,000	17	8	semiannually	.26355	$28,990.50

Solve the following word problems by using either Table 11-2 or the optional present value formula.

$$PV = \frac{A}{(1+i)^n}$$

16. How much must be invested today at 6% compounded quarterly to have $8,000 in 3 years?

$1\frac{1}{2}$%, 12 Periods

Present value = .83639 × 8,000 = $6,691.12

17. Heather Holtz is planning a vacation in Europe in 4 years, after graduation. She estimates that she will need $3,500 for the trip.

a. If her bank is offering 4-year certificates of deposit with 8% interest compounded quarterly, how much must Heather invest now to have the money for the trip?

2%, 16 Periods
Present value = .72845 × 3,500 = $2,549.58

b. How much compound interest will be earned on the investment?
Compound interest = 3,500.00 − 2,549.58 = $950.42

18. Biltmore Homes, a real estate development company, is planning to build five custom homes, each costing $125,000, in $2\frac{1}{2}$ years. The Gables Bank pays 6% interest compounded semiannually. How much should the company invest now to have sufficient funds to build the homes in the future?

3%, 5 Periods

Amount needed = 125,000 × 5 = $625,000

Present value = .86261 × 625,000 = $539,131.25

19. Tri-Star Airlines intends to pay off a $20,000,000 bond issue that comes due in 4 years. How much must the company set aside now, at 6% interest compounded monthly, to accumulate the required amount of money?

Table factor required = $\frac{1}{2}$%, 48 Periods

$\frac{1}{2}$%, 24 Periods: .88719

$\frac{1}{2}$%, 24 Periods: × .88719

.7871061 = .78711 "New" factor $\frac{1}{2}$%, 48 Periods

Present value = .78711 × 20,000,000 = $15,742,200

Corporate bonds are promissory notes, or IOUs, issued by a corporation to borrow money on a long-term basis. They are commonly used to finance company modernization and expansion programs.

The corporate bond market is large and liquid, with daily trading volumes averaging over $22.7 billion. The total market value of outstanding corporate bonds in the United States is over $5.4 trillion.

20. Paul Fraser estimates that he will need $25,000 to set up a law office in 7 years, when he graduates from law school.

    a. How much must Paul invest now at 12% interest compounded quarterly to achieve his goal?
    Table factor required 3%, 28 Periods
    3%, 14 Periods: .66112
    3%, 14 Periods: ×.66112
    28 Periods .4370796 = .43708 "New" factor 3%, 28 Periods
    Present value = .43708 × 25,000 = $10,927

    b. How much compound interest will he earn on the investment?
    Compound interest = 25,000 − 10,927 = $14,073

In the Business World

Present Value of a Songbird! Just as with compounding, the concept of present value of a future amount may also be applied to "other variables" besides money. Use the Present Value Table for Exercises 21 and 22.

21. Summertime songbird population within the Mid-America flyway is predicted to increase over the next 8 years at the rate of 2% per year. If the songbird population is predicted to reach 55 million in 8 years, how many songbirds are there today? Round to the nearest million.
    2%, 8 Periods
    Present value = .85349 × 55,000,000 = 46.9 = 47 million songbirds

22. The requirement for computer server capacity at Acme Industries is expected to increase at a rate of 15% per year for the next five years. If the server capacity is expected to be 1,400 gigabytes in five years, how many gigabytes of capacity are there today? Round to the nearest whole gigabyte.
    15%, 5 Periods
    Present value = .49718 × 1,400 = 696.05 = 696 gigabytes

BUSINESS DECISION THE INFLATION FACTOR

In the Business World

Inflation should be taken into account when making financial plans that cover time periods longer than a year.

"When you take out food, energy, taxes, insurance, housing, transportation, healthcare, and entertainment, inflation remained at a 20 year low."

23. You are the finance manager for Maytag Manufacturing. The company plans to purchase $1,000,000 in new assembly line machinery in 5 years.

    a. How much must be set aside now, at 6% interest compounded semiannually, to accumulate the $1,000,000 in 5 years?
    3%, 10 periods
    Present value = .74409 × 1,000,000 = $744,090

    b. If the inflation rate on this type of equipment is 4% per year, what will be the cost of the equipment in 5 years, adjusted for inflation?
    4%, 5 periods Compound amount = 1.21665 × 1,000,000 = $1,216,650

    c. Use the inflation-adjusted cost of the equipment to calculate how much must be set aside now.
    3%, 10 periods Present value = .74409 × 1,216,650 = $905,297.10

    d. (Optional) Use the present value formula to calculate how much would be required now if you found a bank that offered 6% interest compounded daily.
    5 years = 1,825 days

$$\text{Present value} = \frac{1,216,650}{\left(1 + \frac{.06}{365}\right)^{1825}} = \$901,338.71$$

CHAPTER FORMULAS

Compound Interest

Compound interest = Compound amount − Principal

Compounding periods = Years × Periods per year

$$\text{Interest rate per period} = \frac{\text{Nominal rate}}{\text{Periods per year}}$$

Compound amount = Table factor × Principal

$$\text{Annual percentage yield (APY)} = \frac{\text{Total compound interest earned in 1 year}}{\text{Principal}}$$

$$\text{Compound amount} = \text{Principal}(1 + \text{interest})^{\text{periods}}$$

Present Value

Present value = Table factor × Compound amount

$$\text{Present value} = \frac{\text{Compound amount}}{(1 + \text{interest})^{\text{periods}}}$$

SUMMARY CHART

Section I: Compound Interest—The Time Value of Money

Topic	Important Concepts	Illustrative Examples
Manually Calculating Compound Amount (Future Value) **P/O 11-1, p. 374**	In compound interest, the interest is applied a number of times during the term of an investment. Compound interest yields considerably higher interest than simple interest because the investor is earning interest on the interest. Interest can be compounded annually, semiannually, quarterly, monthly, daily, and continuously. 1. Determine number of compounding periods (years × periods per year). 2. Apply the simple interest formula, $I = PRT$, as many times as there are compounding periods, adding interest to principal before each succeeding calculation.	Manually calculate the compound amount of a \$1,000 investment at 8% interest compounded annually for 2 years. Original principal 1,000.00 Interest—period 1 + 80.00 Principal—period 2 1,080.00 Interest—period 2 + 86.40 Compound amount \$1,166.40
Calculating Amount of Compound Interest **P/O 11-1, p. 374**	Amount of compound interest is calculated by subtracting the original principal from the compound amount. **Compound interest = Compound amount − Principal**	What is the amount of compound interest earned in the problem above? 1,166.40 − 1,000.00 = \$166.40
Computing Compound Amount (Future Value) by Using the Compound Interest Tables **P/O 11-2, p. 375**	1. Scan across the top row of Table 11-1 to find the interest rate per period. 2. Look down that column to the row corresponding to the number of compounding periods. 3. The table factor found at the intersection of the rate per period column and the periods row is the future value of \$1.00 at compound interest. **Compound amount = Table factor × Principal**	Use Table 11-1 to find the compound amount of an investment of \$2,000, at 12% interest compounded quarterly, for 6 years. Rate = 3% per period (12% ÷ 4) Periods = 24 (6 years × 4) Table factor = 2.03279 Compound amount = 2.03279 × 2,000 = \$4,065.58

Section I: (continued)

Topic	Important Concepts	Illustrative Examples
Creating Compound Interest Table Factors for Periods beyond the Table **P/O 11-3, p. 378**	1. For the stated interest rate per period, find the two table factors that represent *half* of the periods required. 2. Multiply the two table factors from Step 1 to form the new factor. 3. Round the new factor to five decimal places.	Create a new table factor for 5% interest for 30 periods. Multiply the 5% factors for 15 and 15 periods from Table 11-1. 5%, 15 periods = 2.07893 5%, 15 periods = × 2.07893 30 4.3219499 New factor, rounded = 4.32195
Calculating Annual Percentage Yield (APY) or Effective Interest Rate **P/O 11-4, p. 379**	To calculate annual percentage yield, divide total compound interest earned in 1 year by the principal. **Annual percentage yield (APY)** $= \dfrac{\textbf{1 year compound interest}}{\textbf{Principal}}$	What is the annual percentage yield of $5,000 invested for 1 year at 12% compounded monthly? From Table 11-1, we use the table factor for 12 periods, 1%, to find the compound amount: 1.12683 × 5,000 = 5,634.15 Interest = Cmp amt − Principal Int = 5,634.15 − 5,000.00 = 634.15 $\text{APY} = \dfrac{634.15}{5,000} = 12.68\%$
(Optional) **Calculating Compound Amount (Future Value) by Using the Compound Interest Formula** **P/O 11-5, p. 380**	In addition to the compound interest tables, another method for calculating compound amount is by the compound interest formula. $A = P(1 + i)^n$ **where:** A = **Compound amount** P = **Principal** i = **Interest rate per period (decimal form)** n = **Number of compounding periods**	What is the compound amount of $3,000 invested at 8% interest compounded quarterly for 10 years? $A = P(1 + i)^n$ $A = 3,000(1 + .02)^{40}$ $A = 3,000(1.02)^{40}$ $A = 3,000(2.2080396)$ $A = \$6,624.12$

Section II: Present Value

Topic	Important Concepts	Illustrative Examples
Calculating the Present Value of a Future Amount by Using the Present Value Tables **P/O 11-6, p. 386**	When the future value, an amount needed in the future, is known, the present value is the amount that must be invested today to accumulate, with compound interest, to that future value. 1. Scan across the top row of Table 11-2 to find the rate per period. 2. Look down that column to the row corresponding to the number of periods. 3. The table factor found at the intersection of the rate per period column and the periods row is the present value of $1.00 at compound interest. **Present value = Table factor × Compound amount**	How much must be invested now at 10% interest compounded semiannually to have $8,000, 9 years from now? Rate = 5% (10% ÷ 2) Periods = 18 (9 years × 2) Table factor = .41552 Present value = .41552 × 8,000 Present value = $3,324.16

Section II: (continued)

Topic	Important Concepts	Illustrative Examples
Creating Present Value Table Factors for Periods beyond the Table **P/O 11-7, p. 388**	1. For the stated interest rate per period, find the two table factors that represent *half* of the periods required. 2. Multiply the two table factors from Step 1 for the new factor. 3. Round the new factor to five decimal places.	Create a new table factor for 6% interest for 41 periods. Multiply the 6% factors for 21 and 20 periods from Table 11-2. 6%, 21 periods = .29416 6%, 20 periods = × .31180 41 .0917191 New factor, rounded = .09172
(Optional) Calculating Present Value of a Future Amount by Using the Present Value Formula **P/O 11-8, p. 389**	If your calculator has an exponential function key, y^x, you can calculate the present value of an investment by using the present value formula. $PV = \frac{A}{(1+i)^n}$ **where:** PV = **Present value** A = **Compound amount** i = **Interest rate per period (decimal form)** n = **Total compounding periods**	How much must be invested now in order to have \$12,000 in 10 years, if the interest rate is 12% compounded quarterly? Present value $= \frac{12{,}000}{(1+.03)^{40}}$ $PV = \frac{12{,}000}{(1.03)^{40}} = \frac{12{,}000}{3.2620378}$ Present value = \$3,678.68

TRY IT EXERCISE SOLUTIONS FOR CHAPTER 11

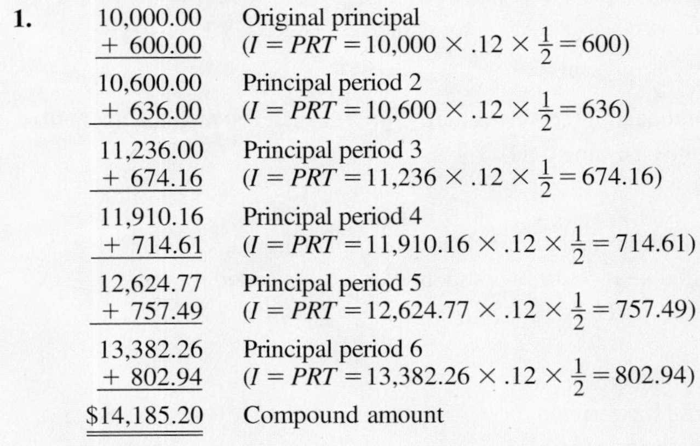

1.

10,000.00	Original principal
+ 600.00	$(I = PRT = 10{,}000 \times .12 \times \frac{1}{2} = 600)$
10,600.00	Principal period 2
+ 636.00	$(I = PRT = 10{,}600 \times .12 \times \frac{1}{2} = 636)$
11,236.00	Principal period 3
+ 674.16	$(I = PRT = 11{,}236 \times .12 \times \frac{1}{2} = 674.16)$
11,910.16	Principal period 4
+ 714.61	$(I = PRT = 11{,}910.16 \times .12 \times \frac{1}{2} = 714.61)$
12,624.77	Principal period 5
+ 757.49	$(I = PRT = 12{,}624.77 \times .12 \times \frac{1}{2} = 757.49)$
13,382.26	Principal period 6
+ 802.94	$(I = PRT = 13{,}382.26 \times .12 \times \frac{1}{2} = 802.94)$
\$14,185.20	Compound amount

Compound Interest = 14,185.20 − 10,000.00 = \$4,185.20

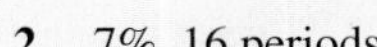

2. 7%, 16 periods

Compound amount = Table factor × Principal

Compound amount = 2.95216 × 20,000 = \$59,043.20

Compound interest = Compound amount − Principal

Compound interest = 59,043.20 − 20,000.00 = \$39,043.20

3. Table factor required = 4%, 28 periods

4%, 14 periods: 1.73168
4%, 14 periods: × 1.73168
28 periods 2.9987156 = 2.99872 New table factor 4%, 28 periods

Compound amount = 2.99872 × 3,500 = \$10,495.52

4. $1\frac{1}{2}$%, 4 periods

Compound amount = 1.06136 × 7,000 = \$7,429.52

Compound interest = 7,429.52 − 7,000.00 = \$429.52

$$\text{Annual percentage yield} = \frac{\text{1 year interest}}{\text{Principal}} = \frac{429.52}{7{,}000.00} = 6.14\%$$

5. $A = P(1 + i)^n$

$P = \$3{,}000$

$i = \frac{8\%}{4} = .02$

$n = 5 \times 4 = 20$

$A = 3{,}000(1 + .02)^{20}$

$A = 3{,}000(1\ .02)^{20}$

$A = 3{,}000(1.4859474)$

$A = \$4{,}457.84$

6. 2%, 12 periods

Present value = Table factor × Compound amount

Present value = .78849 × 3,000,000 = $2,365,470

7. Table factor required = $1\frac{1}{2}$%, 40 Periods

$1\frac{1}{2}$%, 20 periods: .74247

$1\frac{1}{2}$%, 20 periods: × .74247

40 periods = .5512617 = .55126 New table factor $1\frac{1}{2}$%, 40 periods

Present value = .55126 × 8,500 = $4,685.71

8. $PV = \frac{A}{(1+i)^n}$

$A = 30{,}000$

$i = \frac{8\%}{2} = .04$

$n = 17 \times 2 = 34$

$PV = \frac{30{,}000}{(1+.04)^{34}}$

$PV = \frac{30{,}000}{(1.04)^{34}}$

$PV = \frac{30{,}000}{3.7943163} = \$7{,}906.56$

CONCEPT REVIEW

1. Interest calculated solely on the principal is known as ____ interest, whereas interest calculated on the principal and previously earned interest is known as ____ interest. (11-1)

simple, compound

2. The concept that money "now" or in the present, is more desirable than the same amount of money in the future because it can be invested and earn interest as time goes by is known as the ____ ____ of money. (11-1)

time value

3. The total amount of principal and accumulated interest at the end of a loan or investment is known as the ____ amount or ____ value. (11-1)

compound, future

4. An amount of money that must be deposited today at compound interest to provide a specified lump sum of money in the future is known as the ____ amount or ____ value. (11-1, 11-6)

present, present

5. The amount of compound interest is calculated by subtracting the ____ from the compound amount. (11-1)

principal

6. Compound interest is actually the ____ interest formula applied a number of times. (11-1)

simple

7. A compound interest table is a useful set of factors that represent the future value of ____ at various interest rates for a number of compounding periods. (11-2)

$1.00

8. A shortcut method for calculating how long it takes money to double in value at compound interest is called the Rule of ____. (11-2)

72

9. Write the formula for calculating the number of compounding periods of a loan or investment. (11-2)

Compounding periods = Years × Periods per year

10. Write the formula for calculating the interest rate per period of a loan or investment. (11-2)

$\text{Interest rate per period} = \frac{\text{Nominal rate}}{\text{Periods per year}}$

11. Newly created table factors for compound interest and present value should be rounded to ____ decimal places. (11-3, 11-7)

five

12. The annual percentage yield (APY) is equal to the total compound interest earned in ____ year, divided by the ____. (11-4)

one, principal

13. When using the compound interest table or the present value table, the factor is found at the intersection of the rate per ____ column and the number of ____ row. (11-2, 11-6)

period, periods

14. To use the compound interest formula and the present value formula, you need a calculator with an ____ function (y^x) key. (11-5, 11-8)

exponential

ASSESSMENT TEST

CHAPTER 11

Note: Round to the nearest cent, when necessary.

Using Table 11-1, calculate the compound amount and compound interest for the following investments.

	Principal	Term of Investment (years)	Nominal Rate (%)	Interest Compounded	Compound Amount	Compound Interest
1.	$14,000	6	14	semiannually	$31,530.66	$17,530.66
2.	$7,700	5	6	quarterly	$10,370.82	$2,670.82
3.	$3,000	1	18	monthly	$3,586.86	$586.86
4.	$42,000	19	11	annually	$305,060.28	$263,060.28

The following investments require table factors for periods beyond the table. Create the new table factor and calculate the compound amount for each.

	Principal	Term of Investment (years)	Nominal Rate (%)	Interest Compounded	New Table Factor	Compound Amount
5.	$20,000	11	16	quarterly	5.61652	$112,330.40
6.	$10,000	4	6	monthly	1.27049	$12,704.90

For the following investments, compute the amount of compound interest earned in 1 year and the annual percentage yield. Round APY to the nearest hundredth of a percent.

	Principal	Nominal Rate (%)	Interest Compounded	Compound Interest Earned in 1 Year	Annual Percentage Yield (APY)
7.	$8,500	12	monthly	$1,078.06	12.68%
8.	$1,000,000	8	quarterly	$82,430.00	8.24%

Calculate the present value (principal) and the compound interest for the following investments. Use Table 11-2. Round answers to the nearest cent.

	Compound Amount	Term of Investment	Nominal Rate (%)	Interest Compounded	Present Value	Compound Interest
9.	$150,000	22 years	15	annually	$6,930.00	$143,070.00
10.	$20,000	30 months	14	semiannually	$14,259.80	$5,740.20
11.	$900	$1\frac{3}{4}$ years	18	monthly	$658.35	$241.65
12.	$5,500	15 months	8	quarterly	$4,981.52	$518.48

The following investments require table factors for periods beyond the table. Create the new table factor and the present value for each.

	Compound Amount	Term of Investment (years)	Nominal Rate (%)	Interest Compounded	New Table Factor	Present Value
13.	$1,300	4	12	monthly	.62027	$806.35
14.	$100,000	50	5	annually	.08720	$8,720.00

Solve the following word problems by using either Tables 11-1 and 11-2 or the optional compound interest and present value formulas. When necessary, create new table factors. Round dollars to the nearest cent and percents to the nearest hundredth of a percent.

15. What is the compound amount and compound interest of $36,000 invested at 12% compounded semiannually for 7 years?

6%, 14 Periods

Compound amount = 2.26090 × 36,000 = $81,392.40

Compound interest = 81,392.40 − 36,000.00 = $45,392.40

Name

Class

Answers

1.	$31,530.66	$17,530.66
2.	$10,370.82	$2,670.82
3.	$3,586.86	$586.86
4.	$305,060.28	$263,060.28
5.	5.61652	$112,330.40
6.	1.27049	$12,704.90
7.	$1,078.06	12.68%
8.	$82,430.00	8.24%
9.	$6,930.00	$143,070.00
10.	$14,259.80	$5,740.20
11.	$658.35	$241.65
12.	$4,981.52	$518.48
13.	.62027	$806.35
14.	.08720	$8,720.00
15.	$81,392.40	$45,392.40

Complete, worked-out solutions for Exercises 1–14 appear in Appendix B, following the index.

CHAPTER

Name

Class

Answers

16. $30,803.08

17. $17,150.85 $2,150.85

18. 12.68%

19. $92,727.70

20. 83,565

21. a. 12.55%

b. $17,888.55

22. $32,342

16. What is the present value of $73,000 in 11 years if the interest rate is 8% compounded semiannually?

4%, 22 Periods

Present value = .42196 × 73,000 = $30,803.08

17. What is the compound amount and compound interest of $15,000 invested at 6% compounded quarterly for 27 months?

$1\frac{1}{2}$%, 9 Periods

Compound amount = 1.14339 × 15,000 = $17,150.85

Compound interest = 17,150.85 − 15,000.00 = $2,150.85

18. What is the annual percentage yield of a $10,000 investment, for 1 year, at 12% interest compounded monthly?

1%, 12 Periods

Compound amount = 1.12683 × 10,000 = $11,268.30

1 yr interest = 11,268.30 − 10,000 = $1,268.30

$$\text{Annual percentage yield} = \frac{\text{1 yr interest}}{\text{Principal}} = \frac{1{,}268.30}{10{,}000.00} = 12.68\%$$

19. Continental Delivery Service uses vans costing $24,800 each. How much will the company have to invest today to accumulate enough money to buy six new vans at the end of 4 years? Continental's bank is currently paying 12% interest compounded quarterly.

Amount needed = 24,800 × 6 = $148,800

3%, 16 Periods

Present value = .62317 × 148,800 = $92,727.70

20. What is the present value of $100,000 in 3 years if the interest rate is 6% compounded monthly?

Table value required $\frac{1}{2}$%, 36 Periods

$\frac{1}{2}$%, 18 Periods: .91414

$\frac{1}{2}$%, 18 Periods: × .91414

36 Periods .8356519 = .83565 "New" factor $\frac{1}{2}$%, 36 periods

Present value = .83565 × 100,000 = $83,565

21. Sara Morgan invested $8,800 at the Northern Trust Credit Union at 12% interest compounded quarterly.

a. What is the annual percentage yield of this investment?

3%, 4 Periods

Compound amount = 1.12551 × 8,800 = $9,904.49

1 yr interest = 9,904.49 − 8,800.00 = $1,104.49

$$\text{Annual percentage yield} = \frac{\text{1 yr interest}}{\text{Principal}} = \frac{1{,}104.49}{8{,}800.00} = 12.55\%$$

b. What will Sara's investment be worth after 6 years?

3%, 24 Periods

Compound amount = 2.03279 × 8,800 = $17,888.55

© Tammy Hanratty (through R. Brechner)

Home improvement is the weekend hobby of millions of enthusiasts in the United States. In 2006, they spent over $312.1 billion on home improvement projects.

22. Bob and Joy Salkind want to save $50,000 in $5\frac{1}{2}$ years for home improvement projects. If the Bank of Aventura is paying 8% interest compounded quarterly, how much must they deposit now to have the money for the project?

2%, 22 Periods

Present value = .64684 × 50,000 = $32,342

Name

Class

Answers

23. $48,545.40

24. a. 249,235 sq. ft.

b. 240,582 sq. ft.

Build after $3\frac{1}{2}$ years

25. a. $37,243.34

b. $14,243.34

26. 124 Acres of strawberries

27. 3.7 Million fleet miles

23. While rummaging through the attic, you discover a savings account left to you by your rich Uncle David. When you were 5 years old, he invested $20,000 in your name, at 6% interest compounded semiannually. If you are now 20 years old, how much is the account worth?

Table value needed = 3%, 30 Periods

3%, 15 Periods: 1.55797
3%, 15 Periods: × 1.55797
30 Periods 2.4272705 = 2.42727 "New" factor 3%, 30 periods

Compound amount = 2.42727 × 20,000 = $48,545.40

24. Applegate Industries is planning to expand its production facility in a few years. New plant construction costs are estimated to be $4.50 per square foot. The company invests $850,000 today at 8% interest compounded quarterly. Round to the nearest whole square foot.

a. How many square feet of new facility could be built after $3\frac{1}{2}$ years?

2%, 14 Periods
Compound amount = 1.31948 × 850,000 = $1,121,558

$\frac{1,121,558}{4.50} = 249,235$ sq ft

b. If the company waits 5 years, but construction costs increase to $5.25 per square foot, how many square feet could be built? What do you recommend?

2%, 20 Periods
Compound amount = 1.48595 × 850,000 = $1,263,057.50

$\frac{1,263,057.50}{5.25} = 240,582$ sq ft

Recommend: Build after $3\frac{1}{2}$ years

25. Over the past 10 years you've made the following investments:

1. Deposited $10,000 at 8% compounded semiannually, in a 3-year certificate of deposit.
2. After the 3 years, you took the maturity value (principal and interest) of that CD and added another $5,000 to buy a 4-year, 6% certificate compounded quarterly.
3. When that certificate matured, you added another $8,000 and bought a 3-year, 7% certificate compounded annually.

a. What was the total worth of your investment when the last certificate matured?

1. 4%, 6 periods.
Compound amount = 1.26532 × 10,000 = $12,653.20
2. $1\frac{1}{2}$, 16 periods. Principal = 12,653.20 + 5,000.00 = 17,653.20
Compound amount = 1.26899 × 17,653.20 = $22,401.73
3. 7%, 3 Periods. Principal = 22,401.73 + 8,000.00 = 30,401.73
Compound amount = 1.22504 × 30,401.73 = $37,243.34

b. What is the total amount of compound interest earned over the 10-year period?

37,243.34	Total worth
−23,000.00	Total amount invested
$14,243.34	Total interest earned

26. Stan Rockwell owns Redlands Farms, a successful strawberry farm. The strawberry plants increase at a compound rate of 12% per year. Each year Stan brings new land under cultivation for the new strawberry plants. If the farm has 50 acres of strawberry plants today, how many acres of strawberry plants will the farm have in 8 years? Round to the nearest whole acre.

12%, 8 Periods
Compound amount = 2.47596 × 50 = 123.7 = 124 Acres of strawberries

For Exercises 26 and 27, use Table 11-1 to find the future value and 11-2 to find the present value of variables other than money.

27. At Reliable Trucking, Inc., annual sales are predicted to increase over the next 3 years at a rate of 6% per year. Sales equate to "fleet miles." If Reliable's fleet miles are predicted to reach 4.4 million in 3 years, what is the number of fleet miles today? Round to the nearest tenth of a million.

6%, 3 Periods
Present value = .83962 × 4.4 = 3.69 = 3.7 Million fleet miles

CHAPTER

Name

Class

Answers

28. a. $1,414,750.00

b. $1,425,000 now

c. $1,594,175.00

d. $1,500,005.10

Pay Me Now, Pay Me Later is a good example of how the "time value of money" concept can be applied in business.
Remember:
When interest can be earned, money today is more desirable than the same amount of money in the future.

BUSINESS DECISION PAY ME NOW, PAY ME LATER

28. You are the owner of an apartment building that is being offered for sale for $1,500,000. You receive an offer from a prospective buyer who wants to pay you $500,000 now, $500,000 in 6 months, and $500,000 in 1 year.

a. What is the actual present value of this offer, considering you can earn 12% interest compounded monthly on your money?

Offer	Present Value
$500,000 now	500,000.00
$500,000 in 6 months	
1%, 6 Periods (.94205 × 500,000) . .	471,025.00
$500,000 in 1 year	
1%, 12 Periods (.88745 × 500,000) .	443,725.00
Offer worth today	$1,414,750.00

b. If another buyer offers to pay you $1,425,000 cash now, which is a better deal?

$1,425,000.00 Cash now is a better deal

c. Because you understand the "time value of money" concept, you have negotiated a deal with the original buyer from part **a**, whereby you will accept the three-payment offer but will charge 12% interest, compounded monthly, on the two delayed payments. Calculate the total purchase price under this new arrangement.

Offer	Payment
$500,000 now	500,000.00
$500,000 in 6 months plus interest	
1%, 6 Periods (1.06152 × 500,000) . .	530,760.00
$500,000 in 1 year plus interest	
1%, 12 Periods (1.12683 × 500,000)	563,415.00
Total purchase price	$1,594,175.00

d. Now, calculate the present value of the new deal, to verify that you will receive the original asking price of $1,500,000 for your apartment building.

New Offer	Present Value
$500,000 now.	500,000.00
$530,760 in 6 months	
1%, 6 Periods (.94205 × 530,760) . . .	500,002.46
$563,415 in 1 year	
1%, 12 Periods (.88745 × 563,415)	500,002.64
Offer worth today	$1,500,005.10*

* Answer is off by $5.10 due to table rounding. *Note:* Present value formula will yield the exact answer.

COLLABORATIVE LEARNING ACTIVITY

Putting Your Money To Work

As a team, research the financial institutions in your area, as well as on the Internet, to find and list the various certificates of deposit currently being offered. Assume that you want to invest $10,000, for 12 months.

a. What interest rates do these CDs pay? How often is interest compounded?
b. What is the early withdrawal penalty?
c. Are these CDs insured? By whom? What is the limit per account?
d. Overall, which institution offers the CD that would earn the most interest after 12 months?

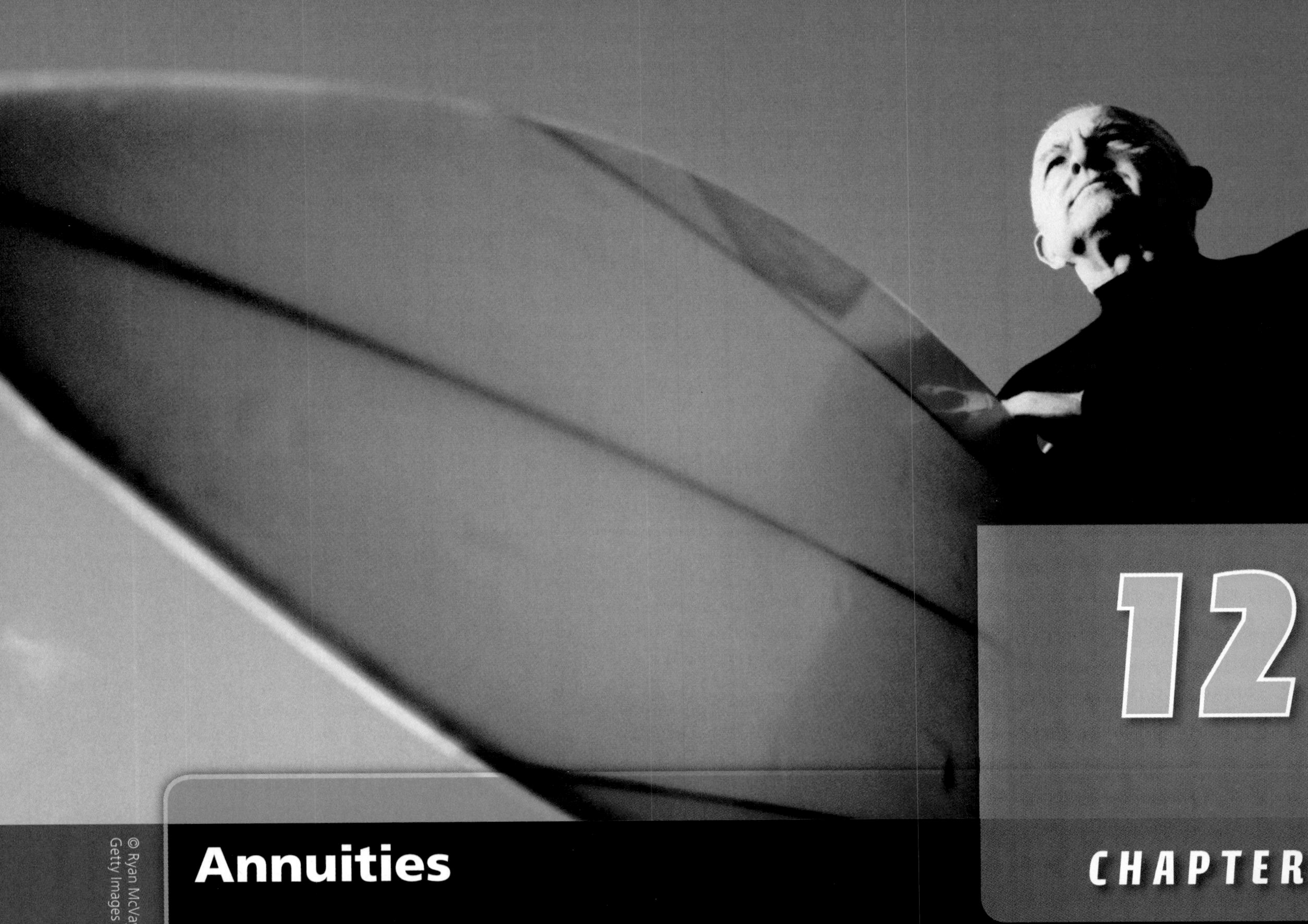

Annuities

PERFORMANCE OBJECTIVES

SECTION I FUTURE VALUE OF AN ANNUITY: ORDINARY AND ANNUITY DUE

The concepts relating to compound interest in Chapter 11 were mainly concerned with lump sum investments or payments. Frequently in business, situations involve a series of equal periodic payments or receipts, rather than lump sums. These are known as annuities. An **annuity** is the payment or receipt of *equal* cash amounts per period for a specified amount of time. Some common applications are insurance and retirement plan premiums and payouts; loan payments; or savings plans for future events such as starting a business, going to college, or purchasing expensive items such as real estate or business equipment.

annuity Payment or receipt of equal amounts of money per period for a specified amount of time.

In this chapter, you learn to calculate the future value of an annuity, the amount accumulated at compound interest from a series of equal periodic payments. You also learn to calculate the present value of an annuity, the amount that must be deposited now at compound interest to yield a series of equal periodic payments. Exhibit 12-1 graphically shows the difference between the future value of an annuity and the present value of an annuity.

All the exercises in this chapter are of the type known as **simple annuities**. This means that the number of compounding periods per year coincides with the number of annuity payments per year. For example, if the annuity payments are monthly, the interest is compounded monthly; if the annuity payments are made every 6 months, the interest is compounded semiannually. **Complex annuities** are those in which the annuity payments and compounding periods do not coincide.

simple annuity Annuity in which the number of compounding periods per year coincides with the number of annuity payments per year.

complex annuity Annuity in which the annuity payments and compounding periods do not coincide.

annuities certain Annuities that have a specified number of time periods.

contingent annuities Annuities based on an uncertain time period, such as the life of a person.

As with compound interest, annuities can be calculated manually, by tables, and by formulas. Manual computation is useful for illustrative purposes; however, it is too tedious because it requires a calculation for each period. The table method is the easiest and most widely used and is the basis for this chapter's exercises. As in Chapter 11, there are formulas to calculate annuities; however, they require calculators with the exponential function key, y^x, and the change-of-sign key, +/−. These optional Performance Objectives are for students with business, financial, or scientific calculators.

12-1 CALCULATING THE FUTURE VALUE OF AN ORDINARY ANNUITY BY USING TABLES

12-1

Annuities are categorized into annuities certain and contingent annuities. **Annuities certain** are those that have a specified number of periods, such as $200 per month for 5 years, or $500 semiannually for 10 years. **Contingent annuities** are based on an uncertain time period,

Exhibit 12-1
Time Line Illustrating Present and Future Value of an Annuity

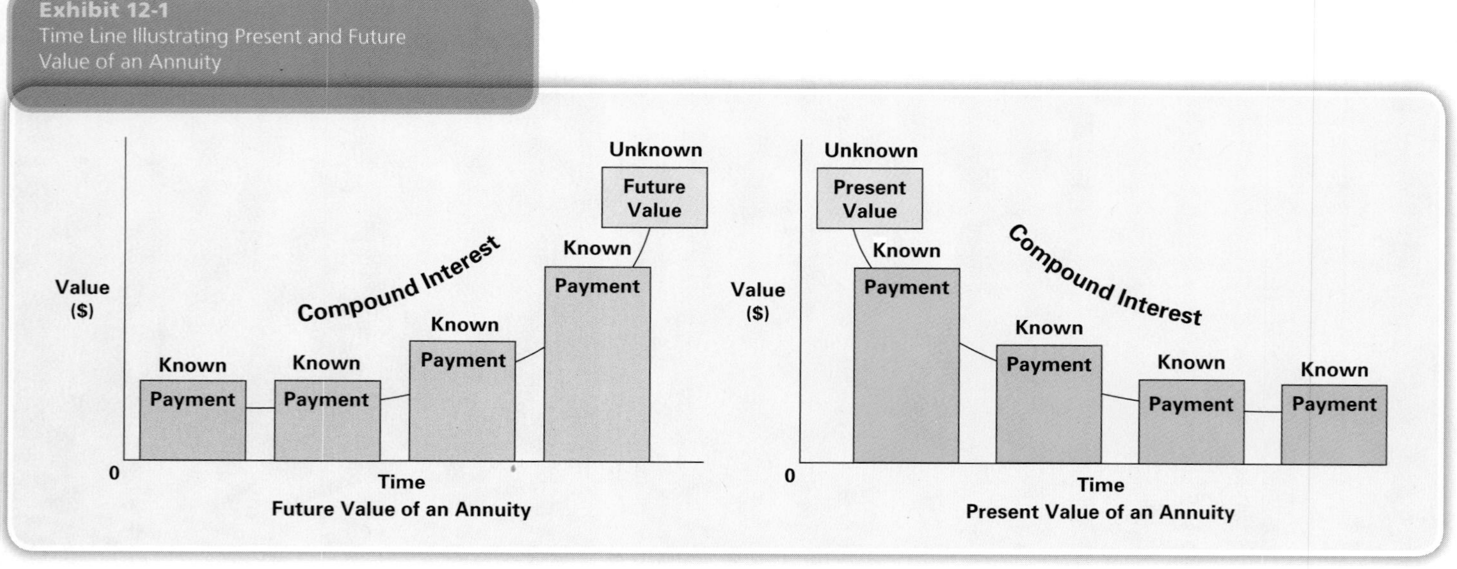

such as a retirement plan that is payable only for the lifetime of the retiree. This chapter is concerned only with annuities certain.

When the annuity payment is made at the end of each period, it is known as an **ordinary annuity**. When the payment is made at the beginning of each period, it is called an **annuity due**. A salary paid at the end of each month is an example of an ordinary annuity. A mortgage payment or rent paid at the beginning of each month is an example of an annuity due.

The **future value of an annuity** is also known as the amount of an annuity. It is the total of the annuity payments plus the accumulated compound interest on those payments.

For illustrative purposes, consider the following annuity, calculated manually.

ordinary annuity Annuity that is paid or received at the end of each time period.

annuity due Annuity that is paid or received at the beginning of each time period.

future value of an annuity The total amount of the annuity payments and the accumulated interest on those payments. Also known as the amount of an annuity.

What is the future value of an ordinary annuity of $10,000 per year, for 4 years, at 6% interest compounded annually?

Because this is an ordinary annuity, the payment is made at the *end* of each period, in this case years. Each interest calculation uses $I = PRT$, with $R = .06$ and $T = 1$ year.

Time	Balance	
Beginning of period 1	0	
	+ 10,000.00	First annuity payment (end of period 1)
End of period 1	10,000.00	
Beginning of period 2	10,000.00	
	600.00	Interest earned, period 2 (10,000.00 × .06 × 1)
	+ 10,000.00	Second annuity payment (end of period 2)
End of period 2	20,600.00	
Beginning of period 3	20,600.00	
	1,236.00	Interest earned, period 3 (20,600.00 × .06 × 1)
	+ 10,000.00	Third annuity payment (end of period 3)
End of period 3	31,836.00	
Beginning of period 4	31,836.00	
	1,910.16	Interest earned, period 4 (31,836.00 × .06 × 1)
	+ 10,000.00	Fourth annuity payment (end of period 4)
End of period 4	$43,746.16	Future value of the ordinary annuity

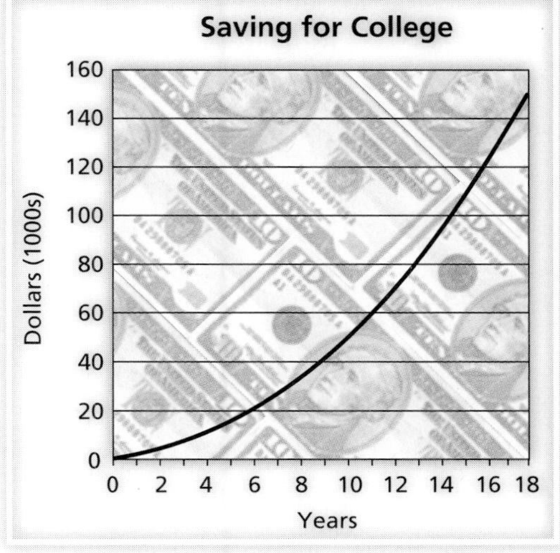

If parents save and invest $10 per work-day at 12% interest from the birthdate of their child, when the child is 18 and ready for college, they would have $150,000 accumulated—through the power of compounding.

As you can see, calculating annuities this way is tedious. An annuity of 10 years, with payments made monthly, would require 120 calculations. As with compound interest, we shall use tables to calculate the future value (amount) of an annuity.

STEPS FOR CALCULATING FUTURE VALUE (AMOUNT) OF AN ORDINARY ANNUITY

Step 1. Calculate the interest rate per period for the annuity (nominal rate ÷ periods per year).

Step 2. Determine the number of periods of the annuity (years × periods per year).

Step 3. From Table 12-1, locate the ordinary annuity table factor at the intersection of the rate per period column and the number of periods row.

Step 4. Calculate the future value of the ordinary annuity.

$$\text{Future value (ordinary annuity)} = \text{Ordinary annuity table factor} \times \text{Annuity payment}$$

Learning Tip

The procedure for using the annuity tables, Tables 12-1 and 12-2, is the same as we used with the compound interest and present value tables in Chapter 11.

Table factors are found at the intersection of the "rate per period" column and the "number of periods" row.

Table 12-1
Future Value (Amount) of an Ordinary Annuity of $1.00

12-2

Periods	$\frac{1}{2}$ %	1%	$1\frac{1}{2}$ %	2%	3%	4%	5%	6%	7%	8%	Periods
1	1.00000	1.00000	1.00000	1.00000	1.00000	1.00000	1.00000	1.00000	1.00000	1.00000	1
2	2.00500	2.01000	2.01500	2.02000	2.03000	2.04000	2.05000	2.06000	2.07000	2.08000	2
3	3.01502	3.03010	3.04522	3.06040	3.09090	3.12160	3.15250	3.18360	3.21490	3.24640	3
4	4.03010	4.06040	4.09090	4.12161	4.18363	4.24646	4.31013	4.37462	4.43994	4.50611	4
5	5.05025	5.10101	5.15227	5.20404	5.30914	5.41632	5.52563	5.63709	5.75074	5.86660	5
6	6.07550	6.15202	6.22955	6.30812	6.46841	6.63298	6.80191	6.97532	7.15329	7.33593	6
7	7.10588	7.21354	7.32299	7.43428	7.66246	7.89829	8.14201	8.39384	8.65402	8.92280	7
8	8.14141	8.28567	8.43284	8.58297	8.89234	9.21423	9.54911	9.89747	10.25980	10.63663	8
9	9.18212	9.36853	9.55933	9.75463	10.15911	10.58280	11.02656	11.49132	11.97799	12.48756	9
10	10.22803	10.46221	10.70272	10.94972	11.46388	12.00611	12.57789	13.18079	13.81645	14.48656	10
11	11.27917	11.56683	11.86326	12.16872	12.80780	13.48635	14.20679	14.97164	15.78360	16.64549	11
12	12.33556	12.68250	13.04121	13.41209	14.19203	15.02581	15.91713	16.86994	17.88845	18.97713	12
13	13.39724	13.80933	14.23683	14.68033	15.61779	16.62684	17.71298	18.88214	20.14064	21.49530	13
14	14.46423	14.94742	15.45038	15.97394	17.08632	18.29191	19.59863	21.01507	22.55049	24.21492	14
15	15.53655	16.09690	16.68214	17.29342	18.59891	20.02359	21.57856	23.27597	25.12902	27.15211	15
16	16.61423	17.25786	17.93237	18.63929	20.15688	21.82453	23.65749	25.67253	27.88805	30.32428	16
17	17.69730	18.43044	19.20136	20.01207	21.76159	23.69751	25.84037	28.21288	30.84022	33.75023	17
18	18.78579	19.61475	20.48938	21.41231	23.41444	25.64541	28.13238	30.90565	33.99903	37.45024	18
19	19.87972	20.81090	21.79672	22.84056	25.11687	27.67123	30.53900	33.75999	37.37896	41.44626	19
20	20.97912	22.01900	23.12367	24.29737	26.87037	29.77808	33.06595	36.78559	40.99549	45.76196	20
21	22.08401	23.23919	24.47052	25.78332	28.67649	31.96920	35.71925	39.99273	44.86518	50.42292	21
22	23.19443	24.47159	25.83758	27.29898	30.53678	34.24797	38.50521	43.39229	49.00574	55.45676	22
23	24.31040	25.71630	27.22514	28.84496	32.45288	36.61789	41.43048	46.99583	53.43614	60.89330	23
24	25.43196	26.97346	28.63352	30.42186	34.42647	39.08260	44.50200	50.81558	58.17667	66.76476	24
25	26.55912	28.24320	30.06302	32.03030	36.45926	41.64591	47.72710	54.86451	63.24904	73.10594	25
26	27.69191	29.52563	31.51397	33.67091	38.55304	44.31174	51.11345	59.15638	68.67647	79.95442	26
27	28.83037	30.82089	32.98668	35.34432	40.70963	47.08421	54.66913	63.70577	74.48382	87.35077	27
28	29.97452	32.12910	34.48148	37.05121	42.93092	49.96758	58.40258	68.52811	80.69769	95.33883	28
29	31.12439	33.45039	35.99870	38.79223	45.21885	52.96629	62.32271	73.63980	87.34653	103.96594	29
30	32.28002	34.78489	37.53868	40.56808	47.57542	56.08494	66.43885	79.05819	94.46079	113.28321	30
31	33.44142	36.13274	39.10176	42.37944	50.00268	59.32834	70.76079	84.80168	102.07304	123.34587	31
32	34.60862	37.49407	40.68829	44.22703	52.50276	62.70147	75.29883	90.88978	110.21815	134.21354	32
33	35.78167	38.86901	42.29861	46.11157	55.07784	66.20953	80.06377	97.34316	118.93343	145.95062	33
34	36.96058	40.25770	43.93309	48.03380	57.73018	69.85791	85.06696	104.18375	128.25876	158.62667	34
35	38.14538	41.66028	45.59209	49.99448	60.46208	73.65222	90.32031	111.43478	138.23688	172.31680	35
36	39.33610	43.07688	47.27597	51.99437	63.27594	77.59831	95.83632	119.12087	148.91346	187.10215	36

Table 12-1
Future Value (Amount) of an Ordinary Annuity of $1.00

Periods	9%	10%	11%	12%	13%	14%	15%	16%	17%	18%	Periods
1	1.00000	1.00000	1.00000	1.00000	1.00000	1.00000	1.00000	1.00000	1.00000	1.00000	1
2	2.09000	2.10000	2.11000	2.12000	2.13000	2.14000	2.15000	2.16000	2.17000	2.18000	2
3	3.27810	3.31000	3.34210	3.37440	3.40690	3.43960	3.47250	3.50560	3.53890	3.57240	3
4	4.57313	4.64100	4.70973	4.77933	4.84980	4.92114	4.99338	5.06650	5.14051	5.21543	4
5	5.98471	6.10510	6.22780	6.35285	6.48027	6.61010	6.74238	6.87714	7.01440	7.15421	5
6	7.52333	7.71561	7.91286	8.11519	8.32271	8.53552	8.75374	8.97748	9.20685	9.44197	6
7	9.20043	9.48717	9.78327	10.08901	10.40466	10.73049	11.06680	11.41387	11.77201	12.14152	7
8	11.02847	11.43589	11.85943	12.29969	12.75726	13.23276	13.72682	14.24009	14.77325	15.32700	8
9	13.02104	13.57948	14.16397	14.77566	15.41571	16.08535	16.78584	17.51851	18.28471	19.08585	9
10	15.19293	15.93742	16.72201	17.54874	18.41975	19.33730	20.30372	21.32147	22.39311	23.52131	10
11	17.56029	18.53117	19.56143	20.65458	21.81432	23.04452	24.34928	25.73290	27.19994	28.75514	11
12	20.14072	21.38428	22.71319	24.13313	25.65018	27.27075	29.00167	30.85017	32.82393	34.93107	12
13	22.95338	24.52271	26.21164	28.02911	29.98470	32.08865	34.35192	36.78620	39.40399	42.21866	13
14	26.01919	27.97498	30.09492	32.39260	34.88271	37.58107	40.50471	43.67199	47.10267	50.81802	14
15	29.36092	31.77248	34.40536	37.27971	40.41746	43.84241	47.58041	51.65951	56.11013	60.96527	15
16	33.00340	35.94973	39.18995	42.75328	46.67173	50.98035	55.71747	60.92503	66.64885	72.93901	16
17	36.97370	40.54470	44.50084	48.88367	53.73906	59.11760	65.07509	71.67303	78.97915	87.06804	17
18	41.30134	45.59917	50.39594	55.74971	61.72514	68.39407	75.83636	84.14072	93.40561	103.74028	18
19	46.01846	51.15909	56.93949	63.43968	70.74941	78.96923	88.21181	98.60323	110.28456	123.41353	19
20	51.16012	57.27500	64.20283	72.05244	80.94683	91.02493	102.44358	115.37975	130.03294	146.62797	20
21	56.76453	64.00250	72.26514	81.69874	92.46992	104.76842	118.81012	134.84051	153.13854	174.02100	21
22	62.87334	71.40275	81.21431	92.50258	105.49101	120.43600	137.63164	157.41499	180.17209	206.34479	22
23	69.53194	79.54302	91.14788	104.60289	120.20484	138.29704	159.27638	183.60138	211.80134	244.48685	23
24	76.78981	88.49733	102.17415	118.15524	136.83147	158.65862	184.16784	213.97761	248.80757	289.49448	24
25	84.70090	98.34706	114.41331	133.33387	155.61956	181.87083	212.79302	249.21402	292.10486	342.60349	25
26	93.32398	109.18177	127.99877	150.33393	176.85010	208.33274	245.71197	290.08827	342.76268	405.27211	26
27	102.72313	121.09994	143.07864	169.37401	200.84061	238.49933	283.56877	337.50239	402.03234	479.22109	27
28	112.96822	134.20994	159.81729	190.69889	227.94989	272.88923	327.10408	392.50277	471.37783	566.48089	28
29	124.13536	148.63093	178.39719	214.58275	258.58338	312.09373	377.16969	456.30322	552.51207	669.44745	29
30	136.30754	164.49402	199.02088	241.33268	293.19922	356.78685	434.74515	530.31173	647.43912	790.94799	30
31	149.57522	181.94342	221.91317	271.29261	332.31511	407.73701	500.95692	616.16161	758.50377	934.31863	31
32	164.03699	201.13777	247.32362	304.84772	376.51608	465.82019	577.10046	715.74746	888.44941	1103.49598	32
33	179.80032	222.25154	275.52922	342.42945	426.46317	532.03501	664.66552	831.26706	1040.48581	1303.12526	33
34	196.98234	245.47670	306.83744	384.52098	482.90338	607.51991	765.36535	965.26979	1218.36839	1538.68781	34
35	215.71075	271.02437	341.58955	431.66350	546.68082	693.57270	881.17016	1120.71295	1426.49102	1816.65161	35
36	236.12472	299.12681	380.16441	484.46312	618.74933	791.67288	1014.34568	1301.02703	1669.99450	2144.64890	36

EXAMPLE 1 CALCULATING THE FUTURE VALUE OF AN ORDINARY ANNUITY

Charles McCormick deposited $3,000 at the *end* of each year for 8 years in his savings account. If his bank paid 5% interest compounded annually, use Table 12-1 to find the future value of Charles' account.

SOLUTION STRATEGY

Step 1. The rate period is 5% (5% ÷ 1 period per year).

Step 2. The number of periods is eight (8 years × 1 period per year).

Step 3. From Table 12-1, the table factor for 5%, eight periods is 9.54911.

Step 4. Future value = Ordinary annuity table factor × Annuity payment

Future value = 9.54911 × 3,000 = $28,647.33

TRY IT EXERCISE 1

12-3

Stargate Bank is paying 8% interest compounded quarterly. Use Table 12-1 to find the future value of $1,000 deposited at the *end* of every 3 months for 6 years.

CHECK YOUR ANSWER WITH THE SOLUTION ON PAGE 432.

12-2 CALCULATING THE FUTURE VALUE OF AN ANNUITY DUE BY USING TABLES

Once again, for illustrative purposes, let's manually calculate the future value of the annuity. This time, however, it is an annuity due.

What is the amount of an annuity due of $10,000 per year, for 4 years, at 6% interest compounded annually?

Because this is an annuity due, the payment is made at the *beginning* of each period. Each interest calculation uses $I = PRT$, with $R = .06$ and $T = 1$ year.

Time	Balance	
Beginning of period 1	10,000.00	First annuity payment (beginning of period 1)
	+ 600.00	Interest earned, period 1 (10,000.00 × .06 × 1)
End of period 1	10,600.00	
Beginning of period 2	10,600.00	
	10,000.00	Second annuity payment (beginning of period 2)
	+ 1,236.00	Interest earned, period 2 (20,600.00 × .06 × 1)
End of period 2	21,836.00	
Beginning of period 3	21,836.00	
	10,000.00	Third annuity payment (beginning of period 3)
	+ 1,910.16	Interest earned, period 3 (31,836.00 × .06 × 1)
End of period 3	33,746.16	
Beginning of period 4	33,746.16	
	10,000.00	Fourth annuity payment (beginning of period 4)
	+ 2,624.76	Interest earned, period 4 (43,746.16 × .06 × 1)
End of period 4	$46,370.92	Future value of the annuity due

TEACHING TIP

Point out to students that the interest earned with an annuity due is *higher* than that of an ordinary annuity because the annuity due starts earning interest from the beginning of the first period, whereas the ordinary annuity starts earning interest at the end.

In these comparative examples, note that the annuity due earned $46,370.92, whereas the ordinary annuity (page 403) earned only $43,746.16.

When calculating the future value of an annuity due, the table factor is found by using the same table as ordinary annuities (Table 12-1), with some modifications in the steps. With annuities due, you must *add* one period to the number of periods and *subtract* 1.00000 from the table factor.

STEPS FOR CALCULATING FUTURE VALUE (AMOUNT) OF AN ANNUITY DUE

Step 1. Calculate the number of periods of the annuity (years × periods per year), and *add* one period to the total.

Step 2. Calculate the interest rate per period (nominal rate ÷ periods per year).

Step 3. From Table 12-1, locate the table factor at the intersection of the rate per period column and the number of periods row.

Step 4. *Subtract* 1.00000 from the ordinary annuity table factor to get the annuity due table factor.

Step 5. Calculate the future value of the annuity due.

Future value (annuity due) = Annuity due table factor × Annuity payment

TEACHING TIP
Use a time line to help illustrate the interest-earning difference between an ordinary annuity and an annuity due.

EXAMPLE 2 CALCULATING THE FUTURE VALUE OF AN ANNUITY DUE

Mark Goodall deposited $60 at the *beginning* of each month, for 2 years, at his credit union. If the interest rate was 12% compounded monthly, use Table 12-1 to calculate the future value of Mark's account.

SOLUTION STRATEGY

Step 1. Number of periods of the annuity due is 24 (2 × 12) + 1 for a total of 25.

Step 2. Interest rate per period is 1% (12% ÷ 12).

Step 3. The ordinary annuity table factor at the intersection of the rate column and the periods row is 28.24320.

Step 4. Subtract 1.00000 from the table factor:

$$\begin{array}{rl} 28.24320 & \text{ordinary annuity table factor} \\ \underline{-1.00000} & \\ 27.24320 & \text{annuity due table factor} \end{array}$$

Step 5. Future value = Annuity due table factor × Annuity payment

Future value = 27.24320 × 60 = $1,634.59

TRY IT EXERCISE 2

Linville Savings & Loan is paying 6% interest compounded quarterly. Use Table 12-1 to calculate the future value of $1,000, deposited at the *beginning* of every 3 months for 5 years.

CHECK YOUR ANSWER WITH THE SOLUTION ON PAGE 432.

12-3 (OPTIONAL) CALCULATING THE FUTURE VALUE OF AN ORDINARY ANNUITY AND AN ANNUITY DUE BY FORMULA

Learning Tip

Note that the annuity due formula is the same as the ordinary annuity formula except it is multiplied by $(1 + i)$. This is to account for the additional period of the annuity due.

Students with financial, business, or scientific calculators may use the following formulas to solve for the future value of an ordinary annuity and the future value of an annuity due.

Future value of an ordinary annuity

$$FV = Pmt \times \frac{(1+i)^n - 1}{i}$$

Future value of an annuity due

$$FV = Pmt \times \frac{(1+i)^n - 1}{i} \times (1+i)$$

where:

FV = future value
Pmt = annuity payment
i = interest rate per period (nominal rate ÷ periods per year)
n = number of periods (years × periods per year)

Ordinary Annuity
Calculator Sequence: 1 [+] i [=] [y^x] n [−] 1 [÷] i [×] Pmt [=] $FV_{\text{ordinary annuity}}$

Annuity Due
Calculator Sequence: 1 [+] i [=] [×] $FV_{\text{ordinary annuity}}$ [=] $FV_{\text{annuity due}}$

TEACHING TIP
As in Chapter 11, answers calculated by formula may vary slightly from those using the tables because the table factors are rounded to five places, whereas the formulas are not.

EXAMPLE 3 USING FORMULAS TO CALCULATE ANNUITIES

a. What is the future value of an ordinary annuity of $100 per month, for 3 years, at 12% interest compounded monthly?

b. What is the future value of this investment if it is an annuity due?

SOLUTION STRATEGY

a. For this future value of an ordinary annuity problem, we use i = 1% (12% ÷ 12) and n = 36 periods (3 years × 12 periods per year).

$$FV = Pmt \times \frac{(1+i)^n - 1}{i}$$

$$FV = 100 \times \frac{(1+.01)^{36} - 1}{.01}$$

$$FV = 100 \times \frac{(1.01)^{36} - 1}{.01}$$

$$FV = 100 \times \frac{1.4307688 - 1}{.01}$$

$$FV = 100 \times \frac{.4307688}{.01}$$

$$FV = 100 \times 43.07688 = \underline{\underline{\$4,307.69}}$$

Calculator Sequence: 1 [+] .01 [=] [y^x] 36 [−] 1 [÷] .01 [×] 100 [=] $4,307.69

b. To solve the problem as an annuity due, rather than an ordinary annuity, multiply $(1 + i)$, for one extra compounding period, by the future value of the ordinary annuity.

$$FV_{\text{annuity due}} = (1+i) \times FV_{\text{ordinary annuity}}$$
$$FV_{\text{annuity due}} = (1+.01) \times 4{,}307.69$$
$$FV_{\text{annuity due}} = (1.01) \times 4{,}307.69 = \$4{,}350.77$$

Calculator Sequence: 1 + .01 = × 4,307.69 = $4,350.77

TRY IT EXERCISE 3

Kim Baker invested $250 at the *end* of every 3-month period, for 5 years, at 8% interest compounded quarterly.

a. How much is Kim's investment worth after 5 years?

b. If Kim would have invested the money at the *beginning* of each 3-month period, rather than at the end, how much would be in the account?

CHECK YOUR ANSWERS WITH THE SOLUTIONS ON PAGE 432.

Review Exercises

SECTION I 12

CLASSROOM ACTIVITY
As a review of Section I, have students work in pairs to solve Review Exercises 1–10.

Complete, worked-out solutions to Exercises 1–10 appear in Appendix B, following the index.

Note: Round to the nearest cent, when necessary.

Use Table 12-1 to calculate the future value of the following ordinary annuities.

	Annuity Payment	Payment Frequency	Time Period (years)	Nominal Rate (%)	Interest Compounded	Future Value of the Annuity
1.	$1,000	every 3 months	4	8	quarterly	$18,639.29
2.	$2,500	every 6 months	5	10	semiannually	$31,444.73
3.	$10,000	every year	10	9	annually	$151,929.30
4.	$200	every month	2	12	monthly	$5,394.69
5.	$1,500	every 3 months	7	16	quarterly	$74,951.37

Use Table 12-1 to calculate the future value of the following annuities due.

	Annuity Payment	Payment Frequency	Time Period (years)	Nominal Rate (%)	Interest Compounded	Future Value of the Annuity
6.	$400	every 6 months	12	10	semiannually	$18,690.84
7.	$1,000	every 3 months	3	8	quarterly	$13,680.33
8.	$50	every month	$2\frac{1}{2}$	18	monthly	$1,905.09
9.	$2,000	every year	25	5	annually	$100,226.90
10.	$4,400	every 6 months	8	6	semiannually	$91,351.00

Solve the following exercises by using Table 12-1.

11. Castle Rock Savings & Loan is paying 6% interest compounded monthly. How much will $100 deposited at the *end* of each month be worth after 2 years?

$R = \frac{1}{2}\%$ $\quad P = 24 \quad$ $F = 25.43196$

Annuity = 25.43196 × 100 = $2,543.20

12. Bay Point Distributors, Inc., deposits $5,000 at the *beginning* of each 3-month period for 6 years in an account paying 8% interest compounded quarterly.

    a. How much will be in the account at the end of the 6-year period?

    $R = 2\%$ $P = 24 + 1 = 25$ $F = 32.03030 - 1.00000$
    Account value = 31.03030 × 5,000 = $155,151.50

    b. What is the total amount of interest earned in this account?

    Total investment = 5,000 × 24 = 120,000
    Interest earned = 155,151.50 − 120,000 = $35,151.50

13. Sandra Shane deposits $85 each payday into an account at 12% interest compounded monthly. She gets paid on the last day of each month. How much will her account be worth at the end of 30 months?

    $R = 1\%$ $P = 30$ $F = 34.78489$
    Account value = 34.78489 × 85 = $2,956.72

14. Wesley Nolan has set up an annuity due with the Granville Island Credit Union. Each month $170 is electronically debited from his checking account and placed into a savings account earning 6% interest, compounded monthly. What is the value of Wesley's account after 18 months?

    $R = \frac{1}{2}\%$ $P = 18 + 1 = 19$ $F = 19.87972 - 1.00000$
    Account value = 18.87972 × 170 = $3,209.55

15. When Tom Reynolds was born, his parents began depositing $500 at the *beginning* of every year into an annuity to save for his college education. If the account paid 7% interest compounded annually for the first 10 years and then dropped to 5% for the next 8 years, how much is the account worth now that Tom is 18 years old and is ready for college?

    Amount $500 $R = 7\%$ $P = 10 + 1 = 11$ $F = 15.78360 - 1.00000$
    500 × 14.78360 = $7,391.80 First 10 years

    Amount $7,391.80 $R = 5\%$ $P = 8$ $F = 1.47746$ (Table 11-1)
    $7,391.80 × 1.47746 = $10,921.09 First 10 years compounded 8 more years

    Amount $500 $R = 5\%$ $P = 8 + 1 = 9$ $F = 11.02656 - 1.00000$
    500 × 10.02656 = 5,013.28 Next 8 years

    $10,921.09 + $5,013.28 = $15,934.37 Total after 18 years

Learning Tip

Exercise #15, Solution Hint
Once you have determined the account value after the first 10 years, don't forget to apply 5% compound interest to that value for the remaining 8 years.

16. Hi-Tech Hardware has been in business for a few years and is doing well. The owner has decided to save for a future expansion to a second location. He invests $1,000 at the *end* of every month at 12% interest compounded monthly.

    a. How much will be available for the second store after $2\frac{1}{2}$ years?

    $R = 1\%$ $P = 30$ $F = 34.78489$
    1,000 × 34.78489 = $34,784.89

    b. (Optional) Use the formula for an ordinary annuity to calculate how much would be in the account if the owner saved for 5 years.

    $R = 1\%$ $P = 60$

    $$FV = 1{,}000\frac{(1+.01)^{60}-1}{.01} = \$81{,}669.67 \text{ Ordinary annuity}$$

    c. (Optional) Use the formula for an annuity due to calculate how much would be in the account after 5 years if it had been an annuity due.

    $FV = (1 + .01) \times 81{,}669.67 = \$82{,}486.37$ Annuity due

BUSINESS DECISION PLANNING YOUR NEST EGG

17. As part of your retirement plan, you have decided to deposit $3,000 at the *beginning* of each year into an account paying 5% interest compounded annually.

   a. How much would the account be worth after 10 years?

   $R = 5\%$ $P = 10 + 1 = 11$ $F = 14.20679 - 1.00000$
   3,000 × 13.20679 = $39,620.37

   b. How much would the account be worth after 20 years?

   $R = 5\%$ $P = 20 + 1 = 21$ $F = 35.71925 - 1.00000$
   3,000 × 34.71925 = $104,157.75

   c. When you retire in 30 years, what will be the total worth of the account?

   $R = 5\%$ $P = 30 + 1 = 31$ $F = 70.76079 - 1.00000$
   3,000 × 69.76079 = $209,282.37

   d. If you found a bank that paid 6% interest compounded annually, rather than 5%, how much more would you have in the account after 30 years?

   $R = 6\%$ $P = 30 + 1 = 31$ $F = 84.80168 - 1.00000$
   3,000 × 83.80168 = $251,405.04

   251,405.04 − 209,282.37 = $42,122.67 More

PRESENT VALUE OF AN ANNUITY

SECTION II 12

In Section I of this chapter, we learned to calculate the future value of an annuity. This business situation requires that a series of equal payments be made into an account, such as a savings account. The annuity starts with nothing and accumulates at compound interest to a future amount. Now, consider the opposite situation. What if we wanted an account from which we could withdraw a series of equal payments over a period of time? This business situation requires that a lump sum amount be deposited at compound interest now to yield the specified annuity payments. The lump sum required at the beginning is known as the **present value of an annuity**.

present value of an annuity Lump sum amount of money that must be deposited now to provide a specified series of equal payments (annuity) in the future.

Let's look at a business situation using this type of annuity. A company owes $10,000 interest to bondholders at the end of each month for the next 3 years. The company decides to set up an account with a lump sum deposit now, which at compound interest will yield the $10,000 monthly payments for 3 years. After 3 years, the debt will have been paid, and the account will be zero.

Just as in Section I, these annuities can be ordinary, whereby withdrawals from the account are made at the *end* of each period, or annuity due, in which the withdrawals are made at the *beginning*. As with the future value of an annuity, we shall use tables to calculate the present value of an annuity. Once again, in addition to tables, these annuities can be solved by using formulas requiring a calculator with a y^x key.

CALCULATING THE PRESENT VALUE OF AN ORDINARY ANNUITY BY USING TABLES

12-4

Table 12-2, Present Value of an Ordinary Annuity, is used to calculate the lump sum required to be deposited now to yield the specified annuity payment.

CLASSROOM ACTIVITY

This chapter provides a good opportunity for a discussion of IRAs and other retirement plans that involve annuities.

- Have students research and report to the class about the various types of individual retirement plans available today, such as traditional and Roth IRAs, SEP pensions, and Keogh plans.
- Invite a stockbroker or an insurance agent to class to speak about annuity-type investments and retirement plans.

STEPS FOR CALCULATING PRESENT VALUE OF AN ORDINARY ANNUITY

Step 1. Calculate the interest rate per period for the annuity (nominal rate ÷ periods per year).

Step 2. Determine the number of periods of the annuity (years × periods per year).

Step 3. From Table 12-2, locate the present value table factor at the intersection of the rate per period column and the number of periods row.

Step 4. Calculate the present value of the ordinary annuity.

$$\text{Present value (ordinary annuity)} = \text{Ordinary annuity table factor} \times \text{Annuity payment}$$

EXAMPLE 4 CALCULATING THE PRESENT VALUE OF AN ORDINARY ANNUITY

How much must be deposited now, at 9% compounded annually, to yield an annuity payment of $5,000 at the end of each year, for 10 years?

SOLUTION STRATEGY

Step 1. The rate per period is 9% (9% ÷ 1 period per year).

Step 2. The number of periods is 10 (10 years × 1 period per year).

Step 3. From Table 12-2, the table factor for 9%, 10 periods is 6.41766.

Step 4. Present value = Ordinary annuity table factor × Annuity payment

Present value = 6.41766 × 5,000 = $32,088.30

TRY IT EXERCISE 4

12-4

The Actor's Playhouse needs $20,000 at the end of each 6-month theater season for renovations and new stage and lighting equipment. How much must be deposited now, at 8% compounded semiannually, to yield this annuity payment for the next 6 years?

CHECK YOUR ANSWER WITH THE SOLUTION ON PAGE 432.

12-5 CALCULATING THE PRESENT VALUE OF AN ANNUITY DUE BY USING TABLES

The present value of an annuity due is calculated by using the same table as ordinary annuities, with some modifications in the steps.

STEPS FOR CALCULATING PRESENT VALUE OF AN ANNUITY DUE

Step 1. Calculate the number of periods of the annuity (years × periods per year), and *subtract* one period from the total.

Step 2. Calculate the interest rate per period (nominal rate ÷ periods per year).

Step 3. From Table 12-2, locate the table factor at the intersection of the rate per period column and the number of periods row.

Step 4. *Add* 1.00000 to the ordinary annuity table factor to get the annuity due table factor.

Step 5. Calculate the present value of the annuity due.

$$\text{Present value (annuity due)} = \text{Annuity due table factor} \times \text{Annuity payment}$$

Learning Tip

The procedure for finding the present value table factor for an annuity due is the *opposite* of that for future value factors. This time you must subtract a period and add a 1.00000.

EXAMPLE 5 CALCULATING THE PRESENT VALUE OF AN ANNUITY DUE

How much must be deposited now, at 10% compounded semiannually, to yield an annuity payment of $2,000 at the beginning of each 6-month period for 7 years?

SOLUTION STRATEGY

Step 1. The number of periods for the annuity due is 14 (7 years × 2 periods per year) less 1 period = 13.

Step 2. The rate per period is 5% (10% ÷ 2 periods per year).

Step 3. From Table 12-2, the ordinary annuity table factor for 5%, 13 periods is 9.39357.

Step 4. Add 1 to the table factor from Step 3 to get 10.39357, the annuity due table factor.

Step 5. Present value (annuity due) = Annuity due table factor × Annuity payment

Present value = 10.39357 × 2,000 = $20,787.14

TRY IT EXERCISE 5

You are the accountant at Crystal City Lumber, Inc. Based on sales and expense forecasts, you have estimated that $10,000 must be sent to the Internal Revenue Service for income tax payments at the *beginning* of each 3-month period for the next 3 years. How much must be deposited now, at 6% compounded quarterly, to yield the annuity payment needed?

Teaching Transparency 12-5

CHECK YOUR ANSWER WITH THE SOLUTION ON PAGE 432.

Table 12-2
Present Value (Amount) of an Ordinary Annuity of $1.00

12-6

Periods	$\frac{1}{2}$%	1%	$1\frac{1}{2}$%	2%	3%	4%	5%	6%	7%	8%	Periods
1	0.99502	0.99010	0.98522	0.98039	0.97087	0.96154	0.95238	0.94340	0.93458	0.92593	1
2	1.98510	1.97040	1.95588	1.94156	1.91347	1.88609	1.85941	1.83339	1.80802	1.78326	2
3	2.97025	2.94099	2.91220	2.88388	2.82861	2.77509	2.72325	2.67301	2.62432	2.57710	3
4	3.95050	3.90197	3.85438	3.80773	3.71710	3.62990	3.54595	3.46511	3.38721	3.31213	4
5	4.92587	4.85343	4.78264	4.71346	4.57971	4.45182	4.32948	4.21236	4.10020	3.99271	5
6	5.89638	5.79548	5.69719	5.60143	5.41719	5.24214	5.07569	4.91732	4.76654	4.62288	6
7	6.86207	6.72819	6.59821	6.47199	6.23028	6.00205	5.78637	5.58238	5.38929	5.20637	7
8	7.82296	7.65168	7.48593	7.32548	7.01969	6.73274	6.46321	6.20979	5.97130	5.74664	8
9	8.77906	8.56602	8.36052	8.16224	7.78611	7.43533	7.10782	6.80169	6.51523	6.24689	9
10	9.73041	9.47130	9.22218	8.98259	8.53020	8.11090	7.72173	7.36009	7.02358	6.71008	10
11	10.67703	10.36763	10.07112	9.78685	9.25262	8.76048	8.30641	7.88687	7.49867	7.13896	11
12	11.61893	11.25508	10.90751	10.57534	9.95400	9.38507	8.86325	8.38384	7.94269	7.53608	12
13	12.55615	12.13374	11.73153	11.34837	10.63496	9.98565	9.39357	8.85268	8.35765	7.90378	13
14	13.48871	13.00370	12.54338	12.10625	11.29607	10.56312	9.89864	9.29498	8.74547	8.24424	14
15	14.41662	13.86505	13.34323	12.84926	11.93794	11.11839	10.37966	9.71225	9.10791	8.55948	15
16	15.33993	14.71787	14.13126	13.57771	12.56110	11.65230	10.83777	10.10590	9.44665	8.85137	16
17	16.25863	15.56225	14.90765	14.29187	13.16612	12.16567	11.27407	10.47726	9.76322	9.12164	17
18	17.17277	16.39827	15.67256	14.99203	13.75351	12.65930	11.68959	10.82760	10.05909	9.37189	18
19	18.08236	17.22601	16.42617	15.67846	14.32380	13.13394	12.08532	11.15812	10.33560	9.60360	19
20	18.98742	18.04555	17.16864	16.35143	14.87747	13.59033	12.46221	11.46992	10.59401	9.81815	20
21	19.88798	18.85698	17.90014	17.01121	15.41502	14.02916	12.82115	11.76408	10.83553	10.01680	21
22	20.78406	19.66038	18.62082	17.65805	15.93692	14.45112	13.16300	12.04158	11.06124	10.20074	22
23	21.67568	20.45582	19.33086	18.29220	16.44361	14.85684	13.48857	12.30338	11.27219	10.37106	23
24	22.56287	21.24339	20.03041	18.91393	16.93554	15.24696	13.79864	12.55036	11.46933	10.52876	24
25	23.44564	22.02316	20.71961	19.52346	17.41315	15.62208	14.09394	12.78336	11.65358	10.67478	25
26	24.32402	22.79520	21.39863	20.12104	17.87684	15.98277	14.37519	13.00317	11.82578	10.80998	26
27	25.19803	23.55961	22.06762	20.70690	18.32703	16.32959	14.64303	13.21053	11.98671	10.93516	27
28	26.06769	24.31644	22.72672	21.28127	18.76411	16.66306	14.89813	13.40616	12.13711	11.05108	28
29	26.93302	25.06579	23.37608	21.84438	19.18845	16.98371	15.14107	13.59072	12.27767	11.15841	29
30	27.79405	25.80771	24.01584	22.39646	19.60044	17.29203	15.37245	13.76483	12.40904	11.25778	30
31	28.65080	26.54229	24.64615	22.93770	20.00043	17.58849	15.59281	13.92909	12.53181	11.34980	31
32	29.50328	27.26959	25.26714	23.46833	20.38877	17.87355	15.80268	14.08404	12.64656	11.43500	32
33	30.35153	27.98969	25.87895	23.98856	20.76579	18.14765	16.00255	14.23023	12.75379	11.51389	33
34	31.19555	28.70267	26.48173	24.49859	21.13184	18.41120	16.19290	14.36814	12.85401	11.58693	34
35	32.03537	29.40858	27.07559	24.99862	21.48722	18.66461	16.37419	14.49825	12.94767	11.65457	35
36	32.87102	30.10751	27.66068	25.48884	21.83225	18.90828	16.54685	14.62099	13.03521	11.71719	36

Table 12-2
Present Value (Amount) of an Ordinary Annuity of $1.00

Periods	9%	10%	11%	12%	13%	14%	15%	16%	17%	18%	Periods
1	0.91743	0.90909	0.90090	0.89286	0.88496	0.87719	0.86957	0.86207	0.85470	0.84746	1
2	1.75911	1.73554	1.71252	1.69005	1.66810	1.64666	1.62571	1.60523	1.58521	1.56564	2
3	2.53129	2.48685	2.44371	2.40183	2.36115	2.32163	2.28323	2.24589	2.20958	2.17427	3
4	3.23972	3.16987	3.10245	3.03735	2.97447	2.91371	2.85498	2.79818	2.74324	2.69006	4
5	3.88965	3.79079	3.69590	3.60478	3.51723	3.43308	3.35216	3.27429	3.19935	3.12717	5
6	4.48592	4.35526	4.23054	4.11141	3.99755	3.88867	3.78448	3.68474	3.58918	3.49760	6
7	5.03295	4.86842	4.71220	4.56376	4.42261	4.28830	4.16042	4.03857	3.92238	3.81153	7
8	5.53482	5.33493	5.14612	4.96764	4.79877	4.63886	4.48732	4.34359	4.20716	4.07757	8
9	5.99525	5.75902	5.53705	5.32825	5.13166	4.94637	4.77158	4.60654	4.45057	4.30302	9
10	6.41766	6.14457	5.88923	5.65022	5.42624	5.21612	5.01877	4.83323	4.65860	4.49409	10
11	6.80519	6.49506	6.20652	5.93770	5.68694	5.45273	5.23371	5.02864	4.83641	4.65601	11
12	7.16073	6.81369	6.49236	6.19437	5.91765	5.66029	5.42062	5.19711	4.98839	4.79322	12
13	7.48690	7.10336	6.74987	6.42355	6.12181	5.84236	5.58315	5.34233	5.11828	4.90951	13
14	7.78615	7.36669	6.98187	6.62817	6.30249	6.00207	5.72448	5.46753	5.22930	5.00806	14
15	8.06069	7.60608	7.19087	6.81086	6.46238	6.14217	5.84737	5.57546	5.32419	5.09158	15
16	8.31256	7.82371	7.37916	6.97399	6.60388	6.26506	5.95423	5.66850	5.40529	5.16235	16
17	8.54363	8.02155	7.54879	7.11963	6.72909	6.37286	6.04716	5.74870	5.47461	5.22233	17
18	8.75563	8.20141	7.70162	7.24967	6.83991	6.46742	6.12797	5.81785	5.53385	5.27316	18
19	8.95011	8.36492	7.83929	7.36578	6.93797	6.55037	6.19823	5.87746	5.58449	5.31624	19
20	9.12855	8.51356	7.96333	7.46944	7.02475	6.62313	6.25933	5.92884	5.62777	5.35275	20
21	9.29224	8.64869	8.07507	7.56200	7.10155	6.68696	6.31246	5.97314	5.66476	5.38368	21
22	9.44243	8.77154	8.17574	7.64465	7.16951	6.74294	6.35866	6.01133	5.69637	5.40990	22
23	9.58021	8.88322	8.26643	7.71843	7.22966	6.79206	6.39884	6.04425	5.72340	5.43212	23
24	9.70661	8.98474	8.34814	7.78432	7.28288	6.83514	6.43377	6.07263	5.74649	5.45095	24
25	9.82258	9.07704	8.42174	7.84314	7.32998	6.87293	6.46415	6.09709	5.76623	5.46691	25
26	9.92897	9.16095	8.48806	7.89566	7.37167	6.90608	6.49056	6.11818	5.78311	5.48043	26
27	10.02658	9.23722	8.54780	7.94255	7.40856	6.93515	6.51353	6.13636	5.79753	5.49189	27
28	10.11613	9.30657	8.60162	7.98442	7.44120	6.96066	6.53351	6.15204	5.80985	5.50160	28
29	10.19828	9.36961	8.65011	8.02181	7.47009	6.98304	6.55088	6.16555	5.82039	5.50983	29
30	10.27365	9.42691	8.69379	8.05518	7.49565	7.00266	6.56598	6.17720	5.82939	5.51681	30
31	10.34280	9.47901	8.73315	8.08499	7.51828	7.01988	6.57911	6.18724	5.83709	5.52272	31
32	10.40624	9.52638	8.76860	8.11159	7.53830	7.03498	6.59053	6.19590	5.84366	5.52773	32
33	10.46444	9.56943	8.80054	8.13535	7.55602	7.04823	6.60046	6.20336	5.84928	5.53197	33
34	10.51784	9.60857	8.82932	8.15656	7.57170	7.05985	6.60910	6.20979	5.85409	5.53557	34
35	10.56682	9.64416	8.85524	8.17550	7.58557	7.07005	6.61661	6.21534	5.85820	5.53862	35
36	10.61176	9.67651	8.87859	8.19241	7.59785	7.07899	6.62314	6.22012	5.86171	5.54120	36

12-6 (OPTIONAL) CALCULATING THE PRESENT VALUE OF AN ORDINARY ANNUITY AND AN ANNUITY DUE BY FORMULA

Students with financial, business, or scientific calculators may use the following formulas to solve for the present value of an ordinary annuity and the present value of an annuity due. Note that the annuity due formula is the same as the ordinary annuity formula, except it is multiplied by $(1 + i)$. This is to account for the fact that with an annuity due each payment earns interest for one additional period, because payments are made at the beginning of each period, not the end.

Present value of an ordinary annuity	Present value of an annuity due
$PV = Pmt \times \frac{1-(1+i)^{-n}}{i}$	$PV = Pmt \times \frac{1-(1+i)^{-n}}{i} \times (1+i)$

where:

PV = present value (lump sum)
Pmt = annuity payment
i = interest rate per period (nominal rate ÷ periods per year)
n = number of periods (years × periods per year)

Ordinary Annuity
Calculator Sequence: 1 [+] i [=] [y^x] n [+/−] [=] [M+] 1 [−] [MR] [÷] i [×] Pmt [=] PV

Annuity Due
Calculator Sequence: 1 [+] i [=] [×] $PV_{\text{ordinary annuity}}$ [=] $PV_{\text{annuity due}}$

EXAMPLE 6 CALCULATING PRESENT VALUE OF AN ANNUITY BY FORMULA

a. What is the present value of an ordinary annuity of $100 per month, for 4 years, at 12% interest compounded monthly?

b. What is the present value of this investment if it is an annuity due?

SOLUTION STRATEGY

a. For this present value of an ordinary annuity problem, we use $i = 1\%$ (12% ÷ 12) and $n = 48$ periods (4 years × 12 periods per year).

$$PV = Pmt \times \frac{1-(1+i)^{-n}}{i}$$

$$PV = 100 \times \frac{1-(1+.01)^{-48}}{.01}$$

$$PV = 100 \times \frac{1-(1.01)^{-48}}{.01}$$

$$PV = 100 \times \frac{1-.6202604}{.01}$$

$$PV = 100 \times \frac{.3797396}{.01}$$

$$PV = 100 \times 37.97396 = \underline{\underline{\$3,797.40}}$$

Calculator Sequence:

1 [+] .01 [=] [y^x] 48 [+/−] [=] [M+] 1 [−] [MR] [÷] .01 [×] 100 [=] $3,797.40

b. To solve as an annuity due, rather than an ordinary annuity, multiply the present value of the ordinary annuity by $(1 + i)$, for one extra compounding period.

$$PV_{\text{annuity due}} = (1+i) \times PV_{\text{ordinary annuity}}$$
$$PV_{\text{annuity due}} = (1+.01) \times 3,797.40$$
$$PV_{\text{annuity due}} = (1.01) \times 3,797.40 = \underline{\underline{\$3,835.37}}$$

Calculator Sequence: 1 [+] .01 [=] [×] 3,797.40 [=] $3,835.37

TRY IT EXERCISE 6

Use the present value of an annuity formula to solve the following.

a. Mike Nolan wants $500 at the *end* of each 3-month period for the next 6 years. If Mike's bank is paying 8% interest compounded quarterly, how much must he deposit now in order to receive the desired ordinary annuity?

b. If Mike wants the payments at the *beginning* of each 3-month period, rather than at the end, how much would he have to deposit?

CHECK YOUR ANSWERS WITH THE SOLUTIONS ON PAGE 432.

Review Exercises

SECTION II 12

Complete, worked-out solutions to Exercises 1–10 appear in Appendix B, following the index.

Note: Round to the nearest cent, when necessary.

Use Table 12-2 to calculate the future value of the following ordinary annuities.

	Annuity Payment	Payment Frequency	Time Period (years)	Nominal Rate (%)	Interest Compounded	Present Value of the Annuity
1.	$300	every 6 months	7	10	semiannually	$2,969.59
2.	$2,000	every year	20	7	annually	$21,188.02
3.	$1,600	every 3 months	6	12	quarterly	$27,096.86
4.	$1,000	every month	$1\frac{3}{4}$	6	monthly	$19,887.98
5.	$8,500	every 3 months	3	16	quarterly	$79,773.10

Use Table 12-2 to calculate the present value of the following annuities due.

	Annuity Payment	Payment Frequency	Time Period (years)	Nominal Rate (%)	Interest Compounded	Present Value of the Annuity
6.	$1,400	every year	10	11	annually	$9,151.87
7.	$1,300	every 3 months	4	12	quarterly	$16,819.32
8.	$500	every month	$2\frac{1}{4}$	18	monthly	$11,199.32
9.	$7,000	every 6 months	12	8	semiannually	$110,997.88
10.	$4,000	every year	18	7	annually	$43,052.88

Solve the following exercises by using Table 12-2.

11. Westchester Savings & Loan is paying 6% interest compounded monthly. How much must be deposited now to withdraw an annuity of \$400 at the end of each month for 2 years?

$R = \frac{1}{2}\%$ $P = 24$ $F = 22.56287$

Amount = 400 × 22.56287 = \$9,025.15

12. Christine Carson wants to receive an annuity of \$2,000 at the beginning of each year for the next 10 years. How much should be deposited now at 6% compounded annually to accomplish this goal?

$R = 6\%$ $P = 10 - 1 = 9$ $F = 6.80169 + 1.00000$

Amount = 2,000 × 7.80169 = \$15,603.38

13. As the chief accountant for Sparkle Industries, you have estimated that the company must pay \$100,000 income tax to the IRS at the end of each quarter this year. How much should be deposited now at 8% interest compounded quarterly to meet this tax obligation?

$R = 2\%$ $P = 4$ $F = 3.80773$

Amount = 100,000 × 3.80773 = \$380,773

14. John Sebastian is the grand prize winner in a college tuition essay contest sponsored by a local scholarship fund. The winner receives \$2,000 at the beginning of each year for the next 4 years. How much should be invested at 7% interest compounded annually to pay the prize?

$R = 7\%$ $P = 4 - 1 = 3$ $F = 2.62432 + 1.00000$

Amount = 2,000 × 3.62432 = \$7,248.64

15. Stewart Creek Golf Course management has contracted to pay a golf green maintenance specialist a \$680 monthly fee at the end of each month to provide advice on improving the quality of the greens on its 18-hole course. How much should be deposited now into an account that earns 6% compounded monthly to be able to make monthly payments to the consultant for the next year?

$R = \frac{1}{2}\%$ $P = 12$ $F = 11.61893$

Amount = 680 × 11.61893 = \$7,900.87

16. Analysts at Sky Blue Airlines did a three-year projection of expenses. They calculated that the company will need \$15,800 at the *beginning* of each six-month period to buy fuel, oil, lube, and parts for aircraft operations and maintenance. Sky Blue can get 6% interest compounded semiannually from its bank. How much should Sky Blue deposit now to support the next three years of operations and maintenance expenses?

$R = 3\%$ $P = 6 - 1 = 5$ $F = 4.57971 + 1.0000 = 5.57971$

15,800 × 5.57971 = \$88,159.42

BUSINESS DECISION THE INSURANCE SETTLEMENT

17. Harper Enterprises has been awarded an insurance settlement of \$5,000 at the end of each 6-month period for the next 10 years.

    a. As their accountant, calculate how much the insurance company must set aside now, at 6% interest compounded semiannually, to pay this obligation to Harper.

    $R = 3\%$ $P = 20$ $F = 14.87747$

    Amount = 5,000 × 14.87747 = \$74,387.35

b. (Optional) Use the present value of an ordinary annuity formula to calculate how much the insurance company would have to invest now if the Harper settlement was changed to $2,500 at the end of each 3-month period for 10 years, and the insurance company could earn 8% interest compounded quarterly.

$R = 2\%$ $P = 40$ Amount $= \$2,500$

$$PV = PMT \times \frac{1-(1+i)^{-n}}{i} \qquad PV = 2,500 \times \frac{1-(1.02)^{-40}}{.02}$$

$$PV = 2,500 \times \frac{1-(1+.02)^{-40}}{.02} \qquad 2,500 \times 27.35547924 = \underline{\underline{\$68,388.70}}$$

c. (Optional) Use the present value of an annuity due formula to calculate how much the insurance company would have to invest now if the Harper settlement was paid at the beginning of each 3-month period rather than at the end.

$R = 2\%$ $P = 40$ Amount $= \$2,500$

PV annuity due $= (1 + i) \times PV$ ordinary annuity

$PV = (1 + .02) \times 68,388.70 = \underline{\underline{\$69,756.47}}$

SINKING FUNDS AND AMORTIZATION

SECTION III 12

Sinking funds and amortization are two common applications of annuities. In the previous sections of this chapter, the amount of the annuity payment was known and you were asked to calculate the future or present value (lump sum) of the annuity. In this section, the future or present value of the annuity is known, and the amount of the payments is calculated.

A sinking fund situation occurs when the future value of an annuity is known, and the payment required each period to amount to that future value is the unknown. **Sinking funds** are accounts used to set aside equal amounts of money at the end of each period, at compound interest, for the purpose of saving for a future obligation. Businesses use sinking funds to accumulate money for such things as new equipment, facility expansion, and other expensive items needed in the future. Another common use is to retire financial obligations such as bond issues that come due at a future date. Individuals can use sinking funds to save for a college education, a car, the down payment on a house, or a vacation.

Amortization is the opposite of a sinking fund. **Amortization** is a financial arrangement whereby a lump-sum obligation is incurred at compound interest now (present value) and is paid off or liquidated by a series of equal periodic payments for a specified amount of time. With amortization the amount of the loan or obligation is given, and the equal payments that will amortize or pay off the obligation must be calculated. Some business uses of amortization would be paying off loans or liquidating insurance or retirement funds.

In this section, you learn to calculate the sinking fund payment required to save for a future amount and the amortization payment required to liquidate a present amount. We assume that all annuities are ordinary, with payments made at the *end* of each period. As in previous sections, these exercises can be calculated by tables or by formulas.

sinking fund Account used to set aside equal amounts of money at the end of each period, at compound interest, for the purpose of saving for a future obligation.

amortization A financial arrangement whereby a lump-sum obligation is incurred at compound interest now, such as a loan, and is paid off or liquidated by a series of equal periodic payments for a specified amount of time.

In the Business World

Mortgages, which are real estate loans, are a common example of amortization. More detailed coverage, including the preparation of amortization schedules, is found in Chapter 14.

12-7 CALCULATING THE AMOUNT OF A SINKING FUND PAYMENT BY TABLE

In a sinking fund, the future value is known; therefore, we use the future value of an annuity table (Table 12-1) to calculate the amount of the payment.

TEACHING TIP
Be sure students are aware that all sinking fund and amortization annuities in this section are ordinary, with payments made at the *end* of each period.

STEPS FOR CALCULATING THE AMOUNT OF A SINKING FUND PAYMENT

Step 1. Using the appropriate rate per period and number of periods of the sinking fund, find the future value table factor from Table 12-1.

Step 2. Calculate the amount of the sinking fund payment.

$$\textbf{Sinking fund payment} = \frac{\textbf{Future value of the sinking fund}}{\textbf{Future value table factor}}$$

EXAMPLE 7 CALCULATING THE AMOUNT OF A SINKING FUND PAYMENT

What sinking fund payment is required at the end of each 6-month period, at 6% interest compounded semiannually, to amount to $12,000 in 4 years?

SOLUTION STRATEGY

TEACHING TIP
In Sections I and II of this chapter, the amount of the annuity payment was "known," and the future and present values were "unknown." In Section III, it is the *opposite*. The future and present values are "known," and the amount of the payment is the "unknown."

Step 1. This sinking fund is for eight periods (4 years × 2 periods per year) at 3% per period (6% ÷ 2 periods per year). From Table 12-1, eight periods, 3% per period gives a future value table factor of 8.89234.

Step 2. $$\text{Sinking fund payment} = \frac{\text{Future value of the sinking fund}}{\text{Future value table factor}}$$

$$\text{Sinking fund payment} = \frac{12{,}000}{8.89234} = \underline{\underline{\$1{,}349.48}}$$

TRY IT EXERCISE 7

Kari La Fontaine wants to accumulate $8,000 in 5 years for a trip to Europe. If her bank is paying 12% interest compounded quarterly, how much must Kari deposit at the end of each 3-month period in a sinking fund to reach her desired goal?

CHECK YOUR ANSWER WITH THE SOLUTION ON PAGE 432.

© Steve Cole/Digital Vision/Getty Images

Sinking funds enable businesses to plan for future purchases of expensive equipment.

CALCULATING THE AMOUNT OF AN AMORTIZATION PAYMENT BY TABLE

12-8

Amortization is the process of "paying off" a financial obligation with a series of equal regular payments over a period of time. With amortization, the original amount of the loan or obligation is known (present value); therefore, we use the present value table (Table 12-2) to calculate the amount of the payment.

STEPS FOR CALCULATING THE AMOUNT OF AN AMORTIZATION PAYMENT

Step 1. Using the appropriate rate per period and number of periods of the amortization, find the present value table factor from Table 12-2.

Step 2. Calculate the amount of the amortization payment.

$$\textbf{Amortization payment} = \frac{\textbf{Original amount of obligation}}{\textbf{Present value table factor}}$$

EXAMPLE 8 CALCULATING THE AMOUNT OF AN AMORTIZATION PAYMENT

What amortization payments are required each month, at 12% interest, to pay off a $10,000 loan in 2 years?

SOLUTION STRATEGY

Step 1. This amortization is for 24 periods (2 years × 12 periods per year) at 1% per period (12% ÷ 12 periods per year). From Table 12-2, 24 periods, 1% per period gives a present value table factor of 21.24339.

Step 2. $\text{Amortization payment} = \dfrac{\text{Original amount of obligation}}{\text{Present value table factor}}$

$$\text{Amortization payment} = \frac{10{,}000}{21.24339} = \underline{\underline{\$470.73}}$$

TRY IT EXERCISE 8

Captain Bob Albrecht purchased a new fishing boat for $130,000. He made a $20,000 down payment and financed the balance at his bank for 7 years. What amortization payments are required every 3 months, at 16% interest, to pay off the boat loan?

CHECK YOUR ANSWER WITH THE SOLUTION ON PAGE 432.

12-9 (OPTIONAL) CALCULATING SINKING FUND PAYMENTS BY FORMULA

In addition to using Table 12-1, sinking fund payments may be calculated by using the formula

$$\textbf{Sinking fund payment} = FV \times \frac{i}{(1+i)^n - 1}$$

where:

FV **= amount needed in the future**
i **= interest rate per period (nominal rate ÷ periods per year)**
n **= number of periods (years × periods per year)**

Calculator Sequence:

1 [+] i [=] [y^x] n [−] 1 [=] [M+] i [÷] [MR] [×] FV [=] Sinking fund payment

EXAMPLE 9 CALCULATING SINKING FUND PAYMENTS BY FORMULA

Ocean Air Corporation needs $100,000 in 5 years to pay off a bond issue. What sinking fund payment is required at the end of each month, at 12% interest compounded monthly, to meet this financial obligation?

SOLUTION STRATEGY

To solve this sinking fund problem, we use 1% interest rate per period (12% ÷ 12) and 60 periods (5 years × 12 periods per year).

$$\text{Sinking fund payment} = \text{Future value} \times \frac{i}{(1+i)^n - 1}$$

$$\text{Sinking fund payment} = 100{,}000 \times \frac{.01}{(1+.01)^{60} - 1}$$

$$\text{Sinking fund payment} = 100{,}000 \times \frac{.01}{.8166967}$$

$$\text{Sinking fund payment} = 100{,}000 \times .0122444 = \underline{\underline{\$1{,}224.44}}$$

Calculator Sequence:

1 [+] .01 [=] [y^x] 60 [−] 1 [=] [M+] .01 [÷] [MR] [×] 100,000 [=] $\underline{\underline{\$1{,}224.44}}$

TRY IT EXERCISE 9

Park City Ski Rental Center will need $40,000 in 6 years to replace aging equipment. What sinking fund payment is required at the end of each month, at 18% interest compounded monthly, to amount to the $40,000 in 6 years?

CHECK YOUR ANSWER WITH THE SOLUTION ON PAGE 432.

(OPTIONAL) CALCULATING AMORTIZATION PAYMENTS BY FORMULA

In addition to using Table 12-2, amortization payments may be calculated by using the formula

$$\textbf{Amortization payment} = PV \times \frac{i}{1-(1+i)^{-n}}$$

where:

PV **= amount of the loan or obligation**
i **= interest rate per period (nominal rate ÷ periods per year)**
n **= number of periods (years × periods per year)**

Calculator Sequence:

Amortization payment

EXAMPLE 10 CALCULATING AMORTIZATION PAYMENTS BY FORMULA

What amortization payment is required each month, at 18% interest, to pay off $5,000 in 3 years?

SOLUTION STRATEGY

To solve this amortization problem, we use 1.5% interest rate per period (18% ÷ 12) and 36 periods (3 years × 12 periods per year).

$$\text{Amortization payment} = \text{Present Value} \times \frac{i}{1-(1+i)^{-n}}$$

$$\text{Amortization payment} = 5{,}000 \times \frac{.015}{1-(1+.015)^{-36}}$$

$$\text{Amortization payment} = 5{,}000 \times \frac{.015}{.4149103}$$

$$\text{Amortization payment} = 5{,}000 \times .0361524 = \underline{\underline{\$180.76}}$$

Calculator Sequence:

1 + .015 = y^x 36 +/− = M+ 1 − MR = M+ .015 ÷ MR × 5,000 = $\underline{\underline{\$180.76}}$

TRY IT EXERCISE 10

Main Street Manufacturing recently purchased a new computer system for $150,000. What amortization payment is required each month, at 12% interest, to pay off this obligation in 8 years?

CHECK YOUR ANSWER WITH THE SOLUTION ON PAGE 432.

SECTION III Review Exercises

Complete, worked-out solutions for Exercises 1–10 appear in Appendix B, following the index.

Note: Round to the nearest cent, when necessary.

For the following sinking funds, use Table 12-1 to calculate the amount of the periodic payments needed to amount to the financial objective (future value of the annuity).

	Sinking Fund Payment	Payment Frequency	Time Period (years)	Nominal Rate (%)	Interest Compounded	Future Value (Objective)
1.	$2,113.50	every 6 months	8	10	semiannually	$50,000
2.	$9,608.29	every year	14	9	annually	$250,000
3.	$55.82	every 3 months	5	12	quarterly	$1,500
4.	$203.93	every month	$1\frac{1}{2}$	12	monthly	$4,000
5.	$859.13	every 3 months	4	16	quarterly	$18,750

CLASSROOM ACTIVITY

To demonstrate their understanding of the subject, have students break into small groups to write and solve some sinking fund and amortization word problems with realistic business scenarios. Next, have each group exchange and solve the problems of another group, check answers, and resolve any differences.

You have just been hired as a loan officer at the Eagle National Bank. Your first assignment is to calculate the amount of the periodic payment required to amortize (pay off) the following loans being considered by the bank (use Table 12-2).

	Loan Payment	Payment Period	Term of Loan (years)	Nominal Rate (%)	Present Value) (Amount of Loan)
6.	$4,189.52	every year	12	9	$30,000
7.	$336.36	every 3 months	5	8	$5,500
8.	$558.65	every month	$1\frac{3}{4}$	18	$10,000
9.	$1,087.48	every 6 months	8	6	$13,660
10.	$51.83	every month	1.5	12	$850

11. Baleen Industries established a sinking fund to pay off a $10,000,000 loan that comes due in 8 years for a corporate jet.

    a. What equal payments must be deposited into the fund every 3 months at 6% interest compounded quarterly for Baleen to meet this financial obligation?

    $R = 1\frac{1}{2}\%$ $\qquad P = 32$ $\qquad PV = 10{,}000{,}000$

    Factor $= 40.68829$

    $$\text{Payment} = \frac{10{,}000{,}000}{40.68829} = \underline{\underline{\$245{,}770.96}}$$

    b. What is the total amount of interest earned in this sinking fund account?

    $245{,}770.96 \times 32 = 7{,}864{,}670.72$

    Amount of interest $= 10{,}000{,}000 - 7{,}864{,}670.72 = \underline{\underline{\$2{,}135{,}329.28}}$

Corporate aircraft are usually powered by jet engines and carry up to 40 passengers. Major U.S. manufacturers in the corporate jet market include the Cessna Aircraft Company, Gulfstream Aerospace Corporation, and Raytheon. According to the General Aviation Manufacturers Association in 2007, there were over 10,550 corporate aircraft in operation in the United States

12. Melissa Jaeger bought a new Nissan Murano for $15,500. She made a $2,500 down payment and is financing the balance at the Imperial Bank over a 3-year period at 12% interest. As her banker, calculate what equal monthly payments will be required by Melissa to amortize the car loan.

    $R = 1\%$ $\qquad P = 36$ $\qquad PV = (15{,}500 - 2{,}500) = 13{,}000$

    Factor $= 30.10751$

    $$\text{Payment} = \frac{13{,}000}{30.10751} = \underline{\underline{\$431.79}}$$

13. Plant World Landscaping buys new lawn equipment every 3 years. It is estimated that $25,000 will be needed for the next purchase. The company sets up a sinking fund to save for this obligation.

    a. What equal payments must be deposited every 6 months if interest is 8% compounded semiannually?

    $R = 4\%$ $\qquad P = 6$ $\qquad FV = 25{,}000$

    Factor $= 6.63298$

    $$\text{Payment} = \frac{25{,}000}{6.63298} = \underline{\underline{\$3{,}769.04}}$$

    b. What is the total amount of interest earned by the sinking fund?

    $6 \times 3{,}769.04 = 22{,}614.24$

    Amount of interest $= 25{,}000.00 - 22{,}614.24 = \underline{\underline{\$2{,}385.76}}$

14. Sandra Gonzalez is ready to retire and has saved up $200,000 for that purpose. She wants to amortize (liquidate) that amount in a retirement fund so that she will receive equal annual payments over the next 25 years. At the end of the 25 years, there will be no funds left in the account. If the fund earns 12% interest, how much will Sandra receive each year?

    $R = 12\%$ $\qquad P = 25$ $\qquad PV = 200{,}000$

    Factor $= 7.84314$

    $$\text{Payment} = \frac{200{,}000}{7.84314} = \underline{\underline{\$25{,}499.99}}$$

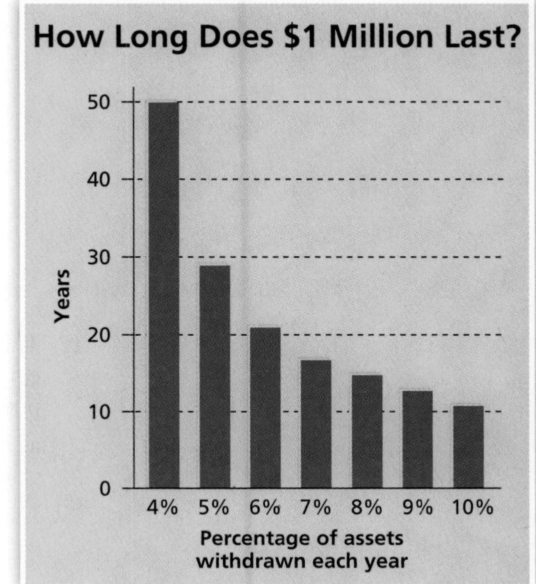

This chart shows the number of years a $1 million portfolio with an annual return of 8.7% can last, based on percentage of assets withdrawn each year.

15. Norm and Alice Scott are planning a Mediterranean Cruise in 4 years and will need \$7,500 for the trip. They decide to set up a sinking fund savings account for the vacation. They intend to make regular payments at the end of each 3-month period into the account that pays 6% interest compounded quarterly. What periodic sinking fund payment will allow them to achieve their vacation goal?

$R = 1.5\%$ $P = 16$ $FV = 7{,}500$

Factor = 17.93237

$$\text{Payment} = \frac{7{,}500}{17.93237} = \underline{\underline{\$418.24}}$$

(Optional) Solve the following exercises by using the sinking fund or amortization formulas.

16. Robby Martin purchased a new home for \$225,000 with a 20% down payment and the remainder amortized over a 15-year period at 9% interest.

a. What is the amount of the house that was financed?

225,000 × .2 = 45,000

Amount financed = 225,000 − 45,000 = $\underline{\underline{\$180{,}000}}$

b. What equal monthly payments are required to amortize this loan over 15 years?

$R = .75\%$ $P = 180$ $PV = 180{,}000$

$$\text{Amortization payment} = PV \times \frac{i}{1-(1+i)^{-n}} = 180{,}000 \times \frac{.0075}{1-(1+.0075)^{-180}}$$

$$= 180{,}000 \times \frac{.0075}{.73945057} = 180{,}000 \times .010142666$$

$$= \underline{\underline{\$1{,}825.68}}$$

c. What equal monthly payments are required if Robby decides to take a 20-year loan rather than a 15?

$R = .75\%$ $P = 240$ $PV = 180{,}000$

$$\text{Amortization payment} = PV \times \frac{i}{1-(1+i)^{-n}} = 180{,}000 \times \frac{.0075}{1-(1+.0075)^{-240}}$$

$$= 180{,}000 \times \frac{.0075}{.833587155} = 180{,}000 \times .00899726$$

$$= \underline{\underline{\$1{,}619.51}}$$

17. The Shangri-La Hotel has a financial obligation of \$1,000,000 due in 5 years for kitchen equipment. A sinking fund is established to meet this obligation at 12% interest compounded monthly.

a. What equal monthly sinking fund payments are required to accumulate the needed amount?

$R = 1\%$ $P = 60$ $FV = 1{,}000{,}000$

$$\text{Payment} = FV \times \frac{i}{(1+i)^n - 1} = 1{,}000{,}000 \times \frac{.01}{(1+.01)^{60} - 1}$$

$$\text{Payment} = 1{,}000{,}000 \times \frac{.01}{.816696699} = \underline{\underline{\$12{,}244.45}}$$

b. What is the total amount of interest earned in the account?

$60 \times 12{,}244.45 = 734{,}667$

Interest earned $= 1{,}000{,}000 - 734{,}667 = \underline{\underline{\$265{,}333}}$

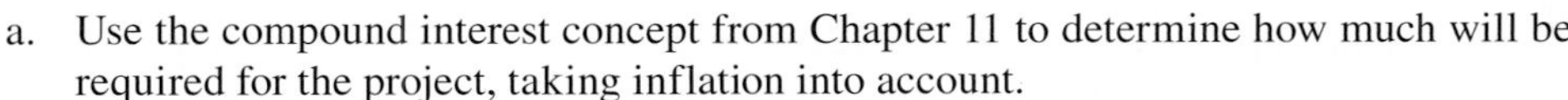

BUSINESS DECISION DON'T FORGET INFLATION!

18. You are the vice president of finance for Neptune Enterprises, Inc., a manufacturer of scuba diving gear. The company is planning a major plant expansion in 5 years. You have decided to start a sinking fund to accumulate the funds necessary for the project. Current bank rates are 8% compounded quarterly. It is estimated that $2,000,000 in today's dollars will be required; however, the inflation rate on construction costs and plant equipment is expected to average 5% per year for the next 5 years.

    a. Use the compound interest concept from Chapter 11 to determine how much will be required for the project, taking inflation into account.

    From Table 11-1, future value at compound interest,

    $R = 5\%$ $\quad P = 5 \quad$ Factor $= 1.27628$

    $FV = 2{,}000{,}000 \times 1.27628 = \underline{\underline{\$2{,}552{,}560}}$

    b. What sinking fund payments will be required at the end of every 3-month period to accumulate the necessary funds?

    $R = 2\% \quad P = 20 \quad FV = \$2{,}552{,}560$

    Factor $= 24.29737$

    $$\text{Payment} = \frac{FV}{\text{Factor}} = \frac{2{,}552{,}560}{24.29737} = \underline{\underline{\$105{,}054.99}}$$

In the Business World

This Business Decision, "Don't Forget Inflation," is a good illustration of how inflation can affect long-range financial planning in business. Notice how much more the project will cost in 5 years because of rising prices.

At www.bls.gov, the Bureau of Labor Statistics has an inflation calculator where you can enter a year and a dollar amount of buying power and then calculate how much buying power would be required for the same amount of goods or services in a subsequent year, after inflation.

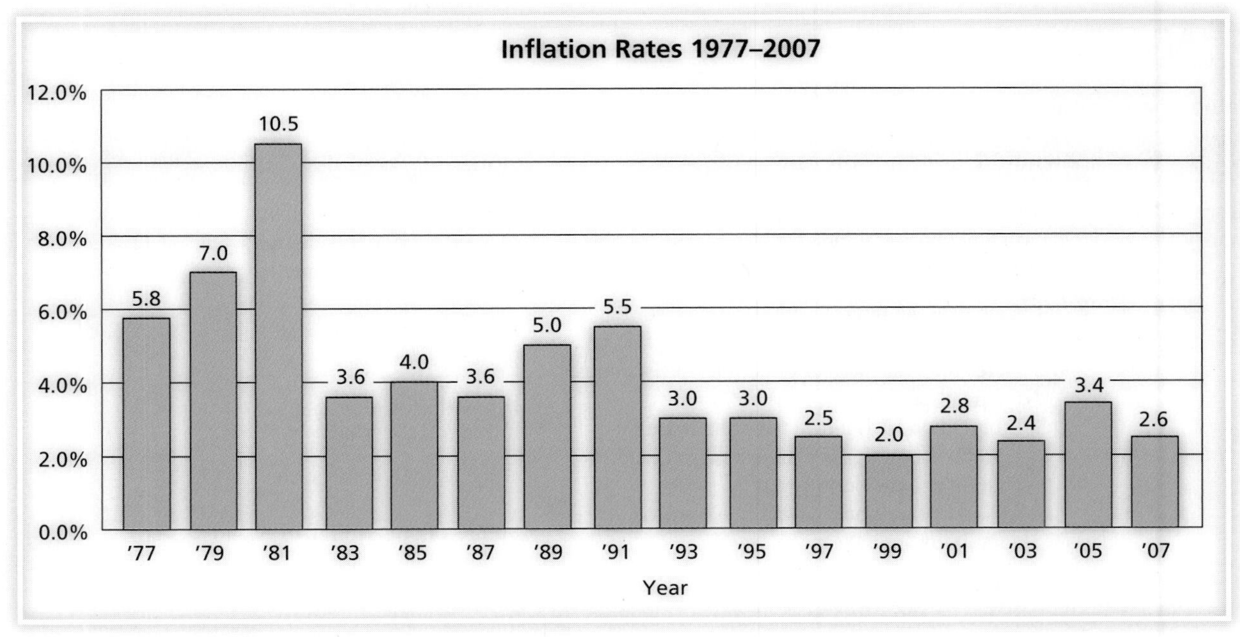

12

CHAPTER FORMULAS

Future value of an annuity

Future value (ordinary annuity) = Ordinary annuity table factor × Annuity payment

$$FV \text{ (ordinary annuity)} = \text{Payment} \times \frac{(1+i)^n - 1}{i}$$

Future value (annuity due) = Annuity due table factor × Annuity payment

$$FV \text{ (annuity due)} = \text{Payment} \times \frac{(1+i)^n - 1}{i} \times (1+i)$$

Present value of an annuity

Present value (ordinary annuity) = Ordinary annuity table factor × Annuity payment

$$PV \text{ (ordinary annuity)} = \text{Payment} \times \frac{1-(1+i)^{-n}}{i}$$

Present value (annuity due) = Annuity due table factor × Annuity payment

$$PV \text{ (annuity due)} = \text{Payment} \times \frac{1-(1+i)^{-n}}{i} \times (1+i)$$

Sinking Fund

$$\text{Sinking fund payment} = \frac{\text{Future value of the sinking fund}}{\text{Future value table factor}}$$

$$\text{Sinking fund payment} = \text{Future value} \times \frac{i}{(1+i)^n - 1}$$

Amortization

$$\text{Amortization payment} = \frac{\text{Original amount of obligation}}{\text{Present value table factor}}$$

$$\text{Amortization payment} = \text{Present value} \times \frac{i}{1-(1+i)^{-n}}$$

SUMMARY CHART

Section I: Future Value of an Annuity

Topic	Important Concepts	Illustrative Examples
Calculating the Future Value of an Ordinary Annuity by Using Tables **P/O 12-1, p. 402**	An annuity is the payment or receipt of *equal* cash amounts per period for a specified amount of time. 1. Calculate the interest rate per period for the annuity (nominal rate ÷ periods per year). 2. Determine the number of periods of the annuity (years × periods per year). 3. From Table 12-1, locate the ordinary annuity table factor at the intersection of the rate column and the periods row. 4. Calculate the future value of an ordinary annuity by **Future value (ordinary annuity) = Table factor × Annuity payment**	Calculate the future value of an ordinary annuity of $500 every 6 months for 5 years at 12% interest compounded semiannually. Rate per period = 6% (12% ÷ 2 periods per year) Periods = 10 (5 years × 2 periods per year) Table factor 6%, 10 periods = 13.18079 Future value = 13.18079 × 500 Future value = $6,590.40

Section I: (continued)

Topic	Important Concepts	Illustrative Examples
Calculating the Future Value of an Annuity Due by Using Tables P/O 12-2, p. 406	1. Calculate the number of periods of the annuity (years × periods per year), and add one period to the total. 2. Calculate the interest rate per period (nominal rate ÷ periods per year). 3. Locate the table factor at the intersection of the rate column and the periods row. 4. Subtract 1 from the ordinary annuity table factor to get the annuity due table factor. 5. Calculate the future value of an annuity due by **Future value (annuity due) = Table factor × Annuity payment**	Calculate the future value of an annuity due to $100 per month, for 2 years, at 12% interest compounded monthly. Periods = 24 (2 × 12) + 1 for a total of 25 Rate per period = 1% (12% ÷ 12) Table factor 1%, 25 periods = 28.24320 28.24320 − 1 = 27.24320 Future value = 27.24320 × 100 Future value = $2,724.32
(Optional) Calculating the Future Value of an Ordinary Annuity and an Annuity Due by Formula P/O 12-3, p. 408	***Future Value: Ordinary Annuity*** $FV = Pmt \times \frac{(1+i)^n - 1}{i}$ ***Future Value: Annuity Due*** $FV = Pmt \times \frac{(1+i)^n - 1}{i} \times (1+i)$ **where:** FV **= future value** Pmt **= annuity payment** i **= interest rate per period (nominal rate ÷ periods per year)** n **= number of periods (years × periods per year)**	a. What is the future value of an *ordinary annuity* of $200 per month for 4 years at 12% interest compounded monthly? $FV = 200 \times \frac{(1+.01)^{48} - 1}{.01}$ $FV = 200 \times 61.222608$ $FV =$ $12,244.52 b. What is the future value of this investment if it was an *annuity due*? $FV = 12{,}244.52 \times (1 + .01)$ $FV = 12{,}244.52 \times 1.01$ $FV =$ $12,366.97

Section II: Present Value of an Annuity

Topic	Important Concepts	Illustrative Examples
Calculating the Present Value of an Ordinary Annuity by Using Tables P/O 12-4, p. 411	1. Calculate the interest rate per period for the annuity (nominal rate ÷ periods per year). 2. Determine the number of periods of the annuity (years × periods per year). 3. From Table 12-2, locate the present value table factor at the intersection of the rate column and the periods row. 4. Calculate the present value of an ordinary annuity by **Present value (ordinary annuity) = Table factor × Annuity payment**	How much must be deposited now, at 5% compounded annually, to yield an annuity payment of $1,000 at the end of each year, for 11 years? Rate per period = 5% (5% ÷ 1 period per year) Number of periods = 11 (11 years × 1 period per year) Table factor 5%, 11 periods is 8.30641 Present value = 8.30641 × 1,000 Present value = $8,306.41

Section II: (continued)

Topic	Important Concepts	Illustrative Examples
Calculating the Present Value of an Annuity Due by Using Tables P/O 12-5, p. 412	1. Calculate the number of periods (years × periods per year), and subtract 1 from the total. 2. Calculate rate per period (nominal rate ÷ periods per year). 3. Locate the table factor at the intersection of the rate column and the periods row. 4. Add 1 to the ordinary annuity table factor to get the annuity due table factor. 5. Calculate the present value of an annuity due by **Present value (annuity due) = Table factor × Annuity payment**	How much must be deposited now, at 8% compounded semiannually, to yield an annuity payment of $1,000 at the beginning of each 6-month period, for 5 years? Number of periods = 10 (5 × 2) less 1 period = 9 Rate per period = 4% (8% ÷ 2) Table factor 4%, 9 periods = 7.43533 7.43533 + 1 = 8.43533 Present value = 8.43533 × 1,000 Present value = $8,435.33
(Optional) Calculating the Present Value of an Ordinary Annuity and an Annuity Due by Formula P/O 12-6, p. 416	***Present Value: Ordinary Annuity*** $PV = Pmt \times \frac{1-(1+i)^{-n}}{i}$ ***Present Value: Annuity Due*** $PV = Pmt \times \frac{1-(1+i)^{-n}}{i} \times (1+i)$ **where:** PV **= present value** Pmt **= annuity payment** i **= interest rate per period (nominal rate ÷ periods per year)** n **= number of periods (years × periods per year)**	a. What is the present value of an ordinary annuity of $100 per month for 5 years at 12% interest compounded monthly? $PV = 100 \times \frac{1-(1+.01)^{-60}}{.01}$ $PV = 100 \times 44.955039$ $PV = \$4{,}495.50$ b. What is the present value of this investment if it was an annuity due? $PV_{\text{annuity due}} = PV_{\text{ordinary annuity}} \times (1+i)$ $PV = 4{,}495.50 \times (1+.01)$ $PV = 4{,}495.50 \times 1.01$ $PV = \$4{,}540.46$

Section III: Sinking Funds and Amortization

Topic	Important Concepts	Illustrative Examples
Calculating the Amount of a Sinking Fund Payment by Table P/O 12-7, p. 420	Sinking funds are accounts used to set aside equal amounts of money at the end of each period, at compound interest, for the purpose of saving for a known future financial obligation. 1. Using the appropriate rate per period and number of periods, find the future value table factor from Table 12-1. 2. Calculate the amount of the sinking fund payment by **Sinking fund payment = Future value of sinking fund / Future value table factor**	What sinking fund payment is required at the end of each 6-month period, at 10% interest compounded semiannually, to amount to $10,000 in 7 years? Number of periods = 14 (7 years × 2 periods per year) Rate per period = 5% (10% ÷ 2 periods per year) Table factor 14 periods, 5% = 19.59863 $\text{Payment} = \frac{10{,}000}{19.59863}$ Payment = $510.24

Section III: (continued)

Topic	Important Concepts	Illustrative Examples
Calculating the Amount of an Amortization Payment by Table **P/O 12-8, p. 421**	Amortization is a financial arrangement whereby a lump-sum obligation is incurred now (present value) and is paid off or liquidated by a series of equal periodic payments for a specified amount of time. 1. Using the appropriate rate per period and number of periods of the amortization, find the present value table factor from Table 12-2. 2. Calculate the amount of the amortization payment by $\text{Amortization payment} = \dfrac{\text{Original amount obligation}}{\text{Present value table factor}}$	What amortization payments are required at the end of each month, at 18% interest, to pay off a $15,000 loan in 3 years? Number of periods = 36 (3 years × 12 periods per year) Rate per period = 1.5% (18% ÷ 12 periods per year) Table factor 36 periods, 1.5% = 27.66068 $\text{Amortization payment} = \dfrac{15{,}000}{27.66068}$ Amortization payment = $542.29
(Optional) Calculating Sinking Fund Payments by Formula **P/O 12-9, p. 422**	Sinking fund payments can be calculated by using the following formula $Pmt = FV \times \dfrac{i}{(1+i)^n - 1}$ where: Pmt = sinking fund payment FV = future value, amount needed in the future i = interest rate per period (nominal rate ÷ periods per year) n = number of periods (years × periods per year)	What sinking fund payment is required at the end of each month, at 12% interest compounded monthly, to amount to $10,000 in 4 years? Rate per period = 1% (12% ÷ 12) Periods = 48 (4 × 12) $Pmt = 10{,}000 \times \dfrac{.01}{(1+.01)^{48} - 1}$ $Pmt = 10{,}000 \times \dfrac{.01}{.6122261}$ $Pmt = 10{,}000 \times .0163338$ Sinking fund payment = $163.34
(Optional) Calculating Amortization Payments by Formula **P/O 12-10, p. 423**	Amortization payments are calculated by using the following formula: $Pmt = PV \times \dfrac{i}{1-(1+i)^{-n}}$ where: Pmt = amortization payment PV = present value, amount of the loan or obligation i = interest rate per period (nominal rate ÷ periods per year) n = number of periods (years × periods per year)	What amortization payment is required each month, at 18% interest, to pay off $3,000 in 2 years? Rate = 1.5% (18% ÷ 12) Periods = 24 (2 × 12) $Pmt = 3{,}000 \times \dfrac{.015}{1-(1+.015)^{-24}}$ $Pmt = 3{,}000 \times \dfrac{.015}{.3004561}$ $Pmt = 3{,}000 \times .0499241$ Amortization payment = $149.77

TRY IT EXERCISE SOLUTIONS FOR CHAPTER 12

1. 2%, 24 periods

Future value = Table factor × Annuity payment

Future value = 30.42186 × 1,000 = $30,421.86

2. Periods = 20 (5 × 4) + 1 = 21

$$\text{Rate} = \frac{6\%}{4} = 1\frac{1}{2}\%$$

Table factor = 24.47052 − 1.00000 = 23.47052

Future value = Table factor × Annuity payment

Future value = 23.47052 × 1,000 = $23,470.52

3. a. 2%, 20 periods

$$FV = Pmt \times \frac{(1+i)^n - 1}{i}$$

$$FV = 250 \times \frac{(1+.02)^{20} - 1}{.02} = 250 \times \frac{(1.02)^{20} - 1}{.02}$$

$$FV = 250 \times 24.297369 = \$6,074.34$$

b. $FV_{\text{annuity due}} = (1 + i) \times FV_{\text{ordinary annuity}}$

$FV_{\text{annuity due}} = (1 + .02)6,074.34 = \$6,195.83$

4. 4%, 12 periods

Present value = Table factor × Annuity payment

Present value = 9.38507 × 20,000 = $187,701.40

5. Periods = 12 (3 × 4) − 1 = 11

$$\text{Rate} = \frac{6\%}{4} = 1\frac{1}{2}\%$$

Table factor = 10.07112 + 1.00000 = 11.07112

Present value = Table factor × Annuity payment

Present value = 11.07112 × 10,000 = $110,711.20

6. a. 2%, 24 periods

$$PV = Pmt \times \frac{1-(1+i)^{-n}}{i}$$

$$PV = 500 \times \frac{1-(1+.02)^{-24}}{.02} = 500 \times \frac{1-.6217215}{.02}$$

$$PV = 500 \times 18.913925 = \$9,456.96$$

b. $PV_{\text{annuity due}} = (1 + i) \times PV_{\text{ordinary annuity}}$

$PV_{\text{annuity due}} = (1 + .02) \times 9,456.96 = \$9,646.10$

7. 3%, 20 periods

$$\text{Sinking fund payment} = \frac{\text{Future value of sinking fund}}{\text{Future value table factor}}$$

$$\text{Sinking fund payment} = \frac{8,000}{26.87037} = \$297.73$$

8. 4%, 28 periods

$$\text{Amortization payment} = \frac{\text{Original amount of obligation}}{\text{Present value table factor}}$$

$$\text{Amortization payment} = \frac{110,000}{16.66306} = \$6,601.43$$

9. $1\frac{1}{2}$%, 72 periods

$$\text{Sinking fund payment} = FV \times \frac{i}{(1+i)^n - 1}$$

$$\text{Sinking fund payment} = 40,000 \times \frac{.015}{(1+.015)^{72} - 1}$$

$$\text{Sinking fund payment} = 40,000 \times .0078078 = \$312.31$$

10. 1%, 96 periods

$$\text{Amortization payment} = PV \times \frac{i}{1-(1+i)^{-n}}$$

$$\text{Amortization payment} = 150,000 \times \frac{.01}{1-(1+.01)^{-96}}$$

$$\text{Amortization payment} = 150,000 \times .0162528 = \$2,437.92$$

CONCEPT REVIEW

1. Payment or receipt of equal amounts of money per period for a specified amount of time is known as a(n) ____. (12-1)

annuity

2. In a simple annuity, the number of compounding ____ per year coincides with the number of annuity ____ per year. (12-1)

periods, payments

3. An ordinary annuity is paid or received at the ____ of each time period. (12-1, 12-2)

end

4. An annuity due is paid or received at the ____ of each time period. (12-1, 12-2)

beginning

5. The total amount of the annuity payments and the accumulated interest on those payments is known as the ____ value of an annuity. (12-1)

future

6. The table factor for an annuity due is found by ____ one period to the number of periods of the annuity, and then subtracting ____ from the resulting table factor. (12-2)

adding, 1.00000

7. Write the formula for calculating the future value of an ordinary annuity when using a calculator with an exponential function, y^x, key. (12-3)

$$\text{Future value} = \text{Payment} \times \frac{(1+i)^n - 1}{i}$$

8. Write the formula for calculating the future value of an annuity due when using a calculator with an exponential function, (y^x), key. (12-3)

$$\text{Future value} = \text{Payment} \times \frac{(1+i)^n - 1}{i} \times (1+i)$$

9. The lump sum amount of money that must be deposited today to provide a specified series of equal payments (annuity) in the future is known as the ____ value of an annuity. (12-4)

present

10. The table factor for the present value of an annuity due is found by ____ one period from the number of periods of the annuity, and then adding ____ to the resulting table factor. (12-5)

subtracting, 1.00000

11. A(n) ____ fund is an account used to set aside equal amounts of money at compound interest for the purpose of saving for a future obligation. (12-7)

sinking

12. ____ is a financial arrangement whereby a lump-sum obligation is incurred at compound interest now, such as a loan, and is then paid off by a series of equal periodic payments. (12-7, 12-8)

Amortization

13. Write the formula for calculating a sinking fund payment by table. (12-7)

$$\text{Sinking fund payment} = \frac{\text{Future value of the sinking fund}}{\text{Future value table factor}}$$

14. Write the formula for calculating an amortization payment by table. (12-8)

$$\text{Amortization payment} = \frac{\text{Original amount of obligation}}{\text{Present value table factor}}$$

ASSESSMENT TEST

CHAPTER 12

Name

Class

Answers

1. $121,687.44
2. $330,659.50
3. $86,445.14
4. $4,694.32
5. $42,646.92
6. $1,363,438.75

Note: Round answer to the nearest cent, when necessary.

Use Table 12-1 to calculate the future value of the following ordinary annuities.

	Annuity Payment	Payment Frequency	Time Period (years)	Nominal Rate (%)	Interest Compounded	Future Value of the Annuity
1.	$4,000	every 3 months	6	8	quarterly	$121,687.44
2.	$10,000	every year	20	5	annually	$330,659.50

Use Table 12-1 to calculate the future value of the following annuities due.

	Annuity Payment	Payment Frequency	Time Period (years)	Nominal Rate (%)	Interest Compounded	Future Value of the Annuity
3.	$1,850	every 6 months	12	10	semiannually	$86,445.14
4.	$200	every month	$1\frac{3}{4}$	12	monthly	$4,694.32

Use Table 12-2 to calculate the present value of the following ordinary annuities.

	Annuity Payment	Payment Frequency	Time Period (years)	Nominal Rate (%)	Interest Compounded	Present Value of the Annuity
5.	$6,000	every year	9	5	annually	$42,646.92
6.	$125,000	every 3 months	3	6	quarterly	$1,363,438.75

Complete, worked-out solutions to Exercises 1–6 appear in Appendix B, following the index.

CHAPTER

Name

____

Class

____

Answers

7. $11,593.58

8. $21,573.70

9. $993.02

10. $227.12

11. $255.66

12. $832.78

13. $20,345.57

14. $154,765.98

15. $6,081.72

16. $42,376.04

Complete, worked-out solutions to Exercises 7–12 appear in Appendix B, following the index.

Use Table 12-2 to calculate the present value of the following annuities due.

	Annuity Payment	Payment Frequency	Time Period (years)	Nominal Rate (%)	Interest Compounded	Present Value of the Annuity
7.	$700	every month	$1\frac{1}{2}$	12	monthly	$11,593.58
8.	$2,000	every 6 months	6	4	semiannually	$21,573.70

Use Table 12-1 to calculate the amount of the periodic payments needed to amount to the financial objective (future value of the annuity) for the following sinking funds.

	Sinking Fund Payment	Payment Frequency	Time Period (years)	Nominal Rate (%)	Interest Compounded	Future Value (Objective)
9.	$993.02	every year	13	7	annually	$20,000
10.	$227.12	every month	$2\frac{1}{4}$	12	monthly	$7,000

Use Table 12-2 to calculate the amount of the periodic payment required to amortize (pay off) the following loans.

	Loan Payment	Payment Period	Term of Loan (years)	Nominal Rate (%)	Interest Compounded	Present Value (Amount of Loan)
11.	$255.66	every 3 months	8	8	quarterly	$6,000
12.	$832.78	every month	$2\frac{1}{2}$	18	monthly	$20,000

13. How much will $800 deposited at the *end* of each month into a savings account be worth after 2 years at 6% interest compounded monthly?

$R = \frac{1}{2}\%$ $P = 24$ Amount = $800

FV ordinary annuity

Factor = 25.43196 × 800

FV = $20,345.57

14. How much will $3,500 deposited at the *beginning* of each 3-month period be worth after 7 years at 12% interest compounded quarterly?

$R = 3\%$ $P = 28 + 1 = 29$ Amount = $3,500

Factor = 45.21885 − 1.00000

= 44.21885 × 3,500

FV of annuity due = $154,765.98

15. What amount must be deposited now to withdraw $200 at the *beginning* of each month for 3 years if interest is 12% compounded monthly?

$R = 1\%$ $P = 36 - 1 = 35$ Amount = $200

Factor = 29.40858 + 1.00000

= 30.40858 × 200

PV annuity due = $6,081.72

16. How much must be deposited now to withdraw $4,000 at the *end* of each year for 20 years if interest is 7% compounded annually?

$R = 7\%$ $P = 20$ Amount = $4,000

Factor = 10.59401 × 4,000

PV ordinary annuity = $42,376.04

CHAPTER 12

Name

Class

Answers

17. $368.62

18. a. $195,350.02

b. $7,071.39

19. $40,012.45

20. a. $4,018.43

b. $42,238.48

17. Brandy Michaels plans to buy a used car when she starts college three years from now, She can make deposits at the end of each month into a 6% sinking fund account compounded monthly. If she wants to have $14,500 available to buy the car, what should be the amount of her monthly sinking fund payments?

$R=\frac{1}{2}\%$ $P=36$ $FV=\$14{,}500$

Factor = 39.33610

$$\text{Payment}=\frac{14{,}500}{39.33610}=\$368.62$$

18. A sinking fund is established by Alliance, Inc., at 8% interest compounded semiannually to meet a financial obligation of $1,800,000 in 4 years.

a. What periodic sinking fund payment is required every 6 months to reach the company's goal?

$R = 4\%$ $P = 8$ $FV = 1{,}800{,}000$

Factor = 9.21423

$$\text{Payment}=\frac{1{,}800{,}000}{9.21423}=\$195{,}350.02$$

b. How much greater would the payment be if the interest rate was 6% compounded semiannually rather than 8%?

$R = 3\%$ $P = 8$ $FV = 1{,}800{,}000$

Factor = 8.89234

$$\text{Payment}=\frac{1{,}800{,}000}{8.89234}=202{,}421.41$$
$$-195{,}350.02$$
Greater by $7,071.39

19. Beach Bowl, a bowling alley, purchased new equipment from Brunswick in the amount of $850,000. Brunswick is allowing Beach Bowl to amortize the cost of the equipment with monthly payments over two years at 12% interest. What equal monthly payments will be required to amortize this loan?

$R = 1\%$ $P = 24$ Obligation = $850,000

Factor = 21.24339

$$\text{Payment}=\frac{850{,}000}{21.24339}=\$40{,}012.45$$

20. Nick Wright buys a home for $120,500. After a 15% down payment, the balance is financed at 8% interest for 9 years.

a. What equal quarterly payments will be required to amortize this mortgage loan?

120,500 × .85 = $102,425 Amount financed

$R = 2\%$ $P = 36$ Obligation = $102,425

Factor = 25.48884

$$\text{Payment}=\frac{102{,}425}{25.48884}=\$4{,}018.43$$

b. What is the total amount of interest Nick will pay on the loan?

4,018.43 × 36 =	$144,663.48	Total paid in
	− 102,425.00	Amount borrowed
	$42,238.48	Total interest

CHAPTER

Name

Class

Answers

21. a. $19,496.56

b. $19,351.43

22. a. $1,709.87

b. $10,426.24

23. $1,678.39

© Global Green, USA/PRNewsFoto/NewsCom

Hybrid cars run off a rechargeable battery and gasoline. With each hybrid car burning 20%–30% less gasoline than comparably sized conventional models, they are in great demand by consumers.

Automobile manufacturers, such as Honda, Toyota, Ford, Dodge, and Lexus, offer hybrids in a variety of sizes and shapes. Most automakers plan to introduce hybrids in the next few years. In 2007, there were more than 500,000 hybrid vehicles in the United States.

(Optional) Use formulas and a financial calculator to solve the following exercises.

21. The Golden View Bank is paying 9% interest compounded monthly.

a. If you deposit $100 at the beginning of each month into a savings plan, how much will it be worth in 10 years?

$R = .75\%$ $P = 120$ Amount = $100

$$FV \text{ of annuity due} = Pmt \times \frac{(1+i)^n - 1}{i} \times (1+i)$$
$$= 100 \times \frac{(1+.0075)^{120} - 1}{.0075} \times (1+.0075)$$
$$= 100 \times \frac{1.451357078}{.0075} \times (1.0075)$$
$$= 100 \times 194.9656342$$
$$= \underline{\underline{\$19,496.56}}$$

b. How much would the account be worth if the payments were made at the end of each month rather than at the beginning?

$$FV \text{ of ordinary annuity} = Pmt \times \frac{(1+i)^n - 1}{i}$$
$$= 100 \times \frac{(1+.0075)^{120} - 1}{.0075}$$
$$= 100 \times 193.5142771$$
$$= \underline{\underline{\$19,351.43}}$$

22. The town of Surfside is planning to buy five new hybrid police cars in 4 years. The cars are expected to cost $18,500 each.

a. What equal monthly payments must the city deposit into a sinking fund at 6% interest compounded monthly to achieve its goal?

$R = .5\%$ $P = 48$ $FV = 5 \times 18{,}500 = \$92{,}500$

$$\text{Sinking fund payment} = FV \times \frac{i}{(1+i)^n - 1}$$
$$= 92{,}500 \times \frac{.005}{(1+.005)^{48} - 1}$$
$$= 92{,}500 \times .018485029$$
$$= \underline{\underline{\$1,709.87}}$$

b. What is the total amount of interest earned in the account?

$48 \times 1{,}709.87 = 82{,}073.76$

	92,500.00
	− 82,073.76
Interest earned =	$10,426.24

23. Niagara Savings & Loan is offering mortgages at 9% interest. What monthly payments would be required to amortize a loan of $200,000 for 25 years?

$R = .75\%$ $P = 300$ Loan = 200,000

$$\text{Payment} = PV \times \frac{i}{1-(1+i)^{-n}}$$
$$= 200{,}000 \times \frac{.0075}{1-(1+.0075)^{-300}}$$
$$= 200{,}000 \times \frac{.0075}{.893712166}$$
$$= 200{,}000 \times .008391964$$
$$= \underline{\underline{\$1,678.39}}$$

CHAPTER 

BUSINESS DECISION TIME IS MONEY!

24. You are one of the retirement counselors at the Grove Park Bank. You have been asked to give a presentation to a class of high school seniors about the importance of saving for retirement. Your boss, the vice president of the trust division, has designed an example for you to use in your presentation. The students are shown 5 retirement scenarios, and are asked to guess which yields the most money. *Note*: All annuities are *ordinary*. Although some stop investing, the money remains in the account at 10% interest compounded annually.

a. Look over each scenario and make an educated guess as to which investor will have the largest accumulation of money invested at 10%, over the next 40 years. Then, for your presentation, calculate the final value for each scenario.

- Ann invests $1,200 per year and stops after 15 years.

  Annuity: 10%, 15 per. 31.77248 × 1,200 = $38,126.98
  Compound interest: 10%, 25 per. 10.83471 × 38,126.98 = $413,094.77

- Boyd waits for 15 years, then invests $1,200 per year for 15 years, then stops.

  Annuity: 10%, 15 per. 31.77248 × 1,200 = $38,126.98
  Compound interest: 10%, 10 per. 2.59374 × 38,126.98 = $98,891.47

- Sam waits for 15 years, then invests $1,200 per year for 25 years.

  Annuity: 10%, 25 per. 98.34706 × 1,200 = $118,016.47

- Nancy waits for 10 years, then invests $1,500 per year for 15 years, then stops.

  Annuity: 10%, 15 per. 31.77248 × 1,500 = $47,658.72
  Compound interest: 10%, 15 per. 4.17725 × 47,658.72 = $199,082.39

- Lindsey waits for 10 years, then invests $1,500 per year for 30 years.

  Annuity: 10%, 30 per. 164.49402 × 1,500 = $246,741.03

b. Based on the results, what message will this presentation convey to the students?

The importance of the time value of money concept: The earlier you start, the more you will have in the future!

c. Recalculate each scenario as an annuity due.

Ann:	$454,404.27	Sam:	$129,818.12	Lindsey:	$271,415.13
Boyd:	$108,780.63	Nancy:	$218,990.66		

(See Appendix B for worked-out solution.)

d. How can the results be used in your presentation?

The results reinforce the original message of starting early. By investing at the *beginning* of each period, additional interest is earned in each scenario.

Name

Class

Answers

24. a. Ann: $413,094.77

Boyd: $98,891.47

Sam: $118,016.47

Nancy: $199,082.39

Lindsey: $246,741.03

b. Importance of the time value of money concept

c. Ann: $454,404.27

Boyd: $108,780.63

Sam: $129,818.12

Nancy: $218,990.66

Lindsey: $271,415.13

d. Starting early

COLLABORATIVE LEARNING ACTIVITY

The "Personal" Sinking Fund

1. As a team, design a "personal" sinking fund for something you to save for in the future.

- **a.** What are the amount and the purpose of the fund?
- **b.** What savings account interest rates are currently being offered at banks and credit unions in your area?
- **c.** Choose the best rate, and calculate what monthly payments would be required to accumulate the desired amount in 1 year, 2 years, and 5 years.

2. As a team, research the annual reports or speak with accountants of corporations in your area that are using sinking funds to accumulate money for a future obligation. Answer the following questions about those sinking funds.

- **a.** What is the name of the corporation?
- **b.** What is the purpose and the amount of the sinking fund?
- **c.** For how many years is the fund?
- **d.** How much are the periodic payments?
- **e.** At what interest rate are these funds growing?

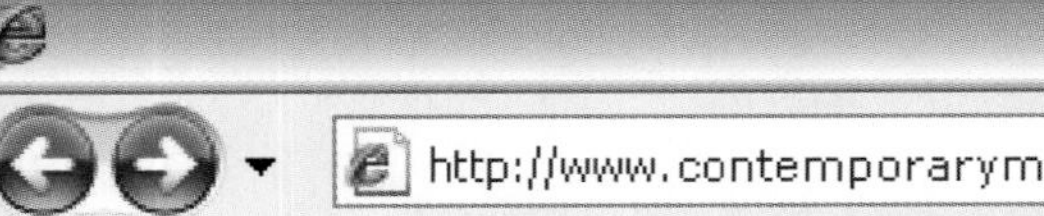

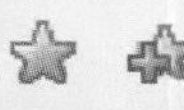

ContemporaryMath.com *All the Math That's Fit to Learn*

Inflation Eats Money!

Inflation is the economic situation in which the average prices of goods and services are rising. See the chart, "Inflation Rates 1977 – 2007," on page 427. When prices rise, consumers can buy less goods and services with their dollars, thus, a decrease in "buying power."

The illustration "Inflation Erodes Buying Power" shows how inflation has affected consumer buying power over the past 50 years. Fifty dollars in buying power in 1957 was worth only $6.58 in buying power in 2007, after inflation. The price comparisons table below lists some interesting 1957 to 2007 price and income differentials.

These inflation illustrations reinforce the all-important time value of money concept, and the importance of "growing" your money. If your money is not put someplace where it can grow, inflation will erode it.

Prices in 1957 . . .		and today
Gas, a gallon	$.23	$2.24
Coffee, a pound	.69	3.14
Milk, a gallon	.97	3.20
Eggs, a dozen	.45	1.26
Sugar, a pound	.11	.51
Harvard tuition	800	31,665
New home	14,200	241,400*
Median income	4,966	46,326

*National Association of Realtors median projection for 2007

Source: "The Power of 50," AARP Bulletin, January 2007, p. 47.

Here's a TIP!

U.S. Treasury Inflation-Indexed Securities, often called Treasury Inflation-Protected Securities or TIPS, are a special type of marketable Treasury security. TIPS are offered in three terms: 5 years, 10 years, and 20-years. When you own TIPS, you receive interest payments every six months and repayment of your principal when the security matures. The difference is this: interest and redemption payments for TIPS are tied to inflation.

Like other marketable securities, TIPS pay a fixed rate of interest. But this fixed rate is applied not to the par amount of the security, but to the inflation-adjusted principal. So, if inflation occurs throughout the life of your security, every interest payment will be greater than the previous one.

Source: www.publicdebt.treas.gov

Quote...UnQuote

- Compounding is mankind's greatest invention because it allows for the reliable, systematic accumulation of wealth.
  –Albert Einstein
- The two most powerful warriors are patience and time.
  –Leo Tolstoy

$50 in 1957 is worth...

$6.58 today after inflation

Inflation Erodes Buying Power

Source: From "Inflation Erodes Buying Power," "The Power of 50," AARP Bulletin, January 2007, p. 47.

"... AND THEN I ADJUSTED FOR INFLATION."

Internet 100%

13

CHAPTER

Consumer and Business Credit

PERFORMANCE OBJECTIVES

OPEN-END CREDIT—CHARGE ACCOUNTS, CREDIT CARDS, AND LINES OF CREDIT

SECTION I 13

"Buy now, pay later" is a concept that has become an everyday part of the way individuals and businesses purchase goods and services. Merchants in all categories, and lending institutions alike, encourage us to just say "charge it!" Consumers are offered a wide variety of charge accounts with many extra services and incentives attached. Many businesses have charge accounts in the company name. These accounts may be used to facilitate employee travel and entertainment expenses or just to fill up the company delivery truck with gasoline, without having to deal with cash. Exhibit 13-1 shows a sample credit card and its parts.

Lending and borrowing money comprise a huge portion of the U.S. economic system. Over the years, as the practice became more and more prevalent, the federal government enacted various legislation to protect the consumer from being misled about credit and finance charges. One of the most important and comprehensive pieces of legislation, known as Regulation Z, covers both installment credit and **open-end credit.**

Regulation Z of the Consumer Credit Protection Act, also known as the Truth in Lending Act, as well as the Fair Credit and Charge Card Disclosure Act, require that lenders fully disclose to the customer, in writing, the cost of the credit and detailed information about their terms. Features such as finance charge, annual percentage rate (APR), cash advances, and annual fees must be disclosed in writing at the time you apply. The **finance charge** is the dollar amount that is paid for the credit. The **annual percentage rate (APR)** is the effective or true annual interest rate being charged. If a card company offers you a written "preapproved" credit solicitation, the offer must include these terms. Also, card issuers must inform customers if they make certain changes in rates or coverage for credit insurance.

open-end credit A loan arrangement in which there is no set number of payments. As the balance of the loan is reduced, the borrower can renew the amount of the loan up to a pre-approved credit limit. A form of revolving credit.

finance charge Dollar amount that is paid for credit. Total of installment payments for an item less the cost price of that item.

annual percentage rate (APR) Effective or true annual interest rate being charged for credit. Must be revealed to borrowers under the Truth in Lending Act.

Teaching Transparency 13-1

Exhibit 13-1
Parts of a Credit Card

If this card is found, please cut in two and return to PO Box 15021, Wilmington, DE 19850. 90288PMC
24 HOUR CUSTOMER SATISFACTION 1-800-635-0581
AUTHORIZED SIGNATURE
Cirrus
MasterCard
5412 3456 7890 1234
VALID DATES
0000 00/00-00/00
LEE M CARDHOLDER
Magnetic strip
Customer service number
Placeholder for signature of account holder
Holograph
Company logo
Account number
Account holder
Expiration date

unsecured loan Loan that is backed simply by the borrower's "promise" to repay, without any tangible asset pledged as collateral. These loans carry more risk for the lender and therefore have higher interest rates than secured loans.

secured loan Loan that is backed by a tangible asset, such as a car, boat, or home, which can be repossessed and sold if the borrower fails to pay back the loan. These loans carry less risk for the lender and therefore have lower interest rates than unsecured loans.

The granting of credit involves a trust relationship between the borrower and the lender. The borrower promises to repay the loan, with interest, in one of many predetermined payment arrangements. Trust on the part of the lender is based on past lending experience with the borrower, the information provided on the credit application, and independent credit reports from credit bureaus. The degree and depth of lender investigation is directly proportional to the amount of money being borrowed. Exhibit 13-2 is an example of a typical online credit application used to secure consumer credit.

When loans are backed by a simple promise to repay, they are known as **unsecured loans**. Most open-end credit accounts are unsecured. Loans that are backed by tangible assets, such as car and boat loans and home mortgage loans, are known as **secured loans**. These loans are backed or secured by an asset that can be repossessed and sold by the lender if the borrower fails to comply with the rules of the loan. Secured loans are covered in Section II of this chapter and in Chapter 14.

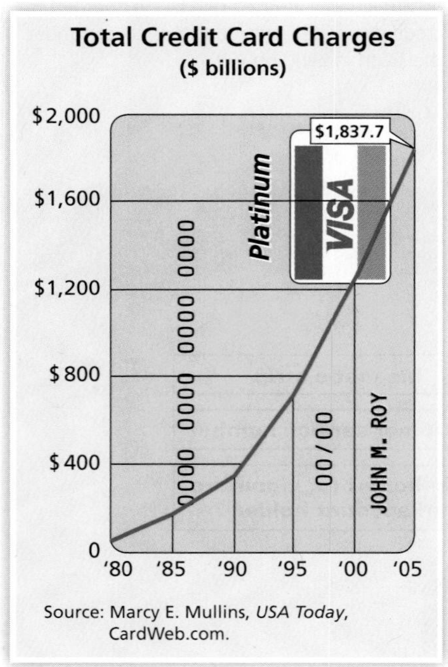

Source: Marcy E. Mullins, *USA Today*, CardWeb.com.

Exhibit 13-2
Typical Online Credit Application

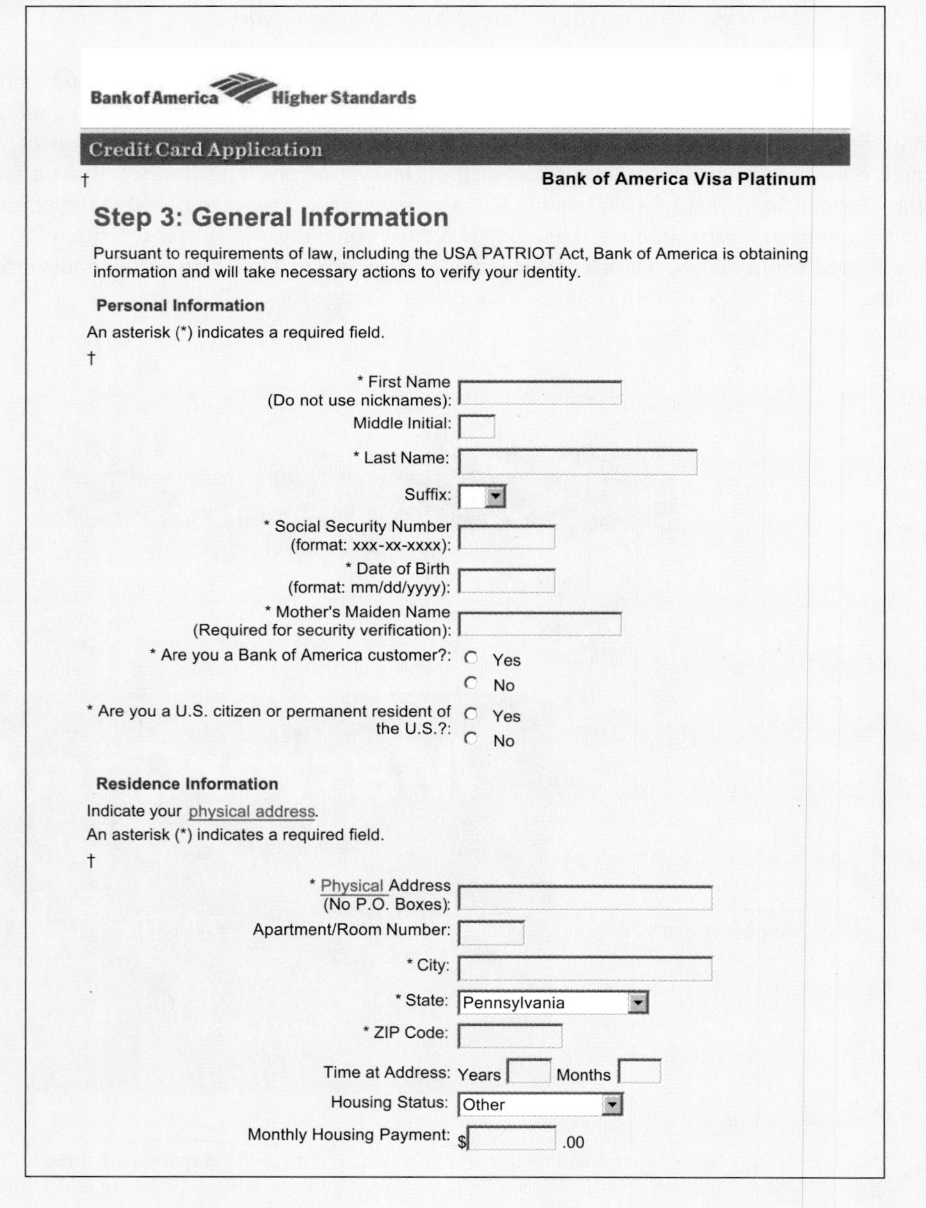
Bank of America Higher Standards

Credit Card Application

† Bank of America Visa Platinum

Step 3: General Information

Pursuant to requirements of law, including the USA PATRIOT Act, Bank of America is obtaining information and will take necessary actions to verify your identity.

Personal Information

An asterisk (*) indicates a required field.

†

* First Name (Do not use nicknames):
Middle Initial:
* Last Name:
Suffix:
* Social Security Number (format: xxx-xx-xxxx):
* Date of Birth (format: mm/dd/yyyy):
* Mother's Maiden Name (Required for security verification):
* Are you a Bank of America customer?: Yes No
* Are you a U.S. citizen or permanent resident of the U.S.?: Yes No

Residence Information

Indicate your physical address.
An asterisk (*) indicates a required field.

†

* Physical Address (No P.O. Boxes):
Apartment/Room Number:
* City:
* State: Pennsylvania
* ZIP Code:
Time at Address: Years Months
Housing Status: Other
Monthly Housing Payment: $ .00

Revolving credit is the most popular type of open-end credit. Under this agreement, the consumer has a prearranged credit limit and two payment options. The first option is to use the account as a regular charge account, whereby the balance is paid off at the end of the month with no finance charge. The second option is to make a minimum payment or portion of the payment but less than the full balance. This option leaves a carryover balance, which accrues finance charges by using the simple interest formula

revolving credit Loans made on a continuous basis and billed periodically. Borrower makes minimum monthly payments or more and pays interest on the outstanding balance. A form of open-end credit extended by many retail stores and credit card companies.

Interest = Principal × Rate × Time

The name *revolving credit* comes from the fact that there is no set number of payments as with installment credit. The account revolves month-to-month, year-to-year—technically never being paid off as long as minimum monthly payments are made. Exhibit 13-3 illustrates a typical revolving credit monthly statement.

CALCULATING THE FINANCE CHARGE AND NEW BALANCE BY THE UNPAID OR PREVIOUS MONTH'S BALANCE METHOD

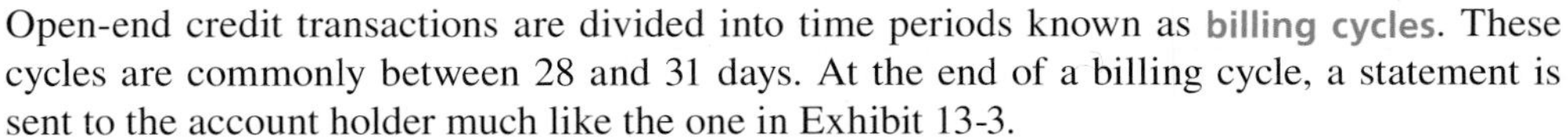

Open-end credit transactions are divided into time periods known as **billing cycles**. These cycles are commonly between 28 and 31 days. At the end of a billing cycle, a statement is sent to the account holder much like the one in Exhibit 13-3.

billing cycle Time period, usually 28 to 31 days, used in billing revolving credit accounts. Account statements are sent to the borrower after each billing cycle.

STEPS TO CALCULATE THE FINANCE CHARGE AND NEW BALANCE BY USING THE UNPAID BALANCE METHOD

Step 1. Divide the annual percentage rate by 12 to find the monthly or periodic interest rate. (Round to the nearest hundredth percent when necessary.)

$$\textbf{Periodic rate} = \frac{\textbf{Annual percentage rate}}{\textbf{12}}$$

Step 2. Calculate the finance charge by multiplying the previous month's balance by the periodic interest rate from Step 1.

Finance charge = Previous month's balance × Periodic rate

Step 3. Total all the purchases and cash advances for the month.

Step 4. Total all the payments and credits for the month.

Step 5. Use the following formula to determine the new balance:

$$\textbf{New balance} = \textbf{Previous balance} + \textbf{Finance charge} + \textbf{Purchases and cash advances} - \textbf{Payments and credits}$$

CLASSROOM ACTIVITY

Ask students who have their own credit cards to read the "fine print" on the back of one of their statements to find:

- interest rate
- method of calculating that rate
- annual fee
- grace period

Next have them compare their features with those of their classmates to determine who has the best and worst "deal."

EXAMPLE 1 CALCULATING THE FINANCE CHARGE AND NEW BALANCE BY USING THE UNPAID BALANCE METHOD

Ron Harper has a revolving department store credit account, with an annual percentage rate of 18%. His previous balance from last month is $322.40. During the month, he purchased shirts for $65.60 and a baseball bat for $43.25. He returned a tie for a credit of $22.95 and made a $50 payment. If the department store uses the unpaid balance method, what is the amount of the finance charge on the account and what is Ron's new balance?

Exhibit 13-3
Typical Monthly Credit Card Statement

Teaching Transparency 13-2

Statement of Account

Bank of America

Payable upon Receipt in U.S. Dollars with a check drawn on a bank located in the U.S. or a money order. Please enter Corporate Account Number on all checks and correspondence.

☐ Check here if address or telephone number has changed. Please note changes on reverse side.

ACCOUNT NUMBER	STATEMENT CLOSING DATE	TOTAL AMOUNT DUE
0000-657421-91226	04-02-09	$266.61

BRYANT CHRZAN
500 OAK ST.
MASON, OH 45040

MAIL PAYMENT TO:

BANK OF AMERICA
P.O. BOX 631
DALLAS TX 73563-0001

Detach here and return upper portion with check or money order. Do not staple or fold.

Summary of Account

Bank of America

Retain this portion for your files.

NEW BALANCE	PAYMENT DUE DATE	STATEMENT CLOSING DATE	CARDMEMBER NAME
$266.61	04-22-09	04-02-09	BRYANT CHRZAN
TOTAL CREDIT LINE	**TOTAL AVAILABLE CREDIT**	**CASH ACCESS LINE**	**ACCOUNT NUMBER**
$3,200	$2,933.39	$2,600	0000-657421-91226

Here is your Account Summary:

	PURCHASES	CASH	TOTAL
Previous Balance	$174.84	$0.00	$174.84
(–) Payments, Credits	174.84	0.00	174.84
(+) Purchases, Cash, Debits	266.61	0.00	266.61
(+) FINANCE CHARGES	0.00	0.00	0.00
(=) New Balance	$266.61	0.00	$266.61
Minimum Payment Due	$10.00	$0.00	$10.00

NEED TO KNOW YOUR CURRENT BALANCE OR AVAILABLE CREDIT? FOR INQUIRIES ABOUT YOUR ACCOUNT CALL TOLL FREE 1-800-635-0581.

Your charges and credits at a glance:

TRAN. DATE	POST DATE	REF. NO.	DESCRIPTION OF TRANSACTIONS		CREDITS	CHARGES
03/19	03/19	835078	Payment - Thank You		$174.84	
03/29	03/30	501065	Wendy's	Food/Beverage		3.97
03/03	03/04	501081	Wal-Mart	Apparel/Housewares		56.94
03/21	03/22	501069	Newsweek	Subscription		26.95
02/18	02/20	501065	Exxon Company USA	Fuel/Misc		13.30
03/29	03/30	501071	Amazon.com	Books		16.00
03/29	03/30	501079	Sports Authority	Tackle Box		18.00
03/29	03/30	501089	Starbucks	Misc.		15.25
03/29	03/30	501092	The Gap	Jacket		116.20
			TOTAL CREDITS AND CHARGES		$174.84	
			BALANCE DUE			$266.61

Here's how we determined your Finance Charge*:

	PURCHASES	CASH
Monthly Periodic Rate	V 1.387%	V 1.629%
(–) Average Daily Balance	$0.00	$0.00
(+) Periodic FINANCE CHARGE	$0.00	$0.00
(=) Total FINANCE CHARGE	$0.00	$0.00

Nominal ANNUAL PERCENTAGE RATE (For Balances)	19.80%
ANNUAL PERCENTAGE RATE (For this billing period-adjusted to include any additional Finance Charges)	19.80%

*Please see reverse side for balance computation method and other important information.
Payments or credits received after closing date above will appear on next month's statement.

SOLUTION STRATEGY

Step 1. $\text{Periodic rate} = \dfrac{\text{Annual percentage rate}}{12}$

$$\text{Periodic rate} = \frac{18\%}{12} = 1.5\%$$

Step 2. Finance charge = Previous month's balance × Periodic rate
Finance charge = 322.40 × .015
Finance charge = 4.836 = $4.84

Step 3. Total the purchases for the month:
$65.60 + 43.25 = $108.85

Step 4. Total the payments and credits for the month:
$50.00 + $22.95 = $72.95

Step 5. Find the new balance for Ron's account by using the formula

New balance = Previous balance + Finance charge + Purchases and cash advances − Payments and credits

New balance = $322.40 + $4.84 + $108.85 − $72.95

New balance = $363.14

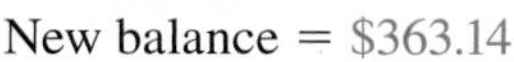

TRY IT EXERCISE 1

Toby Parker has a Bank of America account with an annual percentage rate of 15%. His previous month's balance is $214.90. During the month of July, Toby's account showed the following activity.

Statement of Account — Bank of America

NAME: TOBY PARKER
ACCOUNT NUMBER: 097440
BILLING CYCLE: JULY 1–31

DATE	DESCRIPTION OF TRANSACTIONS	CHARGES
07/06	Royal Cleaners	$35.50
07/09	Payment	40.00
07/15	Coach	133.25
07/16	Antonio's Restaurant	41.10
07/21	CVS Pharmacy	29.00
07/27	CVS Pharmacy (credit)	9.12

How much is the finance charge for July, and what is Toby's new balance?

CHECK YOUR ANSWERS WITH THE SOLUTIONS ON PAGE 479.

TEACHING TIP
Be sure students understand that one month's *ending balance* on a credit card statement is the next month's *beginning balance.*

CALCULATING THE FINANCE CHARGE AND NEW BALANCE BY USING THE AVERAGE DAILY BALANCE METHOD

In business today, the method most widely used to calculate the finance charge on a revolving credit account is known as the **average daily balance**. This method precisely tracks the activity in an account on a daily basis. Each day's balance of a billing cycle is totaled and then divided by the number of days in that cycle. This gives an average of all the daily balances.

average daily balance In revolving credit, the most commonly used method for determining the account balance for a billing cycle. It is the total of the daily balances divided by the number of days in the cycle.

For accounts in which many charges are made each month, the average daily balance method results in much higher interest than the unpaid balance method, because interest starts accruing on the day purchases are made or cash advances are taken.

STEPS TO CALCULATE THE FINANCE CHARGE AND NEW BALANCE BY USING THE AVERAGE DAILY BALANCE

Step 1. Starting with the previous month's balance as the first unpaid balance, multiply each by the number of days that balance existed, until the next account transaction.

Step 2. At the end of the billing cycle, find the sum of all the daily balance figures.

Step 3. Find the average daily balance.

$$\textbf{Average daily balance} = \frac{\textbf{Sum of the daily balances}}{\textbf{Days in billing cycle}}$$

Step 4. Calculate the finance charge.

$$\textbf{Finance charge} = \textbf{Average daily balance} \times \textbf{Periodic rate}$$

Step 5. Compute the new balance as before.

$$\textbf{New balance} = \textbf{Previous balance} + \textbf{Finance charge} + \textbf{Purchases and cash advances} - \textbf{Payments and credits}$$

EXAMPLE 2 USING THE AVERAGE DAILY BALANCE METHOD

Mike Stone has a Bank of America revolving credit account with a 15% annual percentage rate. The finance charge is calculated by using the average daily balance method. The billing date is the first day of each month, and the billing cycle is the number of days in that month. During the month of March, Mike's account showed the following activity.

TEACHING TIP
When discussing the calculation of periodic rate, $\frac{\text{Annual rate}}{12}$, students sometimes get confused converting small percents, such as .75% or 1.25%, to decimals.

Remind them to move the decimal point two places to the left:

.75% = .0075
1.25% = .0125

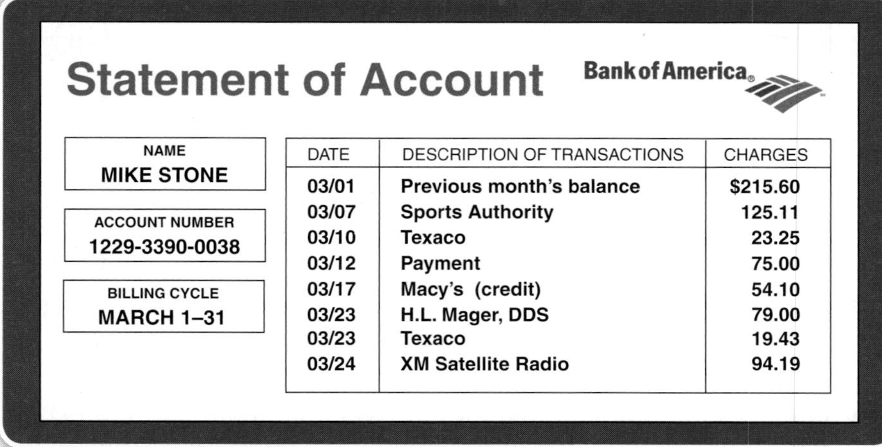

Statement of Account — Bank of America

NAME: MIKE STONE
ACCOUNT NUMBER: 1229-3390-0038
BILLING CYCLE: MARCH 1–31

DATE	DESCRIPTION OF TRANSACTIONS	CHARGES
03/01	Previous month's balance	$215.60
03/07	Sports Authority	125.11
03/10	Texaco	23.25
03/12	Payment	75.00
03/17	Macy's (credit)	54.10
03/23	H.L. Mager, DDS	79.00
03/23	Texaco	19.43
03/24	XM Satellite Radio	94.19

How much is the finance charge for March, and what is Mike's new balance?

SOLUTION STRATEGY

Steps 1 and 2. To calculate the daily balances and their sum, set up a chart such as the one below that lists the activity in the account by dates and number of days.

Dates	Number of Days	Activity/Amount	Unpaid Balance	Daily Balances (unpaid bal. × days)
March 1–6	6	Previous balance	$215.60	$1,293.60
March 7–9	3	Charge +$125.11	340.71	1,022.13
March 10–11	2	Charge +23.25	363.96	727.92
March 12–16	5	Payment −75.00	288.96	1,444.80
March 17–22	6	Credit −54.10	234.86	1,409.16
March 23	1	Charges +79.00		
		+19.43	333.29	333.29
March 24–31	8	Charge +94.19	427.48	3,419.84
	31 days in cycle			Total $9,650.74

Step 3. $\text{Average daily balance} = \frac{\text{Sum of the daily balances}}{\text{Days in billing cycle}} = \frac{9,650.74}{31} = \$311.31$

Step 4. The periodic rate is 1.25% (15% ÷ 12).

Finance charge = Average daily balance × Periodic rate

Finance charge = 311.31 × .0125 = $3.89

Step 5. New balance = Previous balance + Finance charge + Purchases and cash advances − Payments and credits

New balance = $215.60 + $3.89 + $340.98 − $129.10

New balance = $431.37

Learning Tip

Shortcut
"New Balance" can be calculated by adding the finance charge to the last "Unpaid Balance" of the month.
$427.48 + $3.89 = $431.37

TRY IT EXERCISE 2

 13-3

Jill Watson has a Bank of America revolving credit account with an 18% annual percentage rate. The finance charge is calculated by using the average daily balance method. The billing date is the first day of each month, and the billing cycle is the number of days in that month. During the month of August, Jill's account showed the following activity.

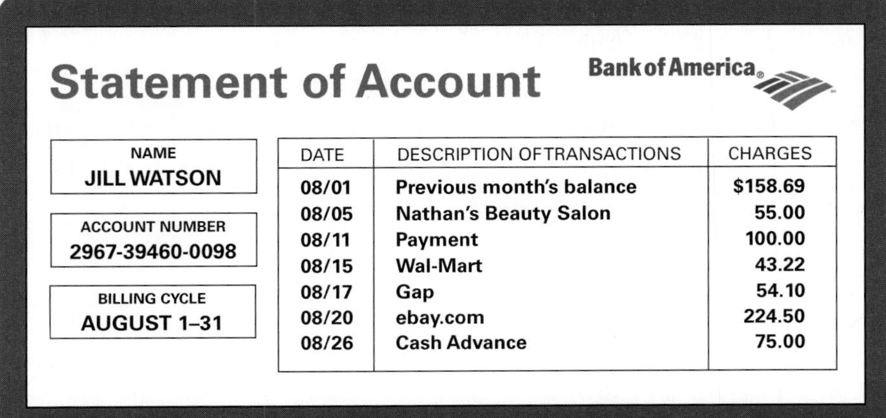

Statement of Account — Bank of America

NAME: JILL WATSON

ACCOUNT NUMBER: 2967-39460-0098

BILLING CYCLE: AUGUST 1–31

DATE	DESCRIPTION OF TRANSACTIONS	CHARGES
08/01	Previous month's balance	$158.69
08/05	Nathan's Beauty Salon	55.00
08/11	Payment	100.00
08/15	Wal-Mart	43.22
08/17	Gap	54.10
08/20	ebay.com	224.50
08/26	Cash Advance	75.00

How much is the finance charge for August, and what is Jill's new balance?

CHECK YOUR ANSWERS WITH THE SOLUTIONS ON PAGE 479.

CLASSROOM ACTIVITY
In small groups, have students work Try It Exercise 2. Determining the finance charge and new balance on a credit card account requires a number of calculations. Splitting up the work, at first, makes learning this procedure easier.

Use Teaching Transparency 13-3 to illustrate the worked-out solution.

13-3 CALCULATING THE FINANCE CHARGE AND NEW BALANCE OF BUSINESS AND PERSONAL LINES OF CREDIT

line of credit Pre-approved amount of open-end credit, based on borrower's ability to pay.

One of the most useful types of open-end credit is the business or personal **line of credit**. In this section, we investigate the unsecured credit line, which is based on your own merit. In Chapter 14, we discuss the home equity line of credit, which is secured by a home or other piece of real estate property.

A line of credit is an important tool for on-going businesses and responsible individuals. For those who qualify, unsecured lines of credit generally range from $2,500 to $250,000. The amount is based on your ability to pay as well as your financial and credit history. This pre-approved borrowing power essentially gives you the ability to become your own private banker. Once the line has been established, you can borrow money by simply writing a check. Lines of credit usually have an annual usage fee of between $50 and $100, and most lenders also require that you update your financial information each year.

U.S. prime rate Lending rate at which the largest and most creditworthy corporations borrow money from banks. The interest rate of most lines of credit is tied to the movement of the prime rate.

With credit lines, you only pay interest on the outstanding average daily balance of your loan. For most lines and some credit cards, the interest rate is variable and is based on, or indexed to, the prime rate. The **U.S. prime rate** is the lending rate at which the largest and most creditworthy corporations in the country borrow money from banks. The current prime rate is published daily in *The Wall Street Journal* in a chart entitled "Borrowing Benchmarks." Exhibit 13-4 shows an example of this chart.

A typical line of credit quotes interest as the prime rate plus a fixed percent, such as "prime + 3%" or "prime + 6.8%." Some lenders have a minimum rate regardless of the prime rate, such as "prime + 3%, minimum 10%." In this case, when the prime is greater than 7%, the rate varies up and down. When the prime falls to less than 7%, the minimum 10% rate applies. This guarantees the lender at least a 10% return on funds loaned. Exhibit 13-5 is an example of a credit card rate disclosure indexed to the prime rate.

Just as with calculating finance charges and new balances on credit cards (see the steps on page 446), the finance charge on a line of credit is based on average daily balance and is calculated by

Finance charge = Average daily balance × Periodic rate

"Well, SOMEONE knows we're here. It's a pre-approved credit card."

This means that interest begins as soon as you write a check for a loan. Typically, the loan is paid back on a flexible schedule. In most cases, balances of $100 or less must be paid in full. Larger balances require minimum monthly payments of $100 or 2% of the outstanding balance, whichever is greater. As you repay, the line of credit renews itself. The new balance of the line of credit is calculated by

New balance = Previous balance + Finance charge + Loans − Payments

Exhibit 13-4
Borrowing Benchmarks
The Wall Street Journal

BORROWING BENCHMARKS

Global Primer

U.S. prime rate is used by banks as a reference point for a range of loans to medium-sized and small business and as a benchmark for consumer rates.

The International Viewpoint

Country	Latest(●)	-52 WEEK RANGE (%)- Low	High
U.S.	8.25	8.25	8.25
Canada	6.25	6.00	6.25
ECB	4.00	2.75	4.00
Japan	1.88	1.38	1.88
Switzerland	4.45	2.74	4.60
U.K.	5.75	4.50	5.75
Hong Kong	8.00	8.00	8.25
Australia	6.25	5.75	6.25

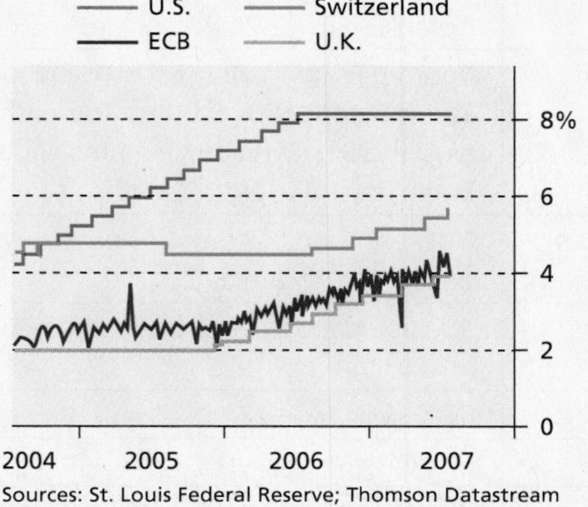

Sources: St. Louis Federal Reserve; Thomson Datastream

Money Rates

July 20,2007

Key annual interest rates paid to borrow or lend money in U.S. and international markets. Rates below are a guide to general levels but don't always represent actual transactions.

Inflation

	June index level	CHG FROM(%) May '07	June '06
U.S. consumer price index			
All items	**208.4**	0.2	2.7
Core	**210.5**	0.1	2.2

International rates

	Latest	Week ago	—52-WEEK— High	Low
Prime rates				
U.S.	**8.25**	**8.25**	**8.25**	**8.25**
Canada	**6.25**	6.25	6.25	6.00
Euro zone	**4.00**	4.00	4.00	2.75
Japan	**1.875**	1.875	1.875	1.375
Switzerland	**4.45**	4.09	4.60	2.74
Britain	**5.75**	5.75	5.75	4.50
Australia	**6.25**	6.25	6.25	5.75
Hong Kong	**8.00**	8.00	8.25	8.00

Other short-term rates

	Latest	Week ago	—52-WEEK— High	Low
Call money				
	7.00	7.00	7.00	7.00
Commercial paper				
30 to 45 days	**5.25**	...	...	...
46 to 60 days	**5.24**	...	...	...
61 to 89 days	**5.23**	...	...	...
90 to 91 days	**5.24**	...	...	...
92 to 122 days	**5.21**	...	...	...
123 to 150 days	**5.20**	...	...	...
151 to 180 days	**5.18**	...	...	...
181 to 210 days	**5.16**	...	...	...
211 to 241 days	**5.14**	...	...	...
242 to 270 days	**5.12**	...	...	...
Dealer commercial paper				
30 days	**5.28**	5.28	5.36	5.25
60 days	**5.30**	5.30	5.41	5.24
90 days	**5.30**	5.30	5.44	5.21

CLASSROOM ACTIVITY

- Have students research and report to the class on the current prime rate and their source of information.
- For discussion, have students bring to class newspaper advertisements promoting lines of credit. What are the typical margins over the prime rate?

Exhibit 13-5
Citibank Credit Card Rate Disclosure Indexed to the U.S. Prime Rate

CITIBANK DISCLOSURES

Annual percentage rate (APR) for purchases	**14.24%** variable
Other APRs	Balance transfer APR: As long as first balance transfer is completed within 4 months from date of account opening, 3.99% until transferred balance is paid in full for balance transfers completed within 4 months from date of first balance transfer. Other balance transfers will be at your variable purchase APR if you qualify. Cash advance APR: 23.24% variable. Default APR: 32.24% variable. See explanation below.*
Variable rate information	Your APRs may vary each billing period. The purchase APR equals the U.S. Prime Rate** plus 5.99%. The cash advance APR equals the U.S. Prime Rate plus 14.99%, with a minimum APR of 19.99%. The Default APR equals the U.S. Prime Rate plus up to 23.99%, or up to 28.99%, whichever is greater.***
Grace period for repayment of balances for purchases	Not less than 20 days if you pay your total new balance in full each billing period by the due date.
Method of computing the balance for purchases	Average daily balance (including new purchases).
Annual fees	$125.
Minimum finance charge	50 cents.
Transaction fee for purchases made in a foreign currency	3% of the amount of each foreign currency purchase after its conversion into U.S. dollars.
Transaction fee for purchases: 3% of the amount of each cash advance, $5 minimum. **Transaction fee for balance transfers:** 3% of the amount of each balance transfer, $5 minimum. **Late fee:** $15 on balances up to $100; $29 on balances of $100 up to $250; and $39 on balances of $250 and over.	

* All your APRs may automatically increase up to the Default APR if you default under any cardmember agreement that you have with us because you fail to make a payment to us when due or you make a payment to us that is not honored.

** For each billing period we use the U.S. Prime Rate published in *The Wall Street Journal* two business days prior to the Statement/Closing Date for that billing period.

*** Factors considered in determining your Default APR may include how long your account has been open, the timing or seriousness of a default, or other indications of account performance.

EXAMPLE 3 CALCULATING FINANCE CHARGES ON A LINE OF CREDIT

Shari's Chocolate Shop has a $20,000 line of credit with The Shangri-La National Bank. The annual percentage rate charged on the account is the current prime rate plus 4%. There is a minimum APR on the account of 10%. The starting balance on April 1 was $2,350. On April 9, Shari borrowed $1,500 to pay for a shipment of assorted gift items. On April 20, she made a $3,000 payment on the account. On April 26, another $2,500 was borrowed to pay for air conditioning repairs. The billing cycle for April has 30 days. If the current prime rate is 8%, what is the finance charge on the account and what is Shari's new balance?

SOLUTION STRATEGY

To solve this problem, we must find the annual percentage rate, the periodic rate, the average daily balance, the finance charge, and finally the new balance.

Annual percentage rate: The annual percentage rate is prime plus 4%, with a minimum of 10%. Because the current prime is 8%, the APR on this line of credit is 12% (8% + 4%).

Periodic rate:

$$\text{Periodic rate} = \frac{\text{Annual percentage rate}}{12 \text{ months}} = \frac{12\%}{12} = 1\%$$

Average daily balance: From the information given, we construct the following chart showing the account activity.

Dates	Number of Days	Activity/Amount	Unpaid Balance	Daily Balances (unpaid balance × days)
April 1–8	8	Previous balance	$2,350	$18,800
April 9–19	11	Borrowed $1,500	3,850	42,350
April 20–25	6	Payment $3,000	850	5,100
April 26–30	5	Borrowed $2,500	3,350	16,750
	30 days in cycle			Total $83,000

$$\text{Average daily balance} = \frac{\text{Sum of the daily balances}}{\text{Days in billing cycle}} = \frac{83{,}000}{30} = \$2{,}766.67$$

Finance charge:

Finance charge = Average daily balance × Periodic rate

Finance charge = 2,766.67 × .01 = $27.67

New balance:

$$\text{New balance} = \text{Previous balance} + \text{Finance charge} + \text{Loan amounts} - \text{Payments}$$

New balance = $2,350 + $27.67 + $4,000 − $3,000

New balance = $3,377.67

TEACHING TIP
Remind students that they can find the new balance by adding the finance charge and the last unpaid balance.
$3,350 + $27.67 = $3,377.67

TRY IT EXERCISE 3

Angler Marine has a $75,000 line of credit with Harborside Bank. The annual percentage rate is the current prime rate plus 4.5%. The balance on November 1 was $12,300. On November 7, Angler borrowed $16,700 to pay for a shipment of fishing equipment, and on November 21 it borrowed another $8,800. On November 26, a $20,000 payment was made on the account. The billing cycle for November has 30 days. If the current prime rate is $8\frac{1}{2}\%$, what is the finance charge on the account and what is Angler's new balance?

CHECK YOUR ANSWERS WITH THE SOLUTIONS ON PAGE 479.

SECTION I Review Exercises

CLASSROOM ACTIVITY
Talk about credit reports and the fact that bad credit stays on a person's record for 7 years. (See In The Business World below.) Ask students to consider and discuss
- the "responsibility" of having credit
- what factors they would consider important in granting credit if they were the lenders

Calculate the missing information on the following revolving credit accounts. Interest is calculated on the unpaid or previous month's balance.

	Previous Balance	Annual Percentage Rate (APR)	Monthly Periodic Rate	Finance Charge	Purchases and Cash Advances	Payments and Credits	New Balance
1.	\$167.88	18%	1.5%	\$2.52	\$215.50	\$50.00	\$335.90
2.	\$35.00	12%	1%	.35	\$186.40	\$75.00	\$146.75
3.	\$455.12	21%	1.75%	7.96	\$206.24	\$125.00	\$544.32
4.	\$2,390.00	15%	$1\frac{1}{4}$%	29.88	\$1,233.38	\$300.00	\$3,353.26

5. Nancy Lozano has a Bank of America revolving credit account with an annual percentage rate of 12% calculated on the previous month's balance. Answer the questions that follow using the Visa monthly statement below.

Statement of Account Bank of America

NAME: NANCY LOZANO
ACCOUNT NUMBER: 2290-0090-4959
BILLING CYCLE: SEPTEMBER 1–30

DATE	DESCRIPTION OF TRANSACTIONS	CHARGES
09/01	Previous month's balance	\$120.00
09/08	Radio Shack	65.52
09/11	Payment	70.00
09/14	Union Oil	23.25
09/22	Cash Advance	60.00
09/26	Safeway Supermarket	59.16

a. What is the amount of the finance charge?

$$\text{Finance charge} = 120 \times \frac{12\%}{12} = \$1.20$$

b. What is Nancy's new balance?

$$\text{New balance} = 120.00 + 1.20 + 207.93 - 70.00 = \$259.13$$

In the Business World

Secret No More!
After years of secrecy, "FICO" scores are now available to consumers nationwide. This all-important credit scoring system, developed by Fair Isaac and Co., provides credit scores and other information to lending institutions everywhere. Most lenders rely heavily on these scores when making credit decisions, especially mortgages.

With proper "financial identification" and \$12.50, you can get your FICO score and other personal credit information at

www.myfico.com

For \$7.95 you can request a credit report from one of the three major credit bureaus listed below. If you have been denied credit, the report is free. These can be ordered online or by phone at

www.annualcreditreport.com

- Equifax—800-685-1111
- Experian—888-397-3742
- TransUnion—800-888-4213

Liz Morgan has a revolving credit account. The finance charge is calculated on the previous month's balance, and the annual percentage rate is 21%. Complete the following 5-month account activity table for Liz.

APR = 21%

$$\text{Periodic rate} = \frac{21}{12} = 1.75\%$$

Month	Previous Month's Balance	Finance Charge	Purchases and Cash Advances	Payments and Credits	New Balance End of Month
6. March	\$560.00	\$9.80	\$121.37	\$55.00	\$636.17
7. April	\$636.17	\$11.13	\$46.45	\$65.00	\$628.75
8. May	\$628.75	\$11.00	\$282.33	\$105.00	\$817.08
9. June	\$817.08	\$14.30	\$253.38	\$400.00	\$684.76
10. July	\$684.76	\$11.98	\$70.59	\$100.00	\$667.33

11. Calculate the average daily balance for the month of October of a revolving credit account with a previous month's balance of $140.00 and the following activity.

Complete, worked-out solutions for Exercises 11–13 appear in Appendix B, following the index.

Average daily balance = $152.29

Date	Activity	Amount
October 3	Cash advance	$50.00
October 7	Payment	$75.00
October 10	Purchase	$26.69
October 16	Credit	$40.00
October 25	Purchase	$122.70

12. Calculate the average daily balance for the month of February of a revolving credit account with a previous month's balance of $69.50 and the following activity.

Average daily balance = $158.51

Date	Activity	Amount
February 6	Payment	$58.00
February 9	Purchase	$95.88
February 15	Purchase	$129.60
February 24	Credit	$21.15
February 27	Cash advance	$100.00

13. Carolyn Salkind has a Bank of America revolving credit account with a 15% annual percentage rate. The finance charge is calculated by using the average daily balance method. The billing date is the first day of each month, and the billing cycle is the number of days in that month. During the month of March, Carolyn's account showed the following activity.

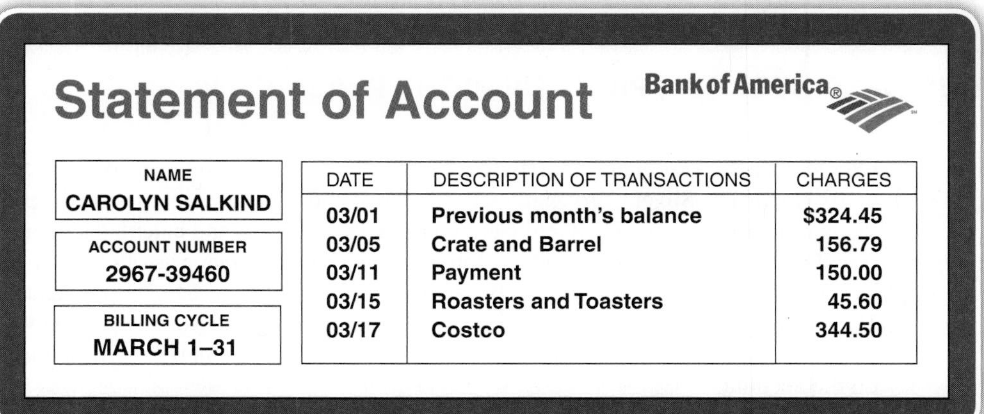

Statement of Account Bank of America

NAME: CAROLYN SALKIND

ACCOUNT NUMBER: 2967-39460

BILLING CYCLE: MARCH 1–31

DATE	DESCRIPTION OF TRANSACTIONS	CHARGES
03/01	Previous month's balance	$324.45
03/05	Crate and Barrel	156.79
03/11	Payment	150.00
03/15	Roasters and Toasters	45.60
03/17	Costco	344.50

© Ted S. Warren/Associated Press

Costco Wholesale is the largest wholesale club operator in the U.S., with 136,000 employees and 2006 sales of over $42 billion. The company operates about 513 membership warehouse stores serving over 49 million cardholders in 38 states and 7 countries.

Stores offer discount prices on 3,700 to 4,500 products—many in bulk packaging—ranging from alcoholic beverages and appliances to fresh food, pharmaceuticals, and tires. Top competitors include Sam's Club, Target, and Wal-Mart.

Average daily balance = $551.10 (See Appendix B)

a. How much is the finance charge for March?

Finance charge = 551.10 × .0125 = $6.89

b. What is Carolyn's new balance?

New balance = 324.45 + 6.89 + 546.89 − 150.00 = $728.23

14. The Freemont Bank offers a business line of credit that has an annual percentage rate of prime rate plus 5.4%, with a minimum of 11%. What is the APR if the prime rate is

a. 7%
$7 + 5.4$
$= \underline{12.4\%}$

b. 10.1%
$10.1 + 5.4$
$= \underline{15.5\%}$

c. 9.25%
$9.25 + 5.4$
$= \underline{14.65\%}$

d. $5\frac{3}{4}\%$
$5.75 + 5.4$
$= \underline{11.15\%}$

15. The Jewelry Exchange has a $30,000 line of credit with NationsBank. The annual percentage rate is the current prime rate plus 4.7%. The balance on March 1 was $8,400. On March 6, the company borrowed $6,900 to pay for a shipment of supplies, and on March 17 it borrowed another $4,500 for equipment repairs. On March 24, a $10,000 payment was made on the account. The billing cycle for March has 31 days. The current prime rate is 9%.

a. What is the finance charge on the account?

Dates	# of Days	Activity	Unpaid Balance	Daily Balance
Mar 1–5	5	Previous balance	8,400	42,000
Mar 6–16	11	+ 6,900	15,300	168,300
Mar 17–23	7	+ 4,500	19,800	138,600
Mar 24–31	8	−10,000	9,800	78,400
	31			$427,300

$$\text{Average daily balance} = \frac{427{,}300}{31} = \$13{,}783.87$$

$$\text{Finance charge} = 13{,}783.87 \times \frac{(9\% + 4.7\%)}{12}$$
$$= 13{,}783.87 \times 1.14\%$$
$$= \underline{\$157.14}$$

b. What is the company's new balance?

New balance = 8,400.00 + 157.14 + 11,400.00 − 10,000.00
= $9,957.14

Shortcut New balance = 9,800.00 + 157.14 = $9,957.14

c. On April 1, how much credit does the Jewelry Exchange have left on the account?

Remaining credit = 30,000.00 − 9,957.14 = $20,042.86

BUSINESS DECISION PICK THE RIGHT PLASTIC

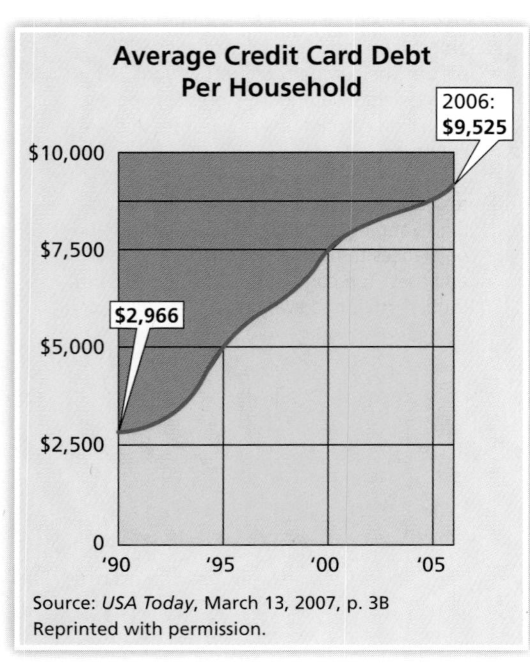

Source: *USA Today*, March 13, 2007, p. 3B
Reprinted with permission.

16. On October 22, you plan to purchase a $3,000 computer by using one of your two credit cards. The Silver Card charges 18% interest and calculates interest on the previous month's balance. The Gold Card charges 18% interest and calculates interest based on the average daily balance. Both cards have a $0 balance as of October 1.

Your plan is to make a $1,000 payment in November, a $1,000 payment in December, and pay off the remaining balance in January. All your payments will be received and posted on the 10th of each month. No other charges will be made on the account.

a. Based on this information, calculate the interest charged by each card for this purchase.

Silver = $45.45

Gold = $73.99 (See Appendix B)

b. Which card is the better deal and by how much?

Gold = $73.99
Silver = − 45.45
$28.54

Silver: Better deal by $28.54

CLOSED-END CREDIT—INSTALLMENT LOANS

SECTION II 13

Closed-end credit, in the form of installment loans, is used extensively today for the purchase of durable goods such as cars, boats, electronic equipment, furniture, and appliances, as well as services such as vacations and home improvements. An **installment loan** is a lump-sum loan whereby the borrower repays the principal plus interest in a specified number of equal monthly payments. These loans generally range in time from 6 months to 10 years, depending on what is being financed.

installment loan Loan made for a specified number of equal monthly payments. A form of closed-end credit used for purchasing durable goods such as cars, boats, and furniture or services such as vacations or home improvements.

When a home or other real estate property is financed, the installment loan is known as a **mortgage**. A mortgage may be for as long as 30 years on a home and even longer on commercial property such as an office building or factory. These loans, along with home equity loans, are discussed in Chapter 14.

mortgage An installment loan made for homes and other real estate property.

Many installment loans are secured by the asset for which the loan was made. For example, when a bank makes a car loan for 3 years, the consumer gets the car to use and monthly payments to make, but the lender still owns the car. Only after the final payment is made on the loan does the lender turn over the title (the proof of ownership document), to the borrower. An additional form of security for the lending institution is that borrowers are often asked to make a down payment as part of the loan agreement.

A **down payment** is a percentage of the purchase price that the buyer must pay in a lump sum at the time of purchase. Down payments on installment loans vary by category of merchandise and generally range from between 0% to 30% of the price of the item. Sometimes, the amount of the down payment is based on the credit rating of the borrower. Usually, the better the credit, the less the down payment.

down payment Portion of the purchase price that the buyer must pay in a lump sum at the time of purchase.

Until the loan on this vehicle is repaid, the lending institution is technically the owner.

CALCULATING THE TOTAL DEFERRED PAYMENT PRICE AND THE AMOUNT OF THE FINANCE CHARGE OF AN INSTALLMENT LOAN

cash or purchase price Price paid for goods and services without the use of financing.

amount financed After the down payment, the amount of money that is borrowed to complete a sale.

Let's take a look at some of the terminology of installment loans. When a consumer buys goods or services without any financing, the price paid is known as the **cash price** or **purchase price**. When financing is involved, the **amount financed** is found by subtracting the down payment from the cash or purchase price. Sometimes, the down payment will be listed as a dollar amount, and other times it will be expressed as a percent of the purchase price.

Amount financed = Purchase price − Down payment

When the down payment is listed as a percent of the purchase price, it can be found by using

Down payment = Purchase price × Down payment percent

As with open-end credit, installment loan consumers are protected by Regulation Z of the Truth in Lending Act.

Advertisers of installment loans, such as car dealers and furniture stores, must disclose in the ad and the loan agreement the following information:

- down payment
- terms and payments
- annual percentage rate
- total payback

A finance charge, including simple interest and any loan origination fees, is then added to the amount financed to give the total amount of installment payments.

Total amount of installment payments = Amount financed + Finance charge

The finance charge can be found by subtracting the amount financed from the total amount of installment payments.

Finance charge = Total amount of installment payments − Amount financed

When the amount of the monthly payments is known, the total amount of installment payments can be found by multiplying the monthly payment amount by the number of payments.

Total amount of installment payments = Monthly payment amount × Number of monthly payments

TEACHING TIP

When purchasing an asset such as a car or a boat, sometimes part of or all the down payment is the buyer's old car or boat rather than cash. This is known as a *trade-in*.

The total deferred payment price is the sum of the total amount of installment payments plus the down payment. This represents the total out-of-pocket expenses incurred by the buyer for an installment purchase.

Total deferred payment price = Total of installment payments + Down payment

EXAMPLE 4 CALCULATING INSTALLMENT LOAN VARIABLES

Jenny Chao is interested in buying a computer. At Circuit City, she picks out a computer and a printer for a total cash price of $2,550. The salesperson informs her that if she qualifies for an installment loan she may pay 20% now, as a down payment, and finance the balance with payments of $110 per month for 24 months.

a. What is the amount of the finance charge on this loan?

b. What is the total deferred payment price of Jenny's computer?

SOLUTION STRATEGY

a. Finance charge:
To calculate the finance charge on this loan, we must first find the amount of the down payment, the amount financed, and the total amount of the installment payments.

Down payment = Purchase price × Down payment percent

Down payment = 2,550 × 20% = 2,550 × .2 = $510

Amount financed = Purchase price − Down payment

Amount financed = 2,550 − 510 = $2,040

Total amount of installment payments = Monthly payment amount × Number of monthly payments

Total amount of installment payments = 110 × 24 = $2,640

Finance charge = Total amount of installment payments − Amount financed

Finance charge = 2,640 − 2,040

Finance charge = $600

b. Total deferred payment price:

Total deferred payment price = Total of installment payments + Down payment

Total deferred payment price = 2,640 + 510

Total deferred payment price = $3,150

TRY IT EXERCISE 4

Manny Garcia found a car he wanted to buy at Autorama Auto Sales. He had the option of paying $12,500 in cash or financing the car with a 4-year installment loan. The loan required a 15% down payment and equal monthly payments of $309.90 for 48 months.

a. What is the finance charge on the loan?
b. What is the total deferred payment price of Manny's car?

CHECK YOUR ANSWERS WITH THE SOLUTIONS ON PAGE 480.

CALCULATING THE AMOUNT OF THE REGULAR MONTHLY PAYMENTS OF AN INSTALLMENT LOAN BY THE ADD-ON INTEREST METHOD

13-5

One of the most common methods of calculating the finance charge on an installment loan is known as **add-on interest**. Add-on interest is essentially the simple interest that we studied in Chapter 10. The term gets its name from the fact that the simple interest is computed and then added on to the amount financed to get the total of installment payments. The interest or finance charge is computed by using the simple interest formula

add-on interest Popular method of calculating the interest on an installment loan. Found by adding the simple interest ($I = PRT$) to the amount financed.

Interest (*finance charge*) = Principal (*amount financed*) × Rate × Time

STEPS TO CALCULATE THE REGULAR MONTHLY PAYMENT OF AN INSTALLMENT LOAN USING ADD-ON INTEREST

Step 1. Calculate the amount to be financed by subtracting the down payment from the purchase price. *Note:* When the down payment is expressed as a percent, the amount financed can be found by the complement method, because the percent financed is 100% minus the down payment percent.

Amount financed = Purchase price(100% − Down payment percent)

Step 2. Compute the add-on interest finance charge by using $I = PRT$.

Step 3. Find the total of installment payments by adding the finance charge to the amount financed.

Total of installment payments = Amount financed + Finance charge

Step 4. Find the regular monthly payments by dividing the total of installment payments by the number of months of the loan.

$$\textbf{Regular monthly payments} = \frac{\textbf{Total of installment payments}}{\textbf{Number of months of the loan}}$$

EXAMPLE 5 CALCULATING MONTHLY PAYMENTS

Lee Childs bought a new boat with a 7% add-on interest installment loan from his credit union. The purchase price of the boat was $19,500. The credit union required a 20% down payment and equal monthly payments for 5 years (60 months). How much are Lee's monthly payments?

SOLUTION STRATEGY

Step 1. Amount financed = Purchase price(100% − Down payment percent)

Amount financed = 19,500(100% − 20%) = 19,500 × .8

Amount financed = $\underline{\$15,600}$

Step 2.

Interest (*finance charge*)	=	Principal (*amount financed*)	×	Rate	×	Time

Finance charge = 15,600 × .07 × 5

Finance charge = $\underline{\$5,460}$

Step 3. Total of installment payments = Amount financed + Finance charge

Total of installment payments = 15,600 + 5,460

Total of installment payments = $\underline{\$21,060}$

Step 4.

$$\text{Regular monthly payments} = \frac{\text{Total of installment payments}}{\text{Number of months of the loan}}$$

$$\text{Regular monthly payments} = \frac{21,060}{60}$$

$$\text{Regular monthly payments} = \underline{\underline{\$351}}$$

TRY IT EXERCISE 5

Donna Roman bought a bedroom set from El Dorado Furniture with a 6% add-on interest installment loan from her bank. The purchase price of the furniture was $1,500.00. The bank required a 10% down payment and equal monthly payments for 2 years. How much are Donna's monthly payments?

CHECK YOUR ANSWER WITH THE SOLUTION ON PAGE 480.

CALCULATING THE ANNUAL PERCENTAGE RATE OF AN INSTALLMENT LOAN BY APR TABLES AND BY FORMULA

As we learned in Objective 13-5, the add-on interest calculation for an installment loan is the same as the procedure we used on the simple interest promissory note. Although the interest is calculated the same way, the manner in which the loans are repaid is different. With promissory notes, the principal plus interest is repaid at the end of the loan period. The borrower has the use of the principal for the full time period of the loan. With an installment loan, the principal plus interest is repaid in equal regular payments. Each month in which a payment is made, the borrower has less and less use of the principal.

For this reason, the effective or true interest rate on an installment loan is considerably higher than the simple add-on rate. As we learned in Section I of this chapter, the effective or true annual interest rate being charged on open- and closed-end credit is known as the APR.

The Federal Reserve Board has published APR tables that can be used to find the APR of an installment loan. APR tables, such as Table 13-1, have values representing the finance charge per $100 of the amount financed. To look up the APR of a loan, we must first calculate the finance charge per $100.

TEACHING TIP
Point out that under Regulation Z, the finance charge includes not only the interest but also other loan origination charges or fees.

STEPS TO FIND THE ANNUAL PERCENTAGE RATE OF AN INSTALLMENT LOAN BY USING APR TABLES

Step 1. Calculate the finance charge per $100.

$$\textbf{Finance charge per \$100} = \frac{\textbf{Finance charge} \times \textbf{100}}{\textbf{Amount financed}}$$

Step 2. From Table 13-1, scan down the Number of Payments column to the number of payments for the loan in question.

Step 3. Scan to the right in that Number of Payments row to the table factor that most closely corresponds to the finance charge per $100 calculated in Step 1.

Step 4. Look to the top of the column containing the finance charge per $100 to find the APR of the loan.

Table 13-1
Annual Percentage Rate (APR) Finance Charge Per $100

ANNUAL PERCENTAGE RATE TABLE FOR MONTHLY PAYMENT PLANS
SEE INSTRUCTIONS FOR USE OF TABLES

FRB-103-M

NUMBER OF PAYMENTS	ANNUAL PERCENTAGE RATE															
	10.00%	10.25%	10.50%	10.75%	11.00%	11.25%	11.50%	11.75%	12.00%	12.25%	12.50%	12.75%	13.00%	13.25%	13.50%	13.75%
	(FINANCE CHARGE PER $100 OF AMOUNT FINANCED)															
1	0.83	0.85	0.87	0.90	0.92	0.94	0.96	0.98	1.00	1.02	1.04	1.06	1.08	1.10	1.12	1.15
2	1.25	1.28	1.31	1.35	1.38	1.41	1.44	1.47	1.50	1.53	1.57	1.60	1.63	1.66	1.69	1.72
3	1.67	1.71	1.76	1.80	1.84	1.88	1.92	1.96	2.01	2.05	2.09	2.13	2.17	2.22	2.26	2.30
4	2.09	2.14	2.20	2.25	2.30	2.35	2.41	2.46	2.51	2.57	2.62	2.67	2.72	2.78	2.83	2.88
5	2.51	2.58	2.64	2.70	2.77	2.83	2.89	2.96	3.02	3.08	3.15	3.21	3.27	3.34	3.40	3.46
6	2.94	3.01	3.08	3.16	3.23	3.31	3.38	3.45	3.53	3.60	3.68	3.75	3.83	3.90	3.97	4.05
7	3.36	3.45	3.53	3.62	3.70	3.78	3.87	3.95	4.04	4.12	4.21	4.29	4.38	4.47	4.55	4.64
8	3.79	3.88	3.98	4.07	4.17	4.26	4.36	4.46	4.55	4.65	4.74	4.84	4.94	5.03	5.13	5.22
9	4.21	4.32	4.43	4.53	4.64	4.75	4.85	4.96	5.07	5.17	5.28	5.39	5.49	5.60	5.71	5.82
10	4.64	4.76	4.88	4.99	5.11	5.23	5.35	5.46	5.58	5.70	5.82	5.94	6.05	6.17	6.29	6.41
11	5.07	5.20	5.33	5.45	5.58	5.71	5.84	5.97	6.10	6.23	6.36	6.49	6.62	6.75	6.88	7.01
12	5.50	5.64	5.78	5.92	6.06	6.20	6.34	6.48	6.62	6.76	6.90	7.04	7.18	7.32	7.46	7.60
13	5.93	6.08	6.23	6.38	6.53	6.68	6.84	6.99	7.14	7.29	7.44	7.59	7.75	7.90	8.05	8.20
14	6.36	6.52	6.69	6.85	7.01	7.17	7.34	7.50	7.66	7.82	7.99	8.15	8.31	8.48	8.64	8.81
15	6.80	6.97	7.14	7.32	7.49	7.66	7.84	8.01	8.19	8.36	8.53	8.71	8.88	9.06	9.23	9.41
16	7.23	7.41	7.60	7.78	7.97	8.15	8.34	8.53	8.71	8.90	9.08	9.27	9.46	9.64	9.83	10.02
17	7.67	7.86	8.06	8.25	8.45	8.65	8.84	9.04	9.24	9.44	9.63	9.83	10.03	10.23	10.43	10.63
18	8.10	8.31	8.52	8.73	8.93	9.14	9.35	9.56	9.77	9.98	10.19	10.40	10.61	10.82	11.03	11.24
19	8.54	8.76	8.98	9.20	9.42	9.64	9.86	10.08	10.30	10.52	10.74	10.96	11.18	11.41	11.63	11.85
20	8.98	9.21	9.44	9.67	9.90	10.13	10.37	10.60	10.83	11.06	11.30	11.53	11.76	12.00	12.23	12.46
21	9.42	9.66	9.90	10.15	10.39	10.63	10.88	11.12	11.36	11.61	11.85	12.10	12.34	12.59	12.84	13.08
22	9.86	10.12	10.37	10.62	10.88	11.13	11.39	11.64	11.90	12.16	12.41	12.67	12.93	13.19	13.44	13.70
23	10.30	10.57	10.84	11.10	11.37	11.63	11.90	12.17	12.44	12.71	12.97	13.24	13.51	13.78	14.05	14.32
24	10.75	11.02	11.30	11.58	11.86	12.14	12.42	12.70	12.98	13.26	13.54	13.82	14.10	14.38	14.66	14.95
25	11.19	11.48	11.77	12.06	12.35	12.64	12.93	13.22	13.52	13.81	14.10	14.40	14.69	14.98	15.28	15.57
26	11.64	11.94	12.24	12.54	12.85	13.15	13.45	13.75	14.06	14.36	14.67	14.97	15.28	15.59	15.89	16.20
27	12.09	12.40	12.71	13.03	13.34	13.66	13.97	14.29	14.60	14.92	15.24	15.56	15.87	16.19	16.51	16.83
28	12.53	12.86	13.18	13.51	13.84	14.16	14.49	14.82	15.15	15.48	15.81	16.14	16.47	16.80	17.13	17.46
29	12.98	13.32	13.66	14.00	14.33	14.67	15.01	15.35	15.70	16.04	16.38	16.72	17.07	17.41	17.75	18.10
30	13.43	13.78	14.13	14.48	14.83	15.19	15.54	15.89	16.24	16.60	16.95	17.31	17.66	18.02	18.38	18.74
31	13.89	14.25	14.61	14.97	15.33	15.70	16.06	16.43	16.79	17.16	17.53	17.90	18.27	18.63	19.00	19.38
32	14.34	14.71	15.09	15.46	15.84	16.21	16.59	16.97	17.35	17.73	18.11	18.49	18.87	19.25	19.63	20.02
33	14.79	15.18	15.57	15.95	16.34	16.73	17.12	17.51	17.90	18.29	18.69	19.08	19.47	19.87	20.26	20.66
34	15.25	15.65	16.05	16.44	16.85	17.25	17.65	18.05	18.46	18.86	19.27	19.67	20.08	20.49	20.90	21.31
35	15.70	16.11	16.53	16.94	17.35	17.77	18.18	18.60	19.01	19.43	19.85	20.27	20.69	21.11	21.53	21.95
36	16.16	16.58	17.01	17.43	17.86	18.29	18.71	19.14	19.57	20.00	20.43	20.87	21.30	21.73	22.17	22.60
37	16.62	17.06	17.49	17.93	18.37	18.81	19.25	19.69	20.13	20.58	21.02	21.46	21.91	22.36	22.81	23.25
38	17.08	17.53	17.98	18.43	18.88	19.33	19.78	20.24	20.69	21.15	21.61	22.07	22.52	22.99	23.45	23.91
39	17.54	18.00	18.46	18.93	19.39	19.86	20.32	20.79	21.26	21.73	22.20	22.67	23.14	23.61	24.09	24.56
40	18.00	18.48	18.95	19.43	19.90	20.38	20.86	21.34	21.82	22.30	22.79	23.27	23.76	24.25	24.73	25.22
41	18.47	18.95	19.44	19.93	20.42	20.91	21.40	21.89	22.39	22.88	23.38	23.88	24.38	24.88	25.38	25.88
42	18.93	19.43	19.93	20.43	20.93	21.44	21.94	22.45	22.96	23.47	23.98	24.49	25.00	25.51	26.03	26.55
43	19.40	19.91	20.42	20.94	21.45	21.97	22.49	23.01	23.53	24.05	24.57	25.10	25.62	26.15	26.68	27.21
44	19.86	20.39	20.91	21.44	21.97	22.50	23.03	23.57	24.10	24.64	25.17	25.71	26.25	26.79	27.33	27.88
45	20.33	20.87	21.41	21.95	22.49	23.03	23.58	24.12	24.67	25.22	25.77	26.32	26.88	27.43	27.99	28.55
46	20.80	21.35	21.90	22.46	23.01	23.57	24.13	24.69	25.25	25.81	26.37	26.94	27.51	28.08	28.65	29.22
47	21.27	21.83	22.40	22.97	23.53	24.10	24.68	25.25	25.82	26.40	26.98	27.56	28.14	28.72	29.31	29.89
48	21.74	22.32	22.90	23.48	24.06	24.64	25.23	25.81	26.40	26.99	27.58	28.18	28.77	29.37	29.97	30.57
49	22.21	22.80	23.39	23.99	24.58	25.18	25.78	26.38	26.98	27.59	28.19	28.80	29.41	30.02	30.63	31.24
50	22.69	23.29	23.89	24.50	25.11	25.72	26.33	26.95	27.56	28.18	28.80	29.42	30.04	30.67	31.29	31.92
51	23.16	23.78	24.40	25.02	25.64	26.26	26.89	27.52	28.15	28.78	29.41	30.05	30.68	31.32	31.96	32.60
52	23.64	24.27	24.90	25.53	26.17	26.81	27.45	28.09	28.73	29.38	30.02	30.67	31.32	31.98	32.63	33.29
53	24.11	24.76	25.40	26.05	26.70	27.35	28.00	28.66	29.32	29.98	30.64	31.30	31.97	32.63	33.30	33.97
54	24.59	25.25	25.91	26.57	27.23	27.90	28.56	29.23	29.91	30.58	31.25	31.93	32.61	33.29	33.98	34.66
55	25.07	25.74	26.41	27.09	27.77	28.44	29.13	29.81	30.50	31.18	31.87	32.56	33.26	33.95	34.65	35.35
56	25.55	26.23	26.92	27.61	28.30	28.99	29.69	30.39	31.09	31.79	32.49	33.20	33.91	34.62	35.33	36.04
57	26.03	26.73	27.43	28.13	28.84	29.54	30.25	30.97	31.68	32.39	33.11	33.83	34.56	35.28	36.01	36.74
58	26.51	27.23	27.94	28.66	29.37	30.10	30.82	31.55	32.27	33.00	33.74	34.47	35.21	35.95	36.69	37.43
59	27.00	27.72	28.45	29.18	29.91	30.65	31.39	32.13	32.87	33.61	34.36	35.11	35.86	36.62	37.37	38.13
60	27.48	28.22	28.96	29.71	30.45	31.20	31.96	32.71	33.47	34.23	34.99	35.75	36.52	37.29	38.06	38.83

continued

13-4

Table 13-1
Annual Percentage Rate (APR) Finance Charge Per $100

ANNUAL PERCENTAGE RATE TABLE FOR MONTHLY PAYMENT PLANS
SEE INSTRUCTIONS FOR USE OF TABLES

FRB-104-M

NUMBER OF PAYMENTS	ANNUAL PERCENTAGE RATE															
	14.00%	14.25%	14.50%	14.75%	15.00%	15.25%	15.50%	15.75%	16.00%	16.25%	16.50%	16.75%	17.00%	17.25%	17.50%	17.75%
	(FINANCE CHARGE PER $100 OF AMOUNT FINANCED)															
1	1.17	1.19	1.21	1.23	1.25	1.27	1.29	1.31	1.33	1.35	1.37	1.40	1.42	1.44	1.46	1.48
2	1.75	1.78	1.82	1.85	1.88	1.91	1.94	1.97	2.00	2.04	2.07	2.10	2.13	2.16	2.19	2.22
3	2.34	2.38	2.43	2.47	2.51	2.55	2.59	2.64	2.68	2.72	2.76	2.80	2.85	2.89	2.93	2.97
4	2.93	2.99	3.04	3.09	3.14	3.20	3.25	3.30	3.36	3.41	3.46	3.51	3.57	3.62	3.67	3.73
5	3.53	3.59	3.65	3.72	3.78	3.84	3.91	3.97	4.04	4.10	4.16	4.23	4.29	4.35	4.42	4.48
6	4.12	4.20	4.27	4.35	4.42	4.49	4.57	4.64	4.72	4.79	4.87	4.94	5.02	5.09	5.17	5.24
7	4.72	4.81	4.89	4.98	5.06	5.15	5.23	5.32	5.40	5.49	5.58	5.66	5.75	5.83	5.92	6.00
8	5.32	5.42	5.51	5.61	5.71	5.80	5.90	6.00	6.09	6.19	6.29	6.38	6.48	6.58	6.67	6.77
9	5.92	6.03	6.14	6.25	6.35	6.46	6.57	6.68	6.78	6.89	7.00	7.11	7.22	7.32	7.43	7.54
10	6.53	6.65	6.77	6.88	7.00	7.12	7.24	7.36	7.48	7.60	7.72	7.84	7.96	8.08	8.19	8.31
11	7.14	7.27	7.40	7.53	7.66	7.79	7.92	8.05	8.18	8.31	8.44	8.57	8.70	8.83	8.96	9.09
12	7.74	7.89	8.03	8.17	8.31	8.45	8.59	8.74	8.88	9.02	9.16	9.30	9.45	9.59	9.73	9.87
13	8.36	8.51	8.66	8.81	8.97	9.12	9.27	9.43	9.58	9.73	9.89	10.04	10.20	10.35	10.50	10.66
14	8.97	9.13	9.30	9.46	9.63	9.79	9.96	10.12	10.29	10.45	10.62	10.78	10.95	11.11	11.28	11.45
15	9.59	9.76	9.94	10.11	10.29	10.47	10.64	10.82	11.00	11.17	11.35	11.53	11.71	11.88	12.06	12.24
16	10.20	10.39	10.58	10.77	10.95	11.14	11.33	11.52	11.71	11.90	12.09	12.28	12.46	12.65	12.84	13.03
17	10.82	11.02	11.22	11.42	11.62	11.82	12.02	12.22	12.42	12.62	12.83	13.03	13.23	13.43	13.63	13.83
18	11.45	11.66	11.87	12.08	12.29	12.50	12.72	12.93	13.14	13.35	13.57	13.78	13.99	14.21	14.42	14.64
19	12.07	12.30	12.52	12.74	12.97	13.19	13.41	13.64	13.86	14.09	14.31	14.54	14.76	14.99	15.22	15.44
20	12.70	12.93	13.17	13.41	13.64	13.88	14.11	14.35	14.59	14.82	15.06	15.30	15.54	15.77	16.01	16.25
21	13.33	13.58	13.82	14.07	14.32	14.57	14.82	15.06	15.31	15.56	15.81	16.06	16.31	16.56	16.81	17.07
22	13.96	14.22	14.48	14.74	15.00	15.26	15.52	15.78	16.04	16.30	16.57	16.83	17.09	17.36	17.62	17.88
23	14.59	14.87	15.14	15.41	15.68	15.96	16.23	16.50	16.78	17.05	17.32	17.60	17.88	18.15	18.43	18.70
24	15.23	15.51	15.80	16.08	16.37	16.65	16.94	17.22	17.51	17.80	18.09	18.37	18.66	18.95	19.24	19.53
25	15.87	16.17	16.46	16.76	17.06	17.35	17.65	17.95	18.25	18.55	18.85	19.15	19.45	19.75	20.05	20.36
26	16.51	16.82	17.13	17.44	17.75	18.06	18.37	18.68	18.99	19.30	19.62	19.93	20.24	20.56	20.87	21.19
27	17.15	17.47	17.80	18.12	18.44	18.76	19.09	19.41	19.74	20.06	20.39	20.71	21.04	21.37	21.69	22.02
28	17.80	18.13	18.47	18.80	19.14	19.47	19.81	20.15	20.48	20.82	21.16	21.50	21.84	22.18	22.52	22.86
29	18.45	18.79	19.14	19.49	19.83	20.18	20.53	20.88	21.23	21.58	21.94	22.29	22.64	22.99	23.35	23.70
30	19.10	19.45	19.81	20.17	20.54	20.90	21.26	21.62	21.99	22.35	22.72	23.08	23.45	23.81	24.18	24.55
31	19.75	20.12	20.49	20.87	21.24	21.61	21.99	22.37	22.74	23.12	23.50	23.88	24.26	24.64	25.02	25.40
32	20.40	20.79	21.17	21.56	21.95	22.33	22.72	23.11	23.50	23.89	24.28	24.68	25.07	25.46	25.86	26.25
33	21.06	21.46	21.85	22.25	22.65	23.06	23.46	23.86	24.26	24.67	25.07	25.48	25.88	26.29	26.70	27.11
34	21.72	22.13	22.54	22.95	23.37	23.78	24.19	24.61	25.03	25.44	25.86	26.28	26.70	27.12	27.54	27.97
35	22.38	22.80	23.23	23.65	24.08	24.51	24.94	25.36	25.79	26.23	26.66	27.09	27.52	27.96	28.39	28.83
36	23.04	23.48	23.92	24.35	24.80	25.24	25.68	26.12	26.57	27.01	27.46	27.90	28.35	28.80	29.25	29.70
37	23.70	24.16	24.61	25.06	25.51	25.97	26.42	26.88	27.34	27.80	28.26	28.72	29.18	29.64	30.10	30.57
38	24.37	24.84	25.30	25.77	26.24	26.70	27.17	27.64	28.11	28.59	29.06	29.53	30.01	30.49	30.96	31.44
39	25.04	25.52	26.00	26.48	26.96	27.44	27.92	28.41	28.89	29.38	29.87	30.36	30.85	31.34	31.83	32.32
40	25.71	26.20	26.70	27.19	27.69	28.18	28.68	29.18	29.68	30.18	30.68	31.18	31.68	32.19	32.69	33.20
41	26.39	26.89	27.40	27.91	28.41	28.92	29.44	29.95	30.46	30.97	31.49	32.01	32.52	33.04	33.56	34.08
42	27.06	27.58	28.10	28.62	29.15	29.67	30.19	30.72	31.25	31.78	32.31	32.84	33.37	33.90	34.44	34.97
43	27.74	28.27	28.81	29.34	29.88	30.42	30.96	31.50	32.04	32.58	33.13	33.67	34.22	34.76	35.31	35.86
44	28.42	28.97	29.52	30.07	30.62	31.17	31.72	32.28	32.83	33.39	33.95	34.51	35.07	35.63	36.19	36.76
45	29.11	29.67	30.23	30.79	31.36	31.92	32.49	33.06	33.63	34.20	34.77	35.35	35.92	36.50	37.08	37.66
46	29.79	30.36	30.94	31.52	32.10	32.68	33.26	33.84	34.43	35.01	35.60	36.19	36.78	37.37	37.96	38.56
47	30.48	31.07	31.66	32.25	32.84	33.44	34.03	34.63	35.23	35.83	36.43	37.04	37.64	38.25	38.86	39.46
48	31.17	31.77	32.37	32.98	33.59	34.20	34.81	35.42	36.03	36.65	37.27	37.88	38.50	39.13	39.75	40.37
49	31.86	32.48	33.09	33.71	34.34	34.96	35.59	36.21	36.84	37.47	38.10	38.74	39.37	40.01	40.65	41.29
50	32.55	33.18	33.82	34.45	35.09	35.73	36.37	37.01	37.65	38.30	38.94	39.59	40.24	40.89	41.55	42.20
51	33.25	33.89	34.54	35.19	35.84	36.49	37.15	37.81	38.46	39.12	39.79	40.45	41.11	41.78	42.45	43.12
52	33.95	34.61	35.27	35.93	36.60	37.27	37.94	38.61	39.28	39.96	40.63	41.31	41.99	42.67	43.36	44.04
53	34.65	35.32	36.00	36.68	37.36	38.04	38.72	39.41	40.10	40.79	41.48	42.17	42.87	43.57	44.27	44.97
54	35.35	36.04	36.73	37.42	38.12	38.82	39.52	40.22	40.92	41.63	42.33	43.04	43.75	44.47	45.18	45.90
55	36.05	36.76	37.46	38.17	38.88	39.60	40.31	41.03	41.74	42.47	43.19	43.91	44.64	45.37	46.10	46.83
56	36.76	37.48	38.20	38.92	39.65	40.38	41.11	41.84	42.57	43.31	44.05	44.79	45.53	46.27	47.02	47.77
57	37.47	38.20	38.94	39.68	40.42	41.16	41.91	42.65	43.40	44.15	44.91	45.66	46.42	47.18	47.94	48.71
58	38.18	38.93	39.68	40.43	41.19	41.95	42.71	43.47	44.23	45.00	45.77	46.54	47.32	48.09	48.87	49.65
59	38.89	39.66	40.42	41.19	41.96	42.74	43.51	44.29	45.07	45.85	46.64	47.42	48.21	49.01	49.80	50.60
60	39.61	40.39	41.17	41.95	42.74	43.53	44.32	45.11	45.91	46.71	47.51	48.31	49.12	49.92	50.73	51.55

continued

Table 13-1
Annual Percentage Rate (APR) Finance Charge Per $100

ANNUAL PERCENTAGE RATE TABLE FOR MONTHLY PAYMENT PLANS
SEE INSTRUCTIONS FOR USE OF TABLES

FRB-105-M

NUMBER OF PAYMENTS	ANNUAL PERCENTAGE RATE															
	18.00%	18.25%	18.50%	18.75%	19.00%	19.25%	19.50%	19.75%	20.00%	20.25%	20.50%	20.75%	21.00%	21.25%	21.50%	21.75%
	(FINANCE CHARGE PER $100 OF AMOUNT FINANCED)															
1	1.50	1.52	1.54	1.56	1.58	1.60	1.62	1.65	1.67	1.69	1.71	1.73	1.75	1.77	1.79	1.81
2	2.26	2.29	2.32	2.35	2.38	2.41	2.44	2.48	2.51	2.54	2.57	2.60	2.63	2.66	2.70	2.73
3	3.01	3.06	3.10	3.14	3.18	3.23	3.27	3.31	3.35	3.39	3.44	3.48	3.52	3.56	3.60	3.65
4	3.78	3.83	3.88	3.94	3.99	4.04	4.10	4.15	4.20	4.25	4.31	4.36	4.41	4.47	4.52	4.57
5	4.54	4.61	4.67	4.74	4.80	4.86	4.93	4.99	5.06	5.12	5.18	5.25	5.31	5.37	5.44	5.50
6	5.32	5.39	5.46	5.54	5.61	5.69	5.76	5.84	5.91	5.99	6.06	6.14	6.21	6.29	6.36	6.44
7	6.09	6.18	6.26	6.35	6.43	6.52	6.60	6.69	6.78	6.86	6.95	7.04	7.12	7.21	7.29	7.38
8	6.87	6.96	7.06	7.16	7.26	7.35	7.45	7.55	7.64	7.74	7.84	7.94	8.03	8.13	8.23	8.33
9	7.65	7.76	7.87	7.97	8.08	8.19	8.30	8.41	8.52	8.63	8.73	8.84	8.95	9.06	9.17	9.28
10	8.43	8.55	8.67	8.79	8.91	9.03	9.15	9.27	9.39	9.51	9.63	9.75	9.88	10.00	10.12	10.24
11	9.22	9.35	9.49	9.62	9.75	9.88	10.01	10.14	10.28	10.41	10.54	10.67	10.80	10.94	11.07	11.20
12	10.02	10.16	10.30	10.44	10.59	10.73	10.87	11.02	11.16	11.31	11.45	11.59	11.74	11.88	12.02	12.17
13	10.81	10.97	11.12	11.28	11.43	11.59	11.74	11.90	12.05	12.21	12.36	12.52	12.67	12.83	12.99	13.14
14	11.61	11.78	11.95	12.11	12.28	12.45	12.61	12.78	12.95	13.11	13.28	13.45	13.62	13.79	13.95	14.12
15	12.42	12.59	12.77	12.95	13.13	13.31	13.49	13.67	13.85	14.03	14.21	14.39	14.57	14.75	14.93	15.11
16	13.22	13.41	13.60	13.80	13.99	14.18	14.37	14.56	14.75	14.94	15.13	15.33	15.52	15.71	15.90	16.10
17	14.04	14.24	14.44	14.64	14.85	15.05	15.25	15.46	15.66	15.86	16.07	16.27	16.48	16.68	16.89	17.09
18	14.85	15.07	15.28	15.49	15.71	15.93	16.14	16.36	16.57	16.79	17.01	17.22	17.44	17.66	17.88	18.09
19	15.67	15.90	16.12	16.35	16.58	16.81	17.03	17.26	17.49	17.72	17.95	18.18	18.41	18.64	18.87	19.10
20	16.49	16.73	16.97	17.21	17.45	17.69	17.93	18.17	18.41	18.66	18.90	19.14	19.38	19.63	19.87	20.11
21	17.32	17.57	17.82	18.07	18.33	18.58	18.83	19.09	19.34	19.60	19.85	20.11	20.36	20.62	20.87	21.13
22	18.15	18.41	18.68	18.94	19.21	19.47	19.74	20.01	20.27	20.54	20.81	21.08	21.34	21.61	21.88	22.15
23	18.98	19.26	19.54	19.81	20.09	20.37	20.65	20.93	21.21	21.49	21.77	22.05	22.33	22.61	22.90	23.18
24	19.82	20.11	20.40	20.69	20.98	21.27	21.56	21.86	22.15	22.44	22.74	23.03	23.33	23.62	23.92	24.21
25	20.66	20.96	21.27	21.57	21.87	22.18	22.48	22.79	23.10	23.40	23.71	24.02	24.32	24.63	24.94	25.25
26	21.50	21.82	22.14	22.45	22.77	23.09	23.41	23.73	24.04	24.36	24.68	25.01	25.33	25.65	25.97	26.29
27	22.35	22.68	23.01	23.34	23.67	24.00	24.33	24.67	25.00	25.33	25.67	26.00	26.34	26.67	27.01	27.34
28	23.20	23.55	23.89	24.23	24.58	24.92	25.27	25.61	25.96	26.30	26.65	27.00	27.35	27.70	28.05	28.40
29	24.06	24.41	24.77	25.13	25.49	25.84	26.20	26.56	26.92	27.28	27.64	28.00	28.37	28.73	29.09	29.46
30	24.92	25.29	25.66	26.03	26.40	26.77	27.14	27.52	27.89	28.26	28.64	29.01	29.39	29.77	30.14	30.52
31	25.78	26.16	26.55	26.93	27.32	27.70	28.09	28.47	28.86	29.25	29.64	30.03	30.42	30.81	31.20	31.59
32	26.65	27.04	27.44	27.84	28.24	28.64	29.04	29.44	29.84	30.24	30.64	31.05	31.45	31.85	32.26	32.67
33	27.52	27.93	28.34	28.75	29.16	29.57	29.99	30.40	30.82	31.23	31.65	32.07	32.49	32.91	33.33	33.75
34	28.39	28.81	29.24	29.66	30.09	30.52	30.95	31.37	31.80	32.23	32.67	33.10	33.53	33.96	34.40	34.83
35	29.27	29.71	30.14	30.58	31.02	31.47	31.91	32.35	32.79	33.24	33.68	34.13	34.58	35.03	35.47	35.92
36	30.15	30.60	31.05	31.51	31.96	32.42	32.87	33.33	33.79	34.25	34.71	35.17	35.63	36.09	36.56	37.02
37	31.03	31.50	31.97	32.43	32.90	33.37	33.84	34.32	34.79	35.26	35.74	36.21	36.69	37.16	37.64	38.12
38	31.92	32.40	32.88	33.37	33.85	34.33	34.82	35.30	35.79	36.28	36.77	37.26	37.75	38.24	38.73	39.23
39	32.81	33.31	33.80	34.30	34.80	35.30	35.80	36.30	36.80	37.30	37.81	38.31	38.82	39.32	39.83	40.34
40	33.71	34.22	34.73	35.24	35.75	36.26	36.78	37.29	37.81	38.33	38.85	39.37	39.89	40.41	40.93	41.46
41	34.61	35.13	35.66	36.18	36.71	37.24	37.77	38.30	38.83	39.36	39.89	40.43	40.96	41.50	42.04	42.58
42	35.51	36.05	36.59	37.13	37.67	38.21	38.76	39.30	39.85	40.40	40.95	41.50	42.05	42.60	43.15	43.71
43	36.42	36.97	37.52	38.08	38.63	39.19	39.75	40.31	40.87	41.44	42.00	42.57	43.13	43.70	44.27	44.84
44	37.33	37.89	38.46	39.03	39.60	40.18	40.75	41.33	41.90	42.48	43.06	43.64	44.22	44.81	45.39	45.98
45	38.24	38.82	39.41	39.99	40.58	41.17	41.75	42.35	42.94	43.53	44.13	44.72	45.32	45.92	46.52	47.12
46	39.16	39.75	40.35	40.95	41.55	42.16	42.76	43.37	43.98	44.58	45.20	45.81	46.42	47.03	47.65	48.27
47	40.08	40.69	41.30	41.92	42.54	43.15	43.77	44.40	45.02	45.64	46.27	46.90	47.53	48.16	48.79	49.42
48	41.00	41.63	42.26	42.89	43.52	44.15	44.79	45.43	46.07	46.71	47.35	47.99	48.64	49.28	49.93	50.58
49	41.93	42.57	43.22	43.86	44.51	45.16	45.81	46.46	47.12	47.77	48.43	49.09	49.75	50.41	51.08	51.74
50	42.86	43.52	44.18	44.84	45.50	46.17	46.83	47.50	48.17	48.84	49.52	50.19	50.87	51.55	52.23	52.91
51	43.79	44.47	45.14	45.82	46.50	47.18	47.86	48.55	49.23	49.92	50.61	51.30	51.99	52.69	53.38	54.08
52	44.73	45.42	46.11	46.80	47.50	48.20	48.89	49.59	50.30	51.00	51.71	52.41	53.12	53.83	54.55	55.26
53	45.67	46.38	47.08	47.79	48.50	49.22	49.93	50.65	51.37	52.09	52.81	53.53	54.26	54.98	55.71	56.44
54	46.62	47.34	48.06	48.79	49.51	50.24	50.97	51.70	52.44	53.17	53.91	54.65	55.39	56.14	56.88	57.63
55	47.57	48.30	49.04	49.78	50.52	51.27	52.02	52.76	53.52	54.27	55.02	55.78	56.54	57.30	58.06	58.82
56	48.52	49.27	50.03	50.78	51.54	52.30	53.06	53.83	54.60	55.37	56.14	56.91	57.68	58.46	59.24	60.02
57	49.47	50.24	51.01	51.79	52.56	53.34	54.12	54.90	55.68	56.47	57.25	58.04	58.84	59.63	60.43	61.22
58	50.43	51.22	52.00	52.79	53.58	54.38	55.17	55.97	56.77	57.57	58.38	59.18	59.99	60.80	61.62	62.43
59	51.39	52.20	53.00	53.80	54.61	55.42	56.23	57.05	57.87	58.68	59.51	60.33	61.15	61.98	62.81	63.64
60	52.36	53.18	54.00	54.82	55.64	56.47	57.30	58.13	58.96	59.80	60.64	61.48	62.32	63.17	64.01	64.86

EXAMPLE 6 CALCULATING APR BY TABLES

Jeff Gordon purchased a used motorcycle for $7,000. He made a down payment of $1,000 and financed the remaining $6,000 for 36 months. With monthly payments of $200 each, the total finance charge on the loan was $1,200 ($200 × 36 = $7,200 − $6,000 = $1,200). Use Table 13-1 to find what annual percentage rate was charged on Jeff's loan.

SOLUTION STRATEGY

Step 1.

$$\text{Finance charge per } \$100 = \frac{\text{Finance charge} \times 100}{\text{Amount financed}}$$

$$\text{Finance charge per } \$100 = \frac{1,200 \times 100}{6,000} = \frac{120,000}{6,000}$$

$$\text{Finance charge per } \$100 = \$20$$

Step 2. Using Table 13-1, scan down the number of payments column to 36 payments.

Step 3. Scan to the right in that number of payments row until we find $20, the finance charge per $100.

Step 4. Looking to the top of the column containing the $20, we find the annual percentage rate for the loan to be 12.25%.

CLASSROOM ACTIVITY
Have half of the class work Try It Exercise 6 using the APR tables, while the other half works the same problem using the APR formula. Compare the results.

TRY IT EXERCISE 6

Kim Williams purchased a living room set for $4,500 from Iberia Designs. She made a $500 down payment and financed the balance with an installment loan for 24 months. If her payments are $190 per month, what APR is she paying on the loan?

Use Teaching Transparency 13-5 to illustrate the APR table solution.

Teaching Transparency 13-5

CHECK YOUR ANSWER WITH THE SOLUTION ON PAGE 480.

Calculating APR by Formula

When APR tables are not available, the annual percentage rate can be closely approximated by the formula

$$\mathbf{APR} = \frac{72I}{3P(n+1) + I(n-1)}$$

where:

I = finance charge on the loan
P = principal, or amount financed
n = number of months of the loan

EXAMPLE 7 CALCULATING APR BY FORMULA

Refer to Example 6, Jeff Gordon's motorcycle purchase. This time use the APR formula to find the annual percentage rate. How does it compare with the APR from the table?

SOLUTION STRATEGY

$$\text{APR} = \frac{72I}{3P(n+1) + I(n\ 1)}$$

$$\text{APR} = \frac{72(1,200)}{3(6,000)\,(36+1) + 1,200\,(36-1)} = \frac{86,400}{666,000 + 42,000} = \frac{86,400}{708,000}$$

$$\text{APR} = .1220338 = \underline{\underline{12.20\%}}$$

Note: In comparing the two answers, we can see that using the formula gives a close approximation of the Federal Reserve Board's APR table value of 12.25%.

TRY IT EXERCISE 7

Judy Morris repaid a $2,200 installment loan with 18 monthly payments of $140 each. Use the APR formula to determine the annual percentage rate of Judy's loan.

CHECK YOUR ANSWER WITH THE SOLUTION ON PAGE 480.

13-7 CALCULATING THE FINANCE CHARGE AND MONTHLY PAYMENT OF AN INSTALLMENT LOAN BY USING THE APR TABLES

When the annual percentage rate and number of months of an installment loan are known, the APR tables can be used in reverse to find the amount of the finance charge. Once the finance charge is known, the monthly payment required to amortize the loan can be calculated as before.

STEPS TO FIND THE FINANCE CHARGE AND THE MONTHLY PAYMENT OF AN INSTALLMENT LOAN BY USING THE APR TABLES

Step 1. Using the APR and the number of payments of the loan, locate the table factor at the intersection of the APR column and the number of payments row. This factor represents the finance charge per $100 financed.

Step 2. Calculate the total finance charge of the loan.

$$\textbf{Finance charge} = \frac{\textbf{Amount financed} \times \textbf{Table factor}}{\textbf{100}}$$

Step 3. Calculate the monthly payment.

$$\textbf{Monthly payment} = \frac{\textbf{Amount financed} + \textbf{Finance charge}}{\textbf{Number of months of the loan}}$$

EXAMPLE 8 CALCULATING FINANCE CHARGE BY APR TABLES

Classic Motors uses Regal Bank to finance automobile and truck sales. This month Regal is offering up to 48-month installment loans with an APR of 15.5%. For qualified buyers, no down payment is required. If Ron Wiser wants to finance a new truck for $17,500, what are the finance charge and the amount of the monthly payment on Ron's loan?

SOLUTION STRATEGY

Step 1. The table factor at the intersection of the 15.5% APR column and the 48 payments row is $34.81.

Step 2. $$\text{Finance charge} = \frac{\text{Amount financed} \times \text{Table factor}}{100}$$

$$\text{Finance charge} = \frac{17{,}500 \times 34.81}{100} = \frac{609{,}175}{100}$$

$$\text{Finance charge} = \underline{\underline{\$6{,}091.75}}$$

Step 3. $$\text{Monthly payment} = \frac{\text{Amount financed} + \text{Finance charge}}{\text{Number of months of the loan}}$$

$$\text{Monthly payment} = \frac{17{,}500 + 6{,}091.75}{48} = \frac{23{,}591.75}{48}$$

$$\text{Monthly payment} = \underline{\underline{\$491.49}}$$

TRY IT EXERCISE 8

Computer Mart uses a finance company that is offering up to 24-month installment loans with an APR of 13.25%. For qualified buyers, no down payment is required. If Mark Gibson wants to finance a computer and printer for $3,550, what are the finance charge and the amount of the monthly payment on Mark's loan?

CHECK YOUR ANSWERS WITH THE SOLUTIONS ON PAGE 480.

In the Business World

Business and personal financial decisions involve a concept known as *opportunity cost*. Like time, money used in one way cannot be used in other ways. Financial choices are always a series of "trade-offs."

If you buy a car with your savings, you give up the interest that money could earn. If you invest the money, you don't get the car. If you borrow money to buy the car, you have to pay interest for its use.

When making financial choices such as saving, spending, investing, or borrowing, you should consider the interest-earning ability of that money as an opportunity cost.

CALCULATING THE FINANCE CHARGE REBATE AND THE AMOUNT OF THE PAYOFF WHEN A LOAN IS PAID OFF EARLY BY USING THE SUM-OF-THE-DIGITS METHOD

13-8

Frequently, borrowers choose to repay installment loans before the full time period of the loan has elapsed. When loans are paid off early, the borrower is entitled to a **finance charge rebate**, because the principal was not kept for the full amount of time on which the finance charge was calculated. At payoff, the lender must return or rebate to the borrower any unearned portion of the finance charge.

A widely accepted method for calculating the finance charge rebate is known as the **sum-of-the-digits method, or Rule of 78**. This method is based on the assumption that the lender earns more interest in the early months of a loan, when the borrower has the use of much of the principal, than in the later months, when most of the principal has already been paid back.

finance charge rebate Unearned portion of the finance charge that the lender returns to the borrower when an installment loan is paid off early.

sum-of-the-digits method, or Rule of 78 Widely accepted method for calculating the finance charge rebate. Based on the assumption that more interest is paid in the early months of a loan, when a greater portion of the principal is available to the borrower.

© Digital Vision/Getty Images

Installment financing is frequently used when consumers purchase big-ticket items such as appliances and electronic equipment.

When using this method, the finance charge is assumed to be divided in parts equal to the sum of the digits of the months of the loan. Because the sum of the digits of a 12-month loan is 78, the technique has become known as the Rule of 78.

$$\text{Sum of the digits of } 12 = 1 + 2 + 3 + 4 + 5 + 6 + 7 + 8 + 9 + 10 + 11 + 12 = 78$$

The amount of finance charge in any given month is represented by a fraction whose numerator is the number of payments remaining, and the denominator is the sum of the digits of the number of months in the loan.

For a 12-month loan, for example, the fraction of the finance charge in the first month would be $\frac{12}{78}$. The numerator is 12, because in the first month no payments have been made; therefore, 12 payments remain. The denominator is 78 because the sum of the digits of 12 is 78. In the second month, the lender earns $\frac{11}{78}$; in the third month, $\frac{10}{78}$. This decline continues until the last month when only $\frac{1}{78}$ remains. Exhibit 13-6 illustrates the distribution of a $1,000 finance charge by using the sum-of-the-digits method.

With the sum-of-the-digits method, a **rebate fraction** is established based on when a loan is paid off. The numerator of the rebate fraction is the sum-of-the-digits of the number of remaining payments and the denominator is the sum of the digits of the total number of payments.

rebate fraction Fraction used to calculate the finance charge rebate. The numerator is the sum of the digits of the number of payments remaining at the time the loan is paid off; the denominator is the sum of the digits of the total number of payments of the loan.

$$\textbf{Rebate fraction} = \frac{\textbf{Sum of the digits of the number of remaining payments}}{\textbf{Sum of the digits of the total number of payments}}$$

Although the sum of the digits is easily calculated by addition, it can become tedious for loans of 24, 36, or 48 months. For this reason, we shall use the sum-of-the-digits formula to find the numerator and denominator of the rebate fraction. In the formula, n represents the number of payments.

$$\textbf{Sum of the digits} = \frac{n(n+1)}{2}$$

Exhibit 13-6
Distribution of a $1,000 Finance Charge over 12 Months

Month Number	Finance Charge Fraction	×	$1,000	=	Finance Charge
1	$\frac{12}{78}$	×	$1,000	=	$153.85
2	$\frac{11}{78}$	×	$1,000	=	$141.03
3	$\frac{10}{78}$	×	$1,000	=	$128.21
4	$\frac{9}{78}$	×	$1,000	=	$115.38
5	$\frac{8}{78}$	×	$1,000	=	$102.56
6	$\frac{7}{78}$	×	$1,000	=	$89.74
7	$\frac{6}{78}$	×	$1,000	=	$76.92
8	$\frac{5}{78}$	×	$1,000	=	$64.10
9	$\frac{4}{78}$	×	$1,000	=	$51.28
10	$\frac{3}{78}$	×	$1,000	=	$38.46
11	$\frac{2}{78}$	×	$1,000	=	$25.64
12	$\frac{1}{78}$	×	$1,000	=	$12.82

In the Business World

This table clearly illustrates that the majority of the finance charge on an installment loan is incurred in the first half of the loan.

STEPS TO CALCULATE THE FINANCE CHARGE REBATE AND LOAN PAYOFF

Step 1. Calculate the rebate fraction.

$$\textbf{Rebate fraction} = \frac{\textbf{Sum of the digits of the number of remaining payments}}{\textbf{Sum of the digits of the total number of payments}}$$

Step 2. Determine the finance charge rebate.

$$\textbf{Finance charge rebate} = \textbf{Rebate fraction} \times \textbf{Total finance charge}$$

Step 3. Find the loan payoff.

$$\textbf{Loan payoff} = \left(\textbf{Payments remaining} \times \textbf{Payments amount}\right) - \textbf{Finance charge rebate}$$

CLASSROOM ACTIVITY

In groups, have students bring to class newspaper advertisements for installment purchase merchandise such as cars, boats, or furniture that display the Regulation Z requirements. From this information, have each group calculate:

- amount financed
- finance charge
- total deferred payments
- amount of the payoff, after half the payments are made

EXAMPLE 9 CALCULATING EARLY LOAN PAYOFF FIGURES

Sandy Lane financed a $1,500 health club membership with an installment loan for 12 months. The payments were $145 per month, and the total finance charge was $240. After 8 months, she decided to pay off the loan. How much is the finance charge rebate and what is her loan payoff?

SOLUTION STRATEGY

Step 1. Rebate fraction:

Set up the rebate fraction by using the sum-of-the-digits formula. Because Sandy has already made eight payments, she has four payments remaining (12 − 8 = 4).

The *numerator* will be the sum of the digits of the number of remaining payments, 4.

$$\text{Sum of the digits of 4} = \frac{n(n+1)}{2} = \frac{4(4+1)}{2} = \frac{4(5)}{2} = \frac{20}{2} = \underline{10}$$

The *denominator* will be the sum of the digits of the number of payments, 12.

$$\text{Sum of the digits of 12} = \frac{n(n+1)}{2} = \frac{12(12+1)}{2} = \frac{12(13)}{2} = \frac{156}{2} = \underline{78}$$

The rebate fraction is therefore $\frac{10}{78}$.

Step 2. Finance charge rebate:

$$\text{Finance charge rebate} = \text{Rebate fraction} \times \text{Total finance charge}$$

$$\text{Finance charge rebate} = \frac{10}{78} \times 240$$

$$\text{Finance charge rebate} = 30.7692 = \underline{\underline{\$30.77}}$$

Step 3. Loan payoff:

Loan payoff = (Payments remaining × Payment amount) − Finance charge rebate

Loan payoff = (4 × 145) − 30.77

Loan payoff = 580.00 − 30.77

Loan payoff = $549.23

TRY IT EXERCISE 9

Chris Hedberg financed a $4,000 piano with an installment loan for 36 months. The payments were $141 per month, and the total finance charge was $1,076. After 20 months Chris decided to pay off the loan. How much is the finance charge rebate and how much is Chris's loan payoff?

CHECK YOUR ANSWERS WITH THE SOLUTIONS ON PAGE 481.

13 SECTION II Review Exercises

Note: Round all answers to the nearest cent, when necessary.

Calculate the amount financed, the finance charge, and the total deferred payment price for the following installment loans.

	Purchase (Cash) Price	Down Payment	Amount Financed	Monthly Payments	Number of Payments	Finance Charge	Total Deferred Payment Price
1.	$1,400	$350	$1,050.00	$68.00	24	$582.00	$1,982.00
2.	$3,500	20%	$2,800.00	$257.00	12	$284.00	$3,784.00
3.	$12,000	10%	$10,800.00	$375.00	36	$2,700.00	$14,700.00
4.	$2,900	0	$2,900.00	$187.69	18	$478.42	$3,378.42
5.	$8,750	15%	$7,437.50	$198.33	48	$2,082.34	$10,832.34

Calculate the amount financed, the finance charge, and the amount of the monthly payments for the following add-on interest loans.

	Purchase (Cash) Price	Down Payment	Amount Financed	Add-On Interest	Number of Payments	Finance Charge	Monthly Payment
6.	$788	10%	$709.20	8%	12	$56.74	$63.83
7.	$1,600	$250	$1,350.00	10%	24	$270.00	$67.50
8.	$4,000	15%	$3,400.00	$11\frac{1}{2}\%$	30	$977.50	$145.92
9.	$17,450	$2,000	$15,450.00	14%	48	$8,652.00	$502.13
10.	$50,300	25%	$37,725.00	12.4%	60	$23,389.50	$1,018.58

Calculate the finance charge, finance charge per $100, and the annual percentage rate for the following installment loans by using the APR table, Table 13-1.

	Amount Financed	Number of Payments	Monthly Payment	Finance Charge	Finance Charge per $100	APR
11.	$2,300	24	$109.25	$322.00	$14.00	13%
12.	$14,000	36	$495.00	$3,820.00	$27.29	16.5%
13.	$1,860	18	$115.75	$223.50	$12.02	14.75%
14.	$35,000	60	$875.00	$17,500.00	$50.00	17.25%

Calculate the finance charge and the annual percentage rate for the following installment loans by using the APR formula.

	Amount Financed	Number of Payments	Monthly Payment	Finance Charge	APR
15.	$500	12	$44.25	$31.00	11.25%
16.	$2,450	36	$90.52	$808.72	19.39%
17.	$13,000	48	$373.75	$4,940.00	16.6%
18.	$100,000	72	$2,055.50	$47,996.00	13.65%

Calculate the finance charge and the monthly payment for the following loans by using the APR table, Table 13-1.

	Amount Financed	Number of Payments	APR	Table Factor	Finance Charge	Monthly Payment
19.	$5,000	48	13.5%	29.97	$1,498.50	$135.39
20.	$7,500	36	12%	19.57	$1,467.75	$249.10
21.	$1,800	12	11.25%	6.20	$111.60	$159.30
22.	$900	18	14%	11.45	$103.05	$55.73

Calculate the missing information for the following installment loans that are being paid off early.

	Number of Payments	Payments Made	Payments Remaining	Sum of the Digits Payments Remaining	Sum of the Digits Number of Payments	Rebate Fraction
23.	12	4	8	36	78	36/78
24.	36	22	14	105	666	105/666
25.	24	9	15	120	300	120/300
26.	60	40	20	210	1,830	210/1,830

You are the loan department supervisor for the Pacific National Bank. The following installment loans are being paid off early, and it is your task to calculate the rebate fraction, the finance charge rebate, and the payoff for each loan.

	Amount Financed	Number of Payments	Monthly Payment	Payments Made	Rebate Fraction	Finance Charge Rebate	Loan Payoff
27.	$3,000	24	$162.50	9	120/300	$360.00	$2,077.50
28.	$1,600	18	$104.88	11	28/171	$47.13	$687.03
29.	$9,500	48	$267.00	36	78/1,176	$219.94	$2,984.06
30.	$4,800	36	$169.33	27	45/666	$87.56	$1,436.41

Solar Energy

According to Solar Home.org, as the financial and environmental cost of relying on traditional fossil fuels rises, harnessing the energy of the sun proves to be a renewable, clean, and affordable solution for a green future. Solar power is inexhaustible and available virtually anywhere, making it an ideal resource for energy generation.

Solar panels are the anchor of portable, residential, or commercial solar energy systems. Solar cells convert solar energy into electricity as part of interconnected module systems that are laminated and framed in a durable, weatherproof package.

31. Brandy Emerson is interested in buying a solar energy system for her home. At Sun-Savers, Inc., she picks out a system for a total cash price of $1,899. The salesperson informs her that if she qualifies for an installment loan, she may pay 10% now, as a down payment, and finance the balance with payments of $88.35 per month for 24 months.

a. What is the amount of the finance charge on this loan?

Amount financed = 1,899(100% − 10%)
= $1,709.10

Total payments = 88.35 × 24
= $2,120.40

Finance charge = 2,120.40 − 1,709.10
= $411.30

b. What is the total deferred payment price of the system?

Total deferred price = 411.30 + 1,899
= $2,310.30

32. Fran Steiner purchased a small sailboat for $8,350. She made a down payment of $1,400 and financed the balance with monthly payments of $239.38 for 36 months.

a. What is the amount of the finance charge on the loan?

Amount financed = 8,350 − 1,400 = $6,950
Total payments = 239.38 × 36 = $8,617.68
Finance charge = 8,617.68 − 6,950.00 = $1,667.68

b. Use Table 13-1 to find what annual percentage rate was charged on Fran's loan.

$$\text{Table factor} = \frac{1{,}667.78 \times 100}{6{,}950} = 24$$

APR = 14.5%

33. Alyssa Newton financed a cruise down the Amazon River with a 5% add-on interest installment loan from her bank. The total price of the trip was $1,500. The bank required equal monthly payments for 2 years. How much are Alyssa's monthly payments?

Finance charge = 1,500 × .05 × 2 = $150
Total payments = 150 + 1,500 = $1,650

$$\text{Monthly payment} = \frac{1{,}650}{24} = \$68.75$$

34. Doug Black bought a snowmobile with a 9% add-on interest installment loan from his credit union. The purchase price was $1,450. The credit union required a 15% down payment and equal monthly payments for 48 months. How much are Doug's monthly payments?

Amount financed = 1,450.00(100% − 15%)
= 1,232.50

$I = PRT$

$I = 1{,}232.50 \times .09 \times 4$

$I = 443.70$

Total payments = 1,232.50 + 443.70
= $1,676.20

$$\text{Monthly payment} = \frac{1{,}676.20}{48} = \$34.92$$

Timeshare is a form of holiday ownership. You own the right (either directly or through a "points club") to use a week (or longer) in an apartment or villa in a holiday resort for a great many years or in perpetuity.

Nearly seven million families have timeshare interests in over 5,000 resorts in 90 countries. Major companies now involved in timeshare include Hilton, Hyatt, Four Seasons, Marriott, Sheraton, Ramada, and De Vere.

35. Olivia Fast found a timeshare condominium she wanted to buy in the Rocky Mountains. She had the option of paying $7,600 in cash or financing the condo with a 2-year installment loan. The loan required a 20% down payment and equal monthly payments of $283.73.

a. What is the finance charge on Olivia's loan?

Amount financed = 7,600(100% − 20%) = $6,080
Total payments = 283.73 × 24 = $6,809.52
Finance charge = 6,809.52 − 6,080.00 = $729.52

b. What is the total deferred payment price of the condo?

Total deferred price = 729.52 + 7,600.00 = $8,329.52

36. Paul Peterson purchased a wall unit for $2,400. He made a $700 down payment and financed the balance with an installment loan for 48 months. If Paul's payments are $42.50 per month, use the APR formula to calculate what annual percentage rate he is paying on the loan.

Amount financed = 2,400 − 700 = 1,700

$$\frac{72 \times 340}{(3 \times 1{,}700 \times 49) + (340 \times 47)} = \frac{24{,}480}{249{,}900 + 15{,}980} = \frac{24{,}480}{265{,}880}$$

APR = 9.21%

Total payments = 42.50 × 48 = $2,040

Finance charge = 2,040 − 1,700 = $340

37. Sound Advice uses the Capital Bank to finance customer purchases. This month, the bank is offering 24-month installment loans with an APR of 15.25%. For qualified buyers, no down payment is required. If Nathan David wants to finance a complete stereo system for $1,300, use the APR tables to calculate the finance charge and the amount of the monthly payment on his loan.

Table factor for 15.25% for 24 months = 16.65

$$\text{Total finance charge} = \frac{1{,}300 \times 16.65}{100} = \underline{\underline{\$216.45}}$$

$$\text{Monthly payment} = \frac{216.45 + 1{,}300}{24} = \underline{\underline{\$63.19}}$$

38. At a recent boat show, Riverside Bank was offering boat loans for up to 5 years, with APRs of 13.5%. On new boats, a 20% down payment was required. Perry Jones wanted to finance a $55,000 boat for 5 years.

a. What would be the finance charge on the loan?

Amount financed = 55,000(100% − 20%) = $44,000

Finance charge = 44,000 × .135 × 5 = $\underline{\underline{\$29{,}700}}$

b. What would be the amount of the monthly payment?

$$\text{Monthly payment} = \frac{29{,}700 + 44{,}000}{60} = \underline{\underline{\$1{,}228.33}}$$

39. Find the sum of the digits of $\quad \text{Sum of digits} = \frac{n(n+1)}{2}$

EXCEL

a. 24

$$\frac{24 \times 25}{2} = \underline{\underline{300}}$$

b. 30

$$\frac{30 \times 31}{2} = \underline{\underline{465}}$$

40. a. What is the rebate fraction of a 36-month loan paid off after the 14th payment?

$36 - 14 = 22$

$$\frac{22 \times 23}{2} = 253 \qquad \frac{36 \times 37}{2} = 666$$

$$\text{Rebate fraction} = \underline{\underline{\frac{253}{666}}}$$

b. What is the rebate fraction of a 42-month loan paid off after the 19th payment?

$42 - 19 = 23$

$$\frac{23 \times 24}{2} = 276 \qquad \frac{42 \times 43}{2} = 903$$

$$\text{Rebate fraction} = \underline{\underline{\frac{276}{903}}}$$

© Robert Brechner/South-Western Cengage Learning

Mountain Bikes

The U.S. bicycle industry was a $5.8 billion industry in 2006, including bicycles, related parts, and accessories, according to research funded by the National Sporting Goods Association. They also report that 43.1 million Americans, age seven and older, rode a bicycle six times or more in 2005.

According to the National Bicycle Dealers Association, in 2006, mountain bikes represented 28.5% of all bicycles sold by the approximately 4,600 specialty bicycle retailers.

41. Brian Singer financed a $3,500 mountain bike with an 8% add-on interest installment loan for 24 months. The loan required a 10% down payment.

a. What is the amount of the finance charge on the loan?

Amount financed = 3,500(100% − 10%) = $3,150

Finance charge = 3,150 × .08 × 2 = $\underline{\underline{\$504}}$

b. How much are Brian's monthly payments?

Monthly payment = 504 + 3,150

$$= \frac{3{,}654}{24} = \underline{\underline{\$152.25}}$$

c. What annual percentage rate is being charged on the loan?

$$\text{APR by formula} = \frac{72 \times 504}{(3 \times 3{,}150 \times 25) + (504 \times 23)} = \frac{36{,}288}{236{,}250 + 11{,}592} = \frac{36{,}288}{247{,}842} = \underline{14.64\%}$$

$$\text{APR by table} = \frac{504 \times 100}{3{,}150} = 16 \text{ factor}$$

Table 13.1, 16.00, 24 periods = $\underline{14.75\%}$

d. If Brian decides to pay off the loan after 16 months, what is his loan payoff?

$$24 - 16 = 8 \quad \frac{8 \times 9}{2} = 36$$

$$\frac{24 \times 25}{2} = 300$$

$$\text{Rebate fraction} = \frac{36}{300}$$

$$\text{Rebate amount} = 504 \times \frac{36}{300} = \$60.48$$

$$\text{Payoff amount} = 8 \times 152.25 = 1{,}218 - 60.48 = \underline{\$1{,}157.52}$$

42. Geraldo Echevaria is planning to buy a used Cessna Skyhawk from an aircraft broker. The listed price is $165,000. Geraldo can get a secured loan from his bank at 7.25% for as long as 60 months, if he pays 15% down. Geraldo's goal is to keep his payments below $3,800 per month and amortize the loan in 42 months.

© R. Alcorn/South-Western Cengage Learning

Cessna Aircraft Company, the world's leading general aviation company based on unit sales, is a subsidiary of Textron, Inc. In its 79-year history, Cessna has delivered more than 189,000 aircraft, including more than 152,000 single-engine airplanes; more than 1,600 Caravans; more than 2,000 military jets and more than 4,800 Citation business jets. In 2006, Cessna had about 13,700 employees and revenue of $4.16 billion.

a. Can he pay off the loan in 42 months and keep his payments under $3,800?

Amount financed = 165,000(100% − 15%) = $140,250

$$\text{Interest} = 140{,}250 \times .0725 \times \frac{42}{12} = \$35{,}588.44$$

$$\text{Payment} = \frac{140{,}250 + 35{,}588.44}{42} = \underline{\$4{,}186.63}$$ No, the payment is too high.

b. What are Geraldo's options to get his payments closer to his goal?

Make a higher down payment; try to negotiate a lower interest rate; try to bargain for a lower sale price; or negotiate some combination of these variables.

c. Geraldo spoke with his bank's loan officer, who has agreed to finance the deal with a 6.95% loan if he can pay 20% down. Will these conditions meet Geraldo's goal?

Amount financed = 165,000(100% − 20%) = $132,000

$$\text{Interest} = 132{,}000 \times .0695 \times \frac{42}{12} = \$32{,}109$$

$$\text{Payment} = \frac{132{,}000 + 32{,}109}{42} = \underline{\$3{,}907.36}$$ No, the payment is still too high.

d. Geraldo has told the seller he cannot buy the airplane at the listed price. If the seller agrees to reduce the listed price by $4,600, and Geraldo pays the 20% down, will he meet his goal?

Amount financed = (165,000 − 4,600)(100% − 20%) = $128,320

$$\text{Interest} = 128{,}320 \times .0695 \times \frac{42}{12} = \$31{,}213.84$$

$$\text{Payment} = \frac{128{,}320.00 + 31{,}213.84}{42} = \underline{\$3{,}798.42}$$ Yes, under these conditions, he meets his goal.

BUSINESS DECISION READING THE FINE PRINT

In the Business World

In 2006, banks levied $14.8 billion in late and over-the-limit penalties on credit card holders.

The advertisement for The Electronic Boutique shown below appeared in your local newspaper this morning. Answer the questions that follow based on the information in the ad.

43. a. If you purchased the TV on January 24th of this year and the billing date of the installment loan is the 15th of each month, when would your first payment be due?

    February of next year

    b. What is the required amount of that payment?

    $1,699.99

    c. If that payment is late or less than required, what happens and how much does that amount to?

    22.73% Interest is charged   Interest = $386.41

    d. If that payment is more than 30 days late, what happens and how much does that amount to?

    24.75% Interest is charged   Interest = $420.75

    e. Explain the advantages and disadvantages of this offer.

    The advantages are that there is no finance charge and no payments are required on the purchase if paid in full by the payment due date. The disadvantage is that if payment is not made by the due date, the finance charge is assessed on the purchase amount from the original date of purchase.

Electronic Boutique

NO INTEREST & NO PAYMENTS* FOR 12 MONTHS

on all Digital Projection TVs

***Offer is subject to credit approval. No finance charges assessed and no monthly payment required on the promotional purchase if you pay this amount in full by the payment due date as shown on the twelfth (12th) billing statement after purchase date. If you do not, finance charges will be assessed on the promotional purchase amount from the purchase date and minimum monthly payment will be required on balance of amount. Standard account terms apply to non-promotional balances and, after the promotion ends, to promotional purchases. APR = 22.73%. APR of 24.75% applies if payment is more than 30 days late. Sales tax will be paid at the time of purchase.**

1699.99 RCA®
61" Projection TV with Built-In Guide Plus+™ Gold for an instant summary of your favorite shows & 2-Tuner Picture-in-Picture for watching two shows at once Features 3-line digital comb filter for optimized color detail and sharpness. Component and S-Video inputs will keep you connected to the latest in digital technology. P61929

CHAPTER FORMULAS

Open-End Credit

$$\text{Periodic rate} = \frac{\text{Annual percentage rate}}{12}$$

Finance charge = Previous month's balance × Periodic rate

$$\text{Average daily balance} = \frac{\text{Sum of the daily balances}}{\text{Days in billing cycle}}$$

Finance charge = Average daily balance × Periodic rate

$$\text{New balance} = \text{Previous balance} + \text{Finance charge} + \text{Purchases and cash advances} + \text{Payments and credits}$$

Closed-End Credit

Amount financed = Purchase price − Down payment

Down payment = Purchase price × Down payment percent

Amount financed = Purchase price(100% − Down payment percent)

Total amount of installment payments = Amount financed + Finance charge

Finance charge = Total amount of installment payments − Amount financed

$$\text{Total amount of installment payments} = \text{Monthly payment amount} \times \text{Number of monthly payments}$$

Total deferred payment price = Total of installment payments + Down payment

Interest (*finance charge*) = Principal (*amount financed*) × Rate × Time

$$\text{Regular monthly payments} = \frac{\text{Total of installment payments}}{\text{Number of months of loan}}$$

$$\text{APR} = \frac{72I}{3P(n+1) + I(n-1)}$$

$$\text{Finance charge} = \frac{\text{Amount financed} \times \text{APR table factor}}{100}$$

$$\text{Sum of the digits} = \frac{n(n+1)}{2}$$

$$\text{Rebate fraction} = \frac{\text{Sum of the digits of remaining payments}}{\text{Sum of the digits of total payment}}$$

Finance charge rebate = Rebate fraction × Total finance charge

Loan payoff = (Payments remaining × Payment amount) − Finance charge rebate

SUMMARY CHART

Section I: Open-End Credit—Charge Accounts, Credit Cards, and Lines of Credit

Topic	Important Concepts	Illustrative Examples
Calculating Finance Charge and New Balance by Using Previous Month's Balance Method **P/O 13-1, p. 443**	1. Divide the annual percentage rate by 12 to find the monthly or periodic interest rate. 2. Calculate the finance charge by multiplying the previous month's balance by the periodic interest rate from Step 1. 3. Total all the purchases and cash advances for the month. 4. Total all the payments and credits for the month. 5. Use the following formula to determine the new balance: $\text{New bal} = \text{Prev bal} + \text{Fin chg} + \text{Purch \& csh} - \text{Pmts \& crd}$	Calculate the finance charge and the new balance of an account with an annual percentage rate of 15%. Previous month's bal = \$186.11 Purchases = \$365.77 Payments = \$200 Periodic rate $= \frac{15}{12} = 1.25\%$ Finance charge = 186.11 × .0125 = \$2.33 New balance = 186.11 + 2.33 + 365.77 − 200.00 = \$354.21
Calculating Finance Charge and New Balance by Using the Average Daily Balance Method **P/O 13-2, p. 445**	1. Starting with the previous month's balance, multiply each by the number of days that balance existed until the next account transaction. 2. At the end of the billing cycle, add all the daily balances × days figures. 3. $\text{Average daily balance} = \frac{\text{Sum of the daily balances}}{\text{Number of days of billing cycle}}$ 4. $\text{Finance charge} = \text{Periodic rate} \times \text{Average daily balance}$ 5. $\text{New bal} = \text{Prev bal} + \text{Fin chg} + \text{Purch \& csh} - \text{Pmts \& crd}$	Calculate the finance charge and the new balance of an account with a periodic rate of 1%, a previous balance of \$132.26, and the following activity. May 5 Purchase \$ 45.60 May 9 Cash advance 100.00 May 15 Credit 65.70 May 23 Purchase 75.62 May 26 Payment 175.00 \$132.26 × 4 days = \$ 529.04 177.86 × 4 days = 711.44 277.86 × 6 days = 1,667.16 212.16 × 8 days = 1,697.28 287.78 × 3 days = 863.34 112.78 × 6 days = 676.68 31 days \$6,144.94 Average daily balance $= \frac{6{,}144.94}{31} = \$198.22$ Finance charge = 1% × 198.22 = \$1.98 New balance = 132.26 + 1.98 + 221.22 − 240.70 = \$114.76

Section I: (continued)

Topic	Important Concepts	Illustrative Examples
Calculating the Finance Charge and New Balance of Business and Personal Lines of Credit **P/O 13-3, p. 448**	With business and personal lines of credit, the annual percentage rate is quoted as the current prime rate plus a fixed percent. Once the APR rate is determined, the finance charge and new balance are calculated as before, using the average daily balance method. **New bal = Previous balance + Finance charge + Loans − Payments**	What are the finance charge and new balance of a line of credit with an APR of the current prime rate plus 4.6%? Previous balance = \$2,000 Average daily balance = \$3,200 Payments = \$1,500 Loans = \$3,600 Current prime rate = 7% APR = 7% + 4.6% = 11.6% $\text{Periodic rate} = \frac{11.6}{12} = .97\%$ Finance charge = 3,200 × .0097 = \$31.04 New balance = 2,000 + 31.04 + 3,600 − 1,500 = \$4,131.04

Section II: Closed-End Credit—Installment Loans

Topic	Important Concepts	Illustrative Examples
Calculating the Total Deferred Payment Price and the Amount of the Finance Charge of an Installment Loan **P/O 13-4, p. 456**	**Finance charge = Total amount of installment pmts − Amount financed** **Total deferred payment price = Total of installment payments + Down payment**	Modern Age sold a \$1,900 bedroom set to Will Baker. Will put down \$400 and financed the balance with an installation loan of 24 monthly payments of \$68.75 each. What are the finance charge and total deferred payment price of the bedroom set? Total amount of payments = \$68.75 × 24 = \$1,650 Finance charge = 1,650 − 1,500 = \$150 Total deferred payment price = 1,650 + 400 = \$2,050
Calculating the Regular Monthly Payment of an Installment Loan by the Add-On Interest Method **P/O 13-5, p. 457**	1. Calculate the amount financed by subtracting the down payment from the purchase price. 2. Compute the add-on interest finance charge by using $I = PRT$. 3. Find the total of the installment payments by adding the interest to the amount financed. 4. Calculate the monthly payment by dividing the total of the installment payments by the number of months of the loan.	Vanessa Cooper financed a new car with an 8% add-on interest loan. The purchase price of the car was \$13,540. The bank required a \$1,500 down payment and equal monthly payments for 48 months. How much are Vanessa's monthly payments? Amount financed = 13,540 − 1,500 = \$12,040 Interest = 12,040 × .08 × 4 = \$3,852.80 Total of installment payments = 12,040.00 + 3,852.80 = \$15,892.80 $\text{Monthly payment} = \frac{15{,}892.80}{48} = \$331.10$

Section II: (continued)

Topic	Important Concepts	Illustrative Examples
Calculating the Annual Percentage Rate (APR) by Using APR Tables **P/O 13-6, p. 459**	1. Calculate the finance charge per \$100 by $\frac{\text{Finance charge} \times 100}{\text{Amount financed}}$ 2. From Table 13-1, scan down the payments column to the number of payments of the loan. 3. Scan to the right in that row to the table factor that most closely corresponds to the finance charge per \$100. 4. Look to the top of the column containing the finance charge per \$100 to find the APR of the loan.	Sean Casey purchased a home gym for \$8,000. He made a \$1,500 down payment and financed the remaining \$6,500 for 30 months. If Sean's total finance charge is \$1,858, what APR is he paying on the loan? $\text{Finance charge per \$100} = \frac{1{,}858 \times 100}{6{,}500} = \$28.58$ From Table 13-1, scan down the payments column to 30. Then scan right to the table factor closest to 28.58, which is 28.64. The top of that column shows the APR to be 20.5%
Calculating the Annual Percentage Rate (APR) by Using the APR Formula **P/O 13-6, p. 463**	When APR tables are not available, the annual percentage rate can be approximated by the formula $\text{APR} = \frac{72I}{3P(n+1)+I(n-1)}$ where I = finance charge on the loan P = principal; amount financed n = number of months of the loan	Using the APR formula, verify the 20.5% found by the table in the previous example. $\text{APR} = \frac{72(1{,}858)}{3(6{,}500)(30+1)+1{,}858(30-1)}$ $= \frac{133{,}776}{658{,}382} = .2031 = 20.3\%$
Calculating the Finance Charge and Monthly Payment of a Loan by Using APR Tables **P/O 13-7, p. 464**	1. From Table 13-1, locate the table factor at the intersection of the APR and number of payments of the loan. This table factor is the finance charge per \$100. 2. Total finance charge $= \frac{\text{Amount financed} \times \text{Table factor}}{100}$ 3. $\text{Monthly payment} = \frac{\text{Amt. financed} + \text{Finance chg}}{\text{Number of months of the loan}}$	Appliance Mart uses Neptune Bank to finance customer purchases. This month Neptune is offering loans up to 36 months with an APR of 13.25%. For qualified buyers, no down payment is required. If Joe Galloway wants to purchase a \$2,350 stove using a 36-month loan, what are the finance charge and monthly payment of the loan? From Table 13-1, the table factor for 36 payments, 13.25% = 21.73 $\text{Total finance charge} = \frac{2{,}350 \times 21.73}{100} = \$510.66$ $\text{Monthly payment} = \frac{2{,}350.00 + 510.66}{36} = \$79.46$
Calculating the Finance Charge Rebate and Payoff for Loans Paid Off Early by Using the Sum-of-the-Digits, or Rule of 78, Method **P/O 13-8, p. 465**	1. Calculate the rebate fraction by $\text{Rebate fraction} = \frac{\text{Sum of the digits of the number of remaining payments}}{\text{Sum of the digits of the total number of payments}}$ 2. Determine the finance charge rebate by Finance charge rebate = Rebate fraction × Total finance charge 3. Find the loan payoff by Loan payoff $= \left(\text{Payments remaining} \times \text{Payments amount}\right) - \text{Finance charge rebate}$	Mel Hart financed a \$2,000 riding lawnmower with an installment loan for 24 months. The payments are \$98 per month, and the total finance charge is \$352. After 18 months, Mel decides to pay off the loan. How much is the finance charge rebate, and what is the amount of the loan payoff? $\text{Rebate fraction} = \frac{\text{Sum of the digits of 6}}{\text{Sum of the digits of 24}}$ $\text{Sum of the digits 6} = \frac{6(7)}{2} = 21$ $\text{Sum of the digits 24} = \frac{24(25)}{2} = 300$ $\text{Rebate fraction} = \frac{21}{300}$ $\text{Finance charge rebate} = \frac{21}{300} \times 352 = \$24.64$ Loan payoff = (6 × 98) − 24.64 = 588.00 − 24.64 = \$563.36

TRY IT EXERCISE SOLUTIONS FOR CHAPTER 13

1. Periodic rate $= \frac{\text{APR}}{12} = \frac{15\%}{12} = 1.25\%$

Finance charge = Previous balance × Periodic rate

Finance charge = 214.90 × .0125 = $2.69

New balance = Previous balance + Finance charge + Purchases & cash advance − Payment & credits

New balance = 214.90 + 2.69 + 238.85 − 49.12 = $407.32

2. Periodic rate $= \frac{\text{APR}}{12} = \frac{18\%}{12} = 1.5\%$

Dates	Days	Activity/Amount		Unpaid Balance	Daily Balances
Aug. 1–4	4	Previous balance	158.69	158.69	634.76
Aug. 5–10	6	Charge	55.00	213.69	1,282.14
Aug. 11–14	4	Payment	–100.00	113.69	454.76
Aug. 15–16	2	Charge	43.22	156.91	313.82
Aug. 17–19	3	Charge	54.10	211.01	633.03
Aug. 20–25	6	Charge	224.50	435.51	2,613.06
Aug. 26–31	6	Cash advance	75.00	510.51	3,063.06
	31				$8,994.63

Average daily balance $= \frac{\text{Sum of the daily balances}}{\text{Days in billing cycle}} = \frac{8{,}994.63}{31} = \$290.15$

Finance charge = Average daily balance × Periodic rate

Finance charge = $290.15 × .015 = $4.35

New balance = Previous balance + Finance charge + Purchases & cash advance − Payments & credits

New balance = 158.69 + 4.35 + 451.82 − 100.00 = $514.86

3. APR = Prime rate + 4.5%

APR = 8.5 + 4.5 = 13%

Periodic rate $= \frac{13\%}{12} = 1.08\%$

Dates	Days	Activity/Amount		Unpaid Balance	Daily Balances
Nov. 1–6	6	Previous balance	12,300	12,300	73,800
Nov. 7–20	14	Borrowed	16,700	29,000	406,000
Nov. 21–25	5	Borrowed	8,800	37,800	189,000
Nov. 26–30	5	Payment	−20,000	17,800	89,000
	30				$757,800

Average daily balance $= \frac{757{,}800}{30} = \$25{,}260$

Finance charge = 25,260 × .0108 = $272.81

New balance = Previous balance + Finance charge + Loan amounts − Payments

New balance = 12,300.00 + 272.81 + 25,500.00 − 20,000.00 = $18,072.81

4. a. Down payment = Purchase price × Down payment percent
Down payment = 12,500 × .15 = $1,875

Amount financed = Purchase price − Down payment
Amount financed = 12,500 − 1,875 = $10,625

Total amount of installment payments = Monthly payment × Number of payments
Total amount of installment payments = 309.90 × 48 = $14,875.20

Finance charge = Total amount of installment payments − Amount financed
Finance charge = 14,875.20 − 10,625.00 = $4,250.20

b. Total deferred payment price = Total amount of installment payments + Down payment
Total deferred payment price = 14,875.20 + 1,875.00 = $16,750.20

5. Amount financed = Purchase price(100% − Down payment %)
Amount financed = 1,500 × .9 = $1,350

Finance charge = Amount financed × Rate × Time
Finance charge = 1,350 × .06 × 2 = $162

Total of installment payments = Amount financed + Finance charge
Total of installment payments = 1,350 + 162 = $1,512

$$\text{Monthly payments} = \frac{\text{Total of installment payments}}{\text{Number of months of loan}}$$

$$\text{Monthly payments} = \frac{1{,}512}{24} = \underline{\underline{\$63}}$$

6. Amount financed = 4,500 − 500 = $4,000
Total payments = 190 × 24 = 4,560
Finance charge = 4,560 − 4,000 = $560

$$\text{Finance charge per 100} = \frac{\text{Finance charge} \times 100}{\text{Amount financed}} = \frac{560 \times 100}{4{,}000} = \$14$$

From Table 13-1 APR for $14 = 13%

7. Total payments = 140 × 18 = 2,520
Finance charge = 2,520 − 2,200 = $320

$$\text{APR} = \frac{72I}{3P(n+1) + I(n-1)}$$

$$\text{APR} = \frac{72(320)}{3(2{,}200)(18+1) + 320(18-1)} = \frac{23{,}040}{125{,}400 + 5{,}440}$$

$$\text{APR} = \frac{23{,}040}{130{,}840} = .17609 = \underline{\underline{17.6\%}}$$

8. 13.25%, 24-month table factor = $14.38

$$\text{Finance charge} = \frac{\text{Amount financed} \times \text{Table factor}}{100}$$

$$\text{Finance charge} = \frac{3{,}550.00 \times 14.38}{100} = \frac{51{,}049}{100} = \underline{\underline{\$510.49}}$$

$$\text{Monthly payment} = \frac{\text{Amount financed} + \text{Finance charge}}{\text{Number of months of loan}}$$

$$\text{Monthly payment} = \frac{3{,}550.00 + 510.49}{24} = \frac{4{,}060.49}{24}$$

$$\text{Monthly payment} = \underline{\underline{\$169.19}}$$

9. 16 months remaining; total of 36 months.

$$\text{Sum of the digits } 16 = \frac{n(n+1)}{2} = \frac{16(16+1)}{2} = \frac{272}{2} = 136$$

$$\text{Sum of the digits } 36 = \frac{n(n+1)}{2} = \frac{36(36+1)}{2} = \frac{1,332}{2} = 666$$

$$\text{Rebate fraction} = \frac{136}{666}$$

$$\text{Finance charge rebate} = \text{Rebate fraction} \times \text{Total finance charge} = \frac{136}{666} \times 1,076$$

Finance charge rebate = $\underline{\underline{\$219.72}}$

Loan payoff = (Payments remaining × Payment amount) − Finance charge rebate

Loan payoff = (16 × 141) − 219.72 = 2,256.00 − 219.72

Loan payoff = $\underline{\underline{\$2,036.28}}$

CONCEPT REVIEW

1. ____ credit is a loan arrangement in which there is no set number of payments. (13-1)

Open-end

2. The effective or true annual interest rate being charged for credit is known as the ____ ____ ____, and is abbreviated ____. (13-1)

annual percentage rate, APR

3. Loans that are backed by the borrower's "promise" to repay are known as ____ loans; whereas loans that are backed by a tangible asset are known as ____ loans. (13-1)

unsecured, secured

4. Loans made on a continuous basis and billed periodically are known as ____ credit. (13-1)

revolving

5. Name the two most common methods used to calculate the finance charge of a revolving credit account. (13-1, 13-2)

- Unpaid or previous month's balance method
- Average daily balance method

6. Write the formula for calculating the average daily balance of a revolving credit account. (13-2)

$$\text{Average daily balance} = \frac{\text{Sum of the daily balances}}{\text{Days in billing cycle}}$$

7. A pre-approved amount of open-end credit is known as a ____ of credit. (13-3)

line

8. The interest rate of most lines of credit is tied to the movement of the ____ rate. (13-3)

prime

9. A loan made for a specified number of equal monthly payments is known as a(n) ____ loan. (13-4)

installment

10. The portion of the purchase price of an asset paid in a lump-sum at the time of purchase is known as the ____ payment. (13-4)

down

11. A popular method for calculating the interest on an installment loan is known as ____ interest. (13-5)

add-on

12. Write the formula for calculating the APR of an installment loan. (13-6)

$$\text{APR} = \frac{72I}{3P(n+1) + I(n-1)}$$

13. The finance charge ____ is the unearned portion of the finance charge that is returned to a borrower when an installment loan is paid off early. (13-8)

rebate

14. The most common method for calculating the finance charge rebate of an installment loan is known as the sum-of-the- ____ method or the Rule of ____. (13-8)

digits, 78

13 CHAPTER ASSESSMENT TEST

Name

Class

Answers

1. a. 1.33%
   b. $4.59
   c. $440.38
2. a. $3.02
   b. $883.70
3. a. $4.46 $724.12
   b. $724.12 $12.09 $839.64
   c. $839.64 $14.02 $859.61

1. Pam Grant's revolving credit account has an annual percentage rate of 16%. The previous month's balance was $345.40. During the current month, Pam's purchases and cash advances amounted to $215.39, and her payments and credits totaled $125.00.

a. What is the monthly periodic rate of the account?

$\text{Periodic rate} = \frac{16\%}{12} = 1.33\%$

b. What is the amount of the finance charge?

$345.40 \times 1.33\% = \$4.59$

c. What is Pam's new balance?

$\text{New balance} = 345.40 + 4.59 + 215.39 - 125.00 = \$440.38$

2. Sam Ullman has a Bank of America revolving credit account with an annual percentage rate of 12% calculated on the previous month's balance. In April, the account had the following activity.

Statement of Account

NAME		
SAM ULLMAN		
ACCOUNT NUMBER		
9595-55-607		
BILLING CYCLE		
APRIL 1–30		

DATE	DESCRIPTION OF TRANSACTIONS	CHARGES
04/01	Previous month's balance	$301.98
04/08	Atlas Gym & Health Club	250.00
04/09	Payment	75.00
04/15	JC Penney	124.80
04/25	Cash Advance	100.00
04/28	Jasper Park Lodge	178.90

a. What is the amount of the finance charge?

$\text{Periodic rate} = 12\% \div 12 = 1\%$

$\text{Finance charge} = 301.98 \times 1\% = \$3.02$

b. What is Sam's new balance?

$\text{New balance} = 301.98 + 3.02 + 653.70 - 75.00 = \$883.70$

3. Laura Granville has a Visa account. The finance charge is calculated on the previous month's balance, and the annual percentage rate is 20%. Complete the following 3-month account activity table for Laura.

Periodic Rate: $20\% \div 12 = 1.67\%$

	Month	Previous Month's Balance	Finance Charge	Purchases and Cash Advances	Payments and Credits	New Balance End of Month
a.	December	$267.00	$4.46	$547.66	$95.00	$724.12
b.	January	$724.12	$12.09	$213.43	$110.00	$839.64
c.	February	$839.64	$14.02	$89.95	$84.00	$859.61

Top Credit Card Issuers

Name of the Banks	Dollars (in billions)	Market share
Bank of America	149.2	20.2%
JPMorgan Chase	140.1	19.0%
Citigroup	111.9	15.1%
American Express	72.6	9.8%
Capital One	53.9	7.3%
Discover	44.3	6.0%
HSBC	27.2	3.7%
Washington Mutual	20.0	2.7%
Wells Fargo	17.4	2.4%
U.S. Bancorp	11.2	1.5%
Total	**$738.6**	**87.7%**

Source: *USA Today*, July 31, 2006, p. 1B Reprinted with permission.

CHAPTER 13

Name

Class

Answers

4. $504.54

5. a. $694.76

b. $7.50

c. $864.74

6. a. $719.35

Complete, worked-out solutions for Exercises 4, 5a, and 6a appear in Appendix B, following the index.

4. Calculate the average daily balance for the month of January of a charge account with a previous month's balance of $480.94 and the following activity.

Date	Activity	Amount
January 7	Cash advance	$80.00
January 12	Payment	$125.00
January 18	Purchase	$97.64
January 24	Credit	$72.00
January 29	Purchase	$109.70
January 30	Purchase	$55.78

$$\text{Average daily balance} = \frac{15{,}640.76}{31} = \underline{\underline{\$504.54}}$$

5. Richard Blake has a Bank of America account with a 13% annual percentage rate calculated on the average daily balance. The billing date is the first day of each month, and the billing cycle is the number of days in that month.

Statement of Account Bank of America

NAME: RICHARD BLAKE

ACCOUNT NUMBER: 4495-5607

BILLING CYCLE: SEPTEMBER 1–30

DATE	DESCRIPTION OF TRANSACTIONS	CHARGES
09/01	Previous month's balance	$686.97
09/04	Ebay	223.49
09/08	Payment	350.00
09/12	Staples	85.66
09/21	Delta Air Lines (credit)	200.00
09/24	Apple.com	347.12
09/28	Ticketmaster	64.00

a. What is the average daily balance for September?

$$\text{Average daily balance} = \frac{20{,}842.71}{30} = \underline{\underline{\$694.76}} \text{ (See Appendix B)}$$

b. How much is the finance charge for September?

$$\text{Periodic rate} = \frac{13\%}{12} = 1.08\%$$

$$\text{Finance Charge} = 694.76 \times .0108 = \underline{\underline{\$7.50}}$$

c. What is Richard's new balance?

$$\text{New balance} = 686.97 + 7.50 + 720.27 - 550.00 = \underline{\underline{\$864.74}}$$

6. Omega Construction, Inc., has a $100,000 line of credit with the Valley National Bank. The annual percentage rate is the current prime rate plus $3\frac{1}{4}\%$. The balance on June 1 was $52,900. On June 8, Precision borrowed $30,600 to pay for a shipment of lumber and roofing materials and on June 18 borrowed another $12,300 for equipment repairs. On June 28, a $35,000 payment was made on the account. The billing cycle for June has 30 days. The current prime rate is $7\frac{3}{4}\%$.

a. What is the finance charge on the account?

$$\text{Average daily balance} = \frac{2{,}345{,}700}{30} = \underline{\underline{\$78{,}190}} \text{ (See Appendix B)}$$

$$\text{Periodic rate} = 7.75 + 3.25 = 11\%$$

$$11\% \div 12 = .92\%$$

$$\text{Finance charge for June} = 78{,}190 \times .0092$$

$$= \underline{\underline{\$719.35}}$$

CHAPTER

Name

Class

Answers

6. b. $61,519.35

7. a. $9,920

b. $39,120

8. a. $1,493.95

b. $54.19

9. a. $10,384

b. 19.25%

10. a. 14.47%

© PhotoLink/Photodisc/Getty Images

According to the U.S. Census Bureau, there are over 1,200 sound recording studios in the United States doing over $540 million in business. This industry comprises establishments primarily engaged in providing the facilities and technical expertise for sound recording in a studio.

b. What is Omega's new balance?

New balance = 52,900.00 + 719.35 + 42,900.00 − 35,000.00 = $61,519.35

7. Fernando Alvarez bought an ultralight airplane for a cash price of $29,200. He made a 15% down payment and financed the balance with payments of $579 per month for 60 months.

EXCEL

a. What is the amount of the finance charge on this loan?

Amount financed = 29,200 × 85% = $24,820

Total payments = 579 × 60 = $34,740

Finance charge = 34,740 − 24,820 = $9,920

b. What is the total deferred payment price of the airplane?

Total deferred price = 9,920 + 29,200 = $39,120

8. Luke Knight bought a saddle with a 9.3% add-on interest installment loan from Bonanza Western Gear. The purchase price of the saddle was $1,290. The loan required a 15% down payment and equal monthly payments for 24 months.

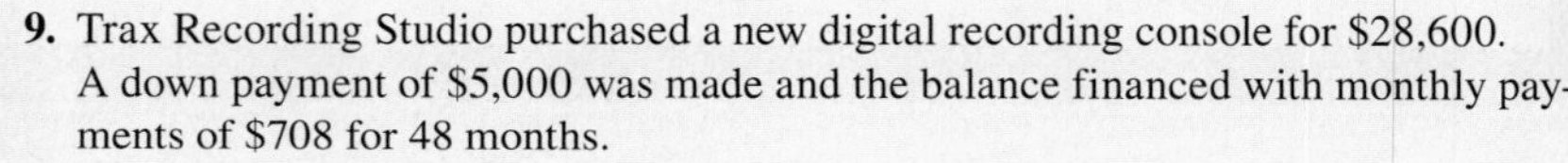

a. What is the total deferred payment price of the saddle?

Amount financed = 1,290 × 85% = $1,096.50

Interest = 1,096.50 × .093 × 2 = $203.95

Total deferred price = 1,290.00 + 203.95 = $1,493.95

b. How much are Luke's monthly payments?

Total payments = 1,096.50 + 203.95 = $1,300.45

$$\text{Monthly payment} = \frac{1{,}300.45}{24} = \$54.19$$

9. Trax Recording Studio purchased a new digital recording console for $28,600. A down payment of $5,000 was made and the balance financed with monthly payments of $708 for 48 months.

a. What is the amount of the finance charge on the loan?

Amount financed = 28,600 − 5,000 = $23,600

Total payments = 708 × 48 = $33,984

Finance charge = 33,984 − 23,600 = $10,384

b. Use Table 13-1 to find what annual percentage rate was charged on the equipment loan.

$$\text{Factor} = \frac{10{,}384 \times 100}{23{,}600} = 44$$

APR = 19.25%

10. Dan Reynolds purchased a $7,590 motorcycle with a 36-month installment loan. The monthly payments are $261.44 per month.

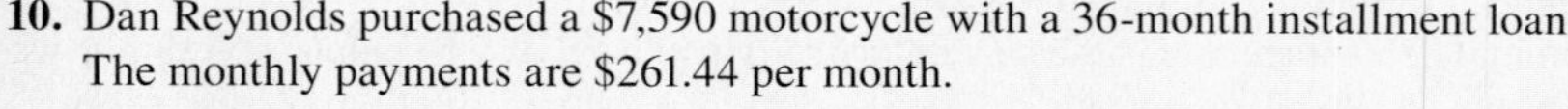

a. Use the APR formula to calculate the annual percentage rate of the loan. Round to the nearest hundredth of a percent.

Total payments = 36 × 261.44 = $9,411.84

Interest = 9,411.84 − 7,590.00 = 1,821.84

$$\text{APR} = \frac{72 \times 1{,}821.84}{(3 \times 7{,}590 \times 37) + (1{,}821.84 \times 35)}$$

$$= \frac{131{,}172.48}{906{,}254.40} = 0.1447413$$

APR = 14.47%

Name

Class

Answers

10. b. 14.5%

11. a. \$66,300

b. \$4,646.67

12. a. 325/666

b. \$634.38

13. a. \$14,144

b. \$1,428

c. 11.75%

b. Use the APR tables to verify your answer from part a.

$$\text{Finance charge per } \$100 = \frac{1{,}821.84 \times 100}{7{,}590} = 24$$

APR = 14.5%

11. SkyHigh Aircraft Sales uses the Midway Bank to finance customer aircraft purchases. This month, Midway is offering 60-month installment loans with an APR of 11.25%. A 15% down payment is required. The president of Radiance Industries wants to finance the purchase of a company airplane for \$250,000.

a. Use the APR tables to calculate the amount of the finance charge.

Table factor = 31.20

Amount financed = 250,000 × 85% = 212,500

$$\text{Finance charge} = \frac{212{,}500 \times 31.20}{100} = \$66{,}300$$

b. How much are the monthly payments on Radiance's aircraft loan?

$$\text{Monthly payment} = \frac{66{,}300 + 212{,}500}{60} = \$4{,}646.67$$

12. After making 11 payments on a 36-month loan, you pay it off.

a. What is your rebate fraction?

Total payments = 36

Payments remaining = 36 − 11 = 25

$$\frac{25 \times 26}{2} = 325 \qquad \frac{36 \times 37}{2} = 666$$

$$\text{Rebate fraction} = \frac{325}{666}$$

b. If the finance charge was \$1,300, what is the amount of your finance charge rebate?

$$\text{Rebate amount} = 1{,}300 \times \frac{325}{666} = \$634.38$$

13. A Subway franchise financed a \$68,000 sandwich oven with a $6\frac{1}{2}\%$ add-on interest installment loan for 48 months. The loan required a 20% down payment.

a. What is the amount of the finance charge on the loan?

Amount financed = 68,000 × 80% = \$54,400

Finance charge = 54,400 × .065 × 4 = \$14,144

b. How much are the monthly payments?

$$\text{Monthly payments} = \frac{54{,}400 + 14{,}144}{48} = \$1{,}428$$

c. What annual percentage rate is being charged on the loan?

$$\text{Finance charge per } \$100 = \frac{14{,}144 \times 100}{54{,}400} = 26$$

APR = 11.75%

Subway

In 1965, 17-year-old Fred DeLuca and family friend Peter Buck opened Pete's Super Submarines in Bridgeport, Connecticut. With a loan from Buck for only \$1,000, DeLuca hoped the tiny sandwich shop would earn enough to put him through college.

After struggling throughout the first few years, the founders changed the company's name to Subway and began franchising in 1974. In 2006, Subway had over 26,500 franchises in 85 countries.

Name ______________________

Class ______________________

Answers

d. $32,906.45

14. a. 14.68%

b. $51,480

c. $11,581.79

15. a. $30,686.75

b. $24,686.75

c. $8,733.25

d. $39,420

e. 12.50%

d. If the company decides to pay off the loan after 22 months, what is the amount of the loan payoff?

Total months = 48

Remaining months = 48 − 22 = 26

Balance remaining = 26 × 1,428 = $37,128

Payoff amount = 37,128.00 − 4,221.55 = $32,906.45

$$\text{Rebate fraction} = \frac{351}{1{,}176}$$

$$\text{Rebate amount} = 14{,}144 \times \frac{351}{1{,}176} = \$4{,}221.55$$

14. You are a salesperson for Grove Key Marina—Boat Sales. A customer is interested in purchasing the 23-foot Sea Ray shown in the accompanying ad and has asked you the following questions.

23' SEA RAY
Sale Price $29,000
NOW $379 per month
$6,000 Down - 120 Months

© Robert Brechner/South-Western Cengage Learning

a. What is the APR of the loan? Use the formula to find the APR of the loan.

APR = 14.68% (See Appendix B)

b. What is the total deferred payment price of the boat?

Total deferred payment = 29,000 + 22,480 = $51,480

c. If the loan is paid off after 7 years, what would be the payoff?

Total months = 120

Remaining months = 120 − 84 = 36

$$\text{Rebate fraction} = \frac{666}{7{,}260}$$

$$\text{Rebate amount} = 22{,}480 \times \frac{666}{7{,}260} = \$2{,}062.21$$

Balance remaining = 36 × 379 = $13,644

Payoff amount = 13,644.00 − 2,062.21 = $11,581.79

Saturn Sky

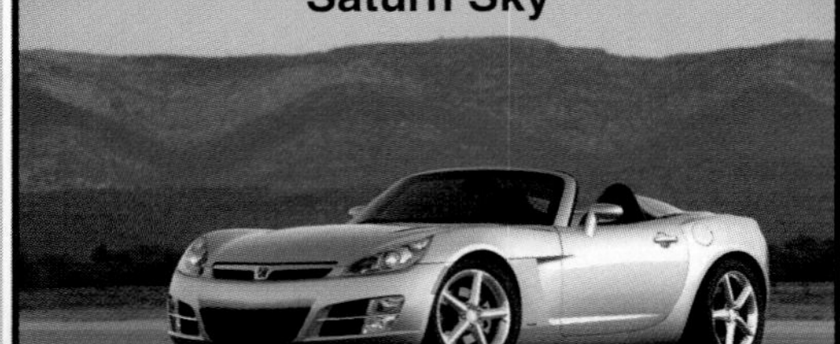

$6,000 DOWN - PLUS TAX, TAG, TITLE
60-MONTHS WITH APPROVED CREDIT

INCLUDES: AUTO TRANS., AIR COND., 4DOOR, AM/FM WITH CD & CASSETTE, POWER WINDOWS AND LOCKS, POWER STEERING

$557 PER MO.

© General Motors/Associated Press

15. Ivan Morales found the accompanying ad for a Saturn Sky in his local newspaper. If the sales tax in his state is 7% and the tag and title fees are $165, calculate the following information for Ivan.

a. The total cost of the car including tax, tag, and title.

Total cost = 28,525.00 + 1,996.75 + 165.00 = $30,686.75

b. The amount financed.

Amount financed = 30,686.75 − 6,000.00 = $24,686.75

c. The amount of the finance charge.

Total payment = 557 × 60 = 33,420

Finance charge = 33,420.00 − 24,686.75 = $8,733.25

d. The total deferred price of the car.

Total deferred price = 33,420 + 6,000 = $39,420

e. The annual percentage rate of the loan. Round to the nearest hundredth.

$$\text{Finance charge per \$100} = \frac{8{,}733.25 \times 100}{24{,}686.75} = 35.38$$

APR = 12.75%

BUSINESS DECISION PURCHASE VS. LEASE

CHAPTER 13

16. You are interested in getting a Honda Element. You have decided to look into leasing, to see how it compares with buying. In recent years, you have noticed that advertised lease payments are considerably lower than those advertised for financing a purchase. It always seemed as if you would be getting "more car for the money!"

In your research, you have found that a closed-end vehicle lease is an agreement in which you make equal monthly payments based on your estimated usage for a set period of time. Then you turn the vehicle back in to the leasing dealer. No equity, no ownership, no asset at the end! You also have the option of purchasing the vehicle at an agreed-on price.

Leasing terminology is different from purchasing, but they are related. The *capitalized cost* is the purchase price; the *capitalized cost reduction* is the down payment; the *money factor* is the interest rate; the *residual value* is the expected market price of the vehicle at the end of the lease.

Use the advertisement below and the purchase vs. lease worksheet on page 488 to compare the total cost of each option. The residual value of the car is estimated to be $13,650. The lease has no termination fees or charges. If you decide to purchase, your bank requires a down payment of $3,800 and will finance the balance with a 10.25% APR loan for 36 months. The sales tax in your state is 6.5%, and the tag and title charges are $75. The *opportunity cost* is the interest your down payment could have earned if you didn't purchase the vehicle. Currently, your money earns 4.5% in a savings account.

a. What is the total purchase price of the vehicle, including tax, tag, and title?
$21,369.68 (See Appendix B)

b. How much are the monthly payments on the loan?
$568.96 (See Appendix B)

c. What is the total cost of purchasing?
$11,145.56

d. What is the total cost of leasing?
$11,801.50

e. In your own words, explain which of these financing choices is a better deal and why.
Answers will vary.

Name

Class

Answers

16. a. $21,369.68

b. $568.96

c. $11,145.56

d. $11,801.50

e. Answers will vary

Honda Element

$19,995

$249

LEASE PER MO.

36 mos.
No security deposit.
$2,500 at signing.
Plus tax, tag & title with approved credit.

“Ownership gives one a real sense of accomplishment. Or skip the whole accomplishment thingy and just lease.”

f. (Optional) Choose an ad from your local newspaper for a lease offer on a vehicle you would like to have. Gather the necessary information needed to complete a purchase vs. lease worksheet. Use local dealers and banks to find the information you need, or do some research on the Internet. Report your findings and conclusions to the class.

Purchase vs. Lease Worksheet

Cost of Purchasing

1.	Total purchase price, including tax, tag, and title	$21,369.68
2.	Down payment	3,800.00
3.	Total of loan payments (monthly payment $568.96 × 36 months)	20,482.56
4.	Opportunity cost on down payment (4.5 % × 3 years × line 2)	513.00
5.	Less: Expected market value of vehicle at the end of the loan	13,650.00
6.	**Total cost of purchasing (lines 2 + 3 + 4 − 5)**	$11,145.56

Cost of Leasing

1.	Capitalized cost, including tax, tag, and title.	$21,369.68
2.	Down payment (capitalized cost reduction $2,500 + security deposit 0)	2,500.00
3.	Total of lease payments (monthly payments $249 × 36 months)	8,964.00
4.	Opportunity cost on down payment (4.5 % × 3 years × line 2)	337.50
5.	End-of-lease termination fees and charges (excess mileage or damage)	0
6.	Less: Refund of security deposit	0
7.	**Total cost of leasing (lines 2 + 3 + 4 + 5 − 6)**	$11,801.50

COLLABORATIVE LEARNING ACTIVITY

Plastic Choices

1. Have each member of the team contact a local bank, credit union, or retail store in your area that offers a credit card. Get a brochure and/or a copy of the credit agreement.
   a. For each card, determine the following:
      - Annual interest rate
      - Method used for computing interest
      - Credit limit
      - Annual fee
      - “Fine-print” features
   b. Based on your research, which cards are the best and worst deals?
2. Log on to CardTrack.com, www.cardtrak.com, or BankRate.com, www.bankrate.com.
   a. Research and list the best credit card deals being offered around the country.
   b. Compare your local banks’ offers with those found on the Internet.
3. Research the Internet for the rules, regulations, and recent changes to:
   a. The Fair Credit and Charge Card Disclosure Act.
   b. Regulation Z of the Consumer Credit Production Act (Truth in Lending Act).
   c. Laws in your state relating to credit cards.

CHAPTER 14

Mortgages

PERFORMANCE OBJECTIVES

SECTION I MORTGAGES—FIXED-RATE AND ADJUSTABLE-RATE

real estate Land, including any permanent improvements such as homes, apartment buildings, factories, hotels, shopping centers, or any other "real" structures.

mortgage A loan in which real property is used as security for a debt.

Federal Housing Administration (FHA) A government agency within the U.S. Department of Housing and Urban Development (HUD) that sets construction standards and insures residential mortgage loans made by approved lenders.

VA mortgage, or GI Loan Long-term, low-down-payment home loans made by private lenders to eligible veterans, the payment of which is guaranteed by the Veterans Administration in the event of a default.

conventional loans Real estate loans made by private lenders that are not FHA-insured or VA-guaranteed.

private mortgage insurance (PMI) A special form of insurance primarily on mortgages for single-family homes, allowing the buyer to borrow more, by putting down a smaller down payment.

Real estate is defined as land, including the air above and the earth below, plus any permanent improvements to the land, such as homes, apartment buildings, factories, hotels, shopping centers, or any other "real" property. Whether for commercial or residential property, practically all real estate transactions today involve some type of financing. The mortgage loan is the most popular method of financing real estate purchases.

A **mortgage** is any loan in which real property is used as security for a debt. During the term of the loan, the property becomes security or collateral for the lender, sufficient to ensure recovery of the amount loaned.

Mortgages today fall into one of three categories: FHA-insured, VA-guaranteed, and conventional. The National Housing Act of 1934 created the **Federal Housing Administration (FHA)** to encourage reluctant lenders to invest their money in the mortgage market, thereby stimulating the depressed construction industry. Today, the FHA is a government agency within the Department of Housing and Urban Development (HUD). The FHA insures private mortgage loans made by approved lenders.

In 1944, the Servicemen's Readjustment Act (GI Bill of Rights) was passed to help returning World War II veterans purchase homes. Special mortgages were established known as **Veterans Affairs (VA) mortgages** or **GI Loans**. Under this and subsequent legislation, the government guarantees payment of a mortgage loan made by a private lender to a veteran/buyer should the veteran default on the loan.

VA loans may be used by eligible veterans, surviving spouses, and active service members to buy, construct, or refinance homes, farm residences, or condominiums. Down payments by veterans are not required but are left to the discretion of lenders, whereas FHA and conventional loans require a down payment from all buyers.

Conventional loans are made by private lenders and generally have a higher interest rate than either FHA or VA loans. Most conventional lenders are restricted to loaning 80% of the appraised value of a property, thus requiring a 20% down payment. If the borrower agrees to pay the premium for **private mortgage insurance (PMI)**, the conventional lender can lend up to 95% of the appraised value of the property.

Historically, high interest rates in the early 1980s caused mortgage payments to skyrocket beyond the financial reach of the average home buyer. To revitalize the slumping

Mortgage loans are the most common form of loan made for real estate property purchases.

mortgage industry, the **adjustable-rate mortgage (ARM)** was created. These are mortgage loans under which the interest rate is periodically adjusted to more closely coincide with changing economic conditions. ARMs are very attractive, particularly to first-time buyers, because a low teaser rate may be offered for the first few years and then adjusted upward to a higher rate later in the loan. Today, the adjustable-rate mortgage has become the most widely accepted option to the traditional 15- and 30-year fixed-rate mortgages.

Extra charges known as **mortgage discount points** are frequently added to the cost of a loan as a rate adjustment factor. This allows lenders to increase their yield without showing an increase in the mortgage interest rate. Each discount point is equal to 1% of the amount of the loan.

By their nature, mortgage loans involve large amounts of money, and long periods of time. Consequently, the monthly payments and the amount of interest paid over the years can be considerable. Exhibit 14-1 illustrates the 30-year mortgage rates in the United States from 1974 to 2007, and the monthly payment on a $100,000 mortgage, at various interest rate levels.

In reality, the higher interest mortgages would have been refinanced as rates declined, but consider the "housing affordability" factor. In 1982, payments on a $100,000 mortgage were $1,548 per month, compared with $550 in 2004!

In this section, you learn to calculate the monthly payments of a mortgage and prepare a partial amortization schedule of that loan. You also calculate the amount of property tax and insurance required as part of each monthly payment. In addition, you learn about the **closing**, the all-important final step in a real estate transaction, and the calculation of the closing costs. Finally, you learn about the important components of an adjustable-rate mortgage: the index, the lender's margin, the interest rate, and the cost caps.

adjustable-rate mortgage (ARM) A mortgage loan in which the interest rate changes periodically, usually in relation to a predetermined economic index.

mortgage discount points Extra charge frequently added to the cost of a mortgage, allowing lenders to increase their yield without showing an increase in the mortgage interest rate.

In the Business World

As a result of declining mortgage rates in recent years, a record 68.8% of families own their own homes today. That amounts to nearly 76 million households.

Purchasing and financing a home is one of the most important financial decisions a person will ever make. Substantial research should be done and much care taken in choosing the correct time to buy, the right property to buy, and the best financial offer to accept. (See Exhibit 14-2, "Mortgage Shopping Worksheet," pages 497–498)

CALCULATING THE MONTHLY PAYMENT AND TOTAL INTEREST PAID ON A FIXED-RATE MORTGAGE

In Chapter 12, we learned that amortization is the process of paying off a financial obligation in a series of equal regular payments over a period of time. We calculated the amount of an amortization payment by using the present value of an annuity table or the optional amortization formula.

Because mortgages run for relatively long periods of time, we can also use a special present-value table in which the periods are listed in years. The table factors represent the monthly payment required per $1,000 of debt to amortize a mortgage. The monthly payment includes mortgage interest and an amount to reduce the principal. See Table 14-1.

closing A meeting at which the buyer and seller of real estate conclude all matters pertaining to the transaction. At the closing, the funds are transferred to the seller, and the ownership or title is transferred to the buyer.

Exhibit 14-1
Historical Mortgage Rates and Monthly Payments

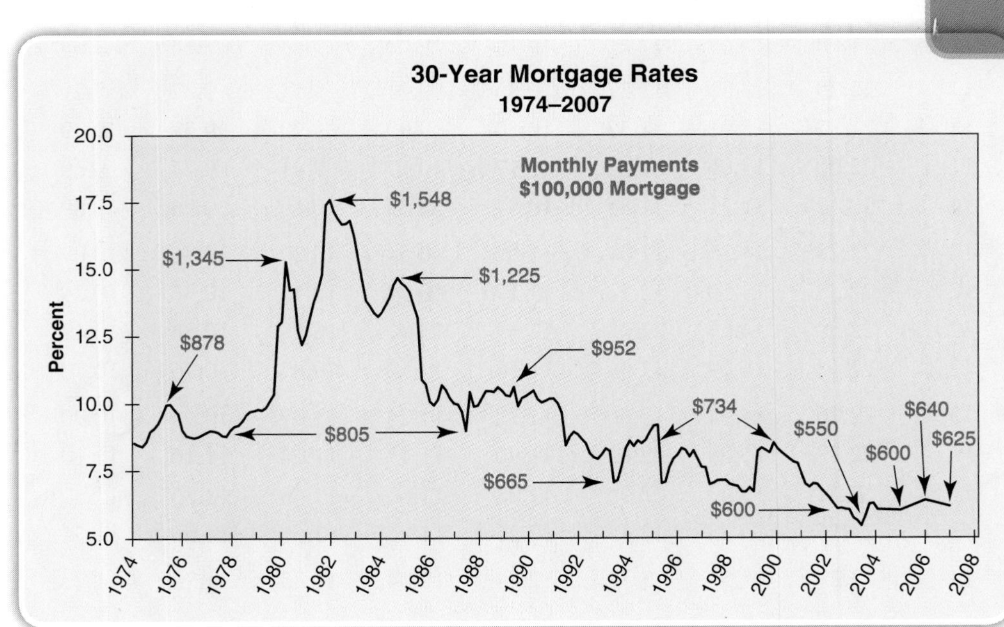

Table 14-1
Monthly Payments to Amortize Principal and Interest per $1,000 Financed

Teaching Transparency 14-1

Learning Tip

Remember that the table values represent monthly payment "per $1,000" financed. When calculating the amount of the monthly payment, you must first determine the number of $1,000s being financed, then multiply that figure by the table factor.

Monthly Payments
(Necessary to amortize a loan of $1,000)

Interest Rate	5 Years	10 Years	15 Years	20 Years	25 Years	30 Years	35 Years	40 Years
5%	18.88	10.61	7.91	6.60	5.85	5.37	5.05	4.83
5¼	18.99	10.73	8.04	6.74	6.00	5.53	5.21	4.99
5½	19.11	10.86	8.18	6.88	6.15	5.68	5.38	5.16
5¾	19.22	10.98	8.31	7.03	6.30	5.84	5.54	5.33
6	19.34	11.11	8.44	7.17	6.45	6.00	5.71	5.51
6¼	19.45	11.23	8.58	7.31	6.60	6.16	5.88	5.68
6½	19.57	11.36	8.72	7.46	6.76	6.33	6.05	5.86
6¾	19.69	11.49	8.85	7.61	6.91	6.49	6.22	6.04
7	19.81	11.62	8.99	7.76	7.07	6.66	6.39	6.22
7¼	19.92	11.75	9.13	7.91	7.23	6.83	6.57	6.40
7½	20.04	11.88	9.28	8.06	7.39	7.00	6.75	6.59
7¾	20.16	12.01	9.42	8.21	7.56	7.17	6.93	6.77
8	20.28	12.14	9.56	8.37	7.72	7.34	7.11	6.96
8¼	20.40	12.27	9.71	8.53	7.89	7.52	7.29	7.15
8½	20.52	12.40	9.85	8.68	8.06	7.69	7.47	7.34
8¾	20.64	12.54	10.00	8.84	8.23	7.87	7.66	7.53
9	20.76	12.67	10.15	9.00	8.40	8.05	7.84	7.72
9¼	20.88	12.81	10.30	9.16	8.57	8.23	8.03	7.91
9½	21.01	12.94	10.45	9.33	8.74	8.41	8.22	8.11
9¾	21.13	13.08	10.60	9.49	8.92	8.60	8.41	8.30
10	21.25	13.22	10.75	9.66	9.09	8.78	8.60	8.50
10¼	21.38	13.36	10.90	9.82	9.27	8.97	8.79	8.69
10½	21.50	13.50	11.06	9.99	9.45	9.15	8.99	8.89
10¾	21.62	13.64	11.21	10.16	9.63	9.34	9.18	9.09
11	21.75	13.78	11.37	10.33	9.81	9.53	9.37	9.29
11¼	21.87	13.92	11.53	10.50	9.99	9.72	9.57	9.49
11½	22.00	14.06	11.69	10.67	10.17	9.91	9.77	9.69
11¾	22.12	14.21	11.85	10.84	10.35	10.10	9.96	9.89
12	22.25	14.35	12.01	11.02	10.54	10.29	10.16	10.09
12¼	22.38	14.50	12.17	11.19	10.72	10.48	10.36	10.29
12½	22.50	14.64	12.33	11.37	10.91	10.68	10.56	10.49
12¾	22.63	14.79	12.49	11.54	11.10	10.87	10.76	10.70
13	22.76	14.94	12.66	11.72	11.28	11.07	10.96	10.90
13¼	22.89	15.08	12.82	11.90	11.47	11.26	11.16	11.10
13½	23.01	15.23	12.99	12.08	11.66	11.46	11.36	11.31
13¾	23.14	15.38	13.15	12.26	11.85	11.66	11.56	11.51
14	23.27	15.53	13.32	12.44	12.04	11.85	11.76	11.72

STEPS TO FIND THE MONTHLY MORTGAGE PAYMENT BY USING AN AMORTIZATION TABLE, AND TOTAL INTEREST

Step 1. Find the number of $1,000s financed.

$$\textbf{Number of \$1,000s financed} = \frac{\textbf{Amount financed}}{\textbf{1,000}}$$

Step 2. Using Table 14-1, locate the table factor, monthly payment per $1,000 financed, at the intersection of the number of years column and the interest rate row.

Step 3. Calculate the monthly payment.

Monthly payment = Number of $1,000s financed × Table factor

Step 4. Find the total interest of the loan.

Total interest = (Monthly payment × Number of payments) − Amount financed

CLASSROOM ACTIVITY
Invite a mortgage loan officer from a bank or mortgage broker to speak to the class about current happenings in real estate financing.

EXAMPLE 1 CALCULATING MONTHLY PAYMENT AND TOTAL INTEREST

What is the monthly payment and total interest on a $50,000 mortgage at 8% for 30 years?

SOLUTION STRATEGY

Step 1. $\text{Number of \$1,000s financed} = \dfrac{\text{Amount financed}}{1,000} = \dfrac{50,000}{1,000} = 50$

Step 2. Table factor for 8%, 30 years is 7.34.

Step 3. Monthly payment = Number of $1,000s financed × Table factor
Monthly payment = 50 × 7.34
Monthly payment = $\underline{\underline{\$367}}$

Step 4. Total interest = (Monthly payment × Number of payments) − Amount financed
Total interest = (367 × 360) − 50,000
Total interest = 132,120 − 50,000
Total interest = $\underline{\underline{\$82,120}}$

TRY IT EXERCISE 1

What is the monthly payment and total interest on an $85,500 mortgage at 7% for 25 years?

CHECK YOUR ANSWERS WITH THE SOLUTIONS ON PAGE 514.

CLASSROOM ACTIVITY
Once students have learned to calculate the total interest on a mortgage, they are usually amazed at how much it costs over a period of 25 or 30 years.

In groups, have students write, solve, and exchange with other groups:

- exercises that compare the interest paid on a 15- and a 30-year mortgage, for a given interest rate.
- exercises that compare the interest paid on a 30-year mortgage at various interest rates.

14-2

14-2 PREPARING A PARTIAL AMORTIZATION SCHEDULE OF A MORTGAGE

level-payment plan Mortgages with regular, equal payments over a specified period of time.

amortization schedule A chart that shows the month-by-month breakdown of each mortage payment into interest and principal and the outstanding balance of the loan.

Mortgages used to purchase residential property generally require regular, equal payments. A portion of the payment is used to pay interest on the loan; the balance of the payment is used to reduce the principal. This type of mortgage is called a **level-payment plan** because the amount of the payment remains the same for the duration of the loan. The amount of the payment that is interest gradually decreases while the amount that reduces the debt gradually increases.

An **amortization schedule** is a chart that shows the status of the mortgage loan after each payment. The schedule illustrates month by month how much of the mortgage payment is interest and how much is left to reduce to principal. The schedule also shows the outstanding balance of the loan after each payment.

In reality, amortization schedules are long, because they show the loan status for each month. A 30-year mortgage, for example, would require a schedule with 360 lines (12 months × 30 years = 360 payments).

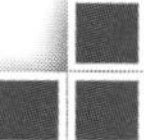

STEPS TO CREATE AN AMORTIZATION SCHEDULE FOR A LOAN

Step 1. Use Table 14-1 to calculate the amount of the monthly payment.

Step 2. Calculate the amount of interest for the current month using $I = PRT$, where P is the current outstanding balance of the loan, R is the annual interest rate, and T is $\frac{1}{12}$.

Step 3. Find the portion of the payment used to reduce principal.

Portion of payment reducing principal = Monthly payment − Interest

Step 4. Calculate the outstanding balance of the mortgage loan.

Outstanding balance = Previous balance − Portion of pmt. reducing principal

Step 5. Repeat Steps 2, 3, and 4 for each succeeding month and enter the values on a schedule with columns labeled as follows.

Payment Number	Monthly Payment	Monthly Interest	Portion Used to Reduce Principal	Loan Balance

In the Business World

In most cases, mortgage interest expense is tax deductible. To increase your deductions for the current year, make your January mortgage payment by December 20. This will allow time for the payment to be credited to your account in December, giving you an extra month of interest deduction this year.

CLASSROOM ACTIVITY

Have students bring to class newspaper ads for houses that tell the price, down payment, and mortgage terms.

In groups, have them calculate

- the total interest that will be paid on the loan.
- an amortization schedule of the first two or three payments.

EXAMPLE 2 PREPARING A PARTIAL AMORTIZATION SCHEDULE

Prepare an amortization schedule for the first 3 months of the $50,000 mortgage at 8% for 30 years from Example 1. Remember, you have already calculated the monthly payment to be $367.

SOLUTION STRATEGY

Step 1. $367 (from Example 1, page 493)

Step 2. **Month 1:**

Interest = Principal × Rate × Time

Interest = $50{,}000 \times .08 \times \frac{1}{12}$

Interest = $333.33

Step 3. Portion of payment reducing principal = Monthly payment − Interest

Portion of payment reducing principal = \$367.00 − \$333.33

Portion of payment reducing principal = \$33.67

Step 4. Outstanding balance = Previous balance − Portion of payment reducing principal

Outstanding balance = 50,000.00 − 33.67

Outstanding balance after one payment = \$49,966.33

Step 5. Repeat Steps 2, 3, and 4, for two more payments and enter the values on the schedule.

Month 2:

Interest = $49{,}966.83 \times .08 \times \frac{1}{12}$ = \$333.11

(*Note:* Although very slightly, interest decreased.)

Portion reducing principal = 367.00 − 333.11 = \$33.89

Outstanding balance after 2 payments = 49,966.33 − 33.89 = \$49,932.44

Month 3:

Interest = $49{,}932.44 \times .08 \times \frac{1}{12}$ = \$332.88

Portion reducing principal = 367.00 − 332.88 = \$34.12

Outstanding balance after three payments = 49,932.44 − 34.12 = \$49,898.32

Amortization Schedule
\$50,000 Loan, 8%, 30 years

Payment Number	Monthly Payment	Monthly Interest	Portion Used to Reduce Principal	Loan Balance
0				\$50,000.00
1	\$367	\$333.33	\$33.67	\$49,966.33
2	\$367	\$333.11	\$33.89	\$49,932.44
3	\$367	\$332.88	\$34.12	\$49,898.32

TRY IT EXERCISE 2

Prepare an amortization schedule of the first four payments of a \$75,000 mortgage at 9% for 15 years. Use Table 14-1 to calculate the amount of the monthly payment.

CHECK YOUR ANSWERS WITH THE SOLUTIONS ON PAGE 515.

14-3

CALCULATING THE MONTHLY PITI OF A MORTGAGE LOAN

In reality, mortgage payments include four parts: principal, interest, taxes, and insurance—thus the abbreviation **PITI**. VA, FHA, and most conventional loans require borrowers to pay $\frac{1}{12}$ of the estimated annual property taxes and hazard insurance with each month's mortgage payment. Each month, the taxes and insurance portions of the payment are placed in a type of savings account for safekeeping known as an **escrow account**. Each year when the property taxes and hazard insurance premiums are due, the lender disburses those payments from the borrower's escrow account. During the next 12 months, the account again builds up to pay for the next year's taxes and insurance.

PITI An abbreviation for the total amount of a mortgage payment; includes principal, interest, property taxes, and hazard insurance.

escrow account Bank account used by mortgage lenders for the safekeeping of the funds accumulating to pay next year's property taxes and hazard insurance.

STEPS TO CALCULATE THE PITI OF A MORTGAGE

Step 1. Calculate the principal and interest portion, PI, of the payment as before using the amortization table, Table 14-1.

Step 2. Calculate the monthly tax and insurance portion, TI.

$$\textbf{Monthly TI} = \frac{\textbf{Estimated property tax + Hazard insurance}}{\textbf{12}}$$

Step 3. Calculate the total monthly PITI.

$$\textbf{Monthly PITI = Monthly PI + Monthly TI}$$

EXAMPLE 3 CALCULATING THE MONTHLY PITI OF A MORTGAGE

In the Business World

Typically, over the years of a mortgage, property taxes and insurance premiums rise. When this happens, the lender must increase the portion set aside in the escrow account by increasing the taxes and insurance parts of the monthly payment.

Tricia Groff purchased a home with a mortgage of \$87,500 at $7\frac{1}{2}$% for 30 years. The property taxes are \$2,350 per year, and the hazard insurance premium is \$567.48. What is the monthly PITI payment of Tricia's loan?

SOLUTION STRATEGY

Step 1. From the amortization table, Table 14-1, the factor for $7\frac{1}{2}$%, 30 years is 7.00. When we divide the amount of Tricia's loan by 1,000 we get 87.5 as the number of 1,000s financed. The principal and interest portion, PI, is therefore 87.5 × 7.00 = \$612.50.

Step 2. $\text{Monthly TI} = \dfrac{\text{Estimated property tax + Hazard insurance}}{12}$

$\text{Monthly TI} = \dfrac{2{,}350.00 + 567.48}{12} = \dfrac{2{,}917.48}{12} = \$243.12$

Step 3. Monthly PITI = PI + TI

Monthly PITI = 612.50 + 243.12

Monthly PITI = \$855.62

TRY IT EXERCISE 3

David Gibson purchased a home with a mortgage of \$125,600 at $9\frac{1}{4}$% for 20 years. The property taxes are \$3,250 per year, and the hazard insurance premium is \$765. What is the monthly PITI payment of David's loan?

CHECK YOUR ANSWER WITH THE SOLUTION ON PAGE 515.

14-4 UNDERSTANDING CLOSING COSTS AND CALCULATING THE AMOUNT DUE AT CLOSING

title, or deed The official document representing the right of ownership of real property.

The term closing, or settlement, is used to describe the final step in a real estate transaction. This is a meeting at which time documents are signed, the buyer pays the agreed upon purchase price, and the seller delivers the **title**, or right of ownership, to the buyer. The official document conveying ownership is known as the **deed**.

Closing costs are the expenses incurred in conjunction with the sale of real estate. In the typical real estate transaction, both the buyer and the seller are responsible for a number of costs that are paid for at the time of closing. The party obligated for paying a particular closing cost is often determined by local custom or by negotiation. Some closing costs are expressed as dollar amounts, whereas others are a percent of the amount financed or the amount of the purchase price.

closing costs Expenses incurred in conjunction with the sale of real estate, including loan origination fees, credit reports, appraisal fees, title search, title insurance, inspections, attorney's fees, recording fees, and broker's commission.

At closing, the buyer is responsible for the purchase price (mortgage + down payment) plus closing costs. The amount received by the seller, after all expenses have been paid, is known as the proceeds. The **settlement statement** or **closing statement** is a document, usually prepared by an attorney, that provides a detailed breakdown of the real estate transaction. This document itemizes closing costs and indicates how they are allocated between the buyer and the seller.

settlement or closing statement A document that provides a detailed accounting of payments, credits, and closing costs of a real estate transaction.

Exhibit 14-2, "Mortgage Shopping Worksheet," can be used to compare mortgage offers from various lenders. It provides a comprehensive checklist of important loan information, typical fees, closing and settlement costs, and other questions and considerations people should be aware of when shopping for a mortgage loan.

Exhibit 14-2
Mortgage Shopping Worksheet

Mortgage Shopping Worksheet

	Lender 1	Lender 2
Name of Lender	________	________
Name of Contact	________	________
Date of Contact	________	________
Mortgage Amount	________	________
Basic Information on the Loans		
Type of Mortgage: fixed rate, adjustable rate, conventional, FHA, other? If adjustable, see page 498	________	________
Minimum down payment required	________	________
Loan term (length of loan)	________	________
Contract interest rate	________	________
Annual percentage rate (APR)	________	________
Points (may be called loan discount points)	________	________
Monthly Private Mortage Insurance (PMI) premiums	________	________
How long must you keep PMI?	________	________
Estimated monthly escrow for taxes and hazard insurance	________	________
Estimated monthly payment (Principal, Interest, Taxes, Insurance, PMI)	________	________
Fees Different institutions may have different names for some fees and may charge different fees. We have listed some typical fees you may see on loan documents.		
Appraisal fee or Loan processing fee	________	________
Origination fee or Underwriting fee	________	________
Lender fee or Funding fee	________	________
Appraisal fee	________	________
Attorney fees	________	________
Document preparation and recording fees	________	________
Broker fees (may be quoted as points, origination fees, or interest rate add-on)	________	________
Credit report fee	________	________
Other fees	________	________

continued

Exhibit 14-2
Mortgage Shopping Worksheet
(continued)

Mortgage Shopping Worksheet

	Lender 1	Lender 2
Name of Lender		
Other Costs at Closing/Settlement		
Title search/Title Insurance		
For lender		
For you		
Estimated prepaid amounts for interest, taxes, hazard insurance, payments to escrow		
State and local taxes, stamp taxes, transfer taxes		
Flood determination		
Prepaid Private Mortgage Insurance (PMI)		
Surveys and home inspections		
Total Fees and Other Closing/Settlement Cost Estimates		
Other Questions and Considerations about the Loan		
Are any of the fees or costs waivable?		
Prepayment penalties		
Is there a prepayment penalty?		
If so, how much is it?		
How long does the penalty period last? (for example, 3 years? 5 years?)		
Are extra principal payments allowed?		
Lock-ins		
Is the lock-in agreement in writing?		
Is there a fee to lock-in?		
When does the lock-in occur—at application, approval, or another time?		
How long will the lock-in last?		
If the rate drops before closing, can you lock-in at a lower rate?		
If the loan is an adjustable rate mortgage:		
What is the initial rate?		
What is the maximum the rate could be next year?		
What are the rate and payment caps each year and over the life of the loan?		
What is the frequency of rate change and of any changes to the monthly payment?		
What is the index that the lender will use?		
What margin will the lender add to the index?		
Credit life insurance		
Does the monthly amount quoted to you include a charge for credit life insurance?		
If so, does the lender require credit life insurance as a condition of the loan?		
How much does the credit life insurance cost?		
How much lower would your monthly payment be without the credit life insurance?		
If the lender does not require credit life insurance, and you still want to buy it, what rates can you get from other insurance providers?		

EXAMPLE 4 CALCULATING MORTGAGE CLOSING COSTS

Barry and Donna Rae Schwartz are purchasing a $180,000 home. The down payment is 25%, and the balance will be financed with a 25-year fixed-rate mortgage at 10% and 2 discount points (each point is 1% of the amount financed). When Barry and Donna Rae signed the sales contract, they put down a deposit of $15,000, which will be credited to their down payment at the time of the closing. In addition, they must pay the following expenses: credit report, $80; appraisal fee, $150; title insurance premium, $\frac{1}{2}$% of amount financed; title search, $200; and attorney's fees, $450.

a. Calculate the amount due from Barry and Donna Rae at the closing.

b. If the sellers are responsible for the broker's commission, which is 6% of the purchase price, $900 in other closing costs, and the existing mortgage, with a balance of $50,000, what proceeds will they receive on the sale of the property?

SOLUTION STRATEGY

a. Down payment = 180,000 × 25% = $45,000

Amount financed = 180,000 − 45,000 = $135,000

Closing Costs, Buyer

Discount points (135,000 × 2%)	$ 2,700
Down payment (45,000 − 15,000 deposit)	30,000
Credit report	80
Appraisal fee	150
Title insurance (135,000 × $\frac{1}{2}$%)	675
Title search	200
Attorney's fees	450
Due at closing	$34,255

TEACHING TIP

Sometimes, students forget how to convert fractional percents to decimals. Remind them that the title insurance, $\frac{1}{2}$%, converts to .005 as a decimal.

b.

Proceeds, Seller

Sale price		$180,000
Less: Broker's commission:		
180,000 × 6%	$10,800	
Closing costs	900	
Mortgage payoff	50,000	
		− 61,700
Proceeds to seller		$ 118,300

TRY IT EXERCISE 4

Justin Schaefer is purchasing a townhouse for $120,000. The down payment is 20%, and the balance will be financed with a 15-year fixed-rate mortgage at 9% and 3 discount points (each point is 1% of the amount financed). When Justin signed the sales contract, he put down a deposit of $10,000, which will be credited to his down payment at the time of the closing. In addition, he must pay the following expenses: loan application fee, $100; condominium transfer fee, $190; title insurance premium, $\frac{3}{4}$% of amount financed; hazard insurance premium, $420; prepaid taxes, $310; and attorney's fees, $500.

a. Calculate the amount due from Justin at the closing.

b. If the seller is responsible for the broker's commission, which is $5\frac{1}{2}\%$ of the purchase price, $670 in other closing costs, and the existing mortgage balance of $65,000, what proceeds will the seller receive on the sale of the property?

CHECK YOUR ANSWERS WITH THE SOLUTIONS ON PAGE 516.

CALCULATING THE INTEREST RATE OF AN ADJUSTABLE-RATE MORTGAGE (ARM)

With a fixed-rate mortgage, the interest rate stays the same during the life of the loan. With an adjustable-rate mortgage (ARM), the interest rate changes periodically, usually in relation to an index, and payments may go up or down accordingly. In recent years, the ARM has become the most widely accepted alternative to the traditional 30-year fixed-rate mortgage.

The primary components of an ARM are the index, lender's margin, calculated interest rate, initial interest rate, and cost caps. With most ARMs, the interest rate and monthly payment change either every year, every 3 years, or every 5 years. The period between one rate change and the next is known as the **adjustment period**. A loan with an adjustment period of 1 year, for example, is called a 1-year ARM.

adjustment period The amount of time between one rate change and the next on an adjustable-rate mortgage; generally 1, 2, or 3 years.

index rate The economic index to which the interest rate on an adjustable-rate mortgage is tied.

margin, or spread The percentage points added to an index rate to get the interest rate of an adjustable-rate mortgage.

Most lenders tie ARM interest rate changes to changes in an **index rate**. These indexes usually go up and down with the general movement of interest rates in the nation's economy. When the index goes up, so does the mortgage rate, resulting in higher monthly payments. When the index goes down, the mortgage rate may or may not go down.

To calculate the interest rate on an ARM, lenders add a few points called the **margin** or **spread** to the index rate. The amount of the margin can differ among lenders and can make a significant difference in the amount of interest paid over the life of a loan.

Calculated interest rate = Index rate + Lender's margin

calculated or initial interest rate The interest rate of an adjustable-rate mortgage to which all future adjustments and caps apply.

teaser rate A discounted interest rate for the first adjustment period of an adjustable-rate mortgage that is below the current market rate of interest.

interest-rate cap Limit on the amount the interest rate can increase on an ARM.

periodic cap Limit on the amount the interest rate of an ARM can increase per adjustment period.

overall cap Limit on the amount the interest rate of an ARM can increase over the life of the loan.

The **calculated** or **initial interest rate** is usually the rate to which all future adjustments and caps apply, although this rate may be discounted by the lender during the first payment period to attract and qualify more potential borrowers. This low initial interest rate, sometimes known as a **teaser rate**, is one of the main appeals of the ARM; however, without some protection from rapidly rising interest rates, borrowers might be put in a position of not being able to afford the rising mortgage payments. To prevent this situation, standards have been established requiring limits or caps on increases.

Interest-rate caps place a limit on the amount the interest rate can increase. These may come in the form of **periodic caps**, which limit the increase from one adjustment period to the next, and **overall caps**, which limit the increase over the life of the mortgage. The following formulas can be used to find the maximum interest rates of an ARM:

Maximum rate per adjustment period = Previous rate + Periodic cap

Maximum overall rate of ARM = Initial rate + Overall cap

EXAMPLE 5 CALCULATING ARM RATES

Michelle Thurber bought a home with an adjustable-rate mortgage. The margin on the loan is 2.5%, and the rate cap is 6% over the life of the loan.

a. If the current index rate is 4.9%, what is the calculated interest rate of the ARM?

b. What is the maximum overall rate of the loan?

SOLUTION STRATEGY

a. Because the loan interest rate is tied to an index, we use the formula

Calculated ARM interest rate = Index rate + Margin

Calculated ARM interest rate = 4.9% + 2.5%

Calculated ARM interest rate = 7.4%

b. Maximum overall rate = Calculated rate + Overall cap

Maximum overall rate = 7.4% + 6%

Maximum overall rate = 13.4%

TRY IT EXERCISE 5

Jennifer Turner bought a home with an adjustable-rate mortgage. The margin on the loan is 3.4%, and the rate cap is 7% over the life of the loan. The current index rate is 3.2%.

a. What is the initial interest rate of the ARM?

b. What is the maximum overall rate of the loan?

CHECK YOUR ANSWERS WITH THE SOLUTIONS ON PAGE 516.

Review Exercises

SECTION I 14

Using Table 14-1 as needed, calculate the required information for the following mortgages.

	Amount Financed	Interest Rate (%)	Term of Loan (years)	Number of $1,000s Financed	Table Factor	Monthly Payment	Total Interest
1.	$80,000	9	20	80	9.00	$720.00	$92,800.00
2.	$72,500	10	30	72.5	8.78	$636.55	$156,658.00
3.	$130,900	$8\frac{1}{2}$	25	130.9	8.06	$1,055.05	$185,615.00
4.	$154,300	$9\frac{1}{4}$	15	154.3	10.30	$1,589.29	$131,772.20
5.	$96,800	$7\frac{3}{4}$	30	96.8	7.17	$694.06	$153,061.60

The month 1, worked-out solution to Exercise 6 appears in Appendix B, following the index.

6. Michael Moyes purchased a home with a $78,500 mortgage at 9% for 15 years. Calculate the monthly payment and prepare an amortization schedule for the first 4 months of Michael's loan.

Payment Number	Monthly Payment	Monthly Interest	Portion Used to Reduce Principal	Loan Balance
0				$78,500
1	$796.78	$588.75	$208.03	$78,291.97
2	$796.78	$587.19	$209.59	$78,082.38
3	$796.78	$585.62	$211.16	$77,871.22
4	$796.78	$584.03	$212.75	$77,658.47

As one of the loan officers for Grove Gate Bank, calculate the monthly principal and interest, PI, using Table 14-1, and the monthly PITI for the following mortgages.

Complete, worked-out solutions to Exercises 7–10 appear in Appendix B, following the index.

	Amount Financed	Interest Rate (%)	Term of Loan (years)	Monthly PI	Annual Property Tax	Annual Insurance	Monthly PITI
7.	$76,400	8	20	$639.47	$1,317	$866	$821.39
8.	$128,800	10	15	$1,384.60	$2,440	$1,215	$1,689.18
9.	$174,200	$7\frac{1}{4}$	30	$1,189.79	$3,505	$1,432	$1,601.21
10.	$250,000	$9\frac{1}{2}$	25	$2,185.00	$6,553	$2,196	$2,914.08

11. Ben and Mal Scott plan to buy a home for $272,900. They will make a 10% down payment, and qualify for a 25-year, 7% mortgage loan.

a. What is the amount of their monthly payment?

Amount financed = 272,900 × 90% = $245,610

$$\text{Number of 1,000s financed} = \frac{245{,}610}{1{,}000} = 245.61$$

7%, 25 years table factor = 7.07

Monthly payment = 7.07 × 245.61 = $1,736.46

b. How much interest will they pay over the life of the loan?

1,736.46 × 300 =	$520,938	Total payments
	− 245,610	Amount financed
	$275,328	Total interest

12. Rick Nicotera purchased a condominium for $88,000. He made a 20% down payment and financed the balance with a 30-year, 9% fixed-rate mortgage.

a. What is the amount of the monthly principal and interest portion, PI, of Rick's loan?

Amount financed = 88,000 × 80% = 70,400

$$\text{Number of \$1,000s financed} = \frac{70{,}400}{1{,}000} = 70.4$$

9%, 30 years table factor = 8.05

Monthly PI = 8.05 × 70.4 = $566.72

b. Construct an amortization schedule for the first 4 months of Rick's mortgage.

Payment Number	Monthly Payment	Monthly Interest	Portion Used to Reduce Principal	Loan Balance
0				$70,400.00
1	$566.72	$528.00	$38.72	$70,361.28
2	$566.72	$527.71	$39.01	$70,322.27
3	$566.72	$527.42	$39.30	$70,282.97
4	$566.72	$527.12	$39.60	$70,243.37

c. If the annual property taxes are $1,650 and the hazard insurance premium is $780 per year, what is the total monthly PITI of Rick's loan?

Taxes $1,650
Insurance + 780
$2,430 ÷ 12 = $202.50

PI $566.72
TI + 202.50
$769.22 Monthly PITI

13. Jeff Von Rosenberg is shopping for a 15-year mortgage for $150,000. Currently, the Fortune Bank is offering an $8\frac{1}{2}$% mortgage with 4 discount points; the Northern Trust Bank is offering an $8\frac{3}{4}$% mortgage with no points. Jeff is unsure which mortgage is a better deal and has asked you to help him decide. (Remember, each discount point is equal to 1% of the amount financed.)

a. What is the total interest paid on each loan?

Fortune Bank

$8\frac{1}{2}$% for 15 years = 9.85 × 150 = 1,477.50

1,477.50 × 180 = 265,950

Total payment $265,950
Amount financed − 150,000
Interest paid over life of loan $115,950

Northern Trust Bank

$8\frac{3}{4}$% for 15 years = 10 × 150 = 1,500

1,500 × 180 = 270,000

Total payment $270,000
Amount financed − 150,000
Interest paid over life of loan $120,000

b. Taking into account the closing points, which bank is offering a better deal and by how much?

Fortune Bank

115,950 + 4% of 150,000

115,950 + 6,000

Interest + points = $121,950

Northern Trust Bank

Interest only = $120,000 $1,950 Less (Better deal)

14. Thomas Edwards is interested in a fixed-rate mortgage for $100,000. He is undecided whether to choose a 15- or 30-year mortgage. The current mortgage rate is 10% for the 15-year mortgage and 11% for the 30-year mortgage.

a. What are the monthly principal and interest payments for each loan?

100,000 10% for 15 years
10.75 × 100 = 1,075
Monthly PI = $1,075

100,000 11% for 30 years
9.53 × 100 = 953
Monthly PI = $953

b. What is the total amount of interest paid on each loan?

$15 \times 12 = 180$ $30 \times 12 = 360$

$180 \times 1{,}075 = 193{,}500$ $360 \times 953 = 343{,}080$

Total payments	$193,500	Total payments	$343,080
Amount financed	− 100,000	Amount financed	− 100,000
Total interest	$93,500	Total interest	$243,080

c. Overall, how much more interest is paid by choosing the 30-year mortgage?

$243{,}080 - 93{,}500 = 149{,}580$

30-year mortgage costs more by $149,580

15. Katie Mergen bought a home with an adjustable-rate mortgage. The margin on the loan is 3.5%, and the rate cap is 8% over the life of the loan.

a. If the current index rate is 3.75%, what is the calculated interest rate of the ARM?

Calculated interest rate of ARM
$3.75 + 3.50 = 7.25\%$

b. What is the maximum overall rate of Katie's loan?

Maximum overall rate
$7.25 + 8.00 = 15.25\%$

16. George and Blanca Gonzalez are purchasing a house in Coral Shores financed with an adjustable-rate mortgage. The margin on the loan is 2.75%, and the rate cap is 6.2% over the life of the loan. The current index rate is 5.8%.

a. What is the calculated interest rate of the ARM?

$2.75\% + 5.8\% = 8.55\%$

b. What is the maximum overall rate of the loan?

$8.55\% + 6.2\% = 14.75\%$

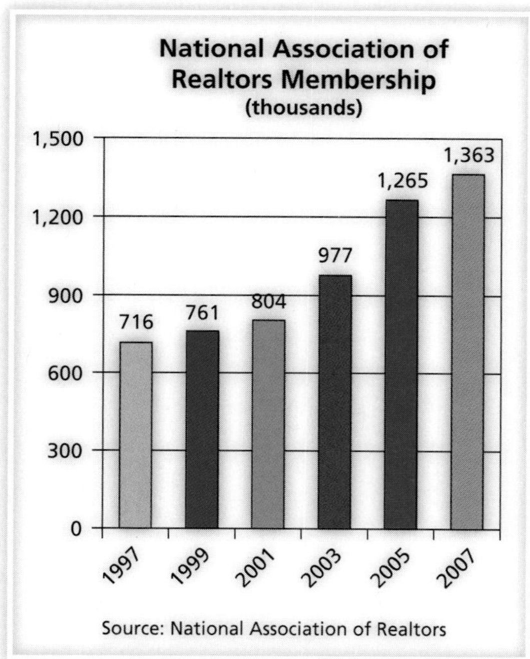

17. You are a real estate broker for Royal Realty. One of your clients, Dawn Fields, has agreed to purchase one of the homes your office has listed for sale for a negotiated price of $235,000. The down payment is 20%, and the balance will be financed with a 15-year fixed-rate mortgage at $8\frac{3}{4}\%$ and $3\frac{1}{2}$ discount points. The annual property tax is $5,475, and the hazard insurance premium is $2,110. When Dawn signed the original contract, she put down a deposit of $5,000, which will be credited to her down payment. In addition, at the time of closing Dawn must pay the following expenses.

Appraisal fee	$215
Credit report	$65
Roof inspection	$50
Mortgage insurance premium	$\frac{1}{2}$% of amount financed
Title search	$125
Attorney's fees	$680
Escrow fee	$210
Prepaid interest	$630

As Dawn's real estate broker, she has asked you the following.

a. What is the total monthly PITI of the mortgage loan?

Amount financed = 235,000 × 80% = $188,000

$8\frac{3}{4}$% for 15 years = 10.00 × 188

PI = $1,880

Tax	5,475
Insurance	2,110
	$7,585 ÷ 12 = $632.08

PI	1,880.00
TI	+ 632.08
	$2,512.08 Monthly PITI

b. What is the total amount of interest that will be paid on the loan?

15 × 12 = 180 Payments

180 × 1,880	$338,400
	− 188,000
Total interest paid on loan	$150,400

c. How much is due from Dawn at the time of the closing?

Appraisal fee	$215		Escrow fee	210	
Credit report	65		Prepaid int.	630	
Roof Inspec.	50		Points	6,580	(188,000 × .035)
Mortgage Ins.	940	(188,000 × .005)	Down payment	+ 47,000	(235,000 × .2)
Title search	125			$56,495	
Attorney's fees	680		Deposit	− 5,000	
			Due at closing	$51,495	

d. If your real estate office is entitled to a commission of $6\frac{1}{2}$% of the price of the home from the seller, how much commission is made on the sale?

$235,000 × .065 = $15,275

BUSINESS DECISION "BUYING DOWN" THE MORTGAGE

18. The buyer of a piece of real estate is often given the option of buying down the loan. This option is done by giving the buyer a choice of loan terms in which various combinations of interest rates and discount points are offered. The choice of how many points and what rate is optimal is often a matter of how long the buyer intends to keep the property.

    Mike Gordon is planning to buy an office building at a cost of $988,000. He must pay 10% down and has a choice of financing terms. He can select from a 7% 30-year loan and pay 4 discount points; a 7.25% 30-year loan and pay 3 discount points; or a 7.5% 30-year loan and pay 2 discount points. Mike expects to hold the building for four years, and then sell it. Except for the three rate and discount point combinations, all other costs of purchasing and selling are fixed and identical.

    a. What is the amount being financed?

    988,000(100% − 10%) = $889,200

    b. If Mike chooses the 4 point 7% loan, what will be his total outlay in points and payments after 48 months?

    Points = .04 × 889,200 = $35,568
    Payments = 48 × 889.2 × 6.66 = $284,259.46
    Total outlay = 35,568.00 + 284,259.46 = $319,827.46

    c. If Mike chooses the 3 point 7.25% loan, what will be his total outlay in points and payments after 48 months?

    Points = .03 × 889,200 = $26,676
    Payments = 48 × 889.2 × 6.83= $291,515.33
    Total outlay = 26,676.00 + 291,515.33 = $318,191.33

d. If Mike chooses the 2 point 7.5% loan, what will be his total outlay in points and payments after 48 months?

Points = .02 × 889,200 = \$17,784
Payments = 48 × 889.2 × 7.00 = \$298,771.20
Total outlay = 17,784.00 + 298,771.20 = \$316,555.20

e. Of the three choices for a loan, which gives Mike the least amount of payments?

7.5%, 2 point loan

SECTION II SECOND MORTGAGES—HOME EQUITY LOANS AND LINES OF CREDIT

Home equity loans and lines of credit increased at an average annual growth rate of 21% between 2002 and 2007. In 2007 and 2008, a cooling housing market and higher interest rates made homeowners more reluctant to tap the equity in their homes. See Exhibit 14-3, Home-Equity Lending. By using the equity in a home, a borrower may qualify for a sizable amount of credit at an interest rate that is relatively low. In addition, under the tax law, the interest may be a tax deduction because the debt is secured by your home.

home equity loan A lump-sum second mortgage loan based on the available equity in a home.

home equity line of credit A revolving credit second mortgage loan made on the available equity in a home.

credit limit A pre-approved limit on the amount of a home equity line of credit.

A **home equity loan** is a lump-sum second mortgage loan based on the available equity in your home. A **home equity line of credit** is a form of revolving credit, also based on the available equity. Because the home is likely to be a consumer's largest asset, many homeowners use these loans and credit lines only for major expenditures such as debt consolidation, education, home improvements, business expansion, medical bills, or vacations.

With home equity lines of credit, the borrower will be approved for a specific amount of credit known as the **credit limit**. This is the maximum amount that can be borrowed at any one time on that line of credit.

14-6 CALCULATING THE POTENTIAL AMOUNT OF CREDIT AVAILABLE TO A BORROWER

Most lenders set the credit limit on a home equity loan or line by taking a percentage of the appraised value of the house and subtracting the balance owed on the existing mortgage. In determining your actual credit limit, the lender also will consider your ability to repay by looking at your income, debts, and other financial obligations, as well as your credit history.

STEPS TO CALCULATE THE POTENTIAL AMOUNT OF CREDIT AVAILABLE TO A BORROWER

Step 1. Calculate the percentage of appraised value.

Percentage of appraised value = Appraised value × Lender's percentage

Step 2. Find the potential amount of credit available.

Potential credit = Percentage of appraised value − First mortgage balance

Exhibit 14-3
Home-Equity Lending

EXAMPLE 6 CALCULATING POTENTIAL CREDIT OF A HOME EQUITY LOAN

Loraine Friedman owns a house that was recently appraised for $115,700. The balance on her existing mortgage is $67,875. If her bank is willing to loan up to 75% of the appraised value, what is the potential amount of credit available to Loraine on a home equity loan?

CLASSROOM ACTIVITY
In groups, have students research and report to the class the typical rates and terms currently being offered in your area for second mortgages and home equity lines of credit.

SOLUTION STRATEGY

Step 1. Percentage of appraised value = Appraised value × Lender's percentage

Percentage of appraised value = 115,700 × .75

Percentage of appraised value = $86,775

Step 2. Potential credit = Percentage of appraised value − First mortgage balance
Potential credit = 86,775 − 67,875
Potential credit = $18,900

TRY IT EXERCISE 6

Walter Zarnoch owns a home that was recently appraised for $92,900. The balance on his existing first mortgage is $32,440. If his credit union is willing to loan up to 80% of the appraised value, what is the potential amount of credit available to Walter on a home equity line of credit?

CHECK YOUR ANSWER WITH THE SOLUTION ON PAGE 516.

14-7 CALCULATING THE HOUSING EXPENSE RATIO AND THE TOTAL OBLIGATIONS RATIO OF A BORROWER

qualifying ratios Ratios used by lenders to determine whether borrowers have the economic ability to repay loans.

housing expense ratio The ratio of a borrower's monthly housing expense (PITI) to monthly gross income.

total obligations ratio The ratio of a borrower's total monthly financial obligations to monthly gross income.

Mortgage lenders use ratios to determine whether borrowers have the economic ability to repay the loan. FHA, VA, and conventional lenders all use monthly gross income as the base for calculating these **qualifying ratios**. Two important ratios used for this purpose are the **housing expense ratio** and the **total obligations ratio**. These ratios are expressed as percents and are calculated by using the following formulas:

$$\textbf{Housing expense ratio} = \frac{\textbf{Monthly housing expense (PITI)}}{\textbf{Monthly gross income}}$$

$$\textbf{Total obligations ratio} = \frac{\textbf{Total monthly financial obligations}}{\textbf{Monthly gross income}}$$

The mortgage business uses widely accepted guidelines for these ratios that should not be exceeded. The ratio guidelines are as follows:

Lending Ratio Guidelines

14-4

Mortgage Type	Housing Expense Ratio	Total Obligations Ratio
FHA	29%	41%
Conventional	28%	36%

Note that the ratio formulas are an application of the percentage formula; the ratio is the rate, the PITI or total obligations are the portion, and the monthly gross income is the base. With this in mind, we are able to solve for any of the variables.

CLASSROOM ACTIVITY
Have students choose what price home they would like to purchase next. Based on a 15% down payment and a reasonable estimate of taxes and insurance, have them use the lending ratio formulas and guidelines to calculate what income they would need to qualify for such a loan.

EXAMPLE 7 CALCULATING MORTGAGE LENDING RATIOS

Ruby Alonso earns a gross income of $2,490 per month. She has applied for a mortgage with a monthly PITI of $556. Ruby has other financial obligations totaling $387.50 per month.

a. What is Ruby's housing expense ratio?
b. What is Ruby's total obligations ratio?
c. According to the lending ratio guidelines above, what type of mortgage would she qualify for, if any?

SOLUTION STRATEGY

a. $$\text{Housing expense ratio} = \frac{\text{Monthly housing expense (PITI)}}{\text{Monthly gross income}}$$

$$\text{Housing expense ratio} = \frac{556}{2{,}490}$$

$$\text{Housing expense ratio} = .2232 = \underline{\underline{22.3\%}}$$

b. $$\text{Total obligations ratio} = \frac{\text{Total monthly financial obligations}}{\text{Monthly gross income}}$$

$$\text{Total obligations ratio} = \frac{556.00 + 387.50}{2{,}490} = \frac{943.50}{2{,}490}$$

$$\text{Total obligations ratio} = .3789 = \underline{\underline{37.9\%}}$$

c. According to the lending ratio guidelines, Ruby would qualify for an FHA mortgage but not a conventional mortgage; her total obligations ratio is 37.9%, which is above the limit for conventional mortgages.

TRY IT EXERCISE 7

Eric Garcia earns a gross income of $3,100 per month. He has made application for a mortgage with a monthly PITI of $669. Eric has other financial obligations totaling $375 per month.

a. What is Eric's housing expense ratio?
b. What is Eric's total obligations ratio?
c. According to the lending ratio guidelines on page 508, what type of mortgage would he qualify for, if any?

14-5

CHECK YOUR ANSWERS WITH THE SOLUTIONS ON PAGE 516.

Review Exercises

SECTION II 14

Note: Round all answers to the nearest cent, when necessary.

For the following second mortgage applications, calculate the percentage of appraised value and the potential credit.

Solution Transparencies

	Appraised Value	Lender's Percentage	Percentage of Appraised Value	Balance of First Mortgage	Potential Credit
1.	$118,700	75%	$89,025	$67,900	$21,125
2.	$89,400	65%	$58,110	$37,800	$20,310
3.	$141,200	80%	$112,960	$99,100	$13,860
4.	$324,600	75%	$243,450	$197,500	$45,950
5.	$98,000	65%	$63,700	$66,000	0

To help home buyers "shop and compare" mortgage offers, the Federal Reserve Board has created a "Mortgage Payment Calculator" website, www.federalreserve.gov/apps/mortcalc/. The site allows consumers to calculate mortgage payments and equity accumulation for a variety of mortgage products, including adjustable-rate mortgages, interest only loans, and fixed-rate mortgages.

Calculate the housing expense ratio and the total obligations ratio for the following mortgage applications.

Applicant	Monthly Gross Income	Monthly (PITI) Expense	Other Monthly Financial Obligations	Housing Expense Ratio (%)	Total Obligations Ratio (%)
6. Parker	$2,000	$455	$380	22.75	41.75
7. Wick	$3,700	$530	$360	14.32	24.05
8. Martin	$3,100	$705	$720	22.74	45.97
9. Panko	$4,800	$1,250	$430	26.04	35.00
10. Emerson	$2,900	$644	$290	22.21	32.21

11. From the lending ratio guidelines on page 508,

a. Which of the applicants in Questions 6-10 would *not* qualify for a conventional mortgage?

6 and 8 Parker and Martin

b. Which of the applicants in Questions 6-10 would *not* qualify for any mortgage?

6 and 8 Parker and Martin

12. The Marlowes own a home that was recently appraised for $219,000. The balance on their existing first mortgage is $143,250. If their bank is willing to loan up to 65% of the appraised value, what is the potential amount of credit available to the Marlowes on a home equity loan?

219,000 × .65 = $142,350
− 143,250
− $900
Available credit 0

13. Jerry and Selina King own a home recently appraised for $418,500. The balance on their existing mortgage is $123,872. If their bank is willing to loan them up to 80% of the appraised value, what is the amount of credit available to them?

418,500 × 80% = $334,800
− 123,872
Available credit $210,928

14. Rhonda Letts is thinking about building an addition on her home. The house was recently appraised at $154,000, and the balance on her existing first mortgage is $88,600. If Rhonda's bank is willing to loan 70% of the appraised value, does she have enough equity in the house to finance a $25,000 addition?

154,000 × .70 = $107,800
− 88,600
Available credit $19,200
No to the addition

15. Steve and Cindy Jordan have a combined monthly gross income of $9,702 and monthly expenses totaling $2,811. They plan to buy a home with a mortgage whose monthly PITI will be $2,002.

a. What is Steve and Cindy's combined housing expense ratio?

$\frac{2,002}{9,702} = 20.6\%$

b. What is their total obligations ratio?

$$\frac{2{,}002 + 2{,}811}{9{,}702} = \underline{\underline{49.6\%}}$$

c. What kind of mortgage can they qualify for, if any?

They can qualify for neither an FHA nor a conventional mortgage under the lending guidelines.

d. (Optional challenge) By how much would they need to reduce their monthly expenses in order to qualify for an FHA mortgage?

$$\frac{2{,}002 + 2{,}811 - x}{9{,}702} = 41\%$$

Let x = Monthly expense reduction needed

$$4{,}813 - x = .41 \times 9{,}702$$
$$4{,}813 - x = 3{,}977.82$$
$$4{,}813 - 3{,}977.82 = x$$
$$\underline{\underline{x = \$835.18}}$$

BUSINESS DECISION QUALIFYING THE BORROWER

16. You are a mortgage broker at The Polaris Bank. One of your clients, Bill Evans, has submitted an application for a mortgage with a monthly PITI of $1,259. His other financial obligations total $654.50 per month. Bill earns a gross income of $4,890 per month.

a. What is his housing expense ratio?

$$\text{Housing expense ratio} = \frac{1{,}259}{4{,}890} = \underline{\underline{25.75\%}}$$

b. What is his total obligations ratio?

$$\text{Total obligations ratio} = \frac{1{,}259.00 + 654.50}{4{,}890} = \underline{\underline{39.13\%}}$$

c. According to the lending ratio guidelines on page 508, what type of mortgage would Bill qualify for, if any?

He qualifies for an FHA mortgage.

© Keith Brofsky/Photodisc/Getty Image

Mortgage brokers are real estate financing professionals acting as the intermediary between consumers and lenders during mortgage transactions. A mortgage broker works with consumers to help them through the complex mortgage origination process.

d. If Bill decided to get a part time job so that he could qualify for a conventional mortgage, how much additional monthly income would he need?

X = gross income required to qualify for conventional mortgage

$$\frac{1{,}259.00 + 654.50}{X} = 36\%$$

$$.36X = 1{,}913.50$$
$$X = 5{,}315.28$$

$5{,}315.28 - 4{,}890.00 = \underline{\underline{\$425.28}}$ Additional monthly income needed

CHAPTER FORMULAS

Fixed-Rate Mortgages

Monthly payment = Number of \$1,000s financed × Table 14-1 factor

Total interest = (Monthly payment × Number of payments) − Amount financed

$$\text{Monthly taxes and Insurance (TI)} = \frac{\text{Estimated property tax} + \text{Hazard insurance}}{12}$$

Monthly PITI = Monthly PI + Monthly TI

Adjustable-Rate Mortgages

ARM-Calculated interest rate = Index rate + Lender's margin

ARM-Maximum rate per adjustment period = Previous rate + Periodic cap

ARM-Maximum overall rate = Initial rate + Overall cap

Home Equity Loans and Lines of Credit

Percentage of appraised value = Appraised value × Lender's percentage

Second mortgage potential credit = Percentage of appraised value − First mtg. balance

$$\text{Housing expense ratio} = \frac{\text{Monthly housing expense (PITI)}}{\text{Monthly gross income}}$$

$$\text{Total obligations ratio} = \frac{\text{Total monthly financial obligations}}{\text{Monthly gross income}}$$

SUMMARY CHART

Section I: Mortgages—Fixed-Rate and Adjustable-Rate

Topic	Important Concepts	Illustrative Examples
Calculating the Monthly Payment and Total Interest Paid on a Fixed-Rate Mortgage **P/O 14-1, p. 491**	1. Find the number of \$1,000s financed by $\text{Number of \$1,000s} = \frac{\text{Amount financed}}{1,000}$ 2. From Table 14-1, locate the table factor, monthly payment per \$1,000 financed, at the intersection of the number of years column and the interest rate row. 3. Calculate the monthly payment by **Monthly payment = Number of 1,000s financed × Table factor** 4. Find the total interest of the loan by $\text{Total interest} = \left(\text{Monthly payments} \times \text{Number of payments}\right) - \text{Amount financed}$	What is the monthly payment and total interest on a \$100,000 mortgage at $9\frac{1}{2}\%$ for 30 years? $\text{Number of 1,000s} = \frac{100,000}{1,000} = 100$ Table factor: $9\frac{1}{2}\%$, 30 years = 8.41 Monthly payment = 100 × 8.41 = \$841 Total interest of the loan = (841 × 360) − 100,000 = 302,760 − 100,000 = \$202,760
Preparing a Partial Amortization Schedule of a Mortgage **P/O 14-2, p. 494**	1. Calculate the monthly payment of the loan as before. 2. Calculate the amount of interest for the current month using $I = PRT$, where P is the current outstanding balance of the loan, R is the annual interest rate, and T is $\frac{1}{12}$.	Prepare an amortization schedule for the first month of a \$70,000 mortgage at 9% for 20 years. Using Table 14-1, we find the monthly payment of the mortgage to be \$630. *Month 1:* Interest = Principal × Rate × Time Interest = $70,000 \times .09 \times \frac{1}{12}$ Interest = \$525

Section I: (continued)

Topic	Important Concepts	Illustrative Examples
	3. Find the portion of the payment used to reduce principal by **Portion of payment reducing principal = Monthly payment − Interest** 4. Calculate outstanding balance of the loan by **Outstanding balance = Previous balance − Portion of payment reducing principal** 5. Repeat Steps 2, 3, and 4 for each succeeding month and enter the values on a schedule labeled appropriately.	Portion of payment reducing principal 630 − 525 = $105 Outstanding balance after one payment 70,000 − 105 = $69,895 An amortization schedule can now be prepared from these data.
Calculating the Monthly PITI of a Mortgage **P/O 14-3, p. 495**	In reality, mortgage payments include four elements: principal, interest, taxes, and insurance, thus the abbreviation PITI. *Monthly PITI of a mortgage:* 1. Calculate the principal and interest portion (PI) of the payment as before, using Table 14-1. 2. Calculate the monthly tax and insurance portion (TI) by **Monthly TI = (Estimated property tax + Hazard Insurance) / 12** 3. Calculate the total monthly PITI by **Monthly PITI = Monthly PI + Monthly TI**	Heather Zamborsky purchased a home for $97,500 with a mortgage at $8\frac{1}{2}$% for 15 years. The property taxes are $1,950 per year, and the hazard insurance premium is $466. What is the monthly PITI payment of Heather's loan? Using a table factor of 9.85 from Table 14-1, we find the monthly PI for this $8\frac{1}{2}$%, 15-year mortgage to be $960.38. Monthly TI $= \frac{1{,}950 + 466}{12}$ $= \frac{2{,}416}{12}$ = $201.33 Monthly PITI = PI + TI = 960.38 + 201.33 = $1,161.71
Calculating the Amount Due at Closing **P/O 14-4, p. 496**	Closing costs are the expenses incurred in conjunction with the sale of real estate. Both buyer and seller are responsible for certain of these costs. The party responsible for paying a particular closing cost is often determined by local custom or by negotiation. Some closing costs are expressed as dollar amounts, whereas others are a percent of the amount financed or the amount of the purchase price. At closing, the buyer is responsible for the purchase price (mortgage + down payment) plus closing costs. The amount received by the seller after all expenses have been paid is known as the proceeds.	*Typical Closing Costs* *Buyer:* Attorney's fee, inspections, credit report, appraisal fee, hazard insurance premium, title exam and insurance premium, escrow fee, prepaid taxes and interest. *Seller:* Attorney's fee, broker's commission, survey expense, inspections, abstract of title, certificate of title, escrow fee, prepayment penalty—existing loan, documentary stamps.
Calculating the Interest Rate of an Adjustable-Rate Mortgage (ARM) **P/O 14-5, p. 500**	Use the following formulas to find the various components of an ARM: **Calculated interest rate = Index rate + Lender's margin** **Max rate per period = Previous rate + Periodic cap** **Maximum overall rate of ARM = Initial rate + Overall cap**	Tim Masters bought a home with an adjustable-rate mortgage. The margin on the loan is 3.5%, and the rate cap is 8% over the life of the loan. If the current index rate is 3.6%, what is the calculated interest rate and the maximum overall rate of the loan? Calculated interest rate = 3.6% + 3.5% = 7.1% Maximum overall rate = 7.1% + 8% = 15.1%

Section II: Second Mortgages—Home Equity Loans and Lines of Credit

Topic	Important Concepts	Illustrative Examples
Calculating the Potential Amount of Credit Available to a Borrower **P/O 14-6, p. 506**	Most lenders set the credit limit on a home equity loan or line by taking a percentage of the appraised value of the home and subtracting the balance owed on the existing first mortgage. In determining your actual credit limit, the lender also will consider your ability to repay by looking at your income, debts, and other financial obligations, as well as your credit history. *Potential amount of credit available to borrower:* 1. Calculate the percentage of appraised value by $\text{Percentage of appraised value} = \text{Appraised value} \times \text{Lender's percentage}$ 2. Find the potential amount of credit available by $\text{Potential credit} = \text{Percentage of appraised value} - \text{First mortgage debt}$	The Blakes own a home that was recently appraised for $134,800. The balance on their existing first mortgage is $76,550. If their bank is willing to loan up to 70% of the appraised value, what is the amount of credit available to the Blakes on a home equity loan? Percentage of appraised value = 134,800 × .70 = $94,360 Available credit = 94,360 − 76,550 = $17,810
Calculating the Housing Expense Ratio and the Total Obligations Ratio of a Borrower **P/O 14-7, p. 508**	Mortgage lenders use ratios to determine if borrowers have the economic ability to repay the loan. Two important ratios used for this purpose are the housing expense ratio and the total obligations ratio. These ratios are expressed as percents and are calculated by using the following formulas: $\text{Housing expense ratio} = \dfrac{\text{Monthly housing expense (PITI)}}{\text{Monthly gross income}}$ $\text{Total obligations ratio} = \dfrac{\text{Total monthly financial obligations}}{\text{Monthly gross income}}$	Vickie Howard earns a gross income of $3,750 per month. She has made application for a mortgage with a monthly PITI of $956. Vickie has other financial obligations totaling $447 per month. a. What is her housing expense ratio? b. What is her total obligations ratio? c. According to the ratio guidelines on page 508, for what type of mortgage would Vickie qualify, if any? $\text{Housing expense ratio} = \dfrac{956}{3,750} = 25.5\%$ $\text{Total obligation ratio} = \dfrac{1,403}{3,750} = 37.4\%$ According to the ratio guidelines, Vickie would qualify for an FHA mortgage but not a conventional mortgage; her total obligations ratio is 37.4%, which is above the limit for conventional mortgages.

TRY IT EXERCISE SOLUTIONS FOR CHAPTER 14

1. $\text{Number of 1,000s financed} = \dfrac{\text{Amount financed}}{1,000}$

$\text{Number of 1,000s financed} = \dfrac{85,500}{1,000} = 85.5$

Table factor 7%, 25 years = 7.07

Monthly payment = Number of 1,000s financed × Table factor
Monthly payment = 85.5 × 7.07 = $604.49

Total interest = (Monthly payment × Number of payments) − Amount financed
Total interest = (604.49 × 300) − 85,500
Total interest = 181,347 − 85,500 = $95,847

2. Number of 1,000s financed $= \dfrac{75{,}000}{1{,}000} = 75$

Table factor 9%, 15 years = 10.15
Monthly payment = 75 × 10.15 = 761.25

Month 1

$$I = PRT = 75{,}000 \times .09 \times \frac{1}{12} = \$562.50$$

Portion of payment reducing principal = 761.25 − 562.50 = $198.75
Outstanding balance = 75,000 − 198.75 = $74,801.25

Month 2

$$I = PRT = 74{,}801.25 \times .09 \times \frac{1}{12} = \$561.01$$

Portion of payment reducing principal = 761.25 − 561.01 = $200.24
Outstanding balance = 74,801.25 − 200.24 = $74,601.01

Month 3

$$I = PRT = 74{,}601.01 \times .09 \times \frac{1}{12} = \$559.51$$

Portion of payment reducing principal = 761.25 − 559.51 = $201.74
Outstanding balance = 74,601.01 − 201.74 = $74,399.27

Month 4

$$I = PRT = 74{,}399.27 \times .09 \times \frac{1}{12} = \$557.99$$

Portion of payment reducing principal = 761.25 − 557.99 = $203.26
Outstanding balance = 74,399.27 − 203.26 = $74,196.01

Amortization Schedule
$75,000, 9%, 15 years

Payment Number	Monthly Payment	Monthly Interest	Portion Used to Reduce Principal	Loan Balance
0				$75,000.00
1	$761.25	$562.50	$198.75	$74,801.25
2	$761.25	$561.01	$200.24	$74,601.01
3	$761.25	$559.51	$201.74	$74,399.27
4	$761.25	$557.99	$203.26	$74,196.01

3. Number of 1,000s $= \dfrac{125{,}600}{1{,}000} = 125.6$

Table factor $9\frac{1}{4}$%, 20 years = 9.16

Monthly payment (PI) = 125.6 × 9.16 = $1,150.50

$$\text{Monthly TI} = \frac{\text{Property tax} + \text{Hazard insurance}}{12}$$

$$\text{Monthly TI} = \frac{3{,}250 + 765}{12} = \frac{4{,}015}{12} = \$334.58$$

Monthly PITI = PI + TI = 1,150.50 + 334.58 = $1,485.08

4. a. Down payment = 120,000 × 20% = $24,000
Amount financed = 120,000 − 24,000 = $96,000

Closing Costs, Buyer:

Discount points (96,000 × 3%)	$ 2,880
Down payment (24,000 − 10,000)	14,000
Application fee	100
Condominium transfer fee	190
Title insurance (96,000 × $\frac{3}{4}$%)	720
Hazard insurance	420
Prepaid taxes	310
Attorney's fees	500
Due at closing	$19,120

b. *Proceeds, Seller:*

Purchase price		$120,000
Less: Broker's commission		
120,000 × $5\frac{1}{2}$%	$6,600	
Closing costs	670	
Mortgage payoff	65,000	
		− 72,270
Proceeds to seller		$47,730

5. a. Calculated ARM rate = Index rate + Margin
Calculated ARM rate = 3.2 + 3.4 = 6.6%

b. Maximum overall rate = Calculated rate + Overall cap
Maximum overall rate = 6.6 + 7.0 = 13.6%

6. Percentage of appraised value = Appraised value × Lender's percentage

Percentage of appraised value = 92,900 × 80% = $74,320

Potential credit = Percentage of appraised value − First mtg. balance

Potential credit = 74,320 − 32,440 = $41,880

7. a. $$\text{Housing expense ratio} = \frac{\text{Monthly housing expense (PITI)}}{\text{Monthly gross income}}$$

$$\text{Housing expense ratio} = \frac{669}{3{,}100} = 21.6\%$$

b. $$\text{Total obligations ratio} = \frac{\text{Total monthly financial obligations}}{\text{Monthly gross income}}$$

$$\text{Total obligations ratio} = \frac{669 + 375}{3{,}100} = \frac{1{,}044}{3{,}100} = 33.7\%$$

c. According to the guidelines, Eric qualifies for both FHA and conventional mortgages.

CONCEPT REVIEW

1. Land, including permanent improvements on that land, is known as ____ ____. (14-1)
real estate

2. A(n) ____ is a loan in which real property is used as security for a debt. (14-1)
mortgage

3. Mortgage ____ points are an extra charge frequently added to the cost of a mortgage. (14-1, 14-4)
discount

4. A chart that shows the month-by-month breakdown of each mortgage payment into interest and principal is known as a(n) ____ schedule. (14-2)
amortization

5. A(n) ____ account is a bank account used by mortgage lenders to accumulate next year's property taxes and hazard insurance. (14-3)
escrow

6. Today, most mortgage payments include four parts, abbreviated PITI. Name these parts. (14-3)
principle, interest, taxes, insurance

7. The final step in a real estate transaction is a meeting at which time the buyer pays the agreed upon purchase price and the seller delivers the ownership documents. This meeting is known as the ____. (14-4)
closing

8. The official document representing the right of ownership of real property is known as the ____ or the ____. (14-4)
title, deed

9. List any four mortgage loan closing costs. (14-4)
- loan origination fees
- appraisal fees
- title search
- attorney's fees
- broker's commission
- credit reports
- inspections
- title insurance
- recording fees

10. A mortgage in which the interest rate changes periodically, usually in relation to a predetermined economic index, is known as a(n) ____ rate mortgage. (14-5)
adjustable

11. A home equity ____ is a lump-sum second mortgage based on the available equity in a home. (14-6)
loan

12. A home equity ____ of credit is a revolving credit second mortgage based on the equity in a home. (14-6)
line

13. Write the formula for the housing expense ratio. (14-7)

$$\frac{\text{Monthly housing expense (PITI)}}{\text{Monthly gross income}}$$

14. Write the formula for the total obligations ratio. (14-7)

$$\frac{\text{Total monthly financial obligations}}{\text{Monthly gross income}}$$

ASSESSMENT TEST

CHAPTER 14

You are one of the branch managers of the Alamo Bank. Today, two loan applications were submitted to your office. Calculate the requested information for each loan.

	Amount Financed	Interest Rate (%)	Term of Loan	Number of $1,000s Financed	Table Factor	Monthly Payment	Total Interest
1.	$134,900	$7\frac{3}{4}$	25 years	134.9	7.56	$1,019.84	$171,052.00
2.	$79,500	$8\frac{1}{4}$	20 years	79.5	8.53	$678.14	$83,253.60

3. Pamela Boyd purchased a home with a $146,100 mortgage at $11\frac{1}{2}$% for 30 years. Calculate the monthly payment and prepare an amortization schedule for the first 3 months of Pamela's loan.

Payment Number	Monthly Payment	Monthly Interest	Portion Used to Reduce Principal	Loan Balance
0				$146,100.00
1	$1,447.85	$1,400.13	$47.72	$146,052.28
2	$1,447.85	$1,399.67	$48.18	$146,004.10
3	$1,447.85	$1,399.21	$48.64	$145,955.46

Calculate the monthly principal and interest by using Table 14-1 and the monthly PITI for the following mortgages.

	Amount Financed	Interest Rate (%)	Term of Loan	Monthly PI	Annual Property Tax	Annual Insurance	Monthly PITI
4.	$54,200	9	25 years	$455.28	$719	$459	$553.45
5.	$132,100	$8\frac{3}{4}$	15 years	$1,321	$2,275	$1,033	$1,596.67

Name

Class

Answers

1. 134.9 7.56
$1,019.84 $171,052.00

2. 79.5 8.53
$678.14 $83,253.60

3. Month 1: $146,052.28
Month 2: $146,004.10
Month 3: $145,955.46

4. $455.28 $553.45

5. $1,321 $1,596.67

Complete, worked-out solutions to Exercises 1, 2, 4, and 5 appear in Appendix B, following the index.

Name

Class

Answers

6. $74,425 0

7. $41,200 $13,800

8. $56,840 $20,840

9. 24.3% 40.15%

10. 25.39% 34.16%

11. Perkins: FHA

Drake: FHA and Conventional

12. a. 8.35%

b. 14.35%

13. a. $5,194.80

b. See table.

c. $6,147.30

Complete, worked-out solutions to Exercises 6–10 appear in Appendix B, following the index.

For the following second mortgage applications, calculate the percentage of appraised value and the potential credit.

	Appraised Value	Lender's Percentage	Percentage of Appraised Value	Amount of First Mortgage	Potential Credit
6.	$114,500	65	$74,425	$77,900	0
7.	$51,500	80	$41,200	$27,400	$13,800
8.	$81,200	70	$56,840	$36,000	$20,840

For the following mortgage applications, calculate the housing expense ratio and the total expense ratio.

	Applicant	Monthly Gross Income	Monthly (PITI) Expense	Other Monthly Financial Obligations	Housing Expense Ratio (%)	Total Obligations Ratio (%)
9.	Perkins	$5,300	$1,288	$840	24.30	40.15
10.	Drake	$3,750	$952	$329	25.39	34.16

11. As a loan officer using the lending ratio guidelines on page 508, what type of mortgage can you offer Perkins and Drake, from Exercises 9 and 10?

Perkins qualifies for FHA

Drake qualifies for FHA and Conventional

12. David Sporn bought the Lazy D Ranch with an adjustable-rate mortgage. The margin on the loan is 3.9%, and the rate cap is 6% over the life of the loan.

a. If the current index rate is 4.45%, what is the calculated interest rate of the ARM?

Calculated interest rate = 4.45% + 3.9%
= 8.35%

b. What is the maximum overall rate of David's loan?

Maximum overall rate = 8.35% + 6%
= 14.35%

13. Diamond Investments purchased a 24-unit apartment building for $650,000. After a 20% down payment, the balance was financed with a 20-year, $10\frac{1}{2}$% fixed-rate mortgage.

a. What is the amount of the monthly principal and interest portion of the loan?

Amount financed = 650,000 × 80% = $520,000

Number of $1,000s financed = 520

10.5%, 20 year table factor = 9.99

520 × 9.99 = $5,194.80 Monthly PI

b. As Diamond's loan officer, construct an amortization schedule for the first 2 months of the mortgage.

Payment Number	Monthly Payment	Monthly Interest	Portion Used to Reduce Principal	Loan Balance
0				$520,000.00
1	$5,194.80	$4,550.00	$644.80	$519,355.20
2	$5,194.80	$4,544.36	$650.44	$518,704.76

c. If the annual property taxes are $9,177 and the hazard insurance premium is $2,253 per year, what is the total monthly PITI of the loan?

$$\text{Monthly PITI} = 5{,}194.80 + \frac{9{,}177 + 2{,}253}{12}$$
$$= \$6{,}147.30$$

Name

Class

Answers

13. d. $13,652.70

14. $25,287.50

15. a. $946,368 $919,584

b. Foremost is better by $9,346.50

16. $154,980 more on 30 years

d. If each apartment rents for $825 per month, how much income will Diamond make per month after the PITI is paid on the building?

24 units × 825 = $19,800.00
− 6,147.30 PITI
Monthly income $13,652.70

14. Larry Mager purchased a ski lodge in Telluride for $850,000. His bank is willing to finance 70% of the purchase price. As part of the mortgage closing costs, Larry had to pay $4\frac{1}{4}$ discount points. How much did this amount to?

850,000 × 70% = $595,000
595,000 × 4.25% = $25,287.50

15. A Wendy's franchisee is looking for a 20-year mortgage, with 90% financing, to build a new location costing $775,000. The Spring Creek Bank is offering a $10\frac{1}{4}$ mortgage with $1\frac{1}{2}$ discount points; Foremost Savings and Loan is offering a 10% mortgage with 4 closing points. The franchisee is unsure which mortgage is a better deal and has asked for your help.

a. What is the total interest paid on each loan?

Spring Creek Bank	Foremost Savings & Loan
775,000 × 90% = $697,500	$697,500 Amount of loan
$10\frac{1}{4}$% 20 years = 9.82	10% 20 years = 9.66
9.82 × 697.5 = 6,849.45 × 20 × 12	9.66 × 697.5 = 6,737.85 × 20 × 12
Total payments = $1,643,868	Total payments = $1,617,084
Amount of loan − 697,500	Amount of loan − 697,500
Total interest $946,368	Total interest $919,584

b. Taking into account the discount points, which lender is offering a better deal and by how much?

Spring Creek Bank	Foremost Savings & Loan
Points = 1.5% × 697,500 = $10,462.50	Points = 4% × 697,500 = $27,900
Interest +946,368.00	Interest +919,584
Total cost $956,830.50	Total cost $947,484

956,830.50 − 947,484.00 = Foremost is better by $9,346.50

16. How much more total interest will be paid by Circuit City on a 30-year fixed-rate mortgage for $100,000 at 11% compared with a 15-year mortgage at $9\frac{1}{2}$%?

15 years

100,000 at 9.5%
10.45 × 100 = 1,045
15 × 12 × 1,045 = $188,100
− 100,000
Interest $88,100

30 years

100,000 at 11%
9.53 × 100 = 953
30 × 12 × 953 = $343,080 $243,080
− 100,000   − 88,100
Interest $243,080 $154,980   More on 30-year loan

© Tgprn Disney Consumer Products/ PR Newswire (NewsCom)

Circuit City Stores, Inc., is a leading specialty retailer of consumer electronics, home office products, entertainment software, and related services. In 2007, the company had over 46,000 employees and generated $12.4 billion in net sales. Circuit City sells products through 642 Superstores in the United States and over 800 retail outlets in other countries as well as on the Internet at www.circuitcity.com. Major competitors include Best Buy and Radio Shack.

CHAPTER

Name

Class

Answers

17. a. $1,230.98

b. $120,236

c. $22,557.40

d. $80,060

18. $149,872.60

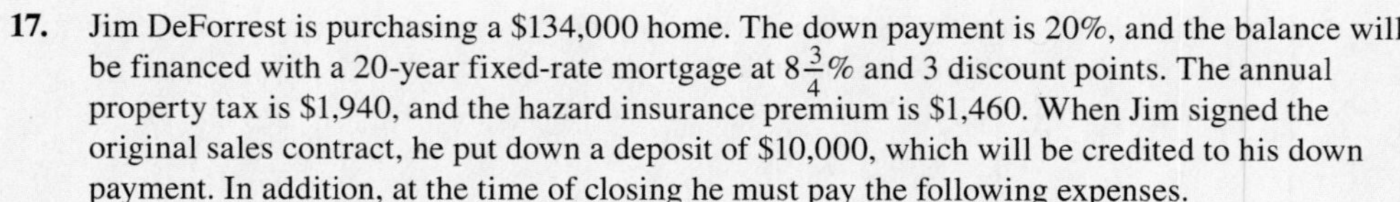

17. Jim DeForrest is purchasing a $134,000 home. The down payment is 20%, and the balance will be financed with a 20-year fixed-rate mortgage at $8\frac{3}{4}$% and 3 discount points. The annual property tax is $1,940, and the hazard insurance premium is $1,460. When Jim signed the original sales contract, he put down a deposit of $10,000, which will be credited to his down payment. In addition, at the time of closing he must pay the following expenses.

Appraisal fee	$165
Credit report	$75
Attorney's fees	$490
Roof inspection	$50
Termite inspection	$88
Title search	$119
Mortgage insurance premium	1.2% of amount financed
Documentary stamps	$\frac{1}{4}$% of amount financed

As Jim's real estate agent, he has asked you the following:

a. What is the total monthly PITI of the mortgage loan?

$$\text{\# of 1,000s} = \frac{134{,}000 \times 80\%}{1{,}000} = 107.2$$

$$107.2 \times 8.84 = \$947.65 = \text{PI}$$

$$\text{PITI} = 947.65 + \frac{1{,}940 + 1{,}460}{12} = \$1{,}230.98$$

b. What is the total amount of interest that will be paid on the loan?

Total payments = 20 × 12 × 947.65 = $227,436

	$227,436
Amount financed	− 107,200
Total interest	$120,236

c. How much is due at the time of the closing?

Appraisal fee	165.00	Mortgage ins.	1,286.40	(107,200 × .012)
Credit report	75.00	Doc stamps	268.00	(107,200 × .0025)
Attorney's fees	490.00	Points	3,216.00	(107,200 × .03)
Roof inspection	50.00	Down payment	+ 26,800.00	
Title search	119.00		32,557.40	
Termite inspection	88.00	Deposit	− 10,000.00	
		Due at closing	$22,557.40	

d. If the sellers are responsible for the 6% broker's commission, $900 in closing costs, and the existing first mortgage with a balance of $45,000, what proceeds will be received on the sale of the property?

Sale price	$134,000	
Less: Closing costs	− 900	
Broker fees	− 8,040	(134,000 × .06)
First mortgage	− 45,000	
Seller's proceeds	$80,060	

18. Branford Martin is negotiating to buy a vacation cottage near the beach at Port St. Joe. The seller of the cottage is asking $186,000. Branford offered him a cash deal, owner-seller (no broker) only if the seller would reduce the price by 12%. The seller agreed. Branford must pay a 10% down payment upon signing the agreement of sale. At closing he must pay the balance of the agreed upon sale price, a $500 attorney fee, a $68 utility transfer fee, a title search and transfer fee of $35 plus $\frac{3}{4}$% of the selling price, and the first six months of the annual insurance of $1,460 per year. How much does Branford owe at closing?

Selling price: $186,000(100% − 12%) =	$163,680.00
less: $163,680 × 10% down payment =	(16,368.00)
Attorney fee:	500.00
Utility transfer fee:	68.00
Title search: 35 + (163,680 × .0075)	1,262.60
Insurance: $1,460(6 ÷ 12)	730.00
Total owed by Branford	$149,872.60

Name

Class

Answers

19 0

20. $155,160

21. a. 27.86%

b. 39.53%

c. FHA

22. a. 25.4%

b. 39.7%

c. FHA

23. a. $980

19. The Taylors own a home that recently appraised for $161,400. The balance on their existing first mortgage is $115,200. If their bank is willing to loan up to 70% of the appraised value, what is the amount of credit available to the Taylors on a home equity line of credit?

$161,400 × 70% = $112,980
Loan balance $115,200
Available credit 0

20. Linda and Doug Mason live in a home they want to make major improvements on. They plan to replace the existing heating and cooling system, remodel the kitchen, and add a room above the garage. To pay for this renovation, they plan to get a home equity line of credit. Their home currently appraises for $298,000. They owe $68,340 on the first mortgage. How much credit will their bank provide if the limit is 75% of their home's value?

$298,000 × 75% = $223,500
− 68,340
Available credit $155,160

21. Paul Scoville earns a gross income of $5,355 per month. He has submitted an application for a fixed-rate mortgage with a monthly PITI of $1,492. Paul has other financial obligations totaling $625 per month.

a. What is his housing expense ratio?

$$\text{Housing expense ratio} = \frac{1,492}{5,355} = 27.86\%$$

b. What is his total obligations ratio?

$$\text{Total obligations ratio} = \frac{1,492 + 625}{5,355} = 39.53\%$$

c. According to the lending ratio guidelines on page 508, for what type of mortgage would Paul qualify for, if any?

FHA

22. Sheryl Stewart is applying for a home mortgage with a monthly PITI of $724. She currently has a gross income of $2,856 and other monthly expense of $411.

a. What is Sheryl's housing expense ratio?

$$\frac{724}{2,856} = 25.4\%$$

b. What is her total obligations ratio?

$$\frac{724 + 411}{2,856} = 39.7\%$$

c. According to the lending ratio guidelines, what type of mortgage would Sheryl qualify for, if any?

FHA

BUSINESS DECISION WHAT SIZE MORTGAGE CAN YOU QUALIFY FOR?

23. You are applying for a conventional mortgage from the Main Street Bank. Your monthly gross income is $3,500, and the bank uses the 28% housing expense ratio guideline.

a. What is the highest PITI you can qualify for? *Hint:* Solve the housing expense ratio formula for PITI. Remember, this is an application of the percentage formula, Portion = Rate × Base, where PITI is the portion, the expense ratio is the rate, and your monthly gross income is the base.

$P = B \times R$
$P = 3,500 \times 28\%$
PITI = $980

CHAPTER

Name

Class

Answers

b. $100,000 maximum

c. $125,000

b. Based on your answer from part **a**, if you are applying for a 30-year, 9% mortgage, and the taxes and insurance portion of PITI is $175 per month, use Table 14-1 to calculate what size mortgage you qualify for. *Hint:* Subtract TI from PITI. Divide the PI by the appropriate table factor to determine how many $1,000s you qualify to borrow.

PI = 980 − 175 = 805 Mortgage can be $100,000 maximum
Factor = 8.05

$$\text{Number of } \$1{,}000\text{s} = \frac{805}{8.05} = 100$$

c. Based on your answer from part **b,** if you are planning on a 20% down payment, what is the most expensive house you can afford? *Hint:* Use the percentage formula again. The purchase price of the house is the base, the amount financed is the portion, and the percent financed is the rate.

$$B = \frac{P}{R} \qquad B = \frac{100{,}000}{80\%} = \$125{,}000$$

Maximum price of house = $125,000

COLLABORATIVE LEARNING ACTIVITY

The Hypothetical Mortgage

Speak with the loan officers at mortgage lending institutions in your area, and ask for their help with a business math class project.

Your assignment is to research the various types of financing deals currently being offered for a hypothetical home you plan to buy. The following assumptions apply to this project:

- The purchase price of the house you plan to buy is $200,000.
- The house was recently appraised for $220,000.
- You plan to make a 25% down payment ($50,000) and are seeking a $150,000 mortgage.
- You have a job that qualifies you for that size mortgage.

Your assignment, as a team, is to compare the current interest rates, costs, and features associated with a 15-year fixed-rate mortgage, a 30-year fixed-rate mortgage, and an adjustable-rate mortgage.

a. What are the current interest rates and discount points of the 15- and 30-year fixed-rate mortgages?

b. What are the monthly payments of the fixed-rate mortgages?

c. What is the initial (teaser) rate, discount points, adjustment period, rate caps, margin, and index for the adjustable-rate mortgage?

d. What are the fees or charges for the loan application, property appraisal, survey, credit report, inspections, title search, title insurance, and document preparation?

e. What other charges or fees can be expected at closing?

f. As a team, decide which type of mortgage is the best deal at this time. Why?

g. Which bank would you choose for the mortgage? Why?

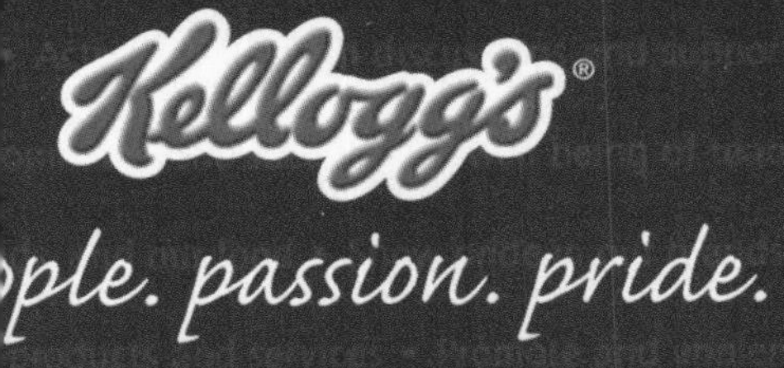
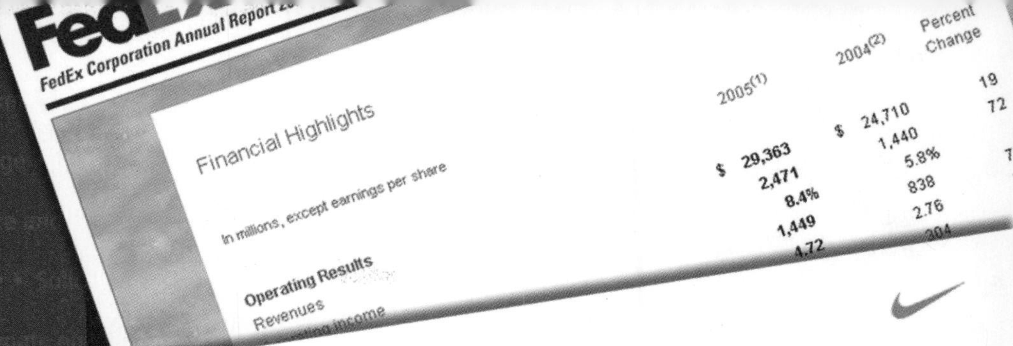

© R. Alcorn/Thomson

CHAPTER 15

Financial Statements and Ratios

PERFORMANCE OBJECTIVES

15 SECTION I THE BALANCE SHEET

financial statements A series of accounting reports summarizing a company's financial data compiled from business activity over a period of time. The four most common are the balance sheet, the income statement, the owner's equity statement, and the cash flow statement.

Financial statements are the periodic report cards of how a business is doing from a monetary perspective. After all, money is the primary way in which the score is kept in the competitive arena of business. These important statements are a summary of a company's financial data compiled from business activity over a period of time.

The four major financial statements used in business today are the balance sheet, the income statement, the owner's equity statement, and the cash flow statement. Together, they tell a story about how a company has performed in the past and is likely to perform in the near future. In this chapter, we focus our attention on the preparation and analysis of the balance sheet and the income statement. The Business Decisions at the ends of the review exercises and the Assessment Test feature actual financial statements from recent annual reports of well-known companies representing various industries. They provide an opportunity to examine real-world statements and apply your own analytical skills.

Typically, a company's accounting department prepares financial statements quarterly for the purpose of management review and government reporting of income tax information. At the end of each year, the accounting department prepares annual financial statements to present the company's yearly financial position and performance. Public corporations, those whose stock can be bought and sold by the general investing public, are required by law to make their statements available to the stockholders and the financial community in the form of quarterly and annual reports. Because it is public information, condensed versions of these reports often appear in financial publications such as *The Wall Street Journal, Business Week, Forbes,* and *Fortune.*

financial analysis The assessment of a company's past, present, and anticipated future financial condition based on the information found on the financial statements.

Financial analysis is the assessment of a company's past, present, and anticipated future financial condition based on the information found on the financial statements. Financial ratios are the primary tool of this analysis. These ratios are a way of standardizing financial data so that they may be compared with ratios from previous operating periods of the same firm or from other similar-size firms in the same industry.

Internally, owners and managers rely on this analysis to evaluate a company's financial strengths and weaknesses and to help make sound business decisions. From outside the firm, creditors and investors use financial statements and ratios to determine a company's creditworthiness or investment potential.

balance sheet A financial statement illustrating the financial position of a company in terms of assets, liabilities, and owner's equity as of a certain date.

financial position The economic resources owned by a company and the claims against those resources at a specific point in time.

The **balance sheet** is the financial statement that lists a company's financial position on a certain date, usually at the end of a month, a quarter, or a year. To fully understand the balance sheet, we must first examine some basic accounting theory.

Financial position refers to the economic resources owned by a company and the claims against those resources at a specific point in time. *Equities* is another term for claims. Keep in mind that a firm's economic resources must always be equal to its equities. A business enterprise can therefore be pictured as an equation:

Economic resources = Equities

creditor One to whom money is owed.

liabilities Debts or obligations of a business resulting from past transactions that require the company to pay money, provide goods, or perform services in the future.

owner's equity The resources claimed by the owner against the assets of a business: Owner's equity = Assets − Liabilities. Also called proprietorship, capital, or net worth.

assets Economic resources, such as cash, inventories, and land, buildings, and equipment owned by a business.

There are two types of equities: the rights of the **creditors** (those who are owed money by the business) and the rights of the owners. The rights of the creditors are known as **liabilities** and represent debts of the business. The rights of the owners are known as **owner's equity.** Owner's equity represents the resources invested in the business by the owners. Theoretically, owner's equity is what would be left over after all the liabilities were paid to the creditors. We can now enhance our equation:

Economic resources = Liabilities + Owner's equity

In accounting terminology, the economic resources owned by a business are known as the **assets.** Our equation now becomes

Assets = Liabilities + Owner's Equity

This all-important equation is known as the **accounting equation**. The balance sheet is a visual presentation of this equation at a point in time. Some balance sheets display the assets on the left and the liabilities and owner's equity on the right. Another popular format lists the assets on the top and the liabilities and owner's equity below. Remember, on a balance sheet the assets must always be equal to the liabilities plus owner's equity.

accounting equation Algebraic expression of a company's financial position:
Assets = Liabilities + Owner's equity.

PREPARING A BALANCE SHEET

15-1

Let's begin by looking at an example of a typical balance sheet and then examining each section and its components more closely. A balance sheet for a corporation, Hypothetical Enterprises, Inc., follows. Carefully look over the statement. Next, read the descriptions of the Balance Sheet Components, pages 526–527, and the Steps to Prepare a Balance Sheet, page 527. Then follow the Example and attempt the Try-It Exercise.

CLASSROOM ACTIVITY
Point out to students that the balance sheet is based on the accounting equation and that both sides must "balance."

To help reinforce the concept, have students use their knowledge of equations to solve the accounting equation for the other variables.

Assets = Liabilities + Owner's equity

Liabilities = Assets − Owner's equity

Owner's equity = Assets − Liabilities

Hypothetical Enterprises, Inc.
Balance Sheet
December 31, 20XX

Assets		
Current Assets		
Cash	$ 13,000	
Accounts Receivable	32,500	
Merchandise Inventory	50,600	
Prepaid Expenses	1,200	
Supplies	4,000	
Total Current Assets		$101,300
Property, Plant, and Equipment		
Land	40,000	
Buildings	125,000	
Machinery and Equipment	60,000	
Total Property, Plant, and Equipment		225,000
Investments and Other Assets		
Investments	10,000	
Intangible Assets	5,000	
Total Investments and Other Assets		15,000
Total Assets		$341,300
Liabilities and Owner's Equity		
Current Liabilities		
Accounts Payable	$ 17,500	
Salaries Payable	5,400	
Taxes Payable	6,500	
Total Current Liabilities		$ 29,400
Long-Term Liabilities		
Mortgage Payable	115,000	
Debenture Bond	20,000	
Total Long-Term Liabilities		135,000
Total Liabilities		164,400
Stockholders' Equity		
Capital Stock	126,900	
Retained Earnings	50,000	
Total Stockholders' Equity		176,900
Total Liabilities and Stockholders' Equity		$341,300

15-2

Annual Meeting
The annual meeting is a company gathering, usually held at the end of each fiscal year, at which the previous year and the outlook for the future are discussed and directors are elected by vote of the common stockholders.

Shortly before each annual meeting, the corporation sends out a document called a proxy statement to each stockholder. The proxy statement contains a list of the business concerns to be addressed at the meeting and a ballot for voting on company initiatives and electing the new Board of Directors.

Balance Sheet Components

ASSETS The asset section of a balance sheet is divided into three components: Current Assets; Property, Plant, and Equipment; and Investments and Other Assets.

Current Assets Assets that are cash or will be sold, used, or converted to cash within 1 year. The following are typical examples of current assets:

- Cash—Cash on hand in the form of bills, coins, checking accounts, and savings accounts.
- Marketable securities—Investments in short-term securities that can be quickly converted to cash, such as stocks and bonds.
- Accounts receivable—Money owed by customers to the firm for goods and services sold on credit.
- Notes receivable—Money owed to the business involving promissory notes.
- Merchandise inventory—The cost of goods a business has on hand for resale to its customers.
- Prepaid expenses—Money paid in advance by the firm for benefits and services not yet received, such as prepaid insurance premiums or prepaid rent.
- Supplies—Cost of assets used in the day-to-day operation of the business. These might include office supplies such as paper, pencils, pens, and computer diskettes or maintenance supplies such as paper towels, soap, lubricants, light bulbs, and batteries.

TEACHING TIP

The concept of *depreciation* should be introduced during the discussion of the balance sheet. Explain that property, plant, and equipment (except land), such as cars, trucks, and business equipment, "wear out" over time and therefore lose value.

- Point out that the "values" of these assets on the balance sheet are at *book value*.

  Book value = Original cost − Accumulated depreciation

- Further point out that depreciation also appears on the income statement as an operating expense (Section II).

Note: For complete coverage of depreciation, see Chapter 17.

Property, Plant, and Equipment Also known as fixed or long-term assets. These assets will be used by the firm in the operation of the business for a period of time longer than 1 year. Some examples follow:

- Land—The original purchase price of land owned by the company. Land is an asset that does not depreciate or lose its value over a period of time.
- Buildings—The cost of the buildings owned by the firm less the accumulated depreciation, or total loss in value, on those buildings since they were new. This is known as the book value of the buildings.
- Machinery and equipment—The book value or original cost less accumulated depreciation of all machinery, fixtures, vehicles, and equipment used in the operation of a business.

Investments and Other Assets This category lists the firm's investments and all other assets.

- Investments—These are investments made by the firm and held for periods longer than 1 year.
- Other assets—This catch-all category is for any assets not previously listed.
- Intangibles—Long-term assets that have no physical substance but have a value based on rights and privileges claimed by the owner. Some examples are copyrights, patents, royalties, and goodwill.

Pepper . . . and Salt

THE WALL STREET JOURNAL

"Feelings of self-worth are important, but never confuse them with *net* worth."

LIABILITIES AND OWNER'S EQUITY The liabilities and owner's equity section of the balance sheet lists the current and long-term liabilities incurred by the company, as well as the owner's *net worth* or claim against the assets of the business. From the accounting equation, it is the difference between the total assets and the total liabilities.

Current Liabilities Debts and financial obligations of the company that are due to be paid within 1 year. Some examples follow:

- Accounts payable—Debts owed by the firm to creditors for goods and services purchased with less than 1 year credit. These might include 30-, 60-, or 90-day terms of sale extended by suppliers and vendors.
- Notes payable—Debts owed by the firm involving promissory notes. An example would be a short-term loan from a bank.

- Salaries payable—Compensation to employees that has been earned but not yet paid.
- Taxes payable—Taxes owed by the firm but not yet paid by the date of the statement.

Don't be overwhelmed by the amount of new terminology associated with financial statements. Start by understanding the function and basic structure of each statement.

Next, learn the purpose of each major category. This should help you determine in which category of the statement each component is listed.

Long-Term Liabilities Debts and financial obligations of the company that are due to be paid in 1 year or more or are to be paid out of noncurrent assets. Some examples follow:

- Mortgage payable—The total obligation a firm owes for the long-term financing of land and buildings.
- Debenture bonds—The total amount a firm owes on bonds at maturity to bondholders for money borrowed on the general credit of the company.

Owner's Equity When a business is organized as a sole proprietorship or partnership, the equity section of the balance sheet is known as owner's equity. The ownership is labeled with the name of the owners or business and the word *capital*. Some examples follow:

- Paul Kelsch, capital
- Lost Sock Laundry, capital.

Stockholders' Equity When the business is a corporation, the equity section of the balance sheet is known as stockholder's equity. The ownership is represented in two categories, capital stock and retained earnings.

- Capital stock—This represents money acquired by selling stock to investors who become stockholders. Capital stock is divided into preferred stock, which has preference over common stock regarding dividends, and common stock, representing the most basic rights to ownership of a corporation.
- Retained earnings—Profits from the operation of the business that have not been distributed to the stockholders in the form of dividends.

STEPS TO PREPARE A BALANCE SHEET

Step 1. Centered at the top of the page, write the company name, type of statement, and date.

Step 2. In a section labeled ASSETS, list and total all the Current Assets; Property, Plant, and Equipment; and Investments and Other Assets.

Step 3. Add the three components of the Assets section to get Total Assets.

Step 4. Double underline Total Assets.

Step 5. In a section labeled LIABILITIES AND OWNER'S EQUITY, list and total all Current Liabilities and Long-Term Liabilities.

Step 6. Add the two components of the Liabilities section to get Total Liabilities.

Step 7. List and total the Owner's or Stockholders' Equity.

Step 8. Add the Total Liabilities and Owner's Equity.

Step 9. Double underline Total Liabilities and Owner's Equity.

Note: In accordance with the accounting equation, check to be sure that

Assets = Liabilities + Owner's Equity

EXAMPLE 1 PREPARING A BALANCE SHEET

Use the following financial information to prepare a balance sheet for Royal Equipment Supply, Inc., as of June 30, 2008: cash, $3,400; accounts receivable, $5,600; merchandise inventory, $98,700; prepaid insurance, $455; supplies, $800; land and building, $147,000; fixtures, $8,600; delivery vehicles, $27,000; forklift, $7,000; goodwill, $10,000; accounts payable, $16,500; notes payable, $10,000; mortgage payable, $67,000; common stock, $185,055; and retained earnings, $30,000.

SOLUTION STRATEGY

The balance sheet for Royal Equipment Supply, Inc., follows. Note that the assets are equal to the liabilities plus stockholders' equity.

Royal Equipment Supply, Inc.
Balance Sheet
June 30, 2008

Assets		
Current Assets		
Cash	$ 3,400	
Accounts Receivable	5,600	
Merchandise Inventory	98,700	
Prepaid Insurance	455	
Supplies	800	
Total Current Assets		$108,955
Property, Plant, and Equipment		
Land and Building	$147,000	
Fixtures	8,600	
Delivery Vehicles	27,000	
Forklift	7,000	
Total Property, Plant, and Equipment		189,600
Investments and Other Assets		
Goodwill	10,000	
Total Investments and Other Assets		10,000
Total Assets		$308,555
Liabilities and Stockholders' Equity		
Current Liabilities		
Accounts Payable	$ 16,500	
Notes Payable	10,000	
Total Current Liabilities		$ 26,500
Long-Term Liabilities		
Mortgage Payable	67,000	
Total Long-Term Liabilities		67,000
Total Liabilities		93,500
Stockholders' Equity		
Common Stock	185,055	
Retained Earnings	30,000	
Total Stockholders' Equity		215,055
Total Liabilities and Stockholders' Equity		$308,555

In the Business World

The stockholders are the owners of a corporation; therefore, the *owner's equity* on the balance sheet of a corporation is known as *stockholders' equity.*

TRY IT EXERCISE 1

Use the following financial information to prepare a balance sheet as of December 31, 2008, for Keystone Auto Repair, a sole proprietorship, owned by Blake Jolin: cash, $5,200; accounts receivable, $2,800; merchandise inventory, $2,700; prepaid salary, $235; supplies, $3,900; land, $35,000; building, $74,000; fixtures, $1,200; tow truck, $33,600; tools and equipment, $45,000; accounts payable, $6,800; notes payable, $17,600; taxes payable, $3,540; mortgage payable, $51,000; Blake Jolin, capital, $124,695.

CHECK YOUR STATEMENT WITH THE SOLUTION ON PAGES 564 & 565.

15-3

CLASSROOM ACTIVITY
In groups, have students prepare the balance sheet for Try It Exercise 1. Use Teaching Transparencies 15-3 and 15-4 to illustrate the solution.

PREPARING A VERTICAL ANALYSIS OF A BALANCE SHEET

Once the balance sheet has been prepared, a number of analytical procedures can be applied to the data to further evaluate a company's financial condition. One common method of analysis of a single financial statement is known as **vertical analysis**. In vertical analysis, each item on the balance sheet is expressed as a percent of total assets (total assets = 100%).

Once the vertical analysis has been completed, the figures show the relationship of each item on the balance sheet to total assets. For analysis purposes, these percents can then be compared with previous statements of the same company, with competitor's figures, or with published industry averages for similar-size companies.

A special form of balance sheet known as a common-size balance sheet is frequently used in financial analysis. **Common-size balance sheets** list only the vertical analysis percentages, not the dollar figures.

vertical analysis A percentage method of analyzing financial statements whereby each item on the statement is expressed as a percent of a base amount. On balance sheet analysis, the base is total assets; on income statement analysis, the base is net sales.

common-size balance sheet A special form of balance sheet that lists only the vertical analysis percentages, not the dollar figures. All items are expressed as a percent of total assets.

STEPS TO PREPARE A VERTICAL ANALYSIS OF A BALANCE SHEET

Step 1. Use the percentage formula, Rate = Portion ÷ Base, to find the percentage of each item on the balance sheet. Use each individual item as the portion and total assets as the base.

Step 2. Round each answer to the nearest tenth of a percent.

Note: A 0.1% differential may sometimes occur due to rounding.

Step 3. List the percent of each balance sheet item in a column to the right of the monetary amount.

EXAMPLE 2 PREPARING A VERTICAL ANALYSIS OF A BALANCE SHEET

Prepare a vertical analysis of the balance sheet for Hypothetical Enterprises, Inc., on page 525.

SOLUTION STRATEGY

Using the steps for vertical analysis, perform the following calculation for each balance sheet item and enter the results on the statement:

(continued)

$$\frac{\text{Cash}}{\text{Total assets}} = \frac{13{,}000}{341{,}300} = .038 = \underline{\underline{3.8\%}}$$

Learning Tip

In vertical analysis, remember that each individual item on the balance sheet is the *portion*, and Total Assets is the *base*.

Because of rounding, the percents may not always add up to exactly 100%. There may be a .1% differential.

Hypothetical Enterprises, Inc.
Balance Sheet
December 31, 20XX

Assets		
Current Assets		
Cash	$ 13,000	3.8%
Accounts Receivable	32,500	9.5
Merchandise Inventory	50,600	14.8
Prepaid Expenses	1,200	0.4
Supplies	4,000	1.2
Total Current Assets	101,300	29.7
Property, Plant, and Equipment		
Land	40,000	11.7
Buildings	125,000	36.6
Machinery and Equipment	60,000	17.6
Total Property, Plant, and Equipment	225,000	65.9
Investments and Other Assets		
Investments	10,000	2.9
Intangible Assets	5,000	1.5
Total Investments and Other Assets	15,000	4.4
Total Assets	$341,300	100.0%
Liabilities and Stockholders' Equity		
Current Liabilities		
Accounts Payable	$ 17,500	5.1%
Salaries Payable	5,400	1.6
Taxes Payable	6,500	1.9
Total Current Liabilities	29,400	8.6
Long-Term Liabilities		
Mortgage Payable	115,000	33.7
Debenture Bond	20,000	5.9
Total Long-Term Liabilities	135,000	39.6
Total Liabilities	164,400	48.2
Stockholders' Equity		
Capital Stock	126,900	37.2
Retained Earnings	50,000	14.6
Total Stockholders' Equity	176,900	51.8
Total Liabilities and Stockholders' Equity	$341,300	100.0%

TRY IT EXERCISE 2

Prepare a vertical analysis of the balance sheet for Royal Equipment Supply, Inc., on page 528.

CHECK YOUR ANSWERS WITH THE SOLUTIONS ON PAGE 565.

PREPARING A HORIZONTAL ANALYSIS OF A BALANCE SHEET

Frequently, balance sheets are prepared with the data from the current year or operating period side-by-side with the figures from one or more previous periods. This type of presentation is known as a **comparative balance sheet** because the data from different periods can be readily compared. This information provides managers, creditors, and investors with important data concerning the progress of the company over a period of time, financial trends that may be developing, and the likelihood of future success.

Comparative balance sheets use horizontal analysis to measure the increases and decreases that have taken place in the financial data between two operating periods. In **horizontal analysis**, each item of the current period is compared in dollars and percent with the corresponding item from a previous period.

comparative balance sheet Balance sheet prepared with the data from the current year or operating period side-by-side with the figures from one or more previous periods.

horizontal analysis Method of analyzing financial statements whereby each item of the current period is compared in dollars and percent with the corresponding item from a previous period.

STEPS TO PREPARE A HORIZONTAL ANALYSIS OF A BALANCE SHEET

Step 1. Set up a comparative balance sheet format with the current period listed first and the previous period listed next.

Step 2. Label the next two columns:

Increase (Decrease)	
Amount	Percent

Step 3. For each item on the balance sheet, calculate the dollar difference between the current and previous period and enter this figure in the Amount column. Enter all decreases in parentheses.

Step 4. Calculate the percent change (increase or decrease) using the percentage formula:

$$\textbf{Percent change (rate)} = \frac{\textbf{Amount of change, step 3 (portion)}}{\textbf{Previous period amount (base)}}$$

Step 5. Enter the percent change, rounded to the nearest tenth percent, in the Percent column. Once again, enter all decreases in parentheses.

TEACHING TIP
In horizontal analysis, be sure students use the "earlier" period as the *base* of the percent change calculation. Remind them that percent decreases are written in parentheses.

EXAMPLE 3 PREPARING A HORIZONTAL ANALYSIS OF A BALANCE SHEET

Using the following comparative balance sheet for the Cudjoe Construction Company, as of December 31, 2008 and 2009, prepare a horizontal analysis of this balance sheet for the owner, Bob Albrecht.

Cudjoe Construction Company
Comparative Balance Sheet
December 31, 2008 and 2009

Assets	**2009**	**2008**
Current Assets		
Cash	$ 3,500	$ 2,900
Accounts Receivable	12,450	7,680
Supplies	2,140	3,200
Total Current Assets	$ 18,090	$ 13,780

(continued)

Assets	2009	2008
Property, Plant, and Equipment		
Land	$ 15,000	$ 15,000
Buildings	54,000	61,000
Machinery and Equipment	134,200	123,400
Total Property, Plant, and Equipment	$203,200	$199,400
Total Assets	$221,290	$213,180
Liabilities and Owner's Equity		
Current Liabilities		
Accounts Payable	$ 5,300	$ 4,100
Notes Payable	8,500	9,400
Total Current Liabilities	$ 13,800	$ 13,500
Long-Term Liabilities		
Mortgage Payable	$ 26,330	$ 28,500
Note Payable on Equipment (5-year)	10,250	11,430
Total Long-Term Liabilities	$ 36,580	$ 39,930
Total Liabilities	$ 50,380	$ 53,430
Owner's Equity		
Bob Albrecht, Capital	$ 170,910	$159,750
Total Liabilities and Owner's Equity	$221,290	$213,180

SOLUTION STRATEGY

Using the steps for horizontal analysis, perform the following operation on all balance sheet items and then enter the results on the statement.

Cash

2009 amount − 2008 amount = 3,500 − 2,900
= $600 increase

$$\text{Percent change} = \frac{\text{Amount of change}}{\text{Previous period amount}} = \frac{600}{2{,}900} = .20689 = 20.7\%$$

Cudjoe Construction Company
Comparative Balance Sheet
December 31, 2008 and 2009

Assets	2009	2008	Increase (Decrease) Amount	Increase (Decrease) Percent
Current Assets				
Cash	$ 3,500	$ 2,900	$ 600	20.7
Accounts Receivable	12,450	7,680	4,770	62.1
Supplies	2,140	3,200	(1,060)	(33.1)
Total Current Assets	$ 18,090	$ 13,780	$4,310	31.3
Property, Plant, and Equipment				
Land	$ 15,000	$ 15,000	$ 0	0
Buildings	54,000	61,000	(7,000)	(11.5)
Machinery and Equipment	134,200	123,400	10,800	8.8
Total Property, Plant, and Equipment	$203,200	$199,400	$3,800	1.9
Total Assets	$221,290	$213,180	$8,110	3.8

(continued)

Liabilities and Owner's Equity				
Current Liabilities				
Accounts Payable	$ 5,300	$ 4,100	$ 1,200	29.3
Notes Payable	8,500	9,400	(900)	(9.6)
Total Current Liabilities	$ 13,800	$ 13,500	$ 300	2.2
Long-Term Liabilities				
Mortgage Payable	$ 26,330	$ 28,500	$ (2,170)	(7.6)
Note Payable on Equipment (5-year)	10,250	11,430	(1,180)	(10.3)
Total Long-Term Liabilities	$ 36,580	$ 39,930	$ (3,350)	(8.4)
Total Liabilities	$ 50,380	$ 53,430	$ (3,050)	(5.7)
Owner's Equity				
Bob Albrecht, Capital	$ 170,910	$159,750	$11,160	7.0
Total Liabilities and Owner's Equity	$221,290	$213,180	$ 8,110	3.8

TRY IT EXERCISE 3

Complete the following comparative balance sheet with horizontal analysis for Gilbert S. Cohen Industries, Inc.

Gilbert S. Cohen Industries, Inc.
Comparative Balance Sheet
December 31, 2008 and 2009

			Increase (Decrease)	
Assets	**2009**	**2008**	**Amount**	**Percent**
Current Assets				
Cash	$ 8,700	$ 5,430		
Accounts Receivable	23,110	18,450		
Notes Receivable	2,900	3,400		
Supplies	4,540	3,980		
Total Current Assets				
Property, Plant, and Equipment				
Land	$ 34,000	$ 34,000		
Buildings	76,300	79,800		
Machinery and Equipment	54,700	48,900		
Total Property, Plant, and Equipment				
Investments and Other Assets	54,230	49,810		
Total Assets				
Liabilities and Stockholders' Equity				
Current Liabilities				
Accounts Payable	$ 15,330	$ 19,650		
Salaries Payable	7,680	7,190		
Total Current Liabilities				
Long-Term Liabilities				
Mortgage Payable	$ 53,010	$ 54,200		
Note Payable (3-year)	32,400	33,560		
Total Long-Term Liabilities				
Total Liabilities				

(continued)

Liabilities and Stockholders' Equity	2009	2008		
Stockholders' Equity				
Common Stock	$130,060	$120,170	______	______
Retained Earnings	20,000	9,000	______	______
Total Liabilities and Stockholders' Equity	______	______	______	______

CHECK YOUR ANSWERS WITH THE SOLUTIONS ON PAGE 566.

15 SECTION I Review Exercises

Solution Transparencies

Calculate the following values according to the accounting equation.

	Assets	Liabilities	Owner's Equity
1.	$283,000	$121,400	$161,600
2.	$548,900	$335,900	$213,000
3.	$ 45,300	$29,000	$16,300

CLASSROOM ACTIVITY

In groups, have students complete Review Exercises 4–25. Next, have the groups compare their answers with those of another group and resolve any differences.

For the following balance sheet items, check the appropriate category.

	Current Asset	Fixed Asset	Current Liability	Long-Term Liability	Owner's Equity
4. Land		✓			
5. Supplies	✓				
6. Marketable securities	✓				
7. Retained earnings					✓
8. Buildings		✓			
9. Mortgage payable				✓	
10. Cash	✓				
11. Notes payable			✓		
12. Equipment		✓			
13. Note receivable (3-month)	✓				
14. Prepaid expenses	✓				
15. Merchandise inventory	✓				
16. Common stock					✓
17. Trucks		✓			
18. Debenture bonds				✓	
19. Accounts receivable	✓				
20. Salaries payable			✓		
21. R. Smith, capital					✓
22. Savings account	✓				
23. Preferred stock					✓
24. Note payable (2-year)				✓	
25. Taxes payable			✓		

Prepare the following statements on separate sheets of paper.

Financial statement solutions for Exercises 26–28 appear in Appendix B, following the index.

26. a. Use the following financial information to calculate the owner's equity and prepare a balance sheet with vertical analysis as of December 31, 2008, for Victory Lane Sporting Goods, a sole proprietorship owned by Kyle Pressman: current assets, $157,600; property, plant, and equipment, $42,000; investments and other assets, $35,700; current liabilities, $21,200; long-term liabilities, $53,400.

Victory Lane Sporting Goods
Balance Sheet
December 31, 2008

b. The following financial information is for Victory Lane Sporting Goods as of December 31, 2009: current assets, $175,300; property, plant, and equipment, $43,600; investments and other assets, $39,200; current liabilities, $27,700; long-term liabilities, $51,000.

Calculate the owner's equity for 2009 and prepare a comparative balance sheet with horizontal analysis for 2008 and 2009.

Victory Lane Sporting Goods
Comparative Balance Sheet
December 31, 2008 and 2009

27. a. Use the following financial information to prepare a balance sheet with vertical analysis as of June 30, 2008, for Flagship Industries, Inc.: cash, $44,300; accounts receivable, $127,600; merchandise inventory, $88,100; prepaid maintenance, $4,100; office supplies, $4,000; land, $154,000; building, $237,000; fixtures, $21,400; vehicles, $64,000; computers, $13,000; goodwill, $20,000; investments, $32,000; accounts payable, $55,700; salaries payable, $23,200; notes payable (6-month), $38,000; mortgage payable, $91,300; debenture bonds, $165,000; common stock, $350,000; and retained earnings, $86,300.

Flagship Industries, Inc.
Balance Sheet
June 30, 2008

b. The following financial information is for Flagship Industries as of June 30, 2009: cash, $40,200; accounts receivable, $131,400; merchandise inventory, $92,200; prepaid maintenance, $3,700; office supplies, $6,200; land, $154,000; building, $231,700; fixtures, $23,900; vehicles, $55,100; computers, $16,800; goodwill, $22,000; investments, $36,400; accounts payable, $51,800; salaries payable, $25,100; notes payable (6-month), $19,000; mortgage payable, $88,900; debenture bonds, $165,000; common stock, $350,000; and retained earnings, $113,800.

Prepare a comparative balance sheet with horizontal analysis for 2008 and 2009.

Flagship Industries, Inc.
Comparative Balance Sheet
June 30, 2008 and 2009

BUSINESS DECISION THE BALANCE SHEET

28. From the consolidated balance sheets for Kellogg on page 536.

a. Prepare a horizontal analysis of the Current assets section comparing 2005 and 2006.

b. Prepare a vertical analysis of the Current liabilities section for 2006.

© PRNewsFoto/Kellogg Company (AP photo)

With 2006 sales of nearly $11 billion, Kellogg Company is the world's leading producer of cereal and a leading producer of convenience foods, including cookies, crackers, toaster pastries, cereal bars, fruit snacks, frozen waffles, and veggie foods. The Company's brands include *Kellogg's, Keebler, Pop-Tarts, Eggo, Cheez-It, Nutri-Grain, Rice Krispies, Murray, Morningstar Farms, Austin, Famous Amos,* and *Kashi*. Kellogg's products are manufactured in 17 countries and marketed in more than 180 countries around the world.

Kellogg Company and Subsidiaries

Consolidated Balance Sheets

(in millions, except share data)	**2006**	2005
Current assets		
Cash and cash equivalents	**$ 410.6**	$ 219.1
Accounts receivable, net	**944.8**	879.1
Inventories	**823.9**	717.0
Other current assets	**247.7**	381.3
Total current assets	**$ 2,427.0**	$ 2,196.5
Property, net	**2,815.6**	2,648.4
Other assets	**5,471.4**	5,729.6
Total assets	**$ 10,714.0**	$10,574.5
Current liabilities		
Current maturities of long-term debt	**$ 723.3**	$ 83.6
Notes payable	**1,268.0**	1,111.1
Accounts payable	**910.4**	883.3
Other current liabilities	**1,118.5**	1,084.8
Total current liabilities	**$ 4,020.2**	$ 3,162.8
Long-term debt	**3,053.0**	3,702.6
Other liabilities	**1,571.8**	1,425.4
Shareholders' equity		
Common stock, $.25 par value, 1,000,000,000 shares authorized	**104.6**	104.6
Capital in excess of par value	**292.3**	58.9
Retained earnings	**3,630.4**	3,266.1
Treasury stock at cost: 20,817,930 shares in 2006 and 13,121,446 shares in 2005	**(912.1)**	(569.8)
Accumulated other comprehensive income (loss)	**(1,046.2)**	(576.1)
Total shareholders' equity	**$ 2,069.0**	$ 2,283.7
Total liabilities and shareholders' equity	**$ 10,714.0**	$10,574.5

THE INCOME STATEMENT

The Bottom Line

When it is all said and done, the question is "how well did the business do?" The real score is found on the income statement. An **income statement** is a summary of the operations of a business over a period of time—usually a month, a quarter, or a year. For any business to exist, it must have earnings and also expenses, either in the form of cash or credit. The income statement shows the **revenue** or earnings of the business from the sale of goods and services; the **expenses**, the costs incurred to generate that revenue; and the bottom line **profit** or **loss**, the difference between revenue and expenses.

income, operating, or profit and loss statement Financial statement summarizing the operations of a business over a period of time. Illustrates the amount of revenue earned, expenses incurred, and the resulting profit or loss: Revenue − Expenses = Profit (or loss).

revenue The primary source of money, both cash and credit, flowing into the business from its customers for goods sold or services rendered over a period of time.

Profit (or Loss) = Revenue − Total Expenses

where: Revenue = Earnings (either cash or credit) from sales during the period
Total expenses = Cost of goods sold + Operating expenses + Taxes

15-4

PREPARING AN INCOME STATEMENT

15-4

Once again, let's begin by looking at a typical income statement. As before, we shall use Hypothetical Enterprises, Inc., to illustrate. Carefully look over the following income statement and then read the descriptions of each section and its components.

expenses Costs incurred by a business in the process of earning revenue.

profit or loss The difference between revenue earned and expenses incurred during an operating period. Profit when revenue is greater than expenses; loss when expenses are greater than revenue. Profit is also known as earnings or income.

Hypothetical Enterprises, Inc.
Income Statement for the year ended December 31, 20XX

Revenue		
Gross Sales	$923,444	
Less: Sales Returns and Allowances	22,875	
Sales Discounts	3,625	
Net Sales		$896,944
Cost of Goods Sold		
Merchandise Inventory, Jan. 1	220,350	
Net Purchases	337,400	
Freight In	12,350	
Goods Available for Sale	570,100	
Less: Merchandise Inventory, Dec. 31	88,560	
Cost of Goods Sold		481,540
Gross Margin		415,404
Operating Expenses		
Salaries and Benefits	152,600	
Rent and Utilities	35,778	
Advertising and Promotion	32,871	
Insurance	8,258	
General and Administrative Expenses	41,340	
Depreciation	19,890	
Miscellaneous Expenses	14,790	
Total Operating Expenses		305,527
Income before Taxes		109,877
Income Tax		18,609
Net Income		$ 91,268

15-5

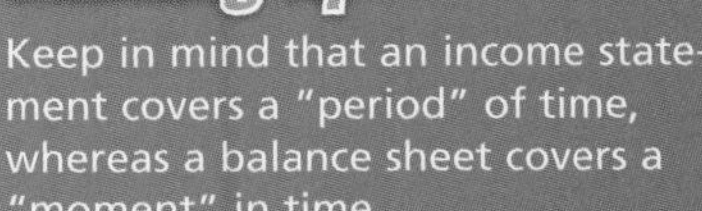

Keep in mind that an income statement covers a "period" of time, whereas a balance sheet covers a "moment" in time.

TEACHING TIP

When discussing income statements,

- Review the definition of *gross*, before deductions, and *net*, after deductions. Remind students that these concepts were covered in Chapter 9, Payroll, when discussing gross pay and net pay.
- Be sure students know that the word *margin* is another way of saying *profit*. The terms *gross margin* and *gross profit* can be used interchangeably.

Income Statement Components

REVENUE The revenue section of the income statement represents the primary source of money, both cash and credit, flowing into the business from its customers for goods sold or services rendered.

  Gross sales
− Sales returns and allowances
− Sales discounts
Net sales

- Gross sales—Total sales of goods and services achieved by the company during the operating period.
- Sales returns and allowances—Amount of merchandise returned for cash or credit by customers for various reasons.
- Sales discounts—Cash discounts given to customers by the business as an incentive for early payment of an invoice. For example, 3/15, n/45, where there is a 3% extra discount if the invoice is paid within 15 days, rather than the net date, 45 days.
- Net sales—Amount received after taking into consideration returned goods, allowances, and sales discounts.

COST OF GOODS SOLD The cost of goods sold section represents the cost to the business of the merchandise that was sold during the operating period.

  Merchandise inventory (beginning)
+ Net purchases
+ Freight in
Goods available for sale
− Merchandise inventory (ending)
Cost of goods sold

- Merchandise inventory (beginning of operating period)—Total value of the goods in inventory at the beginning of the operating period. This *beginning inventory* is last period's ending inventory.
- Net purchases—Amount, at cost, of merchandise purchased during the period for resale to customers after deducting purchase returns and allowances and purchase discounts earned.
- Freight in—Total amount of the freight or transportation charges incurred for the net purchases.
- Goods available for sale—The total amount of the goods available to be sold during the operating period. It is the sum of beginning inventory, net purchases, and freight in.
- Merchandise inventory (end of operating period)—Total value of the goods remaining in inventory at the end of the operating period. This *ending inventory* is next period's beginning inventory.
- Cost of goods sold—Total value of the goods that were sold during the period. It is the difference between goods available for sale and the ending merchandise inventory.

In the Business World

Real-World Connection

The phrase "all to the good" is derived from an old accounting term. The word *good* was used in the nineteenth century to mean *profit*. Thus, after expenses were taken out, the rest "went to the good!"

GROSS MARGIN Gross margin, also known as gross profit, represents the difference between net sales and cost of goods sold.

  Net sales
− Cost of goods sold
Gross margin

TOTAL OPERATING EXPENSES Total operating expenses are the sum of all the expenses incurred by the business during the operating period, except the cost of goods sold and taxes. Operating expenses differ from company to company. Some typical examples are salaries and benefits, sales commissions, rent and utilities, advertising and promotion, insurance, general and administrative expenses, depreciation, and miscellaneous expenses.

INCOME BEFORE TAXES This figure represents the money a company made before paying income tax. It is the difference between gross margin and total operating expenses.

Gross margin
− Total operating expenses
Income before taxes

INCOME TAX This expense figure is the amount of income tax, both state and federal, that is paid by the business during the operating period.

NET INCOME, NET PROFIT or (NET LOSS) Literally the bottom line of the income statement. It is the difference between income before taxes and the income tax paid.

Income before taxes
− Income tax
Net income (loss)

Record Profit
On February 1, 2008, Exxon Mobil Corp. shattered the records for both the largest annual and quarterly profit for a U.S. company, with $40.6 billion and $11.7 billion, respectively. The world's largest publicly traded oil company benefited from historic crude oil prices at 2007 year's end.

STEPS TO PREPARE AN INCOME STATEMENT

Step 1. Centered at the top of the page, write the company name, type of statement, and period of time covered by the statement (example "Year ended Dec. 31, 2008" or "April 2008").

Step 2. In a two-column format, as illustrated on page 537, calculate:

A. *Net Sales:*

Gross sales
− Sales returns and allowances
− Sales discounts
Net sales

B. *Cost of Goods Sold:*

Merchandise inventory (beginning)
+ Net purchases
+ Freight in
Goods available for sale
− Merchandise inventory (ending)
Cost of goods sold

C. *Gross Margin:*

Net sales
− Cost of goods sold
Gross margin

D. *Total Operating Expenses:* Sum of all operating expenses

E. *Income before Taxes:*

Gross margin
− Total operating expenses
Income before taxes

F. *Net Income:*

Income before taxes
− Income tax
Net income (loss)

CLASSROOM ACTIVITY
To help reinforce the concepts in this chapter, have students prepare a "personal" balance sheet and/or income statement.

Point out that you are not interested in their "personal numbers." The lesson here is whether they understand how to set up the financial statement categories.

The popular business term *bottom line* literally comes from the structure of an income statement:

Total revenue
−Total expenses
Income (loss) ←— Bottom line

CLASSROOM ACTIVITY

Demonstrate to students how the "bottom line" of an income statement can be improved by increasing revenue, cutting expenses, or a combination of both.

In groups, have students list ways in which companies in the following categories can reduce their expenses or increase their revenues:

Retail store
Manufacturing firm
Bank
Restaurant
Airline
Hotel
Other

 15-6

EXAMPLE 4 PREPARING AN INCOME STATEMENT

Use the following financial information to prepare an income statement for Royal Equipment Supply, Inc., for the year ended December 31, 2008: gross sales, $458,400; sales returns and allowances, $13,200; sales discounts, $1,244; merchandise inventory, Jan. 1, 2008, $198,700; merchandise inventory, Dec. 31, 2008, $76,400; net purchases, $86,760; freight in, $875; salaries, $124,200; rent, $21,000; utilities, $1,780; advertising, $5,400; insurance, $2,340; administrative expenses, $14,500; miscellaneous expenses, $6,000; and income tax, $17,335.

SOLUTION STRATEGY

The income statement for Royal Equipment Supply, Inc., follows.

Royal Equipment Supply, Inc.
Income Statement
For the year ended December 31, 2008

Revenue		
Gross Sales	$458,400	
Less: Sales Returns and Allowances	13,200	
Sales Discounts	1,244	
Net Sales		$443,956
Cost of Goods Sold		
Merchandise Inventory, Jan. 1	198,700	
Net Purchases	86,760	
Freight In	875	
Goods Available for Sale	286,335	
Less: Merchandise Inventory, Dec. 31	76,400	
Cost of Goods Sold		209,935
Gross Margin		234,021
Operating Expenses		
Salaries	124,200	
Rent	21,000	
Utilities	1,780	
Advertising	5,400	
Insurance	2,340	
Administrative Expenses	14,500	
Miscellaneous Expenses	6,000	
Total Operating Expenses		175,220
Income before Taxes		58,801
Income Tax		17,335
Net Income		$ 41,466

TRY IT EXERCISE 4

Use the following financial information to prepare an income statement for Cutting Edge Manufacturing, Inc., for the year ended December 31, 2009: gross sales, $1,356,000; sales returns and allowances, $93,100; sales discounts, $4,268; merchandise inventory, Jan. 1, 2009, $324,800; merchandise inventory, Dec. 31, 2009, $179,100; net purchases, $255,320; freight in, $3,911; salaries, $375,900; rent, $166,000; utilities, $7,730; advertising, $73,300; insurance, $22,940; administrative expenses, $84,500; miscellaneous expenses, $24,900; and income tax, $34,760.

CHECK YOUR STATEMENT WITH THE SOLUTION ON PAGE 566.

PREPARING A VERTICAL ANALYSIS OF AN INCOME STATEMENT

Vertical analysis can be applied to the income statement just as it was to the balance sheet. Each figure on the income statement is expressed as a percent of net sales (net sales = 100%). The resulting figures describe how net sales were distributed among the expenses and what percent was left as net profit. For analysis purposes, this information can then be compared with the figures from previous operating periods for the company, with competitor's figures, or with published industry averages for similar-size companies.

As with balance sheets, income statements with vertical analysis can be displayed in the format known as **common-size**, in which all figures on the statement appear as percentages.

common-size income statement
A special form of income statement that lists only the vertical analysis percentages, not the dollar figures. All items are expressed as a percent of net sales.

STEPS TO PREPARE A VERTICAL ANALYSIS OF AN INCOME STATEMENT

Step 1. Use the percentage formula, Rate = Portion ÷ Base, to find the rate of each item on the income statement. Use each individual item as the portion and net sales as the base.

Step 2. Round each answer to the nearest tenth of a percent.

Note: A 0.1% differential may sometimes occur due to rounding.

Step 3. List the percentage of each statement item in a column to the right of the monetary amount.

EXAMPLE 5 PREPARING A VERTICAL ANALYSIS OF AN INCOME STATEMENT

Prepare a vertical analysis of the income statement for Hypothetical Enterprises, Inc., on page 537.

SOLUTION STRATEGY

Using the steps for vertical analysis, perform the following calculation for each income statement item and enter the results on the income statement as follows.

$$\frac{\text{Gross sales}}{\text{Net sales}} = \frac{923{,}444}{896{,}944} = 1.0295 = 103.0\%$$

Hypothetical Enterprises, Inc.
Income Statement for the year ended December 31, 20XX

Revenue		
Gross Sales	$923,444	103.0
Less: Sales Returns and Allowances	22,875	2.6
Sales Discounts	3,625	.4
Net Sales	896,944	100.0%
Cost of Goods Sold		
Merchandise Inventory, Jan. 1	220,350	24.6
Net Purchases	337,400	37.6
Freight In	12,350	1.4
Goods Available for Sale	570,100	63.6
Less: Merchandise Inventory, Dec. 31	88,560	9.9
Cost of Goods Sold	481,540	53.7
Gross Margin	415,404	46.3

(continued)

TEACHING TIP
In vertical analysis, remind students that each individual item on the income statement is the *portion* and net sales is the *base*.

As with the balance sheet, the percents may not always add up to exactly 100%. There may be a .1% differential due to rounding.

TEACHING TIP
As with the balance sheet, in horizontal analysis of an income statement, be sure students use the "earlier" period as the *base* of the percent change calculation.

Once again, remind them that percent decreases are written in parentheses.

Operating Expenses		
Salaries and Benefits	152,600	17.0
Rent and Utilities	35,778	4.0
Advertising and Promotion	32,871	3.7
Insurance	8,258	.9
General and Administrative Expenses	41,340	4.6
Depreciation	19,890	2.2
Miscellaneous Expenses	14,790	1.6
Total Operating Expenses	305,527	34.1
Income before Taxes	109,877	12.3
Income Tax	18,609	2.1
Net Income	$ 91,268	10.2%

TRY IT EXERCISE 5

Prepare a vertical analysis of the income statement for Royal Equipment Supply, Inc., on page 540.

CHECK YOUR STATEMENT WITH THE SOLUTION ON PAGE 566.

15-6 PREPARING A HORIZONTAL ANALYSIS OF AN INCOME STATEMENT

As with the balance sheet, the income statement can be prepared in a format that compares the financial data of the business from one operating period to another. This horizontal analysis provides percent increase or decrease information for each item on the income statement. Information such as this provides a very useful progress report of the company. As before, the previous or original period figure is the base.

STEPS TO PREPARE A HORIZONTAL ANALYSIS OF AN INCOME STATEMENT

Step 1. Set up a comparative income statement format with the current period listed first and the previous period listed next.

Step 2. Label the next two columns:

Increase (Decrease)	
Amount	**Percent**

Step 3. For each item on the income statement, calculate the dollar difference between the current and previous period and enter this figure in the Amount column. Enter all decreases in parentheses.

Step 4. Calculate the percent change (increase or decrease) by the percentage formula:

$$\textbf{Percent change (rate)} = \frac{\textbf{Amount of change, Step 3 (portion)}}{\textbf{Previous period amount (base)}}$$

Step 5. Enter the percent change, rounded to the nearest tenth percent, in the Percent column. Once again, enter all decreases in parentheses.

EXAMPLE 6 PREPARING A HORIZONTAL ANALYSIS OF AN INCOME STATEMENT

A comparative income statement for All-Star Appliances, Inc., for the years 2007 and 2008, follows. Prepare a horizontal analysis of the statement for the company.

All-Star Appliances, Inc.
Comparative Income Statement

	2008	2007
Revenue		
Gross Sales	$623,247	$599,650
Less: Sales Returns and Allowances	8,550	9,470
Sales Discounts	3,400	1,233
Net Sales	611,297	588,947
Cost of Goods Sold		
Merchandise Inventory, Jan. 1	158,540	134,270
Purchases	117,290	111,208
Freight In	2,460	1,980
Goods Available for Sale	278,290	247,458
Less: Merchandise Inventory, Dec. 31	149,900	158,540
Cost of Goods Sold	128,390	88,918
Gross Margin	482,907	500,029
Operating Expenses		
Salaries and Benefits	165,300	161,200
Rent and Utilities	77,550	76,850
Depreciation	74,350	75,040
Insurance	4,560	3,900
Office Expenses	34,000	41,200
Warehouse Expenses	41,370	67,400
Total Operating Expenses	397,130	425,590
Income before Taxes	85,777	74,439
Income Tax	27,400	19,700
Net Income	$ 58,377	$ 54,739

SOLUTION STRATEGY

Using the steps for horizontal analysis, perform the following operation on all income statement items and then enter the results on the statement.

Gross Sales 2008 amount − 2007 amount = Amount of change

$$623{,}247 - 599{,}650 = \$23{,}597 \text{ increase}$$

$$\text{Percent change} = \frac{\text{Amount of change}}{\text{Previous period amount}} = \frac{23{,}597}{599{,}650} = 3.9\%$$

All-Star Appliances, Inc.
Comparative Income Statement

			Increase (Decrease)	
	2008	**2007**	**Amount**	**Percent**
Revenue				
Gross Sales	$623,247	$599,650	$23,597	3.9
Less: Sales Returns and Allowances	8,550	9,470	(920)	(9.7)
Sales Discounts	3,400	1,233	2,167	175.8
Net Sales	611,297	588,947	22,350	3.8

(continued)

	2008	2007	Increase (Decrease) Amount	Percent
Cost of Goods Sold				
Merchandise Inventory, Jan. 1	158,540	134,270	24,270	18.1
Purchases	117,290	111,208	6,082	5.5
Freight In	2,460	1,980	480	24.2
Goods Available for Sale	278,290	247,458	30,832	12.5
Less: Merchandise Inventory, Dec. 31	149,900	158,540	(8,640)	(5.4)
Cost of Goods Sold	128,390	88,918	39,472	44.4
Gross Margin	482,907	500,029	(17,122)	(3.4)
Operating Expenses				
Salaries and Benefits	165,300	161,200	4,100	2.5
Rent and Utilities	77,550	76,850	700	.9
Depreciation	74,350	75,040	(690)	(.9)
Insurance	4,560	3,900	660	16.9
Office Expenses	34,000	41,200	(7,200)	(17.5)
Warehouse Expenses	41,370	67,400	(26,030)	(38.6)
Total Operating Expenses	397,130	425,590	(28,460)	(6.7)
Income before Taxes	85,777	74,439	11,338	15.2
Income Tax	27,400	19,700	7,700	39.1
Net Income	$ 58,377	$ 54,739	$ 3,638	6.6

TRY IT EXERCISE 6

Complete the following comparative income statement with horizontal analysis for Timely Watch Company, Inc.

Timely Watch Company, Inc.
Comparative Income Statement

	2008	2007	Increase (Decrease) Amount	Percent
Revenue				
Gross Sales	$1,223,000	$996,500	______	______
Less: Sales Returns and Allowances	121,340	99,600	______	______
Sales Discounts	63,120	51,237	______	______
Net Sales	______	______	______	______
Cost of Goods Sold				
Merchandise Inventory, Jan. 1	311,200	331,000	______	______
Purchases	603,290	271,128	______	______
Freight In	18,640	13,400	______	______
Goods Available for Sale	______	______	______	______
Less: Merchandise Inventory, Dec. 31	585,400	311,200	______	______
Cost of Goods Sold	______	______	______	______
Gross Margin	______	______	______	______

(continued)

Operating Expenses				
Salaries and Benefits	215,200	121,800	______	______
Rent and Utilities	124,650	124,650	______	______
Depreciation	43,500	41,230	______	______
Insurance	24,970	23,800	______	______
Administrative Store Expenses	58,200	33,900	______	______
Warehouse Expenses	42,380	45,450	______	______
Total Operating Expenses	______	______	______	______
Income before Taxes	______	______	______	______
Income Tax	66,280	41,670	______	______
Net Income	______	______	______	______

CHECK YOUR ANSWERS WITH THE SOLUTIONS ON PAGE 567.

Review Exercises

SECTION II 15

Solution Transparencies

Calculate the missing information based on the format of the income statement.

	Net Sales	Cost of Goods Sold	Gross Margin	Operating Expenses	Net Profit
1.	$334,500	$132,300	$202,200	$108,000	$94,200
2.	$1,640,000	$880,000	$760,000	$354,780	$405,220
3.	$675,530	$257,000	$418,530	$334,160	$84,370

EXCEL

4. For the third quarter of 2008, Iberia Tiles had gross sales of $315,450; sales returns and allowances of $23,100; and sales discounts of $18,700. What were the net sales?

Gross sales	$315,450
Less:	
Sales returns + allowance	23,100
Sales discounts	18,700
Net sales	$273,650

5. For the month of August, King Tire Company, Inc., had the following financial information: merchandise inventory, August 1, $244,500; merchandise inventory, August 31, $193,440; gross purchases, $79,350; purchase returns and allowances, $8,700; and freight in, $970.

   a. What is the amount of the goods available for sale?

Inventory (August 1)	$244,500
Net purchases	70,650 (79,350 − 8,700)
Freight in	+ 970
Goods available for sale	$316,120

   b. What is the cost of goods sold for August?

Goods available for sale	$316,120
Inventory (August 31)	−193,440
Cost of goods sold	$122,680

c. If net sales were $335,000, what was the gross margin for August?

Net sales	$335,000
Cost of goods sold	−122,680
Gross margin	$212,320

d. If total operating expenses were $167,200, what was the net profit?

Gross margin	$212,320
Operating expenses	−167,200
Net profit	$ 45,120

Prepare the following statements on separate sheets of paper.

Financial statement solutions for Exercises 6 and 7 appear in Appendix B, following the index.

6. a. As the assistant accounting manager for Jefferson Airplane Parts, Inc., construct an income statement with vertical analysis for the first quarter of 2008 from the following information: gross sales, $240,000; sales discounts, $43,500; beginning inventory, Jan. 1, $86,400; ending inventory, March 31, $103,200; net purchases, $76,900; total operating expenses, $108,000; income tax, $14,550.

Jefferson Airplane Parts, Inc.
Income Statement
January 1 to March 31, 2008

b. You have just received a report with the second quarter figures. Prepare a comparative income statement with horizontal analysis for the first and second quarter of 2008: gross sales, $297,000; sales discounts, $41,300; beginning inventory, April 1, $103,200; ending inventory, June 30, $96,580; net purchases, $84,320; total operating expenses, $126,700; income tax, $16,400.

Jefferson Airplane Parts, Inc.
Comparative Income Statement
First and Second Quarter, 2008

7. a. Use the following financial information to construct a 2008 income statement with vertical analysis for the Sweets & Treats Candy Company, Inc.: gross sales, $2,249,000; sales returns and allowances, $143,500; sales discounts, $54,290; merchandise inventory, Jan. 1, 2008, $875,330; merchandise inventory, Dec. 31, 2008, $716,090; net purchases, $546,920; freight in, $11,320; salaries, $319,800; rent, $213,100; depreciation, $51,200; utilities, $35,660; advertising, $249,600; insurance, $39,410; administrative expenses, $91,700; miscellaneous expenses, $107,500; and income tax, $38,450.

Sweets & Treats Candy Company, Inc.
Income Statement, 2008

b. The following data represents Sweets & Treats' operating results for 2009. Prepare a comparative income statement with horizontal analysis for 2008 and 2009: gross sales, $2,125,000; sales returns and allowances, $126,400; sales discounts, $73,380; merchandise inventory, Jan. 1, 2009, $716,090; merchandise inventory, Dec. 31, 2009, $584,550; net purchases, $482,620; freight in, $9,220; salaries, $340,900; rent, $215,000; depreciation, $56,300; utilities, $29,690; advertising, $217,300; insurance, $39,410; administrative expenses, $95,850; miscellaneous expenses, $102,500; and income tax, $44,530.

Sweets & Treats Candy Company, Inc.
Comparative Income Statement, 2008 and 2009

BUSINESS DECISION THE INCOME STATEMENT

8. From the following income statements for FedEx Corporation,
   a. Prepare a horizontal analysis of the operating income section comparing 2006 and 2007.
   b. Prepare a vertical analysis of the operating expenses section for 2007.

Answers for Exercise 8 appear in Appendix B, following the index.

FedEx Corporation

Consolidated Statements of Income

(In millions, except per share amounts)	Years ended May 31, 2007	2006	2005
REVENUES	**$35,214**	$32,294	$29,363
Operating Expenses:			
Salaries and employee benefits	**13,740**	12,571	11,963
Purchased transportation	**3,873**	3,251	2,935
Rentals and landing fees	**2,343**	2,390	2,299
Depreciation and amortization	**1,742**	1,550	1,462
Fuel	**3,533**	3,256	2,317
Maintenance and repairs	**1,952**	1,777	1,695
Other	**4,755**	4,485	4,221
	31,938	29,280	26,892
OPERATING INCOME	**3,276**	3,014	2,471
Other Income (Expense):			
Interest expense	**(136)**	(142)	(160)
Interest income	**83**	38	21
Other, net	**(8)**	(11)	(19)
	(61)	(115)	(158)
Income Before Income Taxes	**3,215**	2,899	2,313
Provision for Income Taxes	**1,199**	1,093	864
NET INCOME	**$ 2,016**	$ 1,806	$ 1,449
BASIC EARNINGS PER COMMON SHARE	**$ 6.57**	$ 5.94	$ 4.81
DILUTED EARNINGS PER COMMON SHARE	**$ 6.48**	$ 5.83	$ 4.72

© Paul Sakuma/Associated Press

FedEx provides a broad portfolio of transportation, e-commerce, and business services through companies under the FedEx brand. These include FedEx Express, the world's largest express transportation company; FedEx Ground, a leading provider of small-package ground delivery services; FedEx Freight, a leading U.S. provider of less-than-truckload ("LTL") freight services; and FedEx Kinko's, a leading provider of document solutions and business services.

In 2007, its 35th year of continuous operation, FedEx's 280,000 worldwide employees generated revenue of over $35.1 billion, with net income of more than $2 billion, or $6.48 per share.

FINANCIAL RATIOS AND TREND ANALYSIS

SECTION III 15

In addition to vertical and horizontal analysis of financial statements, managers, creditors, and investors also study comparisons among various components on the statements. These comparisons are expressed as ratios and are known as **financial ratios**.

Basically, financial ratios represent an effort by analysts to standardize financial information, which in turn makes comparisons more meaningful. The fundamental purpose of

financial ratios A series of comparisons of financial statement components in ratio form used by analysts to evaluate the operating performance of a company.

To be most meaningful, financial ratios should be compared with ratios from previous operating periods of the company and with industry statistics for similar-sized companies.

This information can be found in an annual publication called *Industry Norms and Ratios*, produced by Dun and Bradstreet, or *The Survey of Current Business*, published by the U.S. Department of Commerce.

ratio analysis is to indicate areas requiring further investigation. Think of them as signals indicating areas of potential strength or weakness of the firm. Frequently, financial ratios have to be examined more closely to discover their true meaning. A high ratio, for example, might indicate that the numerator figure is too high or the denominator figure is too low.

Financial ratios fall into four major categories:

- **Liquidity ratios** tell how well a company can pay off its short-term debts and meet unexpected needs for cash.
- **Efficiency ratios** indicate how effectively a company uses its resources to generate sales.
- **Leverage ratios** show how and to what degree a company has financed its assets.
- **Profitability ratios** tell how much of each dollar of sales, assets, and stockholders' investment resulted in bottom-line net profit.

CALCULATING FINANCIAL RATIOS

ratio A comparison of one amount to another.

As we learned in Chapter 5, a **ratio** is a comparison of one amount to another. A financial ratio is simply a ratio whose numerator and denominator are financial information taken from the balance sheet, income statement, or other important business data.

Ratios may be stated in a number of ways. For example, a ratio of credit sales, $40,000, to total sales, $100,000, in a retail store may be stated as:

a. Credit sales ratio is $\frac{40,000}{100,000}$,
or 4 to 10,
or 2 to 5 (written 2:5).

b. Credit sales are $\frac{4}{10}$, or 40% of total sales.

c. For every $1.00 of sales, $.40 is on credit.

Conversely, the ratio of total sales, $100,000, to credit sales, $40,000, in a retail store may be stated as:

a. Total sales ratio is $\frac{100,000}{40,000}$,
or 10 to 4,
or 2.5 to 1 (written 2.5:1).

b. Total sales are $\frac{10}{4}$, or 250% of credit sales.

c. For every $2.50 of sales, $1.00 is on credit.

To illustrate how ratios are used in financial analysis, let's apply this concept to Hypothetical Enterprises, Inc., a company introduced in Sections I and II of this chapter.

Managers analyze financial statement data to determine a business's strengths and weaknesses.

EXAMPLE 7 CALCULATING FINANCIAL RATIOS

Calculate the financial ratios for Hypothetical Enterprises, Inc., using the data from the financial statements presented on pages 525 and 537.

SOLUTION STRATEGY

Liquidity Ratios

Businesses must have enough cash on hand to pay their bills as they come due. The **liquidity ratios** examine the relationship between a firm's current assets and its maturing obligations. The amount of a firm's working capital and these ratios are good indicators of a firm's ability to pay its bills over the next few months. Short-term creditors pay particular attention to these figures.

The term **working capital** refers to the difference between current assets and current liabilities at a point in time. Theoretically, it is the amount of money that would be left over if all the current liabilities were paid off by current assets.

liquidity ratios Financial ratios that tell how well a company can pay off its short-term debts and meet unexpected needs for cash.

working capital The difference between current assets and current liabilities at a point in time. Theoretically, the amount of money left over if all the current liabilities were paid off by current assets.

Working capital = Current assets − Current liabilities

Current ratio or **working capital ratio** is the comparison of a firm's current assets to current liabilities. This ratio indicates the amount of current assets available to pay off $1 of current debt. A current ratio of 2:1 or greater is considered by banks and other lending institutions to be an acceptable ratio.

current ratio, or working capital ratio The comparison of a firm's current assets to current liabilities.

$$\textbf{Current ratio} = \frac{\textbf{Current assets}}{\textbf{Current liabilities}}$$

CLASSROOM ACTIVITY

In groups, have students discuss which financial ratios would be most important to

- A banker deciding whether to loan money to a company
- A supplier qualifying a company for net/90 merchandise credit
- A prospective investor considering the purchase of stock in a corporation

Hypothetical Enterprises, Inc.:

$$\text{Working capital} = 101{,}300 - 29{,}400 = \underline{\underline{\$71{,}900}}$$

$$\text{Current ratio} = \frac{101{,}300}{29{,}400} = 3.45 = \underline{\underline{3.45{:}1}}$$

Analysis: This ratio shows that Hypothetical has $3.45 in current assets for each $1.00 it owes in current liabilities. A current ratio of 3.45:1 indicates that the company has more than sufficient means of covering short-term debt and is therefore in a strong liquidity position.

Acid test or **quick ratio** indicates a firm's ability to quickly liquidate assets to pay off current debt. This ratio recognizes that a firm's inventories are one of the least liquid current assets. Merchandise inventories and prepaid expenses are not part of quick assets because they are not readily convertible to cash. An acid test ratio of 1:1 or greater is considered to be acceptable.

acid test, or quick ratio A ratio that indicates a firm's ability to quickly liquidate assets to pay off current debt.

Quick assets = Cash + Marketable securities + Receivables

$$\textbf{Acid test ratio} = \frac{\textbf{Quick assets}}{\textbf{Current liabilities}}$$

Hypothetical Enterprises, Inc. (*Note:* Hypothetical has no marketable securities):

$$\text{Quick assets} = 13{,}000 + 32{,}500 = \underline{\$45{,}500}$$

$$\text{Acid test ratio} = \frac{45{,}500}{29{,}400} = 1.55 = \underline{\underline{1.55{:}1}}$$

Analysis: An acid test ratio of 1.55:1 also indicates a strong liquidity position. It means that Hypothetical has the ability to meet all short-term debt obligations immediately if necessary.

Efficiency Ratios

efficiency ratios Financial ratios that indicate how effectively a company uses its resources to generate sales.

average collection period Indicator of how quickly a firm's credit accounts are being collected. Expressed in days.

Efficiency ratios provide the basis for determining how effectively the firm is using its resources to generate sales. A firm with \$500,000 in assets producing \$1,000,000 in sales is using its resources more efficiently than a firm producing the same sales with \$2,000,000 invested in assets.

Average collection period indicates how quickly a firm's credit accounts are being collected and is a good measure of how efficiently a firm is managing its accounts receivable. *Note:* When credit sales figures are not available, net sales may be used instead.

$$\textbf{Average collection period} = \frac{\textbf{Accounts receivable} \times \textbf{365}}{\textbf{Credit sales}}$$

Hypothetical Enterprises, Inc.:

$$\text{Average collection period} = \frac{32{,}500 \times 365}{896{,}944} = \frac{11{,}862{,}500}{896{,}944} = 13.23 = \underline{\underline{13 \text{ days}}}$$

Analysis: This ratio tells us that, on the average, Hypothetical's credit customers take 13 days to pay their bills. Because most industries average between 30 and 60 days, the firm's 13-day collection period is favorable and shows considerable efficiency in handling credit accounts.

inventory turnover The number of times during an operating period that the average inventory was sold.

Inventory turnover is the number of times during an operating period that the average inventory was sold.

$$\textbf{Average inventory} = \frac{\textbf{Beginning inventory} + \textbf{Ending inventory}}{\textbf{2}}$$

$$\textbf{Inventory turnover} = \frac{\textbf{Cost of goods sold}}{\textbf{Average inventory}}$$

Hypothetical Enterprises, Inc.:

$$\text{Average inventory} = \frac{220{,}350 + 88{,}560}{2} = \underline{\underline{\$154{,}455}}$$

$$\text{Inventory turnover} = \frac{481{,}540}{154{,}455} = 3.12 = \underline{\underline{3.1 \text{ times}}}$$

Analysis: Inventory turnover is one ratio that should be compared with the data from previous operating periods and with published industry averages for similar-sized firms in the same industry to draw any meaningful conclusions. When inventory turnover is below average, it may be a signal that the company is carrying too much inventory. Carrying excess inventory can lead to extra expenses such as warehouse costs and insurance. It also ties up money that could be used more efficiently elsewhere.

asset turnover ratio Ratio that tells the number of dollars in sales a firm generates from each dollar it has invested in assets.

Asset turnover ratio tells the number of dollars in sales the firm generates from each dollar it has invested in assets. This ratio is an important measure of a company's efficiency in managing its assets.

$$\textbf{Asset turnover ratio} = \frac{\textbf{Net sales}}{\textbf{Total assets}}$$

Hypothetical Enterprises, Inc.:

$$\text{Asset turnover ratio} = \frac{896{,}944}{341{,}300} = 2.63 = \underline{\underline{2.63{:}1}}$$

Analysis: Asset turnover is another ratio best compared with those of previous operating periods and industry averages to reach any meaningful conclusions. Hypothetical's 2.63:1 ratio means that the company is generating \$2.63 in sales for every \$1.00 in assets.

Leverage Ratios

When firms borrow money to finance assets, they are using financial leverage. Investors and creditors alike are particularly interested in the **leverage ratios** because the greater the leverage a firm has used, the greater the risk of default on interest and principal payments. Such situations could lead the firm into eventual bankruptcy.

leverage ratios Financial ratios that show how and to what degree a company has financed its assets.

Debt-to-assets ratio measures to what degree the assets of the firm have been financed with borrowed funds, or leveraged. This ratio identifies the claim on assets by the creditors. It is commonly expressed as a percent.

debt-to-assets ratio Ratio that measures to what degree the assets of the firm have been financed with borrowed funds, or leveraged.

$$\textbf{Debt-to-assets ratio} = \frac{\textbf{Total liabilities}}{\textbf{Total assets}}$$

Hypothetical Enterprises, Inc.:

$$\text{Debt-to-assets ratio} = \frac{164{,}400}{341{,}300} = .4817 = \underline{\underline{48.2\%}}$$

Analysis: This ratio indicates that Hypothetical's creditors have claim to 48.2% of the company assets, or for each \$1.00 of assets, the company owes \$.48 to its creditors.

Debt-to-equity ratio is used as a safety-factor measure for potential creditors. The ratio compares the total debt of the firm with the owner's equity. It tells the amount of debt incurred by the company for each \$1.00 of equity. It is commonly expressed as a percent.

debt-to-equity ratio A ratio that compares the total debt of a firm to the owner's equity.

$$\textbf{Debt-to-equity ratio} = \frac{\textbf{Total liabilities}}{\textbf{Owner's equity}}$$

Hypothetical Enterprises, Inc.:

$$\text{Debt-to-equity ratio} = \frac{164{,}400}{176{,}900} = .929 = \underline{\underline{.929{:}1 \text{ or } 92.9\%}}$$

Analysis: This ratio indicates that for each \$1.00 of owner's equity, Hypothetical has financed \$.93 in assets. As the debt-to-equity ratio increases, so does the risk factor to potential creditors and investors. This ratio should be compared with previous periods and industry norms.

Profitability Ratios

The **profitability ratios** are important to anyone whose economic interests are tied to the long-range success of the firm. Investors expect a return on their investment in the form of dividends and stock price appreciation. Without adequate profits, firms quickly fall out of favor with current and future investors.

profitability ratios Financial ratios that tell how much of each dollar of sales, assets, and owner's investment resulted in net profit.

Gross profit margin is an assessment of how well the cost of goods sold category of expenses was controlled. This measure particularly spotlights a firm's management of its purchasing and pricing functions. Gross profit margin is expressed as a percent of net sales.

gross profit margin An assessment of how well the cost of goods sold category of expenses was controlled. Expressed as a percent of net sales.

$$\textbf{Gross profit margin} = \frac{\textbf{Gross profit}}{\textbf{Net sales}}$$

Hypothetical Enterprises, Inc.:

$$\text{Gross profit margin} = \frac{415{,}404}{896{,}944} = .463 = \underline{\underline{46.3\%}}$$

Analysis: Hypothetical's gross profit constitutes 46.3% of the company's sales, which means that for each \$1.00 of sales, \$.46 remains as gross margin. For a meaningful analysis, this ratio should be compared with previous operating periods and industry averages.

net profit margin An assessment of management's overall ability to control the cost of goods sold and the operating expenses of a firm. Expressed as a percent of net sales.

Net profit margin is an assessment of management's overall ability to control the cost of goods sold and the operating expenses of the firm. This ratio is the bottom-line score of a firm's profitability and is one of the most important and most frequently used. Net profit margin can be calculated either before or after income tax. As with gross profit margin, it is expressed as a percent.

$$\textbf{Net profit margin} = \frac{\textbf{Net income}}{\textbf{Net sales}}$$

Hypothetical Enterprises, Inc.:

$$\text{Net profit margin} = \frac{91{,}268}{896{,}944} = .1018 = \underline{\underline{10.2\%}}$$

Analysis: This means that for each \$1.00 of net sales, Hypothetical was able to generate \$.10 in net profit. Most firms today have net profit margins between 1% and 8%, depending on the industry. Regardless of industry, Hypothetical's 10.2% net profit margin would be considered very profitable.

return on investment The amount of profit generated by a firm in relation to the amount invested by the owners. Expressed as a percent of owner's equity.

Return on investment is the amount of profit generated by the firm in relation to the amount invested by the owners. Abbreviated ROI, this ratio is commonly expressed as a percent.

$$\textbf{Return on investment} = \frac{\textbf{Net income}}{\textbf{Owner's equity}}$$

"If we factor in possible revenues (pr), excessive expenses (E), the weather (w), our consulting fee (ocf), and your attention span (as-100), we get an enormous profit!"

Hypothetical Enterprises, Inc.:

$$\text{Return on investment} = \frac{91{,}268}{176{,}900} = .5159 = \underline{\underline{51.6\%}}$$

Analysis: This ratio indicates that Hypothetical generated \$.52 in net profit for each \$1.00 invested by the owners. Most investors would consider 51.6% an excellent return on their money.

TRY IT EXERCISE 7

Use the balance sheet and income statement on pages 528 and 540 to calculate the financial ratios for Royal Equipment Supply, Inc.

CHECK YOUR ANSWERS WITH THE SOLUTIONS ON PAGES 567 AND 568.

PREPARING A TREND ANALYSIS OF FINANCIAL DATA

In Sections I and II of this chapter, we used horizontal analysis to calculate and report the *amount* and *percent* change in various balance sheet and income statement items from one operating period to another. When these percentage changes are tracked for a number of successive periods, it is known as **trend analysis**. Trend analysis introduces the element of time into financial analysis. Whereas data from one statement gives a firm's financial position at a given point in time, trend analysis provides a dynamic picture of the firm by showing its financial direction over a period of time.

Index numbers are used in trend analysis to show the percentage change in various financial statement items. With index numbers, a base year is chosen and is equal to 100%. All other years' figures are measured as a percentage of the base year. Once again, we encounter the now familiar percentage formula, Rate = Portion ÷ Base. The index number should be expressed as a percent, rounded to the nearest tenth.

trend analysis The use of index numbers to calculate percentage changes of a company's financial data for several successive operating periods.

index numbers Numbers used in trend analysis indicating changes in magnitude of financial data over a period of time. Calculated by setting a base period equal to 100% and calculating other periods in relation to the base period.

$$\textbf{Index number (rate)} = \frac{\textbf{Yearly amount (portion)}}{\textbf{Base year amount (base)}}$$

For example, if a company had sales of $50,000 in the base year and $60,000 in the index year, the index number would be 1.2 or 120% (60,000 ÷ 50,000). The index number means the sales for the index year were 1.2 times or 120% of the base year.

STEPS FOR PREPARING A TREND ANALYSIS

Step 1. Choose a base year and let it equal 100%.

Step 2. Calculate the index number for each succeeding year.

$$\textbf{Index number} = \frac{\textbf{Yearly amount}}{\textbf{Base year amount}}$$

Step 3. Round each index number to the nearest tenth of a percent.

CLASSROOM ACTIVITY

Have each student write, call, or visit the Web sites of various companies to request a copy of the most recent annual report. In groups, have them

- Choose one company to analyze from the annual reports on hand.
- Locate the consolidated income statement and balance sheet.
- Prepare a trend analysis chart and graph of net sales, net profit, total assets, and stockholders' equity.

As financial analysts, have the groups

- Calculate the financial ratios for the most recent 2 or 3 years.
- Determine for each ratio whether the change was a "positive" or "negative" indicator for the company.
- Discuss and form an opinion about the financial condition of the company.
- Present a report to the class of their group's findings and opinions.

EXAMPLE 8 PREPARING A TREND ANALYSIS

From the following data, prepare a 5-year trend analysis of net sales, net income, and total assets for Hypothetical Enterprises, Inc.

Hypothetical Enterprises, Inc.
5-Year Selected Financial Data

	2008	2007	2006	2005	2004
Net Sales	896,944	881,325	790,430	855,690	825,100
Net Income	91,268	95,550	56,400	75,350	70,100
Total Assets	341,300	320,100	315,600	314,200	303,550

SOLUTION STRATEGY

To prepare the trend analysis, we shall calculate the index number for each year by using the percentage formula and then enter the figures in a trend analysis table. The earliest year, 2004, will be the base year (100%). The first calculation, 2005 net sales index number, is as follows:

In the Business World

Tables illustrate specific data better than charts; however, charts are able to show "relationships" among data more clearly and visually.

Frequently in business presentations tables and charts are used together, with the chart used to clarify or reinforce facts presented in a table.

$$2005 \text{ net sales index number} = \frac{855{,}690}{825{,}100} = 1.037 = \underline{\underline{103.7\%}}$$

Trend Analysis (in percentages)

	2008	2007	2006	2005	2004
Net Sales	108.7	106.8	95.8	103.7 ←	100.0
Net Income	130.2	136.3	80.5	107.5	100.0
Total Assets	112.4	105.5	104.0	103.5	100.0

In addition to the table form of presentation, trend analysis frequently uses charts to visually present the financial data. Multiple-line charts are a particularly good way of presenting comparative data. For even more meaningful analysis, company data can be graphed on the same coordinates as industry averages.

The chart below illustrates Hypothetical's trend analysis figures in a multiple-line-chart format.

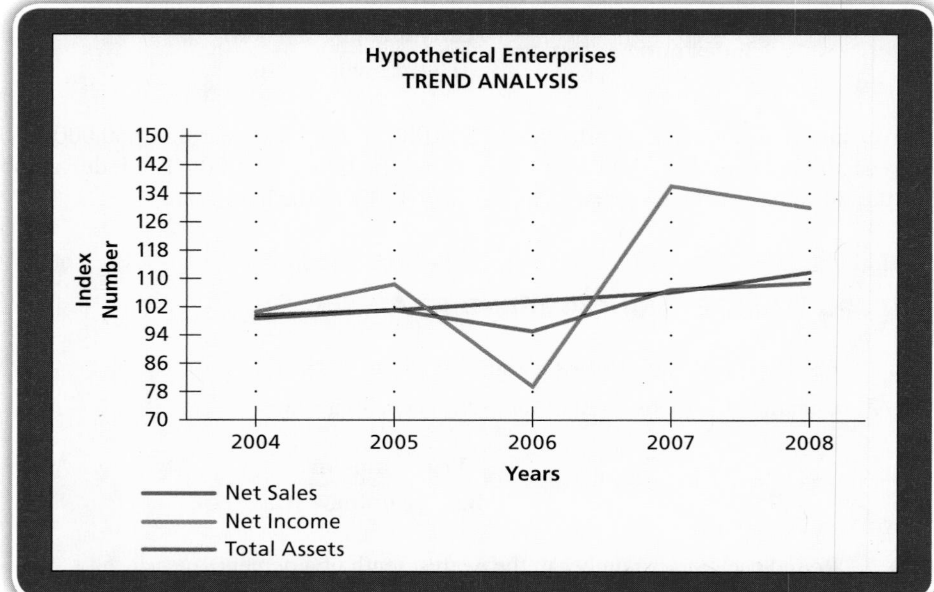

TRY IT EXERCISE 8

Prepare a trend analysis from the following financial data for the Reliance Corporation and prepare a multiple-line chart of the net sales, total assets, and stockholders' equity.

Reliance Corporation
5-Year Selected Financial Data

	2009	2008	2007	2006	2005
Net Sales	245,760	265,850	239,953	211,231	215,000
Total Assets	444,300	489,320	440,230	425,820	419,418
Stockholders' Equity	276,440	287,500	256,239	223,245	247,680

Reliance Corporation
Trend Analysis

	2009	2008	2007	2006	2005
Net Sales	______	______	______	______	______
Total Assets	______	______	______	______	______
Stockholders' Equity	______	______	______	______	______

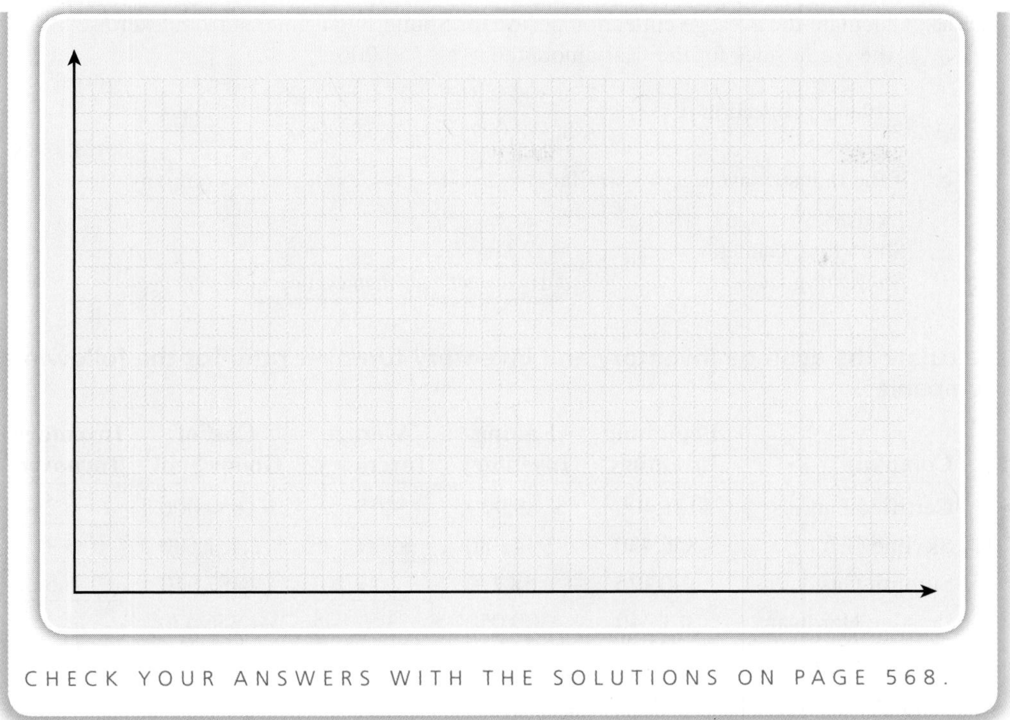

CHECK YOUR ANSWERS WITH THE SOLUTIONS ON PAGE 568.

Review Exercises

SECTION III 15

Calculate the amount of working capital and the current ratio for the following companies.

	Company	Current Assets	Current Liabilities	Working Capital	Current Ratio
1.	Impact Builders, Inc.	$ 125,490	$ 74,330	$51,160	1.69:1
2.	Thunderbird Electronics, Inc.	14,540	19,700	($5,160)	.74:1
3.	Forget-Me-Not Flowers	3,600	1,250	$2,350	2.88:1
4.	Shutterbug Cameras	1,224,500	845,430	$379,070	1.45:1

Use the additional financial information below to calculate the quick assets and acid test ratio for the companies in Questions 1–4.

	Company	Cash	Marketable Securities	Accounts Receivable	Quick Assets	Acid Test Ratio
5.	Impact Builders, Inc.	$12,320	$ 30,000	$ 53,600	$95,920	1.29:1
6.	Thunderbird Electronics, Inc.	2,690	0	4,330	$7,020	.36:1
7.	Forget-me-not Flowers	1,180	0	985	$2,165	1.73:1
8.	Shutterbug Cameras	24,400	140,000	750,300	$914,700	1.08:1

9. Calculate the average collection period for Impact Builders, Inc., from Exercise 5 if the credit sales for the year amounted to $445,000.

$$\text{Average collection period} = \frac{\text{Accounts receivable} \times 365}{\text{Credit sales}}$$

$$\text{Average collection period} = \frac{53{,}600 \times 365}{445{,}000} = \frac{19{,}564{,}000}{445{,}000} = \underline{\underline{44 \text{ Days}}}$$

10. a. Calculate the average collection period for Shutterbug Cameras from Exercise 8 if the credit sales for the year amounted to $8,550,000.

$$\text{Average collection period} = \frac{750{,}300 \times 365}{8{,}550{,}000} = \frac{273{,}859{,}500}{8{,}550{,}000} = \underline{\underline{32 \text{ Days}}}$$

b. If the industry average for similar firms is 48 days, evaluate the company's ratio.

Industry Average	= 48 Days
Shutterbug Cameras average	= 32 Days
Shutterbug Cameras	= 16 Days faster than competition

Calculate the average inventory and inventory turnover ratio for the following companies.

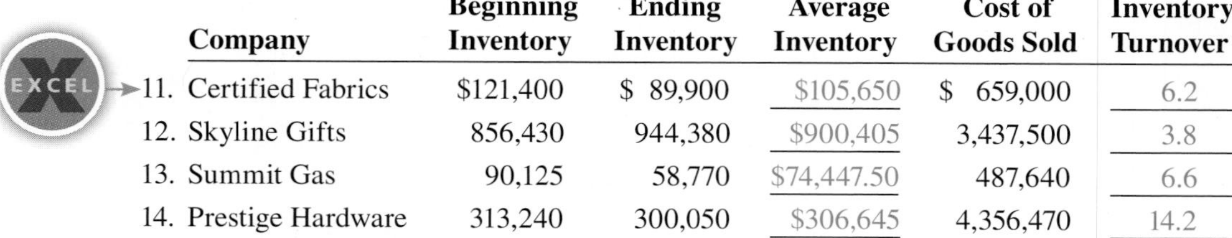

Company	Beginning Inventory	Ending Inventory	Average Inventory	Cost of Goods Sold	Inventory Turnover
11. Certified Fabrics	$121,400	$ 89,900	$105,650	$ 659,000	6.2
12. Skyline Gifts	856,430	944,380	$900,405	3,437,500	3.8
13. Summit Gas	90,125	58,770	$74,447.50	487,640	6.6
14. Prestige Hardware	313,240	300,050	$306,645	4,356,470	14.2

15. Heads or Tails Coin Shop had net sales of $1,354,600 last year. If the total assets of the company are $2,329,500, what is the asset turnover ratio?

$$\text{Asset turnover ratio} = \frac{\text{Net sales}}{\text{Total sales}}$$

$$= \frac{1{,}354{,}600}{2{,}329{,}500} = \underline{\underline{.58:1}}$$

Calculate the amount of owner's equity and the two leverage ratios for the following companies.

Company	Total Assets	Total Liabilities	Owner's Equity	Debt-to-Assets Ratio	Debt-to-Equity Ratio
16. Gateway Imports	$ 232,430	$ 115,320	$117,110	.50:1	.98:1
17. Reader's Choice Books	512,900	357,510	$155,390	.70:1	2.30:1
18. Café Europa	2,875,000	2,189,100	$685,900	.76:1	3.20:1

Calculate the gross and net profits and the two profit margins for the following companies.

Company	Net Sales	Cost of Goods Sold	Gross Profit	Operating Expenses	Net Profit	Gross Profit Margin (%)	Net Profit Margin (%)
19. Timberline Marble	$743,500	$489,560	$253,940	$175,410	$78,530	34.2	10.6
20. Sundance Plumbing	324,100	174,690	$149,410	99,200	$50,210	46.1	15.5
21. Dynamic Optical	316,735	203,655	$113,080	85,921	$27,159	35.7	8.6

Using the owner's equity information below, calculate the return on investment for the companies in Exercises 19–21.

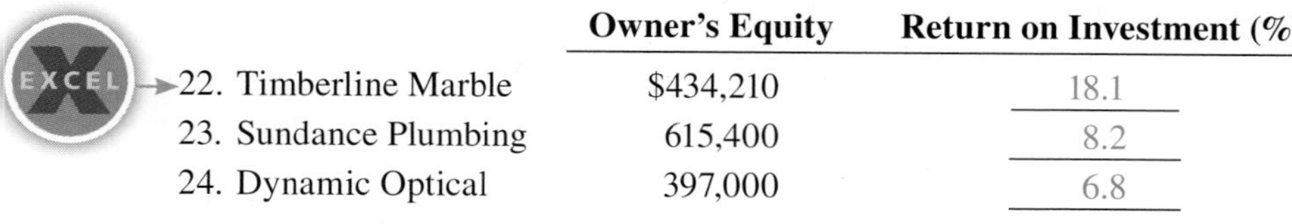

	Owner's Equity	Return on Investment (%)
22. Timberline Marble	$434,210	18.1
23. Sundance Plumbing	615,400	8.2
24. Dynamic Optical	397,000	6.8

25. Prepare a trend analysis from the following financial data for Hook, Line, and Sinker Fishing Supply.

Hook, Line, and Sinker Fishing Supply
5-year Selected Financial Data

	2008	2007	2006	2005	2004
Net Sales	$238,339	$282,283	$239,448	$215,430	$221,800
Net Income	68,770	71,125	55,010	57,680	55,343
Total Assets	513,220	502,126	491,100	457,050	467,720
Stockholders' Equity	254,769	289,560	256,070	227,390	240,600

Hook, Line, and Sinker Fishing Supply
Trend Analysis

	2008	2007	2006	2005	2004
Net Sales	107.5	127.3	108.0	97.1	100.0
Net Income	124.3	128.5	99.4	104.2	100.0
Total Assets	109.7	107.4	105.0	97.7	100.0
Stockholders' Equity	105.9	120.3	106.4	94.5	100.0

BUSINESS DECISION **FINANCIAL RATIOS**

26. Use the financial information for Starbucks on page 558 to answer Exercises 26a through e.

a. Calculate the asset turnover ratio for 2005 and 2006.

$$\text{Asset turnover ratio} = \frac{\text{Net revenue}}{\text{Total assets}}$$

$$2005 = \frac{6{,}369{,}300}{3{,}513{,}693} = \underline{\underline{1.81}}$$

$$2006 = \frac{7{,}786{,}942}{4{,}428{,}941} = \underline{\underline{1.76}}$$

b. Calculate the net profit margin for 2004, 2005, and 2006.

$$\text{Net profit margin} = \frac{\text{Net income (earnings)}}{\text{Net revenue}}$$

$$2004 = \frac{388{,}880}{5{,}294{,}247} = \underline{\underline{7.3\%}}$$

$$2005 = \frac{494{,}370}{6{,}369{,}300} = \underline{\underline{7.8\%}}$$

$$2006 = \frac{564{,}259}{7{,}786{,}942} = \underline{\underline{7.2\%}}$$

Coffee King!

Starbucks is the world's #1 specialty coffee retailer. Starbucks operates and licenses more than 12,500 stores in 37 countries, serving more than 40 million customers each week. The company's long-term store count target is now 40,000 worldwide (20,000 U.S. and 20,000 International).

In 2006, Starbucks employed more than 145,000 people and had revenue of $7.8 billion. Net earnings were $564 million or $0.71 earnings per share. For the past 15 consecutive years, Starbucks has posted five percent or greater comparable store sales growth.

**Starbucks–Selected Fiancial Data
(In thousands, except per share data)**

As of/For Fiscal Year Ended	Oct 1, 2006 (52 Wks)	Oct 2, 2005 (52 Wks)	Oct 3, 2004 (53 Wks)	Sept 28, 2003 (52 Wks)	Sept 29, 2002 (52 Wks)
RESULTS OF OPERATIONS					
Net revenues:					
Company-operated retail	$6,583,098	$5,391,927	$4,457,378	$3,449,624	$2,792,904
Specialty:					
Licensing	860,676	673,015	565,798	409,551	311,932
Food service and other	343,168	304,358	271,071	216,347	184,072
Total specialty	1,203,844	977,373	836,869	625,898	496,004
Total net revenues	7,786,942	6,369,300	5,294,247	4,075,522	3,288,908
Operating income	893,952	780,518	606,494	420,672	313,301
Gain on sale of investment	—	—	—	—	13,361
Earnings before accounting principle change	581,473	494,370	388,880	265,177	210,460
Cumulative effect of accounting change	17,214	—	—	—	—
Net earnings	$ 564,259	$ 494,370	$ 388,880	$ 265,177	$ 210,460
Earnings per common share before cumulative effect of change in accounting principle—diluted	$ 0.73	$ 0.61	$ 0.47	$ 0.33	$ 0.26
Cumulative effect of accounting change per share	0.02	—	—	—	—
Net earnings per common share—diluted	$ 0.71	$ 0.61	$ 0.47	$ 0.33	$ 0.26
Cash dividends per share	—	—	—	—	—
BALANCE SHEET					
Working capital	$ (405,832)	$ (17,662)	$ 604,636	$ 335,767	$ 328,777
Total assets	4,428,941	3,513,693	3,386,266	2,775,931	2,249,432
Short-term borrowings	700,000	277,000	—	—	—
Long-term debt (including current portion)	2,720	3,618	4,353	5,076	5,786
Shareholders' equity	$2,228,506	$2,090,262	$2,469,936	$2,068,507	$1,712,453

c. Calculate the return on investment for 2004, 2005, and 2006.

$$\text{Return on investment} = \frac{\text{Net income (earnings)}}{\text{Total stockholders' equity}}$$

$$2004 = \frac{388{,}880}{2{,}469{,}936} = 15.7\%$$

$$2005 = \frac{494{,}370}{2{,}090{,}262} = 23.7\%$$

$$2006 = \frac{564{,}259}{2{,}228{,}506} = 25.3\%$$

d. Prepare a trend analysis of the net revenue and total assets for 2002 through 2006.

	2006	2005	2004	2003	2002
Net Revenue	236.8	193.7	161.0	123.9	100.0
Total Assets	196.9	156.2	150.5	123.4	100.0

e. Extra credit: Prepare a trend analysis multiple-line chart for the information in part d.

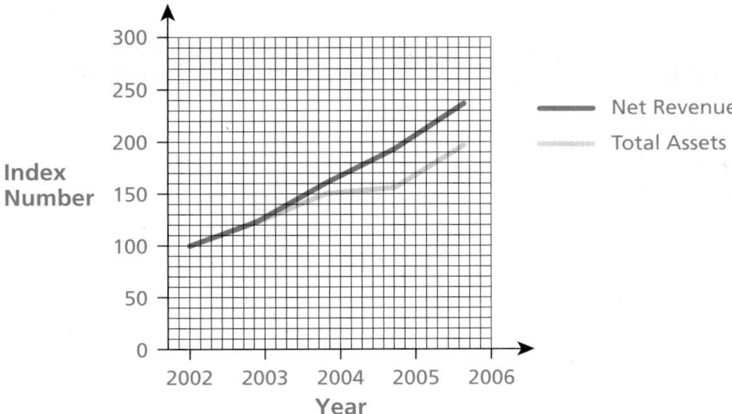

CHAPTER FORMULAS

15

Liquidity Ratios

$$\text{Working capital} = \text{Current assets} - \text{Current liabilities}$$

$$\text{Current ratio} = \frac{\text{Current assets}}{\text{Current liabilities}}$$

$$\text{Quick assets} = \text{Cash} + \text{Marketable securities} + \text{Receivables}$$

$$\text{Acid test ratio} = \frac{\text{Quick assets}}{\text{Current liabilities}}$$

Efficiency Ratios

$$\text{Average collection period} = \frac{\text{Accounts receivable} \times 365}{\text{Credit sales}}$$

$$\text{Average inventory} = \frac{\text{Beginning inventory} + \text{Ending inventory}}{2}$$

$$\text{Inventory turnover} = \frac{\text{Cost of goods sold}}{\text{Average inventory}} \qquad \text{Asset turnover ratio} = \frac{\text{Net sales}}{\text{Total assets}}$$

Leverage Ratios

$$\text{Debt-to-assets ratio} = \frac{\text{Total liabilities}}{\text{Total assets}} \qquad \text{Debt-to-equity ratio} = \frac{\text{Total liabilities}}{\text{Owner's equity}}$$

Profitability Ratios

$$\text{Gross profit margin} = \frac{\text{Gross profit}}{\text{Net sales}} \qquad \text{Net profit margin} = \frac{\text{Net income}}{\text{Net sales}}$$

$$\text{Return on investment} = \frac{\text{Net income}}{\text{Owner's equity}}$$

CHAPTER SUMMARY

Section I: The Balance Sheet

<table>
<tr><th>Topic</th><th>Important Concepts</th><th>Illustrative Examples</th></tr>
<tr>
<td>Preparing a Balance Sheet
P/O 15-1, p. 525</td>
<td>The balance sheet is a financial statement that shows a company's financial position on a certain date. It is based on the fundamental accounting equation:
Assets = Liabilities + Owner's equity

Balance sheet preparation:
1. List and total:
Current assets
+ Property, plant, and equipment
+ Investments and other assets
Total assets

2. List and total:
Current liabilities
+ Long-term liabilities
Total liabilities

3. List and total:
Owner's equity

4. Add the Total liabilities and the Owner's equity. This total should equal the Total assets.</td>
<td>International Industries, Inc.
Balance Sheet
December 31, 2008
Assets
<table>
<tr><td>Cash</td><td>$ 24,000</td></tr>
<tr><td>Receivables</td><td>92,000</td></tr>
<tr><td>Inventory</td><td>68,500</td></tr>
<tr><td>Supplies</td><td>12,100</td></tr>
<tr><td>Total current assets</td><td>$196,600</td></tr>
<tr><td>Land and building</td><td>$546,700</td></tr>
<tr><td>Fixtures & equipment</td><td>88,400</td></tr>
<tr><td>Vehicles</td><td>124,200</td></tr>
<tr><td>Total property & equipment</td><td>$759,300</td></tr>
<tr><td>Total assets</td><td>$955,900</td></tr>
</table>
Liabilities & Owner's Equity
<table>
<tr><td>Accounts payable</td><td>$ 82,400</td></tr>
<tr><td>Note payable (3-month)</td><td>31,300</td></tr>
<tr><td>Total current liabilities</td><td>$ 113,700</td></tr>
<tr><td>Mortgage payable</td><td>$213,400</td></tr>
<tr><td>Note payable (2-year)</td><td>65,800</td></tr>
<tr><td>Total long-term liabilities</td><td>$279,200</td></tr>
<tr><td>Total liabilities</td><td>$392,900</td></tr>
<tr><td>Owner's equity</td><td>563,000</td></tr>
<tr><td>Total liabilities & owner's equity</td><td>$955,900</td></tr>
</table></td>
</tr>
<tr>
<td>Preparing a Vertical Analysis of a Balance Sheet
P/O 15-2, p. 529</td>
<td>In vertical analysis, each item on the balance sheet is expressed as a percent of total assets.
Vertical analysis preparation:
1. Use the percentage formula,
Rate = Portion ÷ Base
Use each balance sheet item as the portion and total assets as the base.
2. Round each answer to the nearest tenth of a percent.
Note: A 0.1% differential may occur due to rounding.</td>
<td>International Industries, Inc.
Balance Sheet—Asset Section
<table>
<tr><td>Cash</td><td>$ 24,000</td><td>2.5</td></tr>
<tr><td>Receivables</td><td>92,000</td><td>9.6</td></tr>
<tr><td>Inventory</td><td>68,500</td><td>7.2</td></tr>
<tr><td>Supplies</td><td>12,100</td><td>1.3</td></tr>
<tr><td>Current assets</td><td>$196,600</td><td>20.6</td></tr>
<tr><td>Land & building</td><td>$546,700</td><td>57.2</td></tr>
<tr><td>Fixtures & equipment</td><td>88,400</td><td>9.2</td></tr>
<tr><td>Vehicles</td><td>124,200</td><td>13.0</td></tr>
<tr><td>Property & equipment</td><td>$759,300</td><td>79.4</td></tr>
<tr><td>Total assets</td><td>$955,900</td><td>100.0</td></tr>
</table></td>
</tr>
<tr>
<td>Preparing a Horizontal Analysis of a Comparative Balance Sheet
P/O 15-3, p. 531</td>
<td>Comparative balance sheets display data from the current period side-by-side with the figures from one or more previous periods. In horizontal analysis, each item of the current period is compared in dollars and percent with the corresponding item from the previous period.
Horizontal analysis preparation:
1. Set up a comparative balance sheet format with the current period listed first.</td>
<td>If the 2007 cash figure for International Industries, Inc. was $21,300, the comparative balance sheet horizontal analysis would be listed as follows:
Cash
<table>
<tr><th></th><th></th><th colspan="2">Increase (Decrease)</th></tr>
<tr><th>2008</th><th>2007</th><th>Amount</th><th>Percent</th></tr>
<tr><td>$24,000</td><td>$21,300</td><td>$2,700</td><td>12.7</td></tr>
</table>
$\frac{2{,}700}{21{,}300} = 12.7\%$</td>
</tr>
</table>

Section I: (continued)

Topic	Important Concepts	Illustrative Examples
	2. Label the next two columns: **Increase (Decrease)** **Amount Percent** 3. For each item, calculate the dollar difference between the current and previous period and enter this figure in the amount column. Enter all decreases in parentheses. 4. Calculate the percent change using: $\text{Percent change (rate)} = \dfrac{\text{Amount of change (portion)}}{\text{Previous period amount (base)}}$ 5. Enter the percent change in the Percent column. Round to the nearest tenth percent. Enter all decreases in parentheses.	For a comprehensive example of a comparative balance sheet with horizontal analysis, see pages 531–533, Cudjoe Construction Company.

Section II: The Income Statement

<table>
<tr><th>Topic</th><th>Important Concepts</th><th>Illustrative Examples</th></tr>
<tr>
<td>Preparing an Income Statement
P/O 15-4, p. 537</td>
<td>An income statement is a summary of the operations of a business over a period of time. It is based on the equation

Profit = Revenue − Total expenses

Income Statement preparation:
1. Label the top of the statement with the company name and period of time covered.
2. In a two-column format, calculate

a. Net sales
Gross sales
− Sales returns & allow.
− Sales discounts
Net sales

b. Cost of goods sold
Beginning inventory
+ Net purchases
+ Freight in
Goods available for sale
− Ending inventory
Cost of goods sold

c. Gross margin
Net sales
− Cost of goods sold
Gross margin

d. Net income
Gross margin
− Total operating expenses
Net income</td>
<td>International Industries, Inc.
Income Statement
Year Ended December 31, 2008
(000)
<table>
<tr><td>Gross sales</td><td>$435.3</td><td></td></tr>
<tr><td>Sales returns</td><td>11.1</td><td></td></tr>
<tr><td>Sales discounts</td><td>8.0</td><td></td></tr>
<tr><td>Net sales</td><td></td><td>$416.2</td></tr>
<tr><td>Inventory, Jan. 1</td><td>124.2</td><td></td></tr>
<tr><td>Net purchases</td><td>165.8</td><td></td></tr>
<tr><td>Freight in</td><td>2.7</td><td></td></tr>
<tr><td>Goods available</td><td>292.7</td><td></td></tr>
<tr><td>Inventory, Dec. 31</td><td>118.1</td><td></td></tr>
<tr><td>Cost of goods sold</td><td></td><td>174.6</td></tr>
<tr><td>Gross margin</td><td></td><td>241.6</td></tr>
<tr><td>Salaries</td><td>87.6</td><td></td></tr>
<tr><td>Rent & utilities</td><td>22.5</td><td></td></tr>
<tr><td>Other expenses</td><td>101.7</td><td></td></tr>
<tr><td>Total operating expenses</td><td></td><td>211.8</td></tr>
<tr><td>Net income</td><td></td><td>$ 29.8</td></tr>
</table></td>
</tr>
</table>

Section II: (continued)

Topic	Important Concepts	Illustrative Examples

Topic: **Preparing a Vertical Analysis of an Income Statement**
P/O 15-5, p. 541

Important Concepts:

In vertical analysis of an income statement, each figure is expressed as a percent of net sales.

Vertical analysis preparation:

1. Use the percentage formula,

   Rate = Portion ÷ Base

   Use each income statement item as the portion and net sales as the base.
2. Round each answer to the nearest tenth of a percent.

   Note: A 0.1% differential may occur due to rounding.

Illustrative Examples:

International Industries, Inc.
Income Statement—2008
(000)

Gross sales	$435.3	104.6
Sales returns	11.1	2.7
Sales discounts	8.0	1.9
Net sales	416.2	100.0
Inventory, Jan. 1	124.2	29.8
Net purchases	165.8	39.8
Freight in	2.7	.6
Goods available for sale	292.7	70.3
Inventory, Dec. 31	118.1	28.4
Cost of goods sold	174.6	42.0
Gross margin	241.6	58.0
Salaries	87.6	21.0
Rent & utilities	22.5	5.4
Other expenses	101.7	24.4
Total operating expenses	211.8	50.9
Net income	$ 29.8	7.2

Topic: **Preparing a Horizontal Analysis of a Comparative Income Statement**
P/O 15-6, p. 542

Important Concepts:

In horizontal analysis of a comparative income statement, each item of the current period is compared in dollars and percent with the corresponding item from the previous period.

Horizontal analysis preparation:

1. Set up a comparative income statement format with the current period listed first.
2. Label the next two columns:

Increase (Decrease)	
Amount	**Percent**

3. For each item, calculate the dollar difference between the current and previous period and enter this figure in the amount column. Enter all decreases in parentheses.
4. Calculate the percent change by using

   $$\text{Percent change (rate)} = \frac{\text{Amount of change (portion)}}{\text{Previous period amount (base)}}$$

5. Enter the percent change in the Percent column. Round to the nearest tenth percent. Enter all decreases in parentheses.

Illustrative Examples:

If the 2007 net income figure for International Industries, Inc., was $23,100, the comparative income statement horizontal analysis would be listed as follows:

Net Income

		Increase (Decrease)	
2008	**2007**	**Amount**	**Percent**
$29,800	$23,100	$6,700	29.0

$$\frac{6,700}{23,100} = 29.0\%$$

For a comprehensive example of a comparative income statement with horizontal analysis, see pages 543–544, All-Star Appliances, Inc.

Section III: Financial Ratios and Trend Analysis

Topic	Important Concepts	Illustrative Examples
Calculating Financial Ratios **P/O 15-7, p. 548**	Financial ratios are standardized comparisons of various items from the balance sheet and the income statement. When compared with ratios of previous operating periods and industry averages, they can be used as signals to analysts of potential strengths or weaknesses of the firm.	A company had net sales of \$100,000 and net income of \$10,000. Express these data as a ratio. $\frac{100{,}000}{10{,}000} = 10$ 1. The ratio of sales to income is 10 to 1, written 10:1. 2. Net income is $\frac{1}{10}$ or 10% of net sales. 3. For every \$1.00 of net sales, the company generates \$.10 in net income.
Liquidity Ratios **P/O 15-7, p. 549**	Liquidity ratios examine the relationship between a firm's current assets and its maturing obligation. They are a good indicator of a firm's ability to pay its bills over the next few months. $\text{Current ratio} = \frac{\text{Current assets}}{\text{Current liabilities}}$ $\text{Acid test ratio} = \frac{\text{Cash} + \text{Marketable securities} + \text{Accounts receivable}}{\text{Current liabilities}}$	International Industries, Inc. Financial Ratios 2008 $\text{Current ratio} = \frac{196{,}600}{113{,}700} = 1.73 = \underline{\underline{1.73:1}}$ $\text{Acid test ratio} = \frac{24{,}000 + 92{,}000}{113{,}700} = 1.02 = \underline{\underline{1.02:1}}$
Efficiency Ratios **P/O 15-7, p. 550**	Efficiency ratios provide the basis for determining how effectively a firm uses its resources to generate sales. $\text{Average collection period} = \frac{\text{Accounts receivable} \times 365}{\text{Credit sales}}$ $\text{Inventory turnover} = \frac{\text{Cost of goods sold}}{\frac{\text{Beg inventory} + \text{End inventory}}{2}}$ $\text{Asset turnover ratio} = \frac{\text{Net sales}}{\text{Total assets}}$	Credit sales for International Industries, Inc. are 50% of net sales. Average collection period = $\frac{92{,}000 \times 365}{208{,}100} = \underline{\underline{161 \text{ days}}}$ Inventory turnover = $\frac{174{,}600}{\frac{124{,}200 + 118{,}100}{2}} = \underline{\underline{1.44 \text{ times}}}$ $\text{Asset turnover ratio} = \frac{416{,}200}{955{,}900} = .44 = \underline{\underline{.44:1}}$
Leverage Ratios **P/O 15-7, p. 551**	Leverage ratios provide information about the amount of money a company has borrowed to finance its assets. $\text{Debt-to-assets ratio} = \frac{\text{Total liabilities}}{\text{Total assets}}$ $\text{Debt-to-equity ratio} = \frac{\text{Total liabilities}}{\text{Owner's equity}}$	$\text{Debt-to-assets ratio} = \frac{392{,}900}{955{,}900} = .411 = \underline{\underline{41.1\%}}$ $\text{Debt-to-equity ratio} = \frac{392{,}900}{563{,}000} = .698 = \underline{\underline{69.8\%}}$
Profitability Ratios **P/O 15-7, p. 551**	Profitability ratios show a firm's ability to generate profits and provide its investors with a return on their investment. $\text{Gross profit margin} = \frac{\text{Gross profit}}{\text{Net sales}}$ $\text{Net profit margin} = \frac{\text{Net income}}{\text{Net sales}}$ $\text{Return on investment} = \frac{\text{Net income}}{\text{Owner's equity}}$	$\text{Gross profit margins} = \frac{241{,}600}{416{,}200} = .580 = \underline{\underline{58.0\%}}$ $\text{Net profit margin} = \frac{29{,}800}{416{,}200} = .072 = \underline{\underline{7.2\%}}$ $\text{Return on investment} = \frac{29{,}800}{563{,}000} = .053 = \underline{\underline{5.3\%}}$

Section III: (continued)

<table>
<tr><th>Topic</th><th>Important Concepts</th><th>Illustrative Examples</th></tr>
<tr>
<td>Preparing a Trend Analysis of Financial Data
P/O 15-8, p. 553</td>
<td>Trend analysis is the process of tracking changes in financial statement items for three or more operating periods.
Trend analysis figures can be displayed on a chart using index numbers or more visually as a line graph or bar chart.

Trend analysis preparation:
1. Choose a base year (usually the earliest year) and let it equal 100%.
2. Calculate the index number for each succeeding year by using
$$\text{Index number (rate)} = \frac{\text{Yearly amount (portion)}}{\text{Base year amount (base)}}$$
3. Round each index number to the nearest tenth of a percent.
4. Optional: Graph the index numbers or the raw data on a line chart.</td>
<td>Prepare a trend analysis for International Industries, Inc. net sales data.

International Industries, Inc.
Net Sales (000)
<table>
<tr><th>2008</th><th>2007</th><th>2006</th><th>2005</th><th>2004</th></tr>
<tr><td>416.2</td><td>401.6</td><td>365.4</td><td>388.3</td><td>375.1</td></tr>
</table>
For this trend analysis, we shall use 2004 as the base year, 100%. Each subsequent year's index number is calculated by using the yearly amount as the portion and the 2004 amount as the base. For example, 2005 index number =
$$\frac{388.3}{375.1} = 103.5$$
<table>
<tr><th>2008</th><th>2007</th><th>2006</th><th>2005</th><th>2004</th></tr>
<tr><td>111.0</td><td>107.1</td><td>97.4</td><td>103.5</td><td>100.0</td></tr>
</table>
International Industries, Inc.
Trend Analysis
Index Number: 120.0, 117.5, 115.0, 112.5, 110.0, 107.5, 105.0, 102.5, 100.0, 97.5, 95.0
Years: 2004, 2005, 2006, 2007, 2008</td>
</tr>
</table>

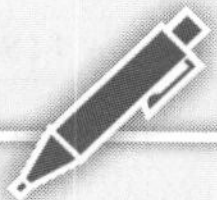

TRY IT EXERCISE SOLUTIONS FOR CHAPTER 15

1.

Keystone Auto Repair
Balance Sheet
December 31, 2008

Assets		
Current Assets		
Cash	$ 5,200	
Accounts Receivable	2,800	
Merchandise Inventory	2,700	
Prepaid Salary	235	
Supplies	3,900	
Total Current Assets		$ 14,835
Property, Plant, and Equipment		
Land	35,000	
Building	74,000	
Fixtures	1,200	
Tow Truck	33,600	
Tools and Equipment	45,000	
Total Property, Plant, and Equipment		188,800
Total Assets		$203,635

Liabilities and Owner's Equity		
Current Liabilities		
Accounts Payable	$ 6,800	
Notes Payable	17,600	
Taxes Payable	3,540	
Total Current Liabilities		$ 27,940
Long-Term Liabilities		
Mortgage Payable	51,000	
Total Long-Term Liabilities		51,000
Owner's Equity		
Blake Jolin, Capital	124,695	
Total Owner's Equity		124,695
Total Liabilities and Owner's Equity		$203,635

2.

Royal Equipment Supply, Inc.
Balance Sheet
June 30, 2008

Assets		
Current Assets		
Cash	$ 3,400	1.1%
Accounts Receivable	5,600	1.8
Merchandise Inventory	98,700	32.0
Prepaid Insurance	455	.1
Supplies	800	.3
Total Current Assets	108,955	35.3
Property, Plant, and Equipment		
Land and Building	147,000	47.6
Fixtures	8,600	2.8
Delivery Vehicles	27,000	8.8
Forklift	7,000	2.3
Total Property, Plant, and Equipment	189,600	61.4
Investments and Other Assets		
Goodwill	10,000	3.2
Total Investments and Other Assets	10,000	3.2
Total Assets	$308,555	100.0%

Liabilities and Stockholders' Equity		
Current Liabilities		
Accounts Payable	$ 16,500	5.3%
Notes Payable	10,000	3.2
Total Current Liabilities	26,500	8.6
Long-Term Liabilities		
Mortgage Payable	67,000	21.7
Total Long-Term Liabilities	67,000	21.7
Total Liabilities	93,500	30.3
Stockholders' Equity		
Common Stock	185,055	60.0
Retained Earnings	30,000	9.7
Total Stockholders' Equity	215,055	69.7
Total Liabilities and Stockholders' Equity	$308,555	100.0%

3.

Gilbert S. Cohen Industries, Inc.
Comparative Balance Sheet
December 31, 2008 and 2009

			Increase (Decrease)	
Assets	**2009**	**2008**	**Amount**	**Percent**
Current Assets				
Cash	$ 8,700	$ 5,430	$ 3,270	60.2%
Accounts Receivable	23,110	18,450	4,660	25.3
Notes Receivable	2,900	3,400	(500)	(14.7)
Supplies	4,540	3,980	560	14.1
Total Current Assets	39,250	31,260	7,990	25.6
Property, Plant, and Equipment				
Land	34,000	34,000	0	0
Buildings	76,300	79,800	(3,500)	(4.4)
Machinery and Equipment	54,700	48,900	5,800	11.9
Total Prop., Plant, and Equip.	165,000	162,700	2,300	1.4
Investments and Other Assets	54,230	49,810	4,420	8.9
Total Assets	$258,480	$243,770	$14,710	6.0
Liabilities and Stockholders' Equity				
Current Liabilities				
Accounts Payable	$ 15,330	$ 19,650	($ 4,320)	(22.0%)
Salaries Payable	7,680	7,190	490	6.8
Total Current Liabilities	23,010	26,840	(3,830)	(14.3)
Long-Term Liabilities				
Mortgage Payable	53,010	54,200	(1,190)	(2.2)
Note Payable (3-year)	32,400	33,560	(1,160)	(3.5)
Total Long-Term Liabilities	85,410	87,760	(2,350)	(2.7)
Total Liabilities	108,420	114,600	(6,180)	(5.4)
Stockholders' Equity				
Common Stock	130,060	120,170	9,890	8.2
Retained Earnings	20,000	9,000	11,000	122.2
Total Liabilities and Stockholders' Equity	$258,480	$243,770	$14,710	6.0

4.

Cutting Edge Manufacturing, Inc.
Income Statement

Revenue		
Gross Sales	$1,356,000	
Less: Sales Returns and Allowances	93,100	
Sales Discounts	4,268	
Net Sales		$1,258,632
Cost of Goods Sold		
Merchandise Inv., Jan. 1	324,800	
Net Purchases	255,320	
Freight In	3,911	
Goods Available for Sale	584,031	
Less: Merchandise Inv., Dec. 31	179,100	
Cost of Goods Sold		404,931
Gross Margin		853,701
Operating Expenses		
Salaries	375,900	
Rent	166,000	
Utilities	7,730	
Advertising	73,300	
Insurance	22,940	
Administrative Expenses	84,500	
Miscellaneous Expenses	24,900	
Total Operating Expenses		755,270
Income before Taxes		98,431
Income Tax		34,760
Net Income		$ 63,671

5.

Royal Equipment Supply, Inc.
Income Statement

Revenue		
Gross Sales	$458,400	103.3%
Less: Sales Returns and Allowances	13,200	3.0
Sales Discounts	1,244	.3
Net Sales	$443,956	100.0%
Cost of Goods Sold		
Merchandise Inventory, Jan. 1	198,700	44.8
Net Purchases	86,760	19.5
Freight In	875	.2
Goods Available for Sale	286,335	64.5
Less: Merchandise Inventory, Dec. 31	76,400	17.2
Cost of Goods Sold	209,935	47.3
Gross Margin	234,021	52.7
Operating Expenses		
Salaries	124,200	28.0
Rent	21,000	4.7
Utilities	1,780	.4
Advertising	5,400	1.2
Insurance	2,340	.5
Administrative Expenses	14,500	3.3
Miscellaneous Expenses	6,000	1.4
Total Operating Expenses	175,220	39.5
Income before Taxes	58,801	13.2
Income Tax	17,335	3.9
Net Income	$ 41,466	9.3%

6.

Timely Watch Company, Inc.
Comparative Income Statement
For the years ended December 31, 2007 and 2008

	2008	2007	Increase (Decrease) Amount	Increase (Decrease) Percent
Revenue				
Gross Sales	$1,223,000	$996,500	$226,500	22.7%
Less: Sales Returns and Allowances	121,340	99,600	21,740	21.8
Sales Discounts	63,120	51,237	11,883	23.2
Net Sales	1,038,540	845,663	192,877	22.8
Cost of Goods Sold				
Merchandise Inventory, Jan. 1	311,200	331,000	(19,800)	(6.0)
Purchases	603,290	271,128	332,162	122.5
Freight In	18,640	13,400	5,240	39.1
Goods Available for Sale	933,130	615,528	317,602	51.6
Less: Merchandise Inventory, Dec. 31	585,400	311,200	274,200	88.1
Cost of Goods Sold	347,730	304,328	43,402	14.3
Gross Margin	690,810	541,335	149,475	27.6
Operating Expenses				
Salaries and Benefits	215,200	121,800	93,400	76.7
Rent and Utilities	124,650	124,650	0	0
Depreciation	43,500	41,230	2,270	5.5
Insurance	24,970	23,800	1,170	4.9
Administrative Store Expenses	58,200	33,900	24,300	71.7
Warehouse Expenses	42,380	45,450	(3,070)	(6.8)
Total Operating Expenses	508,900	390,830	118,070	30.2
Income before Taxes	181,910	150,505	31,405	20.9
Income Tax	66,280	41,670	24,610	59.1
Net Income	$ 115,630	$108,835	$ 6,795	6.2

7. *Royal Equipment Supply—Financial Ratios 2008*

Working capital = Current assets − Current liabilities = 108,955 − 26,500 = $82,455

$$\text{Current ratio} = \frac{\text{Current assets}}{\text{Current liabilities}} = \frac{108{,}955}{26{,}500} = 4.11{:}1$$

$$\text{Acid test ratio} = \frac{\text{Cash} + \text{Marketable securities} + \text{Receivables}}{\text{Current liabilities}} = \frac{3{,}400 + 5{,}600}{26{,}500} = .34{:}1$$

$$\text{Average collection period} = \frac{\text{Accounts receivable} \times 365}{\text{Net sales}} = \frac{5{,}600 \times 365}{443{,}956} = 4.6 \text{ days}$$

$$\text{Average inventory} = \frac{\text{Beginning inventory} + \text{Ending inventory}}{2} = \frac{198{,}700 + 76{,}400}{2} = \$137{,}550$$

$$\text{Inventory turnover} = \frac{\text{Cost of goods sold}}{\text{Average inventory}} = \frac{209{,}935}{137{,}550} = 1.5 \text{ times}$$

$$\text{Asset turnover ratio} = \frac{\text{Net sales}}{\text{Total assets}} = \frac{443{,}956}{308{,}555} = 1.44{:}1$$

$$\text{Debt-to-assets ratio} = \frac{\text{Total liabilities}}{\text{Total assets}} = \frac{93{,}500}{308{,}555} = .303 = 30.3\%$$

$$\text{Debt-to-equity ratio} = \frac{\text{Total liabilities}}{\text{Owner's equity}} = \frac{93{,}500}{215{,}055} = .435 = 43.5\%$$

$$\text{Gross profit margin} = \frac{\text{Gross profit}}{\text{Net sales}} = \frac{234{,}021}{443{,}956} = .527 = \underline{\underline{52.7\%}}$$

$$\text{Net profit margin} = \frac{\text{Net income}}{\text{Net sales}} = \frac{41{,}466}{443{,}956} = .093 = \underline{\underline{9.3\%}}$$

$$\text{Return on investment} = \frac{\text{Net income}}{\text{Owner's equity}} = \frac{41{,}466}{215{,}055} = .193 = \underline{\underline{19.3\%}}$$

8.

Reliance Corporation
Trend Analysis

	2009	2008	2007	2006	2005
Net Sales	114.3	123.7	111.6	98.2	100.0
Total Assets	105.9	116.7	105.0	101.5	100.0
Stockholders' Equity	111.6	116.1	103.5	90.1	100.0

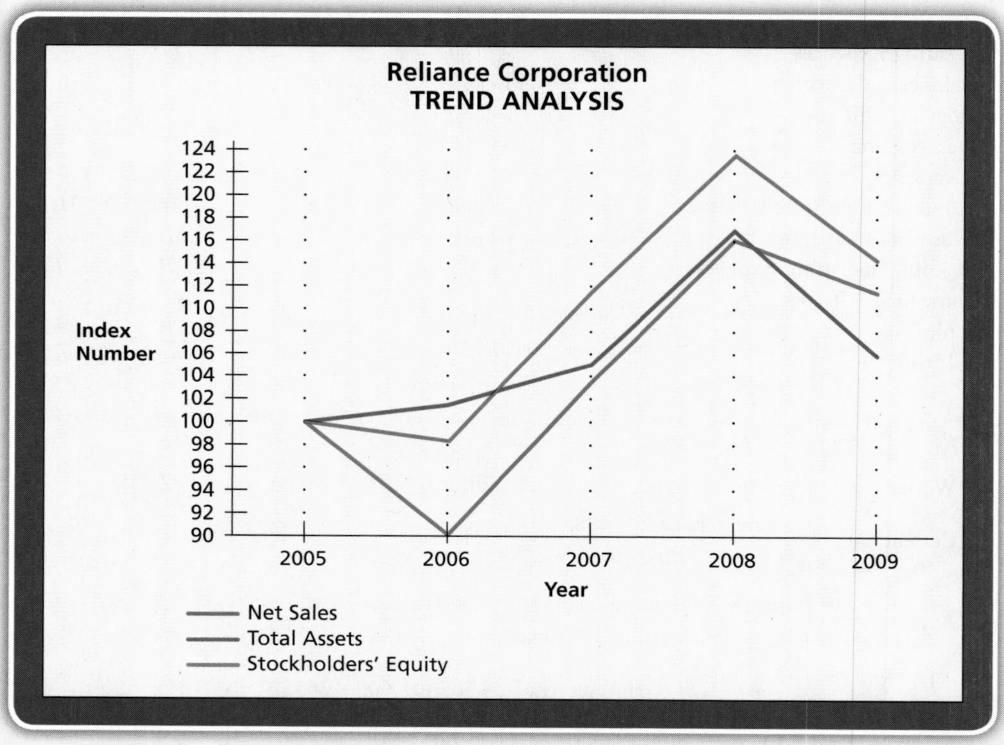

CONCEPT REVIEW

1. In accounting, economic resources owned by a company are known as ____; whereas debts or obligations of a company are known as ____. (15-1)
assets, liabilities

2. The financial statement that illustrates the financial position of a company in terms of assets, liabilities, and owner's equity as of a certain date is known as a(n) ____ sheet. (15-1)
balance

3. The balance sheet is a visual presentation of the all-important "accounting equation." Write this equation. (15-1)
Assets = Liabilities + Owner's Equity

4. In vertical analysis of a balance sheet, each figure on the statement is expressed as a percent of ____ ____. (15-2)
total assets

5. A financial statement prepared with the data from the current operating period side-by-side with the figures from one or more previous periods is known as a(n) ____ statement. (15-3, 15-6)
comparative

6. Horizontal analysis is a method of analyzing financial statements whereby each item of the current period is compared in ____ and ____ with the corresponding item from a previous period. (15-3, 15-6)
dollars, percents

7. A financial statement summarizing the operations of a business over a period of time is known as an income statement, operating statement, or ____ and ____ statement. (15-4)
profit, loss

8. Write the formula that illustrates the structure of an income statement. (15-4)
Profit (or loss) = Revenue – Total expenses

9. In vertical analysis of an income statement, each figure on the statement is expressed as a percent of ____ ____. (15-5)
net sales

10. Name the four major categories of financial ratios. (15-7)
liquidity, efficiency, leverage, profitability

11. Write the formulas for the current ratio and inventory turnover. (15-7)

$$\text{Current ratio} = \frac{\text{Current assets}}{\text{Current liabilities}}$$

$$\text{Inventory turnover} = \frac{\text{Cost of goods sold}}{\text{Average inventory}}$$

12. Write the formulas for the debt-to-assets ratio and return on investment. (15-7)

$$\text{Debt-to-assets ratio} = \frac{\text{Total liabilities}}{\text{Total assets}}$$

$$\text{Return on investment} = \frac{\text{Net income}}{\text{Owner's equity}}$$

13. The use of index numbers to track percentage changes of a company's financial data over successive operating periods is known as ____ analysis. (15-8)
trend

14. With index numbers, a base period is chosen and is equal to ____ percent. (15-8)
100

ASSESSMENT TEST

Prepare the following statements on separate sheets of paper.

1. a. Use the following financial information to calculate the owner's equity and prepare a balance sheet with vertical analysis as of December 31, 2008, for Mountain Magic Tire Company, a sole proprietorship owned by Paul Provost: current assets, $132,500; property, plant, and equipment, $88,760; investments and other assets, $32,400; current liabilities, $51,150; long-term liabilities, $87,490.

Mountain Magic Tire Company
Balance Sheet
As of December 31, 2008

b. The following financial information is for Mountain Magic as of December 31, 2009. Calculate the owner's equity for 2009, and prepare a comparative balance sheet with horizontal analysis for 2008 and 2009: current assets, $154,300; property, plant, and equipment, $124,650; investments and other assets, $20,000; current liabilities, $65,210; long-term liabilities, $83,800.

Financial statement solutions for Exercises 1 and 2 appear in Appendix B, following the index.

Mountain Magic Tire Company
Comparative Balance Sheet
As of December 31, 2008 and 2009

2. a. Use the following financial information to prepare a balance sheet with vertical analysis as of October 31, 2008, for Sticks & Stones Builder's Mart: cash, $45,260; accounts receivable, $267,580; merchandise inventory, $213,200; prepaid expenses, $13,400; supplies, $5,300; land, $87,600; building, $237,200; equipment, $85,630; vehicles, $54,700;

(continued)

CHAPTER

Name

Class

Answers

3. $185,772

4. a. $542,010

b. $225,610

c. $163,840

d. ($15,960)

computers, $31,100; investments, $53,100; accounts payable, $43,200; salaries payable, $16,500; notes payable (6-month), $102,400; mortgage payable, $124,300; notes payable (3-year), $200,000; common stock, $422,000; and retained earnings, $185,670.

Sticks & Stones Builder's Mart
Balance Sheet
As of October 31, 2008

b. The following financial information is for Sticks & Stones Builder's Mart as of October 31, 2009. Prepare a comparative balance sheet with horizontal analysis for 2008 and 2009: cash, $47,870; accounts receivable, $251,400; merchandise inventory, $223,290; prepaid expenses, $8,500; supplies, $6,430; land, $87,600; building, $234,500; equipment, $88,960; vehicles, $68,800; computers, $33,270; investments, $55,640; accounts payable, $48,700; salaries payable, $9,780; notes payable (6-month), $96,700; mortgage payable, $121,540; notes payable (3-year), $190,000; common stock, $450,000; and retained earnings, $189,540.

Sticks & Stones Builder's Mart
Consolidated Balance Sheet
As of October 31, 2008 and 2009

3. For the second quarter of 2009, the Evergreen Plant Nursery had gross sales of $214,300, sales returns and allowances of $26,540, and sales discounts of $1,988. What were Evergreen's net sales?

Gross sales	$214,300
Sales returns	− 26,540
Sales discounts	− 1,988
Net sales	$185,772

4. For the month of January, Consolidated Engine Parts, Inc. had the following financial information: merchandise inventory, January 1, $322,000; merchandise inventory, January 31, $316,400; gross purchases, $243,460; purchase returns and allowances, $26,880; and freight in, $3,430.

a. What are Consolidated's goods available for sale?

Inventory (January 1)	$322,000
Net purchases	216,580 (243,460 − 26,880)
Freight in	+ 3,430
Goods available for sale	$542,010

b. What is the cost of goods sold for January?

Goods available for sale	$542,010
Inventory (January 31)	− 316,400
Cost of goods sold January	$225,610

c. If net sales were $389,450 what was the gross margin for January?

Net sales	$389,450
Cost of goods sold	− 225,610
Gross margin	$163,840

d. If total operating expenses were $179,800, what was the net profit?

Gross margin	$163,840
Operating expenses	− 179,800
Net profit (loss)	($15,960)

Name

Class

Answers

7. $653,300

8. 2.49:1

9. 1.51:1

Prepare the following statements on separate sheets of paper.

5. a. From the following third quarter 2009 information for Woof & Meow Pet Supply, construct an income statement with vertical analysis: gross sales, $224,400; sales returns and allowances, $14,300; beginning inventory, July 1, $165,000; ending inventory, September 30, $143,320; net purchases, $76,500; total operating expenses, $68,600; income tax, $8,790.

Woof & Meow Pet Supply
Income Statement
Third Quarter, 2009

b. The following financial information is for the fourth quarter of 2009 for Woof & Meow Pet Supply. Prepare a comparative income statement with horizontal analysis for the third and fourth quarters: gross sales, $218,200; sales returns and allowances, $9,500; beginning inventory, October 1, $143,320; ending inventory, December 31, $125,300; net purchases, $81,200; total operating expenses, $77,300; income tax, $11,340.

Woof & Meow Pet Supply
Comparative Income Statement
Third and Fourth Quarters, 2009

6. a. Use the following financial information to construct a 2008 income statement with vertical analysis for Touchstone Jewelers: gross sales, $1,243,000; sales returns and allowances, $76,540; sales discounts, $21,300; merchandise inventory, Jan. 1, 2008, $654,410; merchandise inventory, Dec. 31, 2008, $413,200; net purchases, $318,000; freight in, $3,450; salaries, $92,350; rent, $83,100; depreciation, $87,700; utilities, $21,350; advertising, $130,440; insurance, $7,920; miscellaneous expenses, $105,900; and income tax, $18,580.

EXCEL

Financial statement solutions for Exercises 5 and 6 appear in Appendix B, following the index.

Touchstone Jewelers
Income Statement
For the year ended December 31, 2008

b. The following data represent Touchstone's operating results for 2009. Prepare a comparative income statement with horizontal analysis for 2008 and 2009: gross sales, $1,286,500; sales returns and allowances, $78,950; sales discounts, $18,700; merchandise inventory, Jan. 1, 2009, $687,300; merchandise inventory, Dec. 31, 2009, $401,210; net purchases, $325,400; freight in, $3,980; salaries, $99,340; rent, $85,600; depreciation, $81,200; utilities, $21,340; advertising, $124,390; insurance, $8,700; miscellaneous expenses, $101,230; and income tax, $12,650.

Touchstone Jewelers
Comparative Income Statement
For the years ended December 31, 2008 and 2009

As the accounting manager of Spring Creek Plastics, Inc., you have been asked to calculate the following financial ratios for the company's 2008 annual report. Use the balance sheet on page 572 and income statement on page 573 for Spring Creek.

7. Working capital:

$$\text{Working capital} = 1{,}093{,}000 - 439{,}700 = \underline{\underline{\$653{,}300}}$$

8. Current ratio:

$$\text{Current ratio} = \frac{1{,}093{,}000}{439{,}700} = \underline{\underline{2.49{:}1}}$$

9. Acid test ratio:

$$\text{Acid test ratio} = \frac{250{,}000 + 88{,}700 + 325{,}400}{439{,}700} = \underline{\underline{1.51{:}1}}$$

Name

Class

Answers

10. 117 Days
11. 1.74 Times
12. .55:1
13. 37.9%
14. 61.1%
15. 48.3%
16. 4.8%
17. 4.2%

10. Average collection period (credit sales are 60% of net sales):

$$\text{Average collection period} = \frac{325{,}400 \times 365}{(1{,}695{,}900 \times 60\%)} = \frac{118{,}771{,}000}{1{,}017{,}540} = 116.7 = \underline{\underline{117\text{ Days}}}$$

11. Inventory turnover:

$$\text{Inventory turnover} = \frac{876{,}500}{\dfrac{767{,}800 + 239{,}300}{2}} = \frac{876{,}500}{503{,}550} = \underline{\underline{1.74\text{ Times}}}$$

12. Asset turnover ratio:

$$\text{Asset turnover ratio} = \frac{1{,}695{,}900}{3{,}108{,}200} = \underline{\underline{.55:1}}$$

13. Debt-to-assets ratio:

$$\text{Debt-to-assets ratio} = \frac{1{,}178{,}500}{3{,}108{,}200} = \underline{\underline{37.9\%}}$$

14. Debt-to-equity ratio:

$$\text{Debt-to-equity ratio} = \frac{1{,}178{,}500}{1{,}929{,}700} = \underline{\underline{61.1\%}}$$

15. Gross profit margin:

$$\text{Gross profit margin} = \frac{819{,}400}{1{,}695{,}900} = \underline{\underline{48.3\%}}$$

16. Net profit margin:

$$\text{Net profit margin} = \frac{81{,}900}{1{,}695{,}900} = \underline{\underline{4.8\%}}$$

17. Return on investment:

$$\text{Return on investment} = \frac{81{,}900}{1{,}929{,}700} = \underline{\underline{4.2\%}}$$

Spring Creek Plastics, Inc.
Balance Sheet
As of December 31, 2008

Assets		
Cash	$ 250,000	
Accounts Receivable	325,400	
Merchandise Inventory	416,800	
Marketable Securities	88,700	
Supplies	12,100	
Total Current Assets		$1,093,000
Land and Building	1,147,000	
Fixtures and Equipment	868,200	
Total Property, Plant, and Equipment		2,015,200
Total Assets		$3,108,200
Liabilities and Owner's Equity		
Accounts Payable	$ 286,500	
Notes Payable (6-month)	153,200	
Total Current Liabilities		$ 439,700
Mortgage Payable	325,700	
Notes Payable (4-year)	413,100	
Total Long-Term Liabilities		738,800
Total Liabilities		1,178,500
Owner's Equity		1,929,700
Total Liabilities and Owner's Equity		$3,108,200

Spring Creek Plastics, Inc.
Income Statement, 2008

Net Sales		$1,695,900
Merchandise Inventory, Jan. 1	$ 767,800	
Net Purchases	314,900	
Freight In	33,100	
Goods Available for Sale	1,115,800	
Merchandise Inventory, Dec. 31	239,300	
Cost of Goods Sold		876,500
Gross Margin		819,400
Total Operating Expenses		702,300
Income before Taxes		117,100
Taxes		35,200
Net Income		$ 81,900

18. Prepare a trend analysis from the financial data listed below for Coastal Marine International.

Coastal Marine International
4-year Selected Financial Data

	2008	2007	2006	2005
Net Sales	$ 898,700	$ 829,100	$ 836,200	$ 801,600
Net Income	96,300	92,100	94,400	89,700
Total Assets	2,334,000	2,311,000	2,148,700	1,998,900
Stockholders' Equity	615,000	586,000	597,200	550,400

Coastal Marine International
Trend Analysis

	2008	2007	2006	2005
Net Sales	112.1	103.4	104.3	100.00
Net Income	107.4	102.7	105.2	100.00
Total Assets	116.8	115.6	107.5	100.00
Stockholders' Equity	111.7	106.5	108.5	100.00

19. As part of the trend analysis for Coastal Marine International, prepare a multiple-line chart for the annual report comparing net sales and net income for the years 2005 through 2008.

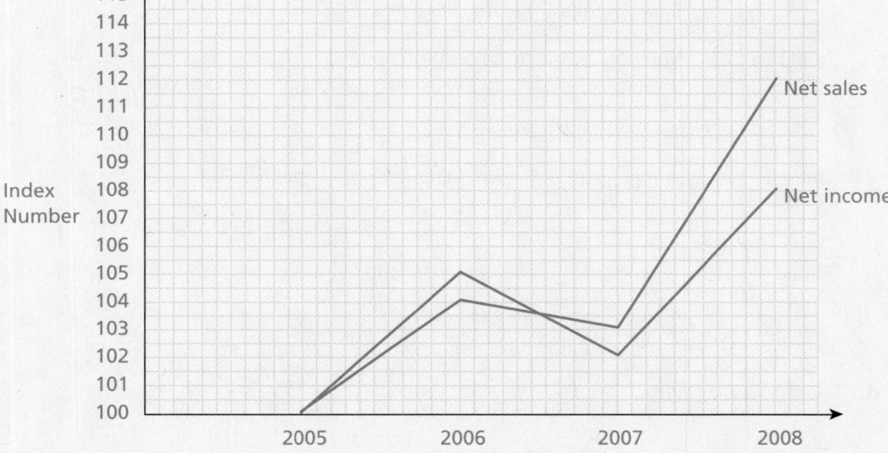

© Apple Inc./PR Newswire Photo Service (Newscom)

Apple Inc., designs, manufactures, and markets personal computers, portable digital music players, and mobile phones and sells a variety of related software, services, peripherals, and networking solutions. The Company sells its products worldwide through its online stores, its retail stores, its direct sales force, and third-party wholesalers, and resellers.

In addition, Apple sells a variety of third-party Macintosh, iPod, and iPhone compatible products including application software, printers, storage devices, speakers, headphones, and various other accessories and supplies through its online and retail stores. The Company sells to education, consumer, creative professional, business, and government customers.

In 2007, Apple generated net sales of over \$24 billion. Net income was nearly \$3.5 billion, or \$4.04 per share.

20. From the following consolidated statements of earnings for Apple, Inc., prepare a vertical analysis in the form of a common-size income statement (percentages only) for 2006.

Apple, Inc.
Consolidated Statements of Operations
(In millions, except share and per share amounts)

Three fiscal years ended September 30, 2006	2006	2005	2004
		As Restated	As Restated
Net sales	\$ 19,315	\$ 13,931	\$ 8,279
Cost of sales	13,717	9,889	6,022
Gross margin	5,598	4,042	2,257
Operating expenses:			
Research and development	712	535	491
Selling, general, and administrative	2,433	1,864	1,430
Restructuring costs	—	—	23
Total operating expenses	3,145	2,399	1,944
Operating income	2,453	1,643	313
Other income and expense	365	165	57
Income before provision for income taxes	2,818	1,808	370
Provision for income taxes	829	480	104
Net income	\$ 1,989	\$ 1,328	\$ 266
Earnings per common share:			
Basic	\$ 2.36	\$ 1.64	\$ 0.36
Diluted	\$ 2.27	\$ 1.55	\$ 0.34

Worked-out solution to Question 20 appears in Appendix B, following the index.

BUSINESS DECISION **EVALUATING FINANCIAL PERFORMANCE**

Name

Class

Answers

21. a.	2006	2.81:1
	2007	3.13:1
b.	2006	1.28:1
	2007	1.68:1
c.	2006	1.52:1
	2007	1.53:1
d.	2006	36.3%
	2007	34.3%

21. From the consolidated statements of income and balance sheets for Nike, Inc, on page 576, prepare the following financial ratios for 2006 and 2007.

a. Current ratio

2006 | 2007

$$\text{Current ratio} = \frac{\text{Current assets}}{\text{Current liabilities}} \qquad \frac{7{,}346.0}{2{,}612.4} = 2.81{:}1 \qquad \frac{8{,}076.5}{2{,}584.0} = 3.13{:}1$$

b. Acid test ratio (Note: Nike, Inc. has no marketable securities.)

2006 | 2007

$$\text{Acid test ratio} = \frac{\text{Cash} + \text{Marketable securities} + \text{Accounts receivable}}{\text{Current liabilities}} \qquad \frac{954.2 + 2{,}382.9}{2{,}612.4} = 1.28{:}1 \qquad \frac{1{,}856.7 + 2{,}494.7}{2{,}584.0} = 1.68{:}1$$

c. Asset turnover ratio

2006 | 2007

$$\text{Asset turnover ratio} = \frac{\text{Net sales}}{\text{Total assets}} \qquad \frac{14{,}954.9}{9{,}869.6} = 1.52{:}1 \qquad \frac{16{,}325.9}{10{,}688.3} = 1.53{:}1$$

d. Debt-to-assets ratio

2006 | 2007

$$\text{Debt-to-assets ratio} = \frac{\text{Total liabilities}}{\text{Total assets}} \qquad \frac{3{,}584.4}{9{,}869.6} = 36.3\% \qquad \frac{3{,}662.9}{10{,}688.3} = 34.3\%$$

e. Debt-to-equity ratio

$$\text{Debt-to-equity ratio} = \frac{\text{Total liabilities}}{\text{Stockholders' equity}} \qquad \underline{2006}: \frac{3{,}584.4}{6{,285.2}} = \underline{\underline{57.0\%}} \qquad \underline{2007}: \frac{3{,}662.9}{7{,}025.4} = \underline{\underline{52.1\%}}$$

f. Net profit margin

$$\text{Net profit margin} = \frac{\text{Net earnings}}{\text{Net sales}} \qquad \underline{2006}: \frac{1{,}392.0}{14{,}954.9} = \underline{\underline{9.3\%}} \qquad \underline{2007}: \frac{1{,}491.5}{16{,}325.9} = \underline{\underline{9.1\%}}$$

g. Return on investment

$$\text{Return on investment} = \frac{\text{Net earnings}}{\text{Stockholders' equity}} \qquad \underline{2006}: \frac{1{,}392.0}{6{,}285.2} = \underline{\underline{22.1\%}} \qquad \underline{2007}: \frac{1{,}491.5}{7{,}025.4} = \underline{\underline{21.2\%}}$$

h. Based on your calculations of the financial ratios for Nike, determine for each ratio whether the 2007 figure was better or worse than 2006.

(a) Current ratio	2007 better than 2006	(e) Debt-to-equity ratio	2007 better than 2006
(b) Acid test ratio	2007 better than 2006	(f) Net profit margin	2007 worse than 2006
(c) Asset turnover ratio	2007 better than 2006	(g) Return on investment	2007 worse than 2006
(d) Debt-to-assets ratio	2007 better than 2006		

i. How would you rate Nike's financial performance from 2006 to 2007?

Answers will vary.
Nike's financial performance was considerably better in 2007 compared with 2006. Revenue increased by almost $1.4 billion while net income increased by close to $100 million. Although net profit margin and return on investment were slightly lower, earnings per share increased by $0.29 and shareholders' dividends increased by $0.12 to $0.71. All in all, an excellent year!

CHAPTER 15

Name

Class

Answers

21. e. 2006 57.0%
2007 52.1%
f. 2006 9.3%
2007 9.1%
g. 2006 22.1%
2007 21.2%
h. (a) 2007 better
(b) 2007 better
(c) 2007 better
(d) 2007 better
(e) 2007 better
(f) 2007 worse
(g) 2007 worse
i. Answers will vary.

Nike is the world's #1 shoemaker and controls over 20% of the U.S. athletic shoe market. The company designs and sells shoes for a variety of sports, including baseball, cheerleading, golf, volleyball, and wrestling.

Nike also sells Cole Haan dress and casual shoes and a line of athletic apparel and equipment. In addition, it operates Niketown shoe and sportswear stores, Nike factory outlets, and Nikewoman shops. Nike sells its products throughout the U.S. and in about 200 other countries.

In 2007 the company employed 30,200 people and had sales of over $16.3 billion. Major competitors include Adidas-Salomon, Fila, USA, Reebok, and New Balance.

NIKE, INC.
CONSOLIDATED BALANCE SHEETS

	May 31, 2007	May 31, 2006
ASSETS	**(In millions)**	
Current assets:		
Cash and equivalents	$ 1,856.7	$ 954.2
Short-term investments	990.3	1,348.8
Accounts receivable, net	2,494.7	2,382.9
Inventories	2,121.9	2,076.7
Deferred income taxes	219.7	203.3
Prepaid expenses and other current assets	393.2	380.1
Total current assets	8,076.5	7,346.0
Property, plant and equipment, net	1,678.3	1,657.7
Identifiable intangible assets, net	409.9	405.5
Goodwill	130.8	130.8
Deferred income taxes and other assets	392.8	329.6
Total assets	$10,688.3	$9,869.6
LIABILITIES AND SHAREHOLDERS' EQUITY		
Current liabilities:		
Current portion of long-term debt	$ 30.5	$ 255.3
Notes payable	100.8	43.4
Accounts payable	1,040.3	952.2
Accrued liabilities	1,303.4	1,276.0
Income taxes payable	109.0	85.5
Total current liabilities	2,584.0	2,612.4
Long-term debt	409.9	410.7
Deferred income taxes and other liabilities	668.7	561.0
Commitments and contingencies	—	—
Redeemable Preferred Stock	0.3	0.3
Shareholders' equity:		
Common stock at stated value		
Class A convertible — 117.6 and 127.8 shares outstanding	0.1	0.1
Class B — 384.1 and 384.2 shares outstanding	2.7	2.7
Capital in excess of stated value	1,960.0	1,447.3
Accumulated other comprehensive income	177.4	121.7
Retained earnings	4,885.2	4,713.4
Total shareholders' equity	7,025.4	6,285.2
Total liabilities and shareholders' equity	$10,688.3	$9,869.6

NIKE, INC.
CONSOLIDATED STATEMENTS OF INCOME

	Year Ended May 31, 2007	2006	2005
	(In millions, except per share data)		
Revenues	$ 16,325.9	$14,954.9	$13,739.7
Cost of sales	9,165.4	8,367.9	7,624.3
Gross margin	7,160.5	6,587.0	6,115.4
Selling and administrative expense	5,028.7	4,477.8	4,221.7
Interest (income) expense, net	(67.2)	(36.8)	4.8
Other (income) expense, net	(0.9)	4.4	29.1
Income before income taxes	2,199.9	2,141.6	1,859.8
Income taxes	708.4	749.6	648.2
Net income	$ 1,491.5	$ 1,392.0	$ 1,211.6
Basic earnings per common share	$ 2.96	$ 2.69	$ 2.31
Diluted earnings per common share	$ 2.93	$ 2.64	$ 2.24
Dividends declared per common share	$ 0.71	$ 0.59	$ 0.475

COLLABORATIVE LEARNING ACTIVITY

Analyzing a Company

As a team, choose an industry you want to research, such as airlines, beverage, computers, entertainment, food, motor vehicles, retail, or wholesale. Next, choose three public companies that directly compete in that industry.

Using the Internet, research key business ratios and other available information about that industry. This may be found in the government's publication, *The Survey of Current Business*, or from private sources, such as *Moody's Index, Dun & Bradstreet*, or *Standard & Poors*.

Next, obtain the most recent annual report and quarterly report for each company from their Web site. This information is usually available under a section entitled "Investor Information." Based on the information your team has accumulated:

a. Calculate the current and previous years' financial ratios for each company.
b. Compare each company's ratios to the industry averages.
c. Evaluate each company's financial condition regarding liquidity, efficiency, leverage, and profitability.
d. If you and your team were going to invest in only one of these companies, which would you choose? Why?

http://www.contemporarymath.com

Contemporary Math

ContemporaryMath.com

All the Math That's Fit to Learn

Doctors Have X-Ray, Lenders Have FICO Scores

When you are applying for credit—whether it's a credit card, a car loan, a personal loan, or a mortgage—lenders want to know your credit risk level. To help them understand your credit risk, most lenders will look at your FICO score, the credit score created by Fair Isaac Corporation, which is available from all three major credit reporting agencies.

A credit score is a number lenders use to help them decide: "If I give this person a loan or credit card, how likely is it that I will get paid back on time?" A score is an estimate of your credit risk based on a snapshot of your credit report at a particular point in time.

FICO scores range from 300 to 850. Higher scores are better scores. The higher your score, the more favorable lenders look upon you as a credit risk. The bar chart "National Distribution of FICO Scores" shows the percentage of U.S. borrowers in each credit score range. For further information about credit scores and to see how various FICO scores affect the interest rates that you pay on loans, visit www.myfico.com.

What Goes Into a Credit Score?

The main criteria and the degree to which they affect your credit score are these:

- **Payment history:** For credit cards, retail accounts, car loans, mortgages, and similar debts. Pay your bills on time.
- **Amounts owed:** Includes the number of accounts with balances, and the amount you owe vs. the amount of credit available. Keep balances low on credit cards and other revolving credit. Pay off debt rather than moving it around.
- **Credit history:** Amount of time you have had each account. The longer your credit history, the better.
- **New credit:** Number of recently opened accounts and recent inquires. Opening several accounts in a short period can hurt your score.
- **Types of credit used:** The "mix" of credit cards, retail accounts, installment loans, finance company accounts, and mortgage loans. The credit mix usually won't be a key factor in determining your FICO score, but it will be more important if your credit report does not have a lot of other information on which to base a score.

Source: www.myfico.com, Understanding Your FICO Score

Quote...UnQuote

- If you think nobody cares if you're alive, try missing a couple of car payments. –**Earl Wilson**
- Education is when you read the fine print. Experience is what you get if you don't. –**Pete Seeger**

National Distribution of FICO Scores

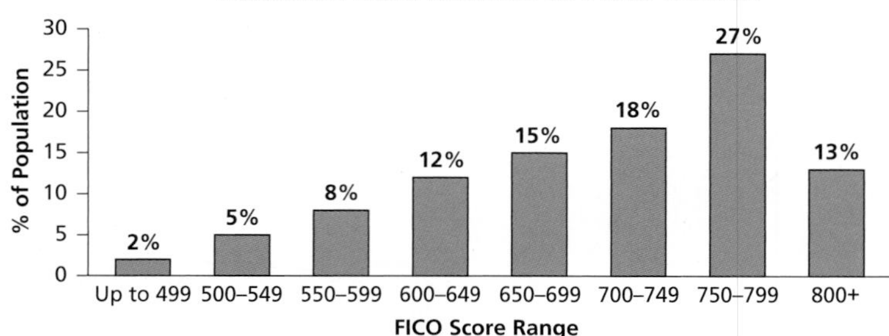

Source: www.myfico.com, Understanding Your FICO Score, page 7

FICO Score Breakdown

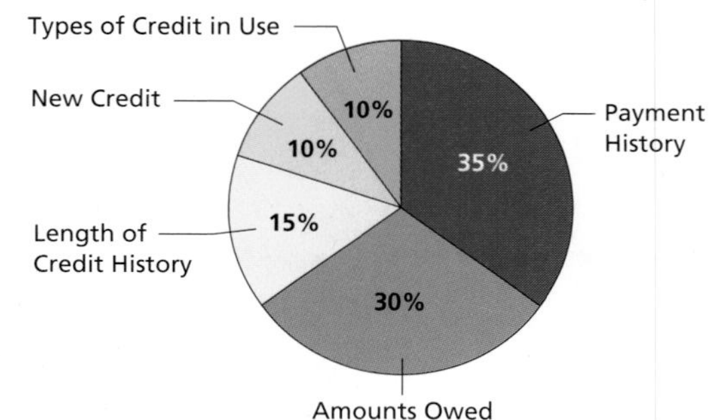

Source: www.myfico.com, Understanding Your FICO Score, page 9

"I know my payment was due four months ago, but my therapist told me to stop dwelling on the past."

Internet 100%

Inventory

PERFORMANCE OBJECTIVES

SECTION I INVENTORY VALUATION

inventory Goods that a company has in its possession at any given time. May be in the form of raw materials, partially finished goods, or goods available for sale.

merchandise inventory Goods purchased by wholesalers and retailers for resale.

In the Business World

Although the material in this chapter essentially deals with accounting procedures, anyone who plans to own or manage a business involving merchandise should have a conceptual understanding of inventory valuation methods.

periodic inventory system Inventory system in which merchandise is physically counted at least once a year to determine the value of the goods available for sale.

perpetual inventory system Inventory system in which goods available for sale are updated on a continuous basis by computer. Purchases by the company are added to inventory, whereas sales to customers are subtracted from inventory.

book inventory The balance of a perpetual inventory system at any given time. Must be confirmed with an actual physical count at least once a year.

specific identification method Inventory valuation method in which each item in inventory is matched or coded with its actual cost. Feasible only for low-volume merchandise flow such as automobiles, boats, or other expensive items.

In business, the term **inventory** is used to describe the goods that a company has in its possession at any given time. For companies engaged in manufacturing activities, inventories are divided into raw materials (used to make other products), partially completed products (work in process), and finished goods (ready for sale to the trade).

Manufacturers sell their finished goods to wholesalers and retailers. These goods, purchased and held expressly for resale, are commonly known as **merchandise inventory**. For wholesalers and retailers, the primary source of revenue is from the sale of this merchandise. In terms of dollars, merchandise inventory is one of the largest and most important assets of a merchandising company. As an expense, the cost of goods sold is the largest deduction from sales in the determination of a company's profit, often larger than the total of operating or overhead expenses.

Interestingly, the merchandise inventory is the only account that is found on both the balance sheet and the income statement. The method used to determine the value of this inventory has a significant impact on a company's bottom-line results. In addition to appearing on the financial statements, the value of the merchandise inventory must also be determined for income tax purposes, insurance, and as a business indicator to management.

To place a value on a merchandise inventory, we must first know the quantity and the cost of the goods remaining at the end of an operating period. Merchandise held for sale must be physically counted at least once a year. Many businesses take inventory on a quarterly or even monthly basis. This is known as a **periodic inventory system**, because the physical inventory is counted periodically.

Today, more and more companies use computers to keep track of merchandise inventory on a continuous or perpetual basis. This is known as a **perpetual inventory system**. For each merchandise category, the purchases made by the company are added to inventory, whereas the sales to customers are subtracted. These balances are known as the **book inventory** of the items held for sale. As accurate as the perpetual system may be, it must be confirmed with an actual physical count at least once a year.

Taking inventory consists of physically counting, weighing, or measuring the items on hand; placing a price on each item; and multiplying the number of items by the price to determine the total cost. The counting part of taking inventory, although tedious, is not difficult. The pricing part, however, is an important and often controversial business decision. To this day, accountants have varying opinions on the subject of inventory valuation techniques.

In most industries, the prices paid by businesses for goods frequently change. A hardware store, for example, may buy a dozen light bulbs for $10.00 one month and $12.50 the next. A gasoline station may pay $1.75 per gallon on Tuesday and $1.69 on Thursday. When taking inventory, it is virtually impossible to determine what price items are left. This means that the *flow of goods* in and out of a business does not always match the *flow of costs* in and out of the business.

The one method of pricing inventory that actually matches the flow of costs to the flow of goods is known as the **specific identification method**. This method is feasible only when the variety of merchandise carried in stock and the volume of sales are relatively low, such as with automobiles or other expensive items. Each car, for example, has a specific vehicle identification number or serial number that makes inventory valuation accurate. A list of the actual vehicles in stock at any given time, and their corresponding costs, can easily be totaled to arrive at an inventory figure.

In reality, most businesses have a wide variety of merchandise and find this method too expensive, because implementation would require sophisticated computer bar-coding systems. For this reason, it is customary to use an *assumption* as to the flow of costs of merchandise in and out of the business. The three most common cost flow assumptions or inventory pricing methods are as follows:

1. **First in, first-out (FIFO):** Cost flow is in the order in which the costs were incurred.
2. **Last-in, first-out (LIFO):** Cost flow is in the reverse order in which the costs were incurred.
3. **Average cost:** Cost flow is an average of the costs incurred.

Although cost is the primary basis for the valuation of inventory, when market prices or current replacement costs fall below the actual cost of those in inventory, the company has incurred a loss. For example, let's say a computer retailer purchases a large quantity of DVD drives at a cost of $200 each. A few months later, due to advances in technology, a faster model is introduced costing only $175 each. Under these market conditions, companies are permitted to choose a method for pricing inventory known as the lower-of-cost-or-market (LCM) rule.

All the inventory valuation methods listed above are acceptable for both income tax reporting and a company's financial statements. As we see in this section, each of these methods has advantages and disadvantages. Economic conditions, such as whether merchandise prices are rising (inflation) or falling (deflation), play an important role in the decision of which method to adopt.

For income tax reporting, once a method has been chosen, the Internal Revenue Service (IRS) requires that it be used consistently from one year to the next. Any changes in the method used for inventory valuation must be for a good reason and must be approved by the IRS.

PRICING INVENTORY BY USING THE FIRST-IN, FIRST-OUT (FIFO) METHOD

The **first-in, first-out (FIFO) method** assumes that the items purchased *first* are the *first* items sold. The items in inventory at the end of the year are matched with the costs of items of the same type that were most recently purchased. This method closely approximates the manner in which most businesses reduce their inventory, especially when the merchandise is perishable or subject to frequent style or model changes.

Essentially, this method involves taking physical inventory at the end of the year or accounting period and assigning cost in reverse order in which the purchases were received.

first-in, first-out (FIFO) method Inventory valuation method that assumes the items purchased by a company *first* are the *first* items to be sold. Items remaining in ending inventory at the end of an accounting period are therefore the most recently purchased.

STEPS TO CALCULATE THE VALUE OF ENDING INVENTORY BY USING FIFO

Step 1. List the number of units on hand at the end of the year and their corresponding costs, starting with the ending balance and working *backward* through the incoming shipments.

Step 2. Multiply the number of units by the corresponding cost per unit for each purchase.

Step 3. Calculate the value of ending inventory by totaling the extensions from Step 2.

Exhibit 16-1
First-In, First-Out—FIFO

16-1

TEACHING TIP
Ask students, "If you worked in a shoe store and were instructed to 'take inventory,' what exactly would you do?" Most will answer, "Count all the boxes."

Next, ask how they would assign a "dollar value" to the boxes. Point out that this chapter deals with the various methods used to determine that "dollar value."

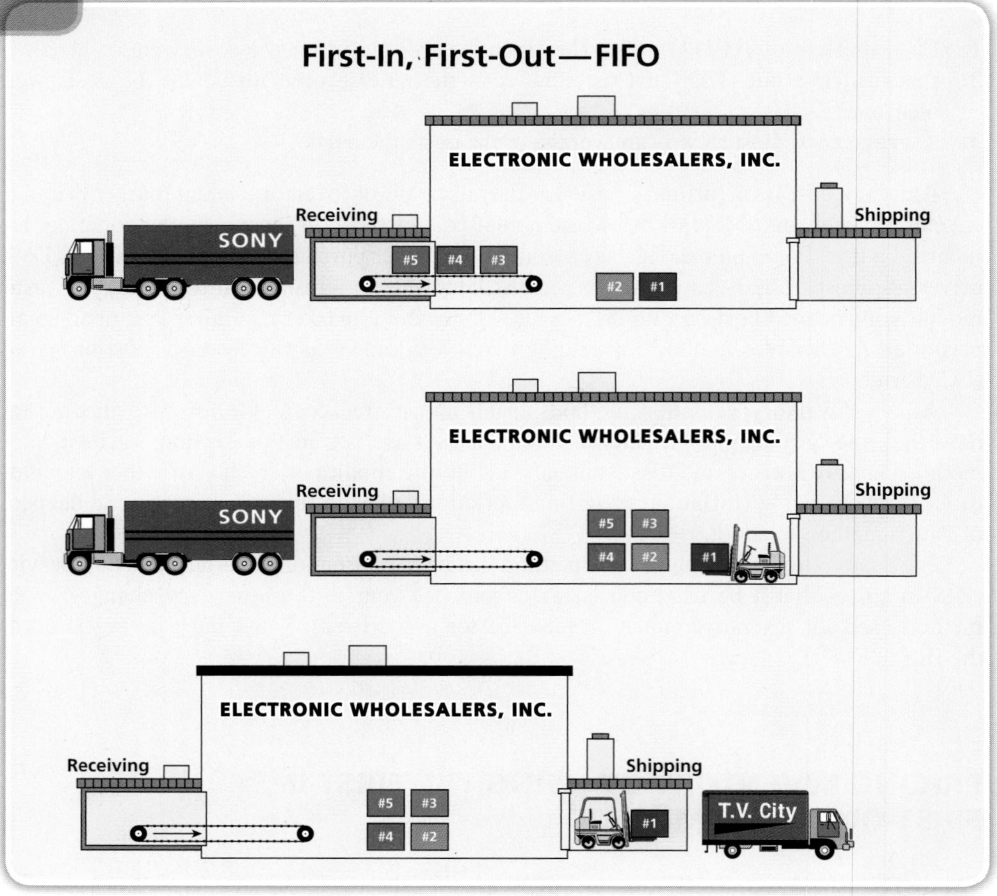

In the Business World

The value placed on inventory can have a significant effect on the *net income* of a company. Because net income is the basis of calculating federal income tax, accountants frequently must decide whether to value inventory to reflect higher net profit to entice investors or lower net profit to minimize income taxes.

To illustrate the application of the FIFO method of inventory pricing, as well as the other methods in this section, we shall use the following annual inventory data for 8 × 10 picture frames at Target.

Target

January 1	Beginning Inventory	400 units @ $5.00	$2,000
April 9	Purchase	200 units @ $6.00	1,200
July 19	Purchase	500 units @ $7.00	3,500
October 15	Purchase	300 units @ $8.00	2,400
December 8	Purchase	200 units @ $9.00	1,800
Picture frames available for sale during the year		1,600	$10,900

EXAMPLE 1 PRICING INVENTORY BY USING THE FIFO METHOD

When physical inventory of the picture frames was taken at Target on December 31, it was found that 700 remained in inventory. Using the FIFO method of inventory pricing, what is the dollar value of this ending inventory?

SOLUTION STRATEGY

With the assumption under FIFO that the inventory cost flow is made up of the *most recent* costs, the 700 picture frames in ending inventory would be valued as follows:

Step 1. Set up a table listing the 700 picture frames with costs in reverse order of acquisition.

200 units @ \$9.00 from the December 8 purchase
300 units @ \$8.00 from the October 15 purchase
200 units @ \$7.00 from the July 19 purchase
700 Inventory, December 31

Steps 2 & 3. Next we extend each purchase, multiplying the number of units by the cost per unit, and find the total of the extensions.

Units	Cost/Unit	Total	
200	\$9.00	\$1,800	
300	8.00	2,400	
200	7.00	1,400	
700		\$5,600	Ending inventory using FIFO

TRY IT EXERCISE 1

You are the merchandise manager at Best Buy. The following data represent your records of the annual inventory figures for a particular video game.

Best Buy

January 1	Beginning Inventory	200 units @ \$8.00	\$1,600
May 14	Purchase	100 units @ \$8.50	850
August 27	Purchase	250 units @ \$9.00	2,250
November 18	Purchase	300 units @ \$8.75	2,625
Video games available for sale		850	\$7,325

Using the FIFO method of inventory pricing, what is the dollar value of ending inventory if there were 380 video games on hand on December 31?

CHECK YOUR ANSWER WITH THE SOLUTION ON PAGE 608.

CLASSROOM ACTIVITY
Have students work Try It Exercises 1, 2, and 3 in pairs. To help them understand inventory valuation, a "continuous scenario" is used to illustrate FIFO, LIFO, and average cost.

- Examples: Picture frames at Target
- Try It Exercises: Video games at Best Buy.

16-2

PRICING INVENTORY BY USING THE LAST-IN, FIRST-OUT (LIFO) METHOD

The **last-in, first-out (LIFO) method** assumes that the items purchased *last* are sold or removed from inventory *first*. The items in inventory at the end of the year are matched with the cost of items of the same type that were purchased earliest. Therefore, items included in your ending inventory are considered to be those from the beginning inventory plus those acquired first from purchases.

This method involves taking physical inventory at the end of the year or accounting period and assigning cost in the same order in which the purchases were received.

last-in, first-out (LIFO) method
Inventory valuation method that assumes the items purchased by a company *last* are the *first* items to be sold. Items remaining in ending inventory at the end of an accounting period are therefore the oldest goods.

STEPS TO CALCULATE THE VALUE OF ENDING INVENTORY BY USING LIFO

Step 1. List the number of units on hand at the end of the year and their corresponding costs starting with the beginning inventory and working *forward* through the incoming shipments.

Step 2. Multiply the number of units by the corresponding cost per unit for each purchase.

Step 3. Calculate the value of ending inventory by totaling the extensions from Step 2.

Exhibit 16-2
Last-In, First-Out—LIFO

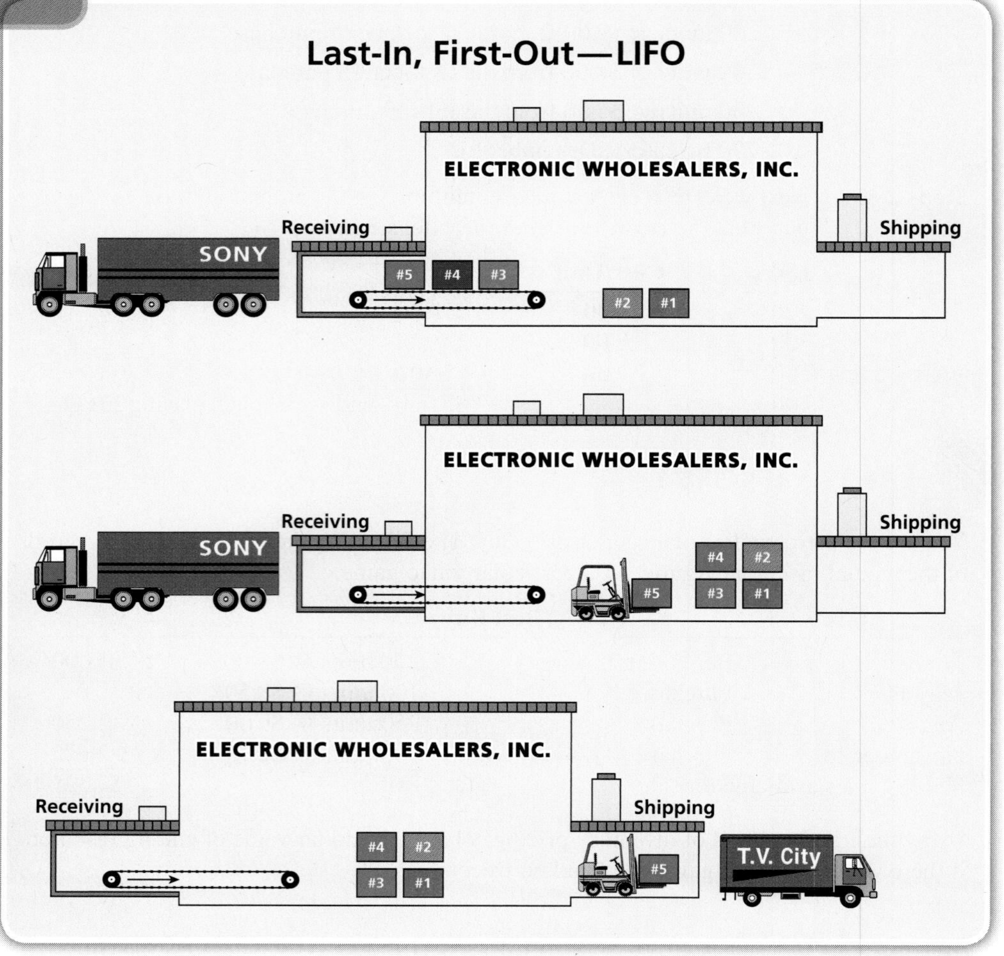

Last-In, First-Out—LIFO

Teaching Transparency 16-3

In the Business World

One of the main reasons for choosing a particular inventory valuation method is for the calculation of *income* for tax purposes.

- When costs are rising:
  FIFO → Higher gross profit
  LIFO → Lower gross profit
- When costs are decreasing:
  FIFO → Lower gross profit
  LIFO → Higher gross profit

EXAMPLE 2 PRICING INVENTORY BY USING THE LIFO METHOD

Let's return to the previous example about the 8×10 picture frames from Target, page 582. Once again, when physical inventory was taken on December 31, it was found that 700 remained in inventory. Using the LIFO method of inventory pricing, what is the dollar value of this ending inventory?

SOLUTION STRATEGY

With the assumption under LIFO that the inventory cost flow is made up of the *earliest* costs, the 700 picture frames in ending inventory would be valued as follows:

Step 1. Set up a table listing the 700 picture frames with costs in the order in which they were acquired.

400 units @ \$5.00 from the January 1 beginning inventory
200 units @ \$6.00 from the April 9 purchase
100 units @ \$7.00 from the July 19 purchase
700 Inventory, December 31

Steps 2 & 3. Next, we extend each purchase, multiplying the number of units by the cost per unit, and find the total of the extensions.

Units	Cost/Unit	Total	
400	$5.00	$2,000	
200	6.00	1,200	
100	7.00	700	
700		$3,900	Ending inventory using LIFO

TRY IT EXERCISE 2

Let's return to Try It Exercise 1, Best Buy. Use the data from page 583 to calculate the dollar value of the 380 video games in ending inventory by using the LIFO method.

CHECK YOUR ANSWER WITH THE SOLUTION ON PAGE 608.

16-4

PRICING INVENTORY BY USING THE AVERAGE COST METHOD

16-3

The **average cost method**, also known as **the weighted average method**, assumes that the cost of each unit of inventory is the *average* cost of all goods available for sale during that accounting period. It is a weighted average because it takes into consideration not only the cost per unit in each purchase but also the number of units purchased at each cost.

average cost, or weighted average, method Inventory valuation method that assumes the cost of each unit of inventory is the *average* cost of all goods available for sale during that accounting period.

STEPS TO CALCULATE THE VALUE OF ENDING INVENTORY BY USING AVERAGE COST

Step 1. Calculate the average cost per unit by using the following formula.

$$\textbf{Average cost per unit} = \frac{\textbf{Cost of goods available for sale}}{\textbf{Total units available for sale}}$$

Step 2. Calculate the value of ending inventory by multiplying the number of units in ending inventory by the average cost per unit.

Ending inventory = Units in ending inventory × Average cost per unit

EXAMPLE 3 PRICING INVENTORY BY USING AVERAGE COST

Let's return once again to the example of the 8×10 picture frames from Target, page 582. Using the average cost method of inventory pricing, what is the dollar value of the 700 frames on hand in ending inventory?

SOLUTION STRATEGY

Under the weighted average cost method, the 700 frames in ending inventory would be valued as follows:

Step 1. Calculate the average cost per unit:

$$\text{Average cost per unit} = \frac{\text{Cost of goods available for sale}}{\text{Total units available for sale}}$$

$$\text{Average cost per unit} = \frac{10{,}900}{1{,}600} = \$6.81$$

Step 2. Ending inventory = Units in ending inventory × Average cost per unit

Ending inventory = 700 × 6.81 = $4,767

TRY IT EXERCISE 3

16-5

Once again, let's use the Best Buy example. This time use the data from page 583 to calculate the value of the 380 video games in ending inventory by using the average cost method.

CHECK YOUR ANSWER WITH THE SOLUTION ON PAGE 608.

16-4 PRICING INVENTORY BY USING THE LOWER-OF-COST-OR-MARKET (LCM) RULE

lower-of-cost-or-market (LCM) rule Inventory valuation method whereby items in inventory are valued either at their actual cost or current replacement value, whichever is lower. This method is permitted under conditions of falling prices or merchandise obsolescence.

The three methods of pricing inventory discussed to this point—FIFO, LIFO, and weighted average—have been based on the cost of the merchandise. When the market price or current replacement price of an inventory item declines below the actual price paid for that item, companies are permitted to use a method known as the **lower-of-cost-or-market (LCM) rule.** This method takes into account such market conditions as severely falling prices, changing fashions or styles, or obsolescence of inventory items. The use of the LCM rule assumes that decreases in replacement costs will be accompanied by proportionate decreases in selling prices.

The lower-of-cost-or-market means comparing the market value (current replacement cost) of each item on hand with its cost, using the lower amount as its inventory value. Under ordinary circumstances, market value means the usual price paid, based on the volume of merchandise normally ordered by the firm.

STEPS TO CALCULATE THE VALUE OF ENDING INVENTORY BY USING THE LOWER-OF-COST-OR-MARKET RULE

Step 1. Calculate the cost for each item in the inventory by using one of the acceptable methods: FIFO, LIFO, or weighted average.

Step 2. Determine the market price or current replacement cost for each item.

Step 3. For each item, select the basis for valuation, cost or market, by choosing the lower figure.

Step 4. Calculate the total amount for each inventory item by multiplying the number of items by the valuation price chosen in Step 3.

Step 5. Calculate the total value of the inventory by adding all the figures in the Amount column.

EXAMPLE 4 PRICING INVENTORY BY USING THE LCM RULE

The following data represent the inventory figures of the Sundance Boutique. Use the lower-of-cost-or-market rule to calculate the extended amount for each item and the total value of the inventory.

Item	Description	Quantity	Unit Price Cost	Unit Price Market	Valuation Basis	Amount
Blouses	Style #44	40	$ 27.50	$ 31.25	______	______
	Style #54	54	36.40	33.20	______	______
Slacks	Style #20	68	42.10	39.80	______	______
	Style #30	50	57.65	59.18	______	______
Jackets	Suede	30	141.50	130.05	______	______
	Wool	35	88.15	85.45	______	______
					Total Value of Inventory	______

SOLUTION STRATEGY

In this example, the cost and market price are given. We begin by choosing the lower of cost or market and then extending each item to the Amount column. For example, the Style #44 blouse will be valued at the cost, $27.50, because it is less than the market price, $31.25. The extension would be 40 × $27.50 = $1,100.00.

Item	Description	Quantity	Unit Price Cost	Unit Price Market	Valuation Basis	Amount
Blouses	Style #44	40	$ 27.50	$ 31.25	Cost	$ 1,100.00
	Style #54	54	36.40	33.20	Market	1,792.80
Slacks	Style #20	68	42.10	39.80	Market	2,706.40
	Style #30	50	57.65	59.18	Cost	2,882.50
Jackets	Suede	30	141.50	130.05	Market	3,901.50
	Wool	35	88.15	85.45	Market	2,990.75
					Total Value of Inventory	$15,373.95

TRY IT EXERCISE 4

Determine the value of the following inventory for the Personal Touch Gift Shop by using the lower-of-cost-or-market rule.

Description	Quantity	Unit Price Cost	Unit Price Market	Valuation Basis	Amount
Lamps	75	$ 9.50	$ 9.20	______	______
Jewelry Boxes	120	26.30	27.15	______	______
16" Vases	88	42.40	39.70	______	______
12" Vases	64	23.65	21.40	______	______
Fruit Bowls	42	36.90	42.00	______	______
				Total Value of Inventory	______

CHECK YOUR ANSWERS WITH THE SOLUTIONS ON PAGE 609.

CLASSROOM ACTIVITY

Ask students to name categories of goods whose current market value might be lower than the cost. Typical responses would be electronic and computer equipment that has been replaced with newer and cheaper models or "out-of-fashion" clothing or accessories.

Specific examples might include computer Ram chips, modems, printers, scanners, beepers, and cellular telephones. Discuss DVDs replacing CDs, high-definition television, flat-panel computer screens, and electronic books.

SECTION I Review Exercises

1. Calculate the total number of units available for sale and the cost of goods available for sale from the following inventory of oil filters for Advance Auto Parts.

Advance Auto Parts
Oil Filter Inventory

Date	Units Purchased	Cost per Unit	Total Cost
Beginning Inventory, Jan. 1	160	$1.45	232.00
Purchase, March 14	210	1.65	346.50
Purchase, May 25	190	1.52	288.80
Purchase, August 19	300	1.77	531.00
Purchase, October 24	250	1.60	400.00
Total Units Available	1,110	**Cost of Goods Available for Sale**	$1,798.30

2. When the merchandise manager of Advance Auto Parts took physical inventory of the oil filters on December 31, it was found that 550 remained in inventory.
   a. What is the dollar value of the oil filter inventory by using FIFO?

   550 filters remaining using FIFO

Units	Cost/Unit	Total	
250	1.60	400.00	
300	1.77	531.00	
550		$931.00	FIFO

   b. What is the dollar value of the oil filter inventory by using LIFO?

   550 filters remaining using LIFO

Units	Cost/Unit	Total	
160	1.45	232.00	
210	1.65	346.50	
180	1.52	273.60	
550		$852.10	LIFO

   c. What is the dollar value of the filters by using the average cost method?

   $$\text{Average cost} = \frac{1{,}798.30}{1{,}110} = \$1.62 \text{ Each}$$

   Total value = 550 × 1.62 = $891

3. The following data represents the inventory for home burglar alarm systems at First Alert Security Corporation.

First Alert Security Corp.
Burglar Alarm Systems Inventory

Date	Units	Cost per Unit	Total Cost
Beginning Inventory, January 1	235	$140.00	$32,900
Purchase, March 10	152	$143.50	21,812
Purchase, May 16	135	$146.80	19,818
Purchase, October 9	78	$150.00	11,700
Alarm Systems Available for Sale	600	**Cost of Goods Available for Sale**	$86,230

a. How many alarm systems did First Alert Security have available for sale?

600

b. What is the total cost of the alarm systems available for sale?

$86,230

c. If physical inventory on December 31 showed 167 alarm systems on hand, what is their value using FIFO?

Units	Cost/Unit	Total
78	150.00	11,700.00
89	146.80	13,065.20
167		$24,765.20

d. What is the value of the 167 alarm systems using LIFO?

Units	Cost/Unit	Total
167	140	$23,380

e. What is the value of the alarm systems using the average cost method?

$$\text{Average cost} = \frac{86{,}230}{600} = \$143.72 \text{ Each}$$

Inventory value $= 167 \times \$143.72 = \$24{,}001.24$

4. The following data represent the inventory figures for 55-gallon fish tanks at Something's Fishy:

Something's Fishy
55-Gallon Fish Tanks Inventory

			Amount
January 1	Beginning Inventory	42 units @ $38.00	1,596.00
March 12	Purchase	80 units @ $36.50	2,920.00
July 19	Purchase	125 units @ $39.70	4,962.50
September 2	Purchase	75 units @ $41.75	3,131.25
	Fish Tanks Available for Sale	322	**Cost of Tanks Available for Sale** $12,609.75

a. How many fish tanks did Something's Fishy have available for sale?

322

b. What is the total cost of the tanks available for sale?

$12,609.75

c. If physical inventory on December 31 was 88 tanks on hand, what is the value of those tanks by using FIFO?

88 tanks using FIFO				
	75	@	41.75	= 3,131.25
	13	@	39.70	= 516.10
	88		Value of tanks	$3,647.35

d. What is the value of the 88 tanks by using LIFO?

88 tanks using LIFO				
	42	@	38.00	= 1,596.00
	46	@	36.50	= 1,679.00
	88		Value of tanks	$3,275.00

e. What is the value of the 88 tanks by using the average cost method?

$$\text{Average cost} = \frac{12{,}609.75}{322} = \$39.16 \text{ Each}$$

$$\text{Inventory value} = 88 \times 39.16 = \underline{\underline{\$3{,}446.08}}$$

True Value Company, headquartered in Chicago, is one of the world's largest retailer-owned hardware cooperatives with approximately 5,800 independent retail locations worldwide. Established as Cotter & Company in 1948 by John Cotter, the co-op originated with 25 members.

Known today as True Value Company, the co-op has grown considerably and today supports its retailers through 12 regional distribution centers and 3,000 associates. In 2006, True Value generated revenue of $2.05 billion.

5. Determine the amount of the following inventory for True Value Hardware by using the lower-of-cost-or-market rule:

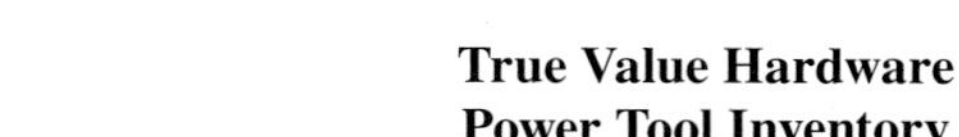

True Value Hardware
Power Tool Inventory

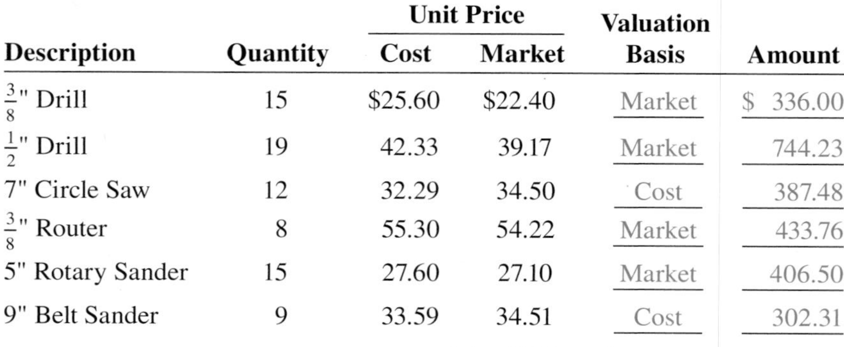

Description	Quantity	Unit Price Cost	Unit Price Market	Valuation Basis	Amount
$\frac{3}{8}$" Drill	15	$25.60	$22.40	Market	$ 336.00
$\frac{1}{2}$" Drill	19	42.33	39.17	Market	744.23
7" Circle Saw	12	32.29	34.50	Cost	387.48
$\frac{3}{8}$" Router	8	55.30	54.22	Market	433.76
5" Rotary Sander	15	27.60	27.10	Market	406.50
9" Belt Sander	9	33.59	34.51	Cost	302.31
				Total Value of Inventory	$2,610.28

6. Use the lower-of-cost-or-market rule to determine the value of the following inventory for the Rainbow Gardens Emporium:

Rainbow Gardens Emporium

Description	Quantity	Unit Price Cost	Unit Price Market	Valuation Basis	Amount
Dish Sets	220	$36	$33	Market	$ 7,260
Table Cloths	180	13	14	Cost	2,340
Barbeque Tools	428	35	33	Market	14,124
Outdoor Lamps	278	56	50	Market	13,900
Ceramic Statues	318	22	17	Market	5,406
				Total Value of Inventory	$43,030

BUSINESS DECISION IN OR OUT?

7. You are the accounting manager of Kleen and Green Janitorial Supply, Inc., of Chicago. One of your junior accountants is working on the December 31 year-end inventory figures and has asked for your help in determining which of several transactions belong in the ending inventory. From the following inventory scenarios, decide which *should* be included in the year-end inventory and which *should not*. *Hint:* Refer to Exhibit 7-3, Shipping Terms, page 209.

a. An order for a floor buffer and three different floor conditioning attachments shipped on December 31, FOB Chicago, and is expected to arrive on January 4.

b. An order for six drums of floor wax and four drums of wax stripper was shipped a to Detroit customer on December 31, FOB Detroit, and should arrive on January 2.

c. An order for 5 foot-operated mop buckets and 12 rag mops will be shipped on January 3.
d. A floor cleaning machine was returned on December 28 for warranty repair and is scheduled to be return shipped on January 6.
e. Two cases of window wipes shipped on December 30 FOB destination and are due to arrive on January 5.
f. A carton of 12 one-gallon bottles of window washing solution and 8 boxes of streak-free window washing cloths were ordered on December 30 and are due to be shipped on January 3.

Included in inventory: b, c, e, f
Not included in inventory: a, d

INVENTORY ESTIMATION

SECTION II 16

In Section I of this chapter, we learned to calculate the value of ending inventory by several methods using a physical count at the end of the accounting year. Most companies, however, require inventory figures more frequently than the once-a-year physical inventory. Monthly and quarterly financial statements, for example, may be prepared with inventory estimates, rather than expensive physical counts or perpetual inventory systems. In addition, when physical inventories are destroyed by fire or other disasters, estimates must be made for insurance claims purposes.

The two generally accepted methods for *estimating* the value of an inventory are the retail method and the gross profit method. For these methods to closely approximate the actual value of inventory, the markup rate for all items bought and sold by the company must be consistent. If they are not, the estimates should be calculated separately for each product category. For example, if a toy store gets a 30% markup on tricycles and 50% on bicycles, these categories should be calculated separately.

In business today, it is common practice for retail stores to use the retail method of inventory valuation, whereas manufacturers and wholesalers use the gross profit method.

ESTIMATING THE VALUE OF ENDING INVENTORY BY USING THE RETAIL METHOD

The **retail method** of inventory estimation is used by retail businesses of all types and sizes, from Wal-Mart and Sears to the corner grocery store. To use this method, the company must have certain figures in its accounting records, including the following:

retail method Method of inventory estimation used by most retailers based on a comparison of goods available for sale at cost and at retail.

a. *Beginning inventory* at cost price and at retail (selling price).
b. *Purchases* during the period at cost price and at retail.
c. *Net sales* for the period.

From these figures, the goods available for sale are determined at both cost and retail. We then calculate a ratio known as the **cost to retail price ratio**, or simply **cost ratio**, by the formula:

cost to retail price ratio, or cost ratio Ratio of goods available for sale at cost to the goods available for sale at retail. Used in the retail method of inventory estimation to represent the cost of each dollar of retail sales.

$$\text{Cost ratio} = \frac{\text{Goods available for sale at cost}}{\text{Goods available for sale at retail}}$$

This ratio represents the cost of each dollar of retail sales. For example, if the cost ratio for a company is .6 or 60%, this means that $.60 is the cost of each $1.00 of retail sales.

STEPS TO ESTIMATE THE VALUE OF ENDING INVENTORY BY USING THE RETAIL METHOD

Step 1. List beginning inventory and purchases at both cost and retail.

Step 2. Add purchases to beginning inventory to determine goods available for sale at both cost and retail.

Beginning inventory
+ Purchases
Goods available for sale

Step 3. Calculate the cost ratio:

$$\textbf{Cost ratio} = \frac{\textbf{Goods available for sale at cost}}{\textbf{Goods available for sale at retail}}$$

Step 4. Subtract net sales from goods available for sale at retail to get ending inventory at retail.

Goods available for sale at retail
− Net sales
Ending inventory at retail

Step 5. Convert ending inventory at retail to ending inventory at cost by multiplying the ending inventory at retail by the cost ratio.

Ending inventory at cost = Ending inventory at retail × Cost ratio

"Yes, it's self-defrosting. It also does a daily inventory, searches for the best deal and runs over to the store for you."

EXAMPLE 5 ESTIMATING INVENTORY USING THE RETAIL METHOD

Using the retail method, estimate the value of the ending inventory at cost on June 30, from the following information for Dependable Distributors, Inc.

Dependable Distributors, Inc.
Financial Highlights
June 1–June 30

	Cost	Retail
Beginning Inventory	$200,000	$400,000
Net Purchases (June)	150,000	300,000
Net Sales (June) $500,000		

SOLUTION STRATEGY

Steps 1 & 2. List the beginning inventory and purchases and calculate the goods available for sale.

	Cost	Retail
Beginning Inventory	$200,000	$400,000
+ Net Purchases (June)	+ 150,000	+ 300,000
Goods Available for Sale	$350,000	$700,000

Step 3. $\text{Cost ratio} = \dfrac{\text{Goods available for sale at cost}}{\text{Goods available for sale at retail}}$

$\text{Cost ratio} = \dfrac{350{,}000}{700{,}000} = .5 = 50\%$

Remember, this 50% figure means that \$.50 was the cost of each \$1.00 of retail sales.

Step 4. Next, find ending inventory at retail:

Goods available for sale at retail	\$700,000
− Net sales	− 500,000
Ending inventory at retail	\$200,000

Step 5. Now, convert the inventory at retail to inventory at cost by using the cost ratio:

Ending inventory at cost = Ending inventory at retail × Cost ratio

Ending inventory at cost = 200,000 × .5 = \$100,000

TRY IT EXERCISE 5

16-6

Using the retail method, estimate the value of the ending inventory at cost on August 31, from the following information for Ripe 'N Ready Fruit Wholesalers, Inc.

Ripe 'N Ready Fruit Wholesalers, Inc.
Financial Highlights
August 1–August 31

	Cost	Retail
Beginning Inventory	\$600,000	\$800,000
Net Purchases (August)	285,000	380,000
Net Sales (August) \$744,000		

CHECK YOUR ANSWER WITH THE SOLUTION ON PAGE 609.

ESTIMATING THE VALUE OF ENDING INVENTORY BY USING THE GROSS PROFIT METHOD

The **gross profit** or **gross margin method** uses a company's gross margin percent to estimate the ending inventory. This method assumes that a company maintains approximately the same gross margin from year to year. Inventories estimated in this manner are frequently used for interim reports and insurance claims; however, this method is not acceptable for inventory valuation on a company's annual financial statements.

gross profit or gross margin method Method of inventory estimation using a company's gross margin percent to estimate the ending inventory. This method assumes that a company maintains approximately the same gross margin from year to year.

From Chapter 15, remember that net sales is comprised of the cost of goods sold and gross margin.

Net sales (100%) = Cost of goods sold (%) + Gross margin (%)

From this equation, we see that when the gross margin percent is known, the cost of goods sold percent would be its complement, because together they equal net sales, which is 100%.

Cost of goods sold percent = 100% − Gross margin percent

Knowing the cost of goods sold percent is the key to this calculation. We use this percent to find the cost of goods sold, which, when subtracted from goods available for sale, gives us the estimated ending inventory.

STEPS TO ESTIMATE THE VALUE OF ENDING INVENTORY BY USING THE GROSS PROFIT METHOD

Step 1. Calculate the goods available for sale.

Beginning inventory
+ Net Purchases
Goods available for sale

Step 2. Find the estimated cost of goods sold by multiplying net sales by the cost of goods sold percent (complement of gross margin percent).

Estimated cost of goods sold = Net sales(100% − Gross margin %)

Step 3. Calculate the estimate of ending inventory by subtracting the estimated cost of goods sold from the goods available for sale.

Goods available for sale
− Estimated cost of goods sold
Estimated ending inventory

EXAMPLE 6 ESTIMATING INVENTORY USING THE GROSS PROFIT METHOD

CLASSROOM ACTIVITY
In groups, have students write and solve word problems involving inventory estimation. Next, have them exchange and solve the problems of another group, compare answers, and resolve any differences.

Angler's Fishing Supply, Inc., maintains a gross margin of 45% on all its wholesale supplies. In April, Angler's had a beginning inventory of $80,000, net purchases of $320,000, and net sales of $500,000. Use the gross profit method to estimate Angler's cost of ending inventory.

SOLUTION STRATEGY

Step 1.

Beginning inventory (April 1)	$ 80,000
+ Net purchases	320,000
Goods available for sale	$400,000

Step 2. Estimated cost of goods sold = Net sales(100% − Gross margin %)

Estimated cost of goods sold = $500,000(100% − 45%) = $275,000

Step 3.

Goods available for sale	$400,000
− Estimated cost of goods sold	275,000
Estimated ending inventory (April 30)	$125,000

TRY IT EXERCISE 6

Fantasy Beauty Supply, Inc., maintains a gross margin of 39% on all its wholesale beauty supplies. In November, the company had a beginning inventory of $137,000, net purchases of $220,000, and net sales of $410,000. Use the gross profit method to estimate the cost of ending inventory for November.

CHECK YOUR ANSWER WITH THE SOLUTION ON PAGE 609.

Teaching Transparency 16-7

Review Exercises

1. Using the retail method, estimate the value of the ending inventory at cost on September 30 from the following information for Tropicana Furniture Designs, Inc. Round the cost ratio to the nearest tenth of a percent.

Tropicana Furniture Designs, Inc.
September 1–September 30

	Cost	Retail
Beginning Inventory, Sept. 1	$150,000	$450,000
Purchases (September)	90,000	270,000
Net Sales (September) $395,000		

	Cost	Retail
Beginning inventory, Sept. 1	150,000	450,000
Purchase (September)	90,000	270,000
Goods available for sale	$240,000	$720,000

$$\text{Cost ratio} = \frac{240,000}{720,000} = 33.3\%$$

Goods available for sale at retail	720,000
Net sales	− 395,000
Ending inventory at retail	$325,000

Ending inventory at cost = 325,000 × 33.3%
= $108,225

2. Castle Industries had net sales of $205,400 in the month of November. Use the retail method to estimate the value of the inventory as of November 30 from the following financial information:

Castle Industries
Financial Highlights
November 1–November 30

	Cost	Retail
Beginning Inventory	$137,211	$328,500
Net Purchases (November)	138,849	313,500
Goods available for sale	$276,060	$642,000

$$\text{Cost ratio} = \frac{276,060}{642,000} = 0.43 = 43\%$$

Goods available for sale at retail	642,000
Net sales	− 205,400
Ending inventory at retail	$436,600

Ending inventory at cost = 436,600 × 43% = $187,738

3. Omni Fitness Equipment, Inc., maintains a gross margin of 55% on all its weight training products. In April, Omni had a beginning inventory of $146,000, net purchases of $208,000, and net sales of $437,000. Use the gross profit method to estimate the cost of ending inventory.

Beginning inventory	146,000	Estimated cost of goods sold	437,000(100% − 55%)
Net purchases	+ 208,000		437,000 × .45
Goods available for sale	$354,000		= $196,650
		Goods available for sale	354,000
		Cost of goods sold	− 196,650
		Estimated ending inventory	$157,350

4. Everlast Engineering Supplies maintains a gross margin of 58% on all of its merchandise. In June the company had a beginning inventory of $622,500, net purchases of $92,400, and net sales of $127,700. Use the gross profit method to estimate the cost of ending inventory as of June 30.

Beginning inventory	622,500	Estimated cost of goods sold	127,700(100% − 58%)
Net purchases	+ 92,400		127,700 × .42 = $53,634
Goods available for sale	$714,900		

Goods available for sale	714,900
Cost of goods sold	− 53,634
Estimated ending inventory	$661,266

5. The following data represent the inventory figures for Hot Shot Welding Supply, Inc. Using the retail method, estimate the value of the ending inventory at cost on January 31. Round the cost ratio to the nearest tenth of a percent.

Hot Shot Welding Supply, Inc.
January 1–January 31

	Cost	Retail
Beginning Inventory, Jan. 1	$50,000	$120,000
Purchases (January)	90,000	216,000
Net Sales (January) $188,000		

$$\text{Cost ratio} = \frac{140,000}{336,000} = 41.7\%$$

	Cost	Retail
Beginning inventory, Jan. 1	50,000	120,000
Purchase (January)	90,000	216,000
Goods available for sale	$140,000	$336,000

Goods available for sale at retail	336,000
Net sales	− 188,000
Ending inventory at retail	$148,000
Ending inventory at cost = 148,000 × .417	
	= $61,716

6. You are the warehouse manager for Discovery Kitchen Supplies. On a Sunday in May, you receive a phone call from the owner. He states that the entire building and contents were destroyed by fire. For the police report and the insurance claim, the owner has asked you to estimate the value of the lost inventory. Your records, which luckily were backed up on the hard drive of your home computer, indicate that at the time of the fire the net sales to date were $615,400 and the purchases were $232,600. The beginning inventory, on January 1, was $312,000. For the past 3 years, the company has operated at a gross margin of 60%. Use the gross profit method to calculate your answer.

Beginning inventory	312,000	Est. cost of goods sold	615,400(100% − 60%)	Total goods available	544,600
Net purchases	+ 232,600		615,400 × .4	Est. cost of goods sold	− 246,160
Total goods available	$544,600		= $246,160	Est. ending inventory	$298,440

BUSINESS DECISION OVER OR UNDER?

7. You own Bristol Marine, a retailer of boats, motors, and marine accessories. The store manager has just informed you that the amount of the physical inventory was incorrectly reported as $540,000 instead of the correct amount of $450,000. Unfortunately, yesterday you sent the quarterly financial statements to the stockholders. Now you must send revised statements and a letter of explanation.

   a. What effect did the error have on the items of the balance sheet for Bristol? Express your answer as *overstated* or *understated* for the items affected by the error.

      Merchandise inventory was overstated by $90,000 ($540,000 − $450,000). Therefore, Current assets, Total assets, and Total stockholders' equity were also overstated by $90,000.

   b. What effect will the error have on the items of the income statement for Bristol?

      Cost of goods sold was understated by $90,000. Therefore, Gross profit and Net income were overstated by $90,000.

   c. Did this error make the Bristol quarterly results look better or worse than they actually are?

      The inventory overstatement made the company's quarterly results look better than they actually were.

INVENTORY TURNOVER AND TARGETS

In Chapter 15, we learned to use inventory turnover as one of the financial statement efficiency ratios. To review, **inventory turnover** or **stock turnover** is the number of times during an operating period that the average dollars invested in merchandise inventory was theoretically sold out or turned over.

inventory or stock turnover The number of times during an operating period that the average dollars invested in merchandise inventory was theoretically sold out or turned over. May be calculated in retail dollars or in cost dollars.

Generally, the more expensive the item, the lower the turnover rate. For example, furniture and fine jewelry items might have a turnover rate of three or four times per year, whereas a grocery store might have a turnover of 15 or 20 times per year, or more. In this section, we revisit the concept of inventory turnover and learn to calculate it at retail and at cost.

Although a company must maintain inventory quantities large enough to meet the day-to-day demands of its operations, it is important to keep the amount invested in inventory to a minimum. In this section, we also learn to calculate target inventories for companies based on published industry standards.

Regardless of the method used to determine inventory turnover, the procedure always involves dividing some measure of sales volume by a measure of the typical or average inventory. This **average inventory** is commonly found by adding the beginning and ending inventories of the operating period, and dividing by 2.

average inventory An estimate of a company's typical inventory at any given time, calculated by dividing the total of all inventories taken during an operating period by the number of times inventory was taken.

$$\textbf{Average inventory} = \frac{\textbf{Beginning inventory} + \textbf{Ending inventory}}{\textbf{2}}$$

Whenever possible, additional interim inventories should be used to increase the accuracy of the average inventory figure. For example, if a mid-year inventory was taken, this figure would be added to the beginning and ending inventories and the total divided by 3. If monthly inventories were available, they would be added and the total divided by 12.

16-7 CALCULATING INVENTORY TURNOVER RATE AT RETAIL

When inventory turnover rate is calculated at retail, the measure of sales volume used is net sales. The average inventory is expressed in retail sales dollars by using the beginning and ending inventories at retail. The inventory turnover rate is expressed in number of *times* the inventory was sold out during the period.

In the Business World

Inventory turnover is an important business indicator, particularly when compared with turnover rates from previous operating periods and with published industry statistics for similar-sized companies.

STEPS TO CALCULATE INVENTORY TURNOVER RATE AT RETAIL

Step 1. Calculate average inventory at retail.

$$\textbf{Average inventory}_{\textbf{at retail}} = \frac{\textbf{Beginning inventory at retail + Ending inventory at retail}}{2}$$

Step 2. Calculate the inventory turnover at retail. Round to the nearest tenth, when necessary.

$$\textbf{Inventory turnover}_{\textbf{at retail}} = \frac{\textbf{Net sales}}{\textbf{Average inventory at retail}}$$

EXAMPLE 7 CALCULATING INVENTORY TURNOVER RATE AT RETAIL

Hobby Town had net sales of $650,900 for the year. If the beginning inventory at retail was $143,000 and the ending inventory at retail was $232,100, what are the average inventory at retail and the inventory turnover at retail, rounded to the nearest tenth?

SOLUTION STRATEGY

Step 1. $\text{Average inventory}_{\text{at retail}} = \dfrac{\text{Beginning inventory at retail + Ending inventory at retail}}{2}$

$$\text{Average inventory}_{\text{at retail}} = \frac{143{,}000 + 232{,}100}{2} = \frac{375{,}100}{2} = \underline{\underline{\$187{,}550}}$$

Step 2. $\text{Inventory turnover}_{\text{at retail}} = \dfrac{\text{Net sales}}{\text{Average inventory at retail}}$

$$\text{Inventory turnover}_{\text{at retail}} = \frac{650{,}900}{187{,}550} = 3.47 = \underline{\underline{3.5 \text{ Times}}}$$

TRY IT EXERCISE 7

Exotic Gardens had net sales of $260,700 for the year. If the beginning inventory at retail was $65,100 and the ending inventory at retail was $52,800, what are the average inventory and the inventory turnover rounded to the nearest tenth?

CHECK YOUR ANSWERS WITH THE SOLUTIONS ON PAGE 609.

© Digital Vision/Getty Images

Inventory turnover rates are important business indicators.

CALCULATING INVENTORY TURNOVER RATE AT COST

16-8

Frequently, the inventory turnover rate of a company is expressed in terms of cost dollars rather than selling price or retail dollars. When this is the case, the cost of goods sold is used as the measure of sales volume and becomes the numerator in the formula. The denominator, average inventory, is calculated at cost.

STEPS TO CALCULATE INVENTORY TURNOVER RATE AT COST

Step 1. Calculate the average inventory at cost.

$$\textbf{Average inventory}_{\text{at cost}} = \frac{\textbf{Beginning inventory at cost} + \textbf{Ending inventory at cost}}{2}$$

Step 2. Calculate the inventory turnover at cost.

$$\textbf{Inventory turnover}_{\text{at cost}} = \frac{\textbf{Cost of goods sold}}{\textbf{Average inventory at cost}}$$

CLASSROOM ACTIVITY

Point out that inventory turnover rates differ from industry to industry.

Ask students to name businesses with high and low inventory turnover rates. Typical responses might include supermarkets for high turnover and jewelry stores for low turnover.

EXAMPLE 8 CALCULATING INVENTORY TURNOVER RATE AT COST

Metro Mechanical, Inc., had cost of goods sold of $416,200 for the year. If the beginning inventory at cost was $95,790 and the ending inventory at cost was $197,100, what are the average inventory at cost and the inventory turnover at cost, rounded to the nearest tenth?

SOLUTION STRATEGY

Step 1. $$\text{Average inventory}_{\text{at cost}} = \frac{\text{Beginning inventory at cost} + \text{Ending inventory at cost}}{2}$$

$$\text{Average inventory}_{\text{at cost}} = \frac{95{,}790 + 197{,}100}{2} = \frac{292{,}890}{2} = \underline{\underline{\$146{,}445}}$$

Step 2. $$\text{Inventory turnover}_{\text{at cost}} = \frac{\text{Cost of goods sold}}{\text{Average inventory at cost}}$$

$$\text{Inventory turnover}_{\text{at cost}} = \frac{416{,}200}{146{,}445} = 2.84 = \underline{\underline{2.8\text{ Times}}}$$

TRY IT EXERCISE 8

E-Z Kwik Grocery Store had cost of goods sold of $756,400 for the year. If the beginning inventory at cost was $43,500 and the ending inventory at cost was $59,300, what are the average inventory at cost and the inventory turnover rounded to the nearest tenth?

CHECK YOUR ANSWERS WITH THE SOLUTIONS ON PAGE 610.

16-9 CALCULATING TARGET INVENTORIES BASED ON INDUSTRY STANDARDS

When inventory turnover is below average for a firm its size, it may be a signal that the company is carrying too much inventory. Carrying extra inventory can lead to extra expenses, such as warehousing costs and insurance. It also ties up money the company could use more efficiently elsewhere. In certain industries, some additional risks of large inventories would be losses due to price declines, obsolescence, or deterioration of the goods.

Trade associations and the federal government publish a wide variety of important industry statistics, ratios, and standards for every size company. When such inventory turnover figures are available, merchandise managers can use the following formulas to calculate the **target average inventory** required by their firm to achieve the published industry standards for a company with similar sales volume.

target average inventory Inventory standards published by trade associations and the federal government for companies of all sizes and in all industries. Used by managers as *targets* for the ideal amount of inventory to carry for maximum efficiency.

$$\textbf{Target average inventory}_{\text{at cost}} = \frac{\textbf{Cost of goods sold}}{\textbf{Published inventory turnover at cost}}$$

$$\textbf{Target average inventory}_{\text{at retail}} = \frac{\textbf{Net sales}}{\textbf{Published inventory turnover at retail}}$$

EXAMPLE 9 CALCULATING TARGET INVENTORIES BASED ON INDUSTRY STANDARDS

F-Stop Photo, Inc., a wholesale photo supply business, had cost of goods sold of \$950,000 for the year. The beginning inventory at cost was \$245,000 and the ending inventory at cost amounted to \$285,000. According to the noted business research firm Dun & Bradstreet, the inventory turnover rate at cost for a photo business of this size is five times. Calculate the average inventory and actual inventory turnover for F-Stop. If the turnover is less than five times, calculate the target average inventory needed by F-Stop to theoretically come up to industry standards.

SOLUTION STRATEGY

Step 1.

$$\text{Average inventory}_{\text{at cost}} = \frac{\text{Beginning inventory at cost} + \text{Ending inventory at cost}}{2}$$

$$\text{Average inventory}_{\text{at cost}} = \frac{245{,}000 + 285{,}000}{2} = \frac{530{,}000}{2} = \underline{\underline{\$265{,}000}}$$

Step 2.

$$\text{Inventory turnover}_{\text{at cost}} = \frac{\text{Cost of goods sold}}{\text{Average inventory at cost}}$$

$$\text{Inventory turnover}_{\text{at cost}} = \frac{950{,}000}{265{,}000} = 3.58 = \underline{\underline{3.6 \text{ Times}}}$$

Step 3. The actual inventory turnover for F-Stop is *3.6 times* per year compared with the industry standard of five times. This indicates that the company is carrying too much inventory. Let's calculate the target average inventory F-Stop should carry to meet industry standards.

$$\text{Target average inventory}_{\text{at cost}} = \frac{\text{Cost of goods sold}}{\text{Published inventory turnover at cost}}$$

$$\text{Target average inventory}_{\text{at cost}} = \frac{950{,}000}{5} = \underline{\underline{\$190{,}000}}$$

The actual average inventory carried by F-Stop for the year was \$265,000 compared with the target inventory of \$190,000. This indicates that, at any given time, the inventory for F-Stop averaged about \$75,000 higher than that of its competition.

TRY IT EXERCISE 9

Satellite Communications, Inc., had net sales of \$2,650,000 for the year. The beginning inventory at retail was \$495,000, and the ending inventory at retail amounted to \$380,000. The inventory turnover at retail published as the standard for a business of this size is seven times. Calculate the average inventory and actual inventory turnover for the company. If the turnover is less than seven times, calculate the target average inventory needed to theoretically come up to industry standards.

CHECK YOUR ANSWERS WITH THE SOLUTIONS ON PAGE 610.

In the Business World

- When industry figures are published at "cost," target inventory is calculated by using *cost of goods sold.*
- When industry figures are published at "retail," target inventory is calculated by using *net sales.*

CLASSROOM ACTIVITY

In groups, have students research the inventory turnover rates for various types of business. This information can be found in U.S. Commerce Department publications such as *The Survey of Current Business*, as well as other government and industry publications.

Have the groups report their findings and sources to the class.

SECTION III Review Exercises

Assuming that all net sales figures are at *retail* and all cost of goods sold figures are at *cost*, calculate the average inventory and inventory turnover for the following. If the actual turnover is less than the published rate, calculate the target average inventory necessary to come up to industry standards.

	Net Sales	Cost of Goods Sold	Beginning Inventory	Ending Inventory	Average Inventory	Inventory Turnover	Published Rate	Target Average Inventory
1.	$500,000		$50,000	$70,000	$60,000	8.3	10.0	$50,000.00
2.		$335,000	48,000	56,000	$52,000	6.4	6.0	Above
3.		1,200,000	443,000	530,000	$486,500	2.5	3.5	$342,857.14
4.	4,570,000		854,000	650,300	$752,150	6.1	8.2	$557,317.07

5. Shop-Rite Shoes, Inc., had net sales of $145,900 for June. The beginning inventory at retail was $24,000, and the ending inventory at retail was $32,900.

   a. What is the average inventory at retail?

   $$\text{Average inventory} = \frac{24{,}000 + 32{,}900}{2} = \$28{,}450$$

   b. What is the inventory turnover rounded to the nearest tenth?

   $$\text{Inventory turnover} = \frac{145{,}900}{28{,}450} = 5.12 = 5.1 \text{ Times}$$

6. Bubbles Bath Boutique had net sales of $245,300 for the year. The beginning inventory at retail was $62,600 and the ending inventory at retail was $54,200.

   a. What is the average inventory at retail?

   $$\text{Average inventory} = \frac{62{,}600 + 54{,}200}{2} = \$58{,}400$$

   b. What is the inventory turnover, rounded to the nearest tenth?

   $$\text{Inventory turnover} = \frac{245{,}300}{58{,}400} = 4.20 = 4.2 \text{ Times}$$

7. The Gourmet's Delight, a cooking equipment wholesaler, had cost of goods sold of $458,900 for the year. The beginning inventory at cost was $83,600, and the ending inventory at cost was $71,700.

   a. What is the average inventory at cost?

   $$\text{Average inventory} = \frac{83{,}600 + 71{,}700}{2} = \$77{,}650$$

   b. What is the inventory turnover, rounded to the nearest tenth?

   $$\text{Inventory turnover} = \frac{458{,}900}{77{,}650} = 5.90 = 5.9 \text{ Times}$$

8. Riverside Industries had cost of goods sold of $359,700 for the year. The beginning inventory at cost was $73,180 and the ending inventory at cost was $79,500.

   a. What is the average inventory at cost?

   $$\text{Average inventory} = \frac{73,180 + 79,500}{2} = \underline{\underline{\$76,340}}$$

   b. What is the inventory turnover rounded to the nearest tenth?

   $$\text{Inventory turnover} = \frac{359,700}{76,340} = 4.71 = \underline{\underline{4.7 \text{ Times}}}$$

9. Delta Supply is a plumbing parts wholesaler. Last year, their average inventory at cost was $154,800, and their cost of goods sold was $738,700. The inventory turnover rate published for a business of this size is 5.5 times.

   a. Calculate the actual inventory turnover rate at cost for Delta. Round to the nearest tenth.

   $$\text{Inventory turnover} = \frac{738,700}{154,800} = 4.77 = \underline{\underline{4.8 \text{ Times}}}$$

   b. If the turnover rate is below the industry average of 5.5 times, calculate the target average inventory needed to match the industry standard.

   $$\text{Target inventory} = \frac{738,700}{5.5} = \underline{\underline{\$134,309.09}}$$

10. Kwik-Mix Concrete Corporation had cost of goods sold of $1,250,000 for the third quarter. The beginning inventory at cost was $135,000, and the ending inventory at cost amounted to $190,900. The inventory turnover rate published as the industry standard for a business of this size is 9.5 times.

   a. Calculate the average inventory and actual inventory turnover rate for the company.

   $$\text{Average inventory} = \frac{135,000 + 190,900}{2} = \underline{\underline{\$162,950}}$$

   $$\text{Inventory turnover} = \frac{1,250,000}{162,950} = 7.67 = \underline{\underline{7.7 \text{ Times}}}$$

   b. If the turnover rate is less than 9.5 times, calculate the target average inventory needed to theoretically come up to industry standards.

   $$\text{Target inventory} = \frac{1,250,000}{9.5} = \underline{\underline{\$131,578.95}}$$

11. Trophy Masters had net sales for the year of $145,000. The beginning inventory at retail was $36,000, and the ending inventory at retail amounted to $40,300. The inventory turnover rate published as the industry standard for a business of this size is 4.9 times.

   a. Calculate the average inventory and actual inventory turnover rate for the company.

   $$\text{Average inventory} = \frac{36,000 + 40,300}{2} = \underline{\underline{\$38,150}}$$

   $$\text{Inventory turnover} = \frac{145,000}{38,150} = 3.80 = \underline{\underline{3.8 \text{ Times}}}$$

   b. If the turnover rate is less than 4.9 times, calculate the target average inventory needed to theoretically come up to industry standards.

   $$\text{Target inventory} = \frac{145,000}{4.9} = \underline{\underline{\$29,591.84}}$$

BUSINESS DECISION KEEP YOUR EYE ON THE FEET

12. Another way to look at the concept of inventory turnover is by measuring sales per square foot. Taking the average inventory at retail and dividing it by the number of square feet devoted to a particular product will give you *average sales per square foot*. When you multiply this figure by the inventory turnover rate you get the *annual sales per square foot*.

Top Five Consumer Electronics Growth Sectors		
Product	2006	2007
DVRs	17%	25%
Network routers/hubs	22	30
MP3 players	25	32
Cable modem	36	42
Digital camera	57	62

Source: CEA Market Research 5/07

It is important to know the amount of sales per square foot your merchandise is producing, both on the average and annually. These figures should be tracked monthly, and compared with industry standards for businesses of similar size and type.

You own Mega Music, a large multiproduct music store in a regional mall. Mega has 10,000 square feet of selling space divided into five departments.

a. From the table below, calculate the average and annual sales per square foot. Then, calculate the annual sales for each department and the total sales for the entire store.

Department	Square Feet	Average Inventory at Retail	Average Sales per Sq. Foot	Inventory Turnover	Annual Sales per Sq. Foot	Departmental Annual Sales
CDs	3,500	$153,000	$43.71	5.2	$227.29	$ 795,515
DVDs	2,800	$141,000	$50.36	4.6	$231.66	$ 648,648
Video tapes	2,100	$38,500	$18.33	4.1	$75.15	$ 157,815
Audio tapes	500	$12,700	$25.40	2.3	$58.42	$ 29,210
Accessories	1,100	$45,000	$40.91	4.7	$192.28	$ 211,508
					Total Sales	$1,842,696

b. If industry standards for this size store and type of merchandise is $200 per square foot in annual sales, which departments are below standards? What can be done to improve the situation?

Answers may vary. Annual sales per square foot in the video and audio tapes departments are significantly below industry standards. These could be *reduced in size* in order to increase the "per square foot" sales figures.

c. (Optional) Use the Internet to research and share with the class the current "industry standard" sales per square foot and inventory turnover rates for the merchandise categories of your store.

CHAPTER FORMULAS

Inventory Valuation—Average Cost Method

$$\text{Average cost per unit} = \frac{\text{Cost of goods available for sale}}{\text{Total units available for sale}}$$

Ending inventory = Units in ending inventory × Average cost per unit

Inventory Estimation—Retail Method

$$\text{Cost ratio} = \frac{\text{Goods available for sale at cost}}{\text{Goods available for sale at retail}}$$

Estimated ending inventory at cost = Ending inventory at retail × Cost ratio

Inventory Estimation—Gross Profit Method

$$\text{Estimated cost of goods sold} = \text{Net sales}(100\% - \text{Gross margin }\%)$$

Inventory Turnover—Retail

$$\text{Average inventory}_{\text{retail}} = \frac{\text{Beginning inventory at retail} + \text{Ending inventory at retail}}{2}$$

$$\text{Inventory turnover}_{\text{retail}} = \frac{\text{Net sales}}{\text{Average inventory at retail}}$$

Inventory Turnover—Cost

$$\text{Average inventory}_{\text{cost}} = \frac{\text{Beginning inventory at cost} + \text{Ending inventory at cost}}{2}$$

$$\text{Inventory turnover}_{\text{cost}} = \frac{\text{Cost of goods sold}}{\text{Average inventory at cost}}$$

Target Inventory

$$\text{Target average inventory}_{\text{cost}} = \frac{\text{Cost of goods sold}}{\text{Published inventory turnover at cost}}$$

$$\text{Target average inventory}_{\text{retail}} = \frac{\text{Net sales}}{\text{Published inventory turnover at retail}}$$

SUMMARY CHART 16

Section I: Inventory Valuation

Topic	Important Concepts	Illustrative Examples
Pricing Inventory by Using the First-In, First-Out (FIFO) Method **P/O 16-1, p. 581**	FIFO assumes that the items purchased first are the first items sold. The items in inventory at the end of the year are matched with the cost of items of the same type that were purchased most recently. *Inventory Pricing—FIFO:* 1. List the number of units on hand at the end of the year and their corresponding costs, starting with the ending balance and working *backward* through the incoming shipments. 2. Multiply the number of units by the corresponding cost per unit for each purchase. 3. Calculate the value of ending inventory by totaling all the extensions from Step 2.	The following data represent the inventory figures for imported ceramic planters at The Gift Collection: **Date** / **Units** / **Cost per Unit** Jan. 1 Beg. Inv. 55 $12.30 Mar. 9 Purch. 60 13.50 Aug. 12 Purch. 45 13.90 Nov. 27 Purch. 75 14.25 On December 31, physical inventory revealed 130 planters in stock. Calculate the value of the ending inventory by using FIFO. With the assumption under FIFO that the inventory cost flow is made up of the most recent costs, the 130 planters would be valued as follows: **Date** / **Units** / **Cost** / **Total** Nov. 27 75 @ 14.25 1,068.75 Aug. 12 45 @ 13.90 625.50 Mar. 9 10 @ 13.50 135.00 130 $1,829.25

Section I: (continued)

Topic	Important Concepts	Illustrative Examples
Pricing Inventory by Using the Last-In, First-Out (LIFO) Method **P/O 16-2, p. 583**	LIFO assumes that the items purchased last are sold or removed from inventory first. The items in inventory at the end of the year are matched with the cost of the same type items purchased earliest. *Inventory Pricing—LIFO:* 1. List the number of units on hand at the end of the year and their corresponding costs, starting with the beginning inventory and working *forward* through the incoming shipments. 2. Multiply the number of units by the corresponding cost per unit for each purchase. 3. Calculate the value of ending inventory by totaling all the extensions from Step 2.	Using the data on page 605 for The Gift Collection, calculate the value of the 130 planters in ending inventory by using LIFO. With the assumption under LIFO that the inventory cost flow is made up of the earliest costs, the 130 planters would be valued as follows: **Date / Units / Cost / Total** Jan. 1 / 55 / @ 12.30 / 676.50 Mar. 9 / 60 / @ 13.50 / 810.00 Aug. 12 / 15 / @ 13.90 / 208.50 130 / $1,695.00
Pricing Inventory by Using the Average Cost Method **P/O 16-3, p. 585**	The average cost method, also known as the weighted average method, assumes that the cost of each unit of inventory is the average cost of all goods available for sale during that accounting period. 1. Calculate the average cost per unit by $\text{Average Cost} = \frac{\text{Cost of goods available for sale}}{\text{Total units available for sale}}$ 2. Calculate the value of ending inventory by multiplying the number of units in ending inventory by the average cost per unit.	Using the average cost method of inventory pricing, what is the dollar value of the 130 planters in ending inventory for The Gift Collection? First, we shall extend and sum each purchase to find the total units available and the total cost of those units available for sale. **Date / Units / Cost per Unit / Total** Jan. 1 / 55 / $12.30 / $676.50 Mar. 9 / 60 / 13.50 / 810.00 Aug. 12 / 45 / 13.90 / 625.50 Nov. 27 / 75 / 14.25 / 1,068.75 235 / $3,180.75 $\text{Av. cost} = \frac{3{,}180.75}{235} = \$13.54$ End. inv. = 130 × 13.54 = $1,760.20
Pricing Inventory by Using the Lower-of-Cost-or-Market (LCM) Rule **P/O 16-4, p. 586**	When the market price or current replacement price of an inventory item declines below the actual price paid for that item, a company is permitted to use the lower-of-cost-or-market rule. 1. Choose lower of cost or market as valuation basis. 2. Multiply the number of units by the valuation basis price. 3. Add the extended totals in the Amount column to get the value of ending inventory.	From the following inventory data for small, medium, and large lamps at The Lighting Center, calculate the value of the ending inventory by using the LCM rule. **Units / Unit Price: Cost / Market / Valuation Basis / Amount** **small** 34 / $40 / $43 / Cost / 1,360 **medium** 55 / 70 / 65 / Market / 3,575 **large** 47 / 99 / 103 / Cost / 4,653 Ending Inventory = $9,588

Section II: Inventory Estimation

<table>
<tr><th>Topic</th><th>Important Concepts</th><th>Illustrative Examples</th></tr>
<tr><td>Estimating the Value of Ending Inventory by Using the Retail Method
P/O 16-5, p. 591</td><td>When it is too costly or not feasible to take a physical inventory count, inventory can be estimated. The retail method, as the name implies, is used by retail operations of all sizes.
1. List beginning inventory and purchases at both cost and retail.
2. Add purchases to beginning inventory to determine goods available for sale.
3. Calculate the cost ratio by
$$\text{Cost ratio} = \frac{\text{Goods available for sale at cost}}{\text{Goods available for sale at retail}}$$
4. Calculate ending inventory at retail by subtracting net sales from goods available for sale at retail.
5. Convert ending inventory at retail to ending inventory at cost by multiplying the ending inventory at retail by the cost ratio.</td><td>Estimate the value of the ending inventory at cost on July 31 from the following information for Central Distributors, Inc.

Cost / Retail
Beg. Inv. $300,000 / $450,000
Net Purch. 100,000 / 150,000
Net Sales $366,000

Cost / Retail
Beg. Inv. $300,000 / $450,000
Net Purch. +100,000 / +150,000
Goods Avail. $400,000 / $600,000

$$\text{Cost ratio} = \frac{400{,}000}{600{,}000} = .67$$
Goods avail. at retail $600,000
− Net sales − 366,000
Ending inventory at retail $234,000

Ending inventory at cost = 234,000 × .67
= $156,780</td></tr>
<tr><td>Estimating the Value of Ending Inventory by Using the Gross Profit Method
P/O 16-6, p. 593</td><td>The gross profit or gross margin method uses a company's gross margin percent to estimate the ending inventory. This method assumes that a company maintains approximately the same gross margin from year to year.
1. Calculate the goods available for sale.
Beginning inventory
+ Net purchases
Goods available for sale
2. Find the estimated cost of goods sold by multiplying net sales by the cost of goods sold percent (complement of gross margin percent).
3. Calculate the estimate of ending inventory by
Goods available for sale
− Estimated cost of goods sold
Estimated ending inventory</td><td>The Stereo Connection maintains a gross margin of 60% on all speakers. In June, the beginning inventory was $95,000, net purchases were $350,600, and net sales were $615,000. What is the estimated cost of ending inventory, using the gross profit method?

Beginning inv. $95,000
+ Net purchases + 350,600
Goods available $445,600

Estimated cost of goods sold =
Net sales(100% − Gr. margin %) =
615,000(100% − 60%) = $246,000

Goods available $445,600
− Estimated CGS − 246,000
Est. ending inv. $199,600</td></tr>
</table>

Section III: Inventory Turnover and Targets

<table>
<tr><th>Topic</th><th>Important Concepts</th><th>Illustrative Examples</th></tr>
<tr><td>Calculating Inventory Turnover Rate at Retail
P/O 16-7, p. 598</td><td>Inventory or stock turnover rate is the number of times during an operating period that the average inventory is sold out or turned over. Average inventory may be expressed either at retail or at cost.
1. Calculate the average inventory at retail by
$$\text{Average inventory}_{\text{retail}} = \frac{\text{Beginning inventory at retail} + \text{Ending inventory at retail}}{2}$$</td><td>Tip Top Roofing Supply had net sales of $66,000 for the year. If the beginning inventory at retail was $24,400 and the ending inventory at retail was $19,600, what are the average inventory and the inventory turnover rate?

$$\text{Average inventory at retail} = \frac{24{,}400 + 19{,}600}{2}$$
= $22,000</td></tr>
</table>

Section III: (continued)

Topic	Important Concepts	Illustrative Examples
	2. Calculate the inventory turnover at retail by $$\text{Inventory turnover}_{retail} = \frac{\text{Net sales}}{\text{Average inventory at retail}}$$	$$\text{Inventory turnover at retail} = \frac{66{,}000}{22{,}000} = \underline{\underline{3\text{ Times}}}$$
Calculating Inventory Turnover Rate at Cost **P/O 16-8, p. 599**	Inventory turnover may also be calculated at cost by using cost of goods sold and the average inventory at cost. 1. Calculate average inventory at cost by $$\text{Average inventory}_{cost} = \frac{\text{Beginning inventory at cost} + \text{Ending inventory at cost}}{2}$$ 2. Calculate the inventory turnover at cost by $$\text{Inventory turnover}_{cost} = \frac{\text{Cost of goods sold}}{\text{Average inventory at cost}}$$	Atlantic Enterprises had $426,000 in cost of goods sold. The beginning inventory at cost was $75,000, and the ending inventory at cost was $95,400. What are Atlantic's average inventory at cost and inventory turnover rate? $$\text{Average inventory at cost} = \frac{75{,}000 + 95{,}400}{2} = \underline{\underline{85{,}200}}$$ $$\text{Inventory turnover at cost} = \frac{426{,}000}{85{,}200} = \underline{\underline{5\text{ Times}}}$$
Calculating Target Average Inventories Based on Industry Standards **P/O 16-9, p. 600**	When inventory turnover is below average, based on published industry standards, it may be a signal that a company is carrying too much inventory. This can lead to extra expenses such as warehousing and insurance. The following formulas can be used to calculate target average inventories at cost or retail to theoretically achieve the published turnover rate. $$\text{Target inventory at cost} = \frac{\text{Cost of goods sold}}{\text{Published rate at cost}}$$ $$\text{Target inventory at retail} = \frac{\text{Net sales}}{\text{Published rate at retail}}$$	Playtime Toys had cost of goods sold of $560,000 for the year. The beginning inventory at cost was $140,000, and the ending inventory was $180,000. The published rate for a firm this size is four times. Calculate the average inventory and turnover rate for Playtime. If the rate is less than four times, calculate the target average inventory. Average inventory at cost $$= \frac{140{,}000 + 180{,}000}{2} = \underline{\underline{\$160{,}000}}$$ $$\text{Inventory turnover at cost} = \frac{560{,}000}{160{,}000} = \underline{\underline{3.5\text{ Times}}}$$ $$\text{Target average inventory} = \frac{560{,}000}{4} = \underline{\underline{\$140{,}000}}$$

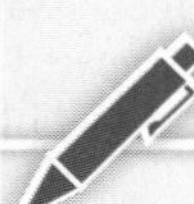

TRY IT EXERCISE SOLUTIONS FOR CHAPTER 16

1. FIFO Inventory Valuation

Units	Cost/Unit	Total
300	$8.75	$2,625
80	9.00	720
380		$3,345

2. LIFO Inventory Valuation

Units	Cost/Unit	Total
200	$8.00	$1,600
100	8.50	850
80	9.00	720
380		$3,170

3. Average Cost Method

$$\text{Average cost/unit} = \frac{\text{Cost of goods available}}{\text{Total units available}} = \frac{7{,}325}{850} = \$8.62$$

Ending inventory = Units in inventory × Average cost per unit

Ending inventory = 380 × 8.62 = $\underline{\underline{\$3{,}275.60}}$

4.

LCM Rule

The Personal Touch Gift Shop

Description	Quantity	Valuation Basis	Price	Amount
Lamps	75	Market	$ 9.20	$ 690.00
Jewelry Boxes	120	Cost	26.30	3,156.00
16" Vases	88	Market	39.70	3,493.60
12" Vases	64	Market	21.40	1,369.60
Fruit Bowls	42	Cost	36.90	1,549.80
			Total Value of Inventory	$10,259.00

5.

	Cost	Retail
Beginning inventory	$600,000	$800,000
+ Net purchases	+ 285,000	+ 380,000
Goods available for sale	$885,000	$1,180,000

$$\text{Cost ratio} = \frac{\text{Goods available at cost}}{\text{Goods available at retail}} = \frac{885{,}000}{1{,}180{,}000} = .75 = 75\%$$

Goods available at retail	1,180,000
− Net sales	− 744,000
Ending inventory at retail	$436,000

Ending inventory at cost = Ending inventory at retail × Cost ratio

Ending inventory at cost = 436,000 × .75 = $327,000

6.

Beginning inventory	$137,000
+ Net purchases	+ 220,000
Goods available for sale	$357,000

Estimated cost of goods sold = Net sales (100% − Gross margin %)

Estimated cost of goods sold = 410,000 (100% − 39%)

Estimated cost of goods sold = 410,000 (.61) = $250,100

Goods available for sale	$357,000
− Estimated cost of goods sold	− 250,100
Estimated ending inventory	$106,900

7.

$$\text{Average inventory}_{retail} = \frac{\text{Beginning inventory at retail} + \text{Ending inventory at retail}}{2}$$

$$\text{Average inventory}_{retail} = \frac{65{,}100 + 52{,}800}{2} = \$58{,}950$$

$$\text{Inventory turnover}_{retail} = \frac{\text{Net sales}}{\text{Average inventory at retail}}$$

$$\text{Inventory turnover}_{retail} = \frac{260{,}700}{58{,}950} = 4.4 \text{ Times}$$

8. $$\text{Average inventory}_{\text{cost}} = \frac{\text{Beginning inventory at cost} + \text{Ending inventory at cost}}{2}$$

$$\text{Average inventory}_{\text{cost}} = \frac{43{,}500 + 59{,}300}{2} = \underline{\underline{\$51{,}400}}$$

$$\text{Inventory turnover}_{\text{cost}} = \frac{\text{Cost of goods sold}}{\text{Average inventory at cost}}$$

$$\text{Inventory turnover}_{\text{cost}} = \frac{756{,}400}{51{,}400} = \underline{\underline{14.7}}\text{ Times}$$

9. $$\text{Average inventory} = \frac{\text{Beginning inventory} + \text{Ending inventory}}{2}$$

$$\text{Average inventory} = \frac{495{,}000 + 380{,}000}{2} = \underline{\underline{\$437{,}500}}$$

$$\text{Inventory turnover} = \frac{\text{Net sales}}{\text{Average inventory at retail}} = \frac{2{,}650{,}000}{437{,}500} = \underline{\underline{6.1}}\text{ Times}$$

$$\text{Target average inventory} = \frac{\text{Net sales}}{\text{Published turnover}}$$

$$\text{Target average inventory} = \frac{2{,}650{,}000}{7} = \underline{\underline{\$378{,}571.43}}$$

CONCEPT REVIEW

1. Goods that a company has in its possession at any given time are known as ____. (16-1)
inventory

2. A ____ inventory system is physically counted at least once a year to determine the value of the goods available for sale. (16-1)
periodic

3. A ____ inventory system updates goods available for sale on a continuous basis by computer. (16-1)
perpetual

4. An inventory valuation method in which each item in inventory is matched or coded with its actual cost is know as the specific ____ method. (16-1)
identification

5. An inventory valuation method that assumes the items purchased by a company *first* are the *first* items to be sold is known as the ____ method. Its abbreviation is ____. (16-1)
first-in, first-out, FIFO

6. An inventory valuation method that assumes the items purchased by the company *last* are the *first* items to be sold is known as the ____ method. Its abbreviation is ____. (16-2)
last-in, first-out, LIFO

7. An inventory valuation method that assumes the cost of each unit of inventory is the *average* cost of all goods available for sale during that accounting period is known as the average cost or ____ average method. (16-3)
weighted

8. An inventory valuation method whereby items in inventory are valued either at their actual cost or current replacement value, whichever is lower is known as the ____ rule. Its abbreviation is ____. (16-4)
lower-of-cost-or-market, LCM

9. The two generally accepted methods for *estimating* the value of an inventory are the ____ method and the gross ____ method. (16-5, 16-6)
retail, profit

10. The number of times during an operating period that the average dollars invested in inventory was theoretically sold out or turned over is known as the ____ turnover or ____ turnover. (16-7, 16-8)
inventory, stock

11. Inventory or stock turnover may be calculated in ____ dollars or in ____ dollars. (16-7, 16-8)
retail, cost

12. Write the formula for average inventory. (16-7, 16-8)

$$\text{Average inventory} = \frac{\text{Beginning inv.} + \text{Ending inv.}}{2}$$

13. The ideal amount of inventory a company should carry for maximum efficiency is known as the ____ average inventory. (16-9)
target

14. When calculating the target average inventory at *cost*, the numerator of the formula is the cost of ____ ____; when calculating the target average inventory at *retail*, the numerator of the formula is net ____. (16-9)
goods sold, sales

ASSESSMENT TEST

CHAPTER 16

Name

Class

Answers

1. 454

$22,053.65

2. a. $6,741.25

b. $5,721.40

c. $6,218.24

3. $178,159

4. $68,475.81

1. Calculate the total number of units available for sale and the cost of goods available for sale from the following inventory of imported silk ties for Ritz Fashions, Inc.

Date	Units Purchased	Cost per Unit	Total Cost
Beginning Inventory, January 1	59	$46.10	2,719.90
Purchase, March 29	75	43.50	3,262.50
Purchase, July 14	120	47.75	5,730.00
Purchase, October 12	95	50.00	4,750.00
Purchase, December 8	105	53.25	5,591.25
Total Units Available	454	**Cost of Goods Available for Sale**	$22,053.65

2. As the manager of Ritz Fashions (Exercise 1), you took physical inventory of the ties on December 31 and found that 128 were still in stock.

a. What is the dollar value of the ending inventory by using FIFO?

Value of 128 ties using FIFO 105 @ 53.25 = 5,591.25
23 @ 50.00 = 1,150.00
128 $6,741.25

b. What is the dollar value of the ending inventory by using LIFO?

Value of 128 ties using LIFO 59 @ 46.10 = 2,719.90
69 @ 43.50 = 3,001.50
128 $5,721.40

c. What is the dollar value of the ending inventory by using the average cost method?

Value of 128 ties using average cost

$$\text{Average cost} = \frac{22{,}053.65}{454} = \$48.58 \text{ Per unit}$$

$128 \times 48.58 = \$6{,}218.24$

3. Determine the value of the following inventory for Allstate Tile by using the lower-of-cost-or-market rule.

Description	Quantity in Square Feet	Unit Price Cost	Unit Price Market	Valuation Basis	Amount
Terracotta 12"	8,400	$4.55	$5.10	Cost	$ 38,220
Super Saltillo 16"	7,300	8.75	8.08	Market	58,984
Monocottura 10"	4,500	3.11	2.90	Market	13,050
Glazed Ceramic	6,200	4.50	5.25	Cost	27,900
Brick Pavers	12,700	3.25	3.15	Market	40,005
				Total Value of Inventory	$178,159

4. Using the retail method, estimate the value of the ending inventory at cost on May 31 from the following information for Neptune Industries, Inc. Round the cost ratio to the nearest tenth of a percent.

Neptune Industries, Inc.
May 1–May 31

	Cost	Retail	
Beginning Inventory, May 1	$145,600	$196,560	
Purchases	79,000	106,650	
Net Sales $210,800	$224,600	$303,210	Goods available for sale

$$\frac{\text{Goods available at cost}}{\text{Goods available at retail}} \quad \frac{224{,}600}{303{,}210} = 74.1\% \text{ Cost ratio}$$

Goods available for sale at retail 303,210
− Net sales − 210,800
Ending inventory at retail $92,410

Ending inventory at cost = 92,410 × .741
= $68,475.81

CHAPTER

Name

Class

Answers

5. $394,885
6. $91,000
3.2
$65,909.09
7. $153,500
5
$111,764.71
8. a. $359,850
b. 2.5 Times
c. $176,800
9. a. $173,200
b. 2.5 Times
c. $114,710.53

5. On July 24, a tornado destroyed Astro Wholesalers' main warehouse and all its contents. Company records indicate that at the time of the tornado the net sales to date were $535,100 and the purchases were $422,900. The beginning inventory, on January 1, was $319,800. For the past 3 years, the company has maintained a gross margin of 35%. Use the gross profit method to estimate the inventory loss for the insurance claim.

Beginning inventory	319,800	Goods available for sale	742,700
Net purchases	+ 422,900	Estimated cost of goods sold	− 347,815
Goods available for sale	$742,700		$394,885

Estimated cost of goods sold = 535,100 (100% − 35%)
= 535,100 × .65
= $347,815

Assuming that all net sales figures are at *retail* and all cost of goods sold figures are at *cost*, calculate the average inventory and inventory turnover for Exercises 6 and 7. If the actual turnover is below the published rate, calculate the target average inventory necessary to come up to industry standards.

	Net Sales	Cost of Goods Sold	Beginning Inventory	Ending Inventory	Average Inventory	Inventory Turnover	Published Rate	Target Average Inventory
6.	$290,000		$88,000	$94,000	$91,000	3.2	4.4	$65,909.09
7.		$760,000	184,000	123,000	$153,500	5	6.8	$111,764.71

8. The Fabric Mart had cost of goods sold for the year of $884,000. The beginning inventory at cost was $305,500, and the ending inventory at cost amounted to $414,200. The inventory turnover rate published as the industry standard for a business of this size is five times.

a. What is the average inventory at cost?

$$\text{Average inventory} = \frac{305{,}500 + 414{,}200}{2} = \$359{,}850$$

b. What is the inventory turnover rounded to the nearest tenth?

$$\text{Inventory turnover} = \frac{884{,}000}{359{,}850} = 2.45 = 2.5 \text{ Times}$$

c. What is the target average inventory needed to theoretically come up to the industry standard?

$$\text{Target Inventory} = \frac{884{,}000}{5} = \$176{,}800$$

© David Young-wolff/PhotoEdit

Aamco began in 1963 as a single transmission repair shop in Philadelphia. Today, Aamco Transmissions is a leading transmission repair franchise, with more than 800 independently owned and operated locations in the U.S. and Canada.

9. An Aamco Transmissions store had net sales of $435,900 for the year. The beginning inventory at retail was $187,600, and the ending inventory at retail was $158,800.

a. What is the average inventory at retail?

$$\text{Average inventory} = \frac{187{,}600 + 158{,}800}{2} = \$173{,}200$$

b. What is the inventory turnover rounded to the nearest tenth?

$$\text{Inventory turnover} = \frac{435{,}900}{173{,}200} = 2.51 = 2.5 \text{ Times}$$

c. If the turnover rate for similar-sized competitors is 3.8 times, calculate the target average inventory needed to theoretically come up to industry standards.

$$\text{Target inventory} = \frac{435{,}900}{3.8} = \$114{,}710.53$$

BUSINESS DECISION INVENTORY VALUATION AND THE BOTTOM LINE

CHAPTER 16

Name

Class

Answers

10. a. **FIFO:** $305,000

LIFO: $245,000

Average cost: $274,400

b. See table.

c. LIFO method

d. FIFO method

10. You are the chief accountant of Pan American Industries, Inc. In anticipation of the upcoming annual stockholders meeting, the president of the company asked you to determine the effect of the FIFO, LIFO, and average inventory valuation methods on the company's income statement.

EXCEL

Beginning inventory, January 1, was 10,000 units at $5.00 each. Purchases during the year consisted of 15,000 units at $6.00 on April 15, 20,000 units at $7.00 on July 19, and 25,000 units at $8.00 on November 2.

a. If ending inventory on December 31 was 40,000 units, calculate the value of this inventory by using the three valuation methods.

FIFO: $305,000 LIFO: $245,000 Average Cost: $274,400

b. Calculate the income statement items below for each of the inventory valuation methods.

Net sales	30,000 units at $12 each
Operating expenses	$100,000
Income tax rate	30%

Pan American Industries, Inc.

	FIFO	LIFO	Average Cost
Net sales	$360,000	$360,000	$360,000
Beginning inventory	50,000	50,000	50,000
Purchases	430,000	430,000	430,000
Cost of goods available for sale	480,000	480,000	480,000
Ending inventory	305,000	245,000	274,400
Cost of goods sold	175,000	235,000	205,600
Gross profit	185,000	125,000	154,400
Operating expenses	100,000	100,000	100,000
Income before taxes	85,000	25,000	54,400
Income tax	25,500	7,500	16,320
Net income	$59,500	$17,500	$38,080

Worked-out solution to Exercise 10a appears in Appendix B, following the index

c. Which inventory method should be used if the objective is to pay the least amount of taxes?

LIFO method has the least amount of taxes

d. Which inventory method should be used if the objective is to show the greatest amount of profit in the annual report to the shareholders?

FIFO method has the greatest profit

In the Business World

This Business Decision, "Inventory Valuation and the Bottom Line," clearly illustrates how the various inventory methods can affect a company's profit picture. Note the significant variation in net income among the three methods.

COLLABORATIVE LEARNING ACTIVITY

The Counting Game!

As a team, choose two or three competitive retail stores in your area, such as supermarkets, drug stores, hardware stores, shoe stores, or clothing stores. Speak with an accounting and/or merchandise manager for each, and determine the following:

a. Approximately how many different items are carried in inventory?
b. What method of inventory valuation is being used? Why?
c. What is their average inventory?
d. How often is a physical inventory count taken? Who does it?
e. Does the company have a computerized perpetual inventory system? How does it work?
f. What is the inventory turnover ratio? How does this compare with the published industry figures for a company that size? Where did you find the published figures?
g. Which of the companies your team researched has the most efficient inventory system? Why?

Depreciation

PERFORMANCE OBJECTIVES

Section I Traditional Depreciation—Methods Used for Financial Statement Reporting

17-1: Calculating depreciation by the straight-line method (p. 617)

17-2: Calculating depreciation by the sum-of-the-years' digits method (p. 618)

17-3: Calculating depreciation by the declining-balance method (p. 621)

17-4: Calculating depreciation by the units-of-production method (p. 623)

Section II Asset Cost Recovery Systems—IRS Prescribed Methods for Income Tax Reporting

17-5: Calculating depreciation by using the Modified Accelerated Cost Recovery System (MACRS) (p. 628)

17-6: Calculating the periodic depletion cost of natural resources (p. 633)

SECTION I TRADITIONAL DEPRECIATION—METHODS USED FOR FINANCIAL STATEMENT REPORTING

long-term or long-lived assets Relatively fixed or permanent assets such as land, buildings, tools, equipment, and vehicles that companies acquire in the course of operating a business.

depreciation, or depreciation expense The decrease in value from the original cost of a long-term asset over its useful life.

book value The value of an asset at any given time. It is the original cost less the accumulated depreciation to that point.

total cost, or original basis The total amount a company pays for an asset, including shipping, handling, and setup charges.

residual, scrap, salvage, or trade-in value The value of an asset at the time it is taken out of service.

useful life The length of time an asset is expected to generate revenue.

In Chapter 15, we learned a firm's assets are divided into three categories: current assets; property, plant, and equipment; and investments and other assets. This chapter deals with the valuation of the **long-term** or **long-lived assets** of the firm: the property, plant, and equipment. Companies acquire these relatively fixed or permanent assets in the course of building and operating a business. Some examples of these assets would be land, buildings, equipment, machinery, vehicles, furniture, fixtures, and tools.

As time goes by, the usefulness or productivity of these assets, except land, decreases. Think of this decrease as a loss of revenue earning power. Accordingly, the cost of these assets is distributed over their useful life to coincide with the revenue earned. This cost write-off is known as **depreciation**. On the income statement, depreciation is listed under operating expenses as **depreciation expense**. On the balance sheet, it is used to determine the current **book value** of an asset, whereby

Book value = Original cost − Accumulated depreciation

Assets depreciate for a number of reasons. They may physically wear out from use and deterioration or they may depreciate because they have become inadequate and obsolete. Four important factors must be taken into account to determine the amount of depreciation expense of an asset.

1. The **total cost**, or **original basis** of the asset. This amount includes such items as shipping, handling, and set-up charges.
2. The asset's estimated **residual value** at the time that it is taken out of service. This is also known as **scrap value**, **salvage value**, or **trade-in value**.
3. An estimate of the **useful life** of the asset or the length of time it is expected to generate revenue. To be depreciated, an asset must have a life greater than 1 year.
4. The method of calculating depreciation must match the way in which the asset will depreciate. Some assets depreciate evenly over the years (straight-line depreciation), whereas others depreciate more quickly at first and then slow down in the later years (accelerated depreciation). Regardless of which method a company chooses, at the end of the useful life of an asset, the total amount of depreciation expense write-off will be the same.

This chapter examines the various methods used to depreciate assets. In Section I, we learn to calculate depreciation by the four traditional methods: straight-line; sum-of-the-years' digits; declining-balance; and units-of-production. Any of these methods may be used for financial statement reporting. However, once a method has been implemented, it cannot be changed.

Frequently, the amount of depreciation reported by a company on its financial statements will differ from the amount reported to the IRS for income tax purposes, because the IRS allows additional options for calculating depreciation expense. Today, the most widely used method for tax purposes is known as the modified accelerated cost recovery system (MACRS). This method is covered in Section II.

Depreciation is most frequently based on time, how many years an asset is expected to last. Certain assets, however, are depreciated more accurately on the basis of some productivity measure such as units of output for production machinery, or mileage for vehicles, regardless of time. This section deals with both time- and productivity-based depreciation methods.

CALCULATING DEPRECIATION BY THE STRAIGHT-LINE METHOD

The **straight-line depreciation** method is by far the most widely used in business today. It provides for equal periodic charges to be written off over the estimated useful life of the asset.

Once the annual depreciation has been determined, we can set up a **depreciation schedule**. The depreciation schedule is a chart illustrating the depreciation activity of the asset for each year of its useful life. The chart shows the amount of depreciation each year, the accumulated depreciation to date, and the book value of the asset.

straight-line depreciation A method of depreciation that provides for equal periodic charges to be written off over the estimated useful life of an asset.

depreciation schedule Chart showing the depreciation activity (depreciation, accumulated depreciation, and book value) of an asset for each year of its useful life.

STEPS TO PREPARE A DEPRECIATION SCHEDULE BY THE STRAIGHT-LINE METHOD

Step 1. Determine the total cost and salvage value of the asset.

Step 2. Subtract salvage value from total cost to find the total amount of depreciation.

$$\textbf{Total depreciation} = \textbf{Total cost} - \textbf{Salvage value}$$

Step 3. Calculate the annual amount of depreciation by dividing the total depreciation by the useful life of the asset.

$$\textbf{Annual depreciation} = \frac{\textbf{Total depreciation}}{\textbf{Estimated useful life (years)}}$$

Step 4. Set up the depreciation schedule in the form of a chart with the following headings:

End of Year	Annual Depreciation	Accumulated Depreciation	Book Value

On a depreciation schedule, the starting book value is the *original cost* of the asset, and the last book value is the *salvage value* of the asset.

EXAMPLE 1 CALCULATING STRAIGHT-LINE DEPRECIATION

Cascade Enterprises purchased a computer system for $9,000. Shipping charges were $125, and setup and programming amounted to $375. The system is expected to last 4 years and has a residual value of $1,500. If Cascade elects to use the straight-line method of depreciation for the computer, calculate the total cost, total depreciation, and annual depreciation. Prepare a depreciation schedule for its useful life.

SOLUTION STRATEGY

Step 1. Total cost = Cost + Shipping charges + Setup expenses

Total cost = 9,000 + 125 + 375 = $9,500

Step 2. Total depreciation = Total cost − Salvage value

Total depreciation = 9,500 − 1,500 = $8,000

Step 3.

$$\text{Annual depreciation} = \frac{\text{Total depreciation}}{\text{Estimated useful life (years)}}$$

$$\text{Annual depreciation} = \frac{8,000}{4} = \$2,000$$

Expensive assets such as this construction equipment are considered long-lived assets, the value of which depreciates over time.

Step 4.

Cascade Enterprises
Straight-Line Depreciation Schedule
Computer System

End of Year	Annual Depreciation	Accumulated Depreciation	Book Value
			(original cost) $9,500
1	$2,000	$2,000	7,500
2	2,000	4,000	5,500
3	2,000	6,000	3,500
4	2,000	8,000	(salvage value) 1,500

TRY IT EXERCISE 1

17-1

Wild Flour Bakery purchased a new bread oven for $125,000. Shipping charges were $1,150, and installation amounted to $750. The oven is expected to last 5 years and has a trade-in value of $5,000. If Wild Flour elects to use the straight-line method, calculate the total cost, total depreciation, and annual depreciation of the oven. Prepare a depreciation schedule for its useful life.

CHECK YOUR ANSWERS WITH THE SOLUTIONS ON PAGE 639.

17-2 CALCULATING DEPRECIATION BY THE SUM-OF-THE-YEARS' DIGITS METHOD

accelerated depreciation Depreciation methods that assume an asset depreciates more in the early years of its useful life than in the later years.

sum-of-the-years' digits A method of accelerated depreciation that allows an asset to depreciate the most during the first year, with decreasing amounts each year thereafter. Total depreciation is based on the total cost of an asset less its salvage value.

TEACHING TIP
Point out to students that although depreciation is primarily an accounting procedure, it is important to understand the underlying "business sense" of the subject.

The sum-of-the-years' digits and the declining-balance methods of calculating depreciation are the two **accelerated depreciation** methods. These methods assume that an asset depreciates more in the early years of its useful life than in the later years. Under the sum-of-the-years' digits method, the yearly charge for depreciation declines steadily over the estimated useful life of the asset because a successively smaller fraction is applied each year to the total depreciation (total cost − salvage value).

This fraction is known as the **sum-of-the-years' digits** fraction. The denominator of the fraction is the sum of the digits of the estimated life of the asset. This number does not change. The numerator of the fraction is the number of years of useful life remaining. This number changes every year as the asset gets older and older. This sum-of-the-years' digits depreciation rate fraction can be expressed as

$$\textbf{SYD depreciation rate fraction} = \frac{\textbf{Years of useful life remaining}}{\textbf{Sum-of-the-digits of the useful life}}$$

The denominator (the sum of the years' digits) can be calculated by adding all the digits of the years, or by the following formula:

$$\text{SYD} = \frac{n(n+1)}{2}$$

where

$$n = \textbf{the number of years of useful life of the asset}$$

For example, let's compute the depreciation rate fractions for an asset that has a useful life of 4 years. The denominator, the sum of the digits of 4, is 10. This is calculated by $4 + 3 + 2 + 1 = 10$ or by the SYD formula, $4(4 + 1) \div 2 = 10$. Remember, the denominator does not change. The numerator of the fractions will be 4, 3, 2, and 1 for each succeeding year.

Year	Depreciation Rate Fraction	Depreciation Rate Decimal	Depreciation Rate Percent
1	$\frac{4}{10}$	.40	40%
2	$\frac{3}{10}$	.30	30%
3	$\frac{2}{10}$	.20	20%
4	$\frac{1}{10}$	.10	10%

From this chart, we can see that an asset with 4 years of useful life will depreciate $\frac{4}{10}$ or 40% in the first year, $\frac{3}{10}$ or 30% in the second year, and so on. The accelerated rate of 40% depreciation write-off in the first year gives the business a reduced tax advantage and therefore an incentive to invest in new equipment.

STEPS TO PREPARE A DEPRECIATION SCHEDULE BY USING THE SUM-OF-THE-YEARS' DIGITS METHOD

Step 1. Find the total depreciation of the asset by

Total depreciation = Total cost − Salvage value

Step 2. Calculate the SYD depreciation rate fraction for each year by

$$\textbf{SYD depreciation rate fraction} = \frac{\textbf{Years of useful life remaining}}{\frac{n(n+1)}{2}}$$

Step 3. Calculate the depreciation for each year by multiplying the total depreciation by that year's depreciation rate fraction.

Annual depreciation = Total depreciation × Depreciation rate fraction

Step 4. Set up a depreciation schedule in the form of a chart with the following headings:

End of Year	Total Depreciation	×	Depreciation Rate Fraction	=	Annual Depreciation	Accumulated Depreciation	Book Value

TEACHING TIP

When applying the sum-of-the-years' digits method, be sure that students use the largest rate fraction in the first year.

Remind them that this is an accelerated method, and therefore the greatest amount of depreciation is taken first.

EXAMPLE 2 CALCULATING SUM-OF-THE YEARS' DIGITS DEPRECIATION

Spectrum Industries purchased a delivery truck for $35,000. The truck is expected to have a useful life of 5 years and a trade-in value of $5,000. Using the sum-of-the-years' digits method, prepare a depreciation schedule for Spectrum.

SOLUTION STRATEGY

Following the steps for preparing a depreciation schedule by using sum-of-the-years' digits:

Step 1. Total depreciation = Total cost − Salvage value

Total depreciation = 35,000 − 5,000 = $30,000

(continued)

Step 2. Year 1: SYD depreciation rate fraction $= \dfrac{\text{Years of useful life remaining}}{\dfrac{n(n+1)}{2}}$

$$\text{SYD depreciation rate fraction} = \frac{5}{\dfrac{5(5+1)}{2}} = \frac{5}{15}$$

The depreciation rate fraction for year 1 is $\frac{5}{15}$. The depreciation fractions for the remaining years will have the same denominator, 15 (the sum of the digits of 5). Only the numerators will change, in descending order. The depreciation fractions for the remaining years are $\frac{4}{15}$, $\frac{3}{15}$, $\frac{2}{15}$, and $\frac{1}{15}$.

Note how accelerated this SYD method is: $\frac{5}{15}$, or $\frac{1}{3}$ of the asset (33.3%), is allowed to be written off in the first year. This is compared with only $\frac{1}{5}$ (20%) per year by using the straight-line method.

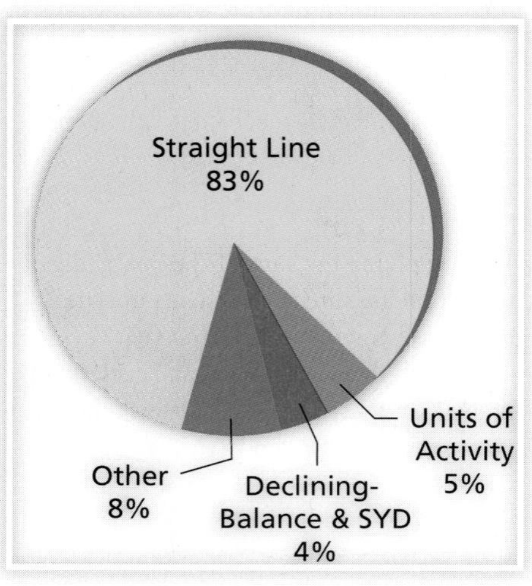

Depreciation Pie
According to an Accounting Trends and Techniques survey conducted by the American Institute of Certified Public Accountants, (AICPA), here is the breakdown of depreciation methods used by the 600 largest U.S. companies.

Step 3. Annual depreciation = Total depreciation × Depreciation rate fraction

$$\text{Annual depreciation (year 1)} = 30{,}000 \times \frac{5}{15} = \underline{\underline{\$10{,}000}}$$

$$\text{Annual depreciation (year 2)} = 30{,}000 \times \frac{4}{15} = \underline{\underline{\$8{,}000}}$$

Continue this calculation for each of the remaining 3 years. Then prepare the schedule.

Step 4.

Spectrum Industries
SYD Depreciation Schedule
Delivery Truck

End of Year	Total Depreciation	×	Depreciation Rate Fraction	=	Annual Depreciation	Accumulated Depreciation	Book Value
							(new) $35,000
1	30,000	×	$\frac{5}{15}$	=	10,000	10,000	25,000
2	30,000	×	$\frac{4}{15}$	=	8,000	18,000	17,000
3	30,000	×	$\frac{3}{15}$	=	6,000	24,000	11,000
4	30,000	×	$\frac{2}{15}$	=	4,000	28,000	7,000
5	30,000	×	$\frac{1}{15}$	=	2,000	30,000	5,000

TRY IT EXERCISE 2

Bow Valley Kitchens purchased new production-line machinery for a total of $44,500. The company expects this machinery to last 6 years and have a residual value of $2,500. Using the sum-of-the-years' digits method, prepare a depreciation schedule for Bow Valley.

CHECK YOUR ANSWERS WITH THE SOLUTIONS ON PAGE 640.

CALCULATING DEPRECIATION BY THE DECLINING-BALANCE METHOD

The second widely accepted method of accelerated depreciation in business is known as the **declining-balance** method. This method uses a *multiple* of the straight-line rate to calculate depreciation. The most frequently used multiples are 1.25, 1.5, and 2. When 1.25 is used, it is known as the 125% declining balance; when 1.5 is used, it is known as the 150% declining balance. When 2 is the multiple, the method is known as the **double-declining balance**.

To calculate the declining-balance rate, we first determine the straight-line rate by dividing 1 by the number of years of useful life, then multiplying by the appropriate declining-balance multiple. For example, when using the double-declining balance, an asset with a useful life of 4 years would have a straight-line rate of 25% per year ($1 \div 4 = \frac{1}{4} = 25\%$). This rate is then multiplied by the declining-balance multiple, 2, to get 50%, the double-declining rate. The following formula should be used for this calculation:

$$\textbf{Declining-balance rate} = \frac{1}{\textbf{Useful life}} \times \textbf{Multiple}$$

declining-balance A method of accelerated depreciation that uses a multiple (125%, 150%, or 200%) of the straight-line rate to calculate depreciation.

double-declining balance Name given to the declining-balance method of depreciation when the straight-line multiple is 200%.

To further accelerate the depreciation, this declining-balance rate is applied to the original total cost of the asset. Salvage value is not considered until the last year of depreciation. When preparing a depreciation schedule by using the declining-balance method, the depreciation stops when the book value of the asset reaches the salvage value. By IRS regulations, the asset cannot be depreciated below the salvage value.

STEPS TO PREPARE A DEPRECIATION SCHEDULE BY USING THE DECLINING-BALANCE METHOD

Step 1. Calculate the declining-balance rate by the formula

$$\textbf{Declining-balance rate} = \frac{1}{\textbf{Useful life}} \times \textbf{Multiple}$$

Step 2. Calculate the depreciation for each year by applying the rate to each year's beginning book value, which is the ending book value of the previous year.

Depreciation for the year = Beginning book value × Declining-balance rate

Step 3. Calculate the ending book value for each year by subtracting the depreciation for the year from the beginning book value:

Ending book value = Beginning book value − Depreciation for the year

Step 4. When the ending book value equals the salvage value, the depreciation is complete.

Step 5. Set up a depreciation schedule in the form of a chart with the following headings:

End of Year	Beginning Book Value	Depreciation Rate	Depreciation for the Year	Accumulated Depreciation	Ending Book Value

From Chapter 15, Financial Statements, remember that depreciation appears on both the balance sheet and the income statement.

- *Balance sheet*—Used to determine book value of an asset.
- *Income statement*—Listed as an operating expense.

EXAMPLE 3 CALCULATING DECLINING BALANCE DEPRECIATION

Allstate Shipping bought a forklift for $20,000. It is expected to have a 5-year useful life and a trade-in value of $2,000. Prepare a depreciation schedule for this asset by using the double-declining balance method.

SOLUTION STRATEGY

Step 1. $\text{Declining-balance rate} = \frac{1}{\text{Useful life}} \times \text{Multiple}$

$\text{Declining-balance rate} = \frac{1}{5} \times 2 = .20 \times 2 = .40 = \underline{\underline{40\%}}$

Step 2. Depreciation for the year = Beginning book value × Declining-balance rate

Depreciation: Year 1 = 20,000 × .40 = $\underline{\underline{\$8{,}000}}$

CLASSROOM ACTIVITY
Discuss depreciation for accounting and tax purposes compared with the actual physical "wearing-out" of an asset. Point out that many assets still have some useful "physical life" remaining, even after they have been fully depreciated.

Ask students to discuss the pros and cons of keeping depreciated assets until they physically wear out, as opposed to purchasing new ones and starting the depreciation process over again.

Step 3. Ending book value = Beginning book value − Depreciation for the year

Ending book value: Year 1 = 20,000 − 8,000 = $\underline{\underline{\$12{,}000}}$

Repeat Steps 2 and 3 for years 2, 3, 4, and 5.

Step 4. In year 5, although the calculated depreciation is $1,036.80 (2,592 × .4), the allowable depreciation is limited to $592 (2,592 − 2,000), because the book value has reached the $2,000 salvage value. At this point, the depreciation is complete.

Step 5.

Allstate Shipping, Inc.
Double-Declining Balance Depreciation Schedule
Forklift

End of Year	Beginning Book Value	Depreciation Rate	Depreciation for the Year	Accumulated Depreciation	Ending Book Value
					(new) $20,000
1	20,000	40%	8,000	8,000	12,000
2	12,000	40%	4,800	12,800	7,200
3	7,200	40%	2,880	15,680	4,320
4	4,320	40%	1,728	17,408	2,592
5	2,592	40%	592*	18,000	2,000

*Maximum allowable to reach salvage value.

TRY IT EXERCISE 3

Jasper Air Service bought a small commuter airplane for $386,000. It is expected to have a useful life of 4 years and a trade-in value of $70,000. Prepare a depreciation schedule for the airplane by using the 150% declining-balance method.

CHECK YOUR ANSWERS WITH THE SOLUTIONS ON PAGE 640.

CALCULATING DEPRECIATION BY THE UNITS-OF-PRODUCTION METHOD

When the useful life of an asset is more accurately defined in terms of how much it is used rather than the passage of time, we may use the **units-of-production** method to calculate depreciation. To apply this method, the life of the asset is expressed in productive capacity, such as miles driven, units produced, or hours used. Some examples of assets typically depreciated by using this method would be cars, trucks, airplanes, production-line machinery, engines, pumps, and electronic equipment.

units-of-production Depreciation method based on how much an asset is used, such as miles, hours, or units produced, rather than the passage of time.

To calculate depreciation by using this method, we begin by determining the depreciation per unit. This number is found by dividing the amount to be depreciated (cost − salvage value) by the estimated units of useful life:

$$\textbf{Depreciation per unit} = \frac{\textbf{Cost} - \textbf{Salvage value}}{\textbf{Units of useful life}}$$

For example, let's say that a hole-punching machine on a production line had a cost of $35,000 and a salvage value of $5,000. If we estimate that the machine had a useful life of 150,000 units of production, the depreciation per unit would be calculated as follows:

$$\text{Depreciation per unit} = \frac{\text{Cost} - \text{Salvage value}}{\text{Units of useful life}} = \frac{35{,}000 - 5{,}000}{150{,}000} = \frac{30{,}000}{150{,}000} = \$.20 \text{ per unit}$$

Once we have determined the depreciation per unit, we can find the annual depreciation by multiplying the depreciation per unit by the number of units produced each year.

$$\textbf{Annual depreciation} = \textbf{Depreciation per unit} \times \textbf{Units produced}$$

In the previous example, if the hole-punching machine produced 30,000 in a year, the annual depreciation for that year would be as follows:

$$\text{Annual depreciation} = \text{Depreciation per unit} \times \text{Units produced} = .20 \times 30{,}000 = \$6{,}000$$

STEPS TO CALCULATE DEPRECIATION BY USING THE UNITS-OF-PRODUCTION METHOD

Step 1. Determine the depreciation per unit by using

$$\textbf{Depreciation per unit} = \frac{\textbf{Cost} - \textbf{Salvage value}}{\textbf{Units of useful life}}$$

(Round to the nearest tenth of a cent when necessary.)

Step 2. Calculate the annual depreciation by using

$$\textbf{Annual depreciation} = \textbf{Depreciation per unit} \times \textbf{Units produced}$$

Step 3. Set up the depreciation schedule in the form of a chart with the following headings:

End of Year	Depreciation per Unit	Units Produced	Annual Depreciation	Accumulated Depreciation	Book Value

CLASSROOM ACTIVITY
In groups, have students create a depreciation scenario, then solve it by using the three methods.

Ask if the units-of-production method could have been applied to their asset.

Based on their findings, have them discuss the balance sheet implications of each method.

EXAMPLE 4 CALCULATING UNITS-OF-PRODUCTION DEPRECIATION

Colorcraft Printing purchased a new printing press for $8,500 with a salvage value of $500. For depreciation purposes, the press is expected to have a useful life of 5,000 hours. From the following estimate of hours of use, prepare a depreciation schedule for the printing press by using the units-of-production method.

Year	Hours of Use
1	1,500
2	1,200
3	2,000
4	500

SOLUTION STRATEGY

Step 1. $$\text{Depreciation per unit (hours)} = \frac{\text{Cost} - \text{Salvage value}}{\text{Hours of useful life}}$$

$$\text{Depreciation per unit} = \frac{8{,}500 - 500}{5{,}000} = \frac{8{,}000}{5{,}000} = \underline{\underline{\$1.60 \text{ per hour}}}$$

Step 2. $$\text{Annual depreciation} = \text{Depreciation per unit} \times \text{Units produced}$$

$$\text{Annual depreciation (year 1)} = 1.60 \times 1{,}500 = \underline{\underline{\$2{,}400}}$$

$$\text{Annual depreciation (year 2)} = 1.60 \times 1{,}200 = \underline{\underline{\$1{,}920}}$$

Continue this procedure for the remaining years.

Step 3.

Colorcraft Printing
Units-of-Production Depreciation Schedule
Printing Press

End of Year	Depreciation per Hour	Hours Used	Annual Depreciation	Accumulated Depreciation	Book Value
					(new) $8,500
1	$1.60	1,500	$2,400	$2,400	6,100
2	1.60	1,200	1,920	4,320	4,180
3	1.60	2,000	3,200	7,520	980
4	1.60	500	480*	8,000	500

*Maximum allowable to reach salvage value.

TRY IT EXERCISE 4

Prestige Limousine Service purchased a limousine with an expected useful life of 75,000 miles. The cost of the limousine was $54,500, and the residual value was $7,500. If the limousine was driven the following amounts of miles per year, prepare a depreciation schedule by using the units-of-production method.

Year	Miles Driven
1	12,500
2	18,300
3	15,900
4	19,100
5	12,400

CHECK YOUR ANSWERS WITH THE SOLUTIONS ON PAGE 640.

Review Exercises

Note: Round to the nearest cent, when necessary.

Calculate the total cost, total depreciation, and annual depreciation for the following assets by using the straight-line method.

	Cost	Shipping Charges	Setup Charges	Total Cost	Salvage Value	Estimated Useful Life (years)	Total Depreciation	Annual Depreciation
1.	$45,000	$150	$500	$45,650	$3,500	10	$42,150	$4,215.00
2.	$88,600	$625	$2,500	91,725	$9,000	7	82,725	11,817.86
3.	$158,200	$0	$1,800	160,000	$20,000	5	140,000	28,000.00
4.	$750,000	$0	$10,300	760,300	$70,000	15	690,300	46,020.00

5. The Fluffy Laundromat purchased new washing machines and dryers for $57,000. Shipping charges were $470, and installation amounted to $500. The machines are expected to last 5 years and have a residual value of $2,000. If Fluffy elects to use the straight-line method of depreciation, prepare a depreciation schedule for these machines.

The Fluffy Laundromat
Straight-Line Depreciation Schedule
Laundry Equipment

End of Year	Annual Depreciation	Accumulated Depreciation	Book Value
			(new) $57,970
1	$11,194	$11,194	46,776
2	11,194	22,388	35,582
3	11,194	33,582	24,388
4	11,194	44,776	13,194
5	11,194	55,970	2,000

Total cost = 57,000 + 470 + 500 = $57,970
Total depreciation = 57,970 − 2,000 = $55,970

$$\text{Annual depreciation} = \frac{55{,}970}{5} = \$11{,}194$$

6. White Mountain Supply Company purchases warehouse shelving for $18,600. Shipping charges were $370, and assembly and setup amounted to $575. The shelves are expected to last for 7 years and have a scrap value of $900. Using the straight-line method of depreciation,

   a. What is the annual depreciation expense of the shelving?

   Total cost = 18,600 + 370 + 575 = $19,545
   Total depreciation = 19,545 − 900 = $18,645

   $$\text{Annual depreciation} = \frac{18{,}645}{7} = \$2{,}663.57$$

   b. What is the accumulated depreciation after the third year?

   Accumulated depreciation after 3rd year = 2,663.57 × 3
   = $7,990.71

   c. What is the book value of the shelving after the fifth year?

   Book value after 5th year = 19,545 − (2,663.57 × 5)
   = $6,227.15

"Tom, you're an asset to the company. It's just that you're depreciating."

Complete Exercises 7–9 as they relate to the sum-of-the-years' digits method of depreciation.

	Useful Life (years)	Sum-of-the-Years' Digits	Depreciation Rate Fraction Year 1	Year 3	Year 5
7.	5	15	$\frac{5}{15}$	$\frac{3}{15}$	$\frac{1}{15}$
8.	7	28	$\frac{7}{28}$	$\frac{5}{28}$	$\frac{3}{28}$
9.	10	55	$\frac{10}{55}$	$\frac{8}{55}$	$\frac{6}{55}$

10. Vanguard Manufacturing, Inc., purchased production-line machinery for $445,000. It is expected to last for 6 years and have a trade-in value of $25,000. Using the sum-of-the-years' digits method, prepare a depreciation schedule for Vanguard.

Original cost	$445,000
Trade-in value	− 25,000
Total depreciation	$420,000

Vanguard Manufacturing, Inc.
SYD Depreciation Schedule
Production-Line Machinery

End of Year	Total Depreciation	Depreciation Rate Fraction	Annual Depreciation	Accumulated Depreciation	Book Value
				(new)	$445,000
1	$420,000	$\frac{6}{21}$	$120,000	$120,000	325,000
2	420,000	$\frac{5}{21}$	100,000	220,000	225,000
3	420,000	$\frac{4}{21}$	80,000	300,000	145,000
4	420,000	$\frac{3}{21}$	60,000	360,000	85,000
5	420,000	$\frac{2}{21}$	40,000	400,000	45,000
6	420,000	$\frac{1}{21}$	20,000	420,000	25,000

Complete Exercises 11–13 as they relate to the declining-balance method of depreciation. Round to the nearest tenth of a percent, when necessary.

	Years	Straight-Line Rate (%)	Multiple (%)	Declining-Balance Rate (%)
11.	4	25	125	31.25
12.	6	16.67	200	33.34
13.	10	10	150	15

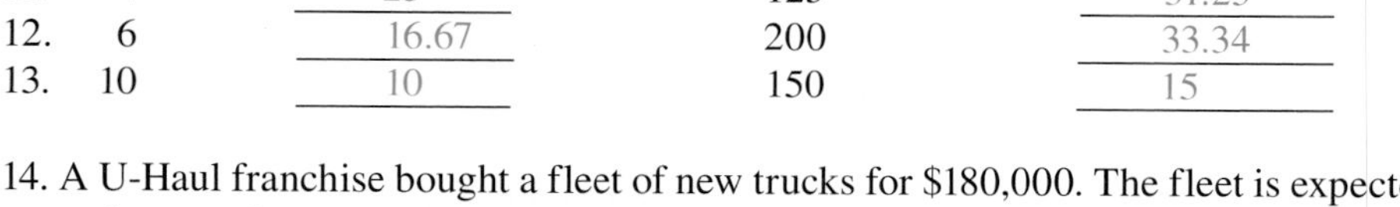

© Kayte M. Deioma/Photo Edit Inc.

U-Haul International, the principal operation of Amerco, Inc., rents trucks, trailers, and tow dollies to do-it-yourself movers through some 14,500 independent dealers and 1,450 company-owned centers in the U.S. and Canada. U-Haul is also a leading provider of self-storage facilities, with over 2,900 affiliates.

In 2007, the company had over 18,000 employees and sales of $2.09 billion. Major competitors include Penske Truck Leasing, Public Storage, and Ryder.

14. A U-Haul franchise bought a fleet of new trucks for $180,000. The fleet is expected to have an 8-year useful life and a trade-in value of $35,000. Prepare a depreciation schedule by using the 150% declining-balance method for the trucks.

U-Haul
150% Declining-Balance Depreciation Schedule
Truck Fleet

End of Year	Beginning Book Value	Depreciation Rate	Depreciation for the Year	Accumulated Depreciation	Ending Book Value
				(new)	$180,000.00
1	$180,000.00	.1875	$33,750.00	$33,750.00	146,250.00
2	146,250.00	.1875	27,421.88	61,171.88	118,828.12
3	118,828.12	.1875	22,280.27	83,452.15	96,547.85
4	96,547.85	.1875	18,102.72	101,554.87	78,445.13
5	78,445.13	.1875	14,708.46	116,263.33	63,736.67
6	63,736.67	.1875	11,950.63	128,213.96	51,786.04
7	51,786.04	.1875	9,709.88	137,923.84	42,076.16
8	42,076.16	.1875	7,076.16*	145,000.00	35,000.00

*Maximum allowed to reach salvage value. Total depreciation = 180,000 − 35,000 = $145,000

Complete the following as they relate to the units-of-production method of depreciation. Round to the nearest tenth of a cent when necessary.

Asset	Cost	Salvage Value	Units of Useful Life	Depreciation per Unit
15. Pump	$15,000	$2,800	100,000 hours	$.122
16. Automobile	$27,400	$3,400	60,000 miles	.40
17. Assembly robot	$775,000	$25,000	3,000,000 units	.25

18. Thunderbird Manufacturing purchased a new stamping machine for $45,000 with a salvage value of $5,000. For depreciation purposes, the machine is expected to have a useful life of 250,000 units of production. Complete the following depreciation schedule by using the units-of-production method:

Thunderbird Manufacturing, Inc.
Units-of-Production Depreciation Schedule
Stamping Machine

End of Year	Depreciation per Unit	Units Produced	Annual Depreciation	Accumulated Depreciation	Book Value
					(new) $45,000
1	$.16	50,000	$8,000	$8,000	37,000
2	.16	70,000	11,200	19,200	25,800
3	.16	45,000	7,200	26,400	18,600
4	.16	66,000	10,560	36,960	8,040
5	.16	30,000	3,040*	40,000	5,000

Total cost = 45,000 − 5,000 = $40,000

$$\text{Depreciation per unit} = \frac{40,000}{250,000} = \$.16$$

*Maximum allowed to reach salvage value

19. You are the accountant for Raleigh Industries, a manufacturer of plastic gears for electric motors. The company's production facility in Pittsburgh has a cost of $3,800,000, an estimated residual value of $400,000, and an estimated useful life of 40 years. You are using the straight-line method of depreciation for this asset.

a. What is the amount of the annual depreciation?

$$\text{Annual depreciation} = \frac{\text{Total depreciation}}{\text{Estimated useful life}} = \frac{3,800,000 - 400,000}{40} = \$85,000$$

b. What is the book value of the property at the end of the twentieth year of use?

Accumulated depreciation = 85,000 × 20 = $1,700,000
Book value = 3,800,000 − 1,700,000 = $2,100,000

c. If at the start of the twenty-first year you revise your estimate so that the remaining useful life is 15 years and the residual value is $120,000, what should be the depreciation expense for each of the remaining 15 years?

$$\text{Annual depreciation} = \frac{\text{Total depreciation}}{\text{Estimated useful life}} = \frac{2,100,000 - 120,000}{15} = \$132,000$$

BUSINESS DECISION THE BALANCING ACT—REPLACING AN ASSET

20. Roll-On Tire Service opened a new service center three decades ago. At the time the center was preparing to open, new equipment was purchased totaling $388,000. Residual value of the equipment was estimated to be $48,000 after 20 years. The company accountant has been using straight-line depreciation on the equipment.

a. How much was the annual depreciation for the original equipment?

$$\text{Annual depreciation} = \frac{\text{Total depreciation}}{\text{Estimated useful life}} = \frac{388,000 - 48,000}{20} = \$17,000$$

b. If the dynamic tire balancing machine had originally cost $11,640, what would its residual value be after 20 years?

$$\text{Tire balancing machine's portion of total equipment purchase} = \frac{11,640}{388,000} = .03 = 3\%$$

$$\text{Tire balancing machine's residual value after 20 years} = 48,000 \times .03 = \underline{\underline{\$1,440}}$$

c. After six years of operation, the original tire balancing machine was replaced with a new model that cost $22,000. Book value was allowed for the old machine as a trade-in. What was the old dynamic tire balancing machine's book value when the replacement machine was bought?

$$\text{Annual depreciation of tire balancing machine} = \frac{11,640 - 1,440}{20} = \$510$$

$$\text{Accumulated depreciation after 6 years} = 510 \times 6 = \$3,060$$

$$\text{Book value after 6 years} = 11,640 - 3,060 = \underline{\underline{\$8,580}}$$

d. What was the book value of the equipment inventory at the six year point, substituting the new tire balancing machine for the original after the new machine had joined the inventory?

$$\text{Book value of the equipment} = 388,000 - (6 \times 17,000) + 22,000 - 8,580$$
$$= \underline{\underline{\$299,420}}$$

17 SECTION II ASSET COST RECOVERY SYSTEMS—IRS PRESCRIBED METHODS FOR INCOME TAX REPORTING

Section I of this chapter described the depreciation methods used by businesses for the preparation of financial statements. For income tax purposes, the Internal Revenue Service (IRS), through federal tax laws, prescribes how depreciation must be taken.

As part of the Economic Recovery Act of 1981, the IRS introduced a depreciation method known as the accelerated cost recovery system (ACRS), which allowed businesses to depreciate assets more quickly than they could with traditional methods. Faster write-offs encouraged businesses to invest in new equipment and other capital assets more frequently, thereby sparking needed economic growth. Essentially, ACRS discarded the concepts of estimated useful life and residual value. In their place, it required that business compute a **cost recovery allowance**.

cost recovery allowance Term used under MACRS meaning the amount of depreciation of an asset that may be written off for tax purposes in a given year.

modified accelerated cost recovery system (MACRS) A 1986 modification of the property classes and the depreciation rates of the accelerated depreciation method; used for assets put into service after 1986.

After the ACRS was modified by the Tax Equity and Fiscal Responsibility Act of 1982 and the Tax Reform Act of 1984, it was significantly overhauled by the Tax Reform Act of 1986. The resulting method was known as the **modified accelerated cost recovery system (MACRS)**. This is the system we shall use to calculate depreciation for federal income tax purposes.

17-5 CALCULATING DEPRECIATION BY USING THE MODIFIED ACCELERATED COST RECOVERY SYSTEM (MACRS)

According to the IRS, the modified accelerated cost recovery system (MACRS) is the name given to tax rules for getting back or recovering through depreciation deductions the cost of property used in a trade or business or to produce income. These rules generally apply to tangible property placed into service *after 1986*.

Before we can calculate the amount of depreciation for a particular asset, we must determine the **basis for depreciation**, or "cost" of that asset, for depreciation purposes. Sometimes the basis for depreciation is the original cost of the asset; however, in many cases the original cost (original basis) is "modified" by various IRS rules, section 179 deductions, and special depreciation allowances. Once the basis for depreciation has been established, the MACRS depreciation deduction can be calculated for each year and the depreciation schedule can be prepared.

basis for depreciation The cost of an asset, for MACRS depreciation purposes. This figure takes into account business usage rules, section 179 deductions, and special depreciation allowances.

Table 17-1 exhibits the eight main property classes of MACRS, with some examples of assets included in each class. Once the **property class** for the asset has been identified, the amount of depreciation each year can be manually calculated or found by using percentage tables. As a general rule, the 3-, 5-, 7-, and 10-year property class assets are depreciated by using the 200% declining-balance method; the 15- and 20-year classes use the 150% declining-balance method; and the 31.5- and 39-year classes use straight-line depreciation.

property class One of several time categories to which property is assigned under MACRS showing how many years are allowed for cost recovery.

Because these calculations were already covered in Section I of this chapter, we shall focus on using one of the **cost recovery percentage** tables provided by the IRS. Table 17-2 is such a table.

cost recovery percentage An IRS-prescribed percentage that is multiplied by the original basis of an asset to determine the depreciation deduction for a given year. Based on property class and year of asset life.

Note that the number of recovery years is one greater than the property class. This is due to a rule known as the **half-year convention**, which assumes that the asset was placed in service in the middle of the first year and therefore begins depreciating at that point. Quarterly tables are listed in IRS Publication 534 for assets placed in service at other times of the year.

half-year convention IRS rule under MACRS that assumes all property is placed in service or taken out of service at the midpoint of the year, regardless of the actual time.

Determining the Asset's Basis for Depreciation

The basis for depreciation of an asset is determined by the percentage of time it is used for business, section 179 deductions, and special depreciation allowances. To qualify for depreciation, an asset must be used for business a "minimum of 50%" of the time. An asset used for business 100% of the time may be depreciated completely. If, for example, an asset is used only 75% of the time for business, then only 75% of the original cost can be depreciated.

Teaching Transparency 17-2

Table 17-1
MACRS Property Classes General Depreciation System

3-Year Property	5-Year Property	7-Year Property
Over-the-road tractors Some horses and hogs Special handling devices for the manufacture of food and beverages Specialty tools used in the manufacture of motor vehicles Specialty tools used in the manufacture of finished products made of plastic, rubber, glass, and metal	Automobiles and taxis Buses and trucks Computers and peripherals Office machinery Research and experimental equipment Breeding or dairy cattle Sheep and goats Airplanes (except those in commercial use) Drilling and timber-cutting equipment Construction equipment	Office furniture and fixtures Railroad cars and engines Commercial airplanes Equipment used in mining, petroleum drilling, and natural gas exploration Equipment used in the manufacture of wood, pulp, and paper products Equipment used to manufacture aerospace products
10-Year Property	**15-Year Property**	**20-Year Property**
Vessels, barges, and tugs Single-purpose agricultural structures Trees and vines bearing fruits or nuts Equipment for grain, sugar, and vegetable oil products	Depreciable improvements made to land such as shrubbery, fences, roads, and bridges Equipment used to manufacture cement Gas utility pipelines	Farm buildings Railroad structures and improvements Communication cable and long-line systems Water utility plants and equipment

31.5-Year Property	39-Year Property
Placed into service before May 13, 1993: Nonresidential real estate Office in the home	*Placed into service after May 12, 1993:* Nonresidential real estate Office in the home

Table 17-2
Cost Recovery Percentage Table
MACRS

Recovery Year	Depreciation Rate for Property Class					
	3-year	5-year	7-year	10-year	15-year	20-year
1	33.33%	20.00%	14.29%	10.00%	5.00%	3.750%
2	44.45	32.00	24.49	18.00	9.50	7.219
3	14.81	19.20	17.49	14.40	8.55	6.677
4	7.41	11.52	12.49	11.52	7.70	6.177
5		11.52	8.93	9.22	6.93	5.713
6		5.76	8.92	7.37	6.23	5.285
7			8.93	6.55	5.90	4.888
8			4.46	6.55	5.90	4.522
9				6.56	5.91	4.462
10				6.55	5.90	4.461
11				3.28	5.91	4.462
12					5.90	4.461
13					5.91	4.462
14					5.90	4.461
15					5.91	4.462
16					2.95	4.461
17						4.462
18						4.461
19						4.462
20						4.461
21						2.231

Teaching Transparency 17-3

Learning Tip

In MACRS, the entire asset is depreciated. There is no salvage value.

Note that the percents for any given property class in the Cost Recovery Percentage Table add up to 100%.

To stimulate business activity, Congress signed into law "The Jobs and Growth Tax Relief Reconciliation Act of 2003" on May 18, 2003. This Federal act contains major depreciation rule changes that affect many individual tax payers and small businesses.

Section 179 Deductions

In 2003, the new law raised the maximum section 179 deduction from $25,000 to $100,000. In an Enterprise Zone or Liberty Zone the tax deduction was raised to $135,000.

Section 179 deductions are a way that small businesses are allowed to "write-off," in one year, all or part of certain business assets that are usually depreciated over many years using MACRS. These assets include most business machinery and equipment, furniture, fixtures, storage facilities, and off-the-shelf software. Table 17-3 lists the section 179 deductions over the past few years.

Special Depreciation Allowance

The new law provided additional depreciation allowances for qualified MACRS assets with a class life of 20 years or less, and acquired and placed into service according to the dates in Table 17-4. This allowance is an additional deduction after the section 179 deduction and before regular depreciation under MACRS. Certain limits and numerous restrictions apply to these depreciation tax rules. For the latest information, see IRS Publication 946, How to Depreciate Property, at www.irs.gov.

Table 17-3
Section 179 Deductions

Year Asset Was Placed into Service	Maximum Section 179 Deduction	
1996	$17,500	
1997	$18,000	
1998	$18,500	
1999	$19,000	
2000	$20,000	
2001	$24,000	
2002	$25,000	
2003	$100,000 ←	**Jobs and Growth Tax Relief Act**
2004–2005	$102,000	
2006	$108,000	
2007	$112,000	

In the Business World

You can allocate the section 179 deduction among qualifying assets in any way you want, thus reducing the basis of each of the assets. It is generally to your advantage to take the deduction on those assets that have the longest life, thus recovering your basis sooner, and use the regular depreciation methods on those assets that have short lives.

Table 17-4
Special Depreciation Allowance

Asset Placed into Service	Special Allowance
September 11, 2001–May 5, 2003	30%
May 6, 2003–January 1, 2005	50%

STEPS TO PREPARE A DEPRECIATION SCHEDULE BY USING MACRS

Step 1. Calculate the basis for depreciation—the **cost** of the particular asset for depreciation purposes.

a. **Percent of business use:** If an asset is used for business less than 100% of the time, multiply the original cost by the business-use percentage of the asset. (*Note:* The minimum percentage for an asset to qualify for depreciation is 50%.)

Business-use basis = Original cost × Business-use percentage

b. **Section 179 deduction:** Determine the amount of the section 179 deduction you choose to take, up to the limit, and subtract that amount from the business-use basis for depreciation.

Tentative basis = Business-use basis − Section 179 deduction

c. **Special Depreciation Allowances:** For qualifying assets, apply any special depreciation allowances, as specified in Table 17-4, to the tentative basis for depreciation.

Basis for depreciation =
Tentative basis(100% − Special depreciation allowance percent)

Step 2. Set up the depreciation schedule in the form of a chart with the following headings:

End of Year	Basis for Depreciation	Cost Recovery Percentage	MACRS Depreciation Deduction	Accumulated Depreciation	Book Value

Use Table 17-1 to determine the property class for the asset and Table 17-2 to find the cost recovery percentages for each year. Calculate the MACRS depreciation deduction for each year by multiplying the basis for depreciation by the cost recovery percentages.

MACRS depreciation deduction =
Basis for depreciation × Cost recovery percentage for that year

EXAMPLE 5 PREPARING A MACRS DEPRECIATION SCHEDULE

On July 27, 2003, Utopia Industries purchased and placed into service new office and computer equipment costing $400,000. This equipment will be used for business 100% of the time. The accountants have elected to take a $30,000 section 179 deduction. Prepare a depreciation schedule for the new asset by using MACRS.

SOLUTION STRATEGY

We begin by calculating the basis for depreciation:

Step 1a. Because the equipment will be used for business 100% of the time, the business-use basis for depreciation is the same as the original cost of the asset.

Business-use basis = Original cost × Business-use percentage

Business-use basis = $400,000 × 100% = $400,000

Step 1b. Next, we find the tentative basis for depreciation by subtracting the section 179 deduction of $30,000 from the business-use basis.

Tentative basis = Business-use basis − Section 179 deduction

Tentative basis = $400,000 − $30,000 = $370,000

Step 1c. Next, we find the basis for depreciation by applying the special depreciation allowance.

Basis for depreciation = Tentative basis(100% − Special depreciation allowance percent)

Basis for depreciation = $370,000(100% − 50%) = $185,000

Step 2. Now let's set up the depreciation schedule. From Table 17-1, we find that office and computer equipment is in the 5-year property class. Table 17-2 provides the cost recovery percentage for each year. Note once again, the extra year is to allow for the assumption that the asset was placed in service at mid-year.

Utopia Industries
MACRS Depreciation Schedule
Office and Computer Equipment

End of Year	Basis for Depreciation	Cost Recovery Percentage	MACRS Depreciation Deduction	Accumulated Depreciation	Book Value
					(new) $185,000
1	$185,000	20.00%	$37,000	$37,000	148,000
2	185,000	32.00	59,200	96,200	88,800
3	185,000	19.20	35,520	131,720	53,280
4	185,000	11.52	21,312	153,032	31,968
5	185,000	11.52	21,312	174,344	10,656
6	185,000	5.76	10,656	185,000	0

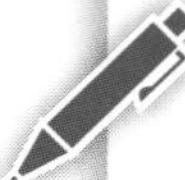

TRY IT EXERCISE 5

Roadway Trucking purchased and placed into service an over-the-road tractor for $135,500 in 2000. The vehicle was used for business 80% of the time. The accountant took the maximum section 179 deduction for the year 2000. Prepare a depreciation schedule for this new asset by using MACRS.

CHECK YOUR ANSWERS WITH THE SOLUTIONS ON PAGE 641.

CALCULATING THE PERIODIC DEPLETION COST OF NATURAL RESOURCES

Just as depreciation is used to write off the useful life of plant assets such as trucks, equipment, and buildings, depletion is used to account for the consumption of natural resources such as coal, petroleum, timber, natural gas, and minerals. **Depletion** is the proportional allocation of the cost of natural resources to the units used up or depleted per accounting period. In accounting, natural resources are also known as **wasting assets**, because they are considered to be exhausted or to be used up as they are converted into inventory by mining, pumping, or cutting.

Depletion of natural resources is calculated in the same way as the units-of-production method of depreciation for plant assets. To calculate the depletion allocation, we must determine the following:

depletion The proportional allocation or write-off of the cost of natural resources to the units used up or depleted per accounting period. Calculated in the same way as units-of-production depreciation.

wasting assets An accounting term used to describe natural resources that are exhausted or used up as they are converted into inventory by mining, pumping, or cutting.

a. *Total cost of the natural resource package*, including the original purchase price, exploration expenses, and extraction or cutting expenses.

b. *Residual or salvage value* of the property after resources have been exhausted.

c. *Estimated total number of units* (tons, barrels, board feet) of resource available.

STEPS TO CALCULATE THE PERIODIC DEPLETION COST OF NATURAL RESOURCES

Step 1. Compute the average depletion cost per unit by

$$\textbf{Average depletion cost per unit} = \frac{\textbf{Total cost of resource} - \textbf{Residual value}}{\textbf{Estimated total units available}}$$

(Round to the nearest tenth of a cent when necessary.)

Step 2. Calculate the periodic depletion cost by

$$\textbf{Periodic depletion cost} = \begin{matrix}\textbf{Units produced in} \\ \textbf{current period}\end{matrix} \times \begin{matrix}\textbf{Average depletion} \\ \textbf{cost per unit}\end{matrix}$$

EXAMPLE 6 CALCULATE THE PERIODIC DEPLETION COST OF NATURAL RESOURCES

Black Gold Oil, Inc., purchased a parcel of land containing an estimated 2 million barrels of crude oil for $850,000. Two oil wells were drilled at a cost of $340,000. The residual value of the property and equipment is $50,000. Calculate the periodic depletion cost for the first year of operation if 325,000 barrels were extracted.

SOLUTION STRATEGY

Step 1. $\text{Average depletion cost per unit} = \dfrac{\text{Total cost of resource} - \text{Residual value}}{\text{Estimated total units available}}$

$$\text{Average depletion cost per barrel} = \frac{(850{,}000 + 340{,}000) - 50{,}000}{2{,}000{,}000} = \$.57 \text{ per barrel}$$

Step 2. Periodic depletion cost = Units produced in current period × Average depl. cost per unit

Periodic depletion cost = 325,000 × .57 = $\underline{\underline{\$185{,}250}}$

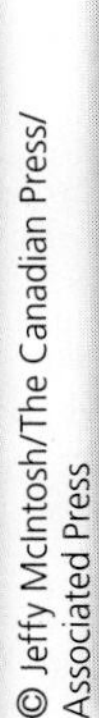

© Jeffy McIntosh/The Canadian Press/ Associated Press

Natural resources are also known as wasting assets, because they are considered to be used up when converted into inventory.

TRY IT EXERCISE 6

The Canmore Mining Company paid $5,330,000 for a parcel of land, including the mining rights. In addition, the company spent $900,000 on labor and equipment to prepare the site for mining operations. After mining is completed, it is estimated that the land and equipment would have a residual value of $400,000. Geologists estimated that the mine contains 7,000,000 tons of coal. If Canmore mined 1,500,000 tons of coal in the first year, what is the amount of the depletion cost?

CHECK YOUR ANSWER WITH THE SOLUTION ON PAGE 641.

SECTION II Review Exercises

1. Trident Developers purchased a computer system for $75,000 on October 4, 2001. The computer system will be used for business 100% of the time. The accountant for the company has elected to take a $10,000 section 179 deduction and the asset qualifies for a special depreciation allowance (see Table 17-4).

   a. What is the basis for depreciation for the computer system?

   Tentative basis = 75,000 − 10,000 = $65,000
   The asset qualifies for a 30% special depreciation allowance.
   Basis for depreciation = 65,000(100% − 30%) = $45,500

   b. What is the amount of the first year's depreciation using MACRS?

   Computers are in the 5-year property class.
   First year depreciation = 20%
   45,500 × 0.2 = $9,100

2. Atlantis Fantasy Company constructed roads and a bridge at AtlantisWorld in Orlando, Florida, at a cost of $15,000,000. Atlantis uses MACRS for tax purposes. No section 179 or special depreciation allowances were taken.

   a. What is the second year's depreciation deduction?

   Roads and bridges are in the 15-year property class.
   Second year cost recovery percent = 9.50%
   MACRS, year 2 = 15,000,000 × 9.50% = $1,425,000

   b. What is the ninth year's depreciation deduction?

   Ninth year cost recovery percent = 5.91%
   MACRS, year 9 = 15,000,000 × 5.91% = $886,500

3. Sunnyland Orange Groves planted fruit trees valued at $375,000 on February 12, 2004. The accountant for the company took a $75,000 section 179 deduction and the asset is entitled to a special depreciation allowance.

   a. What is the basis for depreciation for the fruit trees?

   Tentative basis = 375,000 − 75,000 = $300,000
   The asset qualifies for a 50% special depreciation allowance.
   Basis for depreciation = 300,000(100% − 50%) = $150,000

b. What is the property class for this asset under MACRS?
10-year property

c. What is the percentage for the sixth year of depreciation for this property?
Sixth-year cost recovery percent = 7.37%

d. What is the amount of the depreciation expense in the final year of write-off?
Final year (11th year) depreciation = 150,000 × 3.28% = $4,920

4. Island Hoppers Airways of Hawaii purchased a new commercial airplane for $2,400,000. The airplane is used for business 100% of the time. No section 179 or special allowances are available for this asset. As the accountant for the company, prepare a depreciation schedule for the asset by using MACRS.
Commercial airplanes are in the 7-year property class.
See Appendix B following the index for schedule.

5. Sequoia Timber Company purchased land containing an estimated 6,500,000 board feet of lumber for $3,700,000. The company invested another $300,000 to construct access roads and a company depot. The residual value of the property and equipment is estimated to be $880,000.

a. What is the average depletion cost per board foot of lumber?
Total cost of asset = 3,700,000 + 300,000 − 880,000 = $3,120,000

$$\text{Average depletion cost} = \frac{3,120,000}{6,500,000} = \$.48$$

b. If 782,000 board feet were cut in the second year of operation, what is the amount of the depletion cost for that year?
Second year depletion = 782,000 × .48 = $375,360

BUSINESS DECISION INTANGIBLE WRITE-OFFS

6. As you have seen in this chapter, companies depreciate or write off the expense of *tangible assets*, such as trucks and equipment, over a period of their useful lives. Many companies also have *intangible assets* that must be accounted for as an expense over a period of time.

Intangible assets are resources that benefit the company, but do not have any physical substance. Some examples are copyrights, franchises, patents, trademarks, and leases. In accounting, intangible assets are written off in a procedure known as asset amortization. This is much like straight-line depreciation, but there is no salvage value.

You are the accountant for Front Line Pharmaceuticals, Inc. In January 2000, the company purchased the patent rights for a new medication from Novae, Inc., for $9,000,000. The patent had 15 years remaining as its useful life. In January 2005, Front Line Pharmaceuticals successfully defended its right to the patent in a lawsuit at a cost of $550,000 in legal fees.

a. Using the straight-line method, calculate the patent's annual amortization expense for the years before the lawsuit.

$$\text{Annual amortization expense} = \frac{\text{Asset value}}{\text{Estimated useful life}} = \frac{9,000,000}{15} = \$600,000$$

"All I can say Thompson, is that there should be a Nobel Prize for accountancy."

(continued)

b. Calculate the revised annual amortization expense for the remaining years after the lawsuit.

Accumulated expense = 600,000 × 5 years = $3,000,000

Book value after 5 years = 9,000,000 − 3,000,000 = $6,000,000

$$\text{Revised annual amortization expense} = \frac{\text{Revised asset value}}{\text{Estimated useful life}} = \frac{6{,}000{,}000 + 550{,}000}{10} = \underline{\underline{\$655{,}000}}$$

CHAPTER FORMULAS

Straight-Line Method

Total cost = Cost + Shipping charges + Setup expenses

Total depreciation = Total cost − Salvage value

$$\text{Annual depreciation} = \frac{\text{Total depreciation}}{\text{Estimated useful life (years)}}$$

Sum-of-the-Years' Digits Method

$$\text{SYD depreciation rate fraction} = \frac{\text{Years of useful life remaining}}{\frac{n(n+1)}{2}}$$

Annual depreciation = Total depreciation × Depreciation rate fraction

Declining-Balance Method

$$\text{Declining-balance rate} = \frac{1}{\text{Useful life}} \times \text{Multiple}$$

Beginning book value = Ending book value of the previous year

Ending book value = Beginning book value − Depreciation for the year

Units-of-Production Method

$$\text{Depreciation per unit} = \frac{\text{Cost} - \text{Salvage value}}{\text{Units of useful life}}$$

Annual depreciation = Depreciation per unit × Units produced

MACRS Depreciation

Business-use basis = Original cost × Business-use percentage

Tentative basis = Business-use basis − Section 179 deduction

Basis for depreciation = Tentative basis(100% − Special depr. allowance percent)

MACRS depr. deduction = Basis for depr. × Cost recovery percentage for that year

Natural Resource Depletion

$$\text{Average depletion cost per unit} = \frac{\text{Total cost of resource} - \text{Residual value}}{\text{Estimated total units available}}$$

Periodic depl. cost = Units produced in current period × Average depl. cost per unit

SUMMARY CHART

17

Section I: Traditional Depreciation—Methods Used for Financial Statement Reporting

Topic	Important Concepts	Illustrative Examples
Calculating Depreciation by the Straight-Line Method **P/O 17-1, p. 617**	Straight-line depreciation provides for equal periodic charges to be written off over the estimated useful life of the asset. 1. Determine the total cost and residual value of the asset. 2. Subtract residual value from total cost to find the total amount of depreciation. **Total depr. = Total cost − Residual value** 3. Calculate the annual depreciation by dividing the total depreciation by the useful life of the asset. $\textbf{Annual depreciation} = \dfrac{\textbf{Total depreciation}}{\textbf{Estimated useful life}}$ 4. Set up a depreciation schedule in the form of a chart. **End of Year | Annual Depreciation | Accumulated Depreciation | Book Value**	Golden National Bank purchased a closed-circuit television system for $45,000. Shipping charges were $325, and installation expenses amounted to $2,540. The system is expected to last 5 years and has a residual value of $3,500. Prepare a depreciation schedule for the system. Total cost = 45,000 + 325 + 2,540 = $47,865 Total depr. = 47,865 − 3,500 = $44,365 $\text{Annual depr.} = \dfrac{44{,}365}{5} = \$8{,}873$ **End of Year | Annual Depr. | Accum. Depr. | Book Value** (new) 47,865 1 | 8,873 | 8,873 | 38,992 2 | 8,873 | 17,746 | 30,119 3 | 8,873 | 26,619 | 21,246 4 | 8,873 | 35,492 | 12,373 5 | 8,873 | 44,365 | 3,500
Calculating Depreciation by the Sum-of-the-Years' Digits Method **P/O 17-2, p. 618**	The sum-of-the-years' digits method is one of the accelerated methods of calculating depreciation. 1. Find the total depreciation of the asset: **Total depreciation = Total cost − Residual value** 2. Calculate the SYD depreciation rate fraction for each year: $\textbf{Rate fraction} = \dfrac{\textbf{Years of life remaining}}{\dfrac{n(n+1)}{2}}$ 3. Calculate the depreciation for each year: **Annual depreciation =** **Total depreciation × Depreciation rate fraction**	The Gourmet Diner purchased new kitchen equipment for $165,000 with a 4-year useful life and salvage value of $5,000. Using the sum-of-the-years' digits method, calculate the depreciation expense for year 1 and year 3. Total depr. = 165,000 − 5,000 = 160,000 $\text{Rate fraction year 1} = \dfrac{4}{\dfrac{4(4+1)}{2}} = \dfrac{4}{10}$ $\text{Depr. year 1} = 160{,}000 \times \dfrac{4}{10} = \$64{,}000$ $\text{Rate fraction year 3} = \dfrac{2}{\dfrac{4(4+1)}{2}} = \dfrac{2}{10}$ $\text{Depr. year 3} = 160{,}000 \times \dfrac{2}{10} = \$32{,}000$
Calculating Depreciation by the Declining-Balance Method **P/O 17-3, p. 621**	Declining-balance depreciation, the second accelerated method, uses a multiple of the straight-line rate, such as 125%, 150%, and 200%. Salvage value is not considered until the last year. 1. Calculate the declining-balance rate: $\textbf{Declining-balance rate} = \dfrac{\textbf{1}}{\textbf{Useful life}} \times \textbf{Multiple}$	The Fitness Factory purchased a treadmill for $5,000. It is expected to last 4 years and have a salvage value of $1,000. Use 150% declining-balance depreciation to calculate the book value after each year. Round your answer to dollars. $\text{Declining balance-rate} = \dfrac{1}{4} \times 1.5 = .375$

Section I: (continued)

Topic	Important Concepts	Illustrative Examples
	2. Calculate the depreciation for each year by applying the rate to each year's beginning book value. **Depreciation for year = Beginning book value × Declining balance rate** 3. Calculate the ending book value for each year by subtracting the depreciation for the year from the beginning book value. **Ending book value = Beginning book value − Depreciation for year** 4. The depreciation is complete when the ending book value equals the salvage value.	*Year 1:* Depr. = 5,000 × .375 = 1,875 Book value = 5,000 − 1,875 = $3,125 *Year 2:* Depr. = 3,125 × .375 = 1,172 Book value = 3,125 − 1,172 = $1,953 *Year 3:* Depr. = 1,953 × .375 = 732 Book value = 1,953 − 732 = $1,221 *Year 4:* Depr. = 1,221 × .375 = 458 Book value = 1,221 − 221 = $1,000* **Note:* In year 4, the calculated depreciation is $458. Because the book value of an asset cannot fall below the salvage value, the allowable depreciation is limited to $221 (1,221 − 1,000 = 221).
Calculating Depreciation by the Units-of-Production Method P/O 17-4, p. 623	When the useful life of an asset is more accurately defined in terms of how much it is used, such as miles driven or units produced, we may apply the units-of-production method. 1. Determine the depreciation cost per unit by using $\text{Depreciation per unit} = \dfrac{\text{Cost} - \text{Salvage value}}{\text{Units of useful life}}$ 2. Calculate the depreciation for each year by using **Annual depreciation = Depreciation per unit × Units produced**	Vita Foods purchased a new canning machine for one of its chicken soup production lines at a cost of $455,000. The machine has an expected useful life of 1,000,000 cans and a residual value of $25,000. In the first year, the machine produced 120,000 cans. Calculate the depreciation on the machine for year 1. $\text{Depreciation per unit} = \dfrac{455{,}000 - 25{,}000}{1{,}000{,}000} = \$.43$ Depreciation year 1 = 120,000 × .43 = $51,600

Section II: Asset Cost Recovery Systems—IRS Prescribed Methods for Income Tax Reporting

Topic	Important Concepts	Illustrative Examples
Calculating Depreciation by Using the Modified Accelerated Cost Recovery System (MACRS) P/O 17-5, p. 628	MACRS is used for assets placed in service after 1986. This system uses property classes, Table 17-1 and recovery percentages, Table 17-2. To determine the basis for depreciation, use the section 179 deductions in Table 17-3 and the special depreciation allowance dates, Table 17-4. 1. Calculate the basis for depreciation. a. **Percent of business use:** (Minimum 50% to qualify) **Business-use basis = Original cost × Business-use percentage**	Harbor Helpers purchased a tug boat for $650,000. The boat is used for business 100% of the time. No section 179 or special allowances were available. As their accountant, use MACRS to calculate the depreciation expense for the second and fifth year. Using Table 17-1, we find that tug boats are considered 10-year property. *MACRS Depreciation Expense:* *Year 2* 650,000 × .18 = $117,000 *Year 5* 650,000 × .0922 = $59,930

Section II: (continued)

Topic	Important Concepts	Illustrative Examples
	b. Section 179 deduction: (Table 17-3) **Tentative basis =** **Business-use basis − Section 179 deduction** **c. Special Depreciation Allowances: (Table 17-4)** **Basis for depreciation = Tentative basis (100% − Special depreciation allowance percent)** 2. **MACRS depreciation deduction (Tables 17-1 and 17-2)** **MACRS depreciation deduction =** **Basis for depreciation × Cost recovery percentage for that year**	
Calculating the Periodic Depletion Cost of Natural Resources P/O 17-6, p. 633	Depletion is the proportional allocation of natural resources to the units used up or depleted, per accounting period. Depletion is calculated in the same way as the units-of-production method of depreciation. 1. Compute the average depletion cost per unit: $\text{Average depletion/unit} = \dfrac{\text{Total cost} - \text{Salvage}}{\text{Total units available}}$ 2. Calculate the periodic depletion cost: **Periodic depletion cost =** **Current units × Average depletion per unit**	The Mother Lode Mining Company purchased a parcel of land containing an estimated 800,000 tons of iron ore. The cost of the asset was \$2,000,000. An additional \$350,000 was spent to prepare the property for mining. The estimated residual value of the asset is \$500,000. If the first year's output was 200,000 tons, what is the amount of the depletion allowance? $\text{Av. depl. per unit} = \dfrac{2{,}350{,}000 - 500{,}000}{800{,}000}$ = \$2.31 per ton Depletion cost: Year 1 = 200,000 × 2.31 = \$462,000

TRY IT EXERCISE SOLUTIONS FOR CHAPTER 17

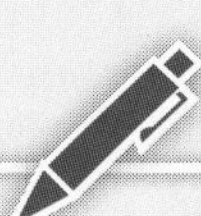

1. Total cost = Cost + Shipping charges + Setup expenses
Total cost = 125,000 + 1,150 + 750 = \$126,900

Total depreciation = Total cost − Salvage value
Total depreciation = 126,900 − 5,000 = \$121,900

$$\text{Annual depreciation} = \frac{\text{Total depreciation}}{\text{Estimated useful life}}$$

$$\text{Annual depreciation} = \frac{121{,}900}{5} = \$24{,}380$$

Wild Flour Bakery
Straight-Line Depreciation Schedule
Bread Oven

End of Year	Annual Depreciation	Accumulated Depreciation	Book Value
			(cost) \$126,900
1	\$24,380	\$24,380	102,520
2	24,380	48,760	78,140
3	24,380	73,140	53,760
4	24,380	97,520	29,380
5	24,380	121,900	(salvage value) 5,000

2. Total depreciation = Total cost − Salvage value
Total depreciation = 44,500 − 2,500 = $42,000

$$\text{SYD depreciation rate fraction} = \frac{\text{Years of useful life remaining}}{\frac{n(n+1)}{2}}$$

$$\text{Rate fraction year 1} = \frac{6}{\frac{6(6+1)}{2}} = \frac{6}{\frac{42}{2}} = \frac{6}{21}$$

Bow Valley Kitchens

End of Year	Total Depreciation	Rate Fraction	Annual Depreciation	Accumulated Depreciation	Book Value
					(new) $44,500
1	$42,000	$\frac{6}{21}$	$12,000	$12,000	32,500
2	42,000	$\frac{5}{21}$	10,000	22,000	22,500
3	42,000	$\frac{4}{21}$	8,000	30,000	14,500
4	42,000	$\frac{3}{21}$	6,000	36,000	8,500
5	42,000	$\frac{2}{21}$	4,000	40,000	4,500
6	42,000	$\frac{1}{21}$	2,000	42,000	2,500

3. $$\text{Declining-balance rate} = \frac{1}{\text{Useful life}} \times \text{Multiple}$$

$$\text{Declining-balance rate} = \frac{1}{4} \times 1.5 = .375$$

Jasper Air Service

End of Year	Regular Book Value	Depreciation Rate	Depreciation for Year	Accumulated Depreciation	Ending Book Value
					(new) $386,000.00
1	$386,000.00	.375	$144,750.00	$144,750.00	241,250.00
2	241,250.00	.375	90,468.75	235,218.75	150,781.25
3	150,781.25	.375	56,542.97	291,761.72	94,238.28
4	94,238.28	.375	24,238.28*	316,000.00	70,000.00

*Maximum allowable to reach salvage value

4. $$\text{Depreciation per unit} = \frac{\text{Cost} - \text{Salvage value}}{\text{Units of useful life}}$$

$$\text{Depreciation per unit} = \frac{54{,}500 - 7{,}500}{75{,}000} = \$.627/\text{mile}$$

Prestige Limousine Service

End of Year	Depreciation per Mile	Miles Used	Annual Depreciation	Accumulated Depreciation	Book Value
					(new) $54,500.00
1	$.627	12,500	$7,837.50	$7,837.50	46,662.50
2	.627	18,300	11,474.10	19,311.60	35,188.40
3	.627	15,900	9,969.30	29,280.90	25,219.10
4	.627	19,100	11,975.70	41,256.60	13,243.40
5	.627	12,400	5,743.40*	47,000.00	7,500.00

*Maximum allowable to reach salvage value

5. MACRS 3-Year Property

Business-use basis = Original cost × Business-use percentage

Business-use basis = 135,500 × 80% = $108,400

Tentative basis = Business-use basis − Section 179 deductions

Tentative basis = 108,400 − 20,000 = $88,400

There are no special allowances available for this asset

Basis for depreciation = $88,400

Roadway Trucking
Over-the-Road Tractor

End of Year	Original Basis	Cost Recovery Percentage	Cost Recovery	Accumulated Depreciation	Book Value
					(new) $88,400.00
1	$88,400	33.33	$29,463.72	$29,463.72	58,936.28
2	88,400	44.45	39,293.80	68,757.52	19,642.48
3	88,400	14.81	13,092.04	81,849.56	6,550.44
4	88,400	7.41	6,550.44	88,400.00	0

6. $\text{Average depletion cost per unit} = \dfrac{\text{Total cost} - \text{Residual value}}{\text{Estimated total units available}}$

$$\text{Average depletion cost per unit} = \frac{(5{,}330{,}000 + 900{,}000) - 400{,}000}{7{,}000{,}000} = \frac{5{,}830{,}000}{7{,}000{,}000} = .8329 = \$.833$$

Periodic depletion cost = Units produced × Average depletion cost per unit

Periodic depletion cost (1st year) = 1,500,000 × .833 = $1,249,500

CONCEPT REVIEW

1. The decrease in value from the original cost of a long-term asset over its useful life is known as ____. (17-1)
depreciation

2. The total cost or original ____ is the total amount a company pays for an asset. The ____ value is an asset's value at any given time during its useful life. (17-1)
basis, book

3. The useful ____ is the length of time an asset is expected to generate revenue. The value of an asset at the time it is taken out of service is known as its ____, scrap, salvage, or trade-in-value. (17-1)
life, residual

4. ____ depreciation is a method of depreciation that provides for equal periodic charges to be written off over the life of an asset. (17-1)
Straight-line

5. Depreciation methods that assume an asset depreciates more in the early years of its useful life are known as ____ depreciation. (17-2)
accelerated

6. ____ digits is a method of accelerated depreciation that allows an asset to depreciate the most during the first year of its useful life. (17-2)
Sum-of-the-years'

7. Write the formula for the sum-of-the-digits of the useful life of an asset, where n is the number of years of useful life. (17-2)

$$SYD = \frac{n(n+1)}{2}$$

8. A method of accelerated depreciation that uses a multiple (125%, 150%, or 200%) of the straight-line rate is known as the ____ method. (17-3)
declining-balance

9. Write the formula for the declining-balance rate. (17-3)

$$\text{Declining-balance rate} = \frac{1}{\text{Useful life}} \times \text{Multiple}$$

10. Write the formula for the depreciation per unit in the units-of-production method. (17-4)

$$\text{Depreciation per unit} = \frac{\text{Cost} - \text{Salvage value}}{\text{Units of useful life}}$$

11. According to the IRS, the depreciation system for getting back or recovering the cost of property used to produce income is known as the ____ ____ ____ ____ system. This system is abbreviated as ____. (17-5)
modified accelerated cost recovery, MACRS

12. The IRS system named in question 11 lists assets in various time categories known as ____ classes. Once an asset's class has been determined, a table is used to find the cost ____ percentage for the recovery year in question. (17-5)
property, recovery

13. The depreciation of natural resources is known as ____. The accounting term used to describe these natural resources is ____ assets. (17-6)
depletion, wasting

14. When depreciating natural resources, the average depletion cost per unit is equal to: ____. (17-6)

$$\frac{\text{Total cost of resource} - \text{Residual value}}{\text{Estimated total units available}}$$

CHAPTER 17 ASSESSMENT TEST

Name

Class

Answers

1. $5,864

$5,264

$877.33

2. $17,210

$15,310

$3,827.50

3. See schedule.

Calculate the total cost, total depreciation, and annual depreciation for the following assets by using the straight-line method.

EXCEL

	Cost	Shipping Charges	Setup Charges	Total Cost	Salvage Value	Estimated Useful Life (years)	Depreciation Total	Depreciation Annual
1.	$5,600	$210	$54	$5,864	$600	6	$5,264	$877.33
2.	$16,900	$310	0	$17,210	$1,900	4	$15,310	$3,827.50

3. Oxford Manufacturing, Inc., purchased new equipment totaling $648,000. Shipping charges were $2,200, and installation amounted to $1,800. The equipment is expected to last 4 years and have a residual value of $33,000. If the company elects to use the straight-line method of depreciation, prepare a depreciation schedule for these assets.

Oxford Manufacturing, Inc.
Straight-Line Depreciation Schedule
Manufacturing Equipment

End of Year	Annual Depreciation	Accumulated Depreciation	Book Value
			(new) $652,000
1	$154,750	$154,750	497,250
2	154,750	309,500	342,500
3	154,750	464,250	187,750
4	154,750	619,000	33,000

CHAPTER 17

Name

Class

Answers

4. 28
6/28
4/28
2/28

5. 45
8/45
6/45
4/45

6. See schedule.

7. 11.111%
13.889%

8. 16.667%
33.333%

9. See schedule.

10. $.017

11. $.024

Complete the following as they relate to the sum-of-the-years' digits method of depreciation.

	Useful Life (years)	Sum-of-the-Years' Digits	Depreciation Rate Fraction Year 2	Year 4	Year 6
4.	7	28	$\frac{6}{28}$	$\frac{4}{28}$	$\frac{2}{28}$
5.	9	45	$\frac{8}{45}$	$\frac{6}{45}$	$\frac{4}{45}$

6. Mr. Fix-It purchased a service truck for $32,400. It has an estimated useful life of 3 years and a trade-in value of $3,100. Using the sum-of-the-years' digits method, prepare a depreciation schedule for the truck.

Mr. Fix-It
SYD Depreciation Schedule
Service Truck

End of Year	Total Depreciation	Depreciation Rate Fraction	Annual Depreciation	Accumulated Depreciation	Book Value
					(new) $32,400.00
1	$29,300	$\frac{3}{6}$	$14,650.00	$14,650.00	17,750.00
2	29,300	$\frac{2}{6}$	9,766.67	24,416.67	7,983.33
3	29,300	$\frac{1}{6}$	4,883.33	29,300.00	3,100.00

Complete the following as they relate to the declining-balance method of depreciation. Round answers to thousandths where applicable.

	Years	Straight-Line Rate (%)	Multiple (%)	Declining-Balance Rate (%)
7.	9	11.111	125	13.889
8.	6	16.667	200	33.333

9. Award Makers bought a computerized engraving machine for $33,800. It is expected to have a 6-year useful life and a trade-in value of $2,700. Prepare a depreciation schedule for the *first 3 years* by using the 125% declining-balance method for the machine.

Award Makers
125% Declining-Balance Depreciation Schedule
Computerized Engraving Machine

End of Year	Beginning Book Value	Depreciation Rate	Depreciation for the Year	Accumulated Depreciation	Ending Book Value
					(new) $33,800.00
1	$33,800.00	.20833	$7,041.55	$7,041.55	26,758.45
2	26,758.45	.20833	5,574.59	12,616.14	21,183.86
3	21,183.86	.20833	4,413.23	17,029.37	16,770.63

Complete the following as they relate to the units-of-production method of depreciation. Round answers to the nearest tenth of a cent.

	Asset	Cost	Salvage Value	Units of Useful Life	Depreciation per Unit
10.	Pump	$8,900	$250	500,000 gallons	$.017
11.	Copier	$3,900	$ 0	160,000 copies	$.024

© Ron Chapple/Thinkstock Images/Jupiter Images

Movie Theaters
In 2006 there were 5,939 movie theaters with a total of 38,415 screens. The average ticket price was $6.55 and the total U.S. box office gross was $9.48 billion for 1.45 billion admissions.

CHAPTER

Name

Class

Answers

12. See schedule.

13. a. $320,000

b. See schedule.

14. a. $25.098

12. Screen Gems Movie Theater purchased a new projector for $155,000 with a salvage value of $2,000. Delivery and installation amounted to $580. The projector is expected to have a useful life of 15,000 hours. Complete the following depreciation schedule for the *first 4 years* of operation by using the units-of-production method:

Total depr. = 155,000 + 580 − 2,000 = $153,580

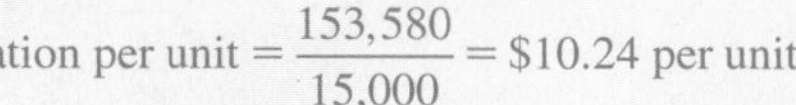

$$\text{Depreciation per unit} = \frac{153{,}580}{15{,}000} = \$10.24 \text{ per unit}$$

Screen Gems Movie Theater
Units-of-Production Depreciation Schedule
Projector

End of Year	Depreciation per Hour	Hours	Annual Depreciation	Accumulated Depreciation	Book Value
					(new) $155,580.00
1	$10.24	2,300	$23,552.00	$23,552.00	132,028.00
2	10.24	1,890	19,353.60	42,905.60	112,674.40
3	10.24	2,160	22,118.40	65,024.00	90,556.00
4	10.24	2,530	25,907.20	90,931.20	64,648.80

13. Stone Age Concrete, Inc., purchased cement manufacturing equipment valued at $344,000 on March 14, 2001. The equipment is used for business 100% of the time. As their accountant, you have elected to take the maximum section 179 deduction.

a. What is the basis for depreciation for this equipment?

Business-use basis = 344,000 × 100% = $344,000
Tentative basis = 344,000 − 24,000 = $320,000
No special allowances available. Basis for depreciation = $320,000
Cement manufacturing equipment depreciates over 15 years

b. Prepare a depreciation schedule for the first 5 years of operation of this equipment by using MACRS.

Stone Age Concrete, Inc.
MACRS Depreciation Schedule
Cement Manufacturing Equipment

End of Year	Original Basis (cost)	Cost Recovery Percentage	Cost Recovery (depreciation)	Accumulated Depreciation	Book Value
					(new) $320,000
1	$320,000	5.00	$16,000	$16,000	304,000
2	320,000	9.50	30,400	46,400	273,600
3	320,000	8.55	27,360	73,760	246,240
4	320,000	7.70	24,640	98,400	221,600
5	320,000	6.93	22,176	120,576	199,424

14. The Platinum Touch Mining Company paid $4,000,000 for a parcel of land, including the mining rights. In addition, the company spent $564,700 to prepare the site for mining operations. When mining is completed, it is estimated that the residual value of the asset will be $800,000. Scientists estimate that the site contains 150,000 ounces of platinum.

a. What is the average depletion cost per ounce?

Total depreciation = 4,000,000 + 564,700 − 800,000 = $3,764,700

$$\text{Average depletion per ounce} = \frac{3{,}764{,}700}{150{,}000} = \$25.098$$

b. If 12,200 ounces were mined in the first year of operation, what is the amount of the depletion cost?

Depletion first year $= 25.098 \times 12{,}200 = \underline{\underline{\$306{,}195.60}}$

15. In January 1998, Marine Science Corporation was awarded a patent for a new boat hull design. The life of the patent is 20 years. They estimate the value of the patent over its lifetime is \$7,500,000. Their accountant amortizes the patent using straight line depreciation to zero value at the end of the 20 years. In January 2006, Marine Science successfully defended their patent in a lawsuit at a legal expense of \$486,000.

a. Using the straight-line method, calculate the patent's annual amortization expense for the years before the lawsuit.

$$\text{Annual amortization expense} = \frac{\text{Asset value}}{\text{Estimated useful life}} = \frac{7{,}500{,}000}{20} = \underline{\underline{\$375{,}000}}$$

b. Calculate the revised annual amortization expense for the remaining years after the lawsuit.

Accumulated expense $= 375{,}000 \times 8$ years $= \$3{,}000{,}000$

Book value after eight years $= 7{,}500{,}000 - 3{,}000{,}000 = \$4{,}500{,}000$

$$\text{Revised annual amortization expense} = \frac{4{,}500{,}000 + 486{,}000}{12} = \underline{\underline{\$415{,}500}}$$

Name

Class

Answers

14. b. \$306,195.60

15. a. \$375,000

b. \$415,500

16. a. \$500,000

b. \$357,250

c. \$42,825

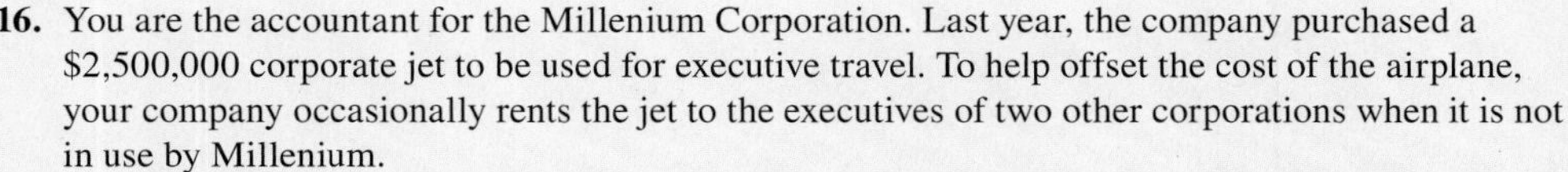

16. You are the accountant for the Millenium Corporation. Last year, the company purchased a \$2,500,000 corporate jet to be used for executive travel. To help offset the cost of the airplane, your company occasionally rents the jet to the executives of two other corporations when it is not in use by Millenium.

When the corporate tax return was filed this year, you began depreciating the jet by using MACRS. Today, you received a letter from the IRS informing you that because your company occasionally rents the airplane to others, it is considered a commercial aircraft and must be depreciated as such. The corporate lawyers are considering disputing this IRS ruling and have asked you the following:

a. How much depreciation did you claim this year?

Private planes depreciate over 5 years.

$2{,}500{,}000 \times 20\% = \underline{\underline{\$500{,}000}}$

b. Under the new category, how much depreciation would be claimed?

Commercial planes depreciate over 7 years.

$2{,}500{,}000 \times 14.29\% = \underline{\underline{\$357{,}250}}$

c. If the company pays 30% income tax, what effect will this change have on the amount of tax owed, assuming the company made a net profit this year?

Less depreciation = Added income

Added income $= 500{,}000 - 357{,}250 = \$142{,}750$

Added tax $= 142{,}750 \times 30\% = \underline{\underline{\$42{,}825}}$

This Business Decision, "A Dispute with the IRS," clearly illustrates how an IRS-prescribed change in property class under MACRS can affect the bottom line of a company's income statement.

COLLABORATIVE LEARNING ACTIVITY

Going, Going, Gone!

1. Have each member of your team choose their favorite vehicle and determine the price of a new one from a dealership. Then check the classified ads of your local newspaper, a publication of used vehicle prices, or the Internet to determine the price of the same vehicle at one, two, three, four, and five years old.

- **a.** Prepare a depreciation schedule based on the information found.
- **b.** Calculate what percent of the vehicle's original value was lost in each year.
- **c.** Construct a line graph of the five years of depreciation of the vehicle.
- **d.** Does it seem to be straight-line or accelerated?
- **e.** Compare the depreciation for each team member's vehicle. Which models depreciated the fastest? The slowest?

2. As a team, choose a local industry. Have each member of the team pick a different company within that industry and speak with an accountant who works there. Identify three major assets that are being depreciated, such as a truck, production-line equipment, a computer system, office furniture and fixtures, etc. For each asset, determine the following:

- **a.** Original purchase price
- **b.** Useful life
- **c.** Salvage value
- **d.** Depreciation method used for financial statement reporting
- **e.** Depreciation method used for income tax purposes

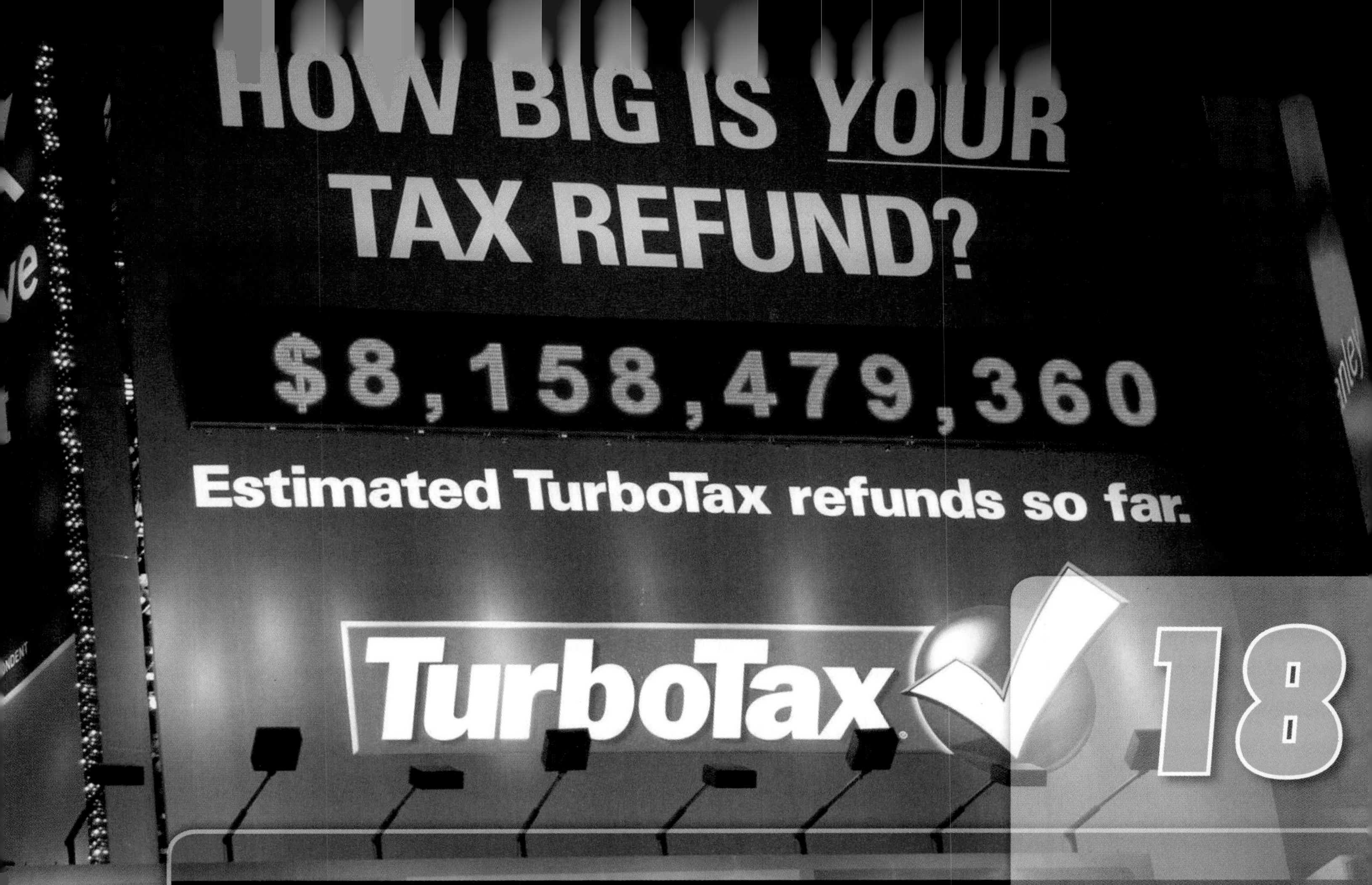

© Turbotax/Feature Photo Service (NewsCom)

CHAPTER 18 Taxes

RMANCE OBJECTIVES

Section I Sales and Excise Taxes

18-1: Determining sales tax by using sales tax tables (p. 649)

18-2: Calculating sales tax by using the percent method (p. 650)

18-3: Calculating selling price and amount of sales tax when total purchase price is known (p. 651)

18-4: Calculating excise tax (p. 652)

Section II Property Tax

18-5: Calculating the amount of property tax (p. 655)

18-6: Calculating tax rate necessary in a community to meet budgetary demands (p. 658)

Section III Income Tax

18-7: Calculating taxable income for individuals (p. 662)

18-8: Using the Tax Table to determine tax liability (p. 665)

18-9: Using the Tax Computation Worksheet to calculate tax liability (p. 671)

18-10: Calculating an individual's tax refund or amount of tax owed (p. 674)

18-11: Calculating corporate income tax and net income after taxes (p. 675)

SECTION I SALES AND EXCISE TAXES

taxation The imposition of a mandatory levy or charge by a government unit to provide financing for public services.

Benjamin Franklin wrote that "nothing can be said to be certain except death and taxes." **Taxation** is the imposition of a mandatory levy on the citizens of a country by their government. In 1904, Supreme Court Justice Oliver Wendell Holmes, Jr. defined taxes as "the price we pay for living in a civilized society." In almost all countries, tax revenue is the major source of financing for publicly provided services. In a democracy, a majority of citizens or their representatives vote to impose taxes on themselves in order to finance, through the public sector, services on which they place value but that they believe cannot be adequately provided by market processes.

In addition to generating revenue to finance public services, taxation can be used for other objectives, such as income redistribution, economic stabilization, and the regulating of consumption of certain commodities or services. In this chapter we shall focus our attention on the three major categories of taxation: sales and excise tax, property tax, and individual and corporate income tax.

sales tax A tax based on the retail selling or rental price of tangible personal property, collected by the retailer at the time of purchase, and paid to the state or local government.

A tax based on the retail selling or rental price of tangible personal property is called a **sales tax**. This tax may also be imposed on admission charges to places of amusement, sport, and recreation, as well as on certain services. Most states, and many other taxing units such as cities, counties, and municipalities, levy or charge a tax on sales. Businesses that purchase merchandise for resale to others are normally exempt from this tax. Only final buyers pay sales tax. Many states allow a sales tax exemption for food, prescription drugs, household medicines, and other selected items.

sales tax rate Sales tax expressed in its most common form, as a percent of the retail price of an item.

The liability for the sales tax is incurred at the time the sale is made. Retail merchants act as agents, collecting sales taxes and periodically remitting them to the proper tax agency. The **sales tax rate** is expressed as a percent and varies from state to state.

excise tax A tax levied by federal, state, and local governments on certain luxury or nonessential products and services such as alcoholic beverages, furs, tobacco products, telephone service, and airline and cruise ship tickets.

Another type of tax levied by federal, state, and local governments on certain products and services is known as an **excise tax**. This tax, which is paid in addition to the sales tax, is imposed on so-called luxury or nonessential items. Some typical examples would be tires, alcoholic beverages, jewelry (except watches), gasoline, furs, firearms, certain recreational equipment and sporting goods, tobacco products, telecommunications services, airline and cruise ship transportation, and telephone service.

In the Business World

The cost of a civilized society: In 2006, federal, state, and local governments in the United States collected over $12,000 in tax revenue for every man, woman, and child in the country!

Revenue from taxes helps pay for many public services, such as the maintenance of roads and highways.

© Florian Frank/Brand X Pictures/Jupiter Images

DETERMINING SALES TAX BY USING SALES TAX TABLES

18-1

Many state and local governments provide retailers with sales tax tables such as those in Exhibit 18-1. These tables are used by businesses that do not have electronic cash register systems that automatically compute the proper amount of sales tax.

STEPS TO DETERMINE SALES TAX DUE ON AN ITEM BY USING SALES TAX TABLES

Step 1. Locate the taxable retail price in the Amount of Sale column.

Step 2. Scan to the right to locate the amount of tax due in the Tax column.

Note: Exhibit 18-1 is only a partial listing. Complete sales tax tables are available in most states from the Department of Revenue.

EXAMPLE 1 USING SALES TAX TABLES

Jana Beck purchased a can of hair spray at CVS Pharmacy for $3.29. Use Exhibit 18-1 to determine the amount of sales tax on this item.

SOLUTION STRATEGY

Step 1. From Exhibit 18-1 we find that the retail price of the hair spray, $3.29, falls in the range of $3.24 to $3.38.

Step 2. Scanning to the right, we find the tax due on this item is $.22.

Exhibit 18-1
$6\frac{1}{2}$% Sales Tax Brackets

$6\frac{1}{2}$% SALES TAX BRACKETS

Amount of Sale	Tax	Amount of Sale	Tax
.10- .15	.01	5.08- 5.23	.34
.16- .30	.02	5.24- 5.38	.35
.31- .46	.03	5.39- 5.53	.36
.47- .61	.04	5.54- 5.69	.37
.62- .76	.05	5.70- 5.84	.38
.77- .92	.06	5.85- 6 09	.39
.93- 1.07	.07	6.10- 6.15	.40
1.08- 1.23	.08	6.16- 6.30	.41
1.24- 1.38	.09	6.31- 6.46	.42
1.39- 1.53	.10	6.47- 6.61	.43
1.54- 1.69	.11	6.62- 6.76	.44
1.70- 1.84	.12	6.77- 6.92	.45
1.85- 2.09	.13	6.93- 7.07	.46
2.10- 2.15	.14	7.08- 7.23	.47
2.16- 2.30	.15	7.24- 7.38	.48
2.31- 2.46	.16	7.39- 7.53	.49
2.47- 2.61	.17	7.54- 7.69	.50
2.62- 2.76	.18	7.70- 7.84	.51
2.77- 2.92	.19	7.85- 8.09	.52
2.93- 3.07	.20	8.10- 8.15	.53
3.08- 3.23	.21	8.16- 8.30	.54
3.24- 3.38	.22	8.31- 8.46	.55
3.39- 3.53	.23	8.47- 8.61	.56
3.54- 3.69	.24	8.62- 8.76	.57
3.70- 3.84	.25	8.77- 8.92	.58
3.85- 4.09	.26	8.93- 9.07	.59
4.10- 4.15	.27	9.08- 9.23	.60
4.16- 4.30	.28	9.24- 9.38	.61
4.31- 4.46	.29	9.39- 9.53	.62
4.47- 4.61	.30	9.54- 9.69	.63
4.62- 4.76	.31	9.70- 9.84	.64
4.77- 4.92	.32	9.85- 10.09	.65
4.93- 5.07	.33		

Amount of Sale	Tax	Amount of Sale	Tax
10.10- 10.15	.66	15.08- 15.23	.99
10.16- 10.30	.67	15.24- 15.38	1.00
10.31- 10.46	.68	15.39- 15.53	1.01
10.47- 10.61	.69	15.54- 15.69	1.02
10.62- 10.76	.70	15.70- 15.84	1.03
10.77- 10.92	.71	15.85- 16.09	1.04
10.93- 11.07	.72	16.10- 16.15	1.05
11.08- 11.23	.73	16.16- 16.30	1.06
11.24- 11.38	.74	16.31- 16.46	1.07
11.39- 11.53	.75	16.47- 16.61	1.08
11.54- 11.69	.76	16.62- 16.76	1.09
11.70- 11.84	.77	16.77- 16.92	1.10
11.85- 12.09	.78	16.93- 17.07	1.11
12.10- 12.15	.79	17.08- 17.23	1.12
12.16- 12.30	.80	17.24- 17.38	1.13
12.31- 12.46	.81	17.39- 17.53	1.14
12.47- 12.61	.82	17.54- 17.69	1.15
12.62- 12.76	.83	17.70- 17.84	1.16
12.77- 12.92	.84	17.85- 18.09	1.17
12.93 13.07	.85	18.10- 18.15	1.18
13.08- 13.23	.86	18.16- 18.30	1.19
13.24- 13.38	.87	18.31- 18.46	1.20
13.39- 13.53	.88	18.47- 18.61	1.21
13.54- 13.69	.89	18.62- 18.76	1.22
13.70- 13.84	.90	18.77- 18.92	1.23
13.85- 14.09	.91	18.93- 19.07	1.24
14.10- 14.15	.92	19.08- 19.23	1.25
14.16- 14.30	.93	19.24- 19.38	1.26
14.31- 14.46	.94	19.39- 19.53	1.27
14.47- 14.61	.95	19.54- 19.69	1.28
14.62- 14.76	.96	19.70- 19.84	1.29
14.77- 14.92	.97	19.85- 20.09	1.30
14.93- 15.07	.98		

In the Business World

Currently, 45 states have a sales tax, with rates that range from 2.9% to 7.25%. In many areas, city and county rates add an additional .5% to 6%. According to the Tax Foundation, in 2006, states collected over $226 billion in sales tax.

States with the highest sales tax rates are California, Mississippi, New Jersey, Rhode Island, and Tennessee. Among the lowest are Colorado (lowest at 2.9%), Alabama, Georgia, Hawaii, Louisiana, New York, South Dakota, and Wyoming. Alaska, Delaware, Montana, New Hampshire, and Oregon have no sales tax.

18-1

TRY IT EXERCISE 1

Use Exhibit 18-1 to determine the amount of sales tax on a calculator with a retail price of $12.49.

CHECK YOUR ANSWER WITH THE SOLUTION ON PAGE 684.

18-2 CALCULATING SALES TAX BY USING THE PERCENT METHOD

When sales tax tables are not available, the percent method may be used to calculate the sales tax on an item or service. Other nontaxable charges, such as packing, delivery, handling, or setup, are added after the sales tax has been computed.

STEPS TO CALCULATE SALES TAX AND TOTAL PURCHASE PRICE BY USING THE PERCENT METHOD

Step 1. Calculate the sales tax by multiplying the selling price of the good or service by the sales tax rate.

Sales tax = Selling price × Sales tax rate

Step 2. Compute the total purchase price by adding the selling price, the sales tax, and any other additional charges.

Total purchase price = Selling price + Sales tax + Other charges

EXAMPLE 2 CALCULATING SALES TAX

Ryan Miller purchased a riding lawnmower for $488.95 at a Wal-Mart store in Atlanta, Georgia. The store charges $25 for delivery and $15 for assembly. If the state sales tax in Georgia is 5%, and Atlanta has a 1.5% city tax, what is the amount of sales tax on the lawnmower and what is the total purchase price?

Remember, there is no sales tax on packing, shipping, handling, or setup charges for merchandise purchased. These charges should be added *after* the sales tax has been computed.

SOLUTION STRATEGY

In this example, the sales tax rate will be the total of the state and city taxes,

Sales tax rate = 5% + 1.5% = 6.5%

Step 1. Sales tax = Selling price × Sales tax rate

Sales tax = 488.95 × .065 = $31.78

Step 2. Total purchase price = Selling price + Sales tax + Other charges

Total purchase price = 488.95 + 31.78 + (25 + 15)

Total purchase price = $560.73

TRY IT EXERCISE 2

Tim Meekma purchased a car for \$38,600 at Auto City in Milwaukee, Wisconsin. If the dealer preparation charges are \$240 and the sales tax rate in Wisconsin is 5%, what is the amount of sales tax on the car, and what is the total purchase price?

CHECK YOUR ANSWERS WITH THE SOLUTIONS ON PAGE 684.

CALCULATING SELLING PRICE AND AMOUNT OF SALES TAX WHEN TOTAL PURCHASE PRICE IS KNOWN

18-3

From time to time, merchants and customers may want to know the actual selling price of an item when the total purchase price, including sales tax, is known.

STEPS TO CALCULATE SELLING PRICE AND AMOUNT OF SALES TAX

Step 1. Calculate the selling price of an item by dividing the total purchase price by 100% plus the sales tax rate.

$$\textbf{Selling price} = \frac{\textbf{Total purchase price}}{\textbf{100\% + Sales tax rate}}$$

Step 2. Determine the amount of sales tax by subtracting the selling price from the total purchase price.

$$\textbf{Sales tax = Total purchase price − Selling price}$$

CLASSROOM ACTIVITY
Invite a certified public accountant or a tax consultant to class to discuss current tax issues and career opportunities with the students.

EXAMPLE 3 CALCULATING SELLING PRICE AND SALES TAX

Elwood Smith bought a television set for a total purchase price of \$477. If his state has a 6% sales tax, what were the actual selling price of the TV and the amount of sales tax?

SOLUTION STRATEGY

Step 1.

$$\text{Selling price} = \frac{\text{Total purchase price}}{100\% + \text{Sales tax rate}}$$

$$\text{Selling price} = \frac{477}{100\% + 6\%} = \frac{477}{1.06} = \underline{\underline{\$450}}$$

Step 2.

$$\text{Sales tax} = \text{Total purchase price} - \text{Selling price}$$

$$\text{Sales tax} = 477 - 450 = \underline{\underline{\$27}}$$

TRY IT EXERCISE 3

At the end of a business day, the cash register at the Galaxy Gift Shop showed total sales, including sales tax, of \$3,520. If the state and local sales taxes amounted to $8\frac{1}{2}$%, what is the amount of Galaxy's actual sales? How much sales tax was collected that day?

CHECK YOUR ANSWERS WITH THE SOLUTIONS ON PAGE 684.

18-4 CALCULATING EXCISE TAX

Learning Tip

Don't tax the tax! The excise tax is *not included* in the selling price when computing the sales tax. Each tax should be calculated *separately* on the actual selling price.

As with the sales tax, an excise tax is usually expressed as a percentage of the purchase price. In certain cases, however, the excise tax may be expressed as a fixed amount per unit purchased, such as \$5 per passenger on a cruise ship, or \$.15 per gallon of gasoline.

When both sales tax and excise tax are imposed on merchandise at the retail level, the excise taxes are *not included* in the selling price when computing the sales tax. Each tax should be calculated independently on the actual selling price.

STEPS TO CALCULATE THE AMOUNT OF EXCISE TAX

Step 1. *When expressed as a percent:* Multiply the selling price of the item by the excise tax rate.

Excise tax = Selling price × Excise tax rate

When expressed as a fixed amount per unit: Multiply the number of units by the excise tax per unit.

Excise tax = Number of units × Excise tax per unit

Step 2. Calculate total purchase price by adding the selling price plus sales tax plus excise tax.

Total purchase price = Selling price + Sales tax + Excise tax

EXAMPLE 4 CALCULATING EXCISE TAX

The round-trip airfare from Miami to New York is \$379. If the federal excise tax on airline travel is 10% and the Florida state sales tax is 6%, what are the amounts of each tax and the total purchase price of the ticket?

SOLUTION STRATEGY

Step 1.

Sales tax = Selling price × Sales tax rate

Sales tax = 379 × .06 = \$22.74

Excise tax = Selling price × Excise tax rate

Excise tax = 379 × .10 = \$37.90

Step 2. Total purchase price = Selling price + Sales tax + Excise tax

Total purchase price = 379.00 + 22.74 + 37.90 = $439.64

TRY IT EXERCISE 4

A bow and arrow set at The Sports Authority in Cincinnati, Ohio, has a retail price of $129.95. The sales tax in Ohio is 5% and the federal excise tax on this type of sporting goods is 11%. What is the amount of each tax, and what is the total purchase price of the bow and arrow set?

CHECK YOUR ANSWERS WITH THE SOLUTIONS ON PAGE 684.

The government "takes its cut" is a good description of the **excise** or **tax** charged on various goods considered luxury items.

The word *excise* is from *excidere*, Latin for "to cut out." In essence, the government cuts out its share!

In 2006, the federal government collected $76.1 billion in excise tax.

Review Exercises

SECTION I

Use Exhibit 18-1 to determine the sales tax and calculate the total purchase price for the following items.

Item	Selling Price	Sales Tax	Total Purchase Price
1. flashlight	$8.95	$.59	$9.54
2. candy	.79	.06	.85
3. notebook	4.88	.32	5.20
4. calculator	18.25	1.19	19.44

Calculate the missing information for the following purchases.

Item	Selling Price	Sales Tax Rate	Sales Tax	Excise Tax Rate	Excise Tax	Total Purchase Price
5. computer	$1,440.00	7%	$100.80	1.1%	$15.84	$1,556.64
6. sofa	$750.00	5	37.50	0	0	787.50
7. fishing rod	$219.95	$4\frac{1}{2}$	9.90	10	22.00	251.85
8. tire	$109.99	6	6.60	5	5.50	122.09
9. automobile	17,847.98	$5\frac{1}{4}$	937.02	0	0	$18,785.00
10. book	14.00	8	1.12	0	0	$15.12

11. Barbara Roberts purchased a refrigerator at Sears for $899.90. The delivery charge was $20 and the ice maker hookup amounted to $55. The state sales tax is $6\frac{1}{2}$% and the city tax is 1.3%.

    a. What is the total amount of sales tax on the refrigerator?

    Total sales tax = 899.90(.065 + .013) = $70.19

    b. What is the total purchase price?

    Total purchase price = 899.90 + 70.19 + 20 + 55 = $1,045.09

CLASSROOM ACTIVITY

As a review of Section I, have students work Review Exercises 5–10 in groups. Next, have the groups compare answers with another group and resolve any differences.

12. Neil Tanner purchased supplies at Office Depot for a total purchase price of $46.71. The state has a 4% sales tax.

    a. What was the selling price of the supplies?

    $$\text{Selling price} = \frac{46.71}{1.04} = \$44.91$$

    b. What was the amount of sales tax?

    Sales tax = 46.71 − 44.91 = $1.80

13. Last month, The Sweet Tooth Candy Shops had total sales, including sales tax, of $57,889. The stores are located in a state that has a sales tax of $5\frac{1}{2}\%$. As the accountant for The Sweet Tooth, calculate:

   a. The amount of sales revenue for the shops last month.

   $$\text{Sales revenue} = \frac{57{,}889}{1.055} = \underline{\underline{\$54{,}871.09}}$$

   b. The amount of sales taxes that must be sent to the state Department of Revenue.

   Sales tax = 57,889.00 − 54,871.09 = $3,017.91

14. Penny Lane purchased a diamond necklace for $17,400 at Abby Road Jewelers. The state sales tax is 8% and the federal excise tax on this type of jewelry is 10% on amounts over $10,000.

   a. What is the amount of the sales tax?

   Sales tax = 17,400 × .08 = $1,392

   b. What is the amount of the federal excise tax?

   Excise tax = .10(17,400 − 10,000) = $740

   c. What is the total purchase price of the necklace?

   Total purchase price = 17,400 + 1,392 + 740 = $19,532

© Gail Burton/Associated Press

In 2007, the per gallon excise tax on aviation fuel was $.219; aviation gasoline was $.194; and aviation fuel for use in commercial aviation (other than foreign trade) was $.044.

15. The federal excise tax on commercial aviation fuel is 4.4 cents per gallon. If Universal Airlines used a total of 6,540,000 gallons of fuel last month, how much excise tax was paid?

   Excise tax = 6,540,000 × .044 = $287,760

BUSINESS DECISION SPLITTING THE TAX

16. You are the owner of Enchantress, a chain of women's clothing boutiques. Your state has a sales tax of 6% and your city has an additional sales tax of 1.5%. Each quarter you are responsible for making these tax deposits to the city and state. Last quarter your stores had total revenue, including sales tax, of $376,250.

   a. How much of this revenue was sales and how much was sales tax?

   $$\text{Sales} = \frac{376{,}250}{1.075} = \underline{\underline{\$350{,}000}}$$

   Sales tax = 376,250 − 350,000 = $26,250

   b. How much tax should be sent to the city?

   $$\text{City tax} = \frac{1.5\%}{7.5\%} \times 26{,}250 = \underline{\underline{\$5{,}250}}$$

   c. How much tax should be sent to the state?

   $$\text{Sales tax} = \frac{6\%}{7.5\%} \times 26{,}250 = \underline{\underline{\$21{,}000}}$$

PROPERTY TAX

SECTION II

Most states have laws that provide for the annual assessment and collection of ad valorem taxes on real and personal property. **Ad valorem tax** means a tax based upon the assessed value of property. The term **property tax** is used interchangeably with the term ad valorem tax. Property taxes are assessed and collected at the county level as the primary source of revenue for counties, municipalities, school districts, and special taxing districts.

ad valorem or property tax A tax based on the assessed value of property, generally collected at the city or county level as the primary source of revenue for counties, municipalities, school districts, and special taxing districts.

Real estate, or **real property** is defined as land, buildings, and all other permanent improvements situated thereon. Real estate is broadly classified based on land use and includes the following:

real estate, or real property Land, buildings, and all other permanent improvements situated thereon.

- Single-family and multifamily residential, condominiums, townhouses, and mobile homes
- Vacant residential and unimproved acreage
- Commercial and industrial land and improvements
- Agriculture

Personal property is divided into two categories for ad valorem tax purposes:

personal property For ad valorem tax purposes, divided into tangible personal property such as business equipment, fixtures, and supplies and household goods such as clothing, furniture, and appliances.

- Tangible personal property—such as business fixtures, supplies, and equipment and machinery for shop, plant, and farm.
- Household goods (exempt from property tax in most states)—apparel, furniture, appliances, and other items usually found in the home.

The value of property for tax purposes is known as the **assessed value**. In some states assessed value of the property is a specified percentage of the **fair market value**, while in other states it is fixed by law at 100%. Typical factors considered in determining the fair market value of a piece of property are location, size, cost, replacement value, condition, and income derived from its use.

The assessed value is determined each year by the **tax assessor** or **property appraiser**. Most states allow specific discounts for early payment of the tax and have serious penalties for delinquency. The Department of Revenue in each state has the responsibility of insuring that all property is assessed and taxes are collected in accordance with the law.

assessed value The value of property for tax purposes, generally a percentage of the fair market value.

fair market value The value of property based on location, size, cost, replacement value, condition, and income derived from its use.

tax assessor, or property appraiser The city or county official designated to determine assessed values of property.

CALCULATING THE AMOUNT OF PROPERTY TAX

18-2

On the basis of the fair market value, less all applicable exemptions, the property tax due is computed by applying the tax rates established by the taxing authorities within that area to the assessed value of the property.

Property tax = Assessed value of property × Tax rate

Property tax rates may be expressed in the following ways:

- Decimal or percent of assessed value—for example, .035 or 3.5%
- Per $100 of assessed value—for example, $3.50 per $100
- Per $1,000 of assessed value—for example, $35.00 per $1,000
- Mills (one one-thousandth of a dollar)—for example, 35 mills

Let's look at the steps to calculate the property tax due when the same tax is expressed in each of the four different ways on a house with an assessed value of $250,000.

In the Business World

Property taxes vary greatly from area to area. Among the highest are: Bridgeport, Connecticut; Des Moines, Iowa; Providence, Rhode Island; Newark, New Jersey; and Manchester, New Hampshire.

Among the lowest are: Honolulu, Hawaii; Denver, Colorado; Birmingham, Alabama; Cheyenne, Wyoming; and New York, New York.

STEPS TO CALCULATE PROPERTY TAX WHEN THE TAX IS EXPRESSED AS A PERCENT

Step 1. Convert the tax rate percent to a decimal by moving the decimal point 2 places to the left.

Step 2. Multiply the assessed value by the tax rate as a decimal.

$$\textbf{Property tax} = \textbf{Assessed value} \times \textbf{Tax rate}$$

EXAMPLE 5 CALCULATING PROPERTY TAX USING PERCENT

Calculate the tax due on a house with an assessed value of $250,000. The tax rate is 7.88% of the assessed value.

SOLUTION STRATEGY

Step 1. Convert tax percent to decimal form: 7.88% = .0788.

Step 2.

Property tax = Assessed value × Tax rate

Property tax = 250,000 × .0788 = $19,700

TRY IT EXERCISE 5

Teaching Transparency 18-3

Calculate the tax due on a condominium with an assessed value of $160,000. The property tax rate is 6.3%.

CHECK YOUR ANSWER WITH THE SOLUTION ON PAGE 684.

© PhotoLink/Photodisc/Getty Images

Property taxes are the primary source of income for most school districts.

STEPS TO CALCULATE PROPERTY TAX WHEN THE TAX IS EXPRESSED PER $100 OF ASSESSED VALUE

Step 1. Divide the assessed value by $100 to determine the number of $100 the assessed value contains.

$$\textbf{Number of \$100} = \frac{\textbf{Assessed value}}{\textbf{100}}$$

Step 2. Calculate the property tax by multiplying the number of $100 by the tax per $100.

$$\textbf{Property tax} = \textbf{Number of \$100} \times \textbf{Tax per \$100}$$

EXAMPLE 6 CALCULATING PROPERTY TAX USING TAX PER $100 OF ASSESSED VALUE

Calculate the tax due on a house with an assessed value of $250,000. The tax rate is $7.88 per $100 of assessed value.

SOLUTION STRATEGY

Step 1. $\text{Number of \$100} = \dfrac{\text{Assessed value}}{100} = \dfrac{250{,}000}{100} = 2{,}500$

Step 2. $\text{Property tax} = \text{Number of \$100} \times \text{Tax per \$100}$

$\text{Property tax} = 2{,}500 \times 7.88 = \underline{\underline{\$19{,}700}}$

TRY IT EXERCISE 6

Calculate the tax due on a three-acre parcel of land with an assessed value of $50,800. The property tax rate is $3.60 per $100 of assessed value.

CHECK YOUR ANSWER WITH THE SOLUTION ON PAGE 685.

CLASSROOM ACTIVITY
Have students research and report to the class on the property tax rates and exemption rules in your area. How do they compare with other cities in your state?

18-3

STEPS TO CALCULATE PROPERTY TAX WHEN THE TAX IS EXPRESSED PER $1,000 OF ASSESSED VALUE

Step 1. Divide the assessed value by $1,000 to determine the number of $1,000 the assessed value contains.

$$\textbf{Number of \$1,000} = \frac{\textbf{Assessed value}}{\textbf{1,000}}$$

Step 2. Calculate the tax due by multiplying the number of $1,000 by the tax per $1,000.

$$\textbf{Property tax} = \textbf{Number of \$1,000} \times \textbf{Tax per \$1,000}$$

EXAMPLE 7 CALCULATING PROPERTY TAX USING TAX PER $1,000 OF ASSESSED VALUE

Calculate the tax due on a house with an assessed value of $250,000. The tax rate is $78.80 per $1,000 of assessed value.

SOLUTION STRATEGY

Step 1. $\text{Number of \$1,000} = \dfrac{\text{Assessed value}}{1{,}000} = \dfrac{250{,}000}{1{,}000} = 250$

Step 2. $\text{Property tax} = \text{Number of \$1,000} \times \text{Tax per \$1,000}$

$\text{Property tax} = 250 \times 78.80 = \underline{\underline{\$19{,}700}}$

 18-4

CLASSROOM ACTIVITY

In groups of twos, have students work:

- Try It Exercises 5 and 6. Use Teaching Transparency 18-3 to illustrate the solution.
- Try It Exercises 7 and 8. Use Teaching Transparency 18-4 to illustrate the solution.

TRY IT EXERCISE 7

Calculate the tax due on a warehouse with an assessed value of $325,400. The property tax rate is $88.16 per $1,000 of assessed value.

CHECK YOUR ANSWER WITH THE SOLUTION ON PAGE 685.

STEPS TO CALCULATE PROPERTY TAX WHEN THE TAX IS EXPRESSED IN MILLS

Step 1. Since mills means $\frac{1}{1000}$ (.001) of a dollar, convert tax rate in mills to tax rate in decimal form by multiplying mills times .001.

Tax rate in decimal form = Tax rate in mills × .001

Step 2. Calculate the tax due by multiplying the assessed value by the tax rate in decimal form.

Property tax = Assessed value × Tax rate in decimal form

EXAMPLE 8 CALCULATING PROPERTY TAX USING MILLS

Calculate the tax due on a house with an assessed value of $250,000. The tax rate is 78.8 mills.

SOLUTION STRATEGY

Step 1.

Tax rate in decimal form = Tax rate in mills × .001

Tax rate in decimal form = 78.8 × .001 = .0788

Step 2.

Property tax = Assessed value × Tax rate in decimal form

Property tax = 250,000 × .0788 = $19,700

TRY IT EXERCISE 8

 18-4

Calculate the tax due on a farm with an assessed value of $85,300. The property tax rate is 54.1 mills.

CHECK YOUR ANSWER WITH THE SOLUTION ON PAGE 685.

18-6 CALCULATING TAX RATE NECESSARY IN A COMMUNITY TO MEET BUDGETARY DEMANDS

Each year local taxing units such as counties and cities must estimate the amount of tax dollars required to pay for all governmental services provided. Typical examples include public schools, law enforcement, fire protection, hospitals, public parks and recreation, roads and highways, sanitation services, and many others. The tax rate necessary to meet these budgetary demands is determined by two factors: (1) the total taxes required, and (2) the total assessed value of the property in the taxing unit. The tax rate is computed by the following formula:

$$\textbf{Tax rate per dollar (decimal form)} = \frac{\textbf{Total taxes required}}{\textbf{Total assessed property value}}$$

As before, the tax rate may be expressed as a percent, per \$100 of assessed value, per \$1,000 of assessed value, or in mills.

CLASSROOM ACTIVITY

Remind students that each year cities and counties must estimate the amount of tax dollars required to pay for all governmental services.

- Have students research and report to the class on your taxing district's budget and the total assessed value of the property.
- Next have them calculate the tax rate using the tax rate per dollar formula. Do their answers agree with the stated property tax rate for your area? Discuss.

STEPS TO COMPUTE TAX RATE

Step 1. Calculate tax rate per dollar of assessed property value by dividing the total taxes required by the total assessed property value.

$$\textbf{Tax rate per dollar (decimal form)} = \frac{\textbf{Total taxes required}}{\textbf{Total assessed property value}}$$

Round your answer to ten-thousandths (4 decimal places). In most states, the rounding is always up, even if the next digit is less than 5.

Step 2. *To convert tax rate per dollar to:*

- **percent**, move the decimal point 2 places to the right and add a percent sign;
- **tax rate per \$100**, multiply by 100;
- **tax rate per \$1,000**, multiply by 1,000;
- **mills**, divide by .001.

Learning Tip

When calculating tax rate per dollar, remember to round your answer to ten-thousandths (4 decimal places) and always round up, even if the next digit is less than 5.

EXAMPLE 9 COMPUTING TAX RATE

The budget planners for the town of Silvertip have determined that \$5,700,000 will be needed to provide all government services for next year. If the total assessed property value in Silvertip is \$68,000,000, what tax rate is required to meet the budgetary demands? Express your answer in each of the four ways.

SOLUTION STRATEGY

Step 1.

$$\text{Tax rate per dollar} = \frac{\text{Total tax required}}{\text{Total assessed property value}}$$

$$= \frac{5{,}700{,}000}{68{,}000{,}000} = .0838235 = \$.0839$$

Step 2. a. To express tax rate as a percent, move the decimal point 2 places to the right, and add a percent sign. Tax rate = 8.39%

b. Tax rate expressed per \$100 = .0839 × 100 = \$8.39

c. Tax rate expressed per \$1,000 = .0839 × 1,000 = \$83.90

d. $\text{Tax rate expressed in mills} = \frac{.0839}{.001} = 83.9 \text{ mills}$

TRY IT EXERCISE 9

The budget planners for Cherry Hill have determined that $3,435,000 will be needed to provide governmental services for next year. The total assessed property value in Cherry Hill is $71,800,000. As the tax assessor, you have been asked by the city council to determine what tax rate will need to be imposed to meet these budgetary demands. Express your answer in each of the four ways.

CHECK YOUR ANSWERS WITH THE SOLUTIONS ON PAGE 685.

18 SECTION II Review Exercises

Calculate the assessed value and the property tax due on the following properties.

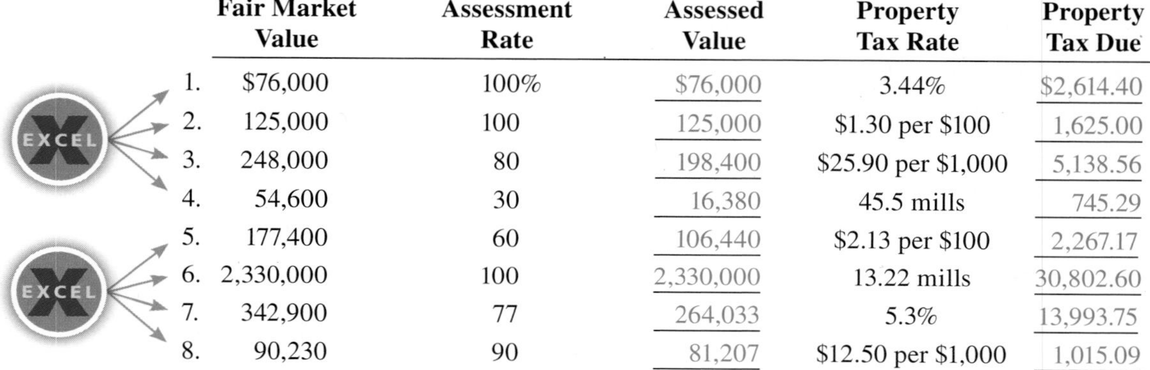

	Fair Market Value	Assessment Rate	Assessed Value	Property Tax Rate	Property Tax Due
1.	$76,000	100%	$76,000	3.44%	$2,614.40
2.	125,000	100	125,000	$1.30 per $100	1,625.00
3.	248,000	80	198,400	$25.90 per $1,000	5,138.56
4.	54,600	30	16,380	45.5 mills	745.29
5.	177,400	60	106,440	$2.13 per $100	2,267.17
6.	2,330,000	100	2,330,000	13.22 mills	30,802.60
7.	342,900	77	264,033	5.3%	13,993.75
8.	90,230	90	81,207	$12.50 per $1,000	1,015.09

Calculate the property tax rate required to meet the budgetary demands of the following communities.

Community	Total Assessed Property Valuation	Total Taxes Required	Property Tax Rate: Percent	Per $100	Per $1,000	Mills
9. Scottsdale	$657,000,000	$32,300,000	4.92%	$4.92	$49.20	49.2
10. Lexington	338,000,000	19,900,000	5.89%	5.89	58.90	58.9
11. Golden Isles	57,000,000	2,100,000	3.68%	3.68	36.80	36.8
12. Bayside	880,000,000	13,600,000	1.55%	1.55	15.50	15.5

13. Maggie Martin purchased a condominium with a market value of $125,000 in Indian Harbor Beach. The assessment rate in that county is 70% and the tax rate is 19.44 mills.

a. What is the assessed value of the condo?

Assessed value = 125,000 × .70 = $87,500

b. What is the amount of property tax?

Property tax = 19.44 × .001 × 87,500 = $1,701

14. As the tax assessor for Caribou County you have been informed that due to budgetary demands a tax increase will be necessary next year. The total market value of the property in the county is $600,000,000. Currently the assessment rate is 45% and the tax rate is 30 mills. The county commission increases the assessment rate to 55% and the tax rate to 35 mills.

    a. How much property tax was collected under the old rates?

    Old assessed value = 600,000,000 × .45 = $270,000,000
    Total taxes at old rate = 30 mills × .001 = .03
    .03 × 270,000,000 = $8,100,000

    b. How much more tax revenue will be collected under the new rates?

    Total taxes at new rate = 600,000,000 × .55 = $330,000,000
    35 mills × .001 = .035
    .035 × 330,000,000 = $11,550,000
    11,550,000 − 8,100,000
    $3,450,000 More

'Relax. It's only money... and taxpayer's money at that."

© Joseph Farris/www.CartoonStock.com

BUSINESS DECISION EARLY PAYMENT, LATE PAYMENT

15. You own an apartment with an assessed value of $185,400. The tax rate is $2.20 per $100 of assessed value.

    a. What is the amount of property tax?

    $$\text{Property tax} = \frac{185{,}400}{100} \times 2.20 = \$4{,}078.80$$

    b. If the state offers a 4% discount for early payment, how much would the tax bill amount to if you paid early?

    Discounted rate = 4,078.80(100% − 4%)
    4,078.80 × 96% = $3,915.65

    c. If the state charges a mandatory $3\frac{1}{2}$% penalty for late payments, how much would the tax bill amount to if you paid late?

    $$\text{Tax} + \text{Late fee} = 4{,}078.80\left(100\% + 3\frac{1}{2}\%\right) = \$4{,}221.56$$

INCOME TAX

SECTION III 18

"The Congress shall have power to lay and collect taxes on incomes, from whatever source derived. . . ." These are the words of the Sixteenth Amendment to the Constitution of the United States. Passed by Congress in 1909 and ratified in 1913, this amendment paved the way for the evolution of the federal income tax system as we know it today. Income taxes, both personal and corporate, compose the largest source of receipts for our federal government. In 2006, individuals paid over $2.5 trillion in federal income taxes and corporations paid more than $380 billion. In addition to the federal income tax, many state governments have also imposed income taxes on their citizens to finance government activities.

income tax A pay-as-you-go tax based on the amount of income of an individual or corporation.

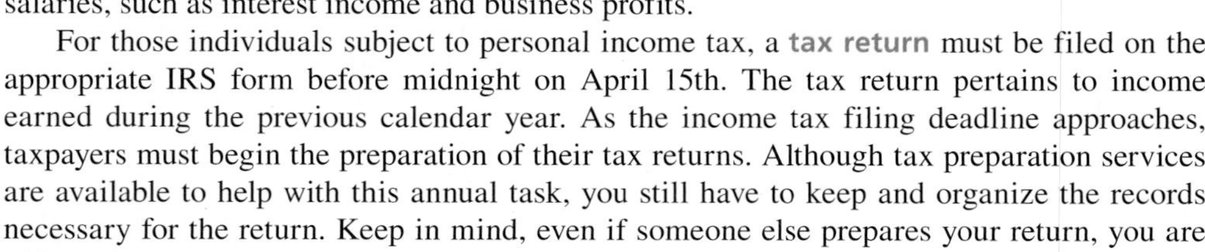

Income tax is a pay-as-you-go tax. The tax is paid as you earn or receive income throughout the year. As we learned in Chapter 9, payment is accomplished through income tax withholdings made by employers on wages and salaries paid to employees, and quarterly estimated tax payments made by people earning substantial income other than wages and salaries, such as interest income and business profits.

tax return The official Internal Revenue Service forms used to report and pay income tax for income earned during the previous calendar year.

For those individuals subject to personal income tax, a **tax return** must be filed on the appropriate IRS form before midnight on April 15th. The tax return pertains to income earned during the previous calendar year. As the income tax filing deadline approaches, taxpayers must begin the preparation of their tax returns. Although tax preparation services are available to help with this annual task, you still have to keep and organize the records necessary for the return. Keep in mind, even if someone else prepares your return, you are ultimately responsible for its accuracy!

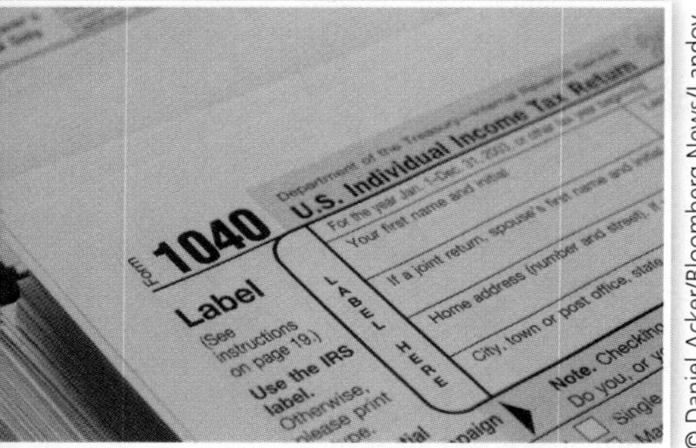

© Daniel Acker/Bloomberg News/Landov

Federal income tax forms must be filed before midnight on April 15th.

Exhibit 18-5 on pages 672 and 673, Form 1040, U.S. Individual Income Tax Return, is the most widely used form for individuals filing tax returns. It is known as the "long form." Based on tax filing options, individuals may qualify to use one of the "short forms," 1040A or 1040EZ. Although the tax rules and forms change almost every year, the method for calculating the amount of income tax due remains generally the same. For the purpose of this chapter, we shall divide the task into two components: (a) calculating the taxable income; and (b) determining the amount of income tax due. The figures and tables used in this section reflect IRS requirements for tax year 2006. For the most recent tax information and tables, consult the instruction booklet that accompanies this year's income tax forms.

CALCULATING TAXABLE INCOME FOR INDIVIDUALS

taxable income The amount of income that tax rates are applied to in order to calculate the amount of tax owed for the year.

Taxable income is the amount of income that tax rates are applied to in order to calculate the amount of tax owed for the year. Exhibit 18-2 is a schematic diagram of the procedure used to calculate taxable income. Look it over carefully, and then use the following steps to calculate taxable income.

STEPS TO CALCULATE TAXABLE INCOME FOR INDIVIDUALS

Step 1. Determine **total income** by adding all sources of taxable income.

Step 2. Calculate **adjusted gross income** by subtracting the sum of all adjustments to income from total income.

Step 3. Subtract the sum of the **itemized deductions** or the **standard deduction** (whichever is larger) from the adjusted gross income.

2006 Standard Deductions

Single	$5,150
Married, filing jointly or Qualifying widow(er)	$10,300
Married, filing separately	$5,150
Head of household	$7,550
65 or older, and/or blind	See IRS instructions to find standard deduction

Step 4. *If adjusted gross income is $112,875 or less:*

Multiply $3,300 by the total number of exemptions claimed and subtract from the amount in Step 3. The result is **taxable income**.

If adjusted gross income is over $112,875:

See IRS instructions to find exemption amounts.

The current standard deductions, tax tables and forms can be found in the IRS publication: *1040 Forms and Instructions.*

This and other tax forms and publications can be obtained by calling the IRS at 1-800-TAX FORM, or from their Web site, www.irs.gov.

For help with doing your taxes, the taxpayer help lines, 1-800-829-1040, are open 24 hours a day, 7 days a week. For recorded tax information and to check on a tax refund, call TeleTax at 1-800-829-4477.

Exhibit 18-2
Procedure to Calculate Taxable Income

Income	Wages, salaries, bonuses, commissions, tips, gratuities Interest and dividend income Rents, royalties, partnerships, S corporations, trusts Pensions and annuities Business income (or loss) Capital gain (or loss) from the sale or exchange of property Farm income Unemployment compensation, social security benefits Contest prizes, gambling winnings
	Less
Adjustments to Income	Alimony payments Retirement fund payments—IRA, Keogh, 401K One-half of self-employment tax Self-employment health insurance Penalty on early withdrawal of savings
	Equals
Adjusted Gross Income	Used in determining limits on certain itemized deductions, such as medical, dental, and employee expenses
	Less
Deductions: Standard or Itemized	Medical and dental expenses (above 7.5% of adjusted gross income) Taxes paid: state and local income taxes; real estate taxes Home mortgage interest and points Charitable contributions Casualty and theft losses Moving expenses Unreimbursed employee expenses—union dues, job travel, education (above 2.0% of adjusted gross income)
and	
Exemptions	Personal exemptions Dependents' exemptions
	Equals
Taxable Income	Income on which the amount of income tax due is based. Used for Tax Table look-up or Tax Computation Worksheet

Teaching Transparency 18-5

In the Business World

There are three basic rules to follow when doing your taxes to avoid arousing IRS suspicion.

1. *Don't Be Greedy*—The IRS uses 35% of your income as the point at which they would like to "take a look" at what you have deducted. Be sure you always **document** your write-offs as fully as possible.
2. *Don't Be Sloppy*—Tax returns that are **incomplete** or have a number of **math errors** will "raise some questions."
3. *Don't "Forget" Income*—The IRS receives **income information** from **all** employers, as well as **all** banks, brokerage houses and other financial institutions that pay interest, dividends or distribute profits of any kind.

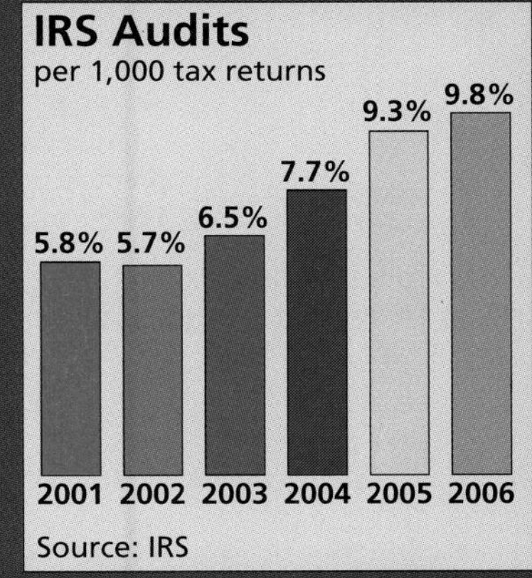

EXAMPLE 10 CALCULATING TAXABLE INCOME

Doug and Beth Nelson are married and file a joint tax return. Doug is a manager and earned $43,500 last year. Beth worked as a secretary and earned $24,660. In addition, they earned $540 interest on their savings account. They each contributed $2,500 to a retirement account, and Doug paid alimony of $4,700 to his first wife. Itemized deductions were as follows: $2,340 in real estate taxes, $4,590 in mortgage interest, $325 in charitable contributions, and $120 in unreimbursed employee expenses (above 2% of adjusted gross income). The Nelsons claim three exemptions: one each for themselves and one for their dependent son Michael. From this information, calculate the Nelsons' taxable income.

SOLUTION STRATEGY

Step 1. Total Income:

$43,500	Doug's income
+ 24,660	Beth's income
+ 540	Interest from savings account
$68,700	Total income

Step 2. Adjusted Gross Income:

$68,700	Total income
− 9,700	Deductions from total income
$59,000	Adjusted gross income

$2,500	Doug's retirement payments
+ 2,500	Beth's retirement payments
+ 4,700	Alimony payments
$9,700	Deductions from total income

Step 3. Deductions:

$2,340	Real estate taxes
+ 4,590	Mortgage interest
+ 325	Charitable contributions
+ 120	Unreimbursed employee expenses (above 2% of adjusted gross income)
$7,375	Total itemized deductions

Since the total itemized deductions, $7,375, is less than the standard deduction for married filing jointly ($10,300) we shall use the standard deduction amount for Doug and Beth's tax return.

Step 4. Exemptions:

Since the Nelsons' adjusted gross income is less than $112,875, multiply $3,300 by their number of exemptions, three:

$59,000	Adjusted gross income
− 10,300	Standard deduction
− 9,900	$3,300 × 3 exemptions
$38,800	Taxable income

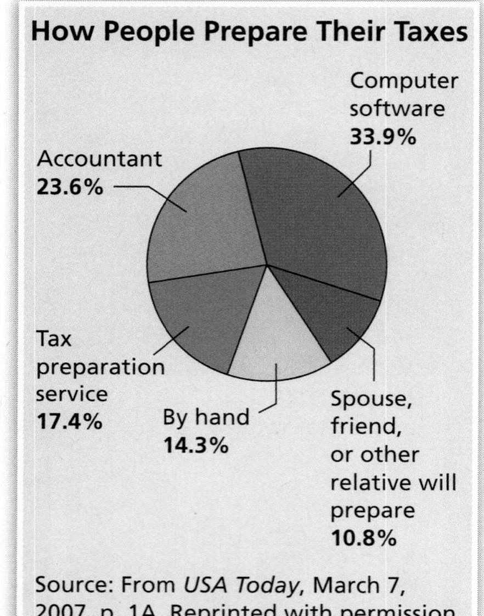

Source: From *USA Today*, March 7, 2007, p. 1A. Reprinted with permission.

TRY IT EXERCISE 10

Nick Bontempo is single, claiming two exemptions. He is a welder, earning $35,000 in wages per year. Last year, he also earned $1,200 in cash dividends from his investments portfolio. Nick contributed $1,500 to his individual retirement account and gained $5,000 from the sale of 100 shares of Consolidated Widget stock. His itemized deductions amounted to medical expenses of $1,000 in excess of IRS exclusions; $1,945 in real estate taxes; $2,500 in mortgage interest; and $300 in charitable contributions. From this information, calculate Nick's taxable income.

CHECK YOUR ANSWER WITH THE SOLUTION ON PAGE 685.

USING THE TAX TABLE TO DETERMINE TAX LIABILITY

If taxable income is less than $100,000, the Tax Table must be used to figure the tax liability. When the taxable income is $100,000 or more, the Tax Rate Schedule for the appropriate filing status must be used. Exhibit 18-3 illustrates a portion of the 2006 **Tax Table** and Exhibit 18-4 shows the 2006 **Tax Computation Worksheet**. The most current version of these may be found in *Instructions for Form 1040*, published by the IRS.

Tax Table The IRS chart used to find the amount of income tax due for individuals with taxable income of under $100,000.

Tax Computation Worksheet The IRS chart used to calculate the amount of income tax due for individuals with taxable income of $100,000 or more.

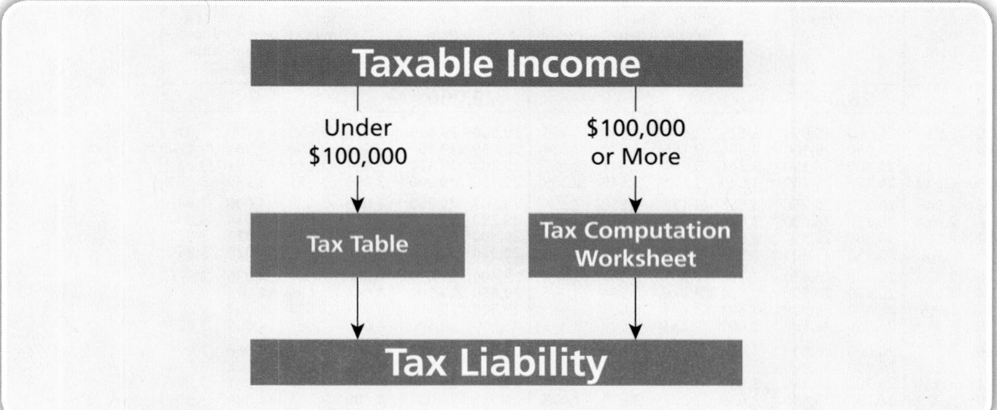

18-6

STEPS TO DETERMINE TAX LIABILITY USING THE TAX TABLE, TAXABLE INCOME UNDER $100,000

Step 1. Read down the "If line 43 (taxable income) is—" columns to find the line that includes the amount of taxable income. *Note:* Line 43 refers to the line on the 1040 tax form where taxable income is listed.

Step 2. Find the tax liability by scanning across to the "And you are—" column containing the appropriate filing status.

Keep in mind that if your marital or dependent status changes, up to December 31, that change counts for the whole year.

Also remember that all W-2 forms must be sent along with your tax returns when filing income tax.

EXAMPLE 11 DETERMINING TAX LIABILITY

Dan Siegel is single with taxable income of $37,440. Use the Tax Table, Exhibit 18-3, to calculate his tax liability.

SOLUTION STRATEGY

Step 1. From the Tax Table, Exhibit 18-3, we read down the "If line 43 (taxable income) is—" column to find Dan's taxable income, $37,440, listed between 37,400 and 37,450.

Step 2. Scan across the "And you are—Single" column to locate Dan's tax liability, $5,914.

TRY IT EXERCISE 11

Tricia Wark and her husband, Barry, had taxable income last year amounting to $64,425. The Warks' filing status is married, filing jointly. Using the Tax Table, determine their tax liability.

CHECK YOUR ANSWER WITH THE SOLUTION ON PAGE 685.

Exhibit 18-3
Tax Table

18-7a

2006 Tax Table — *Continued*

If line 43 (taxable income) is —		And you are —			
At least	But less than	Single	Married filing jointly *	Married filing separately	Head of a household
		Your tax is —			
23,000					
23,000	23,050	3,076	2,699	3,076	2,916
23,050	23,100	3,084	2,706	3,084	2,924
23,100	23,150	3,091	2,714	3,091	2,931
23,150	23,200	3,099	2,721	3,099	2,939
23,200	23,250	3,106	2,729	3,106	2,946
23,250	23,300	3,114	2,736	3,114	2,954
23,300	23,350	3,121	2,744	3,121	2,961
23,350	23,400	3,129	2,751	3,129	2,969
23,400	23,450	3,136	2,759	3,136	2,976
23,450	23,500	3,144	2,766	3,144	2,984
23,500	23,550	3,151	2,774	3,151	2,991
23,550	23,600	3,159	2,781	3,159	2,999
23,600	23,650	3,166	2,789	3,166	3,006
23,650	23,700	3,174	2,796	3,174	3,014
23,700	23,750	3,181	2,804	3,181	3,021
23,750	23,800	3,189	2,811	3,189	3,029
23,800	23,850	3,196	2,819	3,196	3,036
23,850	23,900	3,204	2,826	3,204	3,044
23,900	23,950	3,211	2,834	3,211	3,051
23,950	24,000	3,219	2,841	3,219	3,059
24,000					
24,000	24,050	3,226	2,849	3,226	3,066
24,050	24,100	3,234	2,856	3,234	3,047
24,100	24,150	3,241	2,864	3,241	3,081
24,150	24,200	3,249	2,871	3,249	3,089
24,200	24,250	3,256	2,879	3,256	3,096
24,250	24,300	3,264	2,886	3,264	3,104
24,300	24,350	3,271	2,894	3,271	3,111
24,350	24,400	3,279	2,901	3,279	3,119
24,400	24,450	3,286	2,909	3,286	3,126
24,450	24,500	3,294	2,916	3,294	3,134
24,500	24,550	3,301	2,924	3,301	3,141
24,550	24,600	3,309	2,931	3,309	3,149
24,600	24,650	3,316	2,939	3,316	3,156
24,650	24,700	3,324	2,946	3,324	3,164
24,700	24,750	3,331	2,954	3,331	3,171
24,750	24,800	3,339	2,961	3,339	3,179
24,800	24,850	3,346	2,969	3,346	3,186
24,850	24,900	3,354	2,976	3,354	3,194
24,900	24,950	3,361	2,984	3,361	3,201
24,950	25,000	3,369	2,991	3,369	3,209
25,000					
25,000	25,050	3,376	2,999	3,376	3,216
25,050	25,100	3,384	3,006	3,384	3,224
25,100	25,150	3,391	3,014	3,391	3,231
25,150	25,200	3,399	3,021	3,399	3,239
25,200	25,250	3,406	3,029	3,406	3,246
25,250	25,300	3,414	3,036	3,414	3,254
25,300	25,350	3,421	3,044	3,421	3,261
25,350	25,400	3,429	3,051	3,429	3,269
25,400	25,450	3,436	3,059	3,436	3,276
25,450	25,500	3,444	3,066	3,444	3,284
25,500	25,550	3,451	3,074	3,451	3,291
25,550	25,600	3,459	3,081	3,459	3,299
25,600	25,650	3,466	3,089	3,466	3,306
25,650	25,700	3,474	3,096	3,474	3,314
25,700	25,750	3,481	3,104	3,481	3,321
25,750	25,800	3,489	3,111	3,489	3,329
25,800	25,850	3,496	3,119	3,496	3,336
25,850	25,900	3,504	3,126	3,504	3,344
25,900	25,950	3,511	3,134	3,511	3,351
25,950	26,000	3,519	3,141	3,519	3,359
26,000					
26,000	26,050	3,526	3,149	3,526	3,366
26,050	26,100	3,534	3,156	3,534	3,374
26,100	26,150	3,541	3,164	3,541	3,381
26,150	26,200	3,549	3,171	3,549	3,389
26,200	26,250	3,556	3,179	3,556	3,396
26,250	26,300	3,564	3,186	3,564	3,404
26,300	26,350	3,571	3,194	3,571	3,411
26,350	26,400	3,579	3,201	3,579	3,419
26,400	26,450	3,586	3,209	3,586	3,426
26,450	26,500	3,594	3,216	3,594	3,434
26,500	26,550	3,601	3,224	3,601	3,441
26,550	26,600	3,609	3,231	3,609	3,449
26,600	26,650	3,616	3,239	3,616	3,456
26,650	26,700	3,624	3,246	3,624	3,464
26,700	26,750	3,631	3,254	3,631	3,471
26,750	26,800	3,639	3,261	3,639	3,479
26,800	26,850	3,646	3,269	3,646	3,486
26,850	26,900	3,654	3,276	3,654	3,494
26,900	26,950	3,661	3,284	3,661	3,501
26,950	27,000	3,669	3,291	3,669	3,509
27,000					
27,000	27,050	3,676	3,299	3,676	3,516
27,050	27,100	3,684	3,306	3,684	3,524
27,100	27,150	3,691	3,314	3,691	3,531
27,150	27,200	3,699	3,321	3,699	3,539
27,200	27,250	3,706	3,329	3,706	3,546
27,250	27,300	3,714	3,336	3,714	3,554
27,300	27,350	3,721	3,344	3,721	3,561
27,350	27,400	3,729	3,351	3,729	3,569
27,400	27,450	3,736	3,359	3,736	3,576
27,450	27,500	3,744	3,366	3,744	3,584
27,500	27,550	3,751	3,374	3,751	3,591
27,550	27,600	3,759	3,381	3,759	3,599
27,600	27,650	3,766	3,389	3,766	3,606
27,650	27,700	3,774	3,396	3,774	3,614
27,700	27,750	3,781	3,404	3,781	3,621
27,750	27,800	3,789	3,411	3,789	3,629
27,800	27,850	3,796	3,419	3,796	3,636
27,850	27,900	3,804	3,426	3,804	3,644
27,900	27,950	3,811	3,434	3,811	3,651
27,950	28,000	3,819	3,441	3,819	3,659
28,000					
28,000	28,050	3,826	3,449	3,826	3,666
28,050	28,100	3,834	3,456	3,834	3,674
28,100	28,150	3,841	3,464	3,841	3,681
28,150	28,200	3,849	3,471	3,849	3,689
28,200	28,250	3,856	3,479	3,856	3,696
28,250	28,300	3,864	3,486	3,864	3,704
28,300	28,350	3,871	3,494	3,871	3,711
28,350	28,400	3,879	3,501	3,879	3,719
28,400	28,450	3,886	3,509	3,886	3,726
28,450	28,500	3,894	3,516	3,894	3,734
28,500	28,550	3,901	3,524	3,901	3,741
28,550	28,600	3,909	3,531	3,909	3,749
28,600	28,650	3,916	3,539	3,916	3,756
28,650	28,700	3,924	3,546	3,924	3,764
28,700	28,750	3,931	3,554	3,931	3,771
28,750	28,800	3,939	3,561	3,939	3,779
28,800	28,850	3,946	3,569	3,946	3,786
28,850	28,900	3,954	3,576	3,954	3,794
28,900	28,950	3.961	3,584	3,961	3,801
28,950	29,000	3,969	3,591	3,969	3,809
29,000					
29,000	29,050	3,976	3,599	3,976	3,816
29,050	29,100	3,984	3,606	3,984	3,824
29,100	29,150	3,991	3,614	3,991	3,831
29,150	29,200	3,999	3,621	3,999	3,839
29,200	29,250	4,006	3,629	4,006	3,846
29,250	29,300	4,014	3,636	4,014	3,854
29,300	29,350	4,021	3,644	4,021	3,861
29,350	29,400	4,029	3,651	4,029	3,869
29,400	29,450	4,036	3,659	4,036	3,876
29,450	29,500	4,044	3,666	4,044	3,884
29,500	29,550	4,051	3,674	4,051	3,891
29,550	29,600	4,059	3,681	4,059	3,899
29,600	29,650	4,066	3,689	4,066	3,906
29,650	29,700	4,074	3,696	4,074	3,914
29,700	29,750	4,081	3,704	4,081	3,921
29,750	29,800	4,089	3,711	4,089	3,929
29,800	29,850	4,096	3,719	4,096	3,936
29,850	29,900	4,104	3,726	4,104	3,944
29,900	29,950	4,111	3,734	4,111	3,951
29,950	30,000	4,119	3,741	4,119	3,959
30,000					
30,000	30,050	4,126	3,749	4,126	3,966
30,050	30,100	4,134	3,756	4,134	3,974
30,100	30,150	4,141	3,764	4,141	3,981
30,150	30,200	4,149	3,771	4,149	3,989
30,200	30,250	4,156	3,779	4,156	3,996
30,250	30,300	4,164	3,786	4,164	4,004
30,300	30,350	4,171	3,794	4,171	4,011
30,350	30,400	4,179	3,801	4,179	4,019
30,400	30,450	4,186	3,809	4,186	4,026
30,450	30,500	4,194	3,816	4,194	4,034
30,500	30,550	4,201	3,824	4,201	4,041
30,550	30,600	4,209	3,831	4,209	4,049
30,600	30,650	4,216	3,839	4,216	4,056
30,650	30,700	4,226	3,846	4,226	4,064
30,700	30,750	4,239	3,854	4,239	4,071
30,750	30,800	4,251	3,861	4,251	4,079
30,800	30,850	4,264	3,869	4,264	4,086
30,850	30,900	4,276	3,876	4,276	4,094
30,900	30,950	4,289	3,884	4,289	4,101
30,950	31,000	4,301	3,891	4,301	4,109
31,000					
31,000	31,050	4,314	3,899	4,314	4,116
31,050	31,100	4,326	3,906	4,326	4,124
31,100	31,150	4,339	3,914	4,339	4,131
31,150	31,200	4,351	3,921	4,351	4,139
31,200	31,250	4,364	3,929	4,364	4,146
31,250	31,300	4,376	3,936	4,376	4,154
31,300	31,350	4,389	3,944	4,389	4,161
31,350	31,400	4,401	3,951	4,401	4,169
31,400	31,450	4,414	3,959	4,414	4,176
31,450	31,500	4,426	3,966	4,426	4,184
31,500	31,550	4,439	3,974	4,439	4,191
31,550	31,600	4,451	3,981	4,451	4,199
31,600	31,650	4,464	3,989	4,464	4,206
31,650	31,700	4,476	3,996	4,476	4,214
31,700	31,750	4,489	4,004	4,489	4,221
31,750	31,800	4,501	4,011	4,501	4,229
31,800	31,850	4,514	4,019	4,514	4,236
31,850	31,900	4,526	4,026	4,526	4,244
31,900	31,950	4,539	4,034	4,539	4,251
31,950	32,000	4,551	4,041	4,551	4,259

* This column must also be used by a qualifying widow(er).

(Continued on next page)

Teaching Transparency 18-7b

Exhibit 18-3
Tax Table

2006 Tax Table— *Continued*

If line 43 (taxable income) is —		And you are —			
At least	But less than	Single	Married filing jointly *	Married filing sepa-rately	Head of a house-hold
		Your tax is —			
32,000					
32,000	32,050	4,564	4,049	4,564	4,266
32,050	32,100	4,576	4,056	4,576	4,274
32,100	32,150	4,589	4,064	4,589	4,281
32,150	32,200	4,601	4,071	4,601	4,289
32,200	32,250	4,614	4,079	4,614	4,296
32,250	32,300	4,626	4,086	4,626	4,304
32,300	32,350	4,639	4,094	4,639	4,311
32,350	32,400	4,651	4,101	4,651	4,319
32,400	32,450	4,664	4,109	4,664	4,326
32,450	32,500	4,676	4,116	4,676	4,334
32,500	32,550	4,689	4,124	4,689	4,341
32,550	32,600	4,701	4,131	4,701	4,349
32,600	32,650	4,714	4,139	4,714	4,356
32,650	32,700	4,726	4,146	4,726	4,364
32,700	32,750	4,739	4,154	4,739	4,371
32,750	32,800	4,751	4,161	4,751	4,379
32,800	32,850	4,764	4,169	4,764	4,386
32,850	32,900	4,776	4,176	4,776	4,394
32,900	32,950	4,789	4,184	4,789	4,401
32,950	33,000	4,801	4,191	4,801	4,409
33,000					
33,000	33,050	4,814	4,199	4,814	4,416
33,050	33,100	4,826	4,206	4,826	4,424
33,100	33,150	4,839	4,214	4,839	4,431
33,150	33,200	4,851	4,221	4,851	4,439
33,200	33,250	4,864	4,229	4,864	4,446
33,250	33,300	4,876	4,236	4,876	4,454
33,300	33,350	4,889	4,244	4,889	4,461
33,350	33,400	4,901	4,251	4,901	4,469
33,400	33,450	4,914	4,259	4,914	4,476
33,450	33,500	4,926	4,266	4,926	4,484
33,500	33,550	4,939	4,274	4,939	4,491
33,550	33,600	4,951	4,281	4,951	4,499
33,600	33,650	4,964	4,289	4,964	4,506
33,650	33,700	4,976	4,296	4,976	4,514
33,700	33,750	4,989	4,304	4,989	4,521
33,750	33,800	5,001	4,311	5,001	4,529
33,800	33,850	5,014	4,319	5,014	4,536
33,850	33,900	5,026	4,326	5,026	4,544
33,900	33,950	5,039	4,334	5,039	4,551
33,950	34,000	5,051	4,341	5,051	4,559
34,000					
34,000	34,050	5,064	4,349	5,064	4,566
34,050	34,100	5,076	4,356	5,076	4,574
34,100	34,150	5,089	4,364	5,089	4,581
34,150	34,200	5,101	4,371	5,101	4,589
34,200	34,250	5,114	4,379	5,114	4,596
34,250	34,300	5,126	4,386	5,126	4,604
34,300	34,350	5,139	4,394	5,139	4,611
34,350	34,400	5,151	4,401	5,151	4,619
34,400	34,450	5,164	4,409	5,164	4,626
34,450	34,500	5,176	4,416	5,176	4,634
34,500	34,550	5,189	4,424	5,189	4,641
34,550	34,600	5,201	4,431	5,201	4,649
34,600	34,650	5,214	4,439	5,214	4,656
34,650	34,700	5,226	4,446	5,226	4,664
34,700	34,750	5,239	4,454	5,239	4,671
34,750	34,800	5,251	4,461	5,251	4,679
34,800	34,850	5,264	4,469	5,264	4,686
34,850	34,900	5,276	4,476	5,276	4,694
34,900	34,950	5,289	4,484	5,289	4,701
34,950	35,000	5,301	4,491	5,301	4,709

If line 43 (taxable income) is —		And you are —			
At least	But less than	Single	Married filing jointly *	Married filing sepa-rately	Head of a house-hold
		Your tax is —			
35,000					
35,000	35,050	5,314	4,499	5,314	4,716
35,050	35,100	5,326	4,506	5,326	4,724
35,100	35,150	5,339	4,514	5,339	4,731
35,150	35,200	5,351	4,521	5,351	4,739
35,200	35,250	5,364	4,529	5,364	4,746
35,250	35,300	5,376	4,536	5,376	4,754
35,300	35,350	5,389	4,544	5,389	4,761
35,350	35,400	5,401	4,551	5,401	4,769
35,400	35,450	5,414	4,559	5,414	4,776
35,450	35,500	5,426	4,566	5,426	4,784
35,500	35,550	5,439	4,574	5,439	4,791
35,550	35,600	5,451	4,581	5,451	4,799
35,600	35,650	5,464	4,589	5,464	4,806
35,650	35,700	5,476	4,596	5,476	4,814
35,700	35,750	5,489	4,604	5,489	4,821
35,750	35,800	5,501	4,611	5,501	4,829
35,800	35,850	5,514	4,619	5,514	4,836
35,850	35,900	5,526	4,626	5,526	4,844
35,900	35,950	5,539	4,634	5,539	4,851
35,950	36,000	5,551	4,641	5,551	4,859
36,000					
36,000	36,050	5,564	4,649	5,564	4,866
36,050	36,100	5,576	4,656	5,576	4,874
36,100	36,150	5,589	4,664	5,589	4,881
36,150	36,200	5,601	4,671	5,601	4,889
36,200	36,250	5,614	4,679	5,614	4,896
36,250	36,300	5,626	4,686	5,626	4,904
36,300	36,350	5,639	4,694	5,639	4,911
36,350	36,400	5,651	4,701	5,651	4,919
36,400	36,450	5,664	4,709	5,664	4,926
36,450	36,500	5,676	4,716	5,676	4,934
36,500	36,550	5,689	4,724	5,689	4,941
36,550	36,600	5,701	4,731	5,701	4,949
36,600	36,650	5,714	4,739	5,714	4,956
36,650	36,700	5,726	4,746	5,726	4,964
36,700	36,750	5,739	4,754	5,739	4,971
36,750	36,800	5,751	4,761	5,751	4,979
36,800	36,850	5,764	4,769	5,764	4,986
36,850	36,900	5,776	4,776	5,776	4,994
36,900	36,950	5,789	4,784	5,789	5,001
36,950	37,000	5,801	4,791	5,801	5,009
37,000					
37,000	37,050	5,814	4,799	5,814	5,016
37,050	37,100	5,826	4,806	5,826	5,024
37,100	37,150	5,839	4,814	5,839	5,031
37,150	37,200	5,851	4,821	5,851	5,039
37,200	37,250	5,864	4,829	5,864	5,046
37,250	37,300	5,876	4,836	5,876	5,054
37,300	37,350	5,889	4,844	5,889	5,061
37,350	37,400	5,901	4,851	5,901	5,069
37,400	37,450	5,914	4,859	5,914	5,076
37,450	37,500	5,926	4,866	5,926	5,084
37,500	37,550	5,939	4,874	5,939	5,091
37,550	37,600	5,951	4,881	5,951	5,099
37,600	37,650	5,964	4,889	5,964	5,106
37,650	37,700	5,976	4,896	5,976	5,114
37,700	37,750	5,989	4,904	5,989	5,121
37,750	37,800	6,001	4,911	6,001	5,129
37,800	37,850	6,014	4,919	6,014	5,136
37,850	37,900	6,026	4,926	6,026	5,144
37,900	37,950	6,039	4,934	6,039	5,151
37,950	38,000	6,051	4,941	6,051	5,159

If line 43 (taxable income) is —		And you are —			
At least	But less than	Single	Married filing jointly *	Married filing sepa-rately	Head of a house-hold
		Your tax is —			
38,000					
38,000	38,050	6,064	4,949	6,064	5,166
38,050	38,100	6,076	4,956	6,076	5,174
38,100	38,150	6,089	4,964	6,089	5,181
38,150	38,200	6,101	4,971	6,101	5,189
38,200	38,250	6,114	4,979	6,114	5,196
38,250	38,300	6,126	4,986	6,126	5,204
38,300	38,350	6,139	4,994	6,139	5,211
38,350	38,400	6,151	5,001	6,151	5,219
38,400	38,450	6,164	5,009	6,164	5,226
38,450	38,500	6,176	5,016	6,176	5,234
38,500	38,550	6,189	5,024	6,189	5,241
38,550	38,600	6,201	5,031	6,201	5,249
38,600	38,650	6,214	5,039	6,214	5,256
38,650	38,700	6,226	5,046	6,226	5,264
38,700	38,750	6,239	5,054	6,239	5,271
38,750	38,800	6,251	5,061	6,251	5,279
38,800	38,850	6,264	5,069	6,264	5,286
38,850	38,900	6,276	5,076	6,276	5,294
38,900	38,950	6,289	5,084	6,289	5,301
38,950	39,000	6,301	5,091	6,301	5,309
39,000					
39,000	39,050	6,314	5,099	6,314	5,316
39,050	39,100	6,326	5,106	6,326	5,324
39,100	39,150	6,339	5,114	6,339	5,331
39,150	39,200	6,351	5,121	6,351	5,339
39,200	39,250	6,364	5,129	6,364	5,346
39,250	39,300	6,376	5,136	6,376	5,354
39,300	39,350	6,389	5,144	6,389	5,361
39,350	39,400	6,401	5,151	6,401	5,369
39,400	39,450	6,414	5,159	6,414	5,376
39,450	39,500	6,426	5,166	6,426	5,384
39,500	39,550	6,439	5,174	6,439	5,391
39,550	39,600	6,451	5,181	6,451	5,399
39,600	39,650	6,464	5,189	6,464	5,406
39,650	39,700	6,476	5,196	6,476	5,414
39,700	39,750	6,489	5,204	6,489	5,421
39,750	39,800	6,501	5,211	6,501	5,429
39,800	39,850	6,514	5,219	6,514	5,436
39,850	39,900	6,526	5,226	6,526	5,444
39,900	39,950	6,539	5,234	6,539	5,451
39,950	40,000	6,551	5,241	6,551	5,459
40,000					
40,000	40,050	6,564	5,249	6,564	5,466
40,050	40,100	6,576	5,256	6,576	5,474
40,100	40,150	6,589	5,264	6,589	5,481
40,150	40,200	6,601	5,271	6,601	5,489
40,200	40,250	6,614	5,279	6,614	5,496
40,250	40,300	6,626	5,286	6,626	5,504
40,300	40,350	6,639	5,294	6,639	5,511
40,350	40,400	6,651	5,301	6,651	5,519
40,400	40,450	6,664	5,309	6,664	5,526
40,450	40,500	6,676	5,316	6,676	5,534
40,500	40,550	6,689	5,324	6,689	5,541
40,550	40,600	6,701	5,331	6,701	5,549
40,600	40,650	6,714	5,339	6,714	5,556
40,650	40,700	6,726	5,346	6,726	5,564
40,700	40,750	6,739	5,354	6,739	5,571
40,750	40,800	6,751	5,361	6,751	5,579
40,800	40,850	6,764	5,369	6,764	5,586
40,850	40,900	6,776	5,376	6,776	5,594
40,900	40,950	6,789	5,384	6,789	5,601
40,950	41,000	6,801	5,391	6,801	5,609

* This column must also be used by a qualifying widow(er).

(Continued on next page)

Exhibit 18-3
Tax Table

18-7c

2006 Tax Table — *Continued*

If line 43 (taxable income) is —		And you are —			
At least	But less than	Single	Married filing jointly *	Married filing separately	Head of a household
		Your tax is —			
59,000					
59,000	59,050	11,314	8,099	11,314	10,114
59,050	59,100	11,326	8,106	11,326	10,126
59,100	59,150	11,339	8,114	11,339	10,139
59,150	59,200	11,351	8,121	11,351	10,151
59,200	59,250	11,364	8,129	11,364	10,164
59,250	59,300	11,376	8,136	11,376	10,176
59,300	59,350	11,389	8,144	11,389	10,189
59,350	59,400	11,401	8,151	11,401	10,201
59,400	59,450	11,414	8,159	11,414	10,214
59,450	59,500	11,426	8,166	11,426	10,226
59,500	59,550	11,439	8,174	11,439	10,239
59,550	59,600	11,451	8,181	11,451	10,251
59,600	59,650	11,464	8,189	11,464	10,264
59,650	59,700	11,476	8,196	11,476	10,276
59,700	59,750	11,489	8,204	11,489	10,289
59,750	59,800	11,501	8,211	11,501	10,301
59,800	59,850	11,514	8,219	11,514	10,314
59,850	59,900	11,526	8,226	11,526	10,326
59,900	59,950	11,539	8,234	11,539	10,339
59,950	60,000	11,551	8,241	11,551	10,351
60,000					
60,000	60,050	11,564	8,249	11,564	10,364
60,050	60,100	11,576	8,256	11,576	10,376
60,100	60,150	11,589	8,264	11,589	10,389
60,150	60,200	11,601	8,271	11,601	10,401
60,200	60,250	11,614	8,279	11,614	10,414
60,250	60,300	11,626	8,286	11,626	10,426
60,300	60,350	11,639	8,294	11,639	10,439
60,350	60,400	11,651	8,301	11,651	10,451
60,400	60,450	11,664	8,309	11,664	10,464
60,450	60,500	11,676	8,316	11,676	10,476
60,500	60,550	11,689	8,324	11,689	10,489
60,550	60,600	11,701	8,331	11,701	10,501
60,600	60,650	11,714	8,339	11,714	10,514
60,650	60,700	11,726	8,346	11,726	10,526
60,700	60,750	11,739	8,354	11,739	10,539
60,750	60,800	11,751	8,361	11,751	10,551
60,800	60,850	11,764	8,369	11,764	10,564
60,850	60,900	11,776	8,376	11,776	10,576
60,900	60,950	11,789	8,384	11,789	10,589
60,950	61,000	11,801	8,391	11,801	10,601
61,000					
61,000	61,050	11,814	8,399	11,814	10,614
61,050	61,100	11,826	8,406	11,826	10,626
61,100	61,150	11,839	8,414	11,839	10,639
61,150	61,200	11,851	8,421	11,851	10,651
61,200	61,250	11,864	8,429	11,864	10,664
61,250	61,300	11,876	8,436	11,876	10,676
61,300	61,350	11,889	8,446	11,889	10,689
61,350	61,400	11,901	8,459	11,901	10,701
61,400	61,450	11,914	8,471	11,914	10,714
61,450	61,500	11,926	8,484	11,926	10,726
61,500	61,550	11,939	8,496	11,939	10,739
61,550	61,600	11,951	8,509	11,951	10,751
61,600	61,650	11,964	8,521	11,964	10,764
61,650	61,700	11,976	8,534	11,976	10,776
61,700	61,750	11,989	8,546	11,989	10,789
61,750	61,800	12,001	8,559	12,001	10,801
61,800	61,850	12,014	8,571	12,014	10,814
61,850	61,900	12,026	8,584	12,027	10,826
61,900	61,950	12,039	8,596	12,041	10,839
61,950	62,000	12,051	8,609	12,055	10,851
62,000					
62,000	62,050	12,064	8,621	12,069	10,864
62,050	62,100	12,076	8,634	12,083	10,876
62,100	62,150	12,089	8,646	12,097	10,889
62,150	62,200	12,101	8,659	12,111	10,901
62,200	62,250	12,114	8,671	12,125	10,914
62,250	62,300	12,126	8,684	12,139	10,926
62,300	62,350	12,139	8,696	12,153	10,939
62,350	62,400	12,151	8,709	12,167	10,951
62,400	62,450	12,164	8,721	12,181	10,964
62,450	62,500	12,176	8,734	12,195	10,976
62,500	62,550	12,189	8,746	12,209	10,989
62,550	62,600	12,201	8,759	12,223	11,001
62,600	62,650	12,214	8,771	12,237	11,014
62,650	62,700	12,226	8,784	12,251	11,026
62,700	62,750	12,239	8,796	12,265	11,039
62,750	62,800	12,251	8,809	12,279	11,051
62,800	62,850	12,264	8,821	12,293	11,064
62,850	62,900	12,276	8,834	12,307	11,076
62,900	62,950	12,289	8,846	12,321	11,089
62,950	63,000	12,301	8,859	12,335	11,101
63,000					
63,000	63,050	12,314	8,871	12,349	11,114
63,050	63,100	12,326	8,884	12,363	11,126
63,100	63,150	12,339	8,896	12,377	11,139
63,150	63,200	12,351	8,909	12,391	11,151
63,200	63,250	12,364	8,921	12,405	11,164
63,250	63,300	12,376	8,934	12,419	11,176
63,300	63,350	12,389	8,946	12,433	11,189
63,350	63,400	12,401	8,959	12,447	11,201
63,400	63,450	12,414	8,971	12,461	11,214
63,450	63,500	12,426	8,984	12,475	11,226
63,500	63,550	12,439	8,996	12,489	11,239
63,550	63,600	12,451	9,009	12,503	11,251
63,600	63,650	12,464	9,021	12,517	11,264
63,650	63,700	12,476	9,034	12,531	11,276
63,700	63,750	12,489	9,046	12,545	11,289
63,750	63,800	12,501	9,059	12,559	11,301
63,800	63,850	12,514	9,071	12,573	11,314
63,850	63,900	12,526	9,084	12,587	11,326
63,900	63,950	12,539	9,096	12,601	11,339
63,950	64,000	12,551	9,109	12,615	11,351
64,000					
64,000	64,050	12,564	9,121	12,629	11,364
64,050	64,100	12,576	9,134	12,643	11,376
64,100	64,150	12,589	9,146	12,657	11,389
64,150	64,200	12,601	9,159	12,671	11,401
64,200	64,250	12,614	9,171	12,685	11,414
64,250	64,300	12,626	9,184	12,699	11,426
64,300	64,350	12,639	9,196	12,713	11,439
64,350	64,400	12,651	9,209	12,727	11,451
64,400	64,450	12,664	9,221	12,741	11,464
64,450	64,500	12,676	9,234	12,755	11,476
64,500	64,550	12,689	9,246	12,769	11,489
64,550	64,600	12,701	9,259	12,783	11,501
64,600	64,650	12,714	9,271	12,797	11,514
64,650	64,700	12,726	9,284	12,811	11,526
64,700	64,750	12,739	9,296	12,825	11,539
64,750	64,800	12,751	9,309	12,839	11,551
64,800	64,850	12,764	9,321	12,853	11,564
64,850	64,900	12,776	9,334	12,867	11,576
64,900	64,950	12,789	9,346	12,881	11,589
64,950	65,000	12,801	9,359	12,895	11,601
65,000					
65,000	65,050	12,814	9,371	12,909	11,614
65,050	65,100	12,826	9,384	12,923	11,626
65,100	65,150	12,839	9,396	12,937	11,639
65,150	65,200	12,851	9,409	12,951	11,651
65,200	65,250	12,864	9,421	12,965	11,664
65,250	65,300	12,876	9,434	12,979	11,676
65,300	65,350	12,889	9,446	12,993	11,689
65,350	65,400	12,901	9,459	13,007	11,701
65,400	65,450	12,914	9,471	13,021	11,714
65,450	65,500	12,926	9,484	13,035	11,726
65,500	65,550	12,939	9,496	13,049	11,739
65,550	65,600	12,951	9,509	13,063	11,751
65,600	65,650	12,964	9,521	13,077	11,764
65,650	65,700	12,976	9,534	13,091	11,776
65,700	65,750	12,989	9,546	13,105	11,789
65,750	65,800	13,001	9,559	13,119	11,801
65,800	65,850	13,014	9,571	13,133	11,814
65,850	65,900	13,026	9,584	13,147	11,826
65,900	65,950	13,039	9,596	13,161	11,839
65,950	66,000	13,051	9,609	13,175	11,851
66,000					
66,000	66,050	13,064	9,621	13,189	11,864
66,050	66,100	13,076	9,634	13,203	11,876
66,100	66,150	13,089	9,646	13,217	11,889
66,150	66,200	13,101	9,659	13,231	11,901
66,200	66,250	13,114	9,671	13,245	11,914
66,250	66,300	13,126	9,684	13,259	11,926
66,300	66,350	13,139	9,696	13,273	11,939
66,350	66,400	13,151	9,709	13,287	11,951
66,400	66,450	13,164	9,721	13,301	11,964
66,450	66,500	13,176	9,734	13,315	11,976
66,500	66,550	13,189	9,746	13,329	11,989
66,550	66,600	13,201	9,759	13,343	12,001
66,600	66,650	13,214	9,771	13,357	12,014
66,650	66,700	13,226	9,784	13,371	12,026
66,700	66,750	13,239	9,796	13,385	12,039
66,750	66,800	13,251	9,809	13,399	12,051
66,800	66,850	13,264	9,821	13,413	12,064
66,850	66,900	13,276	9,834	13,427	12,076
66,900	66,950	13,289	9,846	13,441	12,089
66,950	67,000	13,301	9,859	13,455	12,101
67,000					
67,000	67,050	13,314	9,871	13,469	12,114
67,050	67,100	13,326	9,884	13,483	12,126
67,100	67,150	13,339	9,896	13,497	12,139
67,150	67,200	13,351	9,909	13,511	12,151
67,200	67,250	13,364	9,921	13,525	12,164
67,250	67,300	13,376	9,934	13,539	12,176
67,300	67,350	13,389	9,946	13,553	12,189
67,350	67,400	13,401	9,959	13,567	12,201
67,400	67,450	13,414	9,971	13,581	12,214
67,450	67,500	13,426	9,984	13,595	12,226
67,500	67,550	13,439	9,996	13,609	12,239
67,550	67,600	13,451	10,009	13,623	12,251
67,600	67,650	13,464	10,021	13,637	12,264
67,650	67,700	13,476	10,034	13,651	12,276
67,700	67,750	13,489	10,046	13,665	12,289
67,750	67,800	13,501	10,059	13,679	12,301
67,800	67,850	13,514	10,071	13,693	12,314
67,850	67,900	13,526	10,084	13,707	12,326
67,900	67,950	13,539	10,096	13,721	12,339
67,950	68,000	13,551	10,109	13,735	12,351

* This column must also be used by a qualifying widow(er).

(Continued on next page)

18-7d

Exhibit 18-3
Tax Table (concluded)

2006 Tax Table — *Continued*

If line 43 (taxable income) is —		And you are —			
At least	But less than	Single	Married filing jointly *	Married filing separately	Head of a household
		Your tax is —			
68,000					
68,000	68,050	13,564	10,121	13,749	12,364
68,050	68,100	13,576	10,134	13,763	12,376
68,100	68,150	13,589	10,146	13,777	12,389
68,150	68,200	13,601	10,159	13,791	12,401
68,200	68,250	13,614	10,171	13,805	12,414
68,250	68,300	13,626	10,184	13,819	12,426
68,300	68,350	13,639	10,196	13,833	12,439
68,350	68,400	13,651	10,209	13,847	12,451
68,400	68,450	13,664	10,221	13,861	12,464
68,450	68,500	13,676	10,234	13,875	12,476
68,500	68,550	13,689	10,246	13,889	12,489
68,550	68,600	13,701	10,259	13,903	12,501
68,600	68,650	13,714	10,271	13,917	12,514
68,650	68,700	13,726	10,284	13,931	12,526
68,700	68,750	13,739	10,296	13,945	12,539
68,750	68,800	13,751	10,309	13,959	12,551
68,800	68,850	13,764	10,321	13,973	12,564
68,850	68,900	13,776	10,334	13,987	12,576
68,900	68,950	13,789	10,346	14,001	12,589
68,950	69,000	13,801	10,359	14,015	12,601
69,000					
69,000	69,050	13,814	10,371	14,029	12,614
69,050	69,100	13,826	10,384	14,043	12,626
69,100	69,150	13,839	10,396	14,057	12,639
69,150	69,200	13,851	10,409	14,071	12,651
69,200	69,250	13,864	10,421	14,085	12,664
69,250	69,300	13,876	10,434	14,099	12,676
69,300	69,350	13,889	10,446	14,113	12,689
69,350	69,400	13,901	10,459	14,127	12,701
69,400	69,450	13,914	10,471	14,141	12,714
69,450	69,500	13,926	10,484	14,155	12,726
69,500	69,550	13,939	10,496	14,169	12,739
69,550	69,600	13,951	10,509	14,183	12,751
69,600	69,650	13,964	10,521	14,197	12,764
69,650	69,700	13,976	10,534	14,211	12,776
69,700	69,750	13,989	10,546	14,225	12,789
69,750	69,800	14,001	10,559	14,239	12,801
69,800	69,850	14,014	10,571	14,253	12,814
69,850	69,900	14,026	10,584	14,267	12,826
69,900	69,950	14,039	10,596	14,281	12,839
69,950	70,000	14,051	10,609	14,295	12,851
70,000					
70,000	70,050	14,064	10,621	14,309	12,864
70,050	70,100	14,076	10,634	14,323	12,876
70,100	70,150	14,089	10,646	14,337	12,889
70,150	70,200	14,101	10,659	14,351	12,901
70,200	70,250	14,114	10,671	14,365	12,914
70,250	70,300	14,126	10,684	14,379	12,926
70,300	70,350	14,139	10,696	14,393	12,939
70,350	70,400	14,151	10,709	14,407	12,951
70,400	70,450	14,164	10,721	14,421	12,964
70,450	70,500	14,176	10,734	14,435	12,976
70,500	70,550	14,189	10,746	14,449	12,989
70,550	70,600	14,201	10,759	14,463	13,001
70,600	70,650	14,214	10,771	14,477	13,014
70,650	70,700	14,226	10,784	14,491	13,026
70,700	70,750	14,239	10,796	14,505	13,039
70,750	70,800	14,251	10,809	14,519	13,051
70,800	70,850	14,264	10,821	14,533	13,064
70,850	70,900	14,276	10,834	14,547	13,076
70,900	70,950	14,289	10,846	14,561	13,089
70,950	71,000	14,301	10,859	14,575	13,101

If line 43 (taxable income) is —		And you are —			
At least	But less than	Single	Married filing jointly *	Married filing separately	Head of a household
		Your tax is —			
71,000					
71,000	71,050	14,314	10,871	14,589	13,114
71,050	71,100	14,326	10,884	14,603	13,126
71,100	71,150	14,339	10,896	14,617	13,139
71,150	71,200	14,351	10,909	14,631	13,151
71,200	71,250	14,364	10,921	14,645	13,164
71,250	71,300	14,376	10,934	14,659	13,176
71,300	71,350	14,389	10,946	14,673	13,189
71,350	71,400	14,401	10,959	14,687	13,201
71,400	71,450	14,414	10,971	14,701	13,214
71,450	71,500	14,426	10,984	14,715	13,226
71,500	71,550	14,439	10,996	14,729	13,239
71,550	71,600	14,451	11,009	14,743	13,251
71,600	71,650	14,464	11,021	14,757	13,264
71,650	71,700	14,476	11,034	14,771	13,276
71,700	71,750	14,489	11,046	14,785	13,289
71,750	71,800	14,501	11,059	14,799	13,301
71,800	71,850	14,514	11,071	14,813	13,314
71,850	71,900	14,526	11,084	14,827	13,326
71,900	71,950	14,539	11,096	14,841	13,339
71,950	72,000	14,551	11,109	14,855	13,351
72,000					
72,000	72,050	14,564	11,121	14,869	13,364
72,050	72,100	14,576	11,134	14,883	13,376
72,100	72,150	14,589	11,146	14,897	13,389
72,150	72,200	14,601	11,159	14,911	13,401
72,200	72,250	14,614	11,171	14,925	13,414
72,250	72,300	14,626	11,184	14,939	13,426
72,300	72,350	14,639	11,196	14,953	13,439
72,350	72,400	14,651	11,209	14,967	13,451
72,400	72,450	14,664	11,221	14,981	13,464
72,450	72,500	14,676	11,234	14,995	13,476
72,500	72,550	14,689	11,246	15,009	13,489
72,550	72,600	14,701	11,259	15,023	13,501
72,600	72,650	14,714	11,271	15,037	13,514
72,650	72,700	14,726	11,284	15,051	13,526
72,700	72,750	14,739	11,296	15,065	13,539
72,750	72,800	14,751	11,309	15,079	13,551
72,800	72,850	14,764	11,321	15,093	13,564
72,850	72,900	14,776	11,334	15,107	13,576
72,900	72,950	14,789	11,346	15,121	13,589
72,950	73,000	14,801	11,359	15,135	13,601
73,000					
73,000	73,050	14,814	11,371	15,149	13,614
73,050	73,100	14,826	11,384	15,163	13,626
73,100	73,150	14,839	11,396	15,177	13,639
73,150	73,200	14,851	11,409	15,191	13,651
73,200	73,250	14,864	11,421	15,205	13,664
73,250	73,300	14,876	11,434	15,219	13,676
73,300	73,350	14,889	11,446	15,233	13,689
73,350	73,400	14,901	11,459	15,247	13,701
73,400	73,450	14,914	11,471	15,261	13,714
73,450	73,500	14,926	11,484	15,275	13,726
73,500	73,550	14,939	11,496	15,289	13,739
73,550	73,600	14,951	11,509	15,303	13,751
73,600	73,650	14,964	11,521	15,317	13,764
73,650	73,700	14,976	11,534	15,331	13,776
73,700	73,750	14,989	11,546	15,345	13,789
73,750	73,800	15,001	11,559	15,359	13,801
73,800	73,850	15,014	11,571	15,373	13,814
73,850	73,900	15,026	11,584	15,387	13,826
73,900	73,950	15,039	11,596	15,401	13,839
73,950	74,000	15,051	11,609	15,415	13,851

If line 43 (taxable income) is —		And you are —			
At least	But less than	Single	Married filing jointly *	Married filing separately	Head of a household
		Your tax is —			
74,000					
74,000	74,050	15,064	11,621	15,429	13,864
74,050	74,100	15,076	11,634	15,443	13,876
74,100	74,150	15,089	11,646	15,457	13,889
74,150	74,200	15,101	11,659	15,471	13,901
74,200	74,250	15,115	11,671	15,485	13,914
74,250	74,300	15,129	11,684	15,499	13,926
74,300	74,350	15,143	11,696	15,513	13,939
74,350	74,400	15,157	11,709	15,527	13,951
74,400	74,450	15,171	11,721	15,541	13,964
74,450	74,500	15,185	11,734	15,555	13,976
74,500	74,550	15,199	11,746	15,569	13,989
74,550	74,600	15,213	12,759	15,583	14,001
74,600	74,650	15,227	11,771	15,597	14,014
74,650	74,700	15,241	11,784	15,611	14,026
74,700	74,750	15,255	11,796	15,625	14,039
74,750	74,800	15,269	11,809	15,639	14,051
74,800	74,850	15,283	11,821	15,653	14,064
74,850	74,900	15,297	11,834	15,667	14,076
74,900	74,950	15,311	11,846	15,681	14,089
74,950	75,000	15,325	11,859	15,695	14,101
75,000					
75,000	75,050	15,339	11,871	15,709	14,114
75,050	75,100	15,353	11,884	15,723	14,126
75,100	75,150	15,367	11,896	15,737	14,139
75,150	75,200	15,381	11,909	15,751	14,151
75,200	75,250	15,395	11,921	15,765	14,164
75,250	75,300	15,409	11,934	15,779	14,176
75,300	75,350	15,423	11,946	15,793	14,189
75,350	75,400	15,437	11,959	15,807	14,201
75,400	75,450	15,451	11,971	15,821	14,214
75,450	75,500	15,465	11,984	15,835	14,226
75,500	75,550	15,479	11,996	15,849	14,239
75,550	75,600	15,493	12,009	15,863	14,251
75,600	75,650	15,507	12,021	15,877	14,264
75,650	75,700	15,521	12,034	15,891	14,276
75,700	75,750	15,535	12,046	15,905	14,289
75,750	75,800	15,549	12,059	15,919	14,301
75,800	75,850	15,563	12,071	15,933	14,314
75,850	75,900	15,577	12,084	15,947	14,326
75,900	75,950	15,591	12,096	15,961	14,339
75,950	76,000	15,605	12,109	15,975	14,351
76,000					
76,000	76,050	15,619	12,121	15,989	14,364
76,050	76,100	15,633	12,134	16,003	14,376
76,100	76,150	15,647	12,146	16,017	14,389
76,150	76,200	15,661	12,159	16,031	14,401
76,200	76,250	15,675	12,171	16,045	14,414
76,250	76,300	15,689	12,184	16,059	14,426
76,300	76,350	15,703	12,196	16,073	14,439
76,350	76,400	15,717	12,209	16,087	14,451
76,400	76,450	15,731	12,221	16,101	14,464
76,450	76,500	15,745	12,234	16,115	14,476
76,500	76,550	15,759	12,246	16,129	14,489
76,550	76,600	15,773	12,259	16,143	14,501
76,600	76,650	15,787	12,271	16,157	14,514
76,650	76,700	15,801	12,284	16,171	14,526
76,700	76,750	15,815	12,296	16,185	14,539
76,750	76,800	15,829	12,309	16,199	14,551
76,800	76,850	15,843	12,321	16,213	14,564
76,850	76,900	15,857	12,334	16,227	14,576
76,900	76,950	15,871	12,346	16,241	14,589
76,950	77,000	15,885	12,359	16,255	14,601

* This column must also be used by a qualifying widow(er).

18-8

Exhibit 18-4
2006 Tax Computation Worksheet

Section A—Use if your filing status is **Single**. Complete the row below that applies to you.

Taxable income. If line 43 is—	**(a)** Enter the amount from line 43	**(b)** Multiplication amount	**(c)** Multiply (a) by (b)	**(d)** Subtraction amount	**Tax.** Subtract (d) from (c). Enter the result here and on Form 1040, line 44
At least $100,000 but not over $154,800	$	× 28% (.28)	$	$ 5,668.50	$
Over $154,800 but not over $336,550	$	× 33% (.33)	$	$ 13,408.50	$
Over $336,550	$	× 35% (.35)	$	$ 20,139.50	$

Section B—Use if your filing status is **Married filing jointly** or **Qualifying widow(er)**. Complete the row below that applies to you.

Taxable income. If line 43 is—	**(a)** Enter the amount from line 43	**(b)** Multiplication amount	**(c)** Multiply (a) by (b)	**(d)** Subtraction amount	**Tax.** Subtract (d) from (c). Enter the result here and on Form 1040, line 44
At least $100,000 but not over $123,700	$	× 25% (.25)	$	$ 6,885.00	$
Over $123,700 but not over $188,450	$	× 28% (.28)	$	$ 10,596.00	$
Over $188,450 but not over $336,550	$	× 33% (.33)	$	$ 20,018.50	$
Over $336,550	$	× 35% (.35)	$	$ 26,749.50	$

Section C—Use if your filing status is **Married filing separately**. Complete the row below that applies to you.

Taxable income. If line 43 is—	**(a)** Enter the amount from line 43	**(b)** Multiplication amount	**(c)** Multiply (a) by (b)	**(d)** Subtraction amount	**Tax.** Subtract (d) from (c). Enter the result here and on Form 1040, line 44
At least $100,000 but not over $168,275	$	× 33% (.33)	$	$ 10,009.25	$
Over $168,275	$	× 35% (.35)	$	$ 13,374.75	$

Section D—Use if your filing status is **Head of household**. Complete the row below that applies to you.

Taxable income. If line 43 is—	**(a)** Enter the amount from line 43	**(b)** Multiplication amount	**(c)** Multiply (a) by (b)	**(d)** Subtraction amount	**Tax.** Subtract (d) from (c). Enter the result here and on Form 1040, line 44
At least $100,000 but not over $106,000	$	× 25% (.25)	$	$ 4,642.50	$
Over $106,000 but not over $171,650	$	× 28% (.28)	$	$ 7,822.50	$
Over $171,650 but not over $$336,550	$	× 33% (.33)	$	$ 16,405.00	$
Over $336,550	$	× 35% (.35)	$	$ 23,136.00	$

USING THE TAX COMPUTATION WORKSHEET TO CALCULATE TAX LIABILITY

If taxable income is $100,000 or more, the appropriate Tax Computation Worksheet section must be used to calculate the tax liability. Exhibit 18-4 contains the 2006 Tax Computation Worksheet.

In the Business World

The federal individual income tax began relatively modestly in 1913 with 400 pages of rules and a basic rate of 1 percent. From the beginning, CCH Inc. has published an annual collection of federal tax rules containing the tax code, tax regulations, and summaries of federal tax pronouncements. The number of pages in this publication has grown from 400 in 1913 to 66,500 in 2006.

STEPS TO CALCULATE TAX LIABILITY USING THE TAX COMPUTATION WORKSHEET—TAXABLE INCOME OF $100,000 OR ABOVE

Step 1. Locate the Section corresponding to the appropriate filing status:

Section A – Single

Section B – Married filing jointly or qualifying widow(er)

Section C – Married filing separately

Section D – Head of household

Step 2. Read down the first column, "Taxable income. If line 43 is –" to find the range containing the taxable income.

Step 3. Multiply the taxable income by the "multiplication amount" listed in column (b) for that range.

Step 4. Calculate the tax liability by subtracting the "subtraction amount" listed in column (d) for that range from the result in step 3.

EXAMPLE 12 USING THE TAX COMPUTATION WORKSHEET

Casale Hubman had taxable income last year of $121,334. For income tax purposes she files as married, filing separately. Use the appropriate Section (A, B, C, or D) of the Tax Computation Worksheet to calculate her tax liability.

© JEFF MACNELLY

SOLUTION STRATEGY

Step 1. Since Casale files as married filing separately, we shall use the Tax Computation Worksheet, Section C.

Step 2. Reading down the "Taxable income. If line 43 is –" column, we find Casale's taxable income in the range "At least $100,000 but not over $168,275."

Step 3.

121,334.00	Taxable income
× .33	Multiplication amount, column (b), for that range
40,040.22	

Step 4.

40,040.22	Result from Step 3
− 10,009.25	Subtraction amount, column (d), for that range
$30,030.97	Tax liability

TRY IT EXERCISE 12

Mark Batchelor had taxable income of $123,545 last year. If he files as head of household, what is his tax liability?

 18-9

CHECK YOUR ANSWER WITH THE SOLUTION ON PAGE 685.

Exhibit 18-5
Form 1040

Form **1040** Department of the Treasury—Internal Revenue Service
U.S. Individual Income Tax Return **2006** (99) IRS Use Only—Do not write or staple in this space.

For the year Jan. 1–Dec. 31, 2006, or other tax year beginning , 2006, ending , 20 OMB No. 1545-0074

Label (See instructions on page 16.) **Use the IRS label.** Otherwise, please print or type.

LABEL HERE

Your first name and initial	Last name	Your social security number
If a joint return, spouse's first name and initial	Last name	Spouse's social security number
Home address (number and street). If you have a P.O. box, see page 16.	Apt. no.	▲ You **must** enter your SSN(s) above. ▲
City, town or post office, state, and ZIP code. If you have a foreign address, see page 16.		Checking a box below will not change your tax or refund.

Presidential Election Campaign ▶ Check here if you, or your spouse if filing jointly, want $3 to go to this fund (see page 16) ▶ ☐ **You** ☐ **Spouse**

Filing Status

Check only one box.

1 ☐ Single
2 ☐ Married filing jointly (even if only one had income)
3 ☐ Married filing separately. Enter spouse's SSN above and full name here. ▶
4 ☐ Head of household (with qualifying person). (See page 17.) If the qualifying person is a child but not your dependent, enter this child's name here. ▶
5 ☐ Qualifying widow(er) with dependent child (see page 17)

Exemptions

6a ☐ **Yourself.** If someone can claim you as a dependent, **do not** check box 6a . . . . .
b ☐ **Spouse** . . . . .

} Boxes checked on 6a and 6b

c **Dependents:**

(1) First name Last name	(2) Dependent's social security number	(3) Dependent's relationship to you	(4) ✓ if qualifying child for child tax credit (see page 19)
			☐
			☐
			☐
			☐

If more than four dependents, see page 19.

No. of children on 6c who:
- lived with you
- did not live with you due to divorce or separation (see page 20)

Dependents on 6c not entered above

d Total number of exemptions claimed . . . . .

Add numbers on lines above ▶

Income

Attach Form(s) W-2 here. Also attach Forms W-2G and 1099-R if tax was withheld.

If you did not get a W-2, see page 23.

Enclose, but do not attach, any payment. Also, please use **Form 1040-V.**

7	Wages, salaries, tips, etc. Attach Form(s) W-2		7
8a	**Taxable** interest. Attach Schedule B if required		8a
b	**Tax-exempt** interest. **Do not** include on line 8a . . .	8b	
9a	Ordinary dividends. Attach Schedule B if required		9a
b	Qualified dividends (see page 23)	9b	
10	Taxable refunds, credits, or offsets of state and local income taxes (see page 24) .		10
11	Alimony received		11
12	Business income or (loss). Attach Schedule C or C-EZ		12
13	Capital gain or (loss). Attach Schedule D if required. If not required, check here ▶ ☐		13
14	Other gains or (losses). Attach Form 4797		14
15a	IRA distributions . . 15a	b Taxable amount (see page 25)	15b
16a	Pensions and annuities 16a	b Taxable amount (see page 26)	16b
17	Rental real estate, royalties, partnerships, S corporations, trusts, etc. Attach Schedule E		17
18	Farm income or (loss). Attach Schedule F		18
19	Unemployment compensation		19
20a	Social security benefits . 20a	b Taxable amount (see page 27)	20b
21	Other income. List type and amount (see page 29)		21
22	Add the amounts in the far right column for lines 7 through 21. This is your **total income** ▶		22

Adjusted Gross Income

23	Archer MSA deduction. Attach Form 8853	23	
24	Certain business expenses of reservists, performing artists, and fee-basis government officials. Attach Form 2106 or 2106-EZ	24	
25	Health savings account deduction. Attach Form 8889 . .	25	
26	Moving expenses. Attach Form 3903	26	
27	One-half of self-employment tax. Attach Schedule SE . .	27	
28	Self-employed SEP, SIMPLE, and qualified plans . . .	28	
29	Self-employed health insurance deduction (see page 29)	29	
30	Penalty on early withdrawal of savings	30	
31a	Alimony paid b Recipient's SSN ▶	31a	
32	IRA deduction (see page 31)	32	
33	Student loan interest deduction (see page 33)	33	
34	Jury duty pay you gave to your employer	34	
35	Domestic production activities deduction. Attach Form 8903	35	
36	Add lines 23 through 31a and 32 through 35		36
37	Subtract line 36 from line 22. This is your **adjusted gross income** . . . . . ▶		37

For Disclosure, Privacy Act, and Paperwork Reduction Act Notice, see page 80. Cat. No. 11320B Form **1040** (2006)

Exhibit 18-5
Form 1040

Form 1040 (2006) Page **2**

Tax and Credits

38 Amount from line 37 (adjusted gross income) . . . 38

39a Check if: ☐ **You** were born before January 2, 1942, ☐ Blind. / ☐ **Spouse** was born before January 2, 1942, ☐ Blind. } **Total boxes checked** ▶ 39a

b If your spouse itemizes on a separate return or you were a dual-status alien, see page 34 and check here ▶ 39b ☐

Standard Deduction for—
- People who checked any box on line 39a or 39b **or** who can be claimed as a dependent, see page 34.
- All others:

Single or Married filing separately, $5,150

Married filing jointly or Qualifying widow(er), $10,300

Head of household, $7,550

40 **Itemized deductions** (from Schedule A) **or** your **standard deduction** (see left margin) . . 40

41 Subtract line 40 from line 38 . . . 41

42 If line 38 is over $112,875 or you provided housing to a person displaced by Hurricane Katrina, see page 36. Otherwise, multiply $3,300 by the total number of exemptions claimed on line 6d 42

43 **Taxable income.** Subtract line 42 from line 41. If line 42 is more than line 41, enter -0- . 43

44 **Tax** (see page 36). Check if any tax is from: a ☐ Form(s) 8814 b ☐ Form 4972 44

45 **Alternative minimum tax** (see page 39). Attach Form 6251 . . . 45

46 Add lines 44 and 45 . . . ▶ 46

47 Foreign tax credit. Attach Form 1116 if required 47

48 Credit for child and dependent care expenses. Attach Form 2441 48

49 Credit for the elderly or the disabled. Attach Schedule R. 49

50 Education credits. Attach Form 8863 . . . 50

51 Retirement savings contributions credit. Attach Form 8880. 51

52 Residential energy credits. Attach Form 5695. . . . 52

53 Child tax credit (see page 42). Attach Form 8901 if required 53

54 Credits from: a ☐ Form 8396 b ☐ Form 8839 c ☐ Form 8859 54

55 Other credits: a ☐ Form 3800 b ☐ Form 8801 c ☐ Form_____ 55

56 Add lines 47 through 55. These are your **total credits** . . . 56

57 Subtract line 56 from line 46. If line 56 is more than line 46, enter -0- . . . ▶ 57

Other Taxes

58 Self-employment tax. Attach Schedule SE . . . 58

59 Social security and Medicare tax on tip income not reported to employer. Attach Form 4137 . . 59

60 Additional tax on IRAs, other qualified retirement plans, etc. Attach Form 5329 if required . 60

61 Advance earned income credit payments from Form(s) W-2, box 9 . . . 61

62 Household employment taxes. Attach Schedule H . . . 62

63 Add lines 57 through 62. This is your **total tax** . . . ▶ 63

Payments

64 Federal income tax withheld from Forms W-2 and 1099 . 64

65 2006 estimated tax payments and amount applied from 2005 return 65

If you have a qualifying child, attach Schedule EIC.

66a **Earned income credit (EIC)** . . . 66a

b Nontaxable combat pay election ▶ 66b

67 Excess social security and tier 1 RRTA tax withheld (see page 60) 67

68 Additional child tax credit. Attach Form 8812 . . . 68

69 Amount paid with request for extension to file (see page 60) 69

70 Payments from: a ☐ Form 2439 b ☐ Form 4136 c ☐ Form 8885 . 70

71 Credit for federal telephone excise tax paid. Attach Form 8913 if required 71

72 Add lines 64, 65, 66a, and 67 through 71. These are your **total payments** . . . ▶ 72

Refund

Direct deposit? See page 61 and fill in 74b, 74c, and 74d, or Form 8888.

73 If line 72 is more than line 63, subtract line 63 from line 72. This is the amount you **overpaid** 73

74a Amount of line 73 you want **refunded to you.** If Form 8888 is attached, check here ▶ ☐ 74a

▶ b Routing number ▶ c Type: ☐ Checking ☐ Savings

▶ d Account number

75 Amount of line 73 you want **applied to your 2007 estimated tax** ▶ 75

Amount You Owe

76 **Amount you owe.** Subtract line 72 from line 63. For details on how to pay, see page 62 ▶ 76

77 Estimated tax penalty (see page 62) . . . 77

Third Party Designee

Do you want to allow another person to discuss this return with the IRS (see page 63)? ☐ **Yes.** Complete the following. ☐ **No**

Designee's name ▶ Phone no. ▶ ( ) Personal identification number (PIN) ▶

Sign Here

Joint return? See page 17. Keep a copy for your records.

Under penalties of perjury, I declare that I have examined this return and accompanying schedules and statements, and to the best of my knowledge and belief, they are true, correct, and complete. Declaration of preparer (other than taxpayer) is based on all information of which preparer has any knowledge.

Your signature	Date	Your occupation	Daytime phone number ( )
Spouse's signature. If a joint return, **both** must sign.	Date	Spouse's occupation	

Paid Preparer's Use Only

Preparer's signature ▶	Date	Check if self-employed ☐	Preparer's SSN or PTIN
Firm's name (or yours if self-employed), address, and ZIP code ▶		EIN	
		Phone no.	( )

Form **1040** (2006)

18-10 CALCULATING AN INDIVIDUAL'S TAX REFUND OR AMOUNT OF TAX OWED

Once the tax liability has been determined, we must consider the final three items in income tax preparation: tax credits, other taxes, and payments. The following formula is used to complete the tax preparation process. *Note:* When the result is a positive number, it is the amount of tax owed. When the result is a negative number, it indicates a tax overpayment by that amount. When an overpayment occurs, the taxpayer has the option of receiving a refund or applying the amount of the overpayment to next year's estimated tax.

Refund (−) or amount owed (+) = Tax liability − Credits + Other taxes − Payments

tax credit Dollar-for-dollar subtractions from an individual's or corporation's tax liability. Some examples for individuals would be the credit for child and dependent care expenses, the credit for the elderly or disabled, and the foreign tax credit.

Tax Credits. Tax credits are a dollar-for-dollar subtraction from the tax liability. A **tax credit** of one dollar saves a full dollar in taxes, whereas a tax deduction of one dollar results in less than a dollar in tax savings (the amount depends on the tax rate). Some examples are credit for child and dependent care expenses, credit for the elderly or disabled, and the foreign tax credit.

Other Taxes. In addition to the tax liability from the Tax Table or Tax Rate Schedules, other taxes may also be due. These taxes are added to the tax liability. Some examples would be self-employment taxes and Social Security and Medicare taxes on tip income.

Payments. This calculation involves subtracting payments such as employees' federal income tax withheld by employers, estimated tax payments made quarterly, excess Social Security and Medicare paid, and the Earned Income Credit (considered a payment). The Earned Income Credit is available to married taxpayers filing jointly with a child and adjusted gross income of less than $34,001.

© Tony Freeman/PhotoEdit

Internal Revenue Service
Taxes are one of the certainties of life! As long as governments collect taxes, there will be jobs for tax examiners, collectors, and revenue agents.

In 2006, tax examiners, revenue agents, and collectors held about 76,000 jobs at all levels of government. About half worked for the federal government, one-third for state governments, and the remainder in local governments.

STEPS TO CALCULATE AN INDIVIDUAL'S TAX REFUND OR AMOUNT OF TAX OWED

Step 1. Subtract total credits from the tax liability.

Step 2. Add total of other taxes to the tax liability to get total tax.

Step 3. If total payments are greater than total tax, a refund of the difference is due. If total payments are less than total tax, the difference is the tax owed.

EXAMPLE 13 CALCULATING TAX REFUND OR AMOUNT OWED

After preparing her taxes for last year, Linda Ryan determined that she had a tax liability of $5,326. In addition, she owed other taxes of $575. Because of her mother, Linda was entitled to a credit for the elderly of $1,412. If her employer withheld $510 from her paycheck each month, is Linda entitled to a refund or does she owe additional taxes? How much?

SOLUTION STRATEGY

Steps 1 & 2.

$5,326	Tax liability
− 1,412	Tax credits
+ 575	Other taxes
$4,489	Total tax owed

Steps 3. Payments: Federal income tax withheld was $510 × 12 months = $6,120.

$6,120	Payments
− 4,489	Total tax
$1,631	Overpayment

Since Linda's payments are greater than her total tax owed, she has made an overpayment by the amount of the difference, and is therefore entitled to a tax refund of $1,631.

TRY IT EXERCISE 13

Jill Carson had a tax liability of $14,600 last year. In addition, she owed other taxes of $2,336. She was entitled to a credit for child care of $668 and a foreign tax credit of $1,719. If her employer withheld $270 per week for 52 weeks, does Jill qualify for a refund or owe more taxes? How much?

CHECK YOUR ANSWERS WITH THE SOLUTIONS ON PAGE 685.

TAX FACTS

	2007*	Change from '06*
Number of refunds	101.7 million	Up 4.3%
Total dollar amount	$228.86 billion	Up 6.9%
Average refund	$2,250	Up 2.5%

Source: IRS

CALCULATING CORPORATE INCOME TAX AND NET INCOME AFTER TAXES

Just as with individuals, corporations are also taxable entities that must file tax returns and are taxed directly on their earnings. In Chapter 15, we learned to prepare a balance sheet and an income statement based on the operating figures of a company over a period of time. At the bottom of the income statement the net income before taxes was determined. Now let's use the **Corporate Tax Rate Schedule**, Exhibit 18-6 below, to calculate the amount of corporate income tax due.

Corporate Tax Rate Schedule The IRS chart used to calculate the amount of income tax due from corporations.

Exhibit 18-6
Corporate Tax Rate Schedule

 18-10

Corporate Tax Rate Schedule

If taxable income (line 30, Form 1120, or line 26, Form 1120-A) on page 1 is:

Over—	*But not over—*	*Tax is:*	*Of the amount over—*
$0	$50,000	**15%**	$0
50,000	75,000	**$7,500 + 25%**	50,000
75,000	100,000	**13,750 + 34%**	75,000
100,000	335,000	**22,250 + 39%**	100,000
335,000	10,000,000	**113,900 + 34%**	335,000
10,000,000	15,000,000	**3,400,000 + 35%**	10,000,000
15,000,000	18,333,333	**5,150,000 + 38%**	15,000,000
18,333,333	- - - - -	**35%**	0

STEPS TO CALCULATE CORPORATE INCOME TAX AND NET INCOME AFTER TAXES

Step 1. Using the Corporate Tax Rate Schedule, read down the "Over—" and "But not over—" columns to find the range containing the taxable income of the corporation.

Step 2. Subtract the lower number of the range from the taxable income.

Step 3. Multiply the result from Step 2 by the tax rate listed for that range.

Step 4. Calculate the tax liability by adding the result from Step 3 to the dollar amount of tax indicated for that range.

Step 5. Calculate income after taxes by subtracting the tax liability from the net income before taxes.

EXAMPLE 14 CALCULATING CORPORATE INCOME TAX AND AFTER-TAX NET INCOME

North Star Industries had net income before taxes of $7,550,000. Use the Corporate Tax Rate Schedule to calculate the amount of income tax due, and calculate the company's net income after taxes.

SOLUTION STRATEGY

Step 1. North Star's net income falls in the range 335,000 to 10,000,000.

Step 2.	7,550,000	Income before taxes
	− 335,000	Lower number of the range
	7,215,000	
Step 3.	7,215,000	Result from Step 2
	× .34	Tax rate for that range
	2,453,100	
Step 4.	2,453,100	Result from Step 3
	+ 113,900	Dollar amount of tax indicated for that range
	$2,567,000	Tax liability
Step 5.	7,550,000	Income before taxes
	− 2,567,000	Tax liability
	$4,983,000	Net income after taxes

In the Business World

A qualifying domestic corporation with 35 or fewer shareholders may elect to be treated as an **S-corporation**, thus eliminating all corporate liability for federal income taxes.

Instead, any taxable income or loss will be allocated proportionately among the shareholders, who will be responsible for reporting the amounts on their personal income tax returns.

TRY IT EXERCISE 14

The Quarry Restaurant had taxable income of $311,200 last year. Use the Corporate Tax Rate Schedule to calculate the amount of income tax due, and calculate the company's net income after taxes.

CHECK YOUR ANSWERS WITH THE SOLUTIONS ON PAGE 685.

Review Exercises

As a tax return preparer for The Rodriguez Tax & Accounting Service, you have been asked to calculate the missing information for eight of the firm's tax clients. Use the 2006 standard deductions listed on page 662.

Name	Filing Status (exemptions)	Income	Adjustments to Income	Adjusted Gross Income	(circle your choice) Standard Deduction	Itemized Deductions	Exemption Allowances	Taxable Income
1. Andrews	Single (1)	$34,300	$2,120	$32,180	($5,150)	$4,870	$3,300	$23,730
2. Page	Married filing jointly (3)	48,472	1,244	47,228	(10,300)	5,329	9,900	27,028
3. Morris	Qualifying widow (2)	45,670	1,760	43,910	(10,300)	3,870	6,600	27,010
4. Scott	Single (2)	54,700	3,410	51,290	5,150	(6,860)	6,600	37,830
5. Ramirez	Married filing separately (1)	66,210	6,780	59,430	(5,150)	2,245	3,300	50,980
6. Young	Married filing jointly (5)	52,130	1,450	50,680	(10,300)	5,610	16,500	23,880
7. Mills	Head of household (3)	88,600	4,080	84,520	7,550	(21,230)	9,900	53,390
8. Chong	Married filing jointly (4)	38,246	696	37,550	(10,300)	8,400	13,200	14,050

9. Leslie Grant sells wholesale school supplies for Crayola Corporation. She is single, claiming three exemptions. For income tax purposes, she qualifies as a head of household. Last year she earned a total of $54,300 in salary and commission. She contributed $2,500 to her retirement plan and had the following itemized deductions: $1,231 in real estate taxes, $3,450 in mortgage interest, $2,000 in mortgage loan closing points, $420 in charitable contributions, and $3,392 in unreimbursed job expenses above the 2% adjusted gross income exclusion. From this information, calculate Leslie's taxable income.

Total income =	54,300
Adjustments	− 2,500
Adjusted gross income	$51,800

Itemized deductions = 1,231
3,450
2,000
420
+ 3,392
$10,493

Exemptions = 3,300 × 3 = $9,900

$51,800	Adjusted gross income
−10,493	Itemized deductions
− 9,900	Exemptions
$31,407	Taxable income

Use the Tax Table, Exhibit 18-3, to calculate the tax liability for the following taxpayers earning under $100,000.

Name	Filing Status	Taxable Income	Tax Liability
10. Gibbs	Married, Separately	$27,665	$3,774
11. Lundy	Head of household	74,804	$14,064
12. Harris	Single	38,150	$6,101
13. Garcia	Married, Jointly	69,915	$10,596

14. Section B
121,430.00 × .25 = 30,357.50
30,357.50 − 6,885.00 = $23,472.50

15. Section A
247,619.00 × .33 = 81,714.27
81,714.27 − 13,408.50 = $68,305.77

16. Section D
185,188.00 × .33 = 61,112.04
61,112.04 − 16,405.00 = $44,707.04

17. Section C
334,515.00 × .35 = 117,080.25
117,080.25 − 13,374.75 = $103,705.50

Use the Tax Computation Worksheet, Exhibit 18-4, to calculate the tax liability for the following taxpayers earning $100,000 or above.

Name	Filing Status	Taxable Income	Tax Liability
14. Maple	Married, Jointly	$121,430	$23,472.50
15. Cabral	Single	247,619	$68,305.77
16. Burnett	Head of household	185,188	$44,707.04
17. Wolf	Married, Separately	334,515	$103,705.50

As a newly hired IRS trainee, you have been asked to calculate the amount of tax refund or tax owed for the following taxpayers.

EXCEL

Name	Tax Liability	Tax Credits	Other Taxes	Payments	Refund/Owe (circle one)	Amount
18. Lopez	$5,320	$2,110	$325	$4,650	(Refund)/Owe	$1,115
19. Roman	3,229	750	0	3,130	(Refund)/Owe	651
20. Dean	12,280	2,453	1,232	9,540	Refund/(Owe)	1,519
21. Hyde	6,498	1,221	885	7,600	(Refund)/Owe	1,438

22. William and Pearl Pollard had combined income of $97,320 last year. For tax purposes the Pollards claim four exemptions and their filing status is married, filing jointly. They contributed $5,000 to their retirement plan and had total itemized deductions of $17,200. In addition, the Pollards had a tax credit for the disabled of $3,430. If their combined income tax withheld last year amounted to $10,887, calculate:

a. Adjusted gross income.

$97,320 Income
− 5,000 Retirement plan
$92,320 Adjusted gross income

b. Taxable income.

$92,320 Adjusted gross income
−13,200 (4 × 3,300) Exemption allowance
− 17,200 Itemized deductions
$61,920 Taxable income

c. Tax liability.

$8,596 Tax (tax table)
− 3,430 Tax credit for disabled
$5,166 Tax liability

d. Are the Pollards entitled to a refund or do they owe additional taxes? How much?

$10,887 Tax withheld
− 5,166 Tax liability
$5,721 Refund

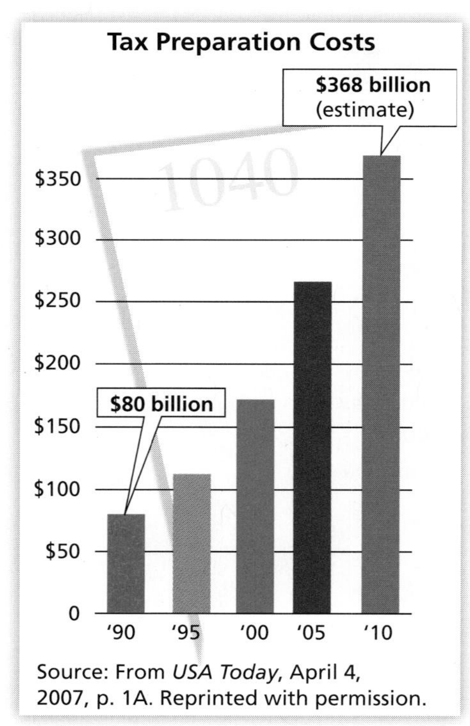

Source: From *USA Today*, April 4, 2007, p. 1A. Reprinted with permission.

Estimated Costs to Individuals and Companies Who Prepare Their Taxes

Calculate the amount of corporate income tax due and the net income after taxes for the following corporations.

	Name	Taxable Income	Tax Liability	Net Income after Taxes
23.	Pyramid Supply, Inc.	$88,955	$18,494.70	$70,460.30
24.	Eagle Corp.	$14,550,000	$4,992,500.00	$9,557,500.00
25.	Starpointe Project, Inc.	$955,000,000	$334,250,000.00	$620,750,000.00

EXCEL

BUSINESS DECISION INVESTING YOUR TAX SAVINGS

26. You are a manager for Overseas International. You earn $50,000 per year, and are in the 28% federal income tax bracket. Each year you contribute $2,500 tax free to your individual retirement account, IRA. The account earns 8% annual interest. In addition, the amount of tax that you save each year by making these "pre-tax" contributions is invested in a taxable aggressive growth mutual fund averaging 15%.

    a. How much tax do you save each year by making the retirement fund contributions?

    Tax savings = 2,500 × .28 = $700

    b. How much will the retirement fund be worth in 30 years?

    From Table 12-1, 8%, 30 periods
    2,500 × 113.28321 = $283,208.03

    c. Although the income from this investment is taxable each year, how much will the "tax savings" fund be worth in 30 years?

    From Table 12-1, 15%, 30 periods
    700 × 434.74515 = $304,321.61

In the Business World

When it comes to income tax, there is a move toward paperless filing and plastic payments.

The IRS will electronically—with your permission—debit your checking account for your income tax payment on April 15th or credit your account with your refund.

You may also use a credit card to make tax payments.

- Official Payments Corporation
  1-800-2PAY-TAX (1-800-272-9829)
  www.officialpayments.com
- Link2Gov Corporation
  1-888-PAY-1040 (1-888-729-1040)
  www.pay1040.com

CHAPTER FORMULAS

18

Sales and Excise Taxes

Sales tax = Selling price × Sales tax rate

Total purchase price = Selling price + Sales tax + Other charges

$$\text{Selling price} = \frac{\text{Total purchase price}}{100\% + \text{Sales tax rate}}$$

Sales tax = Total purchase price − Selling price

Excise tax = Selling price × Excise tax rate

Excise tax = Number of units × Excise tax per unit

Total purchase price = Selling price + Sales tax + Excise tax

Property Tax

Expressed as a Percent

Property tax = Assessed value of property × Tax rate

Expressed per $100 of Assessed Value

Property tax = Number of $100 of assessed value × Tax per $100

Expressed per $1,000 of Assessed Value

Property tax = Number of $1,000 of assessed value × Tax per $1,000

Expressed in Mills

Tax rate in decimal form = Tax rate in mills × .001

Property tax = Assessed value × Tax rate in decimal form

Community Tax Rate

$$\text{Tax rate per dollar (decimal form)} = \frac{\text{Total taxes required}}{\text{Total assessed property value}}$$

Income Tax

Refund (−) or Amount owed (+) = Tax liability − Credits + Other taxes − Payments

SUMMARY CHART 18

Section I: Sales and Excise Taxes

Topic	Important Concepts	Illustrative Examples
Determining Sales Tax by Using Sales Tax Tables **P/O 18-1, p. 649**	Sales tax is a tax based on the total retail price of tangible personal property and certain services and admissions. Exhibit 18-1 is an example of a $6\frac{1}{2}$% sales tax table. *Sales tax tables* 1. Locate the taxable retail price in the Amount of Sale column. 2. Scan to the right to locate the amount of tax due in the Tax column.	Barry Williams purchased food at Boston Market for a total of $16.23. The sales tax in that state is $6\frac{1}{2}$%. Use Exhibit 18-1 to determine the amount of sales tax due on this sale. From Exhibit 18-1 we find that the retail price of the food, $16.23, falls in the range of $16.16 to $16.30. Scanning to the right, we find the tax due on this sale is $1.06.
Calculating Sales Tax by Using the Percent Method **P/O 18-2, p. 650**	Sales tax is expressed as a percentage of the retail selling price. *Percent Method* 1. Calculate the sales tax by multiplying the retail selling price by the sales tax rate: **Sales tax = Selling price × Sales tax rate** 2. Compute total purchase price by adding the selling price, the sales tax, and any other additional charges: **Total purchase price = Selling price + Sales tax + Other charges**	Bob Rich purchased a barbecue grill for $179.95 at JCPenney. The store charged $12.00 for assembly. If the state sales tax is 4% and the city adds an additional $3\frac{1}{2}$%, what is the amount of sales tax on the grill and what is Bob's total purchase price? Sales tax rate $= 4 + 3\frac{1}{2} = 7\frac{1}{2}\%$ Sales tax = 179.95 × .075 = $13.50 Total purchase price = 179.95 + 13.50 + 12.00 = $205.45

Section I: (continued)

Topic	Important Concepts	Illustrative Examples
Calculating Selling Price and Amount of Sales Tax When Total Purchase Price Is Known **P/O 18-3, p. 651**	When the total purchase price of an item or items, including sales tax, is known, actual selling price and amount of sales tax is calculated by: 1. Calculate the selling price of an item by dividing the total purchase price by 100% plus the sales tax rate: $\textbf{Selling price} = \dfrac{\textbf{Total purchase price}}{\textbf{100\% + Sales tax rate}}$ 2. Determine the amount of sales tax by subtracting the selling price from the total purchase price: **Sales tax = Total purchase price − Selling price**	At the end of the day, the cash register at Nancy's Knitting Salon showed total purchases, including sales tax, of $2,251.83. If the sales tax rate in that state is 5%, calculate Nancy's actual sales revenue and sales tax collected. $\text{Sales revenue} = \dfrac{2{,}251.83}{1.05} = \underline{\underline{\$2{,}144.60}}$ $\text{Sales tax} = 2{,}251.83 - 2{,}144.60 = \underline{\underline{\$107.23}}$
Calculating Excise Tax **P/O 18-4, p. 652**	An excise tax is a tax levied by federal, state, and local governments on certain products and services deemed to be luxury or nonessential items. Excise tax is paid in addition to sales tax and is expressed as a percentage of the purchase price or as a fixed amount per unit purchased. *Percentage:* **Excise tax = Selling price × Excise tax rate** *Per Unit:* **Excise tax = Units × Excise tax per unit**	Larry Alison purchased fishing equipment for $244. The sales tax in his state is 4% and the federal excise tax on fishing equipment is 11%. What is the amount of each tax and the total purchase price of the equipment? $\text{Sales tax} = 244 \times .04 = \underline{\underline{\$9.76}}$ $\text{Excise tax} = 244 \times .11 = \underline{\underline{\$26.84}}$ $\text{Total purchase price} = 244 + 9.76 + 26.84 = \underline{\underline{\$280.60}}$

Section II: Property Tax

Topic	Important Concepts	Illustrative Examples
Calculating Property Tax Due with Tax Rate Expressed: **As a Percent** **P/O 18-5, p. 656**	A tax levied on the assessed value of real and certain personal property is known as property tax. *Expressed as a percent* 1. Convert the tax rate to a decimal. 2. Calculate property tax: **Property tax = Assessed value × Tax rate**	The following examples illustrate how to calculate the property tax due when the same tax is expressed in each of the four different ways. A house with an assessed value of $120,000 is subject to a property tax of 2.31%. What is the amount of property tax due? $\text{Property tax} = 120{,}000 \times .0231 = \underline{\underline{\$2{,}772}}$
Per $100 of Assessed Value **P/O 18-5, p. 656**	*Per $100 of assessed value* 1. Calculate number of $100: $\textbf{Number of \$100} = \dfrac{\textbf{Assessed value}}{\textbf{100}}$ 2. Calculate property tax: **Property tax = Number of $100 × Tax per $100**	A house with an assessed value of $120,000 is subject to a property tax of $2.31 per $100 of assessed value. What is the amount of property tax due? $\text{Number of \$100} = \dfrac{120{,}000}{100} = 1{,}200$ $\text{Property tax} = 1{,}200 \times 2.31 = \underline{\underline{\$2{,}772}}$

Section II: (continued)

Topic	Important Concepts	Illustrative Examples
Per $1,000 of Assessed Value **P/O 18-5, p. 657**	*Per $1,000 of assessed value* 1. Calculate number of $1,000: $\text{Number of \$1,000} = \dfrac{\text{Assessed value}}{1{,}000}$ 2. Calculate property tax: **Property tax = Number of $1,000 × Tax per $1,000**	A house with an assessed value of $120,000 is subject to a property tax of $23.10 per $1,000 of assessed value. What is the amount of property tax due? $\text{Number of \$1,000} = \dfrac{120{,}000}{1{,}000} = 120$ Property tax = 120 × 23.10 = $2,772
In Mills **P/O 18-5, p. 658**	*Expressed in mills* 1. Multiply tax rate in mills by .001 to get tax rate as a decimal: **Tax rate (decimal) = Tax rate in mills × .001** 2. Calculate property tax: **Property tax = Assessed value × Tax rate**	A house with an assessed value of $120,000 is subject to a property tax of 23.1 mills. What is the amount of property tax due? Tax rate (decimal) = 23.1 × .001 = .0231 Property tax = 120,000 × .0231 = $2,772
Calculating Tax Rate Necessary in a Community to Meet Budgetary Demands **P/O 18-6, p. 658**	1. **Tax rate per dollar of assessed value =** $\dfrac{\text{Total taxes required}}{\text{Total assessed property value}}$ 2. To convert tax rate per dollar to: • *Percent*—move the decimal point 2 places to the right and add a percent sign. • *Tax rate per $100*—multiply by 100. • *Tax rate per $1,000*—multiply by 1,000. • *Mills*—divide by .001.	Bragg Creek requires $5,000,000 for its annual budget. If the total assessed property value of the town is $80,000,000, what property tax rate is needed to meet those demands? Express your answer in each of the four ways. $\text{Tax rate} = \dfrac{5{,}000{,}000}{80{,}000{,}000} = .0625$ Percent = 6.25% Per $100 = .0625 × 100 = $6.25 per $100 Per $1,000 = .0625 × 1,000 = $62.50 per $1,000 $\text{Mills} = \dfrac{.0625}{.001} = 62.5 \text{ mills}$

Section III: Income Tax

Topic	Important Concepts	Illustrative Examples
Computing Taxable Income for Individuals **P/O 18-7, p. 662**	Taxable income is the amount of income that tax rates are applied to in order to calculate the amount of tax owed for the year. Use Exhibit 18-2 and the following steps to compute taxable income. 1. Determine *gross income* by adding all sources of taxable income. 2. Calculate *adjusted gross income* by subtracting the sum of all adjustments to income from the gross income. 3. Subtract the sum of the *itemized deductions* or the *standard deduction* (whichever is larger) from the adjusted gross income. See Step 3, page 662, for standard deduction amounts.	Dan and Marilyn Dupree are married. For income tax purposes they file jointly and claim four exemptions. Last year they earned a total of $45,460. They had adjustments to income of $3,241, and itemized deductions of $10,676. What is the amount of their taxable income? $45,460 Total income − 3,241 Adjustments to income $42,219 Adjusted gross income

Section III: (continued)

Topic	Important Concepts	Illustrative Examples
	4. If adjusted gross income is $112,875 or less, multiply $3,300 by the number of exemptions claimed and subtract from the amount in Step 3. The result is *taxable income*. For adjusted gross incomes over $112,875 see IRS instructions to find exemption amounts.	Since the itemized deductions are greater than the $10,300 allowed as the standard deduction for married, filing jointly, we shall use the itemized figure. The exemption allowance is 3,300 × 4 = $13,200. $42,219 Adjusted gross income − 10,676 Itemized deductions − 13,200 Exemption allowance $18,343 Taxable income
Using the Tax Table to Determine Personal Income Tax Liability P/O 18-8, p. 665	If taxable income is under $100,000, the Tax Table must be used to figure the tax liability. Exhibit 18-3 illustrates a portion of the 2006 Tax Table. 1. Read down the "If line 43 (taxable income) is—" columns and find the line that includes the amount of taxable income. 2. Find the tax liability by scanning across to the "And you are—" column containing the appropriate filing status.	Laurenzo Picata files his taxes as a head of household. If his taxable income last year was $35,552, what was his tax liability? From Exhibit 18-3, we find Laurenzo's taxable income in the range 35,550 to 35,600. Scanning across to the Head of Household column, we find that Laurenzo's tax liability is $4,799.
Using the Tax Computation Worksheet to Calculate Personal Income Tax Liability P/O 18-9, p. 671	When taxable income is $100,000 or more, the appropriate section of the Tax Computation Worksheet must be used to calculate the tax liability. Exhibit 18-4 contains the 2006 Tax Computation Worksheet. 1. Locate the section corresponding to the appropriate filing status: Section A – Single Section B – Married filing jointly or qualifying widow(er) Section C – Married filing separately Section D – Head of household 2. Read down the first column, "Taxable Income. If line 43 is–" to find the range containing the taxable income. 3. Multiply the taxable income by "multiplication amount" listed in column (b) for that range. 4. Calculate the tax liability by subtracting the "subtraction amount" listed in column (d) for that range from the result in step 3.	Vickie Howard had taxable income last year of $145,000. For income tax purposes she files as married, filing separately. Use the appropriate section of the Tax Computation Worksheet to calculate Vickie's tax liability. Step 1. For Vickie's filing status, we shall use Section C. Step 2. Her taxable income is in the range "At least $100,000 but not over $168,275." Step 3. $145,000 Taxable income × .33 Multiplication amount for that range $47,850 Step 4. $47,850.00 Result from Step 3 − 10,009.25 Subtraction amount for that range $37,840.75 Tax liability
Calculating Tax Refund or Amount of Tax Owed P/O 18-10, p. 674	To calculate the refund or tax owed, we must finally consider tax credits, other taxes, and payments. 1. Subtract total credits from the tax liability. 2. Add total of other taxes to the tax liability to get total tax.	After preparing his taxes, Mike Patterson determined that he had a tax liability of $7,370. In addition, he owed other taxes of $1,225 and was entitled to a tax credit of $3,420. If Mike's employer withheld $445 each month for income tax, is Mike entitled to a refund or does he owe additional taxes? How much?

Section III: (continued)

Topic	Important Concepts	Illustrative Examples
	3. If total payments are greater than total tax, a refund of the difference is due. If total payments are less than total tax, the difference is the tax owed.	\$7,370 Tax liability − 3,420 Tax credits + 1,225 Other taxes \$5,175 Total tax Payments = 445 × 12 = \$5,340 \$5,340 Payments − 5,175 Total tax \$165 Tax refund due (may be applied to next year's taxes)
Calculating Corporate Income Tax and Net Income after Taxes **P/O 18-11, p. 675**	Corporate income tax is calculated using the Corporate Tax Rate Schedule, Exhibit 18-6. 1. Read down the "Over—" and "But not over—" columns to find the range containing the taxable income. 2. Subtract the lower number of the range from the taxable income. 3. Multiply the result from Step 2 by the tax rate listed for that range. 4. Calculate the tax liability by adding the result from Step 3 to the dollar amount of tax indicated for that range. 5. Calculate the net income after taxes by subtracting the tax liability from the taxable income. **Net income after taxes = Income before tax − Tax liability**	The Novelty Nook, Inc., had net income before taxes of \$62,000. What is the amount of income tax due and the net income after taxes? *Step 1.* The taxable income falls in the range 50,000 to 75,000. *Step 2.* \$62,000 Taxable income − 50,000 Lower number of range 12,000 *Step 3.* \$12,000 Result from Step 2 × .25 Tax rate for that range \$3,000 *Step 4.* \$3,000 Result from Step 3 + 7,500 Dollar amount \$10,500 Tax liability *Step 5.* \$62,000 Income before taxes − 10,500 Tax liability \$51,500 Net income after taxes

TRY IT EXERCISE SOLUTIONS FOR CHAPTER 18

1. From Exhibit 18-1, sales tax on \$12.49 = \$.82

2. Sales tax = Selling price × Sales tax rate

Sales tax = 38,600 × .05 = \$1,930

Total purchase price = Selling price + Sales tax + Other charges

Total purchase price = 38,600 + 1,930 + 240 = \$40,770

3. $\text{Selling price} = \dfrac{\text{Total purchase price}}{100\% + \text{Sales tax rate}}$

$\text{Selling price} = \dfrac{3{,}520}{100\% + 8\frac{1}{2}\%} = \dfrac{3{,}520}{1.085} = \$3{,}244.24$

Sales tax = Total purchase price − Selling price

Sales tax = 3,520.00 − 3,244.24 = \$275.76

4. Sales tax = Selling price × Sales tax rate

Sales tax = 129.95 × .05 = \$6.50

Excise tax = Selling price × Excise tax rate

Excise tax = 129.95 × .11 = \$14.29

Total purchase price = Selling price + Sales tax + Excise tax

Total purchase price = 129.95 + 6.50 + 14.29 = \$150.74

5. Tax rate = 6.3% = .063

Property tax = Assessed value × Tax rate

Property tax = 160,000 × .063 = \$10,080

6. $\text{Number of } \$100 = \frac{\text{Assessed value}}{100} = \frac{50{,}800}{100} = 508$

Property tax = Number of $100 × Tax per $100

Property tax = 508 × 3.60 = $1,828.80

7. $\text{Number of } \$1{,}000 = \frac{\text{Assessed value}}{1{,}000} = \frac{325{,}400}{1{,}000} = 325.4$

Property tax = Number of $1,000 × Tax per $1,000

Property tax = 325.4 × 88.16 = $28,687.26

8. Tax rate in decimal form = Tax rate in mills × .001

Tax rate in decimal form = 54.1 × .001 = .0541

Property tax = Assessed value × Tax rate in decimal form

Property tax = 85,300 × .0541 = $4,614.73

9. $\text{Tax rate per dollar} = \frac{\text{Total tax required}}{\text{Total assessed property value}}$

$\text{Tax rate per dollar} = \frac{3{,}435{,}000}{71{,}800{,}000} = .0478412 = \$.0479$

a. *Percent* .0479 = 4.79%

b. *Per $100* .0479 × 100 = $4.79

c. *Per $1,000* .0479 × 1,000 = $47.90

d. *Mills* $\frac{.0479}{.001} = 47.9 \text{ mills}$

10.
$35,000	Wages
+1,200	Cash dividends
+5,000	Sale of stock (gain)
$41,200	Total income

$41,200	Total income
− 1,500	Retirement contributions
$39,700	Adjusted gross income

$1,000	Medical expenses
1,945	Real estate taxes
2,500	Mortgage interest
+ 300	Charitable contributions
5,745	Itemized deductions

$39,700	Adjusted gross income
−5,745	Itemized deductions
−6,600	($3,300 × 2) exemptions
$27,355	Taxable income

11. Using Exhibit 18-3, Tax liability:

Barry and Tricia Wark's tax liability = $9,221

12. Using the Tax Computation Worksheet, Exhibit 18-4, Section D:

123,545.00	Taxable income
× .28	Multiplication amount, column (b), for that range
$ 34,592.60	

34,592.60	
− 7,822.50	Subtraction amount, column (d), for that range
$26,770.10	Mark's tax liability

13.
$14,600	Tax liability
+ 2,336	Other taxes
− 668	Child care credit
− 1,719	Foreign tax credit
$14,549	Total tax

Employer withheld 270 × 52 = $14,040

Tax owed = Total tax − Payments

Tax owed = 14,549 − 14,040 = $509

14. Using Corporate Tax Rate Schedule, Exhibit 18-6:

$311,200	Income before taxes
−100,000	Lower number of range
$211,200	
× .39	Tax rate
82,368	Computed tax
+ 22,250	Dollar amount for that range
$104,618	Tax liability

$311,200	Income before taxes
− 104,618	Tax liability
$206,582	Net income after tax

CONCEPT REVIEW

1. A tax based on the retail selling or rental price of tangible personal property is known as ____ tax. (18-1)
sales

2. Sales tax expressed in its most common form, as a percent of the retail price of an item, is known as the sales tax ____. (18-2)
rate

3. Write the formula for calculating the selling price of an item when the total purchase price, including sales tax, is known. (18-3)

$\text{Selling price} = \frac{\text{Total purchase price}}{100\% + \text{Sales tax rate}}$

4. A tax levied on certain luxury or nonessential products and services such as alcoholic beverages, furs, tobacco products, and airline tickets is known as ____ tax. (18-4)
excise

5. Another name for property tax is _____ _____ tax. (18-5)
ad valorem

6. The value of property for tax purposes is known as the _____ value. The value of property based on location, size, cost, and other such factors is known as the fair _____ value. (18-5)
assessed, market

7. What are the four methods of expressing property tax rates? (18-5)
decimal or percent of assessed value
per $100 of assessed value
per $1,000 of assessed value
mills (one one-thousandths of a dollar)

8. As the tax assessor for your city, what formula would you use to calculate the tax rate per dollar of assessed property value necessary to provide the budgeted government services for next year? (18-6)

$$\text{Tax rate per dollar} = \frac{\text{Total taxes required}}{\text{Total assessed property value}}$$

9. A pay-as-you-go tax based on the amount of income of an individual or corporation is known as _____ tax. The amount of income that tax rates are applied to in order to calculate the amount of tax owed is known as _____ income. (18-7)
income, taxable

10. When calculating an individual's taxable income, we subtract the sum of the _____ deductions or the _____ deduction, whichever is larger, from adjusted gross income. (18-7)
itemized, standard

11. In 2006, if adjusted gross income was $112,875 or less, $3,300 was multiplied by the total number of _____ claimed, and that product subtracted from adjusted gross income to arrive at taxable income. (18-7)
exemptions

12. If an individual's taxable income is less than $100,000, we use the tax _____ to find the tax liability. When the taxable income is $100,000 or more, we use the Tax _____ Worksheet to calculate tax liability. (18-8, 18-9)
table, Computation

13. A tax _____ is a dollar-for-dollar subtraction from an individual's or corporation's tax liability. (18-10)
credit

14. According to the Corporate Tax Rate Schedule, corporate tax rates range from a low of _____ to a high of _____. (18-11)
15%, 38%

CHAPTER 18 ASSESSMENT TEST

Name

Class

Answers

1. $1.17 $19.05
2. $.19 $3.09
3. $6.62 $141.62
4. $1.22
$1.02
$26.64
5. $1,184.63
$755.00
$19,489.63
6. $1,188.00
$89.10
7. a. $25.42
b. $471.30

Use Exhibit 18-1 to determine the sales tax and calculate the total purchase price for the following items.

	Item	Selling Price	Sales Tax	Total Purchase Price
1.	alarm clock	$17.88	$1.17	$19.05
2.	magazine	2.90	.19	3.09

Calculate the missing information for the following purchases.

	Item	Selling Price	Sales Tax Rate	Sales Tax	Excise Tax Rate	Excise Tax	Total Purchase Price
3.	ceiling fan	$135.00	4.9%	$6.62	0	0	$141.62
4.	cable TV bill	24.40	5	1.22	4.2	$1.02	26.64
5.	fur coat	17,550	$6\frac{3}{4}$	1,184.63	10% (over $10,000)	755.00	19,489.63
6.	scanner	1,188.00	$7\frac{1}{2}$	89.10	0	0	$1,277.10

7. Eric Cobbe purchased a microwave oven for $345.88. The delivery charge was $25.00 and the installation amounted to $75.00. The state sales tax is $6\frac{1}{4}$ % and the county tax is 1.1%.

a. What is the total amount of sales tax on the microwave oven?
Total tax = 345.88(6.25% + 1.1%) = $25.42

b. What is the total purchase price?
Total purchase price = 345.88 + 25.42 + 25.00 + 75.00 = $471.30

8. Last week Wood Masters Flooring had total sales, including sales tax, of $16,502.50. The store is located in a state that has a sales tax of $6\frac{3}{4}$%. As the accountant for the store, calculate:

a. The amount of sales revenue.

$$\text{Sales revenue} = \frac{16{,}502.50}{100\% + 6.75\%} = \$15{,}459.02$$

b. The amount of sales taxes that must be sent to the state Department of Revenue.

Sales tax = 16,502.50 − 15,459.02 = $1,043.48

9. Trailside Transport, Inc., purchased 580 tires rated at 50 pounds each for its fleet of trucks. The tires had a retail price of $85 each. The sales tax is 4.5% and the federal excise tax is $.15 per pound.

a. What are the amount of sales tax per tire and the total sales tax?

Sales tax per tire = 85 × 4.5% = $3.83
Total sales tax = 3.83 × 580 = $2,221.40

b. What are the amount of federal excise tax per tire and the total excise tax?

Excise tax per tire = 50 × .15 = $7.50
Total excise tax = 7.50 × 580 = $4,350

c. What is the total purchase price of the tires?

Total purchase price = 85 × 580 = 49,300
49,300.00 + 2,221.40 + 4,350.00 = $55,871.40

Calculate the assessed value and the property tax due on the following properties.

	Fair Market Value	Assessment Rate	Assessed Value	Property Tax Rate	Property Tax Due
10.	$92,200	80%	$73,760	2.33%	$1,718.61
11.	74,430	70	52,101	$12.72 per $1,000	662.72
12.	2,450,900	100	2,450,900	$2.16 per $100	52,939.44
13.	165,230	50	82,615	28.98 mills	2,394.18

Calculate the property tax rate required to meet the budgetary demands of the following communities.

				Property Tax Rate			
	Community	Total Assessed Property Valuation	Total Taxes Required	Percent	Per $100	Per $1,000	Mills
14.	Evergreen	$860,000,000	$32,400,000	3.77%	$3.77	$37.70	37.7
15.	Lakeville	438,000,000	7,200,000	1.64%	1.64	16.40	16.4

16. The Espinosa family is considering the purchase of a home. They have narrowed the choice down to a $162,000 home in Palm Springs and a $151,200 home in Weston. With regard to property taxes, Palm Springs has an assessment rate of 90% and a tax rate of 22.45 mills, while Weston has a 100% assessment rate and a tax rate of $2.60 per $100 of assessed value. Which house has the higher property tax, and by how much?

Palm Springs
162,000 × 90% = 145,800(22.45 × .001)
= $3,273.21

Weston
$$151{,}200 \times 100\% = \frac{151{,}200}{100} \times 2.60$$
= $3,931.20

Weston is higher by $657.99

CHAPTER 18

Name

Class

Answers

8. a. $15,459.02
b. $1,043.48
9. a. $3.83
$2,221.40
b. $7.50
$4,350
c. $55,871.40
10. $73,760
$1,718.61
11. $52,101
$662.72
12. $2,450,900
$52,939.44
13. $82,615
$2,394.18
14. 3.77%
$3.77
$37.70
37.7
15. 1.64%
$1.64
$16.40
16.4
16. Weston is higher by $657.99

CHAPTER

Name

Class

Answers

17. a. 0.07%

b. $.07 per $100

c. $.70 per $1,000

d. 0.7 mills

17. As the tax assessor for Oxford County you have been informed that an additional $4,500,000 in taxes will be required next year for new street lighting and bridge repairs. If the total assessed value of the property in Oxford County is $6,500,000,000, how much will this add to property taxes?

a. As a percent

$$\text{Additional tax} = \frac{4{,}500{,}000}{6{,}500{,}000{,}000} = .00069 = 0.07\%$$

b. Per $100 of assessed value

$.07 per $100

c. Per $1,000 of assessed value

$.70 per $1,000

d. In mills

0.7 mills

Calculate the missing information for the following taxpayers.

	Name	Filing Status (Exemptions)	Income	Adjustments to Income	Adjusted Gross Income	Standard Deduction (circle your choice)	Itemized Deductions (circle your choice)	Exemption Allowance	Taxable Income
18.	Grant	Single (1)	$34,900	$660	$34,240	$5,150	($5,480)	$3,300	$25,460
19.	Collins	Married filing jointly (3)	66,003	2,180	63,823	(10,300)	6,850	9,900	43,623
20.	Lee	Head of household (4)	38,100	2,450	35,650	(7,550)	5,930	13,200	$14,900

18. $25,460

19. $43,623

20. $14,900

21. $44,351.96

22. $14,276.00

23. $2,984.00

24. $29,388.06

25. $61,273.25

26. $6,114.00

27. Owe, $228

28. Refund, $1,527

As an accountant for the Give Me A Break Tax Service, use the Tax Table, Exhibit 18-3, or the Tax Computation Worksheet, Exhibit 18-4, whichever is appropriate, to calculate the tax liability for the following clients.

	Name	Filing Status	Taxable Income	Tax Liability
21.	Demerville	Head of household	$184,112	$44,351.96
22.	Lockhart	Single	70,890	$14,276.00
23.	Walsh	Married, Jointly	24,938	$2,984.00
24.	Chen	Single	125,202	$29,388.06
25.	Kimball	Married, Separately	213,280	$61,273.25
26.	Serrano	Single	38,216	$6,114.00

Calculate the amount of tax refund or tax owed for the following taxpayers.

	Name	Tax Liability	Tax Credits	Other Taxes	Payments	Refund/Owe (circle one)	Amount
27.	O'Reilly	$6,540	$1,219	0	$5,093	Refund/(Owe)	$228
28.	Green	25,112	7,650	2,211	21,200	(Refund)/Owe	1,527

29. Bob Paris is the promotions director for Power 105, a local radio station. He is single and claims two exemptions. Last year Bob earned a salary of $2,450 per month from the station and received a $2,500 Christmas bonus. In addition, he earned royalties of $3,250 from a song he wrote, which was recorded and made popular by a famous musical group. Bob's itemized deductions amounted to $1,850 and he is entitled to a tax credit of $1,765. If the radio station withheld $325 per month for income tax, what is Bob's:

CHAPTER

Name

Class

Answers

29. a. $35,150

b. $23,400

c. $1,371

d. $2,529

30. a. $297,670

b. $577,830

31. a. $12,451

b. Not enough withheld

a. Adjusted gross income?

$29,400 (2,450 × 12) Income
+ 2,500 Bonus
+ 3,250 Royalties
$35,150 Adjusted gross income

b. Taxable income?

$35,150 Adjusted gross income
− 5,150 Standard deduction
− 6,600 (3,300 × 2) Exemption allowance
$23,400 Taxable income

c. Tax liability?

$3,136 Tax (tax table)
− 1,765 Tax credit
$1,371 Tax liability

d. Is Bob entitled to a refund or does he owe additional taxes? How much?

$3,900 (325 × 12) Tax withheld
− 1,371
$2,529 Refund

30. You are the tax consultant for Fairmont Associates, Inc. If the company had taxable income of $875,500 last year, calculate:

a. Corporate tax liability.

Tax liability = 113,900 + 34%(875,500 − 335,000)
= 113,900 + 183,770 = $297,670

b. Net income after taxes.

Net income = 875,500 − 297,670 = $577,830

BUSINESS DECISION THE 90% RULE, HAPPY NEW YEAR!

31. Javier Ramirez, a successful software engineer for Miami–Dade Industries, earns a gross income of $6,000 per month. Javier is single, claims one exemption, and uses the standard deduction. Throughout last year, his company withheld $900 each month from his paycheck for federal income tax.

Today is January 4th. As Javier's accountant, you just informed him that although his tax return is due at the IRS by April 15, 90% of the income tax due for last year must be paid by January 15, or a penalty would be imposed.

a. Calculate the amount of tax Javier owes for the year.

$72,000 (6,000 × 12) Total income
− 5,150 Standard deduction
− 3,300 Exemption allowance
$63,550 Taxable income
Tax liability (tax table) = $12,451

b. Did his company withhold enough from each paycheck to cover the 90% requirement?

900 × 12 = $10,800 Amount withheld

12,451 × 90% = $11,205.90 Amount required

Not enough withheld

In the Business World

Every year the Internal Revenue Service publicizes a taxpayer's right to apply for a four-month extension past April 15, a request rarely denied. In 2006, more than 10 million taxpayers took advantage of this provision by filing an IRS Form 4868.

Not as well known is that these late filers can also get an additional two months extension, until October 15, by filing a Form 2688 or writing a letter of explanation to the IRS.

For many of the late filers, the extension amounts to a free loan from Uncle Sam, as long as they have paid at least 90 percent of their taxes in withholding or installments.

CHAPTER

Name

Class

Answers

31. c. $405.90

d. $18.02

e. $1,068.83

c. How much should Javier send the IRS by January 15, so he will not be penalized?

$11,205.90	Amount required
− 10,800.00	Amount withheld
$405.90	Amount due

d. If Javier waits until April 15 to send the balance of his taxes to the IRS, how much will he be penalized, if the penalty is 18% per year, or 1.5% per month on the shortfall up to 90%? (*Hint:* Use the simple formula, $I = PRT$, with exact interest.)

January 15 to April 15 = 90 Days

$I = PRT$

$I = 405.90 \times .18 \times \frac{90}{365}$

$I =$ $18.02 Penalty charge

e. If Javier gets a 10% raise, all other factors being the same, how much should he tell his payroll department to withhold from each month's paycheck so that 90% of the tax due will have been taken out?

72,000 × 110% = $79,200

$79,200	New salary
− 3,300	Exemption allowance
− 5,150	Standard deduction
$70,750	Taxable income

Taxable liability (tax table) = $14,251

14,251.00 × 90% = $12,825.90 Required by January 15

$\frac{12,825.90}{12}$ = $1,068.83 Withholding per month

COLLABORATIVE LEARNING ACTIVITY

Your Tax Dollars at Work

The primary focus of this chapter has been on calculating the amount of taxes that are due. Now, as a team, do some research into how your local, state, and federal tax dollars are being spent.

1. Local Level. As we have learned, local tax dollars are generally raised from property and local sales taxes. Is this true in your area? Contact your local tax assessor's office to determine the following:
   a. What are the local taxing units: city, county, municipality, district, province, parish, other?
   b. How are local taxes derived for each unit?
   c. What are the tax rates for each unit?
   d. How have the rates changed over the past five years?
   e. What is the latest tax budget for each unit and how is the money being spent?
   f. List five major projects in your area that are currently, recently, or soon-to-be funded by your tax dollars.
   g. As a team, what is your overall opinion of "your local tax dollars at work"?
2. State level. Tax revenue in most states is derived either from sales tax, state income tax, or a combination of both. Is this true in your state? As a team, contact your state taxing authority to determine the following:
   a. How are state taxes derived?
   b. What are the tax rates?
   c. How have the rates changed over the past five years?
   d. What is the latest tax budget and how is the money being spent?

e. List five or more major projects in your state that are currently, recently, or soon-to-be funded by tax dollars.
f. As a team, what is your overall opinion of "your state tax dollars at work"?

3. Federal level. As we have learned, federal tax revenues are derived from excise taxes; individual income taxes; Social Security and Medicare receipts; and corporate income taxes. As a team, research the Internet to determine the following:
   a. What is the current year's amount of excise taxes; individual income taxes; Social Security and Medicare receipts; and corporate income taxes collected by the federal government? Where did you find this information?
   b. From the White House's Office of Management and Budget, research the president's latest federal budget. Construct or find a pie chart of the major categories of the budget by dollar amount and percent breakdown.
   c. How have the categories changed over the past five years?
   d. As a team, what is your overall opinion of "your federal tax dollars at work"?

http://www.contemporarymath.com

Contemporary Math

ContemporaryMath.com

All the Math That's Fit to Learn

A Taxing Situation, AMT!

According to the Internal Revenue Service, the tax laws give preferential treatment to certain kinds of income and allow special deductions and credits for certain kinds of expenses. The **alternative minimum tax, AMT**, enacted in Congress in 1969, attempts to ensure that anyone who benefits from these tax advantages pays at least a minimum amount of tax. Because Congressional "patches" are required each year to prevent the AMT from affecting millions more taxpayers, it has become a political "hot potato."

At today's AMT exemption levels and rules, those hit the hardest are families, those who live in an area with high real estate taxes and costs, and those who own a small business. The AMT adds complexity to an already complex tax code by essentially making people calculate their taxes twice. Taxpayers whose AMT liability exceeds their regular tax liability pay the difference as AMT.

Here's how it works: The AMT replaces personal exemptions and some deductions (most notably, the standard deduction and the deduction of state and local taxes) with an AMT exemption and applies two tax rates—26% on the first $175,000 and 28% on any excess—to the resulting AMT taxable income.

Unlike the regular income tax, the AMT is not indexed for inflation. As that liability rises each year relative to regular income tax liability, more and more taxpayers owe AMT. In the years from 1996 to 2006, the number of people paying the tax has risen from 720,000 to 3.5 million. The charts on the right illustrate what happens if Congress fails to make their annual "patch" to exemption levels.

Source: IRS, www.irs.gov; Tax Policy Center, www.taxpolicycenter.org

Quote...UnQuote

- You have to admire the Internal Revenue Service. Any organization that makes that much money without advertising deserves respect. **–Joe Griffith**
- Education is learning things you didn't even know you didn't know. **–Unknown**

AMT–Number of Taxpayers
(millions)

30, 25, 20, 15, 10, 5, 0

2.1 · 29.3

'02 · '07[1] · '09[1]

Projection

[1] Projection if Congress does not make annual "fixes."

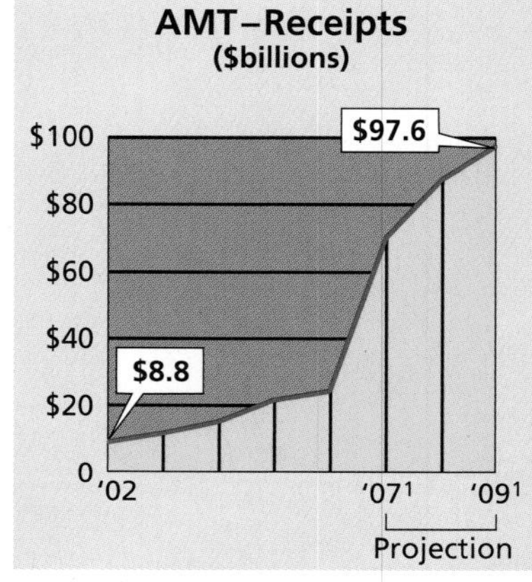

[1] Projection if Congress does not make annual "fixes."

Pepper . . . and Salt

"I've run the AMT numbers. I'll marry you."

Taxing Humor

- When you put the 2 words "The" and "IRS" together, it spells: "Theirs."
- A fool and his money are soon parted. The rest of us wait until income tax time.
- A lot of people still have the first dollar they ever made. The IRS has all the others.
- There are two types of people who complain about paying their taxes, men and women.
- Whoever said that truth never hurts never had to fill out a Form 1040.
- America is the land of opportunity. Everyone can become a taxpayer.

Source: www.butlerWebs.com/jokes/taxes/htm

Internet · 100%

Insurance

CHAPTER 19

PERFORMANCE OBJECTIVES

19 SECTION I LIFE INSURANCE

insurance A mechanism for reducing financial risk and spreading financial loss due to unexpected events.

Insurance is the promise to substitute future economic certainty for uncertainty and to replace the unknown with a sense of security. It is a mechanism for reducing financial risk and spreading financial loss due to unexpected events such as the death or disability of an individual, a home or business fire, a flood, an earthquake, an automobile accident, a negligence lawsuit, or an illness. These are only a few of the uncertainties that businesses and individuals can protect against by purchasing insurance. Companies may even purchase business interruption insurance, which covers the loss of income that may occur as a result of a multitude of perils.

Insurance is a very large and important segment of the U.S. economic system. Today, there are more than 6,000 insurance companies, employing more than 2.3 million persons and collecting close to $240 billion in annual premiums. The insurance industry is second only to commercial banking as a source of investment funds, because insurance companies invest the billions of premium dollars they receive each year in a wide range of investments.

shared risk The theory on which insurance is based; protection is purchased by many whose total payments are pooled together to pay off those few who actually incur a particular loss.

actuaries Statisticians employed by insurance companies who calculate the probability or chance of a certain insurable event occurring.

Insurance is based on the theory of **shared risk**, which means that insurance protection is purchased by many whose total payments are pooled together to pay off those few who actually incur a particular loss. Insurance companies use statisticians known as **actuaries** to calculate the probability or chance of a certain insurable event occurring. Based on a series of complicated calculations, insurance rates are then set. The rates are high enough to cover the cost of expected loss payments in the future and to provide a profit for the insurance company.

This chapter covers three major categories of insurance: life insurance, property insurance, and motor vehicle insurance. Within these three categories are several hundred different products or lines. Each year, companies market new insurance products to meet the needs of a changing society. Recently, for example, insurance was made available to cover the loss of communication satellites during launch, space travel, and reentry.

insurer, carrier, or underwriter The company offering the insurance protection and assuring payment in the event of a loss.

Let's start with some basic terminology of the insurance industry. The company offering the insurance protection and assuring payment in the event of a loss is known as the **insurer**, **carrier**, or **underwriter**. The individual or business purchasing the protection is the

The average insured household is covered by more than $250,000 in life insurance.

insured or **policyholder**. The document stipulating the terms of the contract between the insurer and the insured is the **policy**. The amount of protection provided by the policy is the **face value**, and the amount paid at regular intervals to purchase this protection is known as the **premium**. The **beneficiary** is the person or institution to whom the proceeds of the policy are paid in the event that a loss occurs.

The insurance industry is regulated by a number of authorities, including federal, state, and some inside the industry itself. This regulation is designed to promote the public welfare by maintaining the solvency of insurance companies, providing consumer protection, and ensuring fair trade practices as well as fair contracts at fair prices.

Insurance regulations, procedures, and laws vary widely from state to state. Most states have insurance commissions, departments, divisions, or boards that regulate all aspects of the insurance industry. Some of their responsibilities include premium structure and computation, insurance requirements, and salesperson education and licensing. This chapter focuses on calculating the premiums and the payouts of typical life, property, and motor vehicle insurance policies.

insured, or policyholder The person or business purchasing the insurance protection.

policy The document stipulating the terms of the contract between the insurer and the insured.

face value The amount of protection provided by the policy.

premium The amount paid at regular intervals to purchase insurance protection.

beneficiary The person or institution to whom the proceeds of the policy are paid in the event that a loss occurs.

UNDERSTANDING LIFE INSURANCE AND CALCULATING TYPICAL PREMIUMS FOR VARIOUS TYPES OF POLICIES

Most individuals enjoy feeling that they are in control of their financial destiny. Few products are more important to that sense of security than life insurance. **Life insurance** guarantees a specified sum of money to the surviving beneficiaries on the death of the person who is insured. Over the years, the average amount of life insurance per insured household has been steadily increasing. In 1960, for example, each insured household had an average of $13,000 in life insurance. By 1970, the average had doubled to about $26,000. By 1980, it doubled again, to more than $50,000. Today, the average insured household has more than $250,000 in life insurance coverage. Exhibit 19-1 lists the top 10 life insurance companies by revenue.

life insurance A type of insurance that guarantees a specified sum of money to the surviving beneficiaries upon the death of the person who is insured.

Exhibit 19-1
Top 10 Life Insurance Companies by Revenue

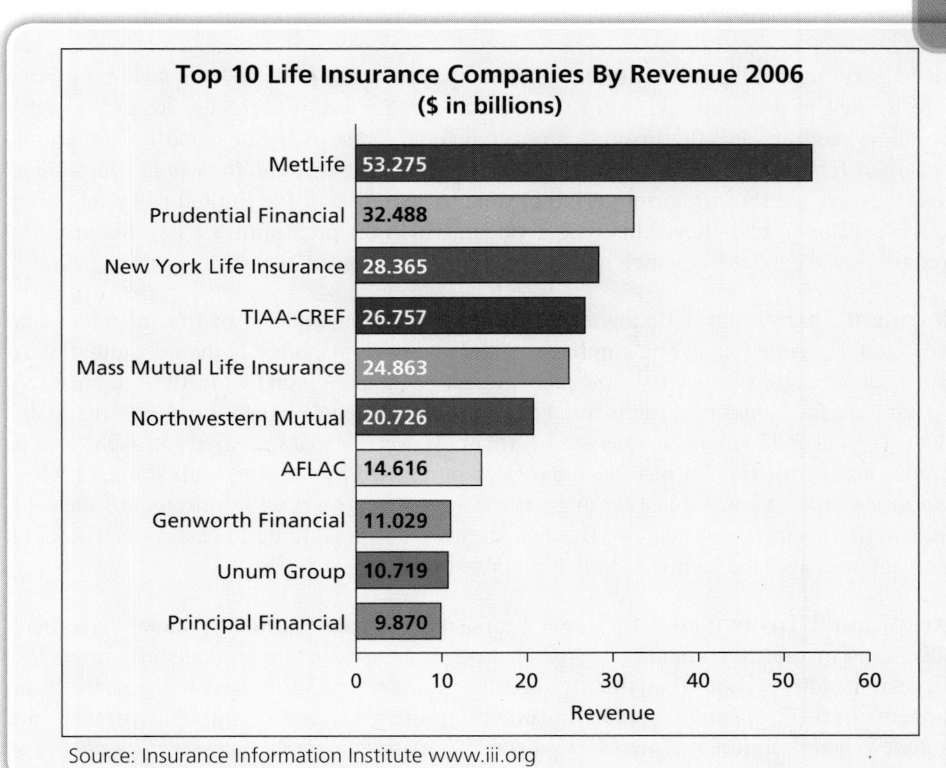

Source: Insurance Information Institute www.iii.org

In the Business World

Should you purchase insurance from an *agent* or a *broker?* Insurance agents are employees of one specific company, such as MetLife, Prudential, or AFLAC. They can only sell policies from the one company they represent.

Insurance brokers, on the other hand, are "independent" agents who represent many insurance companies. They have the advantage of being able to "shop" numerous companies to find the one that offers the best policy at the best price for you. When purchasing any form of insurance, you should either deal with one broker or do the shopping yourself with several agents.

term insurance A type of life insurance that offers pure insurance protection, paying the face value of the policy to the beneficiaries upon the death of the insured.

permanent insurance A type of insurance that combines an investment component with risk protection in order to provide the policyholder with both a death benefit and attractive investment returns.

There are two basic types of policies: those that pay only if the policyholder dies **(term insurance)** and those that pay whether the policyholder lives or dies **(permanent insurance)**. Today, many insurance policies combine an investment component with risk protection to provide the policyholder with both a death benefit if he or she dies and attractive investment returns if he or she lives. In this section, we examine five popular types of life insurance policies: term, whole life, limited payment life, endowment, and nontraditional.

Here are some rules to remember when buying life insurance:

- Evaluate and understand your needs.
- Buy from a company licensed in your state.
- Select an agent who is competent and trustworthy.
- Shop around to compare costs and benefits.
- Buy only the amount you need and can afford.
- Ask about lower premiums for nonsmokers.
- Read and understand your policy.
- Inform your beneficiaries about the insurance you own.
- Keep your policy in a safe place at home and keep the company's name and policy number in a safe deposit box.

For additional information and assistance, contact the Insurance Information Institute at 1-800-331-9146 www.iii.org

Types of Life Insurance

Term Insurance. This type of life insurance offers pure insurance protection, paying the face value of the policy to the beneficiaries on the death of the insured. With term insurance, there is no investment component. All the premium goes toward purchasing the risk coverage. With most term policies, the premium increases periodically, because the risk of death of the insured increases with age. Term policies may be purchased with premiums increasing every year, every 5 years, every 10 years, and so on.

Renewable term insurance allows the policyholder the option of renewing the policy for another 5- or 10-year period, regardless of his or her health. The premiums on these policies are higher than nonrenewable term insurance. Because it is impossible to predict one's future health, many persons opt for the renewable policy. Another common type of insurance, known as convertible term, allows the policyholder to trade in or convert the term policy for permanent insurance with an investment element and cash value, without having to prove one's health status.

Whole Life Insurance. Whole life, also known as ordinary life and straight life, is the most common type of permanent insurance. With whole life insurance, policyholders agree to pay premiums for their entire lives. Whole life insurance offers a guaranteed premium and death benefit as well as a guaranteed minimum cash value, which can be borrowed against if necessary. When the insured dies, the beneficiaries receive the face value of the policy. Having cash value is like having a savings account within the policy that grows each year. If the policyholder lives long enough, the cash value can be received as an annuity to supplement retirement income in later years.

Limited Payment Life Insurance. Limited payment life policies have level premiums that are limited to a certain period of time. After this period, usually 10, 20, or 30 years, the policy is paid up, and the insured is covered for the rest of his or her life. The premiums charged for limited payment policies are higher than premiums for whole life policies because they are paid for a shorter period of time. A variation of the limited payment policy is the life paid-up at 65 policy. This type is one in which the premiums are payable until the insured reaches age 65, after which no more premiums are owed.

TEACHING TIP

Point out to students that term insurance is initially cheaper than other types of policies that offer the same amount of protection. Therefore, it gives the greatest immediate "coverage per dollar."

One common type, *decreasing term*, reduces coverage over time, paying less to the beneficiary as time passes. It is often used to protect a long-term decreasing debt, such as a home mortgage.

Endowment Insurance. Endowment insurance is a combination of life insurance and an accelerated savings plan. The emphasis of the endowment policy is the accumulation of money. Endowment insurance pays the face amount of the policy on the death of the insured. It also pays the face amount if the insured is alive as of a specified date, known as the maturity date. Typical endowment periods are 10, 15, or 20 years or to a specified age such as 65 or 70. Traditionally, this type of insurance has been purchased by families with young children to save money for college education or by those who want to set up a retirement fund with immediate life insurance protection. Because they are designed to build cash values quickly, endowment policies have comparatively high premiums.

Nontraditional Insurance. In recent years, certain nontraditional policies have been introduced by insurance companies. Most of these interest-sensitive products are more flexible in design and provisions than their traditional counterparts. With these policies, the basic components of a life insurance policy, insurance (protection) and savings (investment), are separated. When premium payments are made, a portion known as the *mortality charge* is deducted to pay for the insurance coverage. This mortality charge increases with the age of the policyholder each year because the probability of death increases with age. The remaining amount, after other fees are deducted, goes to the investment *side fund*.

- *Universal life* is the most popular interest-sensitive policy. It features a minimum guaranteed death benefit and flexible premiums and face amounts. The insurance company decides on the type of investments to make, with the earnings credited to the side fund.
- *Variable life* is a higher-risk interest-sensitive policy that allows the policyholder to choose how the side fund will be invested. Typical choices include stocks, bonds, money market accounts, and real estate funds. Although this policy has a guaranteed death benefit, it does not have a guaranteed cash value like universal life.
- *Variable/universal life* is a recently introduced policy that combines features of both variable life and universal life. These policies offer flexible premiums and guaranteed death benefits, both of which can be adjusted by the policyholder. The cash value is not guaranteed and depends on the investment performance of the funds selected by the policyholder.

Calculating Premiums

Insurance premiums are based on the age and sex of the insured as well as the type of policy being purchased. Premiums are less expensive for younger people because their probability of dying is lower than for older people. Females pay lower rates than males of the same age because they have a longer life expectancy than males.

Life insurance is purchased in increments of $1,000 of face value. The actuaries at insurance companies generate comprehensive rate tables, listing the premiums per $1,000 of insurance for males and females of all ages. Table 19-1 is a typical example of such a table.

19-1

Table 19-1
Annual Life Insurance Premiums
(Per $1,000 of Face Value)

	Term Insurance				Permanent Insurance					
	5-Year Term		10-Year Term		Whole Life		20-Payment Life		20-Year Endowment	
Age	Male	Female	Male	Female	Male	Female	Male	Female	Male	Female
18	$ 2.32	$ 1.90	$ 4.33	$ 4.01	$13.22	$11.17	$23.14	$19.21	$33.22	$29.12
19	2.38	1.96	4.42	4.12	13.60	11.68	24.42	20.92	33.68	30.04
20	2.43	2.07	4.49	4.20	14.12	12.09	25.10	21.50	34.42	31.28
21	2.49	2.15	4.57	4.29	14.53	12.53	25.83	22.11	34.90	31.79
22	2.55	2.22	4.64	4.36	14.97	12.96	26.42	22.89	35.27	32.40
23	2.62	2.30	4.70	4.42	15.39	13.41	27.01	23.47	35.70	32.93
24	2.69	2.37	4.79	4.47	15.90	13.92	27.74	24.26	36.49	33.61
25	2.77	2.45	4.85	4.51	16.38	14.38	28.40	25.04	37.02	34.87
26	2.84	2.51	4.92	4.60	16.91	14.77	29.11	25.96	37.67	35.30
27	2.90	2.58	5.11	4.69	17.27	15.23	29.97	26.83	38.23	35.96
28	2.98	2.64	5.18	4.77	17.76	15.66	30.68	27.54	38.96	36.44
29	3.07	2.70	5.23	4.84	18.12	16.18	31.52	28.09	39.42	37.21
30	3.14	2.78	5.30	4.93	18.54	16.71	32.15	28.73	40.19	37.80
35	3.43	2.92	6.42	5.35	24.19	22.52	37.10	33.12	43.67	39.19
40	4.23	3.90	7.14	6.24	27.21	25.40	42.27	36.29	48.20	42.25
45	6.12	5.18	8.81	7.40	33.02	29.16	48.73	39.08	51.11	46.04
50	9.72	8.73	14.19	9.11	37.94	33.57	56.31	44.16	58.49	49.20
55	16.25	12.82	22.03	13.17	45.83	37.02	61.09	49.40	71.28	53.16
60	24.10	19.43	37.70	24.82	53.98	42.24	70.43	52.55	79.15	58.08

premium factor A small surcharge added to the cost of insurance policies when the insured chooses to pay the premiums more frequently than annually; takes into account the increased cost of billing, handling, and bookkeeping.

Annual life insurance premiums are calculated by first determining the number of $1,000 of insurance desired and then multiplying the number of $1,000 by the rate per $1,000 found in Table 19-1. When the insured desires to pay the premiums more frequently than annually, such as semiannually, quarterly, or monthly, a small surcharge is added to account for the increased cost of billing, handling, and bookkeeping. Table 19-2 illustrates typical **premium factors** used by insurance companies for this purpose.

Table 19-2
Life Insurance—Premium Factors

Premium Paid	Percent of Annual Premium
Semiannually	52%
Quarterly	26%
Monthly	9%

STEPS TO CALCULATE LIFE INSURANCE PREMIUMS

Step 1. Calculate the number of $1,000 of insurance desired by dividing the face value of the policy by $1,000. Round to the nearest whole $1,000.

$$\textbf{Number of \$1,000} = \frac{\textbf{Face value of policy}}{\textbf{\$1,000}}$$

Step 2. Locate the appropriate premium rate per $1,000 from Table 19-1. Choose the rate based on the type of policy desired and the age and sex of the applicant.

Step 3. Calculate annual premium by multiplying the number of $1,000 of insurance desired by the Table 19-1 rate.

$$\textbf{Annual premium} = \textbf{Number of \$1,000} \times \textbf{Rate per \$1,000}$$

Step 4. For premiums other than annual, multiply the appropriate Table 19-2 premium factor by the annual premium.

$$\textbf{Premium other than annual} = \textbf{Annual premium} \times \textbf{Premium factor}$$

EXAMPLE 1 CALCULATING LIFE INSURANCE PREMIUMS

Michele Clayton is 24 years old. She is interested in purchasing a whole life insurance policy with a face value of $50,000. As her insurance agent, calculate the annual and monthly insurance premiums for this policy.

SOLUTION STRATEGY

Step 1. $$\text{Number of \$1,000} = \frac{\text{Face value of policy}}{\$1,000} = \frac{50,000}{1,000} = 50$$

Step 2. From Table 19-1, we find the premium per $1,000 for whole life insurance for a 24-year-old woman to be $13.92.

Step 3. Annual premium = Number of $1,000 × Rate per $1,000

= 50 × 13.92 = $696

Step 4. Monthly premium = Annual premium × Monthly premium factor

Monthly premium = 696 × .09 = $62.64

TRY IT EXERCISE 1

Jason Hall, age 26, wants to purchase a 10-year term insurance policy with a face value of $75,000. Calculate his annual and quarterly premiums. How much more will Jason pay per year if he chooses quarterly payments?

CHECK YOUR ANSWERS WITH THE SOLUTIONS ON PAGE 725.

19-2

CALCULATING THE VALUE OF VARIOUS NONFORFEITURE OPTIONS

Because all life insurance policies (except term) build up a **cash value** after the first 2 or 3 years, they should be viewed as being property with a value. Policyholders in effect own these properties and therefore have certain **ownership rights**. For example, policyholders, or policyowners, have the right to change beneficiaries, designate how the death benefits will be paid, borrow money against the policy, assign ownership to someone else, or cancel the policy.

Let's take a closer look at what happens when a policyowner decides to cancel a policy or allows it to terminate or **lapse** by failing to make the required premium payments within 31 days of the due date. The amount of cash value that has accumulated to that point is based on the size of the policy and the amount of time it has been in force. Most policies give the policyowner three choices, known as **nonforfeiture options**.

cash value The amount of money that begins to build up in a permanent life insurance policy after the first 2 or 3 years.

ownership rights The rights of life insurance policyholders, including the right to change beneficiaries, designate how the death benefits will be paid, borrow money against the policy, assign ownership to someone else, or cancel the policy.

lapse Allowing an insurance policy to terminate by failing to make the required premium payments within 31 days of the due date.

nonforfeiture options The options available to the policyholder upon termination of a permanent life insurance policy with accumulated cash value; these include receiving the cash value, using the cash value to purchase a reduced paid-up insurance policy of the same type, or purchasing term insurance with the same face value as the original policy, for as long a time period as the cash value will purchase.

Option 1—Cash Value or Cash Surrender Option. Once a policy has accumulated cash value, the policyowner may choose to surrender (give up) the policy to the company and receive its cash value. At this point, the policy is terminated. If the insured wants to maintain the insurance coverage, the amount of the cash value may be borrowed and later repaid with interest.

Option 2—Reduced Paid-Up Insurance. The second option is that the available cash value is used to purchase a reduced level of paid-up insurance. This policy is of the same type as the original and continues for the life of the policyowner, with no further premiums due.

Option 3—Extended Term Insurance. With this option, the policyholder elects to use the cash value to purchase a term policy with the same face value as the original policy. The new policy will last for as long a time period as the cash value will purchase. When a policyowner simply stops paying on a policy and does not choose a nonforfeiture option, the insurance company automatically implements this extended term option.

Table 19-3 illustrates typical nonforfeiture options per $1,000 of face value, for a policy issued to a woman at age 20.

Teaching Transparency 19-3

Table 19-3
Nonforfeiture Options (Per $1,000 of Face Value Issued to a Woman at Age 20)

	Whole Life Options				20-Payment Life Options				20-Year Endowment Options			
	1	2	3		1	2	3		1	2	3	
			Extended Term				Extended Term				Extended Term	
End of Year	Cash Value	Reduced Paid-Up Insurance	Years	Days	Cash Value	Reduced Paid-Up Insurance	Years	Days	Cash Value	Reduced Paid-Up Insurance	Years	Days
3	$11	$25	2	17	$29	$90	4	217	$39	$97	7	132
5	32	64	9	23	73	212	14	86	91	233	19	204
7	54	99	13	142	101	367	23	152	186	381	26	310
10	98	186	17	54	191	496	30	206	324	512	32	117
15	157	314	21	218	322	789	34	142	647	794	37	350
20	262	491	25	77	505	1,000	-Life-		1,000	1,000	-Life-	

STEPS TO CALCULATE THE VALUE OF VARIOUS NONFORFEITURE OPTIONS

Step 1. Calculate the number of \$1,000 of insurance by dividing the face value of the policy by \$1,000.

Step 2. *Option 1—Cash Value.* Locate the appropriate dollars per \$1,000 in the *cash value* column of Table 19-3, and multiply this figure by the number of \$1,000 of insurance.

Option 2—Reduced Paid-Up Insurance. Locate the appropriate dollars per \$1,000 in the *reduced paid-up insurance* column of Table 19-3, and multiply this figure by the number of \$1,000 of insurance.

Option 3—Extended Term. Locate the length of time of the new extended term policy in the *years* and *days* columns of Table 19-3.

It is important to check your insurance coverage periodically or whenever your situation changes to be sure it meets your current needs.

Some changes that require insurance review might include increased income, getting married, or having a change in family size.

Many insurable assets are tied to inflation and therefore require periodic increases.

- Life insurance—Cost of living increases such as food, clothing, and transportation.
- Property insurance—Rising real estate values and cost of replacement materials.
- Health care insurance—Cost increases in physician, hospital, and other medical-related items.

EXAMPLE 2 CALCULATING NONFORFEITURE OPTIONS

Evelyn Butcher purchased a \$30,000 whole life insurance policy when she was 20 years old. She is now 35 years old and wants to investigate her nonforfeiture options. As her insurance agent, use Table 19-3 to calculate the value of Evelyn's three options.

SOLUTION STRATEGY

Step 1. $\text{Number of \$1,000} = \dfrac{\text{Face value of policy}}{\$1,000} = \dfrac{30,000}{1,000} = 30$

Step 2. *Option 1—Cash Value*. From Table 19-3, we find that after being in force for 15 years, a whole life policy issued to a woman at age 20 has a cash value of \$157 per \$1,000 of insurance.

$$\text{Number of \$1,000} \times \text{Table value} = 30 \times \$157 = \underline{\underline{\$4,710}}$$

Evelyn's cash value option is to receive \$4,710 in cash from the company and have no further insurance coverage.

Option 2—Reduced Paid-Up Insurance. From Table 19-3, we find that after being in force for 15 years, a whole life policy issued to a woman at age 20 will have enough cash value to buy \$314 in paid-up whole life insurance per \$1,000 of face value.

$$\text{Number of \$1,000} \times \text{Table value} = 30 \times 314 = \underline{\underline{\$9,420}}$$

Evelyn's reduced paid-up insurance option is to receive a \$9,420 whole life policy, effective for her entire life, with no further payments.

Option 3—Extended Term Insurance. From Table 19-3, we find that after being in force for 15 years, a whole life policy issued to a woman at age 20 will have enough cash value to purchase \$30,000 of term insurance for a period of 21 years, 218 days.

TRY IT EXERCISE 2

Sarah Hurley purchased a $100,000 20-payment life insurance policy when she was 20 years old. She is now 30 years old and wants to investigate her nonforfeiture options. As her insurance agent, use Table 19-3 to determine the value of Sarah's three options.

CHECK YOUR ANSWERS WITH THE SOLUTIONS ON PAGE 725.

19-4

CALCULATING THE AMOUNT OF LIFE INSURANCE NEEDED TO COVER DEPENDENTS' INCOME SHORTFALL

Evaluating your life insurance needs is a fundamental part of sound financial planning. The amount of insurance and type of policy you should purchase are much less obvious. Life insurance is needed if you keep a household running, support a family, have a mortgage or other major debts, or expect the kids to go to college. Insurance should be used to fill the financial gap a family may incur by the death or disability of the insured.

One so-called rule of thumb is that you carry between seven and ten times your annual income, depending on your lifestyle, number of dependents, and other sources of income. Another estimator of the amount of insurance to purchase is based on a family's additional income requirements needed in the event of the death of the insured. These additional requirements are known as the **income shortfall**.

Let's say, for example, that a family has $30,000 in living expenses per year. If the family's total income, after the death of the insured, decreases to only $20,000, the income shortfall would be $10,000 ($30,000 − $20,000). The theory is to purchase enough life insurance so that the face value of the policy, collected by the family on the death of the insured, can be invested at the prevailing interest rate to generate the additional income needed to overcome the $10,000 shortfall. When prevailing interest rates are low, large amounts of insurance are needed to cover the shortfall. As interest rates rise, less insurance will be needed.

income shortfall The difference between the total living expenses and the total income of a family in the event of the death of the insured; used as an indicator of how much life insurance to purchase.

STEPS TO CALCULATE INSURANCE NEEDED TO COVER DEPENDENTS' INCOME SHORTFALL

Step 1. Determine the dependents' total annual living expenses, including mortgages.

Step 2. Determine the dependents' total annual sources of income, including salaries, investments, and social security.

Step 3. Subtract the income from the living expenses to find the income shortfall.

$$\textbf{Income shortfall} = \textbf{Total living expenses} - \textbf{Total income}$$

Step 4. Calculate the insurance needed to cover the shortfall by dividing the shortfall by the prevailing interest rate (round to the nearest $1,000).

$$\textbf{Insurance needed} = \frac{\textbf{Income shortfall}}{\textbf{Prevailing interest rate}}$$

CLASSROOM ACTIVITY

Divide the class into groups to investigate life, property, and motor vehicle insurance rates in your area.

Ask students to contact local insurance agents to get the current rate tables for each category. Have them share their findings with the class.

EXAMPLE 3 CALCULATING AMOUNT OF INSURANCE NEEDED

With a prevailing interest rate of 6%, how much life insurance is required to cover dependents' income shortfall if their living expenses amount to $48,000 per year and their total income sources amount to $33,000 per year?

SOLUTION STRATEGY

CLASSROOM ACTIVITY
Invite an insurance agent to speak to the class about "current happenings" in the insurance industry and insurance sales as a career.

Step 1. Living expenses per year are $48,000 (given).

Step 2. Dependents' total income is $33,000 (given).

Step 3. Income shortfall = Total expenses − Total income
= 48,000 − 33,000 = $15,000

Step 4. $\text{Insurance needed} = \dfrac{\text{Shortfall}}{\text{Prevailing rate}} = \dfrac{15{,}000}{.06} = \$250{,}000$

TRY IT EXERCISE 3

Pete Nash is evaluating his life insurance needs. His family's total living expenses are $54,000 per year. Kathy, his wife, earns $38,000 per year in salary and receives another $5,000 per year from an endowment fund. If the prevailing interest rate is currently 5%, how much life insurance should Pete purchase to cover his dependents' income shortfall?

CHECK YOUR ANSWER WITH THE SOLUTION ON PAGE 725.

19 SECTION I Review Exercises

Calculate the annual, semiannual, quarterly, and monthly premiums for the following life insurance policies.

	Face Value of Policy	Sex and Age of Insured	Type of Policy	Annual Premium	Semiannual Premium	Quarterly Premium	Monthly Premium
1.	$ 5,000	Male—24	Whole Life	$79.50	$41.34	$20.67	$7.16
2.	10,000	Female—35	10-Year Term	53.50	27.82	13.91	4.82
3.	25,000	Male—19	20-Year Endowment	842.00	437.84	218.92	75.78
4.	75,000	Male—50	20-Payment Life	4,223.25	2,196.09	1,098.05	380.09
5.	100,000	Female—29	5-Year Term	270.00	140.40	70.20	24.30
6.	40,000	Male—35	Whole Life	967.60	503.15	251.58	87.08
7.	35,000	Male—30	20-Payment Life	1,125.25	585.13	292.57	101.27
8.	250,000	Female—45	20-Year Endowment	11,510.00	5,985.20	2,992.60	1,035.90

Complete, worked-out solutions to Exercises 1 and 9 appear in Appendix B, following the index.

Calculate the value of the nonforfeiture options for the following life insurance policies.

	Face Value of Policy	Years in Force	Type of Policy	Cash Value	Reduced Paid-Up Insurance	Extended Term Years	Extended Term Days
9.	$ 50,000	10	Whole Life	$4,900	$9,300	17	54
10.	250,000	7	20-Year Endowment	46,500	95,250	26	310
11.	35,000	15	Whole Life	5,495	10,990	21	218
12.	100,000	3	20-Payment Life	2,900	9,000	4	217

13. Josh Collins is 35 years old and is interested in purchasing a 20-year endowment insurance policy with a face value of $120,000.

a. Calculate the annual premium for this policy.

Face value = $120,000, 20-year endowment, M-35

$$\text{Number of \$1,000s} = \frac{120,000}{1,000} = 120$$

Annual premium = 43.67 × 120 = $5,240.40

b. Calculate the semiannual premium.

Semiannual premium = 5,240.40 × .52 = $2,725.01

14. Ann Crossan, age 27, wants to purchase a 5-year term insurance policy with a face value of $25,000. As her insurance agent, answer the following:

a. What is the annual premium for this policy?

Face value = $25,000, 5-year term, F-27

Number of 1,000s = 25

Annual premium = 2.58 × 25 = $64.50

b. What is the monthly premium?

Monthly premium = 64.50 × .09 = $5.81

c. How much more will Ann pay per year if she chooses monthly payments?

Total payments = 5.81 × 12 = 69.72

69.72 − 64.50

If paid monthly $5.22 More will be paid

"For someone your age, the yearly premium on a $5,000 policy is $8,000."

15. Carolyn Sacco purchased a $75,000, 20-payment life insurance policy when she was 20 years old. She is now 30 years old and wants to investigate her nonforfeiture options. As her insurance agent, calculate the value of Carolyn's three options.

Face value = $75,000, 10 years in force, 20-payment life

Option 1 = 191 × 75 = $14,325 Cash value

Option 2 = 496 × 75 = $37,200 Reduced paid-up insurance

Option 3 = 30 years, 206 days Extended term

16. David Lau is evaluating his life insurance needs. His family's total living expenses are $37,500 per year. Jocelyn, his wife, earns $14,900 per year in salary and receives another $3,500 annually in disability benefits from an insurance settlement for an accident. If the prevailing interest rate is $7\frac{1}{2}\%$, how much life insurance should David purchase to cover his dependents' income shortfall? Round to nearest $1,000.

Total living expenses = $37,500

Total income = 14,900 + 3,500 = $18,400

Income shortfall = 37,500 − 18,400 = $19,100

$$\frac{\text{Income shortfall}}{\text{Prevailing interest rate}} = \frac{19,100}{.075} = 254,666.67 = \$255,000 \text{ Insurance needed}$$

BUSINESS DECISION THE CONSULTATION

17. Lisa Harley, a single mother, is 20 years old. She has called on you for an insurance consultation. Her objective is to purchase life insurance protection for the next 10 years while her children are growing up. Lisa tells you that she can afford about $250 per year for insurance premiums. You have suggested either a 10-year term policy or a whole life policy.

© Comstock/Jupiter Images

Insurance agents help individuals, families, and businesses select insurance policies that provide the best protection for their lives, health, and property. Insurance sales agents who work exclusively for one insurance company are referred to as captive agents. Independent insurance agents, or brokers, represent several companies and place insurance policies for their clients with the company that offers the best rate and coverage.

Insurance sales agents held about 400,000 jobs in 2004. The median annual earnings of insurance sales agents were $41,720. The middle 50 percent earned between $29,980 and $66,160.

a. Rounded to the nearest thousand, how much insurance coverage can Lisa purchase under each policy? ***Hint:*** Divide her annual premium allowance by the rate per $1,000 for each policy.

10-year term policy rate = $4.20

$$\text{Number of 1,000s} = \frac{250}{4.20} = 59.5 = 60$$

She can purchase a $60,000 10-year term policy.

Whole life policy rate = $12.09

$$\text{Number of 1,000s} = \frac{250}{12.09} = 20.6 = 21$$

She can purchase a $21,000 whole life policy.

b. If she should die in the next 10 years, how much more will her children receive under the term insurance?

Term face value = $60,000
Whole life face value = − 21,000
$39,000

Under term policy, $39,000 more would be received.

c. If she should live beyond the 10th year, what are her nonforfeiture options with the whole life policy?

Nonforfeiture options of whole life policy in force 10 years

Option 1 = 98 × 21 = $2,058 Cash value

Option 2 = 186 × 21 = $3,906 Reduced paid-up insurance

Option 3 = 17 years, 54 days Extended term insurance

SECTION II PROPERTY INSURANCE

19-4 UNDERSTANDING PROPERTY INSURANCE AND CALCULATING TYPICAL FIRE INSURANCE PREMIUMS

property insurance Insurance protection for the financial losses that may occur to business and homeowner's property from such perils as fire, lightning, wind, water, negligence, burglary, and vandalism.

Businesses and homeowners alike need insurance protection for the financial losses that may occur to their property from such perils as fire, lightning, wind, water, negligence, burglary, and vandalism. Although the probability that a particular peril will occur is small, no homeowner or business can afford the risk of not having **property insurance**. Most mortgage lenders, in fact, require that sufficient property insurance is purchased by the borrower as a condition for obtaining a mortgage.

In addition to the items listed above, most property insurance policies today have provisions for liability coverage, medical expenses, and additional expenses that may be incurred while the damaged property is being repaired. For example, a business may have to move to

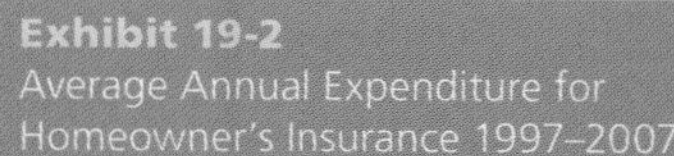
Exhibit 19-2
Average Annual Expenditure for Homeowner's Insurance 1997–2007

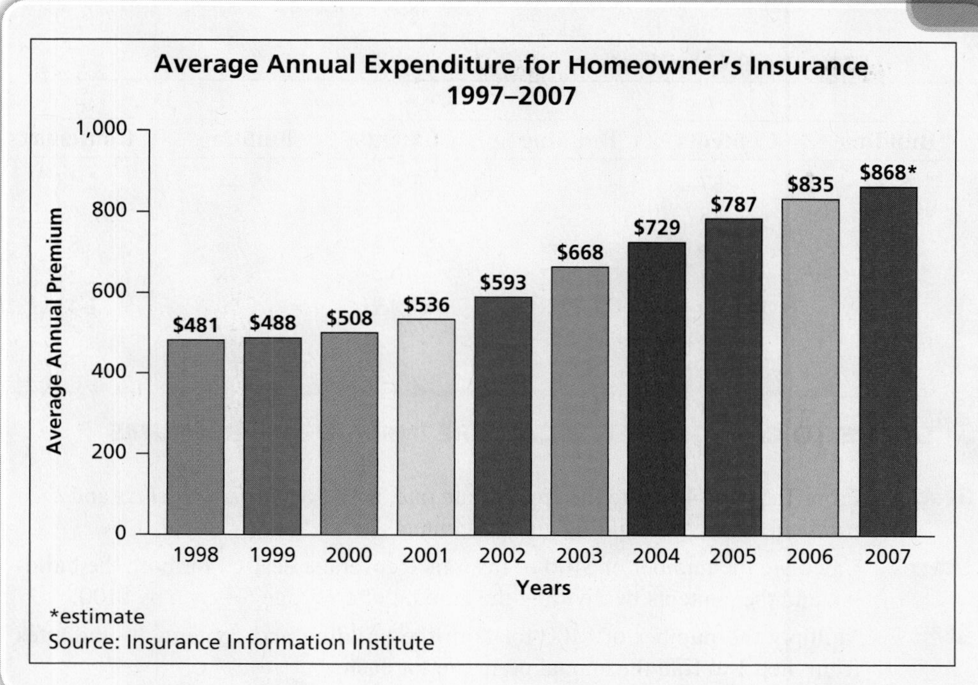

a temporary location during reconstruction, or a family may have to stay in an apartment or motel while their house is being repaired. Insurance companies offer similar policies to meet the needs of apartment and home renters, as well as condominium owners.

In this section, we focus our attention on fire insurance and how these premiums are determined. Fire insurance rates are quoted as an amount per $100 of insurance coverage purchased. Rates are separated into two categories: (a) the structure or building itself and (b) the contents within the building.

A *building's* fire insurance rates are determined by a number of important factors:

1. The *dollar amount* of insurance purchased on the property.
2. The *location of the property*—city, suburbs, and rural areas.
3. The *proximity* and *quality* of fire protection available.
4. The *type of construction* materials used—masonry (brick) or wood (frame).

The *contents* portion of the fire insurance rate is based on

1. The *dollar amount* or value of the contents.
2. The *flammability* of the contents.

From this rate structure, we can see that a building made of concrete, bricks, and steel, located 2 or 3 miles from a fire station, would have a considerably lower rate than a building of the same value, with wood frame construction, located in a rural area, 12 miles from the nearest fire-fighting equipment. Or for that matter, a warehouse filled with explosive chemicals would cost more to insure than the same warehouse filled with Coca-Cola.

Table 19-4 illustrates typical annual fire insurance premiums. Note that the rates are per $100 of insurance coverage. The building and contents are listed separately and divided by the structural class of the building and the location (area rating).

Most businesses and homeowners carry special insurance policies to protect against loss due to fire and other perils. According to the Insurance Information Institute, the average annual homeowner's insurance expenditure was estimated at $868 in 2007.

Teaching Transparency 19-5

Table 19-4
Annual Fire Insurance Premiums
(Per $100 of Face Value)

	Structural Classification							
	A		B		C		D	
Area Rating	Building	Contents	Building	Contents	Building	Contents	Building	Contents
1	$.21	$.24	$.32	$.37	$.38	$.42	$.44	$.48
2	.38	.42	.39	.48	.43	.51	.57	.69
3	.44	.51	.55	.66	.69	.77	.76	.85
4	.59	.68	.76	.83	.87	1.04	.98	1.27
5	.64	.73	.92	1.09	1.08	1.13	1.39	1.43

STEPS TO CALCULATE TYPICAL FIRE INSURANCE PREMIUMS

Step 1. From Table 19-4, locate the appropriate rate, based on *structural class* and *area rating*, for both the building and the contents.

Step 2. Calculate the number of $100 of insurance coverage desired for both the building and the contents by dividing the amount of coverage for each by $100.

Step 3. Multiply the number of $100 for both the building and contents by the rates from Step 1 to find the annual premium for each.

Step 4. Add the annual premiums for the building and the contents to find the total annual premium.

Total annual fire premium = Building premium + Contents premium

EXAMPLE 4 CALCULATING FIRE INSURANCE PREMIUMS

What is the total annual fire insurance premium on a building valued at $200,000 with structural classification B and area rating 4 and contents valued at $40,000?

SOLUTION STRATEGY

Step 1. From Table 19-4, we find the following rates for structural class B and area rating 4:

Building—$.76 per $100 of coverage

Contents—$.83 per $100 of coverage

Step 2. Number of $100 of coverage:

$$\text{Building} = \frac{\text{Amount of coverage}}{\$100} = \frac{200{,}000}{100} = 2{,}000$$

$$\text{Contents} = \frac{\text{Amount of coverage}}{\$100} = \frac{40{,}000}{100} = 400$$

Step 3. Annual fire insurance premiums:

Building = Number of $100 × Table rate = 2,000 × .76 = $1,520

Contents = Number of $100 × Table rate = 400 × .83 = $332

Step 4. Total annual fire premium = Building premium + Contents premium

Total annual fire premium = 1,520 + 332 = $1,852

In the Business World

Before the concept of insurance was invented, people were helped by their neighbors and friends when fire or other peril caused damage to their property.

There was an unwritten code that when someone incurred a loss, such as a house or barn burning down, the people of the town would volunteer labor time and donate materials to help rebuild the property and defray the cost.

This concept is similar to insurance as we know it today; the *many*, each helping a little, to aid the *few* who need it.

TRY IT EXERCISE 4

You are the insurance agent for Diamond Enterprises, Inc. The owner, Ed Diamond, would like you to give him a quote on the total annual premium for a property insurance policy on a new warehouse in the amount of $420,000 and contents valued at $685,000. The warehouse is structural classification A and area rating 2.

CHECK YOUR ANSWER WITH THE SOLUTION ON PAGE 725.

CALCULATING PREMIUMS FOR SHORT-TERM POLICIES AND THE REFUNDS DUE ON CANCELED POLICIES

19-5

From time to time, businesses and individuals cancel insurance policies or require **short-term policies** of less than one year. For example, a family might sell their home two months after paying the annual premium, or a business may require coverage for a shipment of merchandise that will be sold within a few months. When a policy is canceled by the insured or is written for less than one year, the premium charged is known as the **short-rate**.

short-term policy An insurance policy for less than one year.

short-rate The premium charged when a policy is canceled by the insured or is written for less than one year.

Short-Rate Refund

Table 19-5 illustrates typical short-term policy rate factors. These rate factors should be used to calculate the premiums and refunds for short-term policies canceled by the insured. Note that these rate factors are a percentage of the annual premium.

Table 19-5
Property Insurance Short-Rate Schedule

Time Policy Is in Force	Percent of Annual Premium	Time Policy Is in Force (months)	Percent of Annual Premium
5 days	8	4	50
10 days	10	5	60
15 days	14	6	70
20 days	16	7	75
25 days	18	8	80
		9	85
1 month	20	10	90
2 months	30	11	95
3 months	40	12	100

19-6

STEPS TO CALCULATE SHORT-RATE REFUNDS—POLICIES CANCELED BY INSURED

Step 1. Calculate the short-term premium using the short-rate from Table 19-5.

Short-rate premium = Annual premium × Short-rate

Step 2. Calculate the short-rate refund by subtracting the short-rate premium from the annual premium.

Short-rate refund = Annual premium − Short-rate premium

TEACHING TIP
Point out that *short-rate* premiums are more expensive than the rates charged for annual policies because the selling and administrative expenses are charged off over a shorter period of time.

EXAMPLE 5 CALCULATING SHORT-RATE RETURNS

A property insurance policy has an annual premium of $500. What is the short-rate refund if the policy is canceled by the insured after 3 months?

SOLUTION STRATEGY

Teaching Transparency 19-6

Step 1. Short-rate premium = Annual premium × Short-rate

Short-rate premium = 500 × 40% = $200

Step 2. Short-rate refund = Annual premium − Short-rate premium

Short-rate refund = 500 − 200 = $300

TRY IT EXERCISE 5

A property insurance policy has an annual premium of $850. What is the short-rate refund if the policy is canceled by the insured after 8 months?

CHECK YOUR ANSWER WITH THE SOLUTION ON PAGE 725.

Regular Refund

When a policy is canceled by the insurance company, rather than the insured, the company must refund the entire unused portion of the premium. This short-term refund calculation is based on the fraction of a year that the policy was in force and is known as a regular refund.

STEPS TO CALCULATE REGULAR REFUNDS—POLICIES CANCELED BY COMPANY

Step 1. Calculate the premium for the period of time the policy was in force.

$$\textbf{Exact time: Annual premium} \times \frac{\textbf{Days policy in force}}{\textbf{365}}$$

or

$$\textbf{Approximate time: Annual premium} \times \frac{\textbf{Months policy in force}}{\textbf{12}}$$

Step 2. Calculate refund by subtracting premium for period in force from the annual premium.

Regular refund = Annual premium − Premium for period

In the Business World

In addition to homeowners, insurance companies offer similar policies to meet the needs of apartment and home renters, as well as condominium owners.

- *Renter's insurance*—Insurance that covers the renter's personal property and liability. The property owner pays the insurance for the building.
- *Condominium insurance*—Insurance that covers the interior walls, wiring, and contents of the condominium.

EXAMPLE 6 CALCULATING REGULAR REFUNDS

A property insurance policy has an annual premium of $500. What is the regular refund if the policy is canceled by the insurance company after 3 months?

SOLUTION STRATEGY

Step 1. $\text{Premium for period} = \text{Annual premium} \times \dfrac{\text{Months policy in force}}{12}$

$\text{Premium for period} = 500 \times \dfrac{3}{12} = \underline{\$125}$

Step 2. $\text{Regular refund} = \text{Annual premium} - \text{Premium for period}$

$\text{Regular refund} = 500 - 125 = \underline{\underline{\$375}}$

TRY IT EXERCISE 6

A property insurance policy has an annual premium of $850. What is the regular refund if the policy is canceled by the insurance company after 8 months?

CHECK YOUR ANSWER WITH THE SOLUTION ON PAGE 725.

UNDERSTANDING COINSURANCE AND COMPUTING COMPENSATION DUE IN THE EVENT OF A LOSS

19-6

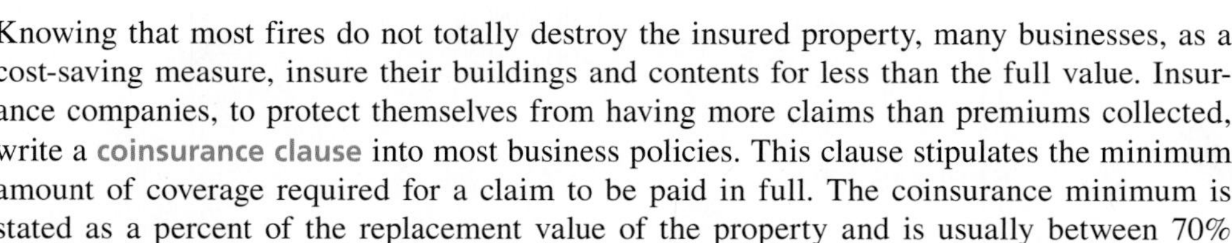

Knowing that most fires do not totally destroy the insured property, many businesses, as a cost-saving measure, insure their buildings and contents for less than the full value. Insurance companies, to protect themselves from having more claims than premiums collected, write a **coinsurance clause** into most business policies. This clause stipulates the minimum amount of coverage required for a claim to be paid in full. The coinsurance minimum is stated as a percent of the replacement value of the property and is usually between 70% and 90%.

coinsurance clause A clause in a property insurance policy stipulating the minimum amount of coverage required for a claim to be paid in full. This requirement is stated as a percent of the replacement value of the property.

Here is an example of how coinsurance works. Let's say that a building has a replacement value of $100,000. If the insurance policy has an 80% coinsurance clause, the building must be insured for $80,000 (80% of the $100,000) to be fully covered for any claim, up to the face value of the policy. Any coverage less than the required 80% would be paid out in proportion to the coverage ratio. The **coverage ratio** is a ratio of the amount of insurance carried by the insured to the amount of insurance required by the insurance company.

coverage ratio A ratio of the amount of insurance carried by the insured to the amount of insurance required according to the coinsurance clause of the insurance policy.

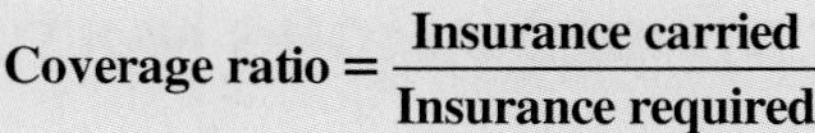

$$\textbf{Coverage ratio} = \frac{\textbf{Insurance carried}}{\textbf{Insurance required}}$$

If, for example, the owner had purchased only $40,000, rather than the required $80,000, the insurance company would only be obligated to pay half, or 50%, of any claim. This is because the ratio of insurance carried to insurance required was 50%.

$$\text{Coverage ratio} = \frac{40{,}000}{80{,}000} = \frac{1}{2} = 50\%$$

STEPS TO CALCULATE AMOUNT OF LOSS TO BE PAID WITH A COINSURANCE CLAUSE

Step 1. Determine the amount of insurance required by the coinsurance clause.

$$\textbf{Insurance required} = \textbf{Replacement value of property} \times \textbf{Coinsurance percent}$$

Step 2. Calculate the amount of the loss to be paid by the insurance company by multiplying the coverage ratio by the amount of the loss.

$$\textbf{Amount of loss paid by insurance} = \frac{\textbf{Insurance carried}}{\textbf{Insurance required}} \times \textbf{Amount of the loss}$$

EXAMPLE 7 CALCULATING INSURANCE LOSS PAYOUT

The Palliser Corporation had property valued at $500,000 and insured for $300,000. If the fire insurance policy contained an 80% coinsurance clause, how much would be paid by the insurance company in the event of a $100,000 fire?

SOLUTION STRATEGY

Step 1. Insurance required = Value of the property × Coinsurance percent

Insurance required = 500,000 × .80 = $400,000

Step 2. $$\text{Amount of loss paid by insurance} = \frac{\text{Insurance carried}}{\text{Insurance required}} \times \text{Amount of loss}$$

$$\text{Amount of loss paid by insurance} = \frac{300,000}{400,000} \times 100,000 = \underline{\underline{\$75,000}}$$

TRY IT EXERCISE 7

19-7

Simplex Systems, Inc. had property valued at $850,000 and insured for $400,000. If the fire insurance policy contained a 70% coinsurance clause, how much would be paid by the insurance company in the event of a $325,000 fire?

CHECK YOUR ANSWER WITH THE SOLUTION ON PAGE 725.

19-7 DETERMINING EACH COMPANY'S SHARE OF A LOSS WHEN LIABILITY IS DIVIDED AMONG MULTIPLE CARRIERS

multiple carriers A situation in which a business is covered by fire insurance policies from more than one company at the same time.

Sometimes businesses are covered by fire insurance policies from more than one company at the same time, which is known as having **multiple carriers**. This situation occurs when one insurance company is unwilling or unable to carry the entire liability of a particular property or because additional coverage was purchased from different insurance companies over a period of time as the business expanded and became more valuable.

Assuming that all coinsurance clause requirements have been met, when a claim is made against multiple carriers, each carrier is responsible for its portion of the total coverage carried. To calculate that portion, we divide the amount of each company's policy by the total insurance carried. This portion is expressed as a percent of the total coverage.

For example, if an insurance company was one of multiple carriers and had a $30,000 fire policy written on a business that had a total of $200,000 in coverage, that insurance company would be responsible for $\frac{30,000}{200,000}$, or 15%, of any loss.

STEPS TO DETERMINE EACH COMPANY'S SHARE OF A LOSS WHEN LIABILITY IS SHARED AMONG MULTIPLE CARRIERS

Step 1. Calculate each carrier's portion by dividing the amount of each policy by the total insurance carried.

$$\textbf{Carrier's percent of total coverage} = \frac{\textbf{Amount of carrier's policy}}{\textbf{Total amount of insurance}}$$

Step 2. Determine each carrier's share of a loss by multiplying the amount of the loss by each carrier's percent of the total coverage.

Carrier's share of loss = Amount of loss × Carrier's percent of total coverage

EXAMPLE 8 CALCULATING MULTI-CARRIER PAYOUTS

Meridian International had multiple carrier fire insurance coverage in the amount of $400,000, as follows.

Travelers:	$80,000	policy
State Farm:	$120,000	policy
Allstate:	$200,000	policy
	$400,000	total coverage

Assuming that all coinsurance clause stipulations have been met, how much would each carrier be responsible for in the event of a $50,000 fire?

SOLUTION STRATEGY

Step 1. $\text{Carrier's percent of total coverage} = \frac{\text{Amount of carrier's policy}}{\text{Total amount of insurance}}$

$$\text{Travelers} = \frac{80,000}{400,000} = \underline{20\%}$$

$$\text{State Farm} = \frac{120,000}{400,000} = \underline{30\%}$$

$$\text{Allstate} = \frac{200,000}{400,000} = \underline{50\%}$$

Step 2. Carrier's share of loss = Amount of loss × Carrier's percent of total coverage

Travelers Share = 50,000 × .20 = $\underline{\underline{\$10,000}}$

State Farm Share = 50,000 × .30 = $\underline{\underline{\$15,000}}$

Allstate Share = 50,000 × .50 = $\underline{\underline{\$25,000}}$

CLASSROOM ACTIVITY

- Ask students to think of insurance risk situations that may require multiple carrier coverage. Some examples might include insuring the Empire State Building or the Sears Tower.
- Have students research Lloyds of London, Goodfellow Rebecca Ingrams Pearson (GRIP), or other insurance companies that have written insurance on "unusual" risks such as movie stars' body parts (dancers' legs, singers' voices) or weather during an event. Have them report their findings to the class.

TRY IT EXERCISE 8

Stellar Industries, Inc., had multiple carrier fire insurance coverage in the amount of $125,000, as follows.

Aetna:	$20,000	policy
USF&G:	$45,000	policy
John Hancock:	$60,000	policy
	$125,000	total coverage

Assuming that all coinsurance clause stipulations have been met, how much would each carrier be responsible for in the event of a $16,800 fire?

CHECK YOUR ANSWERS WITH THE SOLUTIONS ON PAGE 725.

SECTION II Review Exercises

Complete, worked-out solutions for Exercises 1, 6, 7, and 11 appear in Appendix B, following the index.

Calculate the building, contents, and total property insurance premiums for the following policies.

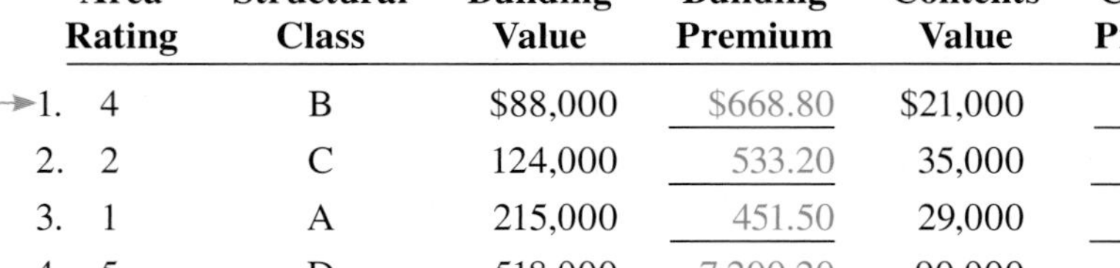

	Area Rating	Structural Class	Building Value	Building Premium	Contents Value	Contents Premium	Total Premium
1.	4	B	$88,000	$668.80	$21,000	$174.30	$843.10
2.	2	C	124,000	533.20	35,000	178.50	711.70
3.	1	A	215,000	451.50	29,000	69.60	521.10
4.	5	D	518,000	7,200.20	90,000	1,287.00	8,487.20
5.	3	C	309,000	2,132.10	57,000	438.90	2,571.00

Calculate the short-term premium and refund for each of the following policies.

	Annual Premium	Canceled After	Canceled By	Short-Term Premium	Short-Term Refund
6.	$450	3 months	insurance company	$112.50	$337.50
7.	560	20 days	insured	89.60	470.40
8.	1,280	9 months	insured	1,088.00	192.00
9.	322	5 months	insurance company	134.17	187.83
10.	630	5 days	insured	50.40	579.60

Calculate the amount to be paid by the insurance company for each of the following claims.

	Replacement Value of Building	Face Value of Policy	Coinsurance Clause (%)	Amount of Loss	Amount of Loss Insurance Company Will Pay
11.	$200,000	$160,000	80	$75,000	$75,000.00
12.	350,000	300,000	90	125,000	119,047.62
13.	70,000	50,000	70	37,000	37,000.00
14.	125,000	75,000	80	50,000	37,500.00
15.	500,000	300,000	80	200,000	150,000.00

16. You are the insurance agent for Alpine Furniture Manufacturing, Inc. The owner, Joey Hill, would like you to give him a quote on the total annual premium for property insurance on a new production facility in the amount of $1,640,000 and equipment and contents valued at $955,000. The building is structural classification B and area rating 4.

$$\text{Building, number of 100s} = \frac{1{,}640{,}000}{100} = 16{,}400$$

$$\text{Contents, number of 100s} = \frac{955{,}000}{100} = 9{,}550$$

Building premium = 16,400 × .76 = $12,464

Contents premium = 9,550 × .83 = $7,926.50

Total annual premium = 12,464.00 + 7,926.50 = $20,390.50

17. A property insurance policy has an annual premium of $1,350. What is the short-rate refund if the policy is canceled by the insured after 9 months?

Annual premium = $1,350 canceled by insured

Short-rate premium = 1,350 × 85% = $1,147.50

Short-rate refund = 1,350.00 − 1,147.50 = $202.50

18. Regency Enterprises has a property insurance policy with an annual premium of $1,320. In recent months, Regency has filed four different claims against the policy: a fire, two burglaries, and a vandalism incident. The insurance company has elected to cancel the policy, which has been in effect for 310 days. What is the regular refund due to Regency?

Annual premium = $1,320, 310 days in force, canceled by insurance company

$$\text{Regular refund} = 1{,}320 \times \frac{310}{365} = 1{,}121.10$$

1,320.00 − 1,121.10 = $198.90

19. Hot Wire Electronics had multiple carrier fire insurance coverage in the amount of $500,000, as follows:

Complete, worked-out solution for Exercise 19 appears in Appendix B, following the index.

Aetna:	$300,000 policy
State Farm:	$125,000 policy
Liberty Mutual:	$75,000 policy
	$500,000 total coverage

Assuming that all coinsurance clause stipulations have been met, how much would each carrier be responsible for in the event of a $95,000 fire?

Aetna: $57,000 State Farm: $23,750 Liberty Mutual: $14,250

BUSINESS DECISION BUSINESS INTERRUPTION INSURANCE

© Digital Vision/Getty Images

Home-Based Business
According to the Small Business Administration (SBA), home-based businesses represent 52 percent of all small firms and provide 10 percent of the total receipts of the economy, about $427 billion. For those running a business from home, a typical home owner's policy is not enough. Typically they provide only $2,500 coverage for business equipment. Home business owners may also need coverage for liability and lost income.

20. As the owner of a successful business, you have just purchased an additional type of property insurance coverage known as *business interruption insurance*. This insurance protects the profits that a company would have earned had there been no problem. Business interruption insurance covers damages caused by all types of perils such as fires, tornadoes, hurricanes, lightning, or any other disaster except floods and earthquakes.

    This insurance pays for "economic" losses incurred when business operations suddenly cease. These include loss of income due to the interruption and additional expenses incurred such as leases; relocation to temporary facilities; overtime to keep up with production demands; recompiling of business, financial and legal records; and even the salaries of key employees.

    Your coverage provides insurance reimbursement for 80% of any losses. Your company pays the other 20%. The annual premium is 2% of the income and extra expenses that you insure.

    a. If you have purchased coverage amounting to $20,000 per month, what is the amount of your annual premium?

    20,000 × 12 = $240,000 annual coverage

    240,000 × .02 = $4,800 annual premium

    b. If a tornado put your company out of business for $5\frac{1}{2}$ months, what would be the amount of the insurance reimbursement for your economic loss?

    20,000 × 5.5 = $110,000 total amount of loss

    110,000 × .8 = $88,000 insurance reimbursement

19 SECTION III MOTOR VEHICLE INSURANCE

19-8 UNDERSTANDING MOTOR VEHICLE INSURANCE AND CALCULATING TYPICAL PREMIUMS

motor vehicle insurance Insurance protection for the financial losses that may be incurred due to a motor vehicle accident or damage caused by fire, vandalism, or other perils.

liability A portion of motor vehicle insurance that includes payment for bodily injury to other persons and damages to the property of others resulting from the insured's negligence.

collision A portion of motor vehicle insurance that covers damage sustained by the insured's vehicle in an accident.

comprehensive Insurance coverage that protects the insured's vehicle for damage caused by fire, wind, water, theft, vandalism, and other perils not caused by accident.

With the steadily increasing costs of automobile and truck repairs and replacement, as well as all forms of medical services, **motor vehicle insurance** today is an absolute necessity! In fact, most states require a certain minimum amount of insurance before a vehicle may even be registered.

Motor vehicle insurance rates, regulations, and requirements vary widely from state to state, but the basic structure is the same. Vehicle insurance is divided into three main categories: **liability**, **collision**, and **comprehensive**.

Liability. This category includes (a) payment for bodily injury to other persons resulting from the insured's negligence and (b) damages to the property of others resulting from the insured's negligence. This property may be other vehicles damaged in the accident or other objects such as fences, landscaping, or buildings.

Collision. This category covers damage sustained by the insured's vehicle in an accident. As a premium reduction measure, collision coverage is often sold with a **deductible** amount, for example, $250 deductible. This means that the insured pays the first $250 in damages for each occurrence, and the insurance company pays the amount over $250. As the deductible amount increases, the premium for the insurance decreases.

Comprehensive. This insurance coverage protects the insured's vehicle for damage caused by fire, wind, water, theft, vandalism, and other perils not caused by an accident.

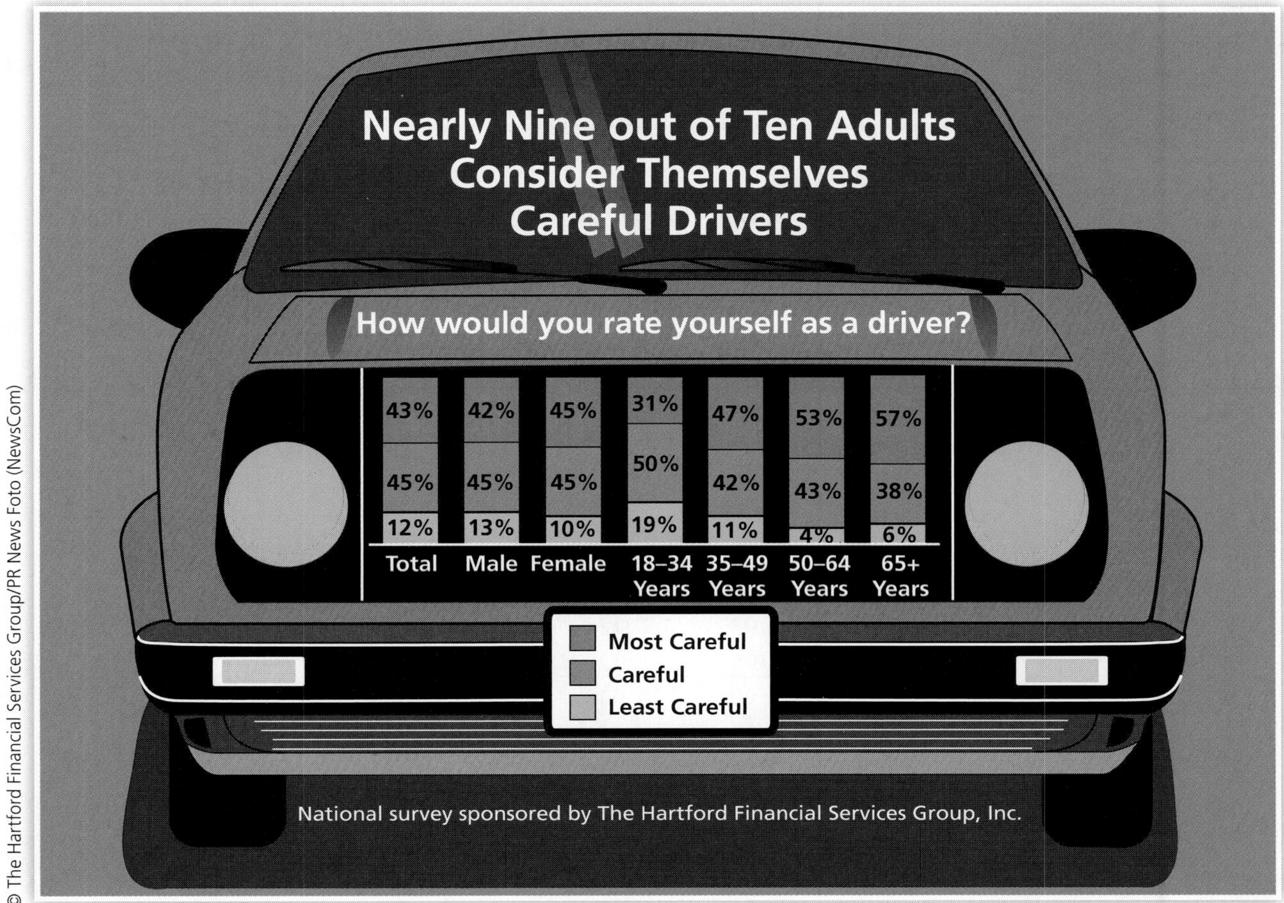

Most states require motor vehicle insurance. According to the National Association of Insurance Commissioners, the average annual cost for auto insurance premiums nationwide for 2007 was estimated at $847 per policy.

Most insurance companies also offer policyholders the option of purchasing policy extras such as uninsured motorist's protection and coverage while driving a rented or borrowed car. Some policies even offer to pay towing expenses in the event of a breakdown or cover the cost for a rental car while the insured's vehicle is being repaired after an accident.

deductible A premium reduction measure in collision insurance whereby the insured pays a stipulated amount of the damage first, the deductible, and the insurance company pays any amount over that; common deductibles are $100, $250, $500, and $1,000.

Liability rates are based on three primary factors: *who* is driving the vehicle, *where* the vehicle is being driven, and the *amount* of insurance coverage desired. Table 19-6 illustrates typical annual liability premiums for bodily injury and property damage. Note that the rates are listed by driver classification (age, sex, and marital status of the driver), territory (metropolitan area, suburbs, small town, rural or farm area), and amount (in thousands of dollars).

Motor vehicle liability premiums are typically stated in a three-number format, such as 50/100/50, with the numbers given in thousands of dollars. The first two numbers, 50/100, refer to the bodily injury portion and means the policy will pay up to $50,000 for bodily injury caused by the insured's vehicle to any one person, with $100,000 maximum per accident, regardless of the number of persons injured. The third number, 50 ($50,000), represents the maximum property damage benefits to be paid per single accident.

Teaching Transparency 19-8

Table 19-7 illustrates typical collision and comprehensive premiums. Note that these rates are listed according to model class (type of vehicle—compact, luxury, truck, or van), vehicle age, territory (where driven), and the amount of the deductible.

Insurance companies often adjust premiums upward or downward by the use of **rating factors**, which are multiples of the base rates found in the tables. For example, if a vehicle is used for business purposes, the risk of an accident is increased and therefore a rating factor of, say, 1.5 might be applied to the base rate to adjust for this risk. A $200 base-rate premium would increase to $300, $200 times the rating factor of 1.5. However, a vehicle driven less than 3 miles to work each way would have less chance of having an accident and might have a rating factor of .9 to lower the rate.

rating factors Multiples of the base rates for motor vehicles; used by insurance companies to adjust premiums upward (factors greater than 1) or downward (factors less than 1), depending on the amount of risk involved in the coverage.

Table 19-6
Motor Vehicle Liability Insurance
Annual Premiums—
Bodily Injury and Property Damage Rates

Territory	Driver Class	Bodily Injury (000) 10/20	15/30	25/50	50/100	100/300	Property Damage (000) 5	10	25	50	100
1	1	$61	$73	$88	$92	$113	$46	$49	$53	$58	$64
	2	63	75	81	94	116	48	51	55	61	66
	3	65	78	84	98	118	52	54	58	63	69
	4	69	81	86	101	121	54	56	60	65	71
2	1	66	75	83	93	114	56	63	68	73	77
	2	69	77	88	98	117	58	64	70	75	79
	3	75	82	92	104	119	59	66	71	76	82
	4	78	86	95	109	122	62	67	73	78	84
3	1	73	77	84	95	116	64	65	72	76	81
	2	78	83	86	99	119	66	69	74	80	83
	3	84	88	92	103	124	70	73	77	82	85
	4	87	93	95	106	128	72	78	81	85	89
4	1	77	81	86	99	118	76	78	83	88	92
	2	81	86	93	103	121	79	83	87	91	95
	3	87	92	100	106	126	80	84	88	93	97
	4	90	94	103	111	132	84	86	91	94	100

Table 19-7
Motor Vehicle Insurance
Annual Premiums—
Collision and Comprehensive Rates

		Territories 1 & 2				Territories 3 & 4			
		Collision		Comprehensive		Collision		Comprehensive	
Model Class	Vehicle Age	$250 Deductible	$500 Deductible	Full Coverage	$100 Deductible	$250 Deductible	$500 Deductible	Full Coverage	$100 Deductible
A–G	0–1	$89	$81	$63	$59	$95	$88	$67	$61
	2–3	87	79	60	57	93	84	63	58
	4–5	86	77	58	54	89	81	60	57
	6+	84	76	55	50	86	78	57	52
H–L	0–1	96	92	78	71	104	95	83	75
	2–3	93	89	76	68	101	90	80	72
	4–5	89	85	74	66	96	87	78	68
	6+	86	81	70	64	92	84	74	66
M–R	0–1	108	104	86	83	112	106	91	88
	2–3	104	101	83	79	109	104	88	82
	4–5	100	98	79	75	104	101	84	77
	6+	94	90	75	71	100	96	80	74
S–Z	0–1	120	115	111	108	124	116	119	113
	2–3	116	112	106	104	121	114	115	109
	4–5	111	107	101	99	116	110	111	106
	6+	108	103	98	96	111	107	108	101

STEPS TO CALCULATE TYPICAL MOTOR VEHICLE INSURANCE PREMIUMS

Step 1. Use Table 19-6 to find the appropriate base premiums for bodily injury and property damage.

Step 2. Use Table 19-7 to find the appropriate base premiums for collision and comprehensive.

Step 3. Add all the individual premiums to find the total base premium.

Step 4. Multiply the total base premium by the rating factor, if any.

Total annual premium = Total base premium × Rating factor

EXAMPLE 9 CALCULATING MOTOR VEHICLE PREMIUMS

Amy Morris wants to purchase a motor vehicle insurance policy with bodily injury and property damage coverage in the amounts of 25/50/25. In addition, she wants collision coverage with $500 deductible and comprehensive with no deductible. Amy is in driver classification 3 and lives in territory 1. Her vehicle, a Ford Mustang, is in model class P and is 3 years old. Because she has taken driver training classes, Amy qualifies for a .95 rating factor. As Amy's insurance agent, calculate her total annual premium.

SOLUTION STRATEGY

Step 1. From Table 19-6, we find the bodily injury premium to be $84 and the property damage premium to be $58.

Step 2. From Table 19-7, we find collision to be $101 and comprehensive to be $83.

Step 3. Total base premium = Bodily injury + Property damage + Collision + Comprehensive

Total base premium = 84 + 58 + 101 + 83 = $326

Step 3. Total annual premium = Total base premium × Rating factor

Total annual premium = 326 × .95 = $309.70

Many insurance companies give money-saving *rating factor* discounts to students who have good grade point averages, usually over 3.0 out of 4.0, or safe-driving records—without tickets or accidents.

19-9

TRY IT EXERCISE 9

Richie Powers, owner of High Performance Marine, wants to purchase truck insurance with bodily injury and property damage coverage in the amounts of 100/300/100. Richie also wants $250 deductible collision and $100 deductible comprehensive. He is in driver classification 4 and lives in territory 3. His vehicle, a Chevy Blazer, is in model class F and is 4 years old. Because Richie uses his truck to make dockside calls and haul boats to his shop, the insurance company has assigned a 2.3 rating factor to his policy. What is Richie's total annual premium?

CHECK YOUR ANSWER WITH THE SOLUTION ON PAGE 725.

Exhibit 19-3
Average Annual Expenditure for Automobile Insurance 1997–2007

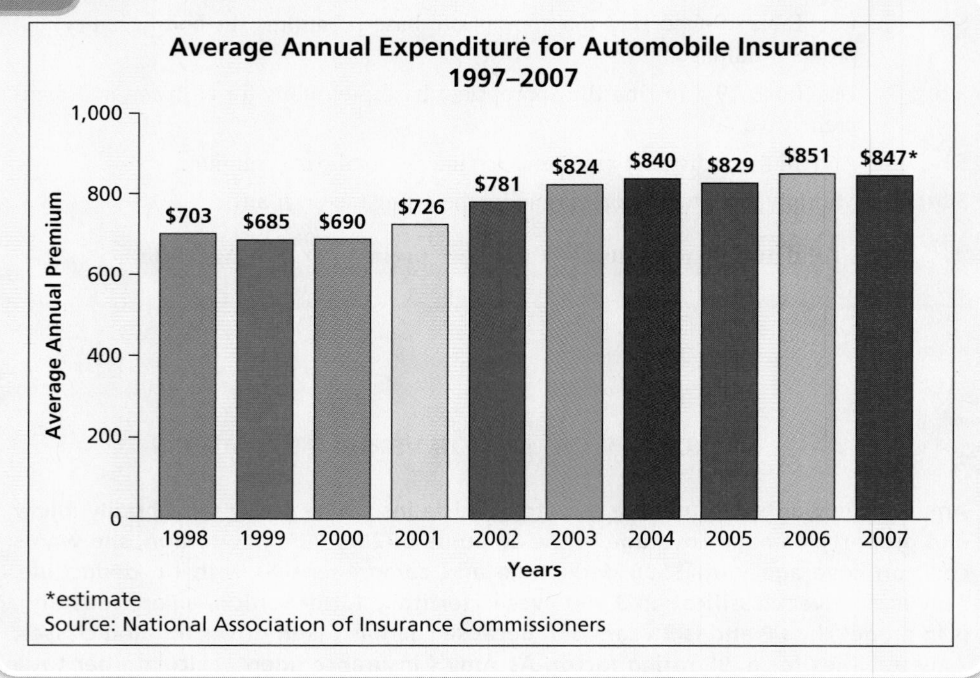

19-9 COMPUTING THE COMPENSATION DUE FOLLOWING AN ACCIDENT

When the insured is involved in a motor vehicle accident in which he or she is at fault, his or her insurance company must pay out the claims resulting from that accident. Any amounts of bodily injury or property damage that exceed the limits of the policy coverage are the responsibility of the insured.

CLASSROOM ACTIVITY
Emphasize that motor vehicle insurance rates, regulations, and requirements vary widely from state to state; however, the basics are the same everywhere.

Have students research and report to the class about the motor vehicle insurance requirements in your state.

EXAMPLE 10 CALCULATING ACCIDENT COMPENSATION

Bill Paxton has motor vehicle insurance in the following amounts: liability, 15/30/5; $500 deductible collision; and $100 deductible comprehensive. Recently, Bill was at fault in an accident in which his van hit a car stopped at a traffic light. Two individuals in the other vehicle, Angel and Martha Cordero, were injured. Angel's bodily injuries amounted to $6,300, whereas Martha's more serious injuries totaled $18,400. In addition, their car sustained $6,250 in damages. Although he was not physically injured, the damage to Bill's van amounted to $4,788.

a. How much will the insurance company have to pay and to whom?

b. What part of the settlement will be Bill's responsibility?

SOLUTION STRATEGY

Liability Portion:

Bill's liability coverage is limited to $15,000 per person. The insurance company will pay the $6,300 for Angel's injuries; however, Bill is responsible for Martha's expenses above the limit.

$18,400	Martha's medical expenses
−15,000	Insurance limit − bodily injury
$ 3,400	Bill's responsibility

Property Damage Portion:

The property damage limit of $5,000 is not sufficient to cover the damage to Angel's car. Bill will have to pay the portion above the limit.

$6,250	Angel's car repairs
−5,000	Insurance limit − property damage
$1,250	Bill's responsibility

The damage to Bill's van will be paid by the insurance company, except for the $500 deductible.

$4,788	Bill's van repairs
− 500	Deductible
$4,288	Insurance company responsibility

TRY IT EXERCISE 10

Jody Cole has automobile liability insurance in the amount of 25/50/10 and also carries $250 deductible collision and full-coverage comprehensive. Recently, Jody was at fault in an accident in which her Volvo went out of control on a rainy day and hit two cars, a fence, and the side of a house. The first car, a Lexus, had $8,240 in damages. The second car, a Ford Taurus, sustained damages of $2,540. The repairs to Jody's car amounted to $3,542. In addition, the fence repairs came to $880, and the house damages were estimated at $5,320.

19-10

a. How much will the insurance company have to pay and to whom?

b. What part of the settlement will be Jody's responsibility?

CHECK YOUR ANSWERS WITH THE SOLUTIONS ON PAGE 725.

Review Exercises — SECTION III 19

As an insurance agent, calculate the annual premium for the following clients.

Name	Territory	Driver Class	Bodily Injury	Property Damage	Model Class	Vehicle Age	Comprehensive Deductible	Collision Deductible	Rating Factor	Annual Premium
1. Schwartz	2	4	50/100	25	J	3	$100	$250	None	$343.00
2. Mager	1	2	10/20	10	R	1	Full Coverage	500	1.5	456.00
3. Almos	3	1	25/50	5	U	5	Full Coverage	250	3.0	1,125.00
4. Denner	2	3	100/300	25	C	4	$100	250	None	330.00
5. Nadler	4	2	50/100	100	H	2	Full Coverage	500	1.7	625.60
6. Manners	1	4	15/30	50	M	3	$100	250	2.5	822.50
7. Hale	2	1	10/20	10	Q	6	$100	250	3.9	1,146.60
8. Coll	3	3	100/300	100	Z	1	Full Coverage	500	None	444.00

9. Don Craven wants to purchase an automobile insurance policy with bodily injury and property damage coverage in the amounts of 50/100/50. In addition, he wants collision coverage with $250 deductible and comprehensive with no deductible. Don is in driver classification 4 and lives in territory 3. His vehicle, a Nissam Maxima, is in model class B and is 1 year old. Don has had two accidents and one ticket in the past 12 months and is therefore considered to be a high risk. Consequently, the insurance company has assigned a rating factor of 4.0 to his policy. As his automobile insurance agent, calculate the total annual premium for Don's policy.

Bodily injury	$106
Property damage	85
Collision	95
Comprehensive	67
	$353

Rating factor 4.0 × 353
Total annual premium = $1,412

10. Howard Marshall's Corvette was hit by a palm tree during a hurricane. The damage was estimated at $1,544. If Howard carried $250 deductible collision and $100 deductible comprehensive, how much of the damages does the insurance company have to pay?

Total damage	$1,544
Less comprehensive deductible	− 100
Insurance company responsibility	$1,444

Liability 50/100/50

Maximum of $50,000 per person
Maximum of $100,000 per accident
Maximum of $50,000 property

Bodily injury (liability)

Hart's injuries	$13,500	Insurance pays all
Black's injuries	11,700	Insurance pays all
Garner's injuries	4,140	Insurance pays all
Williams' injuries	57,800	Insurance pays 50,000
Morgan's injuries	3,590	Insurance pays all

Property damage (liability)

Bus damage	$12,230	Insurance pays all

Collision

Ben's camper	$3,780	
Deductible	− 250	
	$3,530	Insurance portion

11. Ben Crosby has motor vehicle liability insurance in the amount of 50/100/50 and also carries $250 deductible collision coverage and full-coverage comprehensive. Recently, he was at fault in an accident in which his camper hit a bus. Five individuals were injured on the bus and were awarded the following settlements by the courts: Hart, $13,500; Black, $11,700; Garner, $4,140; Williams, $57,800; and Morgan, $3,590. The damage to the bus was $12,230, and Ben's camper sustained $3,780 in damages.

a. How much will the insurance company have to pay and to whom?

Insurance Co.

Hart	$13,500	Morgan	3,590
Black	11,700	Bus	12,230
Garner	4,140	Camper	3,530
Williams	50,000		$98,690

b. What part of the settlement will be Ben's responsibility?

Ben

Williams	$7,800
Deductible	250
	$8,050

BUSINESS DECISION INSURING THE FLEET

12. The Apex Cab Company of Hubman Landing is interested in purchasing $250 deductible collision insurance and full-coverage comprehensive insurance to cover its fleet of 10 taxi cabs. As a requirement for the job, all drivers already carry their own liability coverage in the amount of 100/300/100. Hubman Landing is rated as territory 2. Five of the cabs are 4-year-old Checker Towncars, model class Y. Three of them are 2-year-old Chrysler station wagons, model class R. The remaining two are new Buick sedans, in model class C. Because the vehicles are on the road almost 24 hours a day, they are considered to be very high risk and carry a rating factor of 5.2. They are, however, subject to an 18% multivehicle fleet discount.

a. As the insurance agent for Apex Cab, calculate the total annual premium for the fleet.

10 Cabs, Collision $250 deductible, Comprehensive full coverage, Territory 2

	Comprehensive	Collision
5 Cabs Model Y, 4 years old	@101 × 5 = $505	@111 × 5 = $555
3 Cabs Model R, 2 years old	@ 83 × 3 = $249	@104 × 3 = $312
2 Cabs Model C, 0 years old	@ 63 × 2 = $126	@ 89 × 2 = $178

Total annual premium = 505 + 555 + 249 + 312 + 126 + 178 = $1,925

1,925 × 5.2 = 10,010 × 82% = $8,208.20

b. When the owner saw your rate quote, he exclaimed, "Too expensive! How can I save some money on this insurance?" At that point, you suggested changing the coverage to $500 deductible collision and $100 deductible comprehensive. How much can you save Apex Cab by using the new coverage?

10 Cabs, Collision $500 deductible, Comprehensive $100 deductible, Territory 2

	Comprehensive	Collision
5 Cabs Model Y, 4 years old	@99 × 5 = $495	@107 × 5 = $535
3 Cabs Model R, 2 years old	@79 × 3 = $237	@101 × 3 = $303
2 Cabs Model C, 0 years old	@59 × 2 = $118	@ 81 × 2 = $162

Total annual premium = 495 + 535 + 237 + 303 + 162 + 118 = $1,850

1,850 × 5.2 = 9,620 × 82% = $7,888.40

8,208.20 − 7,888.40 = $319.80 Savings

"We've raised your rates because you haven't had an accident in fourteen years, so you're about due one."

CHAPTER FORMULAS

Life Insurance

$$\text{Number of \$1,000} = \frac{\text{Face value of policy}}{1{,}000}$$

Annual premium = Number of $1,000 × Rate per $1,000

Premium other than annual = Annual premium × Premium factor

Income shortfall = Total living expenses − Total income

$$\text{Insurance needed} = \frac{\text{Income shortfall}}{\text{Prevailing interest rate}}$$

Property Insurance

Total annual fire premium = Building premium + Contents premium

Short-rate premium = Annual premium × Short-rate

Short-rate refund = Annual premium − Short-rate premium

$$\text{Regular refund} = \text{Annual premium} - \text{Premium for period in force}$$

$$\text{Coinsurance coverage ratio} = \frac{\text{Insurance carried}}{\text{Insurance required}}$$

$$\text{Amount of loss paid by insurance} = \frac{\text{Insurance carried}}{\text{Insurance required}} \times \text{Amount of loss}$$

$$\text{Carrier's percent of total coverage} = \frac{\text{Amount of carrier's policy}}{\text{Total amount of insurance}}$$

$$\text{Carrier's share of loss} = \text{Amount of loss} \times \text{Carrier's percent of total coverage}$$

SUMMARY CHART

19

Section I: Life Insurance

Topic	Important Concepts	Illustrative Examples
Understanding Life Insurance and Calculating Typical Premiums for Various Types of Policies P/O 19-1, p. 695	Life insurance guarantees a specified sum of money to the surviving beneficiaries, on the death of the insured. It is purchased in increments of $1,000. Calculating premiums: 1. Calculate the number of $1,000 of insurance desired by dividing the face value of the policy by $1,000. 2. Locate the appropriate premium rate per $1,000 in Table 19-1. 3. Calculate the total annual premium by multiplying the number of $1,000 by the Table 19-1 rate. 4. For premiums other than annual, multiply the annual premium by the appropriate Table 19-2 premium factor.	Margie Gray is 20 years old. She is interested in purchasing a 20-payment life insurance policy with a face value of $25,000. Calculate her annual and monthly premium. $\text{Number of } \$1{,}000 = \frac{25{,}000}{1{,}000} = 25$ Table 19-1 rate = $21.50. Annual premium = 25 × 21.50 = $537.50 Monthly premium = 537.50 × 9% = $48.38
Calculating the Value of Various Nonforfeiture Options P/O 19-2, p. 699	Life insurance policies with accumulated cash value may be converted to one of three nonforfeiture options. Use Table 19-3 and the number of $1,000 of insurance to determine the value of each option. Option 1—Take the cash value of the policy, and cancel the insurance coverage. Option 2—Reduced, paid-up amount of the same insurance. Option 3—Term policy for a certain number of years and days, with the same face value as the original policy.	Ingrid Watson, 30 years old, purchased a $50,000 whole life insurance policy at age 20. What is the value of her nonforfeiture options? $\text{Number of } \$1{,}000 = \frac{50{,}000}{1{,}000} = 50$ Option 1: 50 × $98 = $4,900 Cash Option 2: 50 × $186 = $9,300 Reduced Paid-up Insurance Option 3: 17 years, 54 days Term Policy

Section I: (continued)

Topic	Important Concepts	Illustrative Examples
Calculating the Amount of Life Insurance Needed to Cover Dependents' Income Shortfall **P/O 19-3, p. 701**	When one of the wage-earners in a household dies, the annual living expenses of the dependents may exceed the annual income. This difference is known as the income shortfall. To calculate the amount of insurance needed to cover the shortfall, use $\text{Insurance needed} = \frac{\text{Income shortfall}}{\text{Prevailing interest rate}}$	With a prevailing interest rate of 5%, how much life insurance will be needed to cover dependents' income shortfall if the annual living expenses amount to \$37,600 and the total income is \$21,200? Income shortfall = 37,600 − 21,200 = \$16,400 Insurance needed at 5% = $\frac{16{,}400}{.05}$ = \$328,000

Section II: Property Insurance

Topic	Important Concepts	Illustrative Examples
Understanding Property Insurance and Calculating Typical Fire Insurance Premiums **P/O 19-4, p. 704**	Fire insurance premiums are based on type of construction, location of the property, and availability of fire protection. Fire insurance premiums are quoted per \$100 of coverage, with buildings and contents listed separately. Use Table 19-4 to calculate fire insurance premiums: **Premium = Number of \$100 × Table rate**	What is the total annual fire insurance premium on a building valued at \$120,000, with structural class C and area rating 3, and contents valued at \$400,000? Building: 1,200 × .69 = \$828 Contents: 4,000 × .77 = \$3,080 Total annual fire premium = 828 + 3,080 = \$3,908
Calculating Premiums for Short-Term Policies and the Refunds Due on Canceled Policies **P/O 19-5, p. 707**	Fire policies for less than 1 year are known as short-rate. Use Table 19-5 for these policies. a. Short-rate refund (Policy canceled by insured): **Short-rate premium = Annual premium × Table factor** **Short-rate refund = Annual premium − Short-rate premium** b. Regular refund (Policy canceled by insurance company): **Premium for time in force =** $\text{Annual premium} \times \frac{\text{Months in force}}{12}$ **Regular refund = Annual premium − Premium for time in force**	The Atlas Company has property insurance with State Farm. The annual premium is \$3,000. a. If Atlas cancels the policy after 2 months, what is the short-rate refund? b. If State Farm cancels the policy after 2 months, what is the regular refund? a. Short-rate refund Short-rate premium = 3,000 × 30% = \$900 Short-rate refund = 3,000 − 900 = \$2,100 b. Regular refund Time in force premium = 3,000 × $\frac{2}{12}$ = \$500 Regular refund = 3,000 − 500 = \$2,500
Understanding Coinsurance and Computing Compensation Due in the Event of a Loss **P/O 19-6, p. 709**	A coinsurance clause stipulates the minimum amount of coverage required for a claim to be paid in full. If less than the coinsurance requirement is carried, the payout is proportionately less. **Amount of insurance required = Replacement value × Coinsurance %** **Amount of loss paid =** $\frac{\text{Insurance carried}}{\text{Insurance required}} \times \text{Amount of loss}$	The Shoreline Corporation has a \$150,000 fire insurance policy on a property valued at \$250,000. If the policy has an 80% coinsurance clause, how much would be paid in the event of a \$50,000 fire? Insurance required = 250,000 × .8 = \$200,000 Amount of loss paid = $\frac{150{,}000}{200{,}000} \times 50{,}000$ = \$37,500

Section II: (continued)

Topic	Important Concepts	Illustrative Examples
Determining Each Company's Share of a Loss When Liability Is Divided among Multiple Carriers **P/O 19-7, p. 710**	When more than one insurance company covers a piece of property, the property has multiple carriers. In the event of a claim, each company is responsible for its portion of the total insurance carried. $\text{Carrier's \% of total} = \dfrac{\text{Amount of carrier's policy}}{\text{Total insurance}}$ Carrier's share = Amount of loss × Carrier's %	Briarcliffe Industries had multiple carrier fire insurance on its property as follows: Southwest Mutual . . . . $300,000 Travelers . . . . 100,000 Total . . . . $400,000 Assuming that all coinsurance requirements have been met, how much will each carrier be responsible for in a $20,000 fire? Southwest Mutual: $\dfrac{300,000}{400,000} \times 20,000 = \underline{\underline{\$15,000}}$ Travelers: $\dfrac{100,000}{400,000} \times 20,000 = \underline{\underline{\$5,000}}$

Section III: Motor Vehicle Insurance

Topic	Important Concepts	Illustrative Examples
Understanding Motor Vehicle Insurance and Calculating Typical Premiums **P/O 19-8, p. 714**	Motor vehicle insurance is divided into three main categories: Liability—Covers bodily injury and property damage to others. Use Table 19-6 for these rates. Collision—Covers damage to the insured's vehicle from an auto accident. Use Table 19-7. Comprehensive—Covers damage to the insured's vehicle from fire, wind, water, vandalism, theft, and so on. Use Table 19-7. Rates may be adjusted up or down by multiplying the total table rate by a rating factor.	Beth Merchant wants auto liability coverage of 25/50/25, $250 deductible collision, and $100 deductible comprehensive. She is in driver class 2 and lives in territory 3. Her vehicle, a new SL 500, is in model class L and has a sports car rating factor of 1.7. What is Beth's total auto premium? $86 Bodily injury Table 19-6 74 Property damage Table 19-6 104 Collision Table 19-7 + 75 Comprehensive Table 19-7 $339 Total base × 1.7 Rating factor $576.30 Total premium
Computing the Compensation Due Following an Accident **P/O 19-9, p. 718**	When the policyholder is at fault in an accident, his or her insurance company is responsible for all settlements, up to the limits and deductibles of the policy. Any settlement amounts greater than the policy coverage are the responsibility of the insured.	Warner Bouton has auto liability coverage of 50/100/50, no deductible comprehensive, and $250 deductible collision. Recently, Warner ran a red light and broadsided Sylvia Norton's car. In the court settlement, Sylvia was awarded $75,000 for bodily injury and $14,500 in property damages. Warner's car sustained $7,500 in damages. How much will the insurance company be responsible to pay? How much of the settlement is Warner's responsibility? Liability: Warner's policy limit for bodily injury liability is $50,000. $75,000 Court settlement − 50,000 Paid by insurance $25,000 Paid by Warner The policy limit for property damage is $50,000, therefore the insurance company will pay the full $14,500. Collision: $7,500 Collision damage − 250 Deductible $7,250 Paid by insurance

TRY IT EXERCISE SOLUTIONS FOR CHAPTER 19

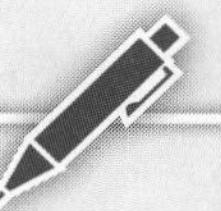

1. $\text{Number of } \$1{,}000 = \dfrac{\text{Face value of policy}}{1{,}000}$

$\text{Number of } \$1{,}000 = \dfrac{75{,}000}{1{,}000} = 75$

Table 19-1 rate = \$4.92 per \$1,000

Annual premium = Number of 1,000 × Rate per \$1,000
Annual premium = 75 × 4.92 = \$369

Quarterly premium = Annual premium × Quarterly factor
Quarterly premium = 369 × .26 = \$95.94

Total payment = Quarterly payment × 4 payments
Total payment = 95.94 × 4 = \$383.76
Jason will pay \$14.76 (383.76 − 369) more if paid quarterly.

2. $\text{Number of } \$1{,}000 = \dfrac{\text{Face value of policy}}{1{,}000} = \dfrac{100{,}000}{1{,}000} = 100$

Option 1

Cash Value = 100 × 191 = \$19,100

Option 2

Reduced Paid-Up Insurance = 100 × 496 = \$49,600

Option 3

Extended Term Insurance = 30 years, 206 days

3. Total income = 38,000 + 5,000 = \$43,000
Income shortfall = Total expenses − Total income
Income shortfall = 54,000 − 43,000 = \$11,000

$\text{Insurance needed} = \dfrac{\text{Shortfall}}{\text{Prevailing rate}}$

$\text{Insurance needed} = \dfrac{11{,}000}{.05} = \$220{,}000$

4. From Table 19-4

Building: .38
Contents: .42

$\text{Building} = \dfrac{\text{Amount of coverage}}{100} = \dfrac{420{,}000}{100} = 4{,}200$

$\text{Contents} = \dfrac{\text{Amount of coverage}}{100} = \dfrac{685{,}000}{100} = 6{,}850$

Building = Number of \$100 × Rate = 4,200 × .38 = \$1,596
Contents = Number of \$100 × Rate = 6,850 × .42 = \$2,877

Total premium = Building + Contents
Total premium = 1,596 + 2,877 = \$4,473

5. From Table 19-5, 8 months = 80%
Short-rate premium = Annual premium × Short-rate
Short-rate premium = 850 × .8 = \$680
Short-rate refund = Annual premium − Short-rate premium
Short-rate refund = 850 − 680 = \$170

6. $\text{Premium for period} = \text{Annual premium} \times \dfrac{\text{Months in force}}{12}$

$\text{Premium for period} = 850 \times \dfrac{8}{12} = \$566.67$

Regular refund = Annual premium − Premium for period
Regular refund = 850.00 − 566.67 = \$283.33

7. Insurance required = Value of property × Coinsurance percent
Insurance required = 850,000 × .7 = \$595,000

$\text{Amount of loss paid} = \dfrac{\text{Insurance carried}}{\text{Insurance required}} \times \text{Loss}$

$\text{Amount of loss paid} = \dfrac{400{,}000}{595{,}000} \times 325{,}000 = \$218{,}487.39$

8. $\text{Carrier's percent of total} = \dfrac{\text{Amount of carrier's policy}}{\text{Total amount of insurance}}$

$\text{Aetna} = \dfrac{20{,}000}{125{,}000} = 16\%$

$\text{USF\&G} = \dfrac{45{,}000}{125{,}000} = 36\%$

$\text{John Hancock} = \dfrac{60{,}000}{125{,}000} = 48\%$

Carrier's share of loss = Amount of loss × Carrier's percent

Aetna = 16,800 × .16 = \$2,688
USF&G = 16,800 × .36 = \$6,048
John Hancock = 16,800 × .48 = \$8,064

9. Base premium =
Bodily injury + Property damage + Collision + Comprehensive
Base premium = 128 + 89 + 89 + 57 = \$363
Total annual premium = Base premium × Rating factor
Total annual premium = 363 × 2.3 = \$834.90

10.

a. Insurance Pays

\$10,000	Property damage
+ 3,292	Jody's car *less* deductible
\$13,292	Total insurance responsibility

b. Jody Pays

\$8,240	Lexus
2,540	Taurus
880	Fence
+ 5,320	House
16,980	Total property damage
− 10,000	Insurance
\$6,980	Jody's portion
+ 250	Collision deductible
\$7,230	Jody's responsibility

CONCEPT REVIEW

1. A mechanism for reducing financial risk and spreading financial loss due to unexpected events is known as ____. The document stipulating the terms of this agreement is known as a(n) ____. (19-1)

   insurance, policy

2. The amount of protection provided by an insurance policy is known as the ____ value. The amount paid to purchase the protection is known as the ____. The ____ is the person or institution to whom the proceeds of the policy are paid in the event that a loss occurs. (19-1)

   face, premium, beneficiary

3. Name the two major categories of life insurance. (19-1)

   term and permanent

4. The ____ factor is a small surcharge added to the cost of insurance policies when the insured chooses to pay the premiums more frequently than annually. (19-1)

   premium

5. The options available to a policyholder upon termination of a permanent life insurance policy with accumulated cash value are known as the ____ options. List these three options. (19-2)

   nonforfeiture,
   - Surrender the policy and take the cash
   - Purchase a reduced level of paid-up insurance
   - Purchase a term policy with the same face value

6. The difference between the total living expenses and the total income of a family in the event of the death of the insured is known as the income ____. Write the formula used to calculate the amount of life insurance needed to cover this difference. (19-3)

   shortfall,

   $$\text{Insurance needed} = \frac{\text{Income shortfall}}{\text{Prevailing interest rate}}$$

7. List any four perils covered by property insurance. (19-4)

   fire, lightning, wind, water, negligence, burglary, vandalism

8. List the four factors used to determine the fire insurance rates on a building. (19-4)
   - dollar amount of insurance coverage purchased
   - location of the property
   - proximity and quality of fire protection available
   - type of construction materials used

9. The premium charged when a policy is canceled by the insured or is written for less than one year is known as the ____. (19-5)

   short-rate

10. The clause in a property insurance policy stipulating the minimum amount of coverage required for a claim to be paid in full is known as the ____ clause. (19-6)

    coinsurance

11. Write the coverage ratio formula used in calculating property insurance rates. (19-6)

    $$\text{Coverage ratio} = \frac{\text{Insurance carried}}{\text{Insurance required}}$$

12. A situation in which a business is covered by fire insurance policies from more than one company at the same time is known as ____ carriers. (19-7)

    multiple

13. In motor vehicle insurance, ____ covers bodily injury to other persons and damages to the property of others resulting from the insured's negligence; ____ covers accident damage to the insured's vehicle; and ____ covers the insured's vehicle for damage caused by fire, wind, water, theft, vandalism, and other perils. (19-8, 19-9)

    liability, collision, comprehensive

14. In motor vehicle insurance, companies often use ____ factors to adjust premiums upward or downward, depending on the amount of the risk involved in the coverage. (19-8, 19-9)

    rating

ASSESSMENT TEST

CHAPTER 19

Name

Class

Calculate the annual, semiannual, quarterly, and monthly premiums for the following life insurance policies.

	Face Value of Policy	Sex and Age of Insured	Type of Policy	Annual Premium	Semiannual Premium	Quarterly Premium	Monthly Premium
1.	$80,000	Male, 29	20-Payment Life	$2,521.60	$1,311.23	$655.62	$226.94
2.	55,000	Female, 21	20-Year Endowment	1,748.45	909.19	454.60	157.36
3.	38,000	Female, 40	5-Year Term	148.20	77.06	38.53	13.34
4.	175,000	Male, 30	Whole Life	3,244.50	1,687.14	843.57	292.01

Calculate the value of the nonforfeiture options for the following life insurance policies.

EXCEL

	Face Value of Policy	Years in Force	Type of Policy	Cash Value	Reduced Paid-up Insurance	Extended Term Years	Extended Term Days
5.	$130,000	15	Whole Life	$20,410	$40,820	21	218
6.	60,000	5	20-Payment Life	$4,380	$ 12,720	14	86

7. Brad Sigler is 19 years old and is interested in purchasing a whole life insurance policy with a face value of $80,000.

a. Calculate the annual insurance premium for this policy.

Annual premium = 13.60 × 80 = $1,088

b. Calculate the monthly insurance premiums.

Monthly premium = 1,088 × 9% = 97.92

c. How much more will Brad pay per year if he chooses monthly payments?

Amount more due to monthly payments =
(97.92 × 12) = 1,175.04 − 1,088.00 = $87.04

8. Deana Jackson purchased a $45,000 20-year endowment life insurance policy when she was 20 years old. She is now 35 years old and wants to look into her nonforfeiture options. As her insurance agent, calculate the value of Deana's three options.

a. Option 1

Nonforfeiture options:
Cash value = 647 × 45 = $29,115

b. Option 2

Reduced paid-up insurance = 794 × 45 = $35,730

c. Option 3

Extended term insurance = 37 years, 350 days

9. Joe Morgan is evaluating his life insurance needs. His family's total annual living expenses are $54,500. Gloria, his wife, earns $28,900 per year in salary. If the prevailing interest rate is 5%, how much life insurance should Joe purchase to cover his dependents' income shortfall in the event of his death?

$54,500
−28,900
Income shortfall = $25,600

$$\text{Insurance needed} = \frac{25,600}{5\%} = \$512,000$$

Answers

1. Annual $2,521.60
Semiannual $1,311.23
Quarterly $655.62
Monthly $226.94

2. Annual $1,748.45
Semiannual $909.19
Quarterly $454.60
Monthly $157.36

3. Annual $148.20
Semiannual $77.06
Quarterly $38.53
Monthly $13.34

4. Annual $3,244.50
Semiannual $1,687.14
Quarterly $843.57
Monthly $292.01

5. $20,410
$40,820
21 years
218 days

6. $4,380
$12,720
14 years
86 days

7. a. $1,088
b. $97.92
c. $87.04

8. a. $29,115
b. $35,730
c. 37 years, 350 days

9. $512,000

Complete, worked-out solutions to Exercises 1, 5, and 6 appear in Appendix B, following the index.

CHAPTER

Name

Class

Answers

10. Building $357.20

Contents $771.90

Total $1,129.10

11. Building $475.00

Contents $672.00

Total $1,147.00

12. Building $6,762.00

Contents $11,550.00

Total $18,312.00

13. Premium $173.33

Refund $86.67

14. Premium $100.80

Refund $619.20

15. $6,057.69

16. $80,000.00

17. $12,392

18. $6,250

19. $153,000

Complete, worked-out solutions to Exercises 10, 13, and 15 appear in Appendix B, following the index.

Calculate the building, contents, and total property insurance premiums for the following property insurance policies.

	Area Rating	Structural Class	Building Value	Building Premium	Contents Value	Contents Premium	Total Premium
10.	4	B	$47,000	$357.20	$93,000	$771.90	$1,129.10
11.	2	A	125,000	475.00	160,000	672.00	1,147.00
12.	3	C	980,000	6,762.00	1,500,000	11,550.00	18,312.00

Calculate the short-term premium and refund for the following policies.

	Annual Premium	Canceled After	Canceled By	Short-Term Premium	Short-Term Refund
13.	$260	8 months	insurance company	$173.33	$86.67
14.	720	15 days	insured	$100.80	$619.20

Calculate the amount to be paid by the insurance company for each of the following claims.

	Replacement Value of Building	Face Value of Policy	Coinsurance Clause (%)	Amount of Loss	Amount of Loss Insurance Company Will Pay
15.	$260,000	$105,000	80	$12,000	$6,057.69
16.	490,000	450,000	90	80,000	$80,000.00

17. You are the insurance agent for Clothes Horse International, a company that imports men's and women's clothing from Europe and the Far East. The owner, Ron Jefferson, wants you to give him a quote on the total annual premium for property insurance on a new warehouse and showroom facility in the amount of $320,000. The building is structural classification B and area rating 4. In addition, Ron will require contents insurance in the amount of $1,200,000.

Property insurance = .76 × 3,200 = $2,432
Contents insurance = .83 × 12,000 = $9,960
Total annual premium = 2,432 + 9,960 = $12,392

18. "Movers of the Stars" has been contracted by Premier Events, Inc., to transport the stage and sound equipment for a 4-month rock-and-roll tour by the Rolling Stones. The moving company purchased property insurance to cover this valuable equipment for an annual premium of $12,500. What is the short-rate premium due for this coverage?

Annual premium $12,500, 4 months in force, Canceled by insured
Short-term premium = 12,500 × 50% = $6,250

19. The Professional Medical Center had property valued at $750,000 and insured for $600,000. The fire insurance policy contained an 80% coinsurance clause. One evening, an electrical short circuit caused a $153,000 fire. How much of the damages will be paid by the insurance company?

Amount of insurance required = 750,000 × 80% = $600,000

$$\text{Amount of loss insurance company will pay} = \frac{600{,}000}{600{,}000} \times 153{,}000 = \$153{,}000$$

20. Jamba Juice Bottling Company had multiple carrier fire insurance coverage on its plant and equipment in the amount of $2,960,000, as follows:

Kemper	$1,350,000 policy
Metropolitan	921,000 policy
The Hartford	689,000 policy
	$2,960,000 total coverage

Assuming that all coinsurance clause stipulations have been met, how much would each carrier be responsible for in the event of a $430,000 fire? Round to the nearest whole percent.

a. Kemper

$\frac{1,350,000}{2,960,000} = .456 = 46\%$

$430,000 \times .46 = \$197,800$

b. Metropolitan

$\frac{921,000}{2,960,000} = .311 = 31\%$

$430,000 \times .31 = \$133,300$

c. The Hartford

$\frac{689,000}{2,960,000} = .232 = 23\%$

$430,000 \times .23 = \$98,900$

Complete, worked-out solutions to Exercises 21–23 appear in Appendix B, following the index.

As an insurance agent, calculate the annual premium for the following clients.

	Name	Territory	Driver Class	Bodily Injury	Property Damage	Model Class	Vehicle Age	Comprehensive Deductible	Collision Deductible	Rating Factor	Annual Premium
21.	Wills	3	2	50/100	25	X	1	$100	$500	0.9	$361.80
22.	Benson	1	1	10/20	5	Q	4	Full Cov.	250	2.2	$629.20
23.	Mays	2	4	100/300	100	F	7	$100	500	1.7	$564.40

24. Kim Kirkland wants to purchase an automobile insurance policy with bodily injury and property damage coverage in the amounts of 25/50/25. In addition, she wants collision coverage with $250 deductible and comprehensive with $100 deductible. Kim is in driver classification 2 and lives in territory 3. Her vehicle, a new Toyota Camry, is in model class B. Because the car has an airbag, an alarm, and antilock brakes, the insurance company has assigned a rating factor of .95 to the policy. As her auto insurance agent, calculate Kim's total annual premium.

Bodily injury 25/50	86
Property damage 25	74
Collision $250 deductible	95
Comprehensive $100 deductible	61
Rating factor .95	316 × .95
Class 2, Territory 3	
Model B, 0 years	$300.20 Annual premium

25. Blake West has automobile liability insurance in the amount of 50/100/50. He also carries $250 deductible collision and full comprehensive coverage. Recently, he was at fault in an accident in which his car went out of control in the rain and struck four pedestrians. In an out-of-court settlement, they were awarded the following: Goya, $45,000; Truman, $68,000; Copeland, $16,000; and Kelly, $11,000. Damages to Blake's car amounted to $3,900.

a. How much will the insurance company pay and to whom?

Insurance company will pay:	
Goya	$45,000
Truman	50,000
Copeland	5,000
Kelly	0
Blake's car	3,650
Total	$103,650

b. What part of the settlement will be Blake's responsibility?

Blake will pay:	
Truman—Per person limit	$18,000
Copeland—Total limit	11,000
Kelly—Total limit	11,000
Deductible	250
Total	$40,250

CHAPTER 19

Name

Class

Answers

20. a. $197,800

b. $133,300

c. $98,900

21. $361.80

22. $629.20

23. $564.40

24. $300.20

25. a. Goya $45,000

Truman 50,000

Copeland 5,000

Kelly 0

Blake's car 3,650

Total $103,650

b. Truman $18,000

Copeland 11,000

Kelly 11,000

Deductible 250

Total $40,250

BUSINESS DECISION GROUP INSURANCE

Name

Class

Answers

26. a. $250,600

b. $13.85, $16.15, $20.77

c. $2,080

26. Many employers purchase group insurance on behalf of their employees. Under a group insurance plan, a master contract issued to the company provides either life insurance, health insurance, or both for the employees who choose to participate. Most plans also provide coverage for dependents of employees. The two major benefits of group plans are lower premiums than individual insurance of the same coverage and no medical exams.

You are the owner of Kingston Industries, Inc., a small manufacturing company with 250 employees. The company has just instituted a group health insurance plan for employees. Under the plan, the employees pay 30% of the premium and the company pays 70%. The insurance company reimburses 80% of all medical expenses over the deductible. The annual rates and deductibles from the insurance company are as follows:

	Annual Premium	Deductible
Employee with no dependents	$1,200	$300
Employee with one dependent	$1,400	$500
Employee with multiple dependents	$1,800	$800

a. If all 250 employees opt for the group health plan, what is the annual cost to the company assuming: 100 employees have no dependents, 80 employees have one dependent, and 70 have multiple dependents?

No dependents: $100 \times 1{,}200 \times .7 = \$84{,}000$
One dependent: $80 \times 1{,}400 \times .7 = \$78{,}400$
Multiple dependents: $70 \times 1{,}800 \times .7 = \$88{,}200$

Total annual cost $= 84{,}000 + 78{,}400 + 88{,}200 = \underline{\underline{\$250{,}600}}$

b. If your employees are paid biweekly, how much should be deducted from each paycheck for each of the three categories?

No dependents: $\frac{1{,}200 \times .3}{26} = \underline{\underline{\$13.85}}$

One dependent: $\frac{1{,}400 \times .3}{26} = \underline{\underline{\$16.15}}$

Multiple dependents: $\frac{1{,}800 \times .3}{26} = \underline{\underline{\$20.77}}$

c. If Yolande Trumble chooses the multiple dependent option, and has a total of $3,400 in medical bills for the year, how much will be reimbursed by the insurance company?

$3{,}400 - 800 = \$2{,}600$ $\quad 2{,}600 \times .8 = \underline{\underline{\$2{,}080}}$

"Sorry sir, you can't claim on your group insurance policy unless the whole group is sick."

COLLABORATIVE LEARNING ACTIVITY

Insurance for Sweetie Pie

As a team, you and your partners are going to hypothetically start a company called The Sweetie Pie Bakery, a company that makes and distributes pies, cakes, cookies, and donuts to restaurants and food stores in your area.

The company will have property and a building valued at $300,000, baking and production-line equipment valued at $400,000, office equipment and fixtures worth $200,000, and four delivery trucks valued at $45,000 each. The expected revenue is $50,000 per month. There will be 18 employees and 4 partners, including you.

Each team member is to consult with a different insurance agent to put together a "package" of business insurance coverage for Sweetie Pie, including property insurance, liability insurance, and business interruption insurance.

In addition, look into a health insurance program for the partners and the employees, as well as $500,000 "key man" life insurance for each partner.

a. Compare and contrast the various insurance packages quoted for Sweetie Pie.
b. Which insurance company came up with life the best package? Why?
c. What other types of coverage did the insurance agent recommend?

CHAPTER 20 Investments

PERFORMANCE OBJECTIVES

Section I Stocks

20-1: Understanding stocks and distributing dividends on preferred and common stock (p. 733)

20-2: Reading a stock quotation table (p. 737)

20-3: Calculating current yield for a stock (p. 739)

20-4: Determining the price-earnings ratio of a stock (p. 740)

20-5: Computing the cost, proceeds, and gain or (loss) on a stock transaction (p. 741)

Section II Bonds

20-6: Understanding bonds and reading a bond quotation table (p. 746)

20-7: Calculating the cost of purchasing bonds and the proceeds from the sale of bonds (p. 750)

20-8: Calculating the current yield for a bond (p. 751)

Section III Mutual Funds

20-9: Understanding mutual funds and reading a mutual fund quotation table (p. 755)

20-10: Calculating the sales charge and sales charge percent of a mutual fund (p. 757)

20-11: Calculating the net asset value of a mutual fund (p. 758)

20-12: Calculating the number of shares purchased of a mutual fund (p. 759)

20-13: Calculating return on investment (p. 760)

STOCKS

SECTION I 20

Financial risk is the chance you take of either making or losing money on an investment. In most cases, the greater the risk, the more money you stand to gain or lose. Investment opportunities range from low-risk **conservative investments**, such as government bonds or certificates of deposit, to high-risk **speculative investments**, such as stocks in new companies, junk bonds, or options and futures. Selecting the right investment depends on personal circumstances as well as general market conditions. See Exhibit 20-1.

Investments are based on *liquidity*, which indicates how easy it is to get your money out; *safety*, how much risk is involved; and *return*, how much you can expect to earn. Investment advice is available from stockbrokers, financial planners, and many other sources. It is generally agreed that over the long run, a **diversified portfolio**, with a mixture of stocks, bonds, cash equivalents, and sometimes other types of investments, is a sensible choice. Determining the correct portfolio mix is a decision that should be based on the amount of assets available, the age of the investor, and the amount of risk desired.

In this chapter, we investigate three major categories of investments: **stocks**, also known as **equities**, which represent an *ownership share* of a corporation; bonds, or debt, which represent IOUs for money borrowed from the investor; and mutual funds, which are investment *pools* of money with a wide variety of investment goals.

financial risk The chance you take of either making or losing money on an investment.

conservative investments Low-risk investments, such as government bonds or certificates of deposit.

speculative investments High-risk investments, such as stocks in new companies, junk bonds, or options and futures.

diversified portfolio An investment strategy that is a mixture of stocks, bonds, cash equivalents, and other types of investments.

stocks, or equities An investment that is an ownership share of a corporation.

UNDERSTANDING STOCKS AND DISTRIBUTING DIVIDENDS ON PREFERRED AND COMMON STOCK

20-1

Corporations are built and expanded with money known as capital, which is raised by issuing and selling **shares** of stock. Investors' ownership in a company is measured by the number of shares they own. Each ownership portion, or share, is represented by a **stock certificate**. In the past, these certificates were sent to the investor, confirming the stock purchase transaction. Today, however, this confirmation comes in the form of a computerized book entry on

share One unit of stock or ownership in a corporation.

stock certificate The official document that represents an ownership share in a corporation.

Exhibit 20-1
Risk vs. Return

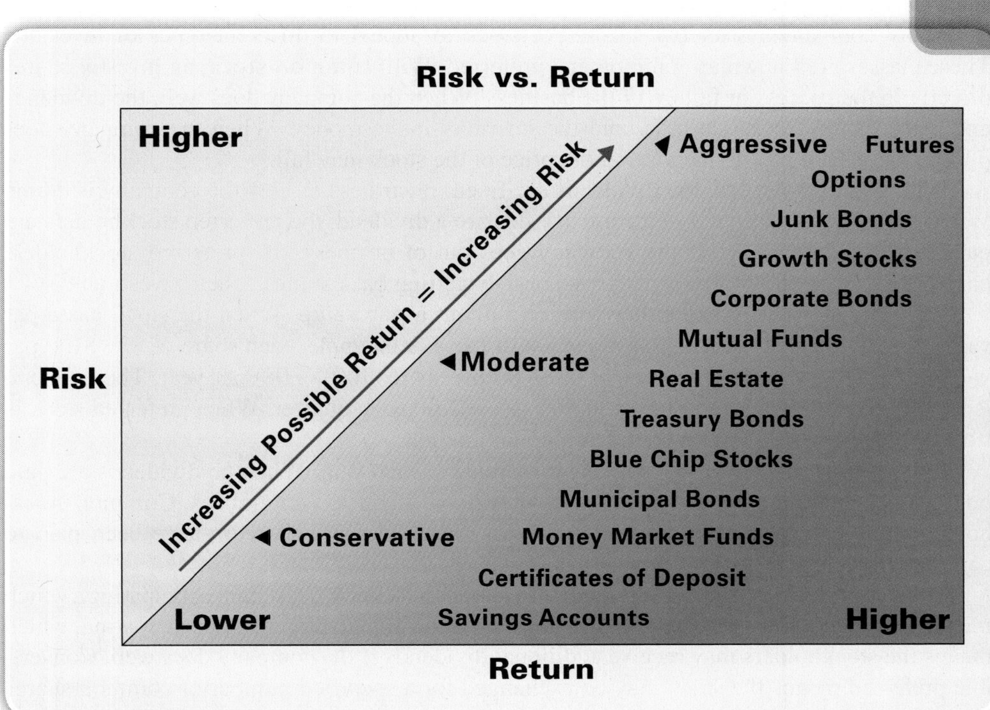

20-1

In the Business World

History has demonstrated repeatedly that a well-diversified portfolio of investments based on careful planning and a focused strategy reduces risk and provides an opportunity for solid returns.

Changing investments too frequently—overreacting to daily economic data or the latest Wall Street fads—can distract investors from reaching their specific goals.

Exhibit 20-2
Stock Certificate

Stock certificate image provided courtesy of OneShare.com

an account statement. Investors who actually want to hold their certificates are charged extra service fees. Exhibit 20-2 is an example of a stock certificate.

shareholder The person who owns shares of stock in a corporation.

dividends A distribution of a company's profits to its shareholders.

publicly held corporation A corporation whose stock is available to be bought and sold by the general investing public. The opposite of a privately held corporation.

common stock A class of corporate stock in which the investor has voting rights and shares directly in the success or failure of the business.

preferred stock A class of corporate stock in which the investor has preferential rights over the common shareholders to dividends and a company's assets.

par value An arbitrary monetary figure specified in the corporate charter for each share of stock and printed on each stock certificate. The dividend for par value preferred stock is quoted as a percent of the par value.

no-par value stock Stock that does not have a par value. The dividend for no-par value preferred stock is quoted as a dollar amount per share.

Generally, if the company does well, the investor or **shareholder** will receive **dividends**, which are a distribution of the company's profits. If the share price goes up, the stockholder can sell the stock at a profit. Today, more than 50 million persons in the United States own stock in thousands of **publicly held corporations**.

Many companies offer two classes of stock to appeal to different types of investors. These classes are known as common and preferred. With **common stock**, an investor shares directly in the success or failure of the business. When the company does well, the dividends and price of the stock may rise, and the investors make money. When the company does poorly, it does not pay dividends and the price of the stock may fall.

With **preferred stock**, the dividends are fixed, regardless of how the company is doing. When the board of directors of a company declare a dividend, the preferred stockholders are paid before the common. If the company goes out of business, the preferred stockholders have priority over the common as far as possibly getting back some of their investment.

Preferred stock is issued either with or without a **par value**. When the stock has a par value, the dividend is specified as a percent of par. For example, each share of 8%, $100 par value preferred stock pays a dividend of $8.00 per share (100 × .08) per year. The dividend is usually paid on a quarterly basis, in this case, $2.00 each quarter. When preferred stock is **no-par value**, the dividend is stated as a dollar amount.

Cumulative preferred stock receives a dividend each year. When no dividends are paid one year, the amount owed, known as **dividends in arrears**, accumulates. Common stockholders cannot receive any dividends until all the dividends in arrears have been paid to cumulative preferred stockholders.

Preferred stock is further divided into categories known as nonparticipating, which means the stockholders receive only the fixed dividend and no more; and participating, which means the stockholders may receive additional dividends if the company does well. Convertible preferred means the stock may be exchanged for a specified number of common shares in the future.

STEPS TO DISTRIBUTE DIVIDENDS ON PREFERRED AND COMMON STOCK

Step 1. If the preferred stock is *cumulative*, any dividends that are in arrears are paid first; then the preferred dividend is paid for the current period. When the dividend per share is stated in dollars (no-par stock), go to Step 2. When the dividend per share is stated as a percent (par stock), multiply the par value by the dividend rate.

$$\textbf{Dividend per share (preferred)} = \textbf{Par value} \times \textbf{Dividend rate}$$

Step 2. Calculate the total amount of the preferred stock dividend by multiplying the number of preferred shares by the dividend per share.

$$\textbf{Total preferred dividend} = \textbf{Number of shares} \times \textbf{Dividend per share}$$

Step 3. Calculate the total common stock dividend by subtracting the total preferred stock dividend from the total dividend declared.

$$\textbf{Total common dividend} = \textbf{Total dividend} - \textbf{Total preferred dividend}$$

Step 4. Calculate the dividends per share for common stock by dividing the total common stock dividend by the number of shares of common stock.

$$\textbf{Dividend per share (common)} = \frac{\textbf{Total common dividend}}{\textbf{Number of shares (common)}}$$

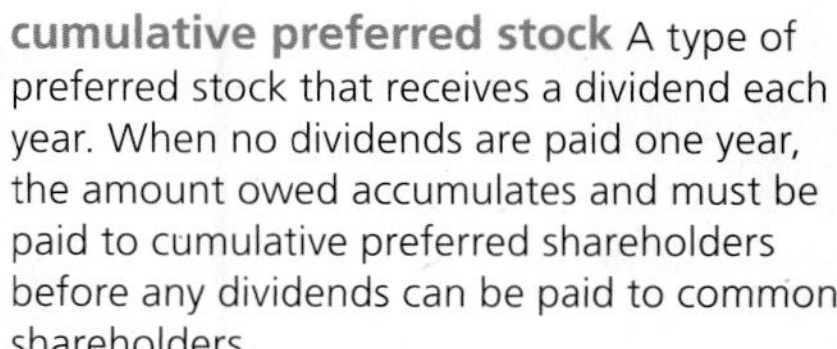

cumulative preferred stock A type of preferred stock that receives a dividend each year. When no dividends are paid one year, the amount owed accumulates and must be paid to cumulative preferred shareholders before any dividends can be paid to common shareholders.

dividends in arrears The amount of dividends that accumulate and are owed to cumulative preferred shareholders for past years in which no dividends were paid.

EXAMPLE 1 DISTRIBUTING COMMON STOCK DIVIDENDS

The Polynomial Corporation has 2,500,000 shares of common stock outstanding. If a dividend of $4,000,000 was declared by the company directors last year, what are the dividends per share of common stock?

SOLUTION STRATEGY

Because Polynomial has no preferred stock, the common shareholders will receive the entire dividend. We go directly to Step 4.

$$\text{Dividend per share (common)} = \frac{\text{Total common dividend}}{\text{Number of shares (common)}} = \frac{4{,}000{,}000}{2{,}500{,}000} = \underline{\underline{\$1.60 \text{ per share}}}$$

TRY IT EXERCISE 1

Kingston Computer, Inc., has 1,400,000 shares of common stock outstanding. If a dividend of $910,000 was declared by the company directors last year, what is the dividend per share of common stock?

CHECK YOUR ANSWER WITH THE SOLUTION ON PAGE 767.

CLASSROOM ACTIVITY

Invite a stockbroker to class to discuss "current happenings" related to investments.

In addition, have him or her talk about career opportunities and the educational requirements for becoming a stockbroker.

EXAMPLE 2 DISTRIBUTING COMMON AND PREFERRED STOCK DIVIDENDS

The board of directors of Bow River Developers, Inc., have declared a dividend of $300,000. The company has 60,000 shares of preferred stock that pay $.50 per share and 100,000 shares of common stock. Calculate the amount of dividends due the preferred shareholders and the dividend per share of common stock.

SOLUTION STRATEGY

Step 1. Because the preferred dividend is stated in dollars ($.50 per share), we skip to Step 2.

Step 2. Total preferred dividend = Number of shares × Dividend per share

Total preferred dividend = 60,000 × .50 = $30,000

Step 3. Total common dividend = Total dividend − Total preferred dividend

Total common dividend = 300,000 − 30,000 = $270,000

Step 4.

$$\text{Dividend per share (common)} = \frac{\text{Total common dividend}}{\text{Number of shares (common)}} = \frac{270{,}000}{100{,}000} = \underline{\underline{\$2.70 \text{ per share}}}$$

TRY IT EXERCISE 2

The board of directors of Digital Technology, Inc., has declared a dividend of $2,800,000. The company has 600,000 shares of preferred stock that pay $1.40 per share and 1,000,000 shares of common stock. Calculate the amount of dividends due the preferred shareholders and the dividend per share of common stock.

CHECK YOUR ANSWERS WITH THE SOLUTIONS ON PAGE 767.

EXAMPLE 3 DISTRIBUTING COMMON AND PREFERRED STOCK DIVIDENDS

Silverlake Enterprises has 100,000 shares of $100 par value, 6%, cumulative preferred stock and 2,500,000 shares of common stock. Although no dividend was declared last year, a $5,000,000 dividend has been declared this year. Calculate the amount of dividends due the preferred shareholders and the dividend per share of common stock.

SOLUTION STRATEGY

Step 1. Because the preferred stock is cumulative and the company did not pay a dividend last year, the preferred shareholders are entitled to the dividends in *arrears* and the dividends for the *current period.*

Dividend per share (preferred) = Par value × Dividend rate

Dividend per share (preferred) = 100 × .06 = $6.00 per share

Step 2.

$$\text{Total preferred dividend (per year)} = \text{Number of shares} \times \text{Dividend per share}$$

$$\text{Total preferred dividend (per year)} = 100{,}000 \times 6.00 = \underline{\$600{,}000}$$

$$\text{Total preferred dividend} = 600{,}000 \text{ (arrears)} + 600{,}000 \text{ (current year)} = \underline{\underline{\$1{,}200{,}000}}$$

Step 3.

$$\text{Total common dividend} = \text{Total dividend} - \text{Total preferred dividend}$$

$$\text{Total common dividend} = 5{,}000{,}000 - 1{,}200{,}000 = \underline{\$3{,}800{,}000}$$

Step 4.

$$\text{Dividend per share (common)} = \frac{\text{Total common dividend}}{\text{Number of shares (common)}} = \frac{3{,}800{,}000}{2{,}500{,}000} = \underline{\underline{\$1.52}}$$

TRY IT EXERCISE 3

Wellington Laboratories has 300,000 shares of $100 par value, 7.5%, cumulative preferred stock, and 5,200,000 shares of common stock. Although no dividend was declared for last year, a $7,000,000 dividend has been declared for this year. Calculate the amount of dividends due the preferred shareholders and the dividend per share of common stock.

CHECK YOUR ANSWERS WITH THE SOLUTIONS ON PAGE 768.

READING A STOCK QUOTATION TABLE

20-2

A stock quotation table provides investors with a summary of what happened in the stock market on a particular trading day. These tables can be found on the Internet or in the business section of most newspapers. Exhibit 20-3 is a sample of such a table from *The Wall Street Journal Online*. The companies listed are the 30 stocks that comprise the Dow Jones Industrial Average, an important economic indicator.

20-2

Let's take a column-by-column look at a particular day's listing for the **Coca-Cola Company**. Stock prices in this table are listed in dollars and cents. The first step in reading the stock quotation table is to locate the alphabetical listing of the company whose stock you want to look up, in this case, Coca-Cola. Each line is divided into 15 columns, as follows.

Column 1 (**Name** Coca-Cola Co.) Company name.

Column 2 (**Symbol** KO) Symbol used to easily identify a particular stock. The symbol for Cola-Cola stock is KO.

Column 3 (**Open** 57.96) Opening price of the stock that trading day. On that day, Coca-Cola stock opened at $57.96.

Column 4 (**High** 58.13) Highest price of the stock during the trading day. During that day, the Coca-Cola stock price reached a high of $58.13.

Column 5 (**Low** 57.69) Lowest price of the stock during the trading day. During that day, the Coca-Cola stock price reached a low of $57.69.

Column 6 (**Close** 57.80) The last price of the trading day. That day, the Coca-Cola stock price closed at $57.80.

Column 7 (**Net Change** −0.27) The difference, or net change, between the "close" price and the previous day's "close" price. Positive change is indicated in green. Negative change is indicated by a minus sign, and in red. That day, the Coca-Cola stock price closed down $0.27 per share.

In the Business World

The New York Stock Exchange began trading stocks in dollars and cents rather than fractions in 2000. For investors, the move to decimals meant that the spreads—the difference between the price of a stock and what a broker will charge investors to buy it—were narrowed.

The minimum spread using fractions was one-eighth, or 12.5 cents. With decimal pricing, the spread could be as little as a penny.

CLASSROOM ACTIVITY

Discuss with students the Dow-Jones Industrial Average. Explain that it is one of many indicators used to follow trends in the stock market.

It is the average value of a group of 30 stocks considered to be typical of today's economic activity, such as AT&T, American Express, Boeing, Coca-Cola, McDonald's, and Microsoft.

Have students research and report to the class:

- Which stocks comprise the current Dow-Jones 30 Industrials?
- How have these changed over the years?

In 1998, for example, Wal-Mart replaced Woolworth on the list. Ask students to comment on why they think this change was made.

Column 8 (**%Change** −0.46) The trading day's percentage change in price. Positive change is indicated in green. Negative change is indicated by a minus sign, and in red. That day, the Coca-Cola stock price went down 0.46%.

Column 9 (**Volume** 3,006,400) The volume or number of shares traded during the day. On that day, more than 3 million shares of Coca-Cola were traded.

Column 10 (**52 Week High** 58.33) Highest price of the stock during the preceding 52-week period. In the past year, the Coca-Cola stock price reached a high of $58.33.

Column 11 (**52 Week Low** 43.72) Lowest price of the stock during the preceding 52-week period. In the past year,the Coca-Cola stock price reached a low of $43.72.

Column 12 (**Dividend** 1.4) The amount of dividends paid out to shareholders in the past year. When there are no dividends, the column shows ". . .". Last year Coca-Cola paid stockholders a dividend of $1.40 per share.

Column 13 (**Yield** 2.4) Yield percent. Last year's dividend as a percent of the current price of the stock. When there are no dividends, the column shows ". . .". Last year, Coca-Cola's dividend yielded stockholders a 2.4% return on their investment.

Column 14 (**P/E** 26) Price-earnings. . . ; ratio. A number that indicates investors' confidence in a stock. It is the ratio of the current price of the stock to the earnings per share for the past year. The price of Coca-Cola stock was selling at a P/E ratio or multiple of 26 times the earnings per share.

Exhibit 20-3
Stock Quotation Table – *The Wall Street Journal Online*

(1)	(2)	(3)	(4)	(5)	(6)	(7)	(8)	(9)	(10)	(11)	(12)	(13)	(14)	(15)
Name	Symbol	Open	High	Low	Close	Net Chg	%Chg	Volume	52 Wk High	52 Wk Low	Div	Yield	P/E	YTD % Chg
3M CO.	MMM	95.75	95.95	95.01	95.41	−0.44	−0.46	2,101,200	95.92	72.90	1.92	2	16	22.40
ALCOA INC.	AA	38.51	38.67	37.86	38.30	−0.49	−1.26	7,254,075	48.77	26.39	0.68	1.8	15	27.60
ALTRIA GROUP INC.	MO	69.46	69.55	69.09	69.28	−0.28	−0.40	4,719,285	72.20	58.24	3	4.3	14	7.60
AMERICAN EXPRESS CO.	AXP	61.11	61.41	60.57	60.69	−0.41	−0.67	3,519,300	65.89	53.91	0.6	1	18	0.00
AMERICAN INT'L GROUP INC.	AIG	69.14	69.65	69.00	69.37	−0.02	−0.03	5,273,700	72.97	60.00	0.8	1.2	11	−3.20
AT&T INC.	T	42.00	42.20	41.78	41.93	−0.21	−0.50	8,897,100	42.97	31.57	1.42	3.4	21	17.30
BOEING CO., THE	BA	103.26	103.26	100.09	101.07	−1.18	−1.15	5,307,400	107.83	77.77	1.4	1.4	22	13.80
CATERPILLAR INC.	CAT	80.74	81.61	80.48	81.34	1.01	1.26	3,592,655	87.00	57.98	1.44	1.8	16	32.60
CITIGROUP INC.	C	48.27	48.28	47.58	47.80	−0.50	−1.04	18,458,758	57.00	44.66	2.16	4.5	11	−14.20
COCA-COLA CO.	**KO**	**57.96**	**58.13**	**57.69**	**57.80**	**−0.27**	**−0.46**	**3,006,400**	**58.33**	**43.72**	**1.4**	**2.4**	**26**	**19.80**
DU PONT CO.	DD	49.42	49.52	48.84	49.00	−0.55	−1.11	2,489,900	53.90	43.40	1.48	3	14	0.60
EXXON MOBIL CORP.	XOM	90.60	90.82	90.16	90.68	−0.68	−0.74	12,768,781	93.99	65.96	1.4	1.5	13	18.30
GENERAL ELECTRIC CO	GE	41.74	41.80	41.41	41.53	−0.24	−0.57	14,400,542	42.15	33.90	1.12	2.7	20	11.60
GENERAL MOTORS CORP	GM	38.22	38.33	37.76	38.11	−0.09	−0.24	7,788,200	38.66	28.49	1	2.6	12	24.10
HEWLETT-PACKARD CO.	HPQ	50.92	52.18	50.91	52.03	1.13	2.22	12,512,240	51.23	37.44	0.32	0.6	21	26.30
HOME DEPOT INC.	HD	34.27	34.32	33.74	33.93	−0.29	−0.85	10,658,220	42.01	31.85	0.9	2.7	13	−15.50
HONEYWELL INT'L INC	HON	59.95	60.86	59.79	60.59	0.77	1.29	2,724,900	61.90	40.77	1	1.7	21	33.90
INTEL CORP.	INTC	25.50	25.76	25.47	25.66	0.12	0.47	34,600,200	26.50	18.75	0.45	1.75	26	27.00
INT'L BUSINESS MACHINES	IBM	116.10	118.23	115.88	117.77	1.47	1.26	4,803,700	119.60	82.50	1.6	1.4	18	21.20
JPMORGAN CHASE & CO.	JPM	47.31	47.58	47.05	47.44	−0.14	−0.29	8,189,700	53.25	42.16	1.52	3.2	10	−1.80
JOHNSON & JOHNSON	JNJ	66.25	66.38	65.95	66.02	−0.23	−0.35	5,642,700	69.41	59.72	1.66	2.5	18	0.00
MCDONALD'S CORP.	MCD	56.11	56.95	56.02	56.87	0.50	0.89	4,187,400	56.56	39.48	1.5	2.6	33	28.30
MERCK & CO	MRK	53.51	53.58	52.80	53.15	−0.36	−0.67	3,988,600	55.14	41.24	1.52	2.9	24	21.90
MICROSOFT CORP.	MSFT	29.66	29.85	29.60	29.84	0.00	0.00	30,265,600	31.84	26.60	0.44	1.45	21	10.90
PFIZER INC.	PFE	25.56	25.67	25.36	25.45	−0.13	−0.51	23,326,300	28.50	23.13	1.16	4.6	10	−1.70
PROCTER & GAMBLE CO.	PG	70.05	70.92	70.05	70.71	−0.12	−0.17	6,043,350	71.32	60.42	1.4	2	23	10.00
UNITED TECHNOLOGIES CORP.	UTX	80.84	81.28	80.21	80.36	−0.48	−0.59	3,205,000	82.50	61.80	1.28	1.6	21	28.50
VERIZON COMMUNICATIONS	VZ	45.07	45.22	44.79	44.96	−0.26	−0.57	5,054,789	45.64	33.99	1.72	3.8	21	20.70
WALT DISNEY CO.	DIS	35.47	35.69	35.13	35.27	−0.20	−0.56	4,613,700	36.30	30.37	. . .	. . .	16	4.30
WAL-MART STORES INC.	WMT	45.20	45.40	45.08	45.27	−0.10	−0.22	7,507,802	52.15	42.09	0.88	1.9	15	−2.00

Column 15 (**YTD %Chg** 19.80) The year-to-date percentage change in the price of the stock. Positive change is indicate in green. Negative change is indicated by a minus sign, and in red. In this example, the value of Coca-Cola stock has risen 19.80% in the past year.

EXAMPLE 4 READING A STOCK QUOTATION TABLE

From Exhibit 20-3, Stock Quotation Table, on page 738, explain the information listed for McDonald's.

SOLUTION STRATEGY

According to the listing for McDonald's, the ticker symbol is MCD. That day, the stock price opened at $56.11, went as high as $56.95 and as low as $56.02, and closed at $56.87. The price of the stock closed up $0.50; a 0.89% increase. During the trading day, over 4 million shares of McDonald's were traded.

In the past year, the stock price was as high as $56.56 and as low as $39.48. The company paid stockholders a dividend of $1.50 per share. That dividend provided a yield of 2.6%. On that day, the stock price of McDonald's was selling at a P/E ratio or multiple of 33 times the earnings per share. In the year to date, the stock price rose 28.30%.

TRY IT EXERCISE 4

Using Exhibit 20-3, Stock Quotation Table, on page 738, explain the information listed for Intel Corp.

CHECK YOUR ANSWERS WITH THE SOLUTIONS ON PAGE 768.

CLASSROOM ACTIVITY
Have students bring in the stock market quotations from the local newspaper.

- Discuss how the format of your local paper's listing differs from that of *The Wall Street Journal.*
- In groups, have them look at the NYSE listing to see how many companies they can identify from the abbreviations.

CALCULATING CURRENT YIELD FOR A STOCK

One way to measure how much you are earning on a stock compared with other investments is by calculating the **current yield**. In the stock quotations, this is listed in the yield % column. The current yield is a way of evaluating the current value of a stock. It tells you how much dividend you get as a percentage of the current price of the stock. When a stock pays no dividend, there is no current yield.

current yield A percentage measure of how much an investor is earning on a stock compared with other investments. It is calculated by dividing the annual dividend per share by the current price of the stock.

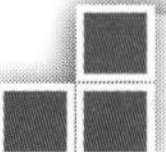

STEPS TO CALCULATE THE CURRENT YIELD OF A STOCK

Step 1. Divide the annual dividend per share by the current price of the stock.

$$\textbf{Current yield} = \frac{\textbf{Annual dividend per share}}{\textbf{Current price of the stock}}$$

Step 2. Convert the answer to a percent, rounded to the nearest tenth.

EXAMPLE 5 CALCULATING CURRENT YIELD

Calculate the current yield for Universal Corporation stock, which pays a dividend of $1.60 per year and is currently selling at $34.06 per share.

SOLUTION STRATEGY

$$\text{Current yield} = \frac{\text{Annual dividend per share}}{\text{Current price of the stock}}$$

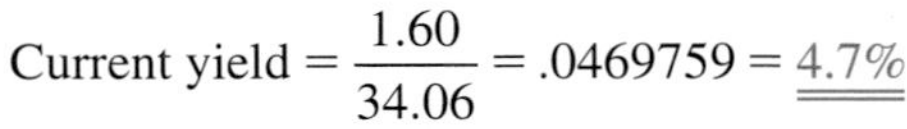

$$\text{Current yield} = \frac{1.60}{34.06} = .0469759 = \underline{\underline{4.7\%}}$$

TRY IT EXERCISE 5

Teaching Transparency 20-3

The Mercantile Corporation paid a dividend of $.68 per share last year. If yesterday's closing price was $12.84, what is the current yield on the stock?

CHECK YOUR ANSWER WITH THE SOLUTION ON PAGE 768.

20-4 DETERMINING THE PRICE-EARNINGS RATIO OF A STOCK

price-earnings ratio, or PE ratio
A ratio that shows the relationship between the price of a stock and a company's earnings for the past 12 months; one of the most widely used tools for analyzing stock.

One of the most widely used tools for analyzing a stock is the **price-earnings ratio**, commonly called the **PE ratio**. This number shows the relationship between the price of a stock and the company's earnings for the past 12 months. The price-earnings ratio is an important indicator because it reflects buyer confidence in a particular stock compared with the stock market as a whole. For example, a PE ratio of 20, or 20:1, means that buyers are willing to pay 20 times the current earnings for a share of stock.

The price-earnings ratio of a stock is most useful when compared with the PE ratios of the company in previous years and with the ratios of other companies in the same industry.

STEPS TO DETERMINE THE PRICE-EARNINGS RATIO OF A STOCK

Step 1. Divide the current price of the stock by the earnings per share for the past 12 months.

$$\textbf{Price-earnings ratio} = \frac{\textbf{Current price per share}}{\textbf{Earnings per share}}$$

Step 2. Round answer to the nearest whole number (may be written as a ratio, X:1).

EXAMPLE 6 CALCULATING PRICE-EARNINGS RATIO

Wakefield Industries stock is currently selling at $104.75. If the company had earnings per share of $3.60 last year, calculate the price-earnings ratio of the stock.

SOLUTION STRATEGY

$$\text{Price-earnings ratio} = \frac{\text{Current price per share}}{\text{Earnings per share}}$$

$$\text{Price-earnings ratio} = \frac{104.75}{3.60} = 29.09722 = \underline{\underline{29}} \text{ or } \underline{\underline{29:1}}$$

This means investors are currently willing to pay 29 times the earnings for one share of Wakefield Industries stock.

TRY IT EXERCISE 6

Crystal Corp. is currently selling for $37.19 per share. If the company had earnings per share of $6.70 in the past 12 months, what is the price-earnings ratio for Crystal?

CHECK YOUR ANSWER WITH THE SOLUTION ON PAGE 768.

20-4

proceeds The amount of money that an investor receives after selling a stock. It is calculated as the value of the shares less the broker's commission.

COMPUTING THE COST, PROCEEDS, AND GAIN OR (LOSS) ON A STOCK TRANSACTION

Investors take on the risks of purchasing stocks in the hope of making money. Although they are more risky than many other types of investment, over the years stocks have shown they are capable of generating spectacular returns in some periods and steady returns in the long run. One investment strategy is to buy stocks and keep them for the dividends paid by the company each quarter. Another strategy is to make money from the profit (or loss) of buying and selling the stock. Simply put, investors generally want to buy low and sell high! The gain or loss is the difference between the cost of purchasing the stock and the **proceeds** received when selling the stock.

Gain or (loss) on stock = Proceeds − Total cost

Stocks are generally purchased and sold through a **stockbroker**. Brokers have representatives at various **stock exchanges**, which are like a marketplace where stocks are bought and sold in the form of an auction. When you ask your broker to buy or sell a stock, the order is transmitted to the representative on the floor of the exchange. It is there that your request is *executed* or transacted.

The charge for this service is a **commission**, which is a percent of the cost of the transaction. Commission rates are competitive and vary from broker to broker. **Full-service brokers**, who provide additional services such as research data and investment advice, charge higher commissions than **discount brokers**, who simply execute the transactions.

Stock exchanges are where brokers execute investors' requests to buy and sell shares of stock.

STEPS TO COMPUTE THE COST, PROCEEDS, AND GAIN OR (LOSS) ON A STOCK TRANSACTION

Cost of purchasing stock

Step 1. Calculate the cost of the shares.

Cost of shares = Price per share × Number of shares

Step 2. Compute the amount of the broker's commission.

Broker's commission = Cost of shares × Commission rate

Step 3. Determine the total cost of the stock purchase.

Total cost = Cost of shares + Broker's commission

Proceeds from selling stock

Step 1. Calculate the value of shares on sale.

Value of shares = Price per share × Number of shares

Step 2. Compute the amount of the broker's commission.

Step 3. Determine the proceeds by subtracting the commission from the value of the shares.

Proceeds = Value of shares − Broker's commission

Gain or (loss) on the transaction

Gain or (loss) on transaction = Proceeds − Total cost

Another factor affecting the commission is whether the amount of shares purchased is a **round lot**, a multiple of 100, or an **odd lot**, less than 100. The commission rate on an odd lot is usually a bit higher than on a round lot. For example, the commission on a 400-share transaction might be 3%, while the commission on a 40-share transaction might be 4%.

stockbroker A professional in stock market trading and investments who acts as an agent in the buying and selling of stocks or other securities.

stock exchanges Marketplaces where stocks, bonds, and mutual funds are bought and sold in the form of an auction.

stockbroker's commission The fee a stockbroker charges for assisting in the purchase or sale of shares of stock; a percent of the cost of the stock transaction.

full-service broker Stockbrokers who provide services such as research and investment advice in addition to assisting in the purchase or sale of stock. Commissions generally range from 3% to 5% of the cost of the transaction.

discount broker Minimum service stockbrokers who simply execute stock purchase and sale transactions. Commissions generally range from 1% to 2% of the cost of the transaction.

round lot Shares of stock purchased in multiples of 100.

odd lot The purchase of less than 100 shares of stock.

TEACHING TIP

Be sure students understand that when a share of stock is purchased, unless it is the initial public offering (IPO), it is being purchased from someone who is selling his or her stock, *not* from the company itself.

Explain that a company has a fixed number of **outstanding shares**, which are bought and sold (traded) among investors each day on various exchanges.

EXAMPLE 7 CALCULATING GAIN OR LOSS ON A STOCK TRANSACTION

You purchase 350 shares of Apollo Industries common stock at $46.50 per share. A few months later, you sell the shares at $54.31. Your stockbroker charges 3% commission on round lots and 4% on odd lots. Calculate (a) the total cost, (b) the proceeds, and (c) the gain or loss on the transaction.

SOLUTION STRATEGY

a. *Cost of purchasing stock*

Step 1.
Cost of shares = Price per share × Number of shares
Cost of shares = 46.50 × 350 = $16,275

Step 2.
Broker's commission = Cost of shares × Commission rate
Round lot commission = 300 shares × 46.50 × .03 = $418.50
Odd lot commission = 50 shares × 46.50 × .04 = $93.00
Broker's commission = 418.50 + 93.00 = $511.50

Step 3.
Total cost = Cost of shares + Broker's commission
Total cost = 16,275 + 511.50 = $16,786.50

b. *Proceeds from selling stock*

Step 1. Value of shares = 54.31 × 350 = $19,008.50

Step 2. Broker's commission = Cost of shares × Commission rate

Round lot commission = 300 shares × 54.31 × .03 = $488.79

Odd lot commission = 50 shares × 54.31 × .04 = $108.62

Broker's commission = 488.79 + 108.62 = $597.41

Step 3. Proceeds = Value of shares − Broker's commission

Proceeds = 19,008.50 − 597.41 = $18,411.09

c. *Gain or (loss) on the transaction*

Gain or (loss) on transaction = Proceeds − Total cost

Gain or (loss) on transaction = 18,411.09 − 16,786.50 = $1,624.59

TRY IT EXERCISE 7

You purchase 225 shares of Saratoga Corporation common stock at $44.80 per share. A few months later, you sell the shares at $53.20. Your stockbroker charges 2% commission on round lots and 3% on odd lots. Calculate (a) the total cost, (b) the proceeds, and (c) the gain or loss on the transaction.

CHECK YOUR ANSWERS WITH THE SOLUTIONS ON PAGE 768.

Learning Tip

Remember, when purchasing stock, commissions are added to the cost of the stock to get total cost; when selling, the commissions are *deducted* by the brokerage firm from the sale price to get the proceeds of the sale.

CLASSROOM ACTIVITY

In groups, have students work Try It Exercise 7, calculating the cost, proceeds, and gain or (loss) on a stock transaction. Next, have the groups compare answers with those of another group and resolve any differences.

Use Teaching Transparencies 20-5, 20-5a, 20-5b, and 20-5c to illustrate the solution.

Teaching Transparency 20-5

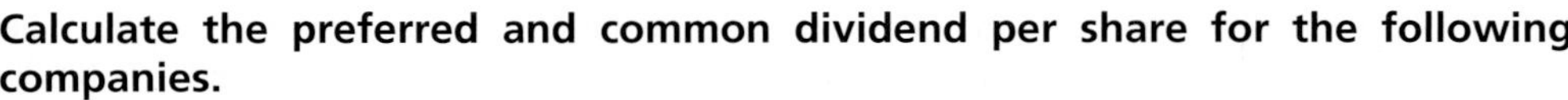

Review Exercises

SECTION I 20

Calculate the preferred and common dividend per share for the following companies.

Solution Transparencies

Company	Common Stock Shares	Preferred Stock Shares	Preferred Stock Div. or Par	Preferred Stock Cum.	Dividend Declared	Arrears	Preferred Div./Share	Common Div./Share
1. Intel	5,000,000		none		$3,000,000	none	—	$.60
2. Alcoa	10,000,000	3,000,000	$5.50	no	25,000,000	none	$5.50	$.85
3. Pepsi	8,000,000	2,000,000	$100 6%	no	10,000,000	none	$5.00	0
4. Wrigley	4,000,000	1,000,000	$100 4%	yes	14,000,000	1 year	$8.00	$1.50
5. IBM	20,000,000	4,000,000	$6.25	yes	none	1 year	0	0

Use Exhibit 20-3, Stock Quotation Table, on page 738, to fill in the blanks for Exercises 6–10.

6. American Express Co. – High and low for the past 52 weeks: High: 65.89, Low: $53.91
7. Hewlett-Packard Co. – Ticker symbol, Close price, and PE ratio: HPQ, $52.03, 21
8. Procter and Gamble Co. – Net change, Volume, and Dividend: down $0.12, 6,043,350 shares, $1.40

Complete, worked-out solutions to Exercises 1–2 appear in Appendix B, following the index.

9. Du Pont Co. – 52-week high, Yield, Year-to-date percent change: $53.90, 3%, 0.60%
10. Johnson & Johnson – Symbol, High for the day, 52-week high: JNJ, $66.38, $69.41

Calculate the missing information for the following stocks.

Company	Earnings per Share	Annual Dividend	Current Price per Share	Current Yield	Price-Earnings Ratio
11. Sears	$6.59	$1.60	$46.13	3.5%	7
12. Wendy's	.77	.24	17.63	1.4%	23
13. Rubbermaid	1.31	.45	27.50	1.6%	21
14. Ford	4.92	1.60	64.00	2.5%	13
15. Disney	1.41	.30	42.38	.7%	30

Calculate the total cost, proceeds, and gain or (loss) for the following stock market transactions.

Company	Number of Shares	Purchase Price	Selling Price	Commissions Buy	Commissions Sell	Commissions Odd Lot	Total Cost	Proceeds	Gain or (Loss)
16. DuPont	100	$47.20	$56.06	3%	3%		$ 4,861.60	$ 5,437.82	$ 576.22
17. Wal-Mart	350	18.42	29.19	2	2	add 1%	6,585.15	9,997.57	3,412.42
18. Heinz	900	28.37	36.25	3	3		26,298.99	31,646.25	5,347.26
19. Goodyear	775	37.75	34.50	1.5	1.5	add 1%	29,723.41	26,310.56	(3,412.85)
20. AmExpress	500	25.11	28.86	3	3		12,931.65	13,997.10	1,065.45

21. The Western Digital Corporation has 500,000 shares of common stock outstanding. If a dividend of $425,000 was declared by the company directors last year, what is the dividend per share of common stock?

$$\text{Dividend per share} = \frac{\text{Total common dividend}}{\text{Number of shares}} = \frac{425{,}000}{500{,}000} = \$.85 \text{ per share}$$

Complete, worked-out solutions to Exercises 11, 13–20 appear in Appendix B, following the index.

22. The board of directors of Prime One Corp. has declared a dividend of $3,000,000. The company has 700,000 shares of preferred stock that pay $.90 per share and 1,600,000 shares of common stock.

    a. What are the dividends due the preferred shareholders?
    Total preferred dividend = Number of shares × Dividend per share
    = 700,000 × .90 = $630,000

    b. What is the dividend per share of common stock?
    Total common dividend = 3,000,000 − 630,000 = $2,370,000

    $$\text{Dividend per common share} = \frac{2{,}370{,}000}{1{,}600{,}000} = \$1.48$$

23. Cobalt Enterprises has 1,800,000 shares of $100 par value, 5%, cumulative preferred stock and 9,750,000 shares of common stock. Although no dividend was declared for the past 2 years, a $44,000,000 dividend has been declared for this year.

    a. How much is due the preferred shareholders?
    Dividend per share preferred = 100 × 5% = $5
    Total dividend due preferred stockholders =
    1,800,000 × 5 × 3 years = $27,000,000

b. What is the dividend per share of common stock?

Dividend per share common stock

$44{,}000{,}000 - 27{,}000{,}000 = \$17{,}000{,}000$

$$\frac{17{,}000{,}000}{9{,}750{,}000} = \underline{\underline{\$1.74}} \text{ per share}$$

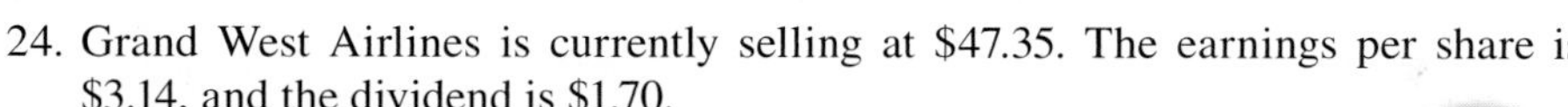

24. Grand West Airlines is currently selling at \$47.35. The earnings per share is \$3.14, and the dividend is \$1.70.

a. What is the current yield of the stock?

$$\text{Current yield} = \frac{\text{Annual dividend}}{\text{Current price}}$$

$$= \frac{1.70}{47.35} = \underline{\underline{3.6\%}}$$

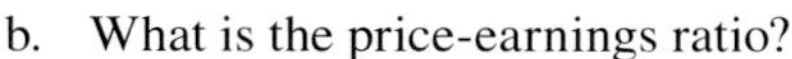

b. What is the price-earnings ratio?

$$\text{Price-earnings ratio} = \frac{\text{Current price per share}}{\text{Earnings per share}}$$

$$\text{Price-earnings ratio} = \frac{47.35}{3.14} = \underline{\underline{15}}$$

Pepper . . . and Salt

THE WALL STREET JOURNAL

"Do you have any personal qualms about losing other people's money?"

25. You purchase 650 shares of Passport Travel common stock at \$44.25 per share. A few months later, you sell the shares at \$57.29. Your stockbroker charges 3% commission on round lots and an extra $1\frac{1}{2}\%$ on odd lots.

a. What is the total cost of the purchase?

Cost of shares	$= 650 \times 44.25$	$= \$28{,}762.50$
Commission	$= 600 \times 44.25 \times 3\%$	$= +\ \ 796.50$
	$= 50 \times 44.25 \times 4.5\%$	$= +\ \ 99.56$
	Total cost	$\$29{,}658.56$

b. What are the proceeds on the sale?

Value of shares	$= 650 \times 57.29$	$= \$37{,}238.50$
Commission	$= 600 \times 57.29 \times 3\%$	$= -\ 1{,}031.22$
	$= 50 \times 57.29 \times 4.5\%$	$= -\ \ 128.90$
	Proceeds	$\$36{,}078.38$

c. What is the gain or (loss) on the transaction?

$\text{Gain} = 36{,}078.38 - 29{,}658.56 = \underline{\underline{\$6{,}419.82}}$

BUSINESS DECISION DOLLAR-COST AVERAGING

26. Though investing all at once works best when stock prices are rising, *dollar-cost averaging* can be a good way to take advantage of a fluctuating market. Dollar-cost averaging is an investment strategy designed to reduce volatility in which securities are purchased in *fixed dollar amounts at regular intervals*, regardless of what direction the market is moving. This strategy is also called *the constant dollar plan*.

You are considering a hypothetical \$1,200 investment in Blue Sky Corporation stock. Your choice is to invest the money all at once or dollar-cost average at the rate of \$100 per month for one year.

a. If you invested all of the money in January, and bought the shares for $10 each, how many shares could you buy?

$$\text{Shares purchased} = \frac{1{,}200}{10} = \underline{\underline{120}}$$

b. From the following chart of share prices, calculate the number of shares that would be purchased each month using dollar-cost averaging and the total shares for the year.

Month	Amount Invested	Cost per Share	Shares Purchased	Month	Amount Invested	Cost per Share	Shares Purchased
January	$100	$10.00	10.0	July	$100	$11.50	8.7
February	100	9.55	10.5	August	100	10.70	9.3
March	100	8.80	11.4	September	100	9.80	10.2
April	100	7.75	12.9	October	100	10.60	9.4
May	100	9.15	10.9	November	100	9.45	10.6
June	100	10.25	9.8	December	100	10.15	9.9

Total shares = 123.6

c. What is the average price you pay per share if you purchase them all in January?

$$\text{Average price} = \frac{1{,}200}{120} = \underline{\underline{\$10.00}}$$

d. What is the average price you pay per share if you purchase them using dollar-cost averaging?

$$\text{Average price} = \frac{1{,}200}{123.6} = \underline{\underline{\$9.71}}$$

SECTION II BONDS

20-6 UNDERSTANDING BONDS AND READING A BOND QUOTATION TABLE

bond A loan or an IOU in the form of an interest-bearing note, in which the bond buyer lends money to the bond issuer. Used by corporations and governments to borrow money on a long-term basis.

secured bonds Bonds that are backed by a lien on specific collateral such as a plant, equipment, or other corporate asset.

unsecured bonds, or debentures Bonds that are backed only by the general credit of the issuing corporation, not on specific collateral pledged as security.

convertible bonds Bonds that can be converted or exchanged at the owner's option for a certain number of shares of common stock.

callable bonds Bonds that the issuer has the right to call or repurchase before the maturity date. Bonds are called when interest rates are falling and the company can issue new bonds at a lower rate.

A **bond** is a loan, or an IOU, where the bond buyer lends money to the bond issuer. With stock, the investor becomes a part-owner of the corporation; with bonds, the investor becomes a creditor. Bonds are known as fixed-income securities because the issuer promises to pay a specified amount of interest on a regular basis, usually semiannually. Although stock is issued only by corporations, bonds are issued by corporations and governments. The federal government, as well as states and local municipalities, issues bonds. The funds raised are used to finance general operations and specific projects such as schools, highways, bridges, and airports. An example of a bond certificate is shown in Exhibit 20-4.

Corporate bonds represent the number one source of corporate borrowing for both large and small companies. Corporations use the money raised from bonds to finance modernization and expansion programs. **Secured bonds** are backed by a lien on a plant, equipment, or other corporate asset. **Unsecured bonds**, also known as **debentures**, are backed only by the general credit of the issuing corporation. Some bonds are **convertible**, which means they can be converted into, or exchanged for, a specified number of shares of common stock. **Callable bonds** give the issuer the right to call or redeem the bonds before the maturity date. Calling bonds might occur when interest rates are falling and the company can issue new bonds at a lower rate.

© Jeremy Edwards/iStockphoto International

You can't buy the Brooklyn Bridge, but you can invest in its repairs! The New York City Transitional Finance Authority, a quasi-independent government agency, sells municipal bonds to finance the city's *capital improvements* programs such as public buildings, roads, bridges, and other municipal projects.

Exhibit 20-4
Bond Certificate

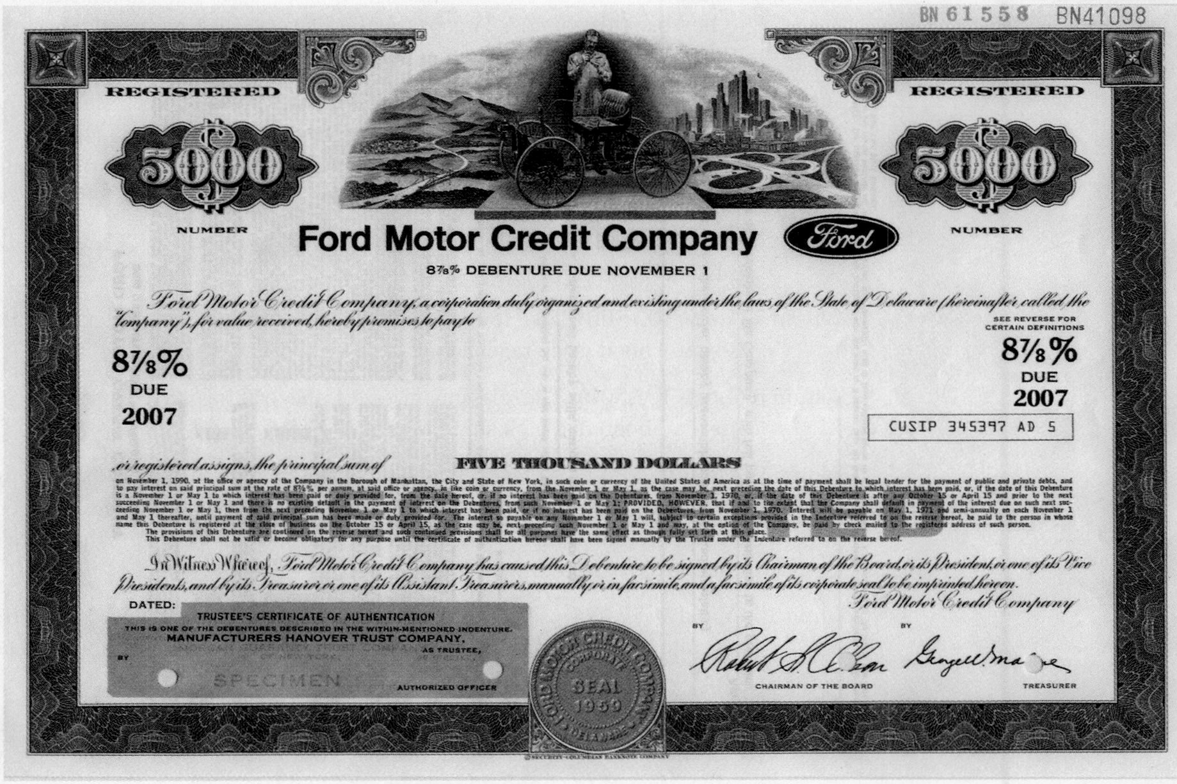

BN 61558 BN41098

REGISTERED | REGISTERED

$5000 | $5000

NUMBER | NUMBER

Ford Motor Credit Company Ford

$8\frac{7}{8}$% DEBENTURE DUE NOVEMBER 1

Ford Motor Credit Company, a corporation duly organized and existing under the laws of the State of Delaware (hereinafter called the "Company"), for value received, hereby promises to pay to

SEE REVERSE FOR CERTAIN DEFINITIONS

$8\frac{7}{8}$% DUE 2007 | $8\frac{7}{8}$% DUE 2007

CUSIP 345397 AD 5

, or registered assigns, the principal sum of **FIVE THOUSAND DOLLARS**

on November 1, 1990, at the office or agency of the Company in the Borough of Manhattan, the City and State of New York, in such coin or currency of the United States of America as at the time of payment shall be legal tender for the payment of public and private debts, and to pay interest on said principal sum at the rate of $8\frac{7}{8}$% per annum, at said office or agency, in like coin or currency, from the November 1 or May 1, as the case may be, next preceding the date of this Debenture to which interest has been paid, or, if the date of this Debenture is a November 1 or May 1 to which interest has been paid or duly provided for, from the date hereof, or, if no interest has been paid on the Debentures, from November 1, 1970, or, if the date of this Debenture is after any October 15 or April 15 and prior to the next succeeding November 1 or May 1 and there is no existing default in the payment of interest on the Debentures, from such November 1 or May 1; PROVIDED, HOWEVER, that if and to the extent that the Company shall default in payment of the interest due on such next succeeding November 1 or May 1, then from the next preceding November 1 or May 1 to which interest has been paid, or if no interest has been paid on the Debentures, from November 1, 1970. Interest will be payable on May 1, 1971 and semi-annually on each November 1 and May 1 thereafter, until payment of said principal sum has been made or duly provided for. The interest so payable on any November 1 or May 1 will, subject to certain exceptions provided in the Indenture referred to on the reverse hereof, be paid to the person in whose name this Debenture is registered at the close of business on the October 15 or April 15, as the case may be, next preceding such November 1 or May 1 and may, at the option of the Company, be paid by check mailed to the registered address of such person.
The provisions of this Debenture are continued on the reverse hereof and such continued provisions shall for all purposes have the same effect as though fully set forth at this place.
This Debenture shall not be valid or become obligatory for any purpose until the certificate of authentication hereon shall have been signed manually by the Trustee under the Indenture referred to on the reverse hereof.

In Witness Whereof, Ford Motor Credit Company has caused this Debenture to be signed by its Chairman of the Board, or its President, or one of its Vice Presidents, and by its Treasurer or one of its Assistant Treasurers, manually or in facsimile, and a facsimile of its corporate seal to be imprinted hereon.

Ford Motor Credit Company

DATED:

TRUSTEE'S CERTIFICATE OF AUTHENTICATION
THIS IS ONE OF THE DEBENTURES DESCRIBED IN THE WITHIN-MENTIONED INDENTURE.
MANUFACTURERS HANOVER TRUST COMPANY, AS TRUSTEE,
BY
SPECIMEN
AUTHORIZED OFFICER

FORD MOTOR CREDIT COMPANY CORPORATE SEAL 1959 DELAWARE

BY CHAIRMAN OF THE BOARD

BY TREASURER

Bond image obtained from Scripopholy.com

When bonds are issued by a corporation, they may be purchased by investors at par value, usually $1,000, and held until the maturity date; or they may be bought and sold through a broker on the secondary or resale market. Bonds pay a fixed interest rate, also known as the **coupon rate**. This rate is a fixed percentage of the par value that will be paid to the bondholder on a regular basis.

coupon rate A fixed percentage of the par value of a bond that is paid to the bondholder on a regular basis.

For example, a company might issue a $1,000 par value, 7% bond, maturing in the year 2025. The bondholder in this case would receive a fixed interest payment of $70 per year (1,000 × .07), or $35 semiannually, until the bond matures. At maturity, the company repays the loan by paying the bondholder the par value of the bond.

During the period between the issue date and the maturity date, bond prices fluctuate in the opposite direction of prevailing interest rates. Let's say you buy a bond with a coupon rate of 8%. If interest rates in the marketplace fall to 7%, newly issued bonds will have a rate lower than yours, thus making yours more attractive and driving the price above the par value. When this occurs, the bonds are said to be selling at a **premium**. However, if interest rates rise to 9%, new bonds would have a higher rate than yours, thus making yours less attractive and pushing the price down, below par. If bonds sell below par, it is known as selling at a **discount**. Remember, at maturity the bond returns to its par value.

premium When a bond is selling for more than its par value, it is said to be selling at a premium. This occurs during periods when prevailing interest rates are declining.

discount When a bond is selling for less than its par value, it is said to be selling at a discount. This occurs during periods when prevailing interest rates are rising.

Just as with stocks, corporate bond quotations may be found on the Internet or in the financial section of most newspapers. Exhibit 20-5 is a portion of such a table, reprinted from *The Wall Street Journal Online*. Let's take a column-by-column look at a particular day's listing for **Dave & Busters.**

Learning Tip

Note that in Exhibit 20-5 the dollar amounts are rounded to tenths of a cent and percents are rounded to thousandths.

20-6

Column 1 (**Issue Name** Dave & Busters) Company name.

Column 2 (**Symbol** DAB.GD) Symbol used to easily identify a particular bond. The symbol for the Dave & Busters' bond is DAB.GD.

Column 3 (**Coupon** 11.250%) The coupon rate of the bond. A fixed percent of the par value of the bond. The Dave and Busters' bond is paying interest of 11.25% of par value.

Column 4 (**Maturity** Mar 2014) The maturity date of the bond. The date the company has to buy back the bonds. This particular Dave & Busters' bond has a maturity date of March 2014.

Column 5 (**Rating** B3/CCC+/−) The rating of the bond from three different rating services: Moody's, S&P, and Fitch. The Dave & Busters' bond is rated B3 by Moody's; CCC+ by S&P; and − by Fitch. For further rating information, consult the web sites of the individual rating services.

Column 6 (**High** 102.625) The highest price of the trading day. That day, the Dave & Busters' bond price reached a high of $102.625.

Column 7 (**Low** 102.500) The lowest price of the trading day. That day, the Dave & Busters' bond price reached a low of $102.50.

Column 8 (**Last** 102.500) The closing price of the trading day. That day, the Dave & Busters' bond had a closing price of $102.50.

Column 9 (**Change** −0.125) The difference, or net change, between the closing price and the previous day's closing price. Positive change is indicated in green. Negative change is indicated by a minus sign, and in red. That day, the Dave & Busters' bond price closed down $0.125.

Column 10 (**Yield%** 10.524) The yield percent of the bond; calculated by dividing the coupon rate by the current price of the bond. That day, the yield on the Dave & Busters' bond was 10.524%.

Note: The coupon rate of a bond does not change. The change in yield occurs as the price of the bond changes. When the price of the bond goes up, the yield goes down; when the price of the bond goes down, the yield goes up.

Exhibit 20-5
Corporate Bond Quotation Table–
The Wall Street Journal Online

(1) Issuer Name	(2) Symbol	(3) Coupon	(4) Maturity	(5) Rating Moody's/S&P/Fitch	(6) High	(7) Low	(8) Last	(9) Change	(10) Yield %
AMERICAN EXPRESS	AXP.IE	3.750%	Nov 2007	A1/A+/A+	99.884	99.837	99.884	0.023	4.660
BANK OF AMERICA	BAC.XQ	4.875%	Sep 2012	Aa1AA/AA	98.930	98.930	98.930	0.345	5.123
CITIGROUP	C.GMV	3.500%	Feb 2008	Aa1/AA/AA+	99.545	99.407	99.545	0.215	4.950
DAVE & BUSTERS	**DAB.GD**	**11.250%**	**Mar2014**	**B3/CCC+/–**	**102.625**	**102.500**	**102.500**	**−0.125**	**10.524**
DIAGEO FINANCE BV	DEO.HL	3.875%	Apr 2011	A3/A–/A	95.843	95.843	95.843	1.680	5.200
FORD MOTOR	F.GU	9.980%	Feb 2047	Caa1/CCC+/B–	94.950	90.469	90.469	−2.781	11.045
FORD MOTOR	F.GL	7.750%	Jun 2043	Caa1/CCC+/B–	78.500	78.500	78.500	0.000	9.958
FORD MOTOR CREDIT	F.IK	7.875%	Jun 2010	B1/B/BB–	100.000	97.250	97.250	−1.375	9.046
GENERAL ELECTRIC CAPITAL	GE.GMY	4.375%	Nov 2011	Aaa/AAA/–	98.040	96.950	98.040	1.759	4.906
GENERAL MOTORS	GM.HB	8.375%	Jul 2003	Caa1/B–/B–	93.849	89.000	90.600	−0.400	9.343
GENERAL MOTORS	GM.HC	8.250%	Jul 2023	Caa1/B–/B–	92.250	89.000	92.250	−0.875	9.188
GENERAL MOTORS	GM.GC	9.400%	Jul 2021	Caa1/B–/B–	99.000	97.712	98.500	1.000	9.595
GENERAL MOTORS ACC.	GMA.GT	5.850%	Jan 2009	Ba1/BB+/BB+	99.250	99.150	99.250	1.500	6.470
H. J. HEINZ	HNZ.GC	6.000%	Mar 2008	Baa2/BBB/BBB	100.331	100.226	100.331	0.000	5.187
HARRAHS OPERATING	HET.GF	5.375%	Dec 2013	Baa3/BB/BB+	84.000	83.500	83.500	−0.500	8.902
LEHMAN BROTHERS HLDS.	LEH.JAF	7.000%	Sep 2037	A1/–/–	100.000	100.000	100.000	0.000	7.000
MERRIL LYNCH	MER.GHM	5.000%	Jan 2015	Aa3/AA–/AA–	97.130	94.250	94.250	−3.385	5.986
MGM MIRAGE	MGG.HA	7.625%	Jan 2017	Ba2/BB/BB	100.870	100.870	100.870	0.370	7.490
MONSANTO	MON.GB	4.000%	May 2008	Baa1/A–/A–	99.268	99.268	99.268	0.029	5.260
SBC COMM	SBC.OB	5.100%	Sep 2014	A2/A/A	99.600	97.801	99.600	0.000	5.169

EXAMPLE 8 READING A BOND QUOTATION TABLE

Using Exhibit 20-5, Corporate Bond Quotation Table above, explain the information listed for the MGM Mirage bond.

SOLUTION STRATEGY

According to the listing for MGM Mirage, the symbol for the bond is MGG.HA. The coupon rate of the bond is 7.625%, maturing in January 2017. The bond has ratings of Ba2/BB/BB. That day, the bond price went as high as $100.87 and as low as $100.87, and closed at $100.87. The price of the bond closed up $0.37 from the previous close. The yield at that price was 7.49.

TRY IT EXERCISE 8

Using Exhibit 20-5, Corporate Bond Quotation Table above, explain the information listed for General Electric Capital.

CHECK YOUR ANSWERS WITH THE SOLUTIONS ON PAGE 768.

CLASSROOM ACTIVITY

Have students research and report to the class on the bond rating systems published by Standard & Poor's and Moody's Investors Service.

Treasury bonds are fully guaranteed by the U.S. government and therefore have lower interest rates than those of other issuers such as corporations and municipalities.

Because corporate and municipal bonds carry a "risk factor," prospective purchasers can use **bond ratings** to evaluate how safe one bond is compared with another.

Bonds with lower ratings carry a higher risk and therefore must offer higher interest rates to attract investors. Bonds with low ratings are often referred to as **junk bonds**.

20-7 CALCULATING THE COST OF PURCHASING BONDS AND THE PROCEEDS FROM THE SALE OF BONDS

Similar to stocks, when bonds are bought and sold a brokerage charge is commonly added to the price of each bond. Although there is no standard commission, the charge is generally between \$5 and \$10 per bond. As noted earlier, bonds pay interest semiannually, such as on January 1 and July 1. When bonds are traded between the stated interest payment dates, the interest accumulated from the last payment date must be paid to the seller by the buyer. This interest due to the seller is known as the **accrued interest**.

accrued interest When bonds are traded between the stated interest payment dates, the interest accumulated from the last payment date that must be paid to the seller by the buyer.

Accrued interest of a bond is calculated by using the simple interest formula, $I = PRT$, where P is the face value of the bond, R is the coupon rate, and T is the number of days since the last payment date divided by 360. When time is stated in months, divide by 12.

STEPS TO CALCULATE THE COST OF PURCHASING A BOND

Step 1. Calculate the accrued interest on the bond since the last payment date using $I = PRT$.

Step 2. Calculate the price to purchase the bond.

Price per bond = Current market price + Accrued interest + Commission

Step 3. Calculate total purchase price.

Total purchase price = Price per bond × Number of bonds purchased

EXAMPLE 9 CALCULATING THE PURCHASE PRICE OF A BOND

What is the purchase price of 10 Sterling Industries bonds with a coupon rate of 9.5% and a current market price of 107? The commission charge is \$5 per bond. The date of the transaction is April 1, and the bond pays interest on January 1 and July 1.

SOLUTION STRATEGY

Step 1. Because the time since the last payment is 3 months, we shall use $T = \frac{3}{12}$.

$$\text{Accrued interest} = 1{,}000 \times .095 \times \frac{3}{12} = \underline{\$23.75}$$

Step 2. Price per bond = Current market price + Accrued interest + Commission

Price per bond = 1,070.00 + 23.75 + 5.00 = $\underline{\text{\$1,098.75 per bond}}$

Step 3. Total purchase price = Price per bond × Number of bonds

Total purchase price = 1,098.75 × 10 = $\underline{\underline{\$10{,}987.50}}$

TRY IT EXERCISE 9

What is the purchase price of 20 Monarch Corporation bonds with a coupon rate of 6.25% and a current market price of \$91.375? The commission charge is \$10 per bond. The date of the transaction is October 1, and the bond pays interest on February 1 and August 1.

CHECK YOUR ANSWER WITH THE SOLUTION ON PAGE 768.

CLASSROOM ACTIVITY
In groups, have students work Try It Exercise 9, calculating the cost of purchasing a bond, and Try It Exercise 10, calculating the proceeds of the sale.

Next, have the groups compare answers with those of another group and resolve any differences.

STEPS TO CALCULATE THE PROCEEDS FROM THE SALE OF A BOND

Step 1. Calculate the accrued interest on the bond since the last payment date by using $I = PRT$.

Step 2. Calculate the proceeds per bond.

$$\textbf{Proceeds} = \textbf{Current market price} + \textbf{Accrued interest} - \textbf{Commission}$$

Step 3. Calculate the total proceeds from the sale.

$$\textbf{Total proceeds} = \textbf{Proceeds per bond} \times \textbf{Number of bonds sold}$$

EXAMPLE 10 CALCULATING THE PROCEEDS OF A BOND SALE

What are the proceeds of the sale of 15 Slick Oil bonds with a coupon rate of 7.125% and a current market price of $111? The commission charge is $7.50 per bond. The date of the transaction is 71 days since the last interest payment.

SOLUTION STRATEGY

Step 1. $\text{Accrued interest} = 1{,}000 \times .07125 \times \frac{71}{360} = \underline{\$14.05}$

Step 2. Proceeds per bond = Current market price + Accrued interest − Commission

Proceeds per bond = $1{,}110.00 + 14.05 - 7.50 = \underline{\$1{,}116.55}$

Step 3. Total proceeds = Proceeds per bond × Number of bonds sold

Total proceeds = $1{,}116.55 \times 15 = \underline{\underline{\$16{,}748.25}}$

TRY IT EXERCISE 10

What are the proceeds of the sale of five Pioneer Corporation bonds with a coupon rate of 8.875% and a current market price of $99? The commission charge is $10 per bond. The date of the transaction is 122 days since the last interest payment.

CHECK YOUR ANSWER WITH THE SOLUTION ON PAGE 768.

CALCULATING THE CURRENT YIELD FOR A BOND

20-8

Just as with stocks, the current yield of a bond is a simple measure of the return on investment based on the current market price. When bonds are purchased at par, the current yield is equal to the coupon rate. For example, a bond purchased at par for $1,000, with a coupon rate of 7%, pays interest of $70 per year (1,000 × .07), and has a yield of 7% $\left(\frac{70}{1{,}000} = .07\right)$. If the bond is purchased at a discount, say, $875, it still pays $70; however, the yield is 8% $\left(\frac{70}{875} = .08\right)$. If the bond is purchased at a premium, say, $1,165, it still pays $70; however, now the yield is only 6% $\left(\frac{70}{1{,}165} = .06\right)$.

STEPS TO CALCULATE CURRENT YIELD FOR A BOND

Step 1. Calculate the annual interest and current price of the bond.

Step 2. Divide the annual interest of the bond by the current market price.

$$\textbf{Current yield} = \frac{\textbf{Annual interest}}{\textbf{Current market price}}$$

Step 3. Convert the answer to a percent, rounded to the nearest tenth.

EXAMPLE 11 CALCULATING THE CURRENT YIELD OF A BOND SALE

Calculate the current yield for a G. Tech Scientific bond with a coupon rate of 13.5% and currently selling at a premium of $107.25.

SOLUTION STRATEGY

Annual interest = Par value × Coupon rate = 1,000 × .135 = $135

Current price = Par value × Price percent = 1,000 × 1.0725 = $1,072.50

$$\text{Current yield} = \frac{\text{Annual interest}}{\text{Current market price}} = \frac{135}{1,072.50} = .12587 = \underline{\underline{12.6\%}}$$

TRY IT EXERCISE 11

Calculate the current yield for a Webster Electronics bond with a coupon rate of 9.375% and currently selling at a discount of $84.75.

CHECK YOUR ANSWER WITH THE SOLUTION ON PAGE 768.

Learning Tip

Remember, bond interest is always constant, regardless of what you paid for the bond; the yield is what varies, depending on the current price of the bond.

20 SECTION II Review Exercises

Use Exhibit 20-5, Corporate Bond Quotation Table, on page 749, to fill in the blanks for Exercises 1–10.

1. Ford Motor (F.GU) – Coupon, High: 9.98%, $94.95
2. H. J. Heinz – Maturity, Yield %: March 2008, 5.187%
3. Bank of America – Symbol, Change: BAC.XQ, up $0.345
4. Which bond is selling for exactly par value? Lehman Brothers Hlds.
5. Which bond has the lowest coupon rate? Citicorp
6. Merrill Lynch – Ratings: Aa3/AA-/AA-
7. General Motors (GM.HC) – Coupon, Yield %: 8.25%, 9.188%

8. Which bond has the highest current price? How much? Dave & Busters, $102.50
9. Monsanto – Ratings, Yield % Baa1/A-/A-,5.26%
10. Which bond has the furthest maturity date? When? Ford Motor (F.GU), February 2047

Calculate the accrued interest and the total purchase price of the following bond purchases.

Company	Coupon Rate	Market Price	Time Since Last Interest	Accrued Interest	Commission per Bond	Bonds purchased	Total Price
11. Xerox	5.5%	$86.25	2 months	$9.17	$5.00	1	$876.67
12. U.S. West	7.25	102.50	78 days	15.71	4.50	5	5,226.05
13. AT&T	8.375	95.00	5 months	34.90	10.00	8	7,959.20
14. Hilton	9.5	79.75	23 days	6.07	9.75	15	12,199.80
15. Ford	6.625	111.875	3 months	16.56	8.00	10	11,433.10

11. Accrued interest = 1,000 × Coupon rate × Time

$$I = 1{,}000 \times .055 \times \frac{2}{12} = \$9.17$$

Total price = (Current market price + Accrued interest + Commission) × Number of bonds

= (862.50 + 9.17 + 5.00) × 1
= $876.67

EXCEL

Calculate the accrued interest and the total proceeds of the following bond sales.

Company	Coupon Rate	Market Price	Time Since Last Interest	Accrued Interest	Commission per Bond	Bonds purchased	Total Price
16. Textron	6.25%	$91.50	21 days	$3.65	$6.00	10	$9,126.50
17. Apple	8.50	108.75	4 months	28.33	8.50	4	4,429.32
18. USX	10.625	77.00	85 days	25.09	12.00	15	11,746.35
19. Mobil	9.75	89.375	1 month	8.13	7.25	7	6,262.41
20. Nabisco	6.625	104.125	39 days	7.18	9.00	20	20,788.60

16. $I = PRT$

Proceeds = Current market price + Accrued interest − Commission

$$I = 1{,}000 \times .0625 \times \frac{21}{360} = \$3.65$$

Proceeds = (915.00 + 3.65 − 6.00) × 10
= $9,126.50

Calculate the annual interest and current yield for the following bonds.

Company	Coupon Rate	Annual Interest	Market Price	Current Yield
21. Kroger	6.625%	$66.25	$91.125	7.3%
22. Bordens	9.25	92.50	108.00	8.6
23. Blockbuster	7.50	75.00	125.25	6
24. McDonald's	11.875	118.75	73.50	16.2
25. Pacific Telesis	5.375	53.75	84.375	6.4

21. Accrued interest = Par value × Coupon rate
Kroger, annual interest = 1,000 × .06625
= $66.25

$$\text{Current yield} = \frac{\text{Annual interest}}{\text{Current market price}}$$

$$\text{Current yield} = \frac{66.25}{911.25} = 0.0727 = 7.3\%$$

EXCEL

EXCEL

26. On March 1, Larry Winters bought 10 Great Eastern Financial bonds with a coupon rate of 9.125%. The purchase price was $88.875, and the commission was $6 per bond. Great Eastern Financial bonds pay interest on February 1 and August 1.

(continued)

a. What is the current yield of the bond?

Annual interest = Par value × Coupon rate
Annual interest = 1,000 × .09125 = $91.25

$$\text{Current yield} = \frac{\text{Annual interest}}{\text{Market price}}$$

$$\text{Current yield} = \frac{91.25}{888.75} = \underline{\underline{10.3\%}}$$

b. What is the total purchase price of the bonds?

Total purchase price =
(Current market price + Accrued interest + Commission) × Number of bonds

$$\text{Accrued interest} = 1{,}000 \times .09125 \times \frac{1}{12} = \$7.60$$

Total purchase price = (888.75 + 7.60 + 6.00) × 10 = $\underline{\underline{\$9{,}023.50}}$

c. If Larry sold the bonds on November 1 for 93.875, what are the proceeds from the sale?

Proceeds of sale =
Current market price + Accrued interest − Commission × Number of bonds

$$\text{Accrued interest} = 1{,}000 \times .09125 \times \frac{3}{12} = \$22.81$$

Proceeds = (938.75 + 22.81 − 6.00) × 10 = $\underline{\underline{\$9{,}555.60}}$

BUSINESS DECISION TAXABLE OR TAX-FREE BONDS

27. More than 50,000 state and local governments and their agencies borrow money by issuing **municipal bonds** to build, repair, or improve schools, streets, highways, hospitals, sewer systems, and so on. When the federal income tax law was adopted in 1913, interest on municipal bonds was excluded from federal taxation. As a result, municipal bond investors are willing to accept lower yields than those they can obtain from taxable bonds.

As part of your portfolio, you are considering investing $50,000 in bonds. You have the choice of investing in tax-exempt municipal bonds yielding 5.5% or corporate bonds yielding 7.5% in taxable interest income.

a. What is the annual interest income and tax status of the municipal bond investment?

Annual income = 50,000 × .055 = $\underline{\underline{\$2{,}750, \text{tax free}}}$

b. What is the annual interest income and tax status of the corporate bond investment?

Annual income = 50,000 × .075 = $\underline{\underline{\$3{,}750, \text{taxable}}}$

c. If you are in the 30% marginal tax bracket for federal income taxes and your state and local taxes on that income amount to an additional 6%, what is the after-tax income on the corporate bonds?

After-tax income = 3,750 × .64 = $\underline{\underline{\$2{,}400}}$

d. What is the actual percent yield realized on the corporate bonds after taxes?

$$\text{Yield} = \frac{2{,}400}{50{,}000} = \underline{\underline{4.8\%}}$$

MUTUAL FUNDS

SECTION III 20

UNDERSTANDING MUTUAL FUNDS AND READING A MUTUAL FUND QUOTATION TABLE

20-9

mutual funds, or investment trusts Corporations that are investment pools of money with a wide variety of investment goals.

Mutual funds are a very popular way of investing. Essentially, mutual funds are professionally managed investment companies that pool the money from many individuals and invest it in stocks, bonds, and other securities. Most individual investors do not have the time or the ability to research the literally thousands of investment possibilities. By pooling the financial resources of thousands of shareholders, mutual funds can use the expertise of the country's top professional money managers.

Mutual funds are corporations known as **investment trusts**. Their assets are stocks and bonds purchased with the hope that the value of the securities will increase. Investors purchase shares of stock of the fund. If the fund is successful in its investments, it pays dividends and capital gains to its shareholders.

With mutual funds, instead of choosing individual stocks and bonds, investors pick a fund with financial goals similar to their own. These range from high-risk aggressive growth goals, such as investing in new and unproven companies and industries, to more moderate-risk goals, such as steady income and balanced growth and income, which is achieved by investing in large and established companies. Most mutual fund companies offer several different funds known as a *family*. Investors are free to move their money back and forth among them as their investment goals or market conditions change.

Just as with stock prices, mutual fund share prices fluctuate up and down on a daily basis and can be tracked on the Internet and in the financial section of most newspapers. Let's take a column-by-column look at a typical day's listing for a mutual fund in the **Harbor Funds** family, known as **CapAplnst**. Exhibit 20-6 is a portion of such a table, as listed in *The Wall Street Journal Online*.

In the Business World

Mutual funds are big business! In recent years, the popularity of mutual funds as an investment has skyrocketed. According to the Investment Company Institute, in 1990, there were 3,079 different mutual funds with total net assets of just over $1 billion. In 2006, there were over 8,120 funds with assets over $10.4 billion.

Column 1 (**Family/Fund** Harbor Funds/CapAplnst) Mutual funds are listed aplhabetically by the fund's family name and in subcategories by the various funds available within that family. In this example, the family name is Harbor Funds and the particular fund is CapAplnst.

Column 2 (**Symbol** HACAX) Symbol used to easily identify a particular fund. The symbol for the CapAplnst Harbor Fund is HACAX.

Column 3 (**NAV** 38.12) Net asset value; the dollar value of one share of the fund's stock. This is the price you receive when you sell your shares of the fund. That day, the net asset value for the CapAplnst Harbor Fund was $38.12. Positive change is indicated in green. Negative change is indicated by a minus sign and in red.

Column 4 (**Change** 0.04) The difference, or net change, between the net asset value and the previous day's net asset value. That day, the CapAplnst Harbor Fund net asset value was up $0.04. Positive change is indicated in green. Negative change is indicated by a minus sign and in red.

Column 5 (**YTD %Return** 14.3) The year-to-date percentage return on investment. That day, the CapAplnst Harbor Fund year-to-date return was 14.3%. Positive change is indicated in green. Negative change is indicated by a minus sign and in red.

Column 6 (**3-yr %Change** 13.6) The 3-year percentage change in the net asset value. In the past 3 years, the CapAplnst Harbor Fund has returned 13.6%. Positive change is indicated in green. Negative change is indicated by a minus sign and in red.

Exhibit 20-6
Mutual Fund Quotation Table – *The Wall Street Journal Online*

Teaching Transparency 20-7

(1) Family/Fund	(2) Symbol	(3) NAV	(4) Chg	(5) YTD % return	(6) 3-yr % chg
Delaware Invest B					
CorPlsBd t	DEGBX	7.35	. . .	2.1	2.0
DelBalB t	DELBX	19.13	−0.06	3.9	9.0
SelGrowBt	DVEBX	28.11	0.09	15.4	15.2
Delaware Invest C					
LgeCapValC	DECCX	21.65	−0.11	4.6	12.1
SelGrowC p	DVECX	27.81	0.09	15.4	15.2
SmCpValC p	DEVCX	36.08	−0.23	2.2	12.5
HSBC Investor					
FxdInc	RFXIX	10.27	. . .	3.8	4.7
IntlEqY	RINEX	24.46	−0.29	15.1	25.3
SmC Eq Y	RESCX	18.48	0.04	22.6	20.8
Harbor Funds					
Bond	HABDX	11.62	−0.01	4.2	3.9
BondRet p	HRBDX	11.61	−0.01	3.9	3.6
CapAplnst	**HACAX**	**38.12**	**0.04**	**14.3**	**13.6**
HiYBdInst r	HYFAX	10.88	. . .	4.1	6.5
IntlRet p	HRINX	75.62	−0.71	22.4	29.0
Oak Associates Funds					
BlkOakEmrg	BOGSX	2.87	0.01	27.0	12.6
LivOakHlth	LOGSX	12.55	. . .	15.5	10.5
Oak Value					
Oak Value	OAKVX	26.43	−0.10	12.1	11.0
Old Mutual Adv Funds					
AAllocBalA r	OMABX	13.26	−0.03	10.7	11.9
AAllocGrC t	OMCGX	15. 60	−0.06	13.4	16.8
ANDefEqZ	ANDEX	14.23	0.02	2.4	10.6
Oppenheimer A					
AMTFrMuniA p	OPTAX	9.45	. . .	−5.0	4.2
DiscovA p	OPOCX	59.81	0.02	29.7	15.4
EmerTech p	OETAX	4.00	0.02	28.2	16.1
EmgGrA	OEGAX	14.29	0.01	27.1	17.6
IntlSmCoA	OSMAX	34.75	−0.37	29.3	38.3
IntlVFA	OIVAX	20.61	−0.22	9.7	21.0
PIA Funds					
OCMGold t	OCMGX	21.02	−0.27	16.8	23.8
PIAModDurBd	PIATX	18.54	. . .	3.6	3.9
PIAShTSec	PIASX	9.98	. . .	3.9	3.6

EXAMPLE 12 READING A BOND QUOTATION TABLE

Using Exhibit 20-6, Mutual Fund Quotation Table, on page 756, explain the information listed for the Oppenheimer A, EmgGrA fund.

SOLUTION STRATEGY

According to the listing, for the Oppenheimer A, EmgGrA fund, the symbol for the fund is OEGAX. The net asset value of the fund is $14.29, up $0.01 from the previous day's net asset value. The year-to-date return on investment is up 27.1%. The 3-year percent change in net asset value is 17.6%.

TRY IT EXERCISE 12

Using Exhibit 20-6, Mutual Fund Quotation Table, on page 756, explain the information listed for the Old Mutual Adv Funds, ANDefEqZ.

CHECK YOUR ANSWERS WITH THE SOLUTIONS ON PAGE 768.

In the Business World

For further information about stocks, bonds, and mutual funds, contact the Securities and Exchange Commission's Investor Information Service at 1-800-SEC-0330 to get free publications and investor alerts. This information is also available at www.sec.gov.

20-10 CALCULATING THE SALES CHARGE AND SALES CHARGE PERCENT OF A MUTUAL FUND

Two important terms in mutual funds are net asset value and offer price. The **net asset value** is the dollar value of one share of a fund's stock. This is the per share price you receive when you sell the fund. The **offer price** is the per share price investors pay when purchasing a mutual fund. The offer price includes the net asset value and the broker's commission.

With mutual funds, the sales charge or broker's commission is known as the **load**. These charges vary from 1% to more than 8% of the amount invested. The load is paid either when purchasing the stock, in a **front-end load**, or when selling the stock, in a **back-end load**. Some mutual funds do not charge a commission and are known as no-load funds. For load funds, the difference between the offer price and the net asset value is the sales charge.

net asset value (NAV) The dollar value of one share of a mutual fund's stock. It is the price investors receive when they sell their shares of the fund.

offer price The price per share investors pay when purchasing a mutual fund. Offer price includes the net asset value plus the broker's commission.

load The sales charge or broker's commission on a mutual fund.

front-end load The sales charge or commission on a mutual fund when it is paid at the time of purchase.

back-end load The sales charge or commission on a mutual fund when it is paid at the time of sale.

STEPS TO CALCULATE MUTUAL FUND SALES CHARGE AND SALES CHARGE PERCENT

Step 1. Calculate mutual fund sales charge by subtracting the net asset value from the offer price.

Mutual fund sales charge = Offer price − Net asset value

Step 2. Calculate sales charge percent by dividing the sales charge by the net asset value.

$$\textbf{Sales charge percent} = \frac{\textbf{Sales charge}}{\textbf{Net asset value}}$$

EXAMPLE 13 CALCULATING MUTUAL FUND SALES CHARGE PERCENT

A mutual fund has an offer price of $6.75 per share and a net asset value of $6.44. What are the sales charge and the sales charge percent?

SOLUTION STRATEGY

Step 1.

$$\text{Mutual fund sales charge} = \text{Offer price} - \text{Net asset value}$$

$$\text{Mutual fund sales charge} = 6.75 - 6.44 = \underline{\underline{\$.31 \text{ per share}}}$$

Step 2.

$$\text{Sales charge percent} = \frac{\text{Sales charge}}{\text{Net asset value}}$$

$$\text{Sales charge percent} = \frac{.31}{6.44} = .0481 = \underline{\underline{4.8\%}}$$

TRY IT EXERCISE 13

What are the sales charge and the sales charge percent for a mutual fund with an offer price of $9.85 per share and net asset value of $9.21?

CHECK YOUR ANSWERS WITH THE SOLUTIONS ON PAGE 769.

20-11 CALCULATING THE NET ASSET VALUE OF A MUTUAL FUND

The assets of a mutual fund consist of the total current value of the stocks or bonds that the fund owns. As stated earlier, a mutual fund's net asset value is the per share price of the fund's stock.

TEACHING TIP
Point out to students that although newspapers list the daily net asset value (NAV) of a fund, to get the true measure of a fund's performance, dividends or capital gains paid out to the shareholders must also be taken into account.

It is interesting to note that a capital gains distribution may actually depress the share price, as the distribution amount was previously included in the fund's portfolio, which is lowered accordingly, when the distribution is made.

STEPS TO CALCULATE NET ASSET VALUE OF A MUTUAL FUND

Step 1. Calculate net asset value by subtracting the total liabilities from the total assets of the fund and dividing by the number of shares outstanding.

$$\textbf{Net asset value (NAV)} = \frac{\textbf{Total assets} - \textbf{Total liabilities}}{\textbf{Number of shares outstanding}}$$

Step 2. Round the answer to dollars and cents.

EXAMPLE 14 CALCULATING NET ASSET VALUE

A mutual fund has total assets of $40,000,000 and liabilities of $6,000,000. If there are 12,000,000 shares outstanding, what is the net asset value of the fund?

SOLUTION STRATEGY

$$\text{Net asset value} = \frac{\text{Total assets} - \text{Total liabilities}}{\text{Number of shares outstanding}}$$

$$\text{Net asset value} = \frac{40{,}000{,}000 - 6{,}000{,}000}{12{,}000{,}000} = \underline{\underline{\$2.83 \text{ per share}}}$$

TRY IT EXERCISE 14

A mutual fund has total assets of $80,000,000 and liabilities of $5,000,000. If there are 17,000,000 shares outstanding, what is the net asset value of the fund?

CHECK YOUR ANSWER WITH THE SOLUTION ON PAGE 769.

CALCULATING THE NUMBER OF SHARES PURCHASED OF A MUTUAL FUND

Investors frequently purchase shares of mutual funds by using lump-sum amounts of money. To accommodate this practice, most funds sell fractional shares of their stock.

STEPS TO CALCULATE NUMBER OF SHARES PURCHASED OF A MUTUAL FUND

Step 1. Calculate number of shares by dividing the amount of the investment by the offer price of the fund. For no-load funds, use the net asset value as the denominator.

$$\textbf{Number of shares purchased} = \frac{\textbf{Total investment}}{\textbf{Offer price}}$$

Step 2. Round the number of shares to thousandths, three decimal places.

EXAMPLE 15 CALCULATING NUMBER OF SHARES PURCHASED

Richard Avalon invested a lump sum of $5,000 in a mutual fund with an offer price of $6.55. How many shares did Richard purchase?

SOLUTION STRATEGY

$$\text{Number of shares purchased} = \frac{\text{Total investment}}{\text{Offer price}}$$

$$\text{Number of shares purchased} = \frac{5{,}000}{6.55} = \underline{\underline{763.359 \text{ shares}}}$$

TRY IT EXERCISE 15

Haydee Navarro invested $10,000 in a no-load mutual fund with a net asset value of $12.25. How many shares did she purchase?

CHECK YOUR ANSWER WITH THE SOLUTION ON PAGE 769.

20-13 CALCULATING RETURN ON INVESTMENT

return on investment (ROI) The basic measure of how an investment is doing. Used to compare various investments on an equal basis. Calculated as a percent, by dividing the total gain on the investment by the total cost of purchase.

Regardless of whether you are investing in stocks, bonds, or mutual funds, the basic measure of how your investments are doing is known as the **return on investment (ROI)**. This performance yardstick allows investors to compare various investments on an equal basis. Return on investment takes into account all transaction charges, such as broker's commissions and fees, as well as income received, such as dividends and interest payments. ROI is expressed as a percent, rounded to the nearest tenth.

STEPS TO CALCULATE RETURN ON INVESTMENT

Step 1. Calculate the dollar gain or (loss) on the sale of the investment by subtracting the total cost from the proceeds of the sale.

Gain or (loss) on investment = Proceeds − Total cost

Step 2. Compute total gain by adding any dividends received on stocks, or interest received on bonds, to the gain or loss on sale.

Total gain or (loss) = Gain or (loss) + Dividends or interest

Step 3. Calculate return on investment by dividing the total gain by the total cost of purchase. Round your answer to the nearest tenth percent.

$$\textbf{Return on investment (ROI)} = \frac{\textbf{Total gain}}{\textbf{Total cost of purchase}}$$

Google Flies High
On Monday, October 9, 2007, Google shares closed over $600 for the first time. If you would have purchased 100 shares of Google stock at the August 2004 opening price, $85, the investment would have cost you $8,500. At the close of trading on October 26, 2007, the 100 shares were worth $67,460!

EXAMPLE 16 CALCULATING RETURN ON INVESTMENT

Bertha Hill purchased 1,000 shares of Classic Mutual Fund for an offer price of $5.30 per share. She later sold the shares at a net asset value of $5.88 per share. During the time Bertha owned the shares, Classic paid a dividend of $.38 per share. What is Bertha's return on investment?

SOLUTION STRATEGY

Step 1.

Total cost of purchase = 1,000 shares × 5.30 = $5,300

Proceeds from sale = 1,000 shares × 5.88 = $5,880

Gain on sale = Proceeds − Total cost

Gain on sale = 5,880 − 5,300 = $\underline{\$580}$

Step 2. In addition to the gain on sale, Bertha also made \$380 (1,000 × .38) in dividends.

$$\text{Total gain} = \text{Gain on sale} + \text{Dividends}$$
$$\text{Total gain} = 580 + 380 = \underline{\$960}$$

Step 3. $\text{Return on investment} = \dfrac{\text{Total gain}}{\text{Total cost of purchase}} = \dfrac{960}{5{,}300} = .18113 = \underline{\underline{18.1\%}}$

CLASSROOM ACTIVITY
In groups, have students work Try It Exercise 16, calculating return on investment. Next, have the groups compare answers with another group and resolve any differences.
Use Teaching Transparencies 20-8 and 20-8a to illustrate the solution.

TRY IT EXERCISE 16

Gabe Hopen purchased 2,000 shares of Berkeley National Mutual Fund for an offer price of \$8.60 per share. He later sold the shares at a net asset value of \$9.18 per share. During the time Gabe owned the shares, Berkeley National paid dividends of \$.27 and \$.42 per share. What is Gabe's return on investment?

CHECK YOUR ANSWER WITH THE SOLUTION ON PAGE 769.

20-8

"Yes, our investments are diversified: 20% out the window, 65% down the drain, and 15% gone with the wind."

Review Exercises

SECTION III 20

Use Exhibit 20-6, Mutual Fund Data, on page 756, to fill in the blanks for Exercises 1–8.

1. Oak Value, Oak Value – Symbol and Net asset value: OAKVX, \$26.43
2. Delaware Invest C, SmCpValC p – YTD % return and 3-year % change: 2.2%, 12.5%
3. Which mutual fund has the lowest net asset value? How much? Oak Associates Funds, BlkOakEmrg, \$2.87

Complete, worked-out solutions to Exercises 9, 13, and 17 appear in Appendix B, following the index.

4. Which mutual fund has the highest year-to-date percent return? How much? Oppenheimer A. DiscovA p, 29.7%
5. Which mutual fund has the lowest 3-year percent change? How much? Delaware Invest B, CorPlsBd t, 2%
6. PIA Funds, OCMGold t – Net asset value and change: $21.02, down $0.27
7. Which Harbor Fund has the best 3-year percent change? How much? IntRet p, 29%
8. What is the symbol of the HSBC Investor fund that went down that day? How much? RINEX, $0.29

Calculate the sales charge and sales charge percent for the following mutual funds.

Fund	Offer Price	Net Asset Value	Sales Charge	Sales Charge %
9. Smith Barney A: MuFl A	$13.35	$12.82	$.53	4.1
10. Retire Invst Trust: Income	15.44	15.44	0	0
11. Rightime Group:	26.97	25.69	1.28	5.0
12. Smith Barney A: USGvtA	13.64	13.09	.55	4.2

Calculate the net asset value and number of shares purchased for the following mutual funds. Round shares to thousandths, three decimal places.

	Total Assets	Total Liabilities	Shares Outstanding	Net Asset Value	Offer Price	Total Investment	Shares Purchased
13.	$80,000,000	$2,300,000	5,000,000	$15.54	$16.10	$10,000	621.118
14.	52,000,000	1,800,000	6,100,000	8.23	9.50	5,000	526.316
15.	95,400,000	4,650,000	8,500,000	10.68	11.15	50,000	4,484.305
16.	15,000,000	750,000	1,300,000	10.96	NL	25,000	2,281.022

Calculate the total cost, proceeds, total gain or (loss), and return on investment for the following mutual fund investments. The offer price is the purchase price of the shares, and the net asset value is the price at which the shares were later sold.

	Shares	Offer Price	Total Cost	Net Asset Value	Proceeds	Per Share Dividends	Total Gain or (Loss)	Return on Investment %
17.	100	$15.30	$1,530	$18.80	$1,880	$.45	$395	25.8
18.	500	10.40	5,200	12.90	6,450	.68	1,590	30.6
19.	1,000	4.85	4,850	6.12	6,120	1.25	2,520	52
20.	700	7.30	5,110	5.10	3,570	0	(1,540)	(30.1)

21. A mutual fund has an offer price of $13.10 and a net asset value of $12.35.
    a. What is the sales charge?
    Sales charge = 13.10 − 12.35 = $.75
    b. What is the sales charge percent?
    $$\text{Sales percent} = \frac{.75}{12.35} = 6.1\%$$

22. A mutual fund has total assets of $25,000,000 and liabilities of $3,500,000. If there are 8,600,000 shares outstanding, what is the net asset value of the fund?

$$\text{Net asset value} = \frac{25{,}000{,}000 - 3{,}500{,}000}{8{,}600{,}000} = \underline{\underline{\$2.50}}$$

23. Ken Warrren invested a lump sum of $10,000 in a mutual fund with an offer price of $14.50. How many shares did he purchase?

$$\text{Shares purchased} = \frac{10{,}000}{14.50} = \underline{\underline{689.655}}$$

24. Charlie Beavin purchased 500 shares of Advantage Resource Fund for an offer price of $8.90 per share. He later sold the shares at a net asset value of $10.50 per share. During the time that he owned the shares the fund paid a dividend of $.75 per share three times. What is Charlie's return on investment?

$\text{Cost} = 500 \times 8.90 = \$4{,}450$
$\text{Proceeds} = 500 \times 10.50 = \$5{,}250$
$\text{Dividends} = .75 \times 500 \times 3 = \$1{,}125$

$$\text{Return on investment} = \frac{5{,}250 - 4{,}450 + 1{,}125}{4{,}450} = \underline{\underline{43.3\%}}$$

BUSINESS DECISION CAPITAL GAINS

25. There are many tax rules and regulations that you should be aware of when investing; whether it be in stocks, bonds, mutual funds, real estate, or collectibles. **Capital gains** are proceeds derived from your investments. Unless they are specified as being tax-free, such as municipal bonds, you must pay capital gains taxes on these funds.

In the Business World

In addition to the capital gains tax rates of 5% and 15% for stock, bonds, and mutual funds, there are two other rates:

25% Rate

This rate applies to part of the gain from selling real estate that has already been depreciated. This higher rate keeps the seller from getting a double tax break—depreciation and long-term capital gains.

28% Rate

Two categories of capital gains are subject to this rate: small business stock (half of gain excluded from tax if the stock was held for more than 5 years) and collectibles, such as artwork, antiques, gems, memorabilia, stamps, and coins.

The Ultimate Collectible

In 2007, Gustav Klimt's 1907 society portrait, *Adele Block-Bauer 1*, was sold to cosmetics entrepreneur, Ronald S. Lauder, for a record $135 million, the most ever paid for a work of art.

Capital gains are taxed in one of two ways. If the investment was held for one year or less, this is considered **short-term** and is taxed as ordinary income at your regular income tax rate. If the investment was held for more than one year, it is considered **long-term** and qualifies for various tax discounts, as follows:

	Capital Gains Rates	
Stocks Held	**10% or 15% tax bracket**	**Over 15% tax bracket**
1 year or less	10% or 15%	25%–35%
Over 1 year	5%	15%

a. If you are in the 15% tax bracket, how much tax would be saved by waiting for an investment to become long-term before selling, if your taxable profit from this investment was $25,000?

Long-term tax savings = 15% − 5% = 10%
25,000 × .10 = $2,500

b. How much would you save if you were in the 35% tax bracket?

Long-term tax savings = 35% − 15% = 20%
25,000 × .20% = $5,000

CHAPTER FORMULAS

Stocks

Dividend per share (preferred) = Par value + Dividend rate

$$\text{Dividend per share (common)} = \frac{\text{Total common dividend}}{\text{Number of shares (common)}}$$

$$\text{Current yield} = \frac{\text{Annual dividend per share}}{\text{Current price of the stock}}$$

$$\text{Price-earnings ratio} = \frac{\text{Current price per share}}{\text{Earnings per share}}$$

Gain or (loss) on stock = Proceeds − Total cost

Bonds

Price per bond = Current market price + Accrued interest + Commission

Proceeds = Current market price + Accrued interest − Commission

$$\text{Current yield} = \frac{\text{Annual interest}}{\text{Current market price}}$$

Mutual funds

Mutual fund sales charge = Offer price − Net asset value

$$\text{Sales charge percent} = \frac{\text{Sales charge}}{\text{Net asset value}}$$

$$\text{Net asset value (NAV)} = \frac{\text{Total assets} - \text{Total liabilities}}{\text{Number of shares outstanding}}$$

$$\text{Number of shares purchased} = \frac{\text{Total investment}}{\text{Offer price}}$$

$$\text{Return on investment (ROI)} = \frac{\text{Total gain}}{\text{Total cost of purchase}}$$

SUMMARY CHART

20

Section I: Stocks

Topic	Important Concepts	Illustrative Examples
Distributing Dividends on Preferred and Common Stock **P/O 20-1, p. 733**	Companies raise capital by selling stock. Common stock shares in the success or failure of the business. Preferred stock receives a fixed dividend and is paid before common. Cumulative preferred receives dividends in arrears, those not paid in past years. Preferred dividends are stated as a percent of par value or as a dollar amount for no-par preferred. Dividends are distributed as follows: 1. Preferred—Arrears 2. Preferred—Current period 3. Common—Current period **Dividend per share (preferred) = Par value + Dividend rate** **Dividend per share (common) =** $\frac{\textbf{Total common dividend}}{\textbf{Number of shares (common)}}$	Apex Corp. has 100,000 shares of $100 par, 7%, cumulative preferred and 300,000 shares of common stock. No dividend was declared last year. This year, a $2,000,000 dividend was declared. Distribute the dividends among the two classes of stock. Preferred stockholders receive 100 × .07 = $7.00 per share. Preferred—Arrears: 100,000 shares × 7 = $700,000 Preferred—Current: 100,000 shares × 7 = 700,000 Total due preferred = $1,400,000 Common: $2,000,000 Total dividend − 1,400,000 Preferred dividend $600,000 Common dividend Div. per share = $\frac{600{,}000}{300{,}000}$ = $2.00
Calculating Current Yield for a Stock **P/O 20-3, p. 739**	Current yield is a measure of how much you are earning on a stock compared with other investments. **Current yield =** $\frac{\textbf{Annual dividend per share}}{\textbf{Current price of the stock}}$	What is the current yield for Calder Corporation stock, which pays a dividend of $2.35 per share and is currently selling for $57.25? Current Yield = $\frac{2.35}{57.25}$ = 4.1%
Determining the Price-Earnings Ratio of a Stock **P/O 20-4, p. 740**	The price-earnings ratio of a stock shows the relationship between the price of a stock and the company's earnings for the past 12 months. **PE ratio =** $\frac{\textbf{Current price per share}}{\textbf{Earnings per share}}$	General Dynamo stock is selling at $34.35. If the company had earnings per share of $4.27, calculate the price-earnings ratio. PE ratio = $\frac{34.35}{4.27}$ = 8.04 = 8
Computing the Cost, Proceeds, and Gain or (Loss) on a Stock Transaction **P/O 20-5, p. 741**	Stocks are purchased and sold through stockbrokers, who charge a commission for these services. Round lots are purchases in multiples of 100 shares. Odd lots are purchases of less than 100 shares. Extra commission is usually charged for odd lots. **Total cost of purchase = Cost of shares + Broker's commission** **Proceeds = Value of shares − Broker's commission** **Gain or (loss) = Proceeds − Total cost**	You purchase 450 shares of Keller Corp. common stock at $19.75 per share. A few months later, you sell the shares at $27.50. Your stockbroker charges 3% on round lots and 4% on odd lots. What are the total cost, the proceeds, and the gain or loss on your investment? ***Purchase*** Cost of shares = 450 × 19.75 = $8,887.50 Commission = 400 × 19.75 × .03 = $237.00 50 × 19.75 × .04 = 39.50 Total commission = $276.50 Total cost of purchase = 8,887.50 + 276.50 = $9,164 ***Sale*** Value of shares = 450 × 27.50 = $12,375 Commission = 400 × 27.50 × .03 = $330 50 × 27.50 × .04 = 55 Total commission = $385 Proceeds = 12,375 − 385 = $11,990 ***Gain*** 11,990 − 9,164 = $2,826

Section II: Bonds

Topic	Important Concepts	Illustrative Examples
Calculating the Cost of Purchasing Bonds **P/O 20-7, p. 750**	Bonds are loans to companies or governments that pay fixed interest semiannually. *Buying Bonds:* 1. Calculate accrued interest since the last payment by $I = PRT$. 2. Calculate the price to purchase the bond by **Purchase price per bond = Current price + Accrued interest + Commission** 3. Calculate total purchase price by **Total purchase price = Price per bond × Number of bonds**	What is the purchase price of 10 Tornado bonds with a coupon rate of 5.5% and a current market price of $96.25? The commission charge is $6.00 per bond. The date of the purchase is November 1; the bond pays interest on Jan. 1 and July 1. Accrued interest $= 1{,}000 \times .055 \times \frac{4}{12} = \$18.33$ Price per bond = 962.50 + 18.33 + 6.00 = $986.83 Total purchase price = 986.83 × 10 = $9,868.30
Calculating Proceeds from the Sale of Bonds **P/O 20-7, p. 751**	*Selling Bonds:* 1. Calculate accrued interest since last payment by $I = PRT$. 2. Calculate the proceeds per bond by **Proceeds = Current market price + Accrued interest − Commission** 3. Calculate the total proceeds of the sale by **Total proceeds = Proceeds per bond × Number of bonds**	Bill Elliott sold 5 Crystal Corp. bonds with a coupon rate of 6.375% and a current market price of $107.75. The commission charge is $8 per bond. The date of sale is 100 days since the last interest payment. What are Bill's proceeds? Accrued interest $= 1{,}000 \times .06375 \times \frac{100}{360} = \$17.71$ Proceeds per bond = 1,077.50 + 17.71 − 8.00 = $1,087.21 Total proceeds = 1,087.21 × 5 = $5,436.05
Calculating the Current Yield for a Bond **P/O 20-8, p. 751**	Current yield is a simple measure of the return on investment based on the current market price of the bond. **Annual interest = Par value × Coupon rate** $\textbf{Current yield} = \frac{\textbf{Annual interest}}{\textbf{Market price}}$	Calculate the current yield for a Hi-Volt Electronics bond with a coupon rate of 9.25% and currently selling at a premium of $112.50. Annual interest = 1,000 × .0925 = $92.50 Current yield $= \frac{92.50}{1{,}125} = 8.2\%$

Section III: Mutual Funds

Topic	Important Concepts	Illustrative Examples
Calculating the Sales Charge and Sales Charge Percent of a Mutual Fund **P/O 20-10, p. 757**	Mutual fund sales charge or load may vary from 1% to 8% of the amount invested. When it is paid at the time of purchase, it is known as a front-end load. It is the difference between the offer price and the net asset value of the fund. **Sales charge = Offer price − NAV** $\textbf{Sales charge \%} = \frac{\textbf{Sales charge}}{\textbf{Net asset value}}$	What are the sales charge and the sales charge percent for a mutual fund with an offer price of $12.35 per share and a net asset value of $11.60? Sales charge = 12.35 − 11.60 = $.75 per share Sales charge % $= \frac{.75}{11.60} = 6.5\%$

Section III: (continued)

Topic	Important Concepts	Illustrative Examples
Calculating Net Asset Value of a Mutual Fund **P/O 20-11, p. 758**	The assets of a mutual fund are the total current value of its investments. The net asset value is the per share figure. $\text{Net asset value (NAV)} = \dfrac{\text{Total assets} - \text{Total liabilities}}{\text{Number of shares outstanding}}$	A mutual fund has total assets of \$20,000,000 and liabilities of \$5,000,000. If there are 4,000,000 shares outstanding, what is the net asset value of the fund? $\text{Net asset value} = \dfrac{20,000,000 - 5,000,000}{4,000,000} = \underline{\underline{\$3.75}}$
Computing Number of Shares Purchased of a Mutual Fund **P/O 20-12; p. 759**	Mutual fund stock is sold in fractional shares to accommodate those investing lump sums of money. Shares are rounded to thousandths (three decimal places). $\text{Number of shares} = \dfrac{\text{Total investment}}{\text{Offer price}}$ *Note*: For no-load funds, use net asset value as the denominator.	Cindy Montana invested a lump sum of \$10,000 in a mutual fund with an offer price of \$8.75. How many shares did she purchase? $\text{Number of shares} = \dfrac{10,000}{8.75} = \underline{\underline{1,142.857}}$
Calculating Return on Investment **P/O 20-13, p. 760**	Return on investment is the basic measure of how your stocks, bonds, or mutual fund investments are doing. 1. Calculate the gain or (loss) on the investment by **Gain or (loss) = Proceeds − Total cost** 2. Compute total gain or (loss) by **Total gain or (loss) = Gain or (loss) + Dividends or interest** 3. Calculate return on investment by $\text{Return on investment} = \dfrac{\text{Total gain}}{\text{Total cost of purchase}}$	Noah Gomberg purchased 1,000 shares of Lincoln mutual fund for an offer price of \$7.50 per share. He later sold the shares at a net asset value of \$8.75. During the time he owned the shares, Lincoln paid a dividend of \$.85 per share. What is his return on investment? Total cost = 1,000 × 7.50 = \$7,500 Proceeds = 1,000 × 8.75 = \$8,750 Gain = 8,750 − 7,500 = \$1,250 Dividends = 1,000 × .85 = \$850 Total gain = 1,250 + 850 = \$2,100 $\text{ROI} = \dfrac{2,100}{7,500} = .28 = \underline{\underline{28\%}}$

TRY IT EXERCISE SOLUTIONS FOR CHAPTER 20

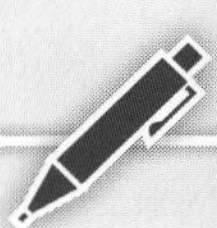

1. $\text{Dividend per share} = \dfrac{\text{Total common dividend}}{\text{Number of shares}}$

$\text{Dividend per share} = \dfrac{910,000}{1,400,000} = \underline{\underline{\$.65}}$

2. Total preferred dividend = Number of shares × Dividend per share

Total preferred dividend = 600,000 × 1.40 = $\underline{\underline{\$840,000}}$

Total common dividend = Total dividend − Total preferred dividend

Total common dividend = 2,800,000 − 840,000 = \$1,960,000

$\text{Dividend per share} = \dfrac{\text{Total common dividend}}{\text{Number of shares}}$

$\text{Dividend per share} = \dfrac{1,960,000}{1,000,000} = \underline{\underline{\$1.96}}$

3. Dividend per share = Par value × Dividend rate

Dividend per share = 100 × 7.5% = $7.50

Total preferred div. (per year) = Number of shares × Div. per share

Total preferred div. (per year) = 300,000 × 7.50 = $2,250,000

Total preferred div. = 2,250,000 (arrears) + 2,250,000 (this year) = $\underline{\underline{\$4,500,000}}$

Total common div. = Total div. − Total preferred div.

Total common div. = 7,000,000 − 4,500,000 = $2,500,000

$$\text{Dividend per share} = \frac{2,500,000}{5,200,000} = \underline{\underline{\$.48}}$$

4.

Name	Intel Corp.
Symbol	INTC
Open	$25.50
High	$25.76
Low	$25.47
Close	$25.66
Net Change	up $0.12
Percent Change	up 0.47%
Volume	34,600,200 shares
52-Week High	$26.50
52-Week Low	$18.75
Dividend	$0.45 per share
Yield	1.75%
P/E	26
YTD % Change	up 27%

5. $$\text{Current yield} = \frac{\text{Annual dividend per share}}{\text{Current price of stock}}$$

$$\text{Current yield} = \frac{.68}{12.84} = \underline{\underline{5.3\%}}$$

6. $$\text{Price-earnings ratio} = \frac{\text{Current price per share}}{\text{Earnings per share}}$$

$$\text{Price-earnings ratio} = \frac{37.19}{6.70} = 5.55 = \underline{\underline{6}}$$

7. a. ***Cost of stock:***

Cost of shares = Price per share × Number of shares

Cost of shares = 44.80 × 225 = $\underline{\$10,080}$

Broker's commission = Cost of shares × Comm. Rate

Round lot = 200 × 44.80 × .02 = $179.20

Odd lot = 25 × 44.80 × .03 = $33.60

Total commission = 179.20 + 33.60 = $\underline{\$212.80}$

Total cost = Cost of shares + Commission

Total cost = 10,080.00 + 212.80 = $\underline{\underline{\$10,292.80}}$

b. ***Proceeds from sale:***

Value of shares = Price per share × Number of shares

Value of shares = 53.20 × 225 = $\underline{\$11,970}$

Commission:

Round lot = 200 × 53.20 × .02 = $212.80

Odd lot = 25 × 53.20 × .03 = $39.90

Total commission = 212.80 + 39.90 = $\underline{\$252.70}$

Proceeds = Value of shares − Broker's commission

Proceeds = 11,970.00 − 252.70 = $\underline{\underline{\$11,717.30}}$

c. ***Gain or (loss) on transaction:***

Gain = Proceeds − Total cost

Gain = 11,717.30 − 10,292.80 = $\underline{\underline{\$1,424.50}}$

8.

Issuer Name	General Electric Capital
Symbol	GE.GMY
Coupon	4.375%
Maturity	November 2011
Rating	Aaa/AAA/−
High	$98.04
Low	$96.95
Last	$98.04
Change	up $1.759
Yield Percent	4.906%

9. $$\text{Accrued interest} = 1,000 \times .0625 \times \frac{2}{12} = \$10.42$$

Price per bond = Market price + Accrued int + Comm.

Price per bond = 913.75 + 10.42 + 10.00 = $\underline{\$934.17}$

Total purchase price = Price per bond × Number of bonds

Total purchase price = 934.17 × 20 = $\underline{\underline{\$18,683.40}}$

10. $$\text{Accrued interest} = 1,000 \times .08875 \times \frac{122}{360} = \$30.08$$

Proceeds per bond = Market price + Accrued interest − Comm.

Proceeds per bond = 990 + 30.08 − 10.00 = $\underline{\$1,010.08}$

Total proceeds = Proceeds per bond × Number of bonds

Total proceeds = 1,010.08 × 5 = $\underline{\underline{\$5,050.40}}$

11. Annual interest = Par value × Coupon rate

Annual interest = 1,000 × .09375 = $\underline{\$93.75}$

Current price = Par value × Price percent

Current price = 1,000 × .8475 = $\underline{\$847.50}$

$$\text{Current yield} = \frac{\text{Annual interest}}{\text{Market price}}$$

$$\text{Current yield} = \frac{93.75}{847.50} = .1106 = \underline{\underline{11.1\%}}$$

12.

Family/Fund	Old Mutual Adv Funds, ANDefEqZ
Symbol	ANDEX
Net asset value	$14.23
Change	up $0.02
YTD % Return	up 2.4%
3-year % Change	up 10.6%

13. Mutual fund sales charge = Offer price − Net asset value

Mutual fund sales charge = 9.85 − 9.21 = $.64

$$\text{Sales charge percent} = \frac{\text{Sales charge}}{\text{NAV}} = \frac{.64}{9.21} = 6.9\%$$

14. $$\text{Net asset value} = \frac{\text{Total assets} - \text{Total liabilities}}{\text{Number of shares}}$$

$$\text{Net asset value} = \frac{80{,}000{,}000 - 5{,}000{,}000}{17{,}000{,}000} = \$4.41$$

15. $$\text{Number of shares purchased} = \frac{\text{Total investment}}{\text{Offer price}}$$

$$\text{Number of shares purchased} = \frac{10{,}000}{12.25} = 816.327 \text{ shares}$$

16. Total cost of purchase = 2,000 × 8.60 = $17,200

Proceeds from sale = 2,000 × 9.18 = $18,360

Gain on sale = Proceeds − Total cost

Gain on sale = 18,360 − 17,200 = $1,160

Dividends: 2,000 × .27 = $540

2,000 × .42 = $840

Total dividends = 540 + 840 = $1,380

Total gain = Gain on sale + Dividends

Total gain = 1,160 + 1,380 = $2,540

$$\text{Return on investment} = \frac{\text{Total gain}}{\text{Total cost of purchase}}$$

$$\text{ROI} = \frac{2{,}540}{17{,}200} = .1476 = 14.8\%$$

CONCEPT REVIEW

1. ____, or equities, are a major investment category represented by an ownership share of a corporation. (20-1)
Stocks

2. A distribution of a company's profits to its shareholders is known as ____. (20-1)
dividends

3. ____ stock is a class of stock in which the investor has voting rights. A class of stock in which the investor has preferential rights to dividends and company assets is known as ____ stock. (20-1)
Common, preferred

4. When reading a stock table, which two columns indicate a stock's performance in the past full year? Which column indicates how a stock has done so far in the current year? (20-2)
52 Week High and 52 Week Low;
Year-To-Date % Change

5. The current ____ is a percentage measure of how much an investor is earning on a stock compared with other investments. Write the formula used to calculate this measure. (20-3)
yield,

$$\text{Current yield} = \frac{\text{Annual dividend per share}}{\text{Current price of the stock}}$$

6. The ____ ratio shows the relationship between the price of a stock and the company's earnings for the past 12 months. (20-4)
price-earnings

7. Write the formula used to calculate the gain or loss on an investment in stocks. (20-5)
Gain or (loss) on stock = Proceeds − Total cost

8. A ____ is a loan or an IOU in the form of an interest-bearing note, in which the buyer lends money to the issuer. (20-6)
bond

9. When you sell a bond, your proceeds from the sale are the current market price plus ____ interest, minus the broker's ____. (20-7)
accrued, commission

10. Write the formula used to calculate the current yield of a bond. (20-8)

$$\text{Current yield} = \frac{\text{Annual interest}}{\text{Current market price}}$$

11. ____ ____ are professionally managed collective investment accounts that pool the money from many individuals and invest it in stocks, bonds, and other securities. (20-9)
Mutual funds

12. The dollar value of one share of a mutual fund's stock is known as the net ____ ____. (20-10, 20-11)
asset value

13. The price per share investors pay when purchasing a mutual fund is known as the ____ price. (20-12)
offer

14. The basic measure of how well an investment is doing is known as the ____ on investment. Write the formula used to calculate this measure. (20-13)
return,

$$\text{Return on investment} = \frac{\text{Total gain}}{\text{Total cost of purchase}}$$

ASSESSMENT TEST

Calculate the preferred and common stock dividend per share for the following companies.

Company	Common Stock Shares	Preferred Stock Shares	Div. or Par.	Cum.	Dividend Declared	Arrears	Preferred Div./Share	Common Div./Share
1. Goodyear	22,000,000		none		$ 7,900,000	none	0	$.36
2. Hasbro	5,000,000	1,000,000	$3.20	yes	8,500,000	1 year	$6.40	$.42
3. Chrysler	80,000,000	3,400,000	$100, 5%	yes	58,000,000	2 years	$15.00	$.09

CHAPTER 20

Name

Class

Answers

1. 0 $.36
2. $6.40 $.42
3. $15.00 $.09
4. $80.74, $81.61, $80.48, $81.34
5. 3M Company, 2,101.200 shares
6. $0.88, 1.9%, 15
7. Honeywell Int'l Inc. 33.90%
8. 2.2% 22
9. $2.09 3.3%
10. $40.00 19
11. $8.98 $1.71
12. $16,014, $17,542, $1,528.00
13. $15,665.20, $12,142.70, ($3,522.50)
14. $12,546, $13,965, $1,419.00
15. $39,277.88, $44,975.31, $5,697.43
16. a. $3,920,000
  b. $1.47

Use Exhibit 20-3, Stock Market Quotation Table, on page 738, to fill in the blanks for Exercises 4–7.

4. Caterpillar Inc. – Open, High, Low, and Close: $80.74, $81.61, $80.48, $81.34
5. Which stock had the lowest volume? How Much? 3M Company, 2,101,200 shares
6. Wal-Mart Stores Inc. – Dividend, Yield, P/E: $0.88, 1.9%, 15
7. Which stock had the highest year-to-date percent change? How much? Honeywell Int'l Inc. 33.90%

Calculate the missing information for the following stocks.

Company	Earnings per Share	Annual Dividend	Current Price per Share	Current Yield %	Price-Earnings Ratio
8. Federal Express	$3.20	$1.50	$69.25	2.2	22
9. Merck	$2.09	$1.12	$33.50	3.3	16
10. Office Depot	$2.10	$.48	$40.00	1.2	19
11. Loews Corp.	$8.98	$1.71	$89.75	1.9	10

Calculate the total cost, proceeds, and gain or (loss) for the following stock market transactions.

Company	Number of Shares	Purchase Price	Selling Price	Commissions Buy	Sell	Odd Lot	Total Cost	Proceeds	Gain or (Loss)
12. Olin	400	$39.25	$44.75	2%	2%	—	$16,014.00	$17,542.00	$ 1,528.00
13. Limited	630	24.13	19.88	3	3	add 1%	15,665.20	12,142.70	(3,522.50)
14. Exxon	200	61.50	71.25	2	2	—	12,546.00	13,965.00	1,419.00
15. IBM	850	45.50	53.75	1.5	1.5	add 1%	39,277.88	44,975.31	5,697.43

16. The board of directors of Eastwood Corp. has declared a dividend of $16,000,000. The company has 800,000 shares of preferred stock that pay $4.90 per share and 8,200,000 shares of common stock.

   a. What are the dividends due the preferred shareholders?

   Preferred shareholders get $4.90 per share × 800,000 = $3,920,000

   b. What is the dividend per share of common stock?

   Total common stock dividend = 16,000,000 − 3,920,000 = $12,080,000

   $$\text{Dividend per share of common stock} = \frac{12{,}080{,}000}{8{,}200{,}000} = \$1.47 \text{ Per share}$$

17. Flamingo Financial has 500,000 shares of $100 par value, 6.5%, cumulative preferred stock and 8,400,000 shares of common stock. Although no dividend was declared for the past 3 years, a $19,000,000 dividend has been declared for this year.

a. How much is due the preferred shareholders?

Preferred shareholders due: 100 × 6.5% × 4 years = $26 per share
Total due preferred shareholders = 26 × 500,000 = $13,000,000

b. What is the dividend per share of common stock?

Total common stock dividend = 19,000,000 − 13,000,000 = $6,000,000

$$\text{Dividend per share of common stock} = \frac{6{,}000{,}000}{8{,}400{,}000} = \$.71 \text{ Per share}$$

18. Fuller Laboratories is currently selling at $27.48. The earnings per share are $2.69, and the dividend is $.70.

a. What is the current yield of the stock?

$$\text{Current yield} = \frac{.70}{27.48} = 2.5\%$$

b. What is the price-earnings ratio?

$$\text{Price-earnings ratio} = \frac{27.48}{2.69} = 10$$

19. You purchase 350 shares of Universal Airlines common stock at $12.38 per share. A few months later, you sell the shares at $9.88. Your stockbroker charges 3% commission on round lots and an extra 1.5% on odd lots.

a. What is the total cost of the purchase?

300 × 12.38 = 3,714.00 × 103% = $3,825.42
50 × 12.38 = 619.00 × 104.5% = 646.86
Total cost = $4,472.28

b. What are the proceeds on the sale?

300 × 9.88 = 2,964.00 × 97% = $2,875.08
50 × 9.88 = 494.00 × 95.5% = 471.77
Proceeds = $3,346.85

c. What is the gain or loss on the transaction?

4,472.28 − 3,346.85 = ($1,125.43) Loss

Use Exhibit 20-5, Corporate Bond Quotation Table, on page 749, to fill in the blanks for Questions 20–25.

20. MGM Mirage – Symbol, Coupon, Maturity: MGG.HA, 7.625%, January 2017

21. Diageo Finance BV – Rating, Yield %: A3/A–/A, 5.2%

22. Which bond had the lowest "Last" price? How much? Ford Motor, F.GL., $78.50

23. Which bond had the greatest "Change"? How much? Merrill Lynch, down $3.385

24. General Motors, GM, GC – High, Low, Last: $99.00, $97.712, $98.50

25. Monsanto – Rating, Change, Yield %: Baa1/A–/A–, up $0.029, 5.26%

CHAPTER 20

Name

Class

Answers

17. a. $13,000,000

b. $.71

18. a. 2.5%

b. 10

19. a. $4,472.28

b. $3,346.85

c. ($1,125.43)

20. MGG, HA, 7.625%, January 2017

21. A3/A – /A, 5.200%

22. Ford Motor, F. GL. $78.50

23. Merrill Lynch, down $3.385

24. $99.00, 97.712, $98.50

25. Baal/A–/A –, up $0.029, 5.26%

Complete worked-out solutions to Exercises 1, 2, and 8–13 appear in Appendix B, following the index.

Calculate the accrued interest and the total purchase price of the following bond purchases.

Company	Coupon Rate	Market Price	Time Since Last Interest	Accrued Interest	Commission per Bond	Bonds Purchased	Total Price
26. Conagra	8.25%	$95.375	65 days	$14.90	$5.00	10	$9,736.50
27. Dell	7.375	78.50	100 days	$20.49	9.50	5	$4,074.95
28. Chevron	5.625	105.75	3 months	$14.06	7.00	15	$16,178.40

26. Interest $= 1{,}000 \times .0825 \times \frac{65}{360} = \$14.90$

Total cost $= (953.75 + 14.90 + 5.00) \times 10$
$= \$9{,}736.50$

Calculate the accrued interest and the total proceeds of the following bond sales.

Company	Coupon Rate	Market Price	Time Since Last Interest	Accrued Interest	Commission per Bond	Bonds Sold	Total Proceeds
29. Upjohn	7.375%	$94.50	10 days	$2.05	$6.00	10	$9,410.50
30. Brunswick	8.875	109.25	4 months	$29.58	5.00	20	$22,341.60
31. Pet	9.25	98.00	85 days	$21.84	8.00	5	$4,969.20

29. Interest $= 1{,}000 \times .07375 \times \frac{10}{360} = \$2.05$

Proceeds $= (945.00 + 2.05 - 6.00) \times 10$
$= \$9{,}410.50$

Calculate the annual interest and current yield for the following bonds.

Company	Coupon Rate	Annual Interest	Market Price	Current Yield
32. Duracell	5.375%	$53.75	$94.125	5.7%
33. Seaboard	9.5	$95.00	$105.75	9%

32. Annual interest $= 1{,}000 \times 5.375\% = 53.75$

Current yield $= \frac{53.75}{941.25} = 5.7\%$

Complete worked-out solutions to Exercises 27–28, 30–31, and 33 appear in Appendix B, following the index.

34. On May 1, Emerson Fast bought 10 Serenity Ridge bonds with a coupon rate of 7.875%. The purchase price was $101.375, and the commission was $8.00 per bond. Serenity Ridge bonds pay interest on April 1 and October 1.

a. What is the current yield of the bond?

$$\text{Current yield} = \frac{\text{Annual interest}}{\text{Current market price}}$$

Interest $= 1{,}000 \times .07875 = \$78.75$

$$\text{Yield} = \frac{78.75}{1{,}013.75} = 7.8\%$$

b. What is the total purchase price of the bonds?

Accrued interest $= 1{,}000 \times .07875 \times \frac{1}{12} = \$6.56$

Total purchase price $= (1{,}013.75 + 6.56 + 8.00) \times 10 = \$10{,}283.10$

c. If Emerson sold the bonds on August 1 for $109.50, what are the proceeds from the sale?

Accured interest $= 1{,}000 \times .07875 \times \frac{4}{12} = \$26.25$

Proceeds $= (1{,}095.00 + 26.25 - 8.00) \times 10 = \$11{,}132.50$

Use Exhibit 20-6, Mutual Fund Quotation Table, on page 756, to fill in the blanks for Questions 35–38.

35. Which mutual fund has the highest net asset value? How much? Harbor Funds, IntlRet p, $75.62

36. Delaware Invest B, SelGrowBt – Symbol, Year-to-date percent return: DVEBX, 15.4%

20 CHAPTER

Name

Class

Answers

26.	$14.90	$9,736.50
27.	$20.49	$4,074.95
28.	$14.06	$16,178.40
29.	$2.05	$9,410.50
30.	$29.58	$22,341.60
31.	$21.84	$4,969.20
32.	$53.75	5.7%
33.	$95.00	9%
34. a.	7.8%	
b.	$10,283.10	
c.	$11,132.50	
35.	Harbor Funds, IntlRet p, $75.62	
36.	DVEBX, 15.4%	

37. Harbor Funds, Bond – Net asset value, Change: $11.62, down $0.01

38. Which mutual fund has the highest 3-year percent change? How much? Oppenheimer A, IntlSmCoA, 38.3%

Calculate the sales charge and sales charge percent for the following mutual funds.

Fund	Offer Price	Net Asset Value (NAV)	Sales Charge	Sales Charge %
39. Quest for Value: CA TE	$10.88	$10.36	$.52	5
40. Sentinel Group: EmGr	$5.59	$5.31	$.28	5.3

Calculate the net asset value and number of shares purchased for the following mutual funds. Round shares to thousandths, three decimal places.

	Total Assets	Total Liabilities	Shares Outstanding	Net Asset Value (NAV)	Offer Price	Total Investment	Shares Purchased
41.	$30,000,000	$1,800,000	4,000,000	$7.05	$7.80	$50,000	6,410.256
42.	58,000,000	3,700,000	7,100,000	$7.65	NL	25,000	3,267.974

Calculate the total cost, proceeds, total gain or (loss), and return on investment for the following mutual fund investments. The offer price is the purchase price of the shares and the net asset value is the price at which the shares were later sold.

	Shares	Offer Price	Total Cost	Net Asset Value (NAV)	Proceeds	Per Share Dividends	Total Gain or (Loss)	Return on Investment %
43.	100	$13.40	$1,340	$11.80	1,180	$.75	($85.00)	(6.3)
44.	500	12.65	$6,325	15.30	7,650	.63	$1,640	25.9
45.	1,000	9.40	$9,400	12.82	12,820	.96	$4,380	46.6

46. A mutual fund has an offer price of $8.90 and a net asset value of $8.35.

a. What is the sales charge?

Sales charge = Offer price − NAV = 8.90 − 8.35 = $.55

b. What is the sales charge percent?

$$\text{Sales charge percent} = \frac{\text{Sales charge}}{\text{NAV}} = \frac{.55}{8.35} = 6.6\%$$

47. A mutual fund has total assets of $25,000,000 and liabilities of $1,500,000. If there are 2,600,000 shares outstanding, what is the net asset value of the fund?

$$\text{NAV} = \frac{25{,}000{,}000 - 1{,}500{,}000}{2{,}600{,}000} = \$9.04$$

48. Karl Hellman invested a lump sum of $20,000 in a mutual fund with an offer price of $11.80. How many shares did he purchase?

$$\text{Number of shares} = \frac{20{,}000}{11.80} = 1{,}694.915$$

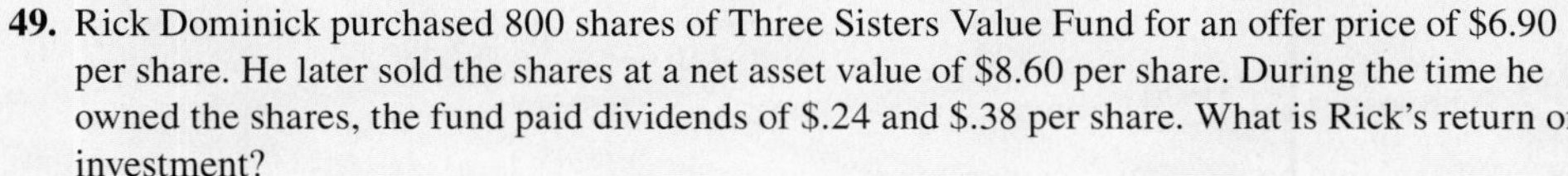

49. Rick Dominick purchased 800 shares of Three Sisters Value Fund for an offer price of $6.90 per share. He later sold the shares at a net asset value of $8.60 per share. During the time he owned the shares, the fund paid dividends of $.24 and $.38 per share. What is Rick's return on investment?

Cost = 800 × 6.90 = $5,520
Proceeds = 800 × 8.60 = $6,880
Dividends = (.24 + .38) × 800 = $496

Gain = 6,880 + 496 − 5,520 = $1,856

$$\text{Return on investment} = \frac{1{,}856}{5{,}520} = 33.6\%$$

Name

Class

Answers

37. $11.62, down $0.01

38. Oppenheimer A, InstlSmCoA, 38.3 %

39. $.52 5%

40. $.28 5.3%

41. $7.05 6,410.256

42. $7.65 3,267.974

43. $1,340 1,180 ($85.00) (6.3%)

44. $6,325 7,650 $1,640 25.9%

45. $9,400 12,820 $4,380 46.6%

46. a. $.55 **b.** 6.6%

47. $9.04

48. 1,694.915

49. 33.6%

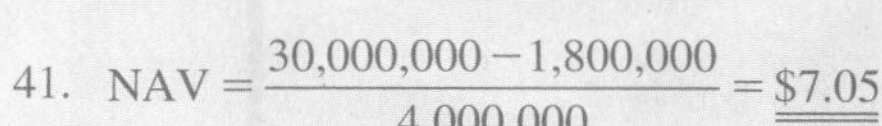

41. $\text{NAV} = \frac{30{,}000{,}000 - 1{,}800{,}000}{4{,}000{,}000} = \$7.05$

$\text{Shares purchased} = \frac{50{,}000}{7.80} = 6{,}410.256$

42. $\text{NAV} = \frac{58{,}000{,}000 - 3{,}700{,}000}{7{,}100{,}000} = \$7.65$

$\text{Shares purchased} = \frac{25{,}000}{7.65} = 3{,}267.974$

20 CHAPTER

BUSINESS DECISION PAPER PROFIT

Name

Class

Answers

50. a. $3,544.50

b. 3.3%

c. Total loss = ($1,477.71)

d. (1.3%) Loss

50. You have received your investment portfolio year-end statement from your broker, Rich Waldman. All investments were purchased at the January prices and held the entire year.

Portfolio Year-End Statement

Investment	Number	Dividend	Price—Jan. 1	Price—Dec. 31
Disney	400 shares	$.30	38.38	45.75
Federal Express	500 shares	0	74.50	70.13
McDonald's	200 shares	.24	27.88	29.25
Exxon	300 shares	3.00	68.75	64.63
AT&T 7.125% 12	20 bonds		98.50	101.38
Ryder 9.875% 17	10 bonds		103.88	100.75

a. Calculate how much profit or loss you made for the year, including stock dividends and bond interest.

Company	Value Jan. 1	Value Dec. 31	Dividend/ Interest	Gain or (Loss)
Disney	$ 15,352	$ 18,300	$ 120.00	$3,068.00
Federal Express	37,250	35,065	0	(2,185.00)
McDonald's	5,576	5,850	48.00	322.00
Exxon	20,625	19,389	900.00	(336.00)
AT&T 7.125% 12	19,700	20,276	1,425.00	2,001.00
Ryder 9.875% 17	10,388	10,075	987.50	674.50
	$108,891	$108,955	$3,480.50	$3,544.50

Total profit for the year = $3,544.50

b. What was the total return on investment for your portfolio?

$$\text{Return on investment} = \frac{\text{Total gain}}{\text{Value Jan. 1}} = \frac{3,544.50}{108,891.00} = 3.3\%$$

c. Using a broker's commission of 3% buying and 3% selling on the stocks, and $5 buying and $5 selling per bond, how much profit or loss would you make if you liquidated your entire portfolio at the December 31 prices?

	Total Cost Jan. 1	Proceeds Dec. 31	Dividend/ Interest	Gain or (Loss)
Disney	$ 15,812.56	$ 17,751.00	$ 120.00	$2,058.44
Federal Express	38,367.50	34,013.05	0	(4,354.45)
McDonald's	5,743.28	5,674.50	48.00	(20.78)
Exxon	21,243.75	18,807.33	900.00	(1,536.42)
AT&T 7.125% 12	19,800.00	20,176.00	1,425.00	1,801.00
Ryder 9.875% 17	10,438.00	10,025.00	987.50	574.50
	$111,405.09	$106,446.88	$3,480.50	($1,477.71)

Total loss = ($1,477.71)

d. What would be the return on investment?

$$\text{Return on investment} = \frac{(1,477.71)}{111,405.09} = (1.3\%) \text{ Loss}$$

Among the largest full-service brokerages in the country are Merrill Lynch, Smith Barney, UBS, Edward Jones, Wachovia, Morgan Stanley, A.G. Edwards, and CharlesSchwab.

COLLABORATIVE LEARNING ACTIVITY

Yesterday, Today, and Tomorrow!

In this activity, you and your team will research the meaning and direction of some of the more important investment and money indicators in our economy. Your best source of information for this project will be the Internet, stockbrokers, and financial newspapers such as *The Wall Street Journal*, *Barron's*, or *The New York Times*.

a. Research and explain what the economic indicators mean and how they are derived.

b. Look up the current figure for each indicator.

c. Look up historical figures (every 3 or 6 months) and prepare a visual presentation (line graph or bar graph) of each indicator's performance trend since October 2007.

d. As a team, discuss and report what each trend indicates.

Economic Indicator	October 12, 2007
Dow Jones Industrial Average	14,093.08
Standard & Poor's 500	1,561.80
NASDAQ Composite Average	2,805.68
30-year U.S. Treasury bond	4.76%
10-year U.S. Treasury note—Yield	4.649%
Japanese yen (per U.S. dollar)	117.26
Euro (in U.S. dollars)	$1.4147
Canadian dollars (in U.S. dollars)	$1.0201
Gold (troy oz.)	$740.40
Oil, W. Texas (per barrel)	$83.69
U.S. Prime Rate	7.75%
Certificate of deposit (6-month)	4.75%
30-year mortgage	6.30%
Consumer price index (C.P.I.)	207.917
Gross Domestic Product ($billions)	$13,632.6
Unemployment rate	4.4%
Average hourly earnings	$17.22

©Adam Odoie/ PhotoEdit Inc.

Business Statistics and Data Presentation

CHAPTER 21

PERFORMANCE OBJECTIVES

DATA INTERPRETATION AND PRESENTATION

SECTION I 21

Information, the Name of the Game!

Statistical ideas and methods are used in almost every aspect of human activity, from the natural sciences to the social sciences. Statistics has special applications in such areas as medicine, psychology, education, engineering, and agriculture. In business, statistical methods are applied extensively in production, marketing, finance, and accounting.

Business statistics is the systematic process of collecting, interpreting, and presenting numerical data about business situations. In business, statistics is organized into two categories, descriptive statistics and statistical inference. **Descriptive statistics** deals with the tabular or graphical presentation of data, whereas **statistical inference** is the process of arriving at conclusions, predictions, forecasts, or estimates based on that data. To make sound managerial decisions, today's managers must understand the meaning and implications of vast amounts of numerical data generated by their companies.

Business statistics starts with the collection of raw data concerning a particular business situation or question. For example, if management wants the next annual report to present a comparison chart of company sales and profit figures with current industry trends, two types of information would be required. First are the company records of sales and profits. These data would be readily available from *internal* company sources. Most large corporations today use a vast array of computer systems to collect and store incredible amounts of information relating to all aspects of business activity. Management information systems are then used to deliver these data, on request, in an electronic instant.

Information gathered from sources outside the firm, such as current industry statistics, are known as *external* data and are readily available from a variety of private and government publications. The federal government is by far the largest researcher and publisher of business data. The Departments of Commerce and Labor periodically publish information relating to all aspects of the economy and the country. Some of these publications are the *Statistical Abstract of the United States, Survey of Current Business, Monthly Labor Review, Federal Reserve Bulletin, Census of the United States*, and the *Census of Business*.

The Statistical Abstract of the United States, published by the U.S. Census Bureau since 1878, is the standard summary of statistics on the social, political, and economic organization of the United States. It is designed to serve as a convenient volume for statistical reference and as a guide to other statistical publications and sources.

Private statistical services such as Moody's Investors Service and Standard and Poor's offer a wealth of information for business decision making. Other private sources are periodicals such as *The Wall Street Journal, Fortune, Business Week, Forbes*, and *Money*, as well as hundreds of industry and trade publications, and Web sites.

Numerical data form the raw material on which analyses, forecasts, and managerial plans are based. In business, tables and charts are used extensively to summarize and display data in a clear and concise manner. In this section, you learn to read, interpret, and construct information from tables and charts.

business statistics The systematic process of collecting, interpreting, and presenting numerical data about business situations.

descriptive statistics Statistical procedures that deal with the collection, classification, summarization, and the tabular or graphical presentation of data.

21-1 READING AND INTERPRETING INFORMATION FROM A TABLE

statistical inference The process of arriving at conclusions, predictions, forecasts, or estimates based on the data under study.

table A collection of related data arranged for ease of reference or comparison, usually in parallel columns with meaningful titles.

A **table** is a collection of related data arranged for ease of reference or comparison, usually in parallel columns with meaningful titles. Tables are a very useful tool in summarizing statistical data and are found everywhere in business. Once the data have been obtained from the table, they can be compared with other data by arithmetic or percentage analysis.

STEPS TO READING A TABLE

Step 1. Scan the titles above the columns for the category of information being sought.

Step 2. Look down the column for the specific fact required.

Table 21-1 shows the sales figures in dollars for Magnum Enterprises over a 6-month period. Magnum manufactures and sells standard and deluxe computer components. Note that the table is divided into columns representing sales per month of each product type by territory.

Table 21-1
Magnum Enterprises
6-Month Sales Report

Magnum Enterprises
6-Month Sales Report

	January		February		March		April		May		June	
	Standard	**Deluxe**	**Standard**	**Deluxe**	**Standard**	**Deluxe**	**Standard**	**Deluxe**	**Standard**	**Deluxe**	**Standard**	**Deluxe**
Northwest	$123,200	$ 86,400	$115,800	$ 73,700	$133,400	$ 91,100	$136,700	$ 92,600	$112,900	$ 65,300	$135,000	$ 78,400
Northeast	214,700	121,300	228,400	133,100	246,600	164,800	239,000	153,200	266,100	185,000	279,300	190,100
Southwest	88,300	51,000	72,100	45,700	97,700	58,300	104,000	67,800	125,000	78,300	130,400	74,500
Southeast	143,200	88,700	149,900	91,300	158,400	94,500	127,700	70,300	145,700	79,400	162,000	88,600

EXAMPLE 1 READING A TABLE

Answer the following questions about Magnum Enterprises from Table 21-1.

a. What were the sales of deluxe units in April in the Northeast?
b. What were the sales of standard units in May in the Southwest?
c. What were the total sales for February and March in the Southeast?
d. What months showed a decrease in sales of deluxe units in the Northwest?
e. How many more standard units were sold companywide in June than in January?
f. What percent of the total units sold in March were deluxe?

In the Business World

The material in this chapter presents concepts and procedures that will help you understand and evaluate statistical information that you encounter as both a consumer and businessperson.

Statistical information may be in the form of daily media, such as radio and television reports or newspaper and magazine articles, or they may be business-related statistics such as company reports, presentations, budgets, and schedules.

SOLUTION STRATEGY

Questions a, b, and d can be answered by inspection. Questions c, e, and f require numerical or percentage calculations.

a. Deluxe unit sales in April in the Northeast = $153,200

b. Standard unit sales in May in the Southwest = $125,000

c. Total sales in February and March in the Southeast:

$$149{,}900 + 91{,}300 + 158{,}400 + 94{,}500 = \$494{,}100$$

d. Decrease in sales of deluxe units in the Northwest occurred in February and May.

e. Standard unit sales in January = $569,400

Standard unit sales in June = $706,700

$$706{,}700 - 569{,}400 = \$137{,}300 \text{ more in June}$$

f. To solve this problem, we use the percentage formula Rate = Portion ÷ Base. In this case, the rate is the unknown, the total sales in March is the base, and the deluxe sales in March is the portion.

$$\text{Rate} = \frac{408{,}700}{1{,}044{,}800} = .3911 = 39.1\%$$

TRY IT EXERCISE 1

Answer the following questions about Magnum Enterprises from Table 21-1.

a. What were the sales of standard units in February in the Northeast?
b. What were the sales of deluxe units in April in the Southeast?
c. What were the total sales for May and June in the Northwest?
d. What months showed an increase in sales of standard units in the Southwest?
e. How many more deluxe units were sold companywide in May than in April?
f. What percent of the total units sold in the Northwest were standard?

CHECK YOUR ANSWERS WITH THE SOLUTIONS ON PAGE 815.

READING AND CONSTRUCTING A LINE CHART

Charts are used to display a picture of the relationships among selected data. **Line charts** show data changing over a period of time. A single glance at a line chart gives the viewer a general idea of the direction or trend of the data: up, down, or up and down.

The horizontal or ***x*-axis** is used to measure units of time, such as days, weeks, months, or years, whereas the vertical or ***y*-axis** depicts magnitude, such as sales dollars or production units. Frequently, the y-axis is used to measure the percentage of something.

Line charts are actually a series of data points on a grid, continuously connected by straight lines. They may contain a single line, representing the change of one variable such as interest rates; or they may contain multiple lines, representing the change of interrelated variables such as interest rates and stock prices or sales and profits.

line chart A series of data points on a grid, continuously connected by straight lines, that display a picture of selected data changing over a period of time.

***x*-axis** The horizontal axis of a chart, usually used to measure units of time such as days, weeks, months, or years.

***y*-axis** The vertical axis of a chart, usually used to measure the quantity or magnitude of something, such as sales dollars or production units. The *y*-axis is frequently used to measure the percentage of something.

STEPS FOR READING A LINE CHART

Step 1. Scan either the *x*- or *y*-axis for the known variable: *x* for time, *y* for amount.

Step 2. Draw a perpendicular line from that axis to the point where it intersects the chart.

Step 3. Draw a line from that point perpendicular to the opposite axis.

Step 4. The answer is read where that line intersects the opposite axis.

Exhibit 21-1 and Exhibit 21-2 are examples of single- and multiple-line charts.

EXAMPLE 2 READING A LINE CHART

Answer the following questions from the line charts in Exhibits 21-1 and 21-2.

a. How much was a 30-second Super Bowl advertisement in 2007?
b. Which year had the lowest 30-second Super Bowl advertising rate? How much?
c. In what year were 10 million high definition television sets sold?
d. In what year did high definition television set sales first surpass analog set sales?

Exhibit 21-1
Single-Line Chart

Teaching Transparency 21-1

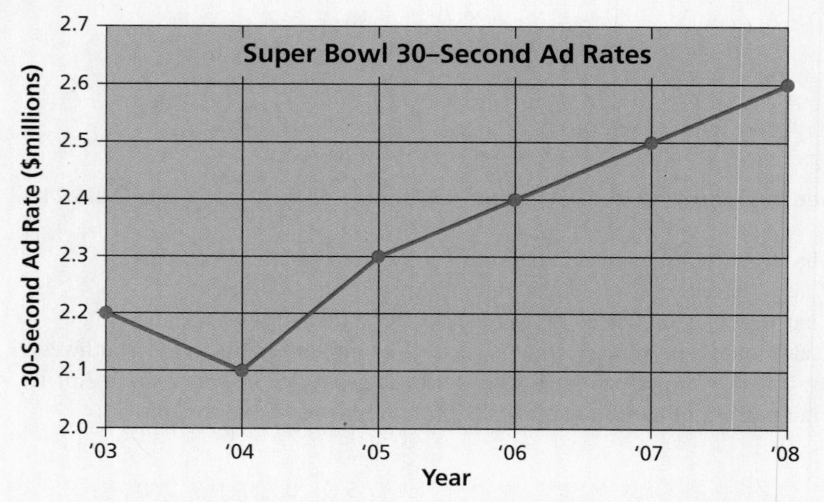

Source: *USA Today*, 10-11-2007, Page 36 Chart, Nielson Monitor-Plus. Reprinted with permission.

Exhibit 21-2
Multiple-Line Chart

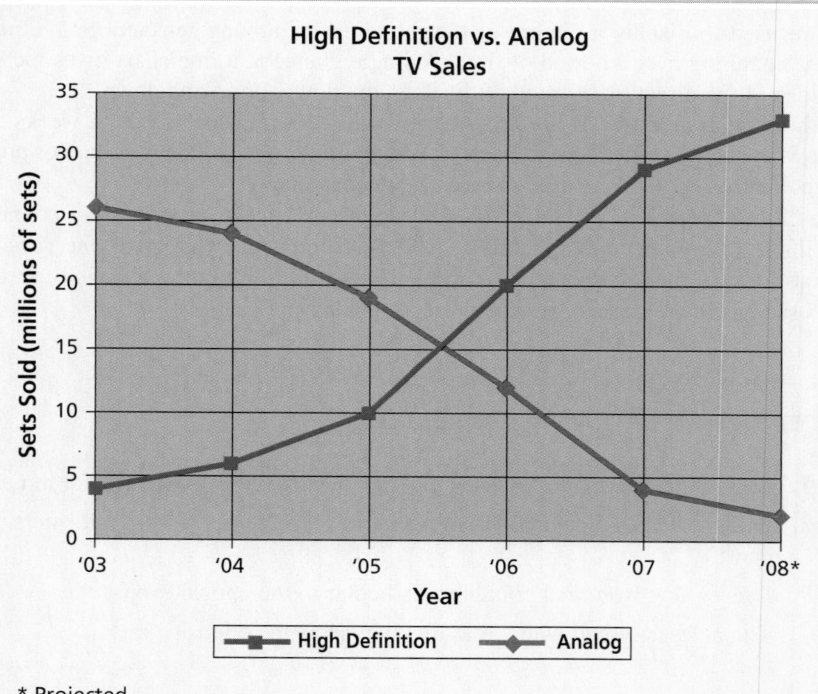

* Projected
Source: Wired 6/2006, Pg. 146 Chart

In the Business World

Tables illustrate specific data better than line charts; however, line charts are able to show relationships among data more clearly.

Frequently, in business presentations they are used together, with the chart used to clarify or reinforce facts presented in a table.

SOLUTION STRATEGY

a. In Exhibit 21-1, locate 2007 on the x-axis and then scan up to where the line chart is intersected. Look to the left, perpendicular to the y-axis, to find the answer, $2.5 million.

b. In Exhibit 21-1, scan the line chart for the lowest point. Look down perpendicular to the x-axis, to find the year, 2004. From the lowest point, look left perpendicular to the y-axis, to find the amount, $2.1 million.

c. In Exhibit 21-2, locate 10 million sets on the y-axis and then scan to the right until the high definition line is intersected. Look down, perpendicular to the x-axis, to find the answer, 2005.

d. In Exhibit 21-2, scan the lines for the point where high definition sales are greater than analog sales. Look down, perpendicular to the x-axis, to find the year, 2006.

TRY IT EXERCISE 2

Answer the following questions from the line charts in Exhibits 21-1 and 21-2.

a. In which year was the 30-second Super Bowl advertising rate $2.3 million?

b. How much was a 30-second Super Bowl advertisement in 2008?

c. How many high definition television sets were sold in 2006?

d. What was the last year that analog sets outsold high definition sets?

CHECK YOUR ANSWERS WITH THE SOLUTIONS ON PAGE 816.

In the Business World

Frequently, the word *graph* is used instead of *chart*. Graph is short for graphic formula. That is, a means of providing information graphically, rather than in words. Graph is from the Greek, *graphein*, to draw!

STEPS TO CONSTRUCT A LINE CHART

Step 1. Evenly space and label the time variable on the x-axis.

Step 2. Evenly space and label the amount variable on the y-axis.

Step 3. Show each data point by placing a dot above the time period and across from the corresponding amount.

Step 4. Connect the plotted points with straight lines to form the chart.

Step 5. When multiple lines are displayed, they should be labeled or differentiated by various colors or line patterns.

EXAMPLE 3 CONSTRUCTING A LINE CHART

You are the manager of Handy Hardware Stores, Inc. The company has one store in Centerville and one in Carson City. The following table shows the monthly sales figures, in thousands of dollars, for each store last year. From this information, construct a line chart of the total sales for each month.

TEACHING TIP
Call attention to the importance of the "scale" chosen for a chart. Demonstrate on the board how different scales can change the "look" of a chart. Show students how small changes can be made to appear more important than they are by changing the scale.

To illustrate, plot the same information on two charts, one using whole numbers as the scale and the other using tenths. Notice the difference in the shape of the line. The chart using whole numbers appears flat compared with the "dramatic rise" in the chart using tenths.

Handy Hardware: Monthly Sales Report ($000)

	Jan.	Feb.	Mar.	Apr.	May	June	July	Aug.	Sept.	Oct.	Nov.	Dec.
Centerville	16	18	24	21	15	13	17	18	16	23	24	20
Carson City	8	11	14	12	10	16	13	13	9	13	14	17
Total	24	29	38	33	25	29	30	31	25	36	38	37

SOLUTION STRATEGY

For this chart, show the months on the x-axis and the sales on the y-axis. Use a range of 0 to 40 on the y-axis. Plot each month with a dot and connect all the dots with straight lines.

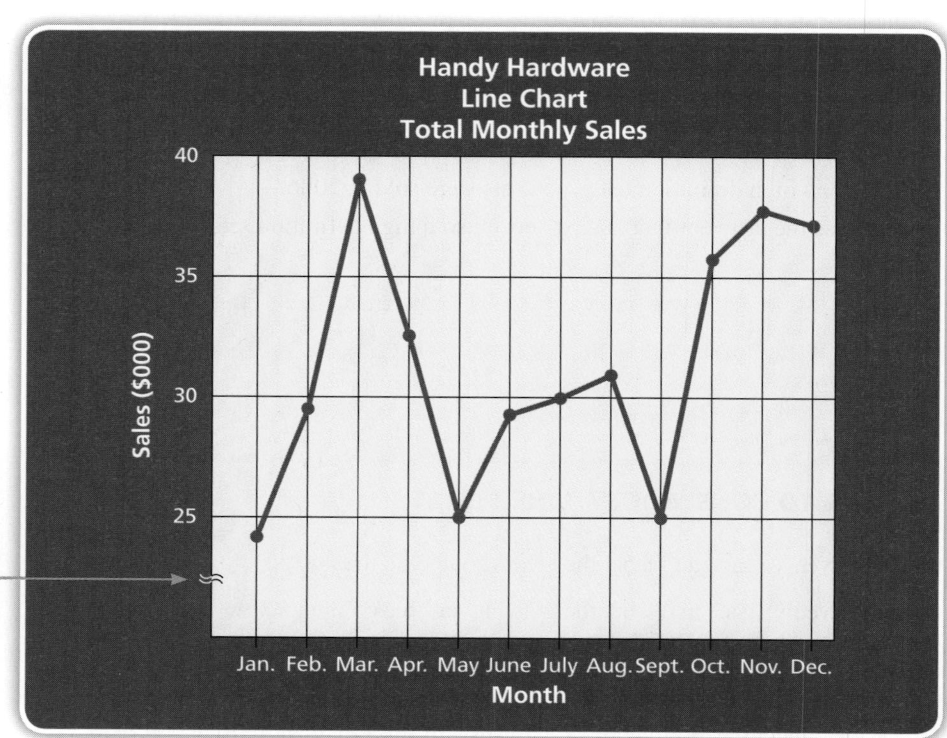

Learning Tip
Sometimes the x- or y-axis of a chart is "shortened" to better display the required scale. A pair of wavy lines (≈) intersecting the axis are used to indicate when this occurs.

TRY IT EXERCISE 3

The following data represent the audience statistics for a circus that performed in your town last week. Use the grid below to draw a line chart of the total attendance for each day.

Circus Attendance

	Monday	Tuesday	Wednesday	Thursday	Friday	Saturday	Sunday
Adults	2,300	2,100	1,900	2,200	2,400	2,700	2,600
Children	3,300	2,600	2,400	1,900	2,700	3,100	3,600
Total	5,600	4,700	4,300	4,100	5,100	5,800	6,200

CHECK YOUR CHART WITH THE SOLUTION ON PAGE 816.

© David Young-Wolff/PhotoEdit Inc.

Statistical information is recorded and used in many different ways at sporting events, including measuring attendance and athlete performance.

EXAMPLE 4 CONSTRUCTING A MULTIPLE-LINE CHART

From the Handy Hardware table on page 782 construct a multiple-line chart of the monthly sales for each of the stores. Show the Centerville store with a solid line and the Carson City store with a dashed line.

SOLUTION STRATEGY

As in the last example, the x-axis, time, will be months. The y-axis should range from 0 to 25 to include all the data.

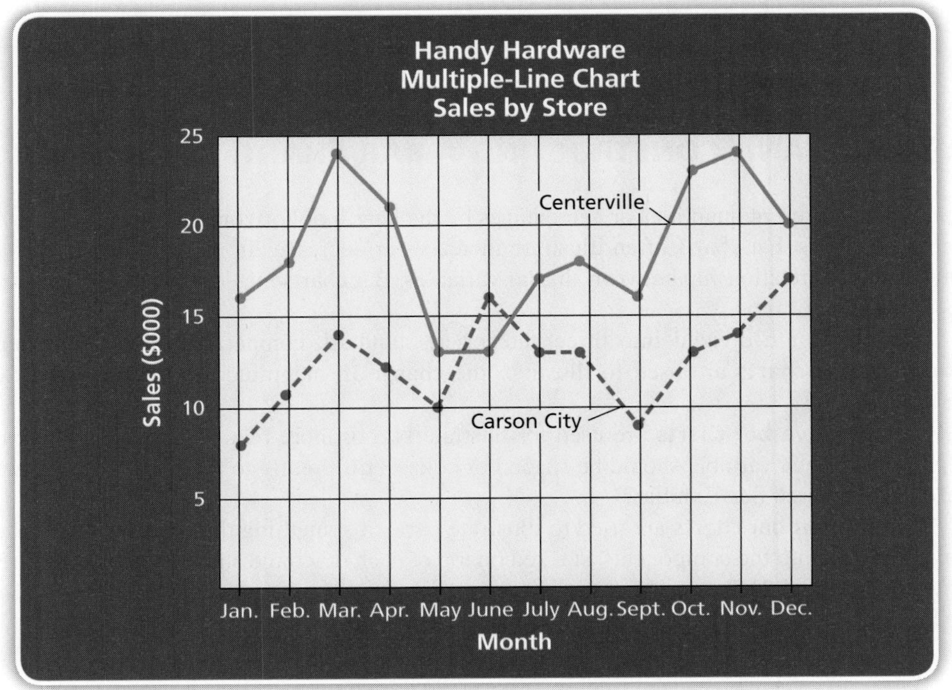

CLASSROOM ACTIVITY

Invite an insurance company actuary or a marketing research person to class as a guest speaker. Have him or her discuss

- The importance and variety of uses of statistics in today's business world
- How statistics can be misleading
- Career opportunities and educational requirements of their profession

TRY IT EXERCISE 4

From the Circus Attendance table on page 782 draw a multiple-line chart showing the number of adults and children attending the circus last week. Use a solid line for the adults and a dashed line for the children.

© Digital Vision/Getty Images

One of the most common uses of statistical information and data interpretation is for business presentations.

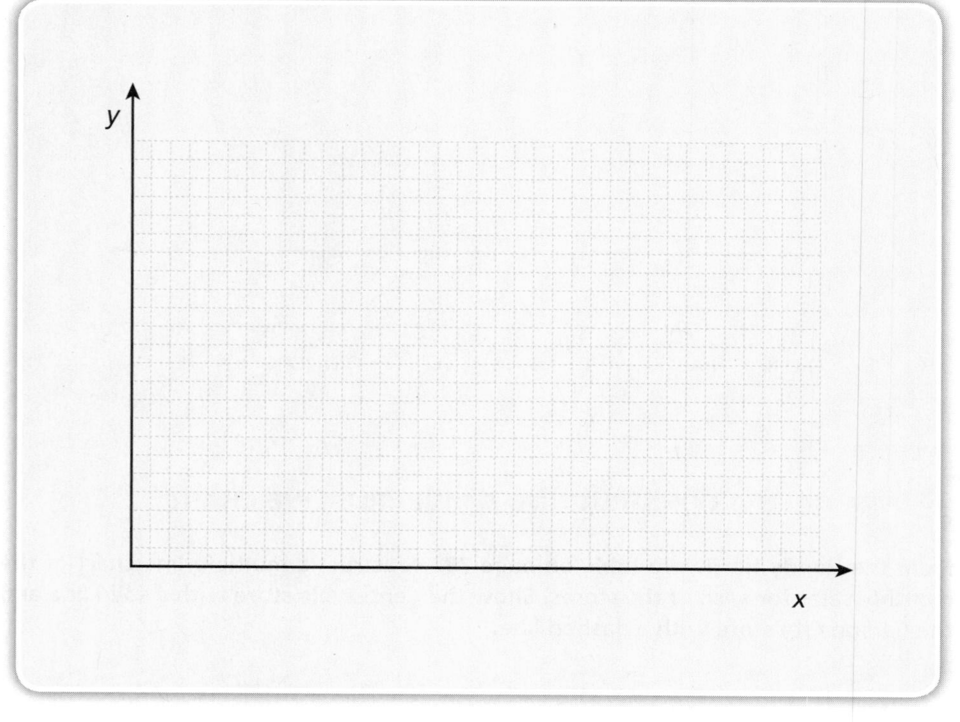

CHECK YOUR CHART WITH THE SOLUTION ON PAGE 816.

READING AND CONSTRUCTING A BAR CHART

bar chart Graphical presentations that represent quantities or percentages by the length of horizontal or vertical bars. These charts may or may not be based on the movement of time.

standard bar chart A bar chart that illustrates increases or decreases in magnitude of one variable.

comparative bar chart A bar chart used to illustrate the relationship between two or more similar variables.

component bar chart A bar chart used to illustrate the parts of something that add to a total; each bar is divided into the components stacked on top of each other and shaded or colored differently.

Bar charts represent quantities or percentages by the length of horizontal or vertical bars. As with line charts, bar charts often illustrate increases or decreases in magnitude of a certain variable or the relationship between similar variables. Bar charts may or may not be based on the movement of time.

Bar charts are divided into three categories: standard, comparative, and component. **Standard bar charts** are used to illustrate the change in magnitude of one variable. See Exhibit 21-3.

Comparative bar charts are used to illustrate two or more related variables. The bars representing each variable should be shaded or colored differently to make the chart easy to read and interpret. See Exhibit 21-4.

Component bar charts are used to illustrate parts of something that add to a total. Each bar is divided into the components, stacked on top of each other and shaded or colored differently. See Exhibit 21-5.

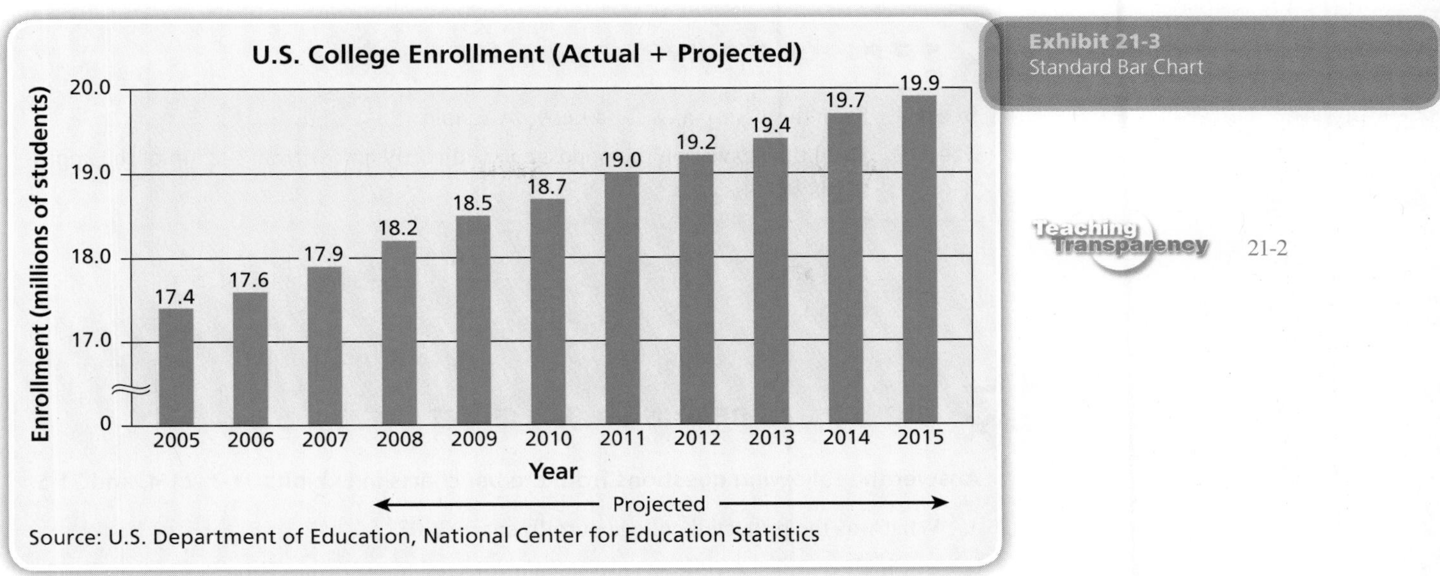

Exhibit 21-3
Standard Bar Chart

Teaching Transparency 21-2

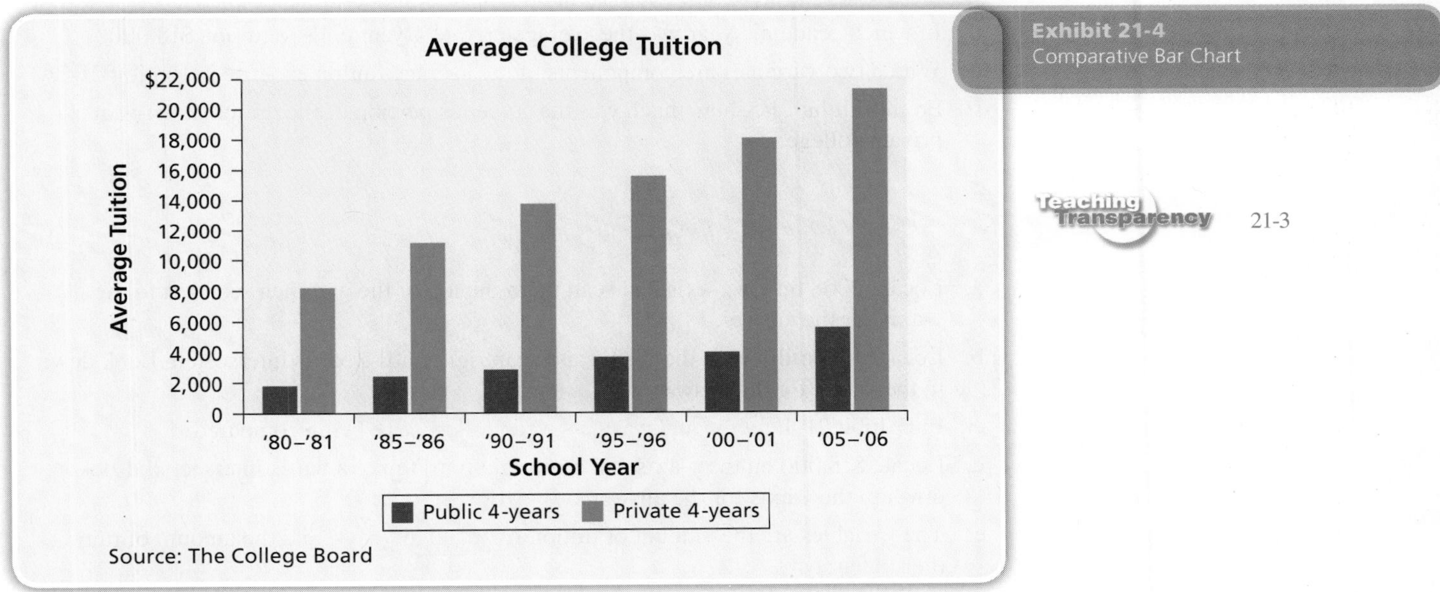

Exhibit 21-4
Comparative Bar Chart

Teaching Transparency 21-3

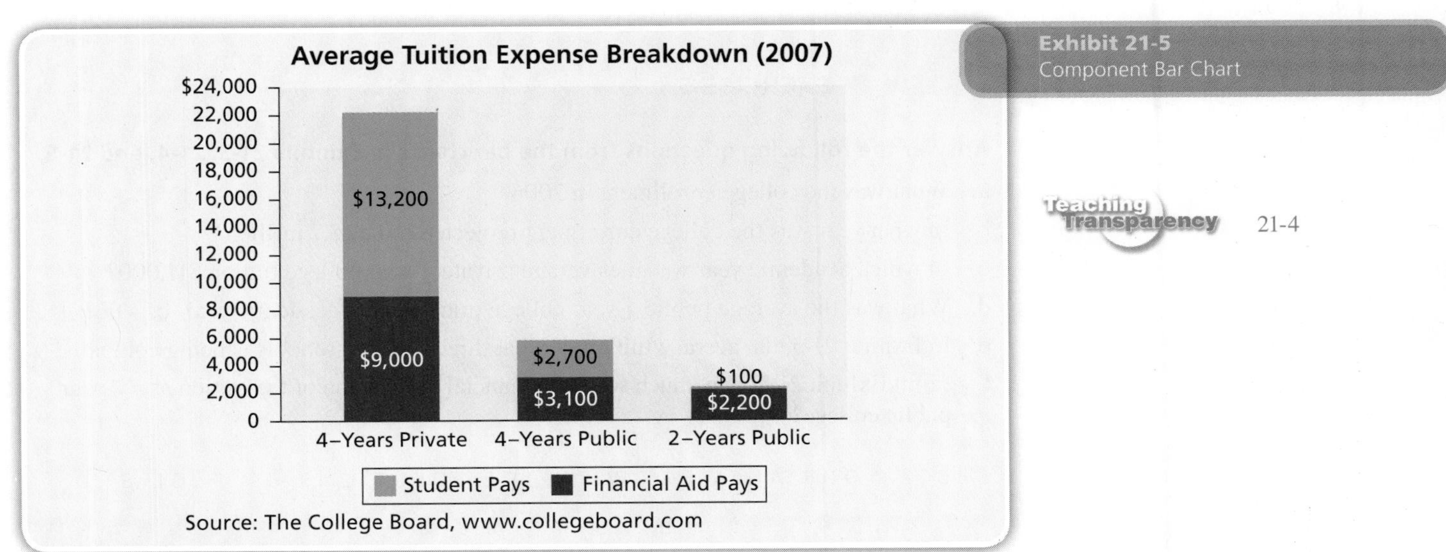

Exhibit 21-5
Component Bar Chart

Teaching Transparency 21-4

STEPS FOR READING A BAR CHART

Step 1. Scan the x- or y-axis for a known variable.

Step 2. Read the answer on the opposite axis directly across from the top of the appropriate bar.

EXAMPLE 5 READING A BAR CHART

Answer the following questions from the bar charts in Exhibits 21-3, 21-4, and 21-5.

a. What was the projected college enrollment in 2008?
b. In which year is the college enrollment projected to be 19.4 million?
c. Which two variables are being compared in Exhibit 21-4?
d. In which academic year was the average private 4-year college tuition $18,000?
e. Which two variables are components of the average tuition expense in Exhibit 21-5?
f. From Exhibit 21-5, how much was the student's portion of the tuition at a 4-year private college?

SOLUTION STRATEGY

a. Locate 2008 on the x-axis and scan up to the top of the bar, then scan left to the y-axis for the answer, 18,200,000.
b. Locate 19.4 million on the y-axis and scan right until a bar is intersected. Look down to the x-axis for the answer, 2013.
c. In Exhibit 21-4, public and private 4-year colleges are being compared.
d. Locate $18,000 on the y-axis and scan right until top of a bar is intersected. Look down to the x-axis for the answer, '00–'01.
e. The variables are the amount of tuition financial aid pays, and the amount of tuition the student pays.
f. The student's portion of the tuition at a 4-year private college was $13,200.

TRY IT EXERCISE 5

Answer the following questions from the bar charts in Exhibits 21-3, 21-4, and 21-5.

a. What was the college enrollment in 2006?
b. In what year was the college enrollment projected to be 18.7 million?
c. In which academic year was the average private 4-year college tuition $11,000?
d. What was the average public 4-year college tuition in the academic year '05–'06?
e. In Exhibit 21-5, the average tuition of what three types of schools is being compared?
f. From Exhibit 21-5, how much was the financial aid portion of the tuition at a 4-year public college?

CHECK YOUR ANSWERS WITH THE SOLUTIONS ON PAGE 817.

STEPS TO CONSTRUCT A BAR CHART

Step 1. Evenly space and label the *x*-axis. The space between bars should be one-half the width of the bars.

Step 2. Evenly space and label the *y*-axis. Be sure to include the full range of values needed to represent the variable. The lowest values should start at the bottom of the *y*-axis and increase upward.

Step 3. Draw each bar up from the *x*-axis to the point opposite the *y*-axis that corresponds to its value.

Step 4. For comparative and component bar charts, differentiate the bars by color or shading pattern. For complex presentations, provide a key or legend that shows which pattern or color represents each variable. This will help the reader to interpret the chart.

Learning Tip

The steps shown here are used to construct charts with *vertical* bars. For charts with *horizontal* bars, lay out the bars on the *y*-axis and the magnitude variable on the *x*-axis.

EXAMPLE 6 CONSTRUCTING A STANDARD BAR CHART

From the Handy Hardware sales report table on page 782, construct a standard bar chart of total sales for January through June.

SOLUTION STRATEGY

For this chart, the time variable, January through June, is shown on the *x*-axis. A range of 0 to 40 is used on the *y*-axis.

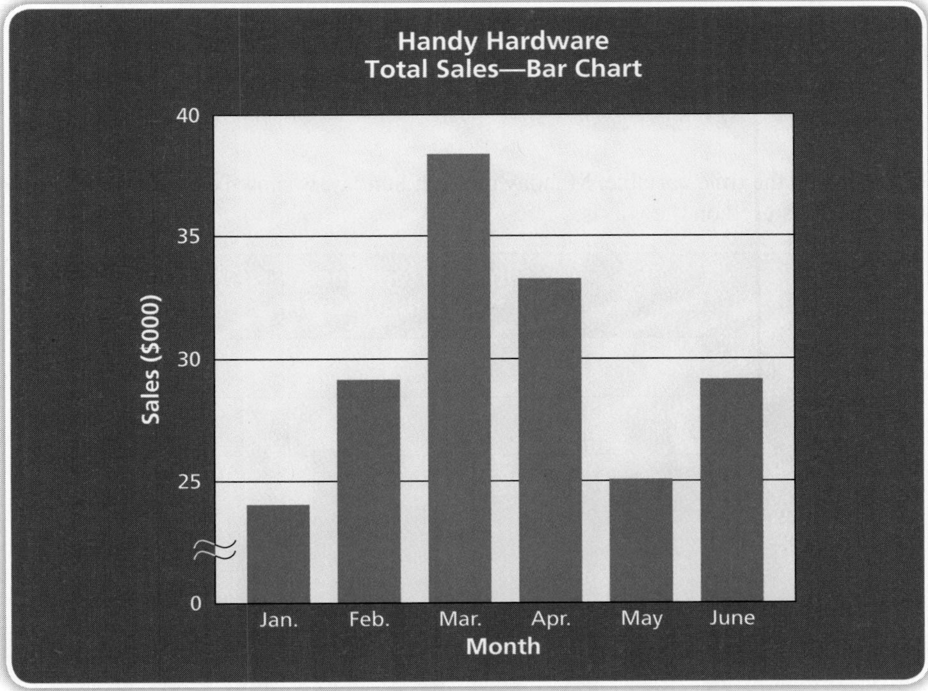

TRY IT EXERCISE 6

From the table for Circus Attendance on page 782 use the following grid to construct a standard bar chart of the total attendance for each day.

CHECK YOUR CHART WITH THE SOLUTION ON PAGE 817.

EXAMPLE 7 CONSTRUCTING A COMPONENT BAR CHART

From the table for Circus Attendance on page 782 construct a component bar chart that displays the adults and the children as components of each day's total audience. Plot the adults at the bottom of the bars in blue shading, and the children stacked above the adults in green shading.

SOLUTION STRATEGY

For this chart, the time variable, Monday through Sunday, is shown on the x-axis. A range of 0 to 7,000 is used on the y-axis.

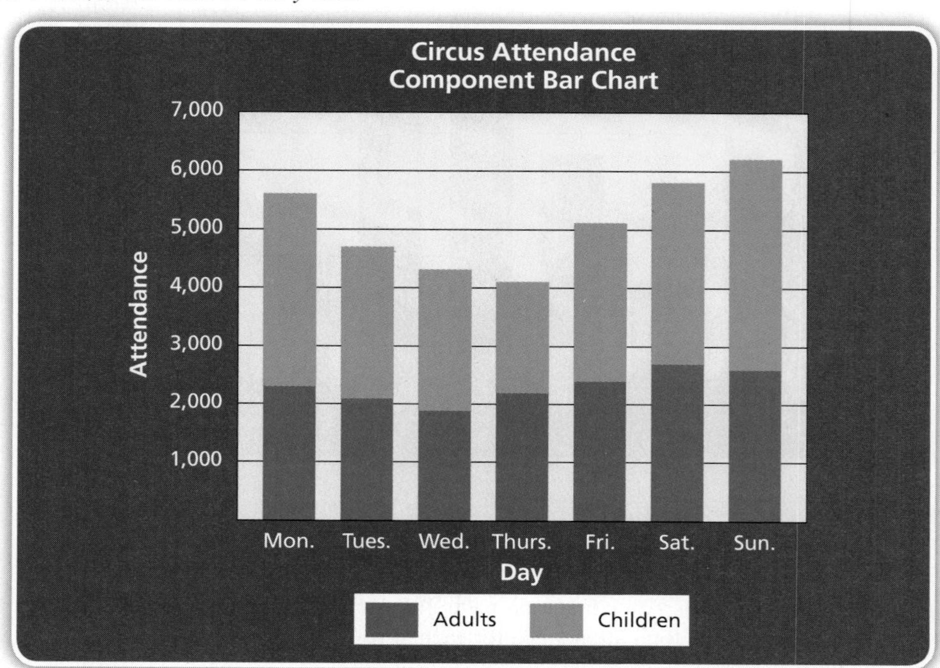

TRY IT EXERCISE 7

Use a separate sheet of graph paper to construct a component bar chart that displays the Centerville and the Carson City stores as components of the total monthly sales for July through December from the Handy Hardware sales report table on page 782.

CHECK YOUR CHART WITH THE SOLUTION ON PAGE 817.

EXAMPLE 8 CONSTRUCTING A COMPARATIVE BAR CHART

From the table below, construct a comparative bar chart of the freshmen and sophomore enrollment. Let the *x*-axis represent the time variable. For each term, group the bars together and differentiate them by shading.

Interstate Business College: Annual Enrollment

	Fall	Winter	Spring	Summer
Freshmen	1,800	1,400	1,350	850
Sophomores	1,200	1,200	1,150	700
Juniors	1,200	1,100	750	650
Seniors	850	700	500	400

SOLUTION STRATEGY

This chart is constructed in the same way as the standard bar chart except that the variables being compared are drawn side by side. The space between the bars is one-half the width of each bar. The *y*-axis ranges from 0 to 2,000 students. Note that the bars are shaded to differentiate the variables and that an explanation key is provided.

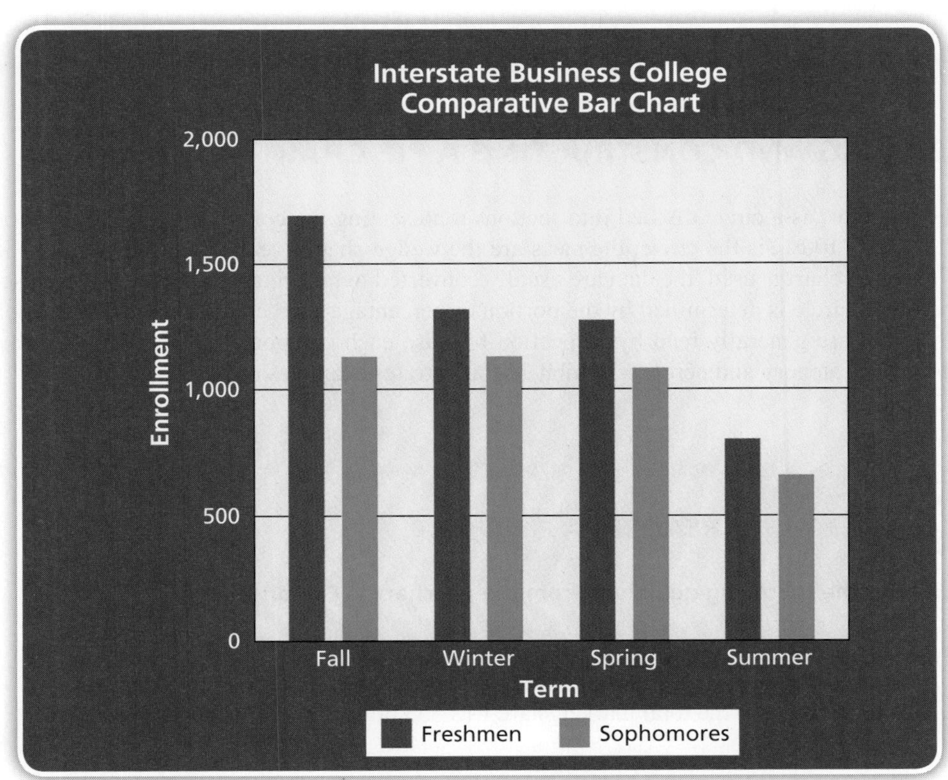

In the Business World

Many popular software programs, such as Microsoft's Excel and PowerPoint, Lotus 123, and Harvard Graphics, are designed to generate data in visually appealing chart form. These can be used to enhance your homework assignments at school or business presentations at work.

TRY IT EXERCISE 8

From the Interstate Business College enrollment figures in the table on page 789, construct a comparative bar chart of the junior and senior enrollment. Let the x-axis represent the time variable. For each term, group the bars together and differentiate them by shading.

CLASSROOM ACTIVITY
Ask students who have Microsoft Excel, PowerPoint, or Lotus 123 to create a hypothetical set of data and bring to class examples of the various types of charts these programs can generate.

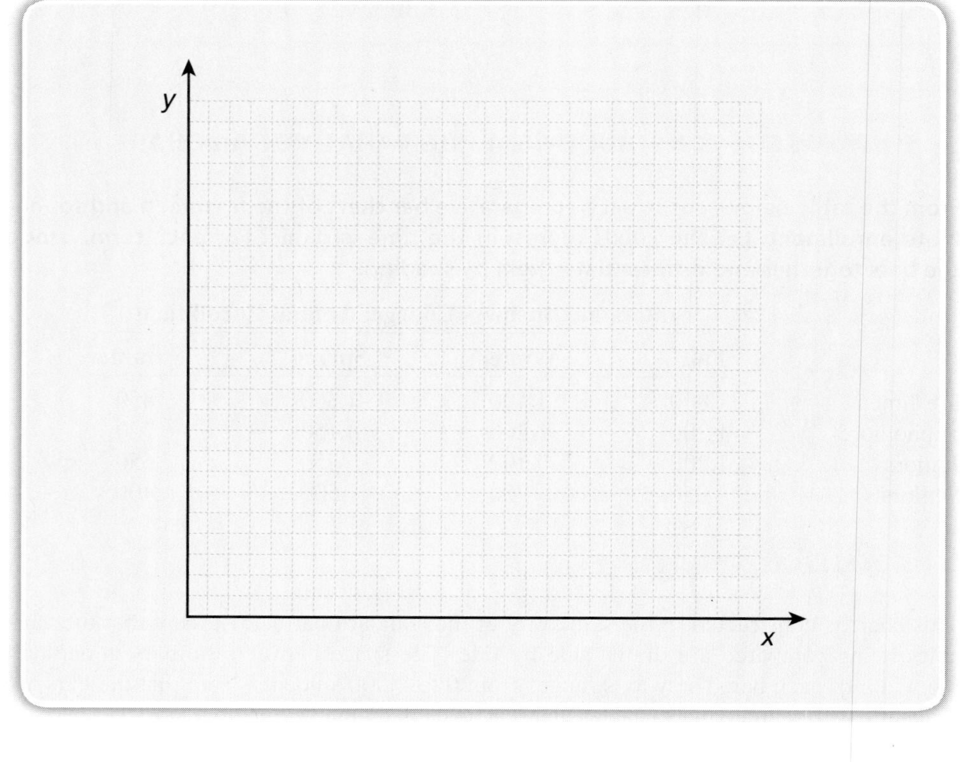

CHECK YOUR CHART WITH THE SOLUTION ON PAGE 817.

READING AND CONSTRUCTING A PIE CHART

pie chart A circle divided into sections, usually expressed in percentage form, representing the component parts of a whole.

The **pie chart** is a circle divided into sections representing the component parts of a whole. The whole, 100%, is the circle; the parts are the wedge-shaped sections of the circle. When this type of chart is used, the data are usually converted to percentages. The size of each section of the circle is determined by the portion or percentage each component is of the whole. Pie charts are generally read by inspection because each component of the data is clearly labeled by category and percent. Exhibit 21-6 illustrates examples of pie charts.

EXAMPLE 9 READING A PIE CHART

Answer the following questions from the pie chart in Exhibit 21-6.

a. What percent of the market did Starbucks have?
b. What was the combined market share of Wendy's and Burger King?
c. Considering that the total market share was $55 billion, how much was McDonald's revenue?

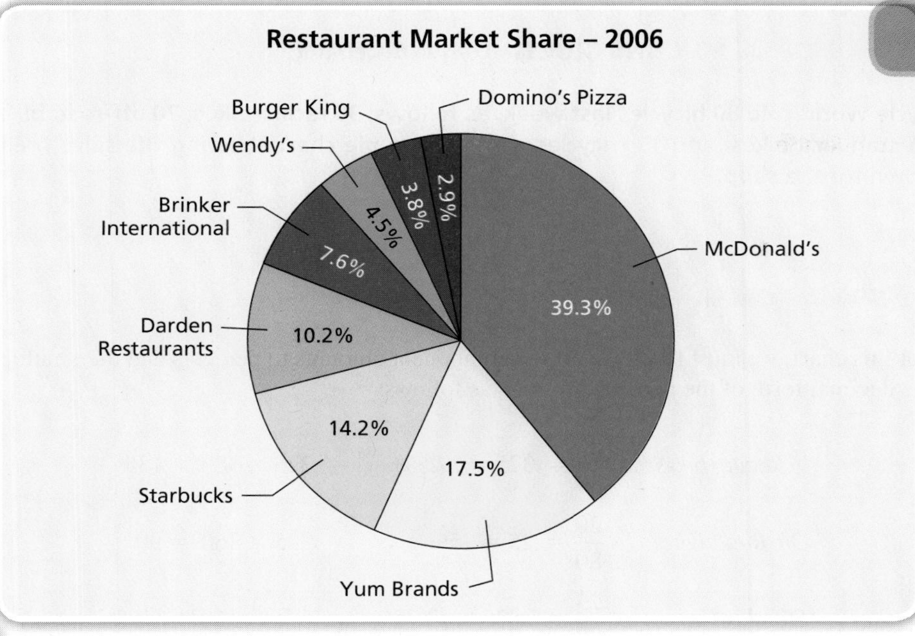

Exhibit 21-6
Pie Chart

Footnotes:
Yum Brands: KFC, Pizza Hut, Taco Bell

Darden Restaurants: Olive Garden, Red Lobster, Long John Silver's

Brinker International: Chili's, Macaroni Grill, On the Border

SOLUTION STRATEGY

a. Starbucks had 14.2% of the market.

b. The combined market share of Wendy's and Burger King was: 4.5% + 3.8% = 8.3%.

c. McDonald's revenue was: 39.3% of $55 billion = $21.615 billion.

Teaching Transparency 21-5

TRY IT EXERCISE 9

Answer the following questions from the pie chart in Exhibit 21-6.

a. What was the market share for Darden Restaurants?

b. What restaurant company had a 17.5% share of the market? What restaurants do they own?

c. Considering that the total market share was $55 billion, how much was Domino's revenue?

CHECK YOUR ANSWERS WITH THE SOLUTIONS ON PAGE 818.

STEPS TO CONSTRUCT A PIE CHART

Step 1. Convert the amount of each component to a percent by using the percentage formula Rate = Portion ÷ Base. Let the portion be the amount of each component and the base the total amount. Round each percent to hundredths.

Step 2. Because a full circle is made up of 360° representing 100%, multiply each component's percent (decimal form) by 360° to determine how many degrees each component's slice will be. Round to the nearest whole degree.

Step 3. Draw a circle with a compass and mark the center.

Step 4. Using a protractor, mark off the number of degrees on the circle that represents each component.

Step 5. Connect each point on the circle with the center by a straight line to form a segment or slice for each component.

Step 6. Label the segments clearly by name, color, or shading.

Pepper . . . and Salt

THE WALL STREET JOURNAL

LITZLER

"The secret to a crowd-pleasing pie chart is the crust."

EXAMPLE 10 CONSTRUCTING A PIE CHART

Cycle World sold 80 bicycles last week, as follows: 30 racing bikes, 20 off-road bikes, 15 standard bikes, and 15 tricycles. Construct a pie chart showing the sales breakdown for the shop.

SOLUTION STRATEGY

For this chart, we must first convert the component amounts to percents and then multiply the decimal form of the percents by 360° as follows:

Racing bikes: $\frac{30}{80} = .375 = 37.5\%$ $\quad .375 \times 360° = 135°$

Off-Road bikes: $\frac{20}{80} = .25 = 25\%$ $\quad .25 \times 360° = 90°$

Standard bikes: $\frac{15}{80} = .1875 = 18.75\%$ $\quad .1875 \times 360° = 67.5°$

Tricycles: $\frac{15}{80} = .1875 = 18.75\%$ $\quad .1875 \times 360° = 67.5°$

Learning Tip

Although a full circle has exactly 360°, sometimes the total may be slightly higher or lower than 360° because of rounding.

Next, draw a circle and use a protractor to mark the degree points of each component. Connect the points with the center of the circle to form the segments, and label each appropriately. The completed chart follows.

CLASSROOM ACTIVITY

In groups, have students bring to class examples of tables and charts found in newspapers and magazines.

Next, have each group mount them by categories on poster board and discuss which chart is best suited to various types of information. Some typical responses might include

- Line charts—Show changes of something over a period of time
- Bar charts—Describe magnitude or quantity comparisons
- Pie charts—Illustrate the parts of a whole

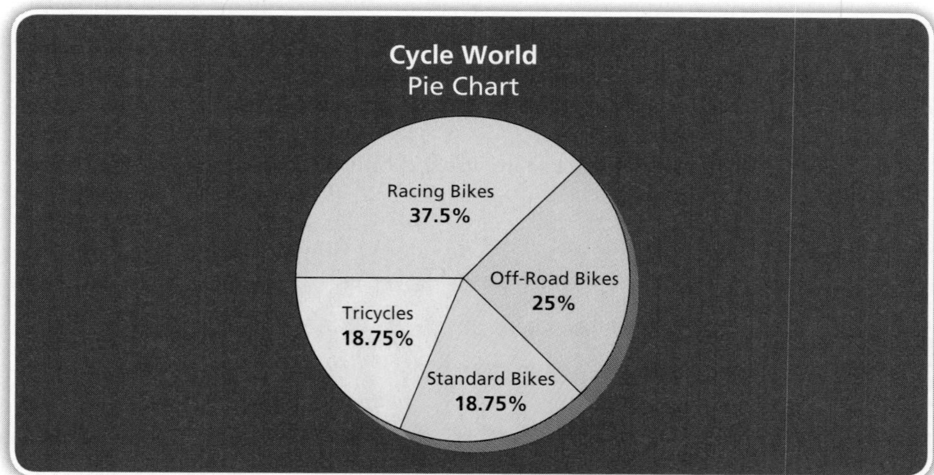

TRY IT EXERCISE 10

From the Interstate Business College enrollment figures in the table on page 789, construct a pie chart illustrating the Winter Term enrollment.

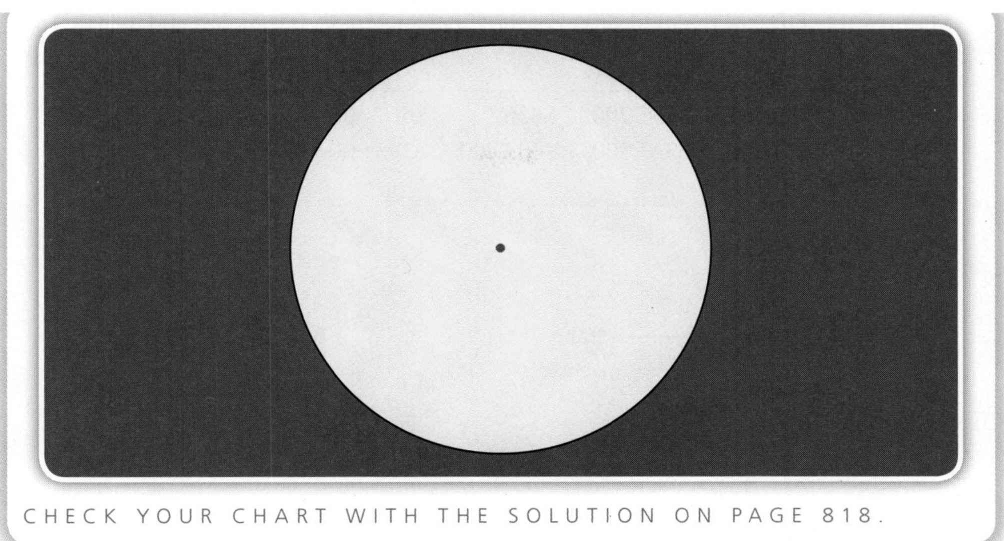

CHECK YOUR CHART WITH THE SOLUTION ON PAGE 818.

Review Exercises

SECTION I 21

As the sales manager for Magnum Enterprises, you have been asked by the president to prepare the following charts for the shareholders' meeting next week. Use the 6-month sales report, Table 21-1 on page 778, as the database for these charts. Calculate totals as required.

1. Single-line chart of the total company sales per month.

	Jan	Feb	Mar	Apr	May	June
Standard	$569,400	$566,200	$636,100	$607,400	$649,700	$706,700
Deluxe	347,400	343,800	408,700	383,900	408,000	431,600
Total	$916,800	$910,000	$1,044,800	$991,300	$1,057,700	$1,138,300

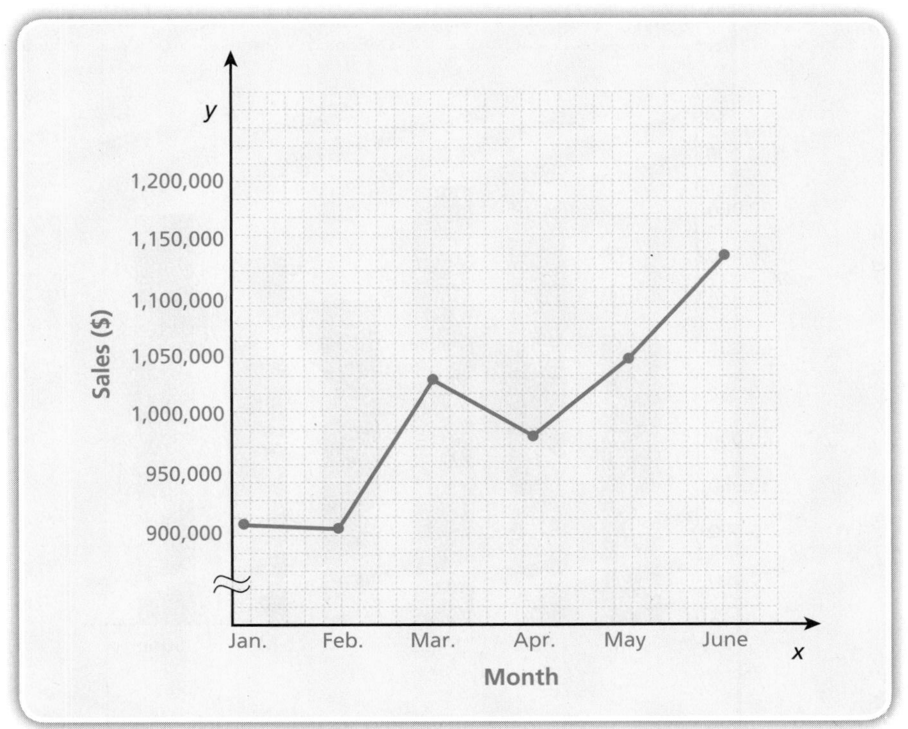

2. Multiple-line chart of the total sales per month of each model, standard and deluxe.

	Jan	Feb	Mar	Apr	May	June
Standard	$569,400	$566,200	$636,100	$607,400	$649,700	$706,700
Deluxe	$347,400	$343,800	$408,700	$383,900	$408,800	$431,600

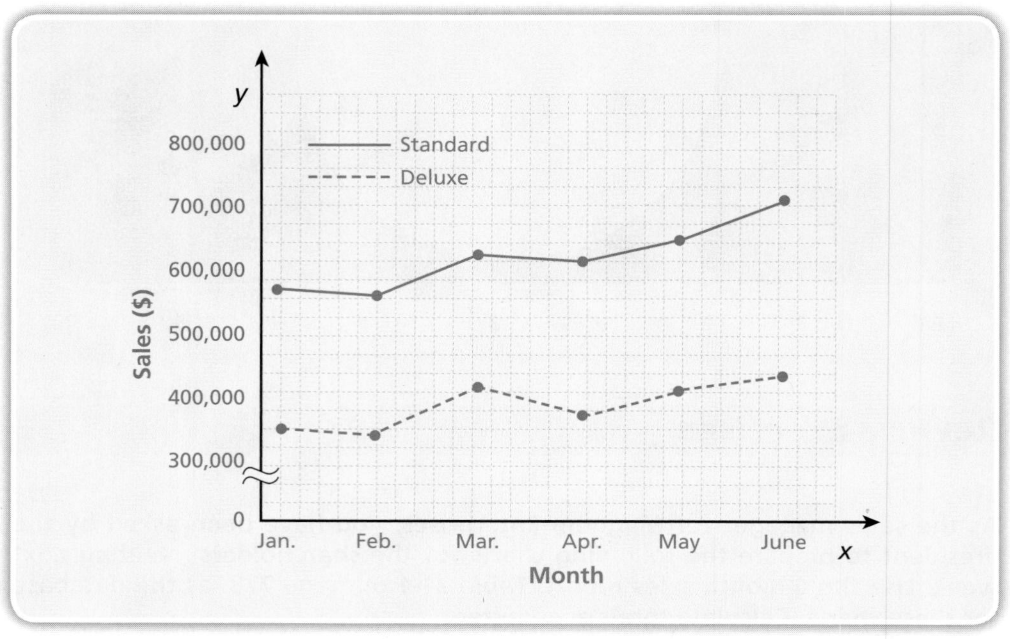

3. Standard bar chart of the deluxe sales per month in the Southeast territory.

Jan	Feb	Mar	Apr	May	June
$88,700	$91,300	$94,500	$70,300	$79,400	$88,600

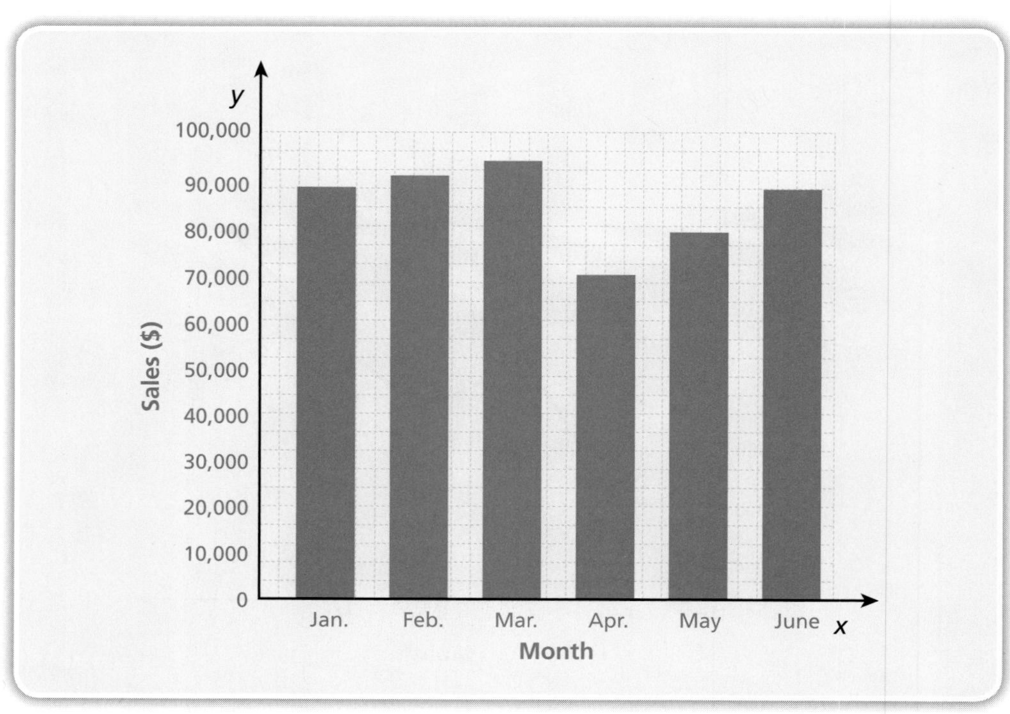

4. Component bar chart of the standard and deluxe model sales as components of total monthly sales in the Northeast territory.

	Jan	Feb	Mar	Apr	May	June
Standard	$214,700	$228,400	$246,600	$239,000	$266,100	$279,300
Deluxe	121,300	133,100	164,800	153,200	185,000	190,100
Total	$336,000	$361,500	$411,400	$392,200	$451,100	$469,400

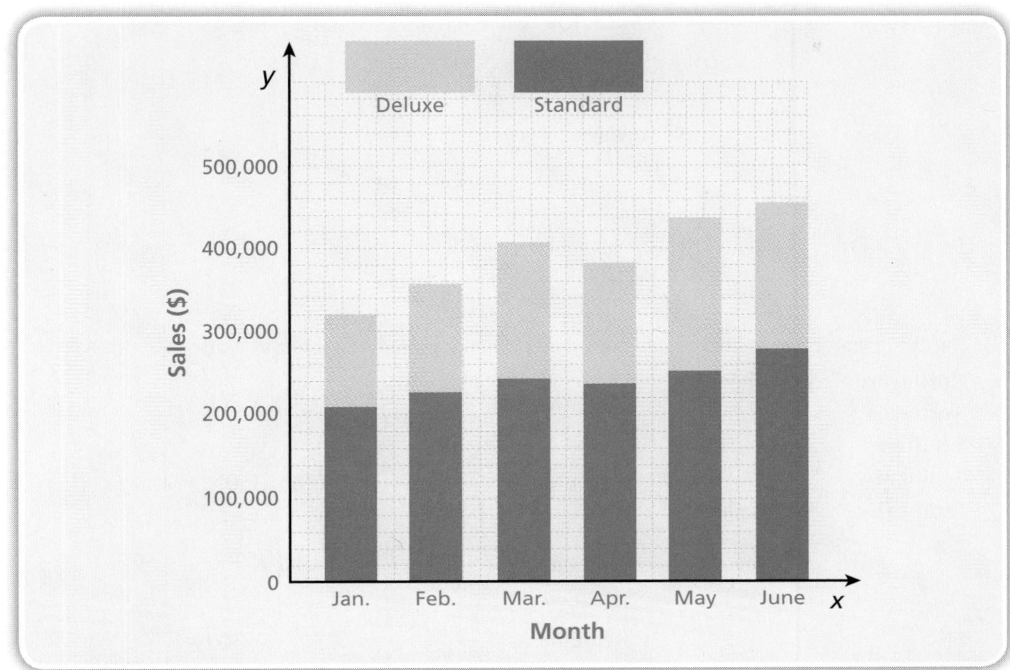

5. Comparative bar chart of the standard and deluxe model sales per month in the Northwest territory.

	Jan	Feb	Mar	Apr	May	June
Standard	$123,200	$115,800	$133,400	$136,700	$112,900	$135,000
Deluxe	86,400	73,700	91,100	92,600	65,300	78,400

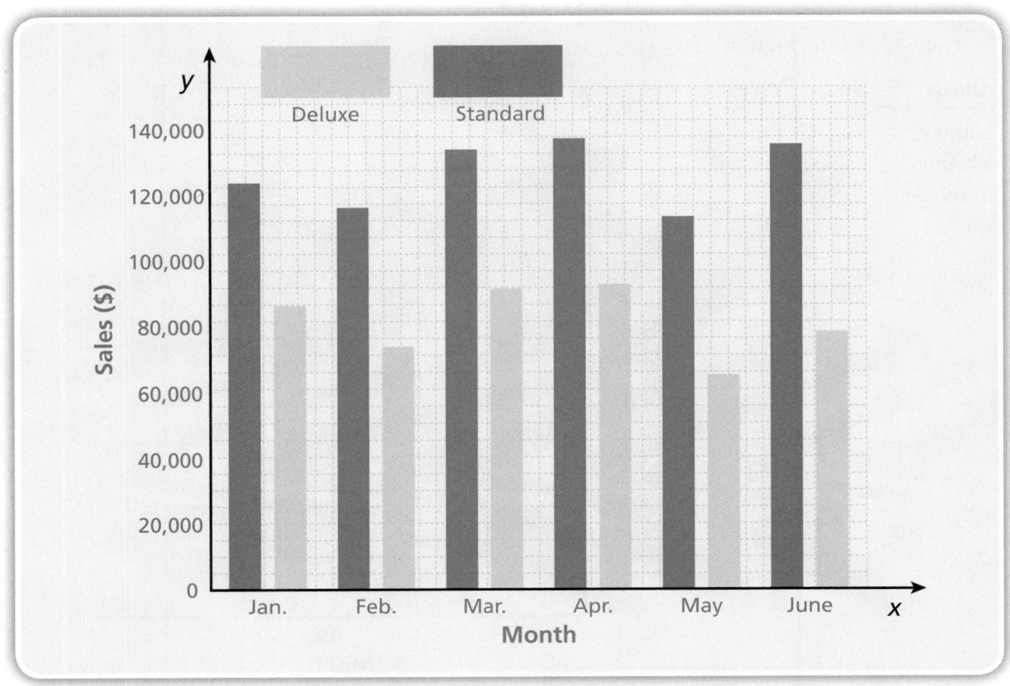

© Stockbyte/Getty Images

Public Relations

Tables, charts, and graphs are used extensively in public relations. Public relations (PR) specialists serve as advocates for businesses, nonprofit associations, universities, hospitals, and other organizations. It is their job to build and maintain positive relationships with the various "publics" their client or employer relies on for support.

Public relations specialists held about 188,000 jobs in 2004. Employment is expected to increase faster than the average for all occupations through 2014. Median annual earnings for salaried PR specialists were $43,830 in 2004. The middle 50 percent earned between $32,970 and $59,360.

6. Pie chart of the total 6-month sales of the four territories.

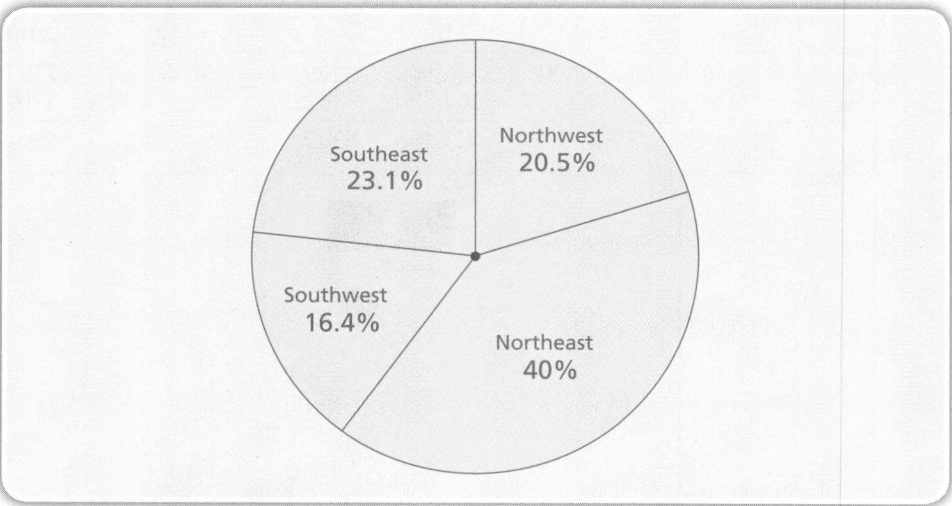

Northwest	$1,244,500
Northeast	2,421,600
Southwest	993,100
Southeast	1,399,700
Total sales	$6,058,900

Northwest $\frac{1,244,500}{6,058,900} = 20.5\% \times 360 = 74°$

Northeast $\frac{2,421,600}{6,058,900} = 40\% \times 360 = 144°$

Southwest $\frac{993,100}{6,058,900} = 16.4\% \times 360 = 59°$

Southeast $\frac{1,399,700}{6,058,900} = 23.1\% \times 360 = 83°$

$360°$

BUSINESS DECISION CHOOSING A CHART

7. You have been asked to prepare a chart of stock prices for the upcoming semiannual stockholders' meeting for Magnum Enterprises. The following table shows Magnum's stock prices on the first day of each month. Choose and prepare a chart that best illustrates this information.

Month	Stock Price
January	$ 35.50
February	$ 32.75
March	$ 37.25
April	$ 38.50
May	$ 40.25
June	$ 39.75

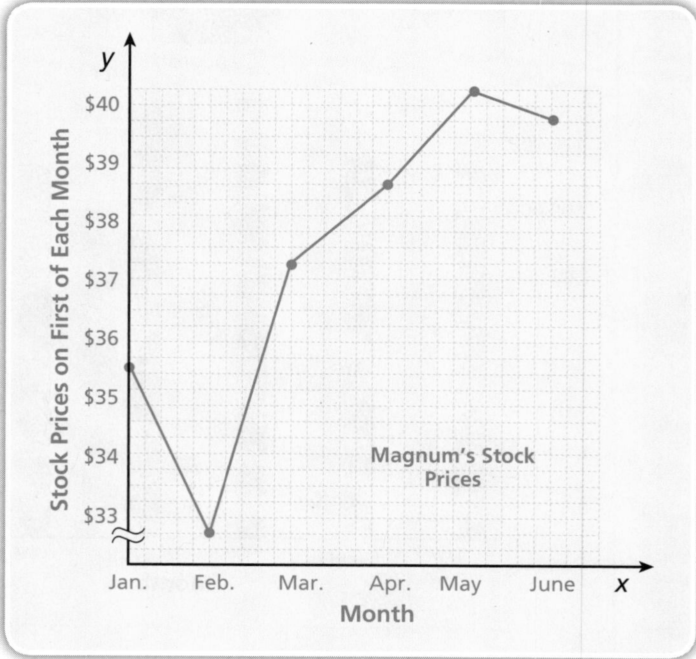

MEASURES OF CENTRAL TENDENCY AND DISPERSION—UNGROUPED DATA

SECTION II 21

A numerical **average** is a value that is representative of a whole set of values. In business, managers use averages extensively to describe or represent a variety of situations. Imagine a payroll director being asked to describe the hourly wages of his 650 factory workers. On the one extreme, he might produce a list of his 650 workers along with their hourly wages. This action answers the question, but it provides too much information. A more appropriate response might be to calculate the average hourly wage and report that "$9.75 was the average hourly wage of the workers."

Because an average is numerically located within the range of values that it represents, averages are often referred to as measures of central tendency. In this section, we study the three most commonly used averages in business statistics: the arithmetic mean, the median, and the mode. We also study a measure of dispersion known as the range.

average A numerical value that is representative of a whole set of values.

CLASSROOM ACTIVITY
Ask students to discuss what *average* means. Point out that *average* can mean "typical" in a nonmathematical sense. Have them describe the "average" student in the class.

CALCULATING THE ARITHMETIC MEAN OF UNGROUPED DATA

The **arithmetic mean** corresponds to the generally accepted meaning of the word *average*. It is customary to abbreviate the term *arithmetic mean* and refer to this average simply as the **mean**.

mean, or arithmetic mean The sum of the values of a set of data divided by the number of values in that set.

STEPS TO CALCULATE THE ARITHMETIC MEAN OF UNGROUPED DATA

Step 1. Find the sum of all the values in the data set.

Step 2. Divide the sum in Step 1 by the number of values in the set.

$$\textbf{Mean of ungrouped data} = \frac{\textbf{Sum of values}}{\textbf{Number of values}}$$

EXAMPLE 11 CALCULATING THE MEAN

Galaxy Travel had daily sales of $4,635 on Monday, $3,655 on Tuesday, $3,506 on Wednesday, $2,870 on Thursday, $4,309 on Friday, and $5,475 on Saturday. What is the mean sales per day?

SOLUTION STRATEGY

To calculate the mean (average sales per day), we find the sum of the values (sales per day) and divide this sum by the number of values (6 days).

$$\text{Mean of ungrouped data} = \frac{\text{Sum of values}}{\text{Number of values}}$$

$$\text{Mean} = \frac{4{,}635 + 3{,}655 + 3{,}506 + 2{,}870 + 4{,}309 + 5{,}475}{6} = \frac{24{,}450}{6} = \underline{\underline{\$4{,}075}}$$

The word *average* is derived from maritime laws dating back to the 16th century. When a cargo vessel was in danger of sinking during a storm at sea, the heavy cargo was usually thrown overboard to save the ship. By law, the cost of the lost or damaged goods was equally divided among all the concerned parties. In French, this practice was known as *avarié*, which later became the English word average!

TRY IT EXERCISE 11

21-6

The attendance figures for a series of management seminars are as follows: 432, 247, 661, 418, and 512. What was the mean number of individuals attending per seminar?

CHECK YOUR ANSWER WITH THE SOLUTION ON PAGE 818.

DETERMINING THE MEDIAN

median The *midpoint* value of a set of data when the numbers are ranked in ascending or descending order.

Another measure of central tendency, and a very useful way of describing a large quantity of data, is the median. The **median** of a set of numbers is the *midpoint* value when the numbers are ranked in ascending or descending order. The median is a more useful measure of central tendency than the mean when one or more of the values of the set is significantly higher or lower than the rest of the set. For example, if the ages of five individuals in a group are 22, 26, 27, 31, and 69, the mean of this set is 35. However, the median is 27, a value that better describes the set.

When there is an odd number of values in the set, the middle value is the median. For example, in a set of seven ranked values, the fourth value is the midpoint. There are three values greater than and three values less than the median.

When there is an even number of values in the set, the median is the midpoint or average between the two middle values. For example, in a set with 10 values, the median is the midpoint between the fifth and the sixth value.

TEACHING TIP
In determining the median of a set of numbers, students often forget to rank the numbers in ascending or descending order.

STEPS TO DETERMINE THE MEDIAN

Step 1. Rank the numbers in ascending or descending order.

Step 2a. For an *odd number of values*—The median is the middle value.

Step 2b. For an *even number of values*—The median is the average or midpoint of the two middle values.

$$\textbf{Median} = \frac{\textbf{Middle value} + \textbf{Middle value}}{\textbf{2}}$$

EXAMPLE 12 DETERMINING THE MEDIAN

Determine the median for the following set of values:

2 8 5 13 11 6 9 15 4

SOLUTION STRATEGY

Step 1. Rank the data in ascending order as follows:

2 4 5 6 8 9 11 13 15

Step 2. Because the number of values in this set is *odd* (nine), there are four values less than and four values greater than the median. Therefore, the median is the fifth value, $\underline{\underline{8}}$.

TRY IT EXERCISE 12

21-7

Determine the median for the following set of values:

4,589 6,558 4,237 2,430 3,619 5,840 1,220

CHECK YOUR ANSWER WITH THE SOLUTION ON PAGE 818.

EXAMPLE 13 DETERMINING THE MEDIAN

Determine the median for the following set of values representing phones sold at a Sprint/Nextel store this week.

56 34 87 12 45 49

SOLUTION STRATEGY

Step 1. Rank the data in ascending order:

12 34 45 49 56 87

Step 2. Because the number of values in this set is *even* (six), the median is the midpoint between the third and the fourth values, 45 and 49.

$$\text{Median} = \frac{\text{Middle value} + \text{Middle value}}{2} = \frac{45+49}{2} = \frac{94}{2} = \underline{\underline{47}}$$

CLASSROOM ACTIVITY

Divide the class into two groups. Have each group calculate the mean, median, and mode of the age of the group members.

Next, have them calculate the same information for the class as a whole. Discuss the difference in the results, if any.

TRY IT EXERCISE 13

Determine the median for the following set of values representing the number of plants sold at Tropical Gardens in the past 10 days.

12 33 42 13 79 29 101 54 76 81

21-8

CHECK YOUR ANSWER WITH THE SOLUTION ON PAGE 818.

DETERMINING THE MODE

The **mode** is the third measure of central tendency that we consider. It is the value or values in a set that occur *most often*. It is possible for a set of data to have more than one mode or no mode at all.

mode The value or values in a set of data that occur *most often*.

STEPS TO DETERMINE THE MODE

Step 1. Count the number of times each value in a set occurs.

Step 2a. If one value occurs more times than any other, it is the mode.

Step 2b. If two or more values occur more times than any other, they are all modes of the set.

Step 2c. If all values occur the same number of times, there is no mode.

One common business application of the mode is in merchandising, in which it is used to keep track of the most frequently purchased goods, as in the following example. Note that the mean and median of this set of data would provide little useful information regarding sales.

In the Business World

The *mode* is used extensively in marketing research to measure the most frequent responses on survey questions. In advertising, the mode translates into persuasive headlines, "4 Out of 5 Doctors Recommend . . . . "

EXAMPLE 14 DETERMINING THE MODE

Find the mode of the following set of values representing the wattage of light bulbs sold in a Home Depot yesterday.

25 25 60 60 60 75 75 75 75 100 100 150

SOLUTION STRATEGY

From these data, we see that the mode is 75 watts, because the value 75 occurs most often. This would indicate to the retailer that 75-watt bulbs were the most frequently purchased.

TRY IT EXERCISE 14

Teaching Transparency 21-9

Calculate the mode of the following set of values representing the size, in gallons, of fish tanks sold at Aquarium Adventures.

10 10 20 10 55 20 10 65 85 20 10 20 55 10 125 55 10 20

CHECK YOUR ANSWER WITH THE SOLUTION ON PAGE 818.

21-8 DETERMINING THE RANGE

range The difference between the lowest and the highest values in a data set; used as a measure of *dispersion*.

Although it does not measure central tendency like the mean, median, and mode, the range is another useful measure in statistics. The **range** is a measure of *dispersion*; it is the difference between the lowest and the highest values in a data set. It is used to measure the scope or broadness of a set of data. A small range indicates that the data in a set are narrow in scope; the values are close to each other. A large range indicates that the data in a set are wide in scope; the values are spread far apart.

CLASSROOM ACTIVITY

"Olympic-type" events are scored by dropping the highest and lowest numbers in the set of judges' scores. Ask students how this can affect the outcome and why this scoring system is used.

Using a hypothetical set of "scores," demonstrate how dropping the highest and lowest numbers changes the mean and range but not the median.

STEPS TO DETERMINE THE RANGE

Step 1. Locate the highest and lowest values in a set of numbers.

Step 2. Subtract the lowest from the highest to get the range.

Range = Highest value − Lowest value

EXAMPLE 15 DETERMINING THE RANGE

Determine the range of the following shirt prices at Vogue Men's Shop.

\$37.95 \$15.75 \$24.75 \$18.50 \$33.75 \$42.50 \$14.95 \$27.95 \$19.95

SOLUTION STRATEGY

To determine the range of shirt prices, subtract the lowest price from the highest price:

Range = Highest value − Lowest value = 42.50 − 14.95 = \$27.55

Note that the range for shirts, $27.55, is relatively large. It might be said that customers shopping in this shirt department have a wide range of prices to choose from.

TRY IT EXERCISE 15

Determine the range of the following temperature readings from the oven at Bon Appétit Bakery.

367° 351° 349° 362° 366° 358° 369° 355° 354°

CHECK YOUR ANSWER WITH THE SOLUTION ON PAGE 818.

 21-10

Review Exercises

SECTION II 21

Calculate the mean of the following sets of values. Round to the nearest tenth when applicable.

1. 4 6 1 8 9 2 3 5 5 6 8 9 10

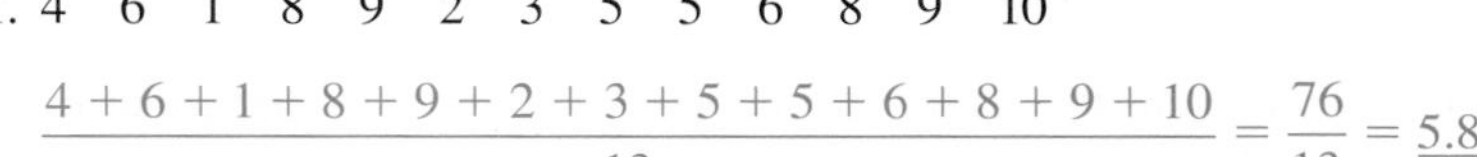

$$\frac{4+6+1+8+9+2+3+5+5+6+8+9+10}{13} = \frac{76}{13} = \underline{\underline{5.8}}$$

2. 324 553 179 213 423 336 190 440 382 111 329 111 397

$$\frac{324+553+179+213+423+336+190+440+382+111+329+111+397}{13}$$

$$= \frac{3{,}988}{13} = \underline{\underline{306.8}}$$

3. .87 .32 1.43 2.3 5.4 3.25 .5

$$\frac{.87+.32+1.43+2.3+5.4+3.25+.5}{7} = \frac{14.07}{7} = \underline{\underline{2}}$$

Determine the median of the following sets of values. Round to the nearest tenth when applicable.

4. 57 38 29 82 71 90 11 94 26 18 18

11 18 18 26 29 (38) 57 71 82 90 94

<u>38</u> is the median.

5. $2.50 $3.25 $4.35 $1.22 $1.67 $4.59

$1.22 $1.67 $2.50 $3.25 $4.35 $4.59

$$\frac{2.50+3.25}{2} = \frac{5.75}{2} = \underline{\underline{\$2.88}}$$

6. 35% 51% 50% 23% 18% 67% 44% 52%

18% 23% 35% 44% 50% 51% 52% 67%

$$\frac{44\% + 50\%}{2} = \underline{\underline{47\%}}$$

In the Business World

Your grade point average (GPA) is actually the *mean* of your grades. It is calculated by assigning a "value" to each grade, such as A=4, B=3, C=2, and multiplying those values by the number of credits earned for each.

The sum of those values divided by the number of credits earned is your GPA.

Determine the mode of the following sets of values.

7. 21 57 46 21 34 76 43 68 21 76 18 12

   12 × 1 (21 × 3) 34 × 1 43 × 1 46 × 1 68 × 1 76 × 2 57 × 1 18 × 1

   The mode is 21.

8. $1,200 $7,300 $4,500 $3,450 $1,675

   $1,200 × 1 $7,300 × 1 $4,500 × 1 $3,450 × 1 $1,675 × 1

   There is no mode in this set.

9. 4 9 3 5 4 7 1 9 9 4 7 1 8 1 4 6 7 4 6 9 9 2

   (4 × 5) (9 × 5) 3 × 1 5 × 1 7 × 3 1 × 3 8 × 1 6 × 2 2 × 1

   4 and 9 are both modes in this set.

Determine the range of the following sets of values.

10. 12 42 54 28 112 76 95 27 36 11 96 109 210

Highest	210
Lowest	− 11
Range	199

11. $2.35 $4.16 $3.42 $1.29 $.89 $4.55

Highest	4.55
Lowest	− .89
Range	$3.66

12. 1,099 887 1,659 1,217 2,969 790

Highest	2,969
Lowest	− 790
Range	2,179

13. The following numbers represent the gallons of chocolate syrup used per month by a Baskin-Robbins to make milk shakes and hot fudge sundaes:

Jan.—225	Feb.—254	March—327	April—370	May—425	June—435
July—446	Aug.—425	Sept.—359	Oct.—302	Nov.—270	Dec.—241

    a. What is the mean of this set of data?

    $$\frac{225 + 254 + 327 + 370 + 425 + 435 + 446 + 425 + 359 + 302 + 270 + 241}{12}$$

    $$\frac{4{,}079}{12} = 339.9$$

    b. What is the median of this set of data?

    225, 241, 254, 270, 302, 327, 359, 370, 425, 425, 435, 446

    $$\frac{327 + 359}{2} = 343$$

    c. What is the mode of this set of data?

    425 occurs twice; it is the mode.

    d. What is the range of this set of data?

    446 − 225 = 221

© Sandy Huffaker/Bloomberg News/Landov

Ice Cream

According to the U.S. Department of Agriculture (USDA) U.S. production of ice cream and related frozen desserts in 2006 amounted to about 1.6 billion gallons, which translates to over 21 quarts per person. Sales of ice cream and related products, one of the U.S. food industry's largest sectors, amounts to over $20 billion per year.

Baskin-Robbins, with more than 5,600 retail stores in over 30 countries, is the world's largest chain of ice cream specialty stores. Major competitors include Dairy Queen, Haagen-Dazs, and Carvel.

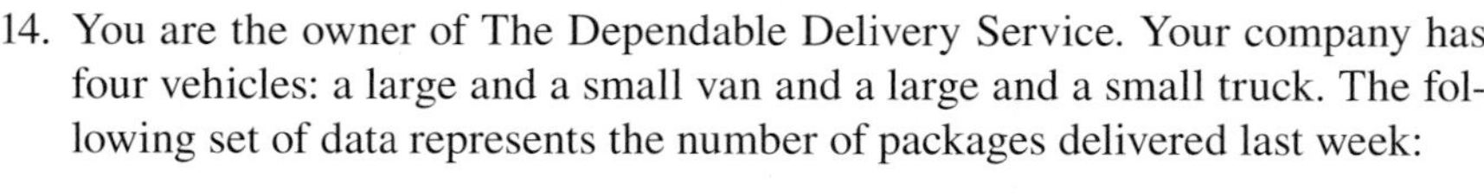

14. You are the owner of The Dependable Delivery Service. Your company has four vehicles: a large and a small van and a large and a small truck. The following set of data represents the number of packages delivered last week:

	Monday	Tuesday	Wednesday	Thursday	Friday
Small Van	67	86	94	101	86
Large Van	142	137	153	165	106
Small Truck	225	202	288	311	290
Large Truck	322	290	360	348	339

a. What is the mean number of packages delivered for each van?

Small van $\frac{67+86+94+101+86}{5} = \underline{\underline{86.8}}$

Large van $\frac{142+137+153+165+106}{5} = \underline{\underline{140.6}}$

b. What is the median number of packages delivered for each truck?

Small truck	202	225	(288)	290	311	Median = 288
Large truck	290	322	(339)	348	360	Median = 339

c. What is the mean number of packages delivered on Monday?

$\frac{67+142+225+322}{4} = \underline{\underline{189}}$

d. What is the median number of packages delivered on Thursday?

101 165 311 348 $\frac{165+311}{2} = \underline{\underline{238}}$

e. What is the mode of all the packages delivered during the week?

86 occurs twice.

290 occurs twice.

These are both modes of this set of numbers.

f. What is the range of all the packages delivered during the week?

Highest 360
Lowest −67
Range 293

CLASSROOM ACTIVITY

Have students apply their knowledge of equations to solve the following "challenge" problem:

Yesterday, a car dealer sold four cars with a *mean* cost of $30,000. If three of the cars were valued at $22,000, $28,000, and $34,000, what was the value of the fourth car?

Solution:

$$\frac{22{,}000+28{,}000+34{,}000+X}{4} = 30{,}000$$

$$\frac{84{,}000+X}{4} = 30{,}000$$

$$84{,}000 + X = 4(30{,}000)$$

$$84{,}000 + X = 120{,}000$$

$$X = 120{,}000 - 84{,}000$$

$$X = \underline{\underline{\$36{,}000}}$$

BUSINESS DECISION INTERPRETING THE NUMBERS

15. You are the manager of a production plant that makes computer hard drives for Digital Masters Corporation. Last week your plant had the following production numbers during a 6-day production run:

2,300 2,430 2,018 2,540 2,675 4,800

a. What is the mean, median, mode, and range of this set of production data?

$$\text{Mean} = \frac{2{,}300+2{,}430+2{,}018+2{,}540+2{,}675+4{,}800}{6}$$

$$= \frac{16{,}763}{6} = \underline{\underline{2{,}793.8}}$$

Mode = No mode

Range = 4,800 − 2,018 = 2,782

Median = 2,018 2,300 2,430 2,540 2,675 4,800

$$= \frac{2{,}430+2{,}540}{2} = \underline{\underline{2{,}485}}$$

b. Which average best describes the production at your plant? Why?

2,485, the median, best describes the production data because the last number is uncharacteristically high. The mean is therefore too high.

SECTION III FREQUENCY DISTRIBUTIONS—GROUPED DATA

ungrouped data Data that have not been grouped into a distribution-type format.

grouped data Data that have been divided into equal-size groups known as classes. Frequently used to represent data when dealing with large amounts of values in a set.

frequency The number of values in each class of a frequency distribution.

In the previous section, the values in the sets are listed individually and are known as **ungrouped data**. Frequently, business statistics deals with hundreds or even thousands of values in a set. In dealing with such a large amount of values, it is often easier to represent the data by dividing the values into equal-size groups known as classes, creating **grouped data**.

The number of values in each class is called the **frequency**, with the resulting chart called a **frequency distribution** or **frequency table**. The purpose of a frequency distribution is to organize large amounts of data into a more compact form without changing the essential information contained in those values.

21-9 CONSTRUCTING A FREQUENCY DISTRIBUTION

STEPS TO CONSTRUCT A FREQUENCY DISTRIBUTION

frequency distribution, or frequency table The chart obtained by dividing data into equal-size classes; used to organize large amounts of data into a more compact form without changing the essential information contained in those values.

Step 1. Divide the data into equal-size classes. Be sure to use a range that includes all values in the set.

Step 2. Use tally marks to record the frequency of values within each class.

Step 3. Rewrite the tally marks for each class numerically in a column labeled "frequency (f)." The data are now grouped.

EXAMPLE 16 CONSTRUCTING A FREQUENCY DISTRIBUTION

From the following ungrouped data representing the weight of packages shipped by Monarch Manufacturing this month, construct a frequency distribution by using classes with an interval of 10 pounds each.

13	16	65	45	44	35	22	46	36	49	56	26
68	27	35	15	43	62	32	57	48	23	43	44

SOLUTION STRATEGY

First, we find the range of the data by subtracting the lowest value, 13, from the highest value, 68. This gives a range of 55 pounds. Second, by using 60 pounds as the range for the classes of our frequency distribution we are sure to include all values in the set. Class intervals of 10 pounds each allow for six equal classes:

Frequency Distribution for Monarch Manufacturing

Class (lb)	Tally	Frequency (f)
10 to 19	III	3
20 to 29	IIII	4
30 to 39	IIII	4
40 to 49	~~IIII~~ III	8
50 to 59	II	2
60 to 69	III	3

CLASSROOM ACTIVITY

In groups, have students work Try It Exercise 16.

Next, have the groups compare answers with those of another group and resolve any differences.

TRY IT EXERCISE 16

You are the manager of The Dress Code Boutique. From the following ungrouped data representing the dollar sales of each transaction at the store today, construct a frequency distribution using classes with an interval of $10 each.

21-11

14	19	55	47	44	39	22	71	35	49	64	22	88	78	16
88	37	29	71	74	62	54	59	18	93	49	74	26	66	75

CHECK YOUR ANSWER WITH THE SOLUTION ON PAGE 818.

CALCULATING THE MEAN OF GROUPED DATA

Just as with ungrouped data, we can calculate the arithmetic mean of grouped data in a frequency distribution. Keep in mind, however, that the means for grouped data are calculated by using the midpoints of each class rather than the actual values of the data and are therefore only approximations. Because the actual values of the data in each class of the distribution are lost, we must make the assumption that the midpoints of each class closely approximate the values in that class. In most cases, this is true because some class values fall below the midpoint and some above, thereby canceling the inaccuracy.

STEPS TO CALCULATE THE MEAN OF A FREQUENCY DISTRIBUTION

Step 1. Add a column to the frequency distribution listing the midpoints of each class. Label it "midpoints" (m).

Step 2. In a column labeled ($f \times m$), multiply the frequency for each class by the midpoint of that class.

Step 3. Find the sum of the frequency column.

Step 4. Find the sum of the ($f \times m$) column.

Step 5. Find the mean by dividing the sum of the ($f \times m$) column by the sum of the frequency column.

$$\textbf{Mean of grouped data} = \frac{\textbf{Sum of (frequency} \times \textbf{midpoint)}}{\textbf{Sum of frequency}}$$

EXAMPLE 17 CALCULATING THE MEAN OF GROUPED DATA

21-11

Calculate the mean of the grouped data from the frequency distribution for Monarch Manufacturing in the previous example.

SOLUTION STRATEGY

Begin by attaching the midpoint (m) and frequency $\times$ midpoint ($f \times m$) columns to the frequency distribution as follows:

Frequency Distribution for Monarch Manufacturing

Class (lb)	Tally	Frequency (f)	Midpoint (m)	$f \times m$
10 to 19	|||	3	14.5	43.5
20 to 29	||||	4	24.5	98.0
30 to 39	||||	4	34.5	138.0
40 to 49	~~||||~~ |||	8	44.5	356.0
50 to 59	||	2	54.5	109.0
60 to 69	|||	3	64.5	193.5
		24		938.0

After finding the sum of the frequency and $f \times m$ columns, use these sums to calculate the mean of the grouped data:

$$\text{Mean of grouped data} = \frac{\text{Sum of (frequency} \times \text{midpoint)}}{\text{Sum of frequency}} = \frac{938}{24} = \underline{\underline{39.1 \text{ lb}}}$$

TRY IT EXERCISE 17

From the frequency distribution previously prepared in Try It Exercise 16 for The Dress Code Boutique, calculate the mean of the grouped data.

CHECK YOUR ANSWER WITH THE SOLUTION ON PAGE 819.

21-11 PREPARING A HISTOGRAM OF A FREQUENCY DISTRIBUTION

histogram A special type of bar chart, without space between the bars, which is used to display the data from a frequency distribution.

A **histogram** is a special type of bar chart that is used in business to display the data from a frequency distribution. A histogram is drawn in the same way as a standard bar chart but without space between the bars.

STEPS TO PREPARE A HISTOGRAM OF A FREQUENCY DISTRIBUTION

Step 1. Locate the classes of the frequency distribution adjacent to each other along the x-axis, increasing from left to right.

Step 2. Evenly space the frequencies on the y-axis, increasing from bottom to top.

Step 3. Plot the frequency for each class in the form of a rectangular bar whose top edge is opposite the frequency of that class on the y-axis.

EXAMPLE 18 PREPARING A HISTOGRAM

Prepare a histogram from the Monarch Manufacturing frequency distribution above.

SOLUTION STRATEGY

On page 807 is the histogram prepared from the data in the Monarch Manufacturing frequency distribution. Note that the x-axis displays the adjacent classes and the y-axis displays their frequencies.

Because a frequency distribution has classes whose numbers are continuous, the histogram bars depicting that distribution are made to look continuous by drawing them adjacent to each other—no space between them.

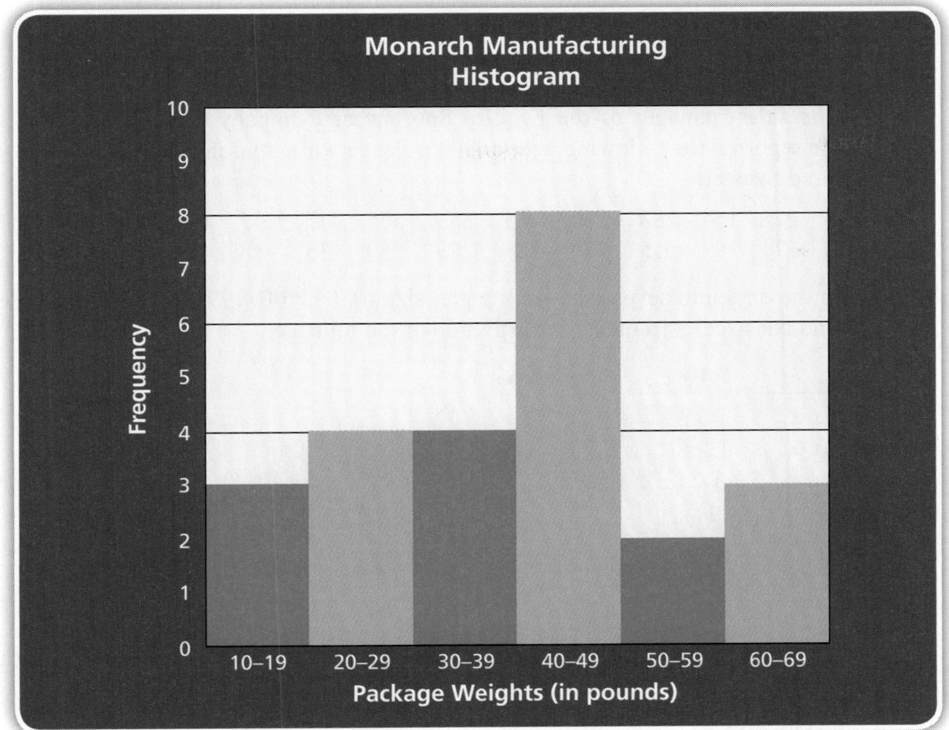

TRY IT EXERCISE 18

Using the grid provided below, construct a histogram from the data in The Dress Code Boutique frequency distribution you prepared in Try It Exercise 16.

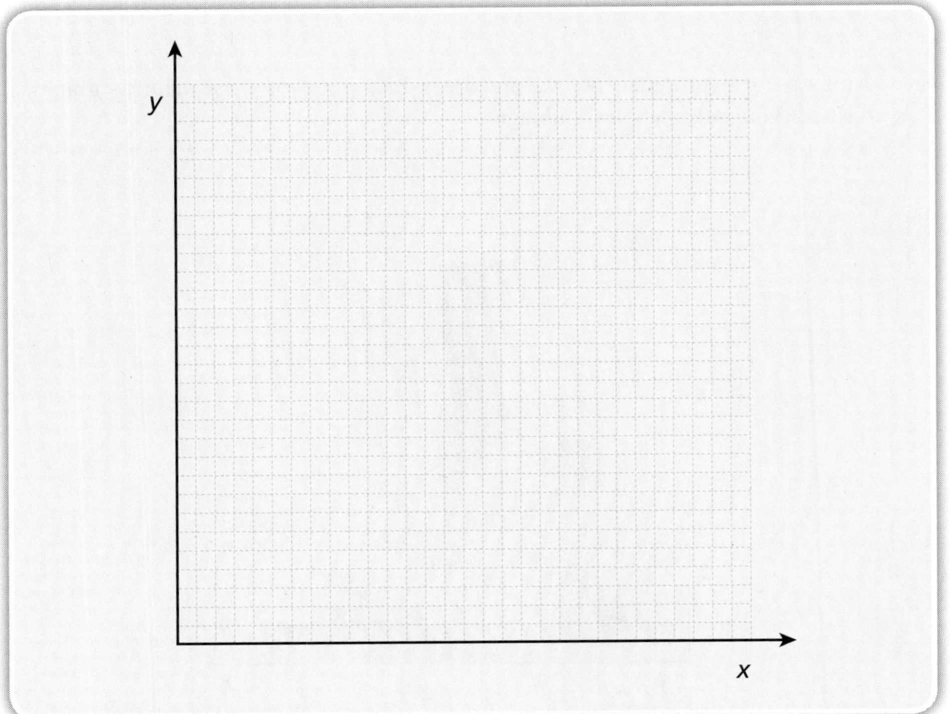

CHECK YOUR HISTOGRAM WITH THE SOLUTION ON PAGE 819.

SECTION III Review Exercises

1. You are the sales manager of the Esquire Sportswear Company. Last week, your 30 salespeople reported the following automobile mileage while making sales calls to retail stores around the state:

385	231	328	154	283	86	415	389	575	117	75	173	247	316	357
211	432	271	93	515	376	328	183	359	136	88	438	282	375	637

a. Group the data into seven classes of equal size (0–99, 100–199, 200–299, 300–399, etc.) and construct a frequency distribution of the mileage.

Class	Tally	Frequency
0–99	||||	4
100–199	~~||||~~	5
200–299	~~||||~~ |	6
300–399	~~||||~~ ||||	9
400–499	|||	3
500–599	||	2
600–699	|	1

b. Calculate the mean of the grouped data by using 49.5, 149.5, 249.5, etc., as the midpoints.

Class	Tally	Frequency (f)	Midpoint (m)	$f \times m$
0–99	||||	4	49.5	198.0
100–199	~~||||~~	5	149.5	747.5
200–299	~~||||~~ |	6	249.5	1,497.0
300–399	~~||||~~ ||||	9	349.5	3,145.5
400–499	|||	3	449.5	1,348.5
500–599	||	2	549.5	1,099.0
600–699	|	1	649.5	649.5
		30		8,685.0

$$\text{Mean} = \frac{8{,}685}{30} = \underline{\underline{289.5}}$$

c. Using the grid provided below, prepare a histogram of these data to graphically illustrate your salespeoples' mileage.

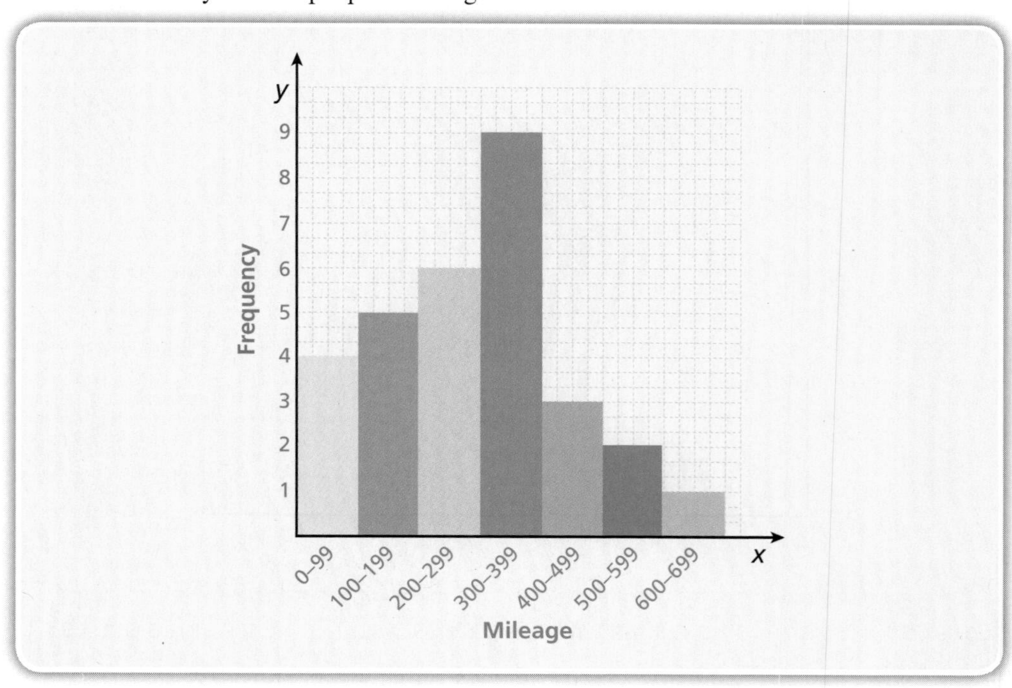

2. You are the owner of the Brava Java Cyber Café. As part of a marketing effort to increase the "average sale" per customer, you recently did a survey of the lunch-hour sales receipts for a busy Saturday. The following are the results of that survey.

\$4.15	\$5.60	\$4.95	\$6.70	\$5.40	\$7.15	\$6.45	\$8.25	\$7.60	\$6.25
\$5.50	\$4.90	\$7.60	\$6.40	\$7.75	\$5.25	\$6.70	\$8.45	\$7.10	\$8.80
\$9.65	\$8.40	\$6.50	\$5.25	\$6.75	\$8.50	\$5.35	\$6.80	\$4.25	\$9.95

a. Group the sales receipts into six classes of equal size (\$4.00–\$4.99, \$5.00–\$5.99, etc.) and construct a frequency distribution.

Class	Tally	Frequency
\$4.00–4.99	IIII	4
5.00–5.99	~~IIII~~ I	6
6.00–6.99	~~IIII~~ III	8
7.00–7.99	~~IIII~~	5
8.00–8.99	~~IIII~~	5
9.00–9.99	II	2

b. Calculate the mean of the grouped data.

Class	Tally	Frequency (f)	Midpoint (m)	$f \times m$
\$4.00–4.99	IIII	4	4.495	17.980
5.00–5.99	~~IIII~~ I	6	5.495	32.970
6.00–6.99	~~IIII~~ III	8	6.495	51.960
7.00–7.99	~~IIII~~	5	7.495	37.475
8.00–8.99	~~IIII~~	5	8.495	42.475
9.00–9.99	II	2	9.495	18.990
		30		201.850

$$\text{Mean} = \frac{201.85}{30} = \underline{\underline{\$6.73}}$$

c. Using the grid provided below, prepare a histogram of the sales receipts.

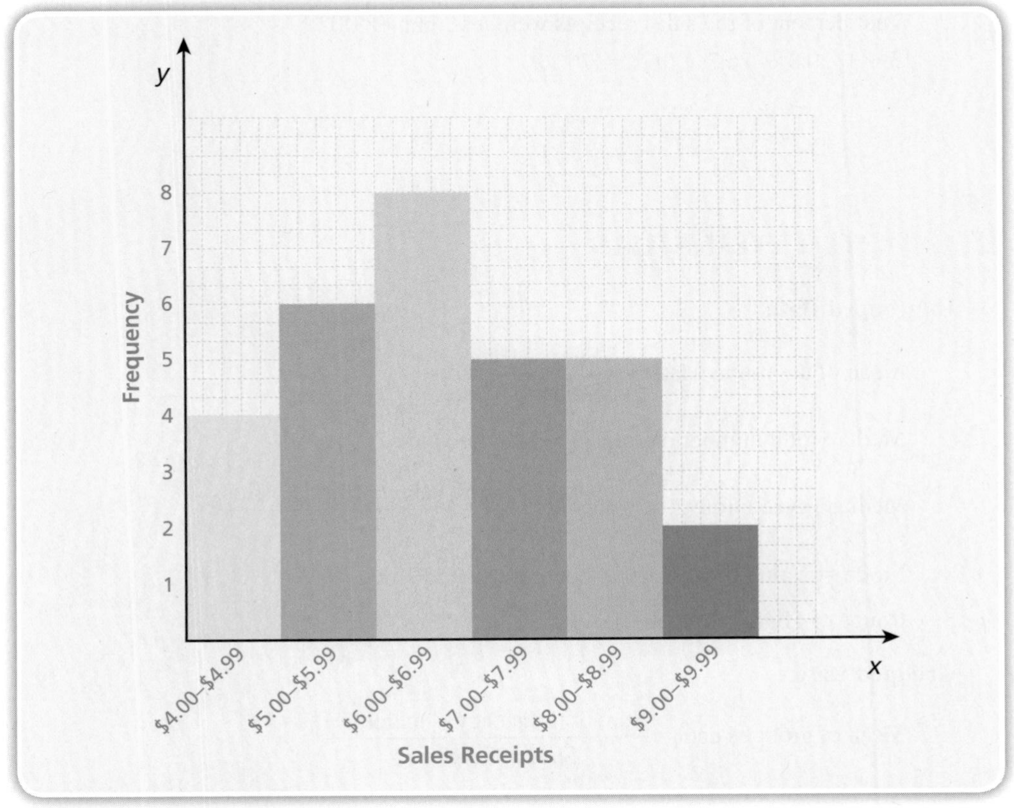

© R. Alcorn/Cengage

The trend today is for coffee establishments to provide wireless Internet connections for their customers.

BUSINESS DECISION RELATIVE FREQUENCY DISTRIBUTION

3. In business, percents are frequently used to express the number of observations in a frequency distribution of business data. A **relative frequency distribution** expresses the distribution as percents. To convert a frequency distribution to a relative frequency distribution, each of the class frequencies (portion) is divided by the total number of observations (base). Remember, Rate = Portion ÷ Base.

a. From the frequency distribution you constructed for Brava Java Café in Exercise 2a, convert each class frequency to a relative class frequency; percents. Round your answers to tenths.

Class	Frequency (from 2a.)	Relative frequency
$4.00–4.99	4	13.3%
5.00–5.99	6	20.0
6.00–6.99	8	26.7
7.00–7.99	5	16.7
8.00–8.99	5	16.7
9.00–9.99	2	6.7
	Total 30	100.1%*

*due to rounding

b. What percent of the sales receipts were paid between $5.00 and $5.99?
20%

c. What percent of the sales receipts were $7.00 or more?
16.7 + 16.7 + 6.7 = 40.1%

d. What percent of the sales receipts were less than $8.00?
13.3 + 20.0 + 26.7 + 16.7 = 76.7%

CHAPTER FORMULAS

Ungrouped Data

$$\text{Mean of ungrouped data} = \frac{\text{Sum of values}}{\text{Number of values}}$$

Median (odd number of values) = Middle value

$$\text{Median (even number of values)} = \frac{\text{Middle value} + \text{Middle value}}{2}$$

Mode = Value or values that occur most frequently

Range = Highest value − Lowest value

Grouped Data

$$\text{Mean of grouped data} = \frac{\text{Sum of (frequency} \times \text{midpoint)}}{\text{Sum of frequency}}$$

SUMMARY CHART

Section I: Data Interpretation and Presentation

Topic	Important Concepts	Illustrative Examples

Reading and Interpreting Information from a Table
P/O 21-1, p. 778

Tables are a collection of related data arranged for ease of reference or comparison, usually in parallel columns with meaningful titles. They are a very useful tool in summarizing statistical data and are found everywhere in business.

Reading tables:

1. Scan the titles above the columns for the category of information being sought.
2. Look down the column for the specific fact required.

FRIENDLY AUTO SALES
90-Day Sales Report
($000)

	April	May	June
Autos	56	61	64
Trucks	68	58	66
Parts	32	41	37
Total	156	160	167

Reading and Constructing a Line Chart
P/O 21-2, p. 779

Charts are used to display a picture of the relationships among selected data. Line charts show data changing over a period of time. They are a graph of a series of data points on a grid, continuously connected by straight lines.

Reading line charts:

1. Scan either the x- or y-axis for the known variable; x for time or y for amount.
2. Draw a perpendicular line from that axis to the point where it intersects the chart.
3. Draw a line from that point perpendicular to the opposite axis.
4. The answer is read where that line intersects the opposite axis.

Constructing line charts:

1. Evenly space and label the time variable on the x-axis.
2. Evenly space and label the amount variable on the y-axis.
3. Show each data point by placing a dot above the time period and across from the corresponding amount.
4. Connect the plotted points with straight lines to form the chart.
5. Lines should be differentiated by various line patterns or colors.

Single-Line Chart

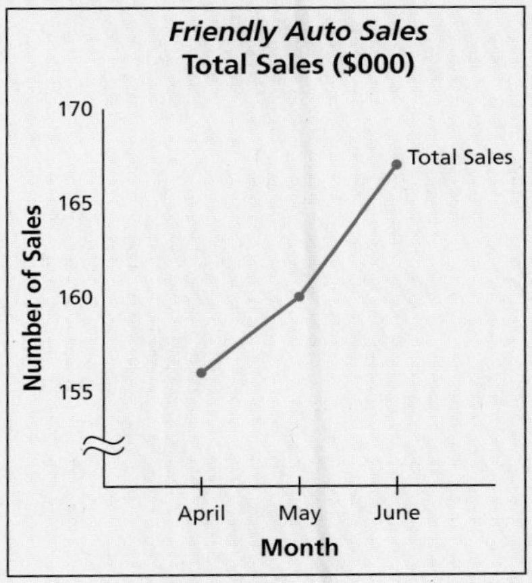

Multiple-Line Chart

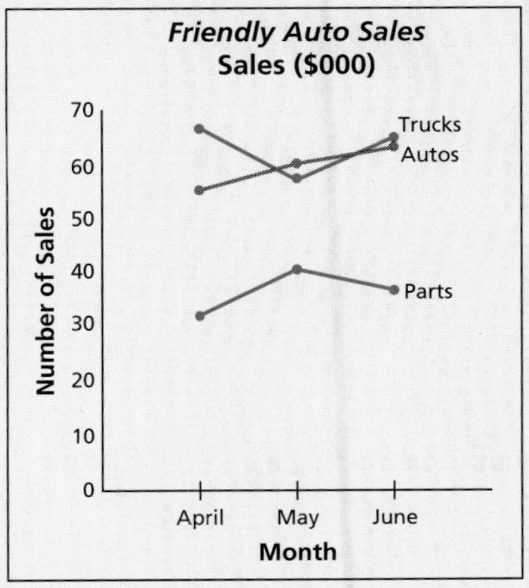

Section I: (continued)

<table>
<tr><th>Topic</th><th>Important Concepts</th><th>Illustrative Examples</th></tr>
<tr><td>Reading and Constructing a Bar Chart
P/O 21-3, p. 784</td><td>Bar charts represent data by the length of horizontal bars or vertical columns. As with line charts, bar charts often illustrate increases or decreases in magnitude of a certain variable, or the relationship between similar variables.
Comparative bar charts illustrate two or more related variables. In this chart, the bars of the related variables are drawn next to each other but do not touch.
Component bar charts illustrate parts of something that add to a total. Each bar is divided into components stacked on top of each other and shaded or colored differently.
Reading bar charts:
1. Scan the x- or y-axis for a known variable.
2. Read the answer on the opposite axis directly across from the top of the appropriate bar.
Constructing bar charts:
1. Evenly space and label the x-axis. The space between bars should be one-half the width of the bars.
2. Evenly space and label the y-axis.
3. Draw each bar up from the x-axis to the point opposite the y-axis that corresponds to its value.
4. For comparative and component bar charts, differentiate the bars by color or shading pattern.</td><td>Standard Bar Chart
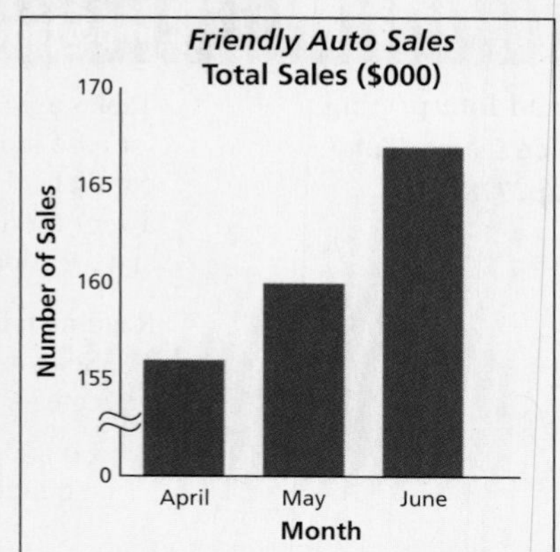

Comparative Bar Chart
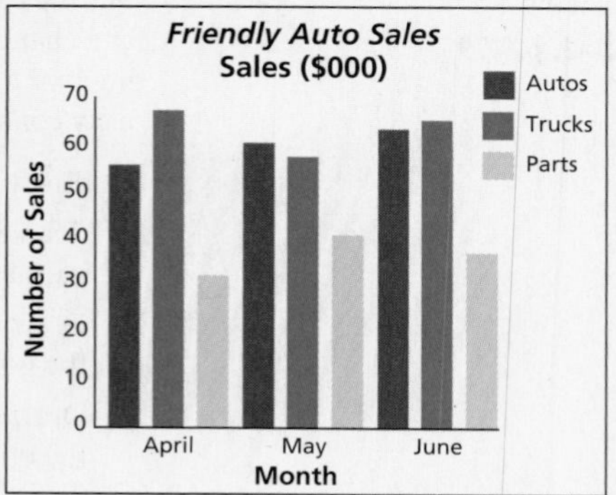

Component Bar Chart
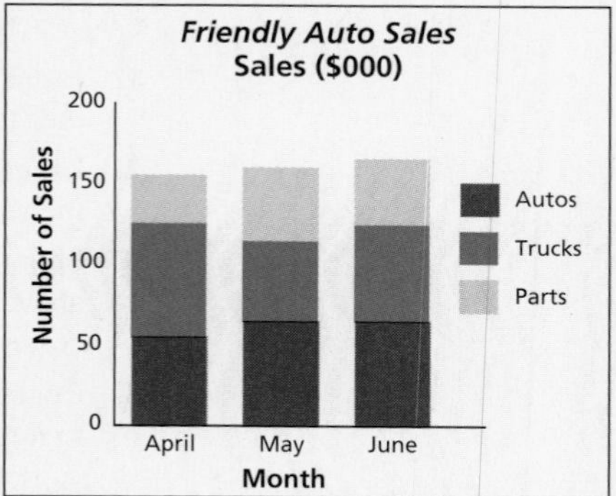
</td></tr>
<tr><td>Reading and Constructing a Pie Chart
P/O 21-4, p. 790</td><td>The pie chart is a circle divided into sections representing the component parts of a whole, usually in percentage terms.
Constructing pie charts:
1. Convert the amount of each component to a percent using the formula Rate = Portion ÷ Base. Let the percentage be the amount of each component, and the base the total amount. Round each percent to hundredths.</td><td>$\text{April} = \frac{156}{483} = .323 = 32.3\%$
$\text{April} = .323 \times 360° = 116°$
$\text{May} = \frac{160}{483} = .331 = 33.1\%$
$\text{May} = .331 \times 360° = 119°$
$\text{June} = \frac{167}{483} = .346 = 34.6\%$
$\text{June} = .346 \times 360° = 125°$</td></tr>
</table>

Section I: (continued)

Topic	Important Concepts	Illustrative Examples
	2. Because a full circle is made up of 360° representing 100%, multiply each component's percent (decimal form) by 360° to determine how many degrees each component's slice will be. Round to the nearest whole degree. 3. Draw a circle with a compass and mark the center. 4. Using a protractor, mark off the number of degrees on the circle that represents each component. 5. Connect each point on the circle with the center by a straight line to form a segment or slice for each component. 6. Label the segments clearly by name, color, or shading.	*Pie Chart* 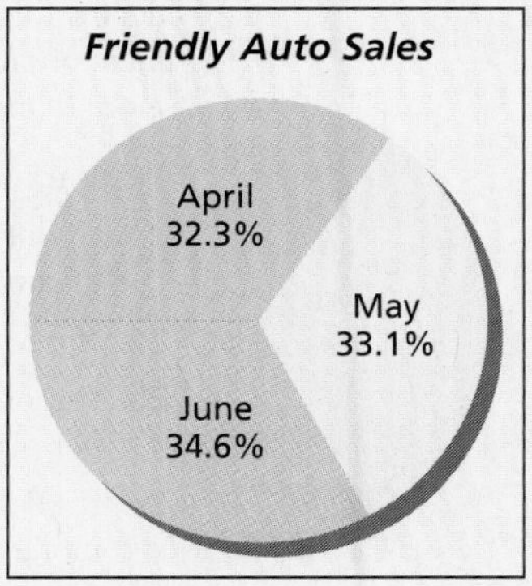 ***Friendly Auto Sales*** April 32.3% May 33.1% June 34.6%

Section II: Measure of Central Tendency and Dispersion—Ungrouped Data

Topic	Important Concepts	Illustrative Examples
Calculating the Arithmetic Mean of Ungrouped Data P/O 21-5, p. 797	A numerical average is a value that is representative of a whole set of values. The arithmetic mean corresponds to the generally accepted meaning of the word *average*. Computing the mean: 1. Find the sum of all the values in the set. 2. Divide by the number of values in the set. $\text{Mean} = \frac{\text{Sum of values}}{\text{Number of values}}$	If a grocery store had sales of \$4,600 on Monday, \$3,650 on Tuesday, and \$3,500 on Wednesday, what is the mean sales for the 3 days? $\text{Mean} = \frac{4,600 + 3,650 + 3,500}{3}$ $= \frac{11,750}{3} = \underline{\underline{\$3,916.67}}$
Calculating the Median P/O 21-6, p. 798	Another measure of central tendency, and a very useful way of describing a large quantity of data, is the median. The median of a set of numbers is the *midpoint* value when the numbers are ranked in increasing or decreasing order. Determining the median: 1. Rank the numbers in increasing or decreasing order. 2a. For an *odd number* of values in the set, the median is the middle value. 2b. For an *even number* of values in the set, the median is the average or midpoint of the two middle values. $\text{Median} = \frac{\text{Middle value} + \text{Middle value}}{2}$	Find the median for the following set of values: 2 8 5 13 11 6 9 15 4 Rank the data as follows: 2 4 5 6 8 9 11 13 15 Because the number of values in the set is odd (nine), the median is the middle value, $\underline{\underline{8}}$. Find the median for the following set of values: 56 34 87 12 45 49 Rank the data as follows: 12 34 45 49 56 87 Because the number of values in this set is even (six), the median is the midpoint between the third and the fourth values, 45 and 49. $\text{Median} = \frac{45 + 49}{2} = \frac{94}{2} = \underline{\underline{47}}$

Section II: (Continued)

Topic	Important Concepts	Illustrative Examples
Determining the Mode **P/O 21-7, p. 799**	The mode is the third measure of central tendency. It is the value or values in a set that occur most often. It is possible for a set of data to have more than one mode or no mode at all. Determining the mode: 1. Count the number of times each value in a set occurs. 2a. If one value occurs most often, it is the mode. 2b. If more than one value occur the same number of times, they are all modes of the set. 2c. If all values occur only once, there is no mode.	Find the mode of the following set representing television screen sizes sold in a Circuit City store yesterday: 25 25 27 25 17 19 12 12 17 25 17 5 25 Because the value 25 occurs most often, the mode is 25 inches.
Determining the Range **P/O 21-8, p. 800**	The range is a measure of dispersion, equal to the difference between the lowest and the highest values in a set. It is used to measure the scope or broadness of a set of data. Determining the range: 1. Locate the highest and lowest values in a set of numbers. 2. Subtract these values to determine the range. **Range = Highest value − Lowest value**	Find the range of the following modem prices at Computers USA: 237 215 124 185 375 145 199 Highest = \$375 Lowest = \$124 Range = 375 − 124 = \$251

Section III: Frequency Distributions—Grouped Data

Topic	Important Concepts	Illustrative Examples
Constructing a Frequency Distribution **P/O 21-9, p. 804**	Business statistics frequently deals with hundreds or even thousands of values in a set. In dealing with large amounts of values, it is often easier to represent the data by dividing the values into equal-size groups known as classes, forming grouped data. The number of values in each class is called the frequency, with the resulting chart called a frequency distribution. Constructing a frequency distribution: 1. Divide the data into equal-size classes. Be sure to use a range that includes all values in the set. 2. Use tally marks to record the frequency of values within each class. 3. Rewrite the tally marks for each class numerically in a column labeled "frequency (f)." The data are now grouped.	The following ungrouped data represent the number of sales calls made by the sales force of Northwest Supply Company last month. Construct a frequency distribution of these data by using six equal classes with an interval of ten. 13 26 65 45 44 35 46 36 49 56 16 68 27 35 43 62 32 57 23 43 44 **Class** / **Tally** / **Freq (f)** 10 to 19 / II / 2 20 to 29 / III / 3 30 to 39 / IIII / 4 40 to 49 / ~~IIII~~ II / 7 50 to 59 / II / 2 60 to 69 / III / 3
Computing the Mean of Grouped Data **P/O 21-10, p. 805**	Calculating the mean of a frequency distribution: 1. Add a column to the frequency distribution listing the midpoints (m) of each class.	Calculate the mean number of sales calls for Northwest Supply. The mean of the grouped data is computed by first attaching the midpoint (m) and frequency × midpoint ($f \times m$) columns to the frequency distribution as follows:

Section III: (continued)

<table>
<tr><th>Topic</th><th>Important Concepts</th><th>Illustrative Examples</th></tr>
<tr>
<td></td>
<td>2. In a column labeled ($f \times m$), multiply the frequency for each class by the midpoint of that class.
3. Find the sum of the frequency column.
4. Find the sum of the ($f \times m$) column.
5. Find the mean by dividing the sum of the ($f \times m$) column by the sum of the frequency column.

$$\text{Mean} = \frac{\text{Sum of } (f \times m)}{\text{Sum of frequencies}}$$</td>
<td>
<table>
<tr><th>Class</th><th>Freq (f)</th><th>Midpt (m)</th><th>$f \times m$</th></tr>
<tr><td>10–19</td><td>2</td><td>14.5</td><td>29.0</td></tr>
<tr><td>20–29</td><td>3</td><td>24.5</td><td>73.5</td></tr>
<tr><td>30–39</td><td>4</td><td>34.5</td><td>138.0</td></tr>
<tr><td>40–49</td><td>7</td><td>44.5</td><td>311.5</td></tr>
<tr><td>50–59</td><td>2</td><td>54.5</td><td>109.0</td></tr>
<tr><td>60–69</td><td>3</td><td>64.5</td><td>193.5</td></tr>
<tr><td></td><td>21</td><td></td><td>854.5</td></tr>
</table>
$$\text{Mean} = \frac{854.5}{21} = \underline{\underline{40.7 \text{ calls}}}$$
</td>
</tr>
<tr>
<td>Preparing a Histogram of a Frequency Distribution
P/O 21-11, p. 806</td>
<td>A histogram is a special type of bar chart that is used in business to display the data from a frequency distribution. A histogram is drawn in the same way as a standard bar chart except there are no spaces between the bars.
Constructing a histogram:
1. Locate the classes of the frequency distribution adjacent to each other along the x-axis, increasing from left to right.
2. Evenly space the frequencies on the y-axis, increasing from bottom to top.
3. Plot each class's frequency in the form of a rectangular bar whose top edge is opposite the frequency of that class on the y-axis.</td>
<td>Histogram
</td>
</tr>
</table>

TRY IT EXERCISE SOLUTIONS FOR CHAPTER 21

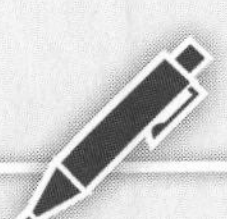

1. a. Standard units—February—Northeast = $\underline{\underline{\$228,400}}$

b. Deluxe units—April—Southeast = $\underline{\underline{\$70,300}}$

c. Total sales—May and June—Northwest

May = 112,900 + 65,300 = 178,200

June = 135,000 + 78,400 = 213,400

Total $\underline{\underline{\$391,600}}$

d. Months with increase in standard unit sales—Southwest

$\underline{\underline{\text{March, April, May, June}}}$

e. April—Deluxe = 92,600 + 153,200 + 67,800 + 70,300 = 383,900

May—Deluxe = 65,300 + 185,000 + 78,300 + 79,400 = 408,000

408,000 − 383,900 = $\underline{\underline{\$24,100}}$

f. $$\text{Northwest—Percent standard units} = \frac{\text{Standard units}}{\text{Total units}}$$

$$\text{Northwest—Percent standard units} = \frac{757,000}{1,244,500} = .6082 = \underline{\underline{60.8\%}}$$

2. **a.** 2005
   b. $2.6 million
   c. 20 million TV sets
   d. 2005

3.

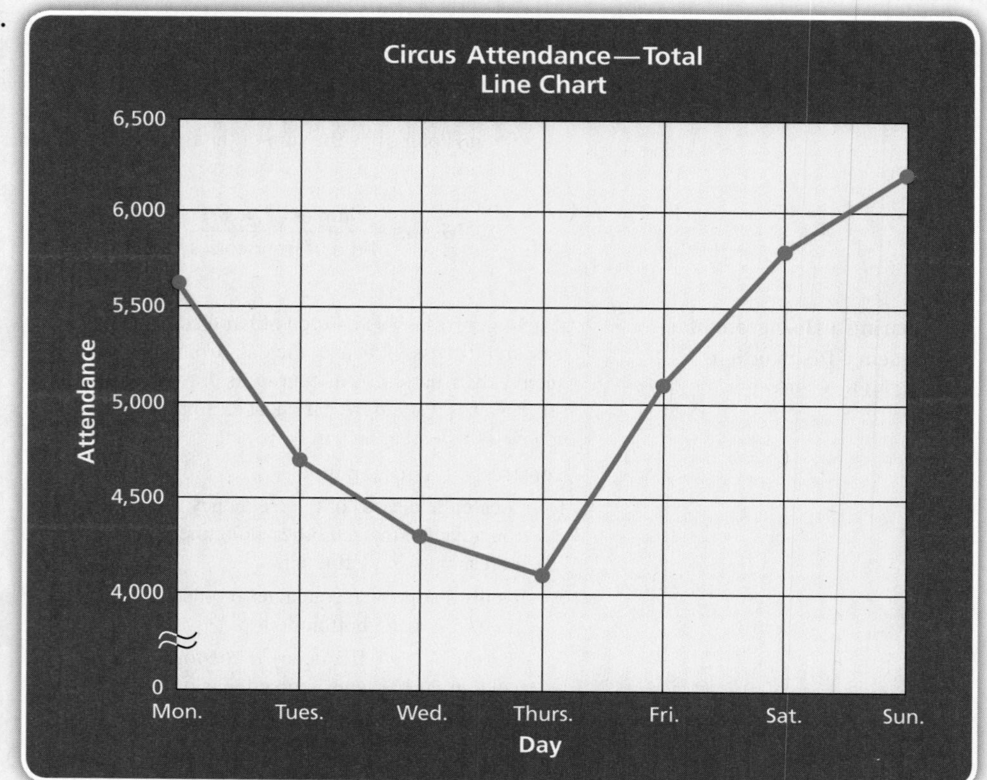

4.

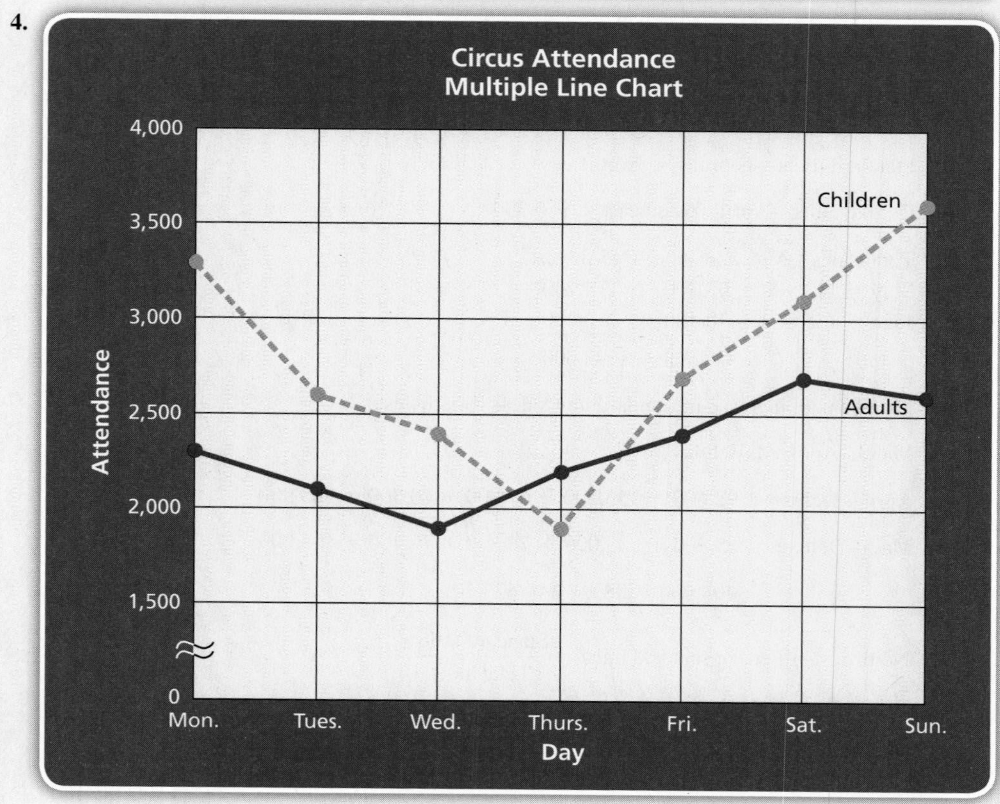

5. **a.** 17.6 million students
   b. 2010
   c. ’85–’86
   d. $5,500
   e. 4-year private, 4-year public, and 2-year public college
   f. $3,100

6.

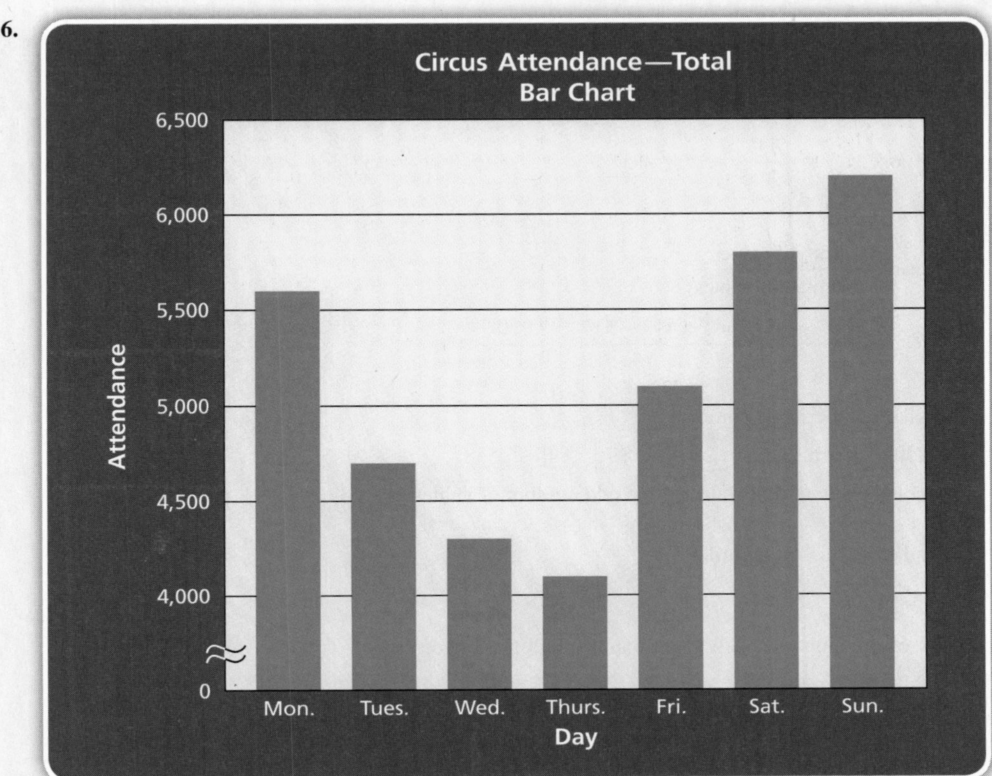

7.

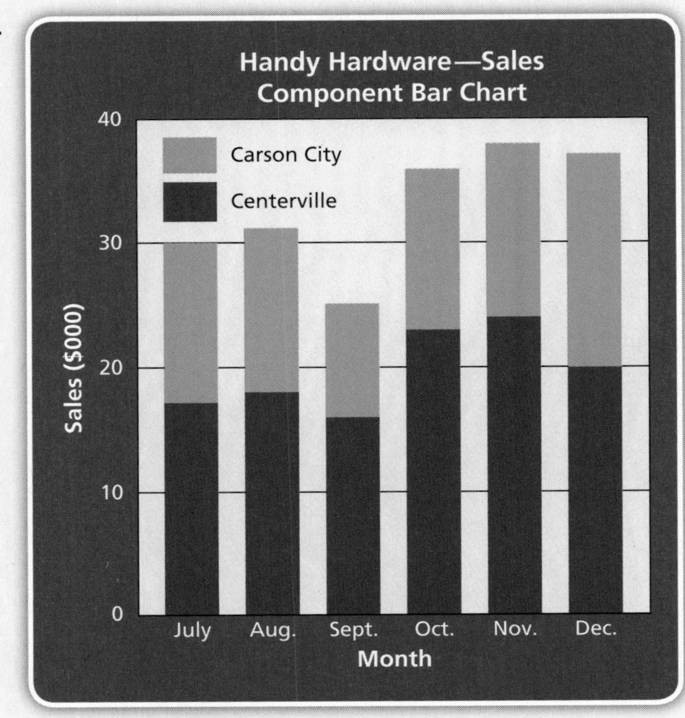

8.

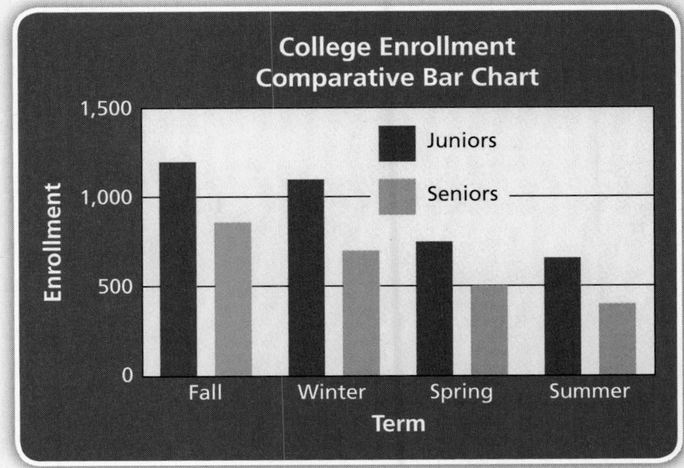

9. a. 10.2%

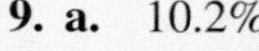

b. Yum Brands; KFC, Pizza Hut, and Taco Bell

c. $1.595 billion

10.

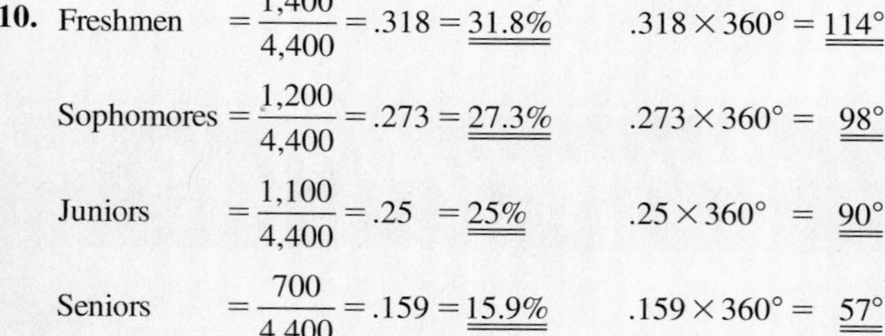

$$\text{Freshmen} = \frac{1{,}400}{4{,}400} = .318 = \underline{\underline{31.8\%}} \qquad .318 \times 360° = \underline{\underline{114°}}$$

$$\text{Sophomores} = \frac{1{,}200}{4{,}400} = .273 = \underline{\underline{27.3\%}} \qquad .273 \times 360° = \underline{\underline{98°}}$$

$$\text{Juniors} = \frac{1{,}100}{4{,}400} = .25 = \underline{\underline{25\%}} \qquad .25 \times 360° = \underline{\underline{90°}}$$

$$\text{Seniors} = \frac{700}{4{,}400} = .159 = \underline{\underline{15.9\%}} \qquad .159 \times 360° = \underline{\underline{57°}}$$

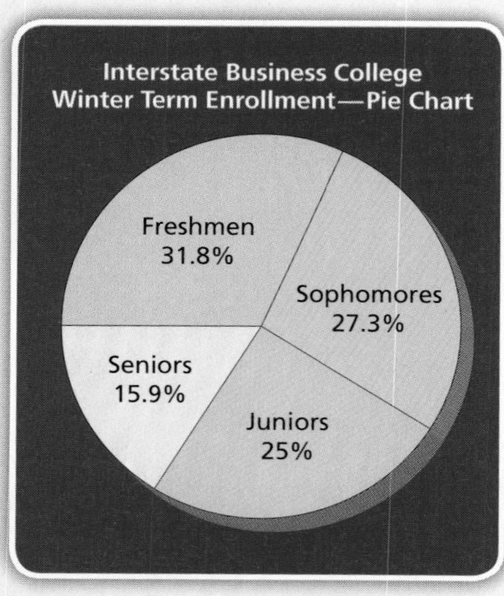

11.

$$\text{Mean} = \frac{\text{Sum of values}}{\text{Number of values}}$$

$$\text{Mean} = \frac{432 + 247 + 661 + 418 + 512}{5} = \frac{2{,}270}{5} = \underline{\underline{454}}$$

12. Ranked in increasing order:

1,220 2,430 3,619 (4,237) 4,589 5,840 6,558

Median is the middle value of the odd number of values = $\underline{\underline{4{,}237}}$

13. Ranked in increasing order:

12 13 29 33 42 54 76 79 81 101

For even number of values, median is midpoint between the two middle values.

$$\text{Midpoint} = \frac{42 + 54}{2} = \frac{96}{2} = \underline{\underline{48}}$$

14. $\underline{\underline{10 = 7}}$ 20 = 5 55 = 3 65 = 1 85 = 1 125 = 1

The mode of these values is $\underline{\underline{10}}$ because it occurred the most number of times, seven.

15. Range = Highest value − Lowest value

Range = 369° − 349° = $\underline{\underline{20°}}$

16. *The Dress Code*

Frequency Distribution

$ Sales per transaction

Class ($)	Tally	Frequency
10–19	||||	4
20–29	||||	4
30–39	|||	3
40–49	||||	4
50–59	|||	3
60–69	|||	3
70–79	~~||||~~ |	6
80–89	||	2
90–99	|	1

17. *The Dress Code* *$ Sales per transaction*

Class ($)	Tally	Freq (f)	Midpoint (m)	($f \times m$)
10–19	||||	4	14.5	58.0
20–29	||||	4	24.5	98.0
30–39	|||	3	34.5	103.5
40–49	||||	4	44.5	178.0
50–59	|||	3	54.5	163.5
60–69	|||	3	64.5	193.5
70–79	~~||||~~ |	6	74.5	447.0
80–89	||	2	84.5	169.0
90–99	|	1	94.5	94.5
		30		1,505.0

$$\text{Mean} = \frac{\text{Sum of } (f \times m)}{\text{Sum of frequency}}$$

$$\text{Mean} = \frac{1{,}505}{30} = 50.166 = \underline{\underline{\$50.17}}$$

18.

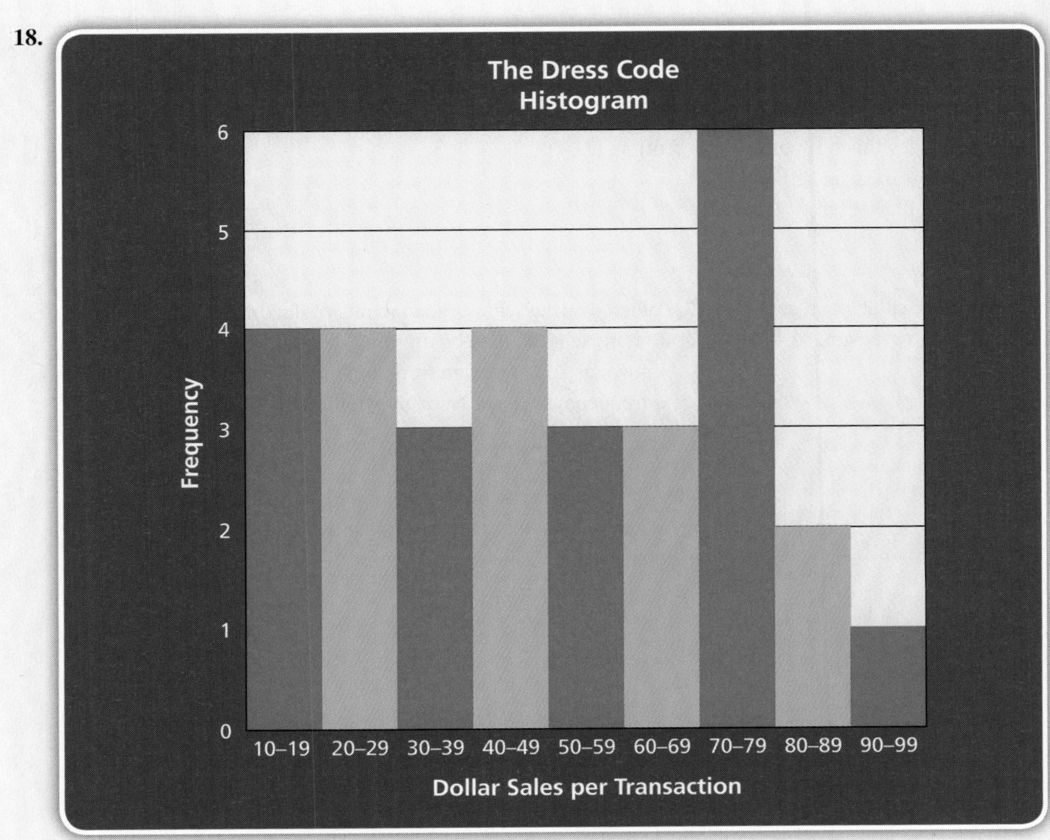

CONCEPT REVIEW

1. The systematic process of collecting, interpreting, and presenting numerical data about business situations is known as business ____. (21-1)

statistics

2. Statistical procedures that deal with the collection classification, summarization, and presentation of data are known as ____ statistics. The process of arriving at conclusions, predictions, forecasts, or estimates based on the data under study is known as statistical ____. (21-1)

descriptive, inference

3. A collection of related data arranged for ease of reference or comparison, usually in parallel columns with meaningful titles, is known as a(n) ____. (21-1)

table

4. A(n) ____ chart is a series of data points on a grid continuously connected by straight lines that display a picture of selected data changing over a period of time. (21-2)

line

5. The horizontal axis of a line chart is known as the ____ and is used to measure units of time; the vertical axis of a line chart is known as the ____ and is used to measure the quantity or magnitude of something. (21-2)

x-axis, y-axis

6. When a bar chart is used to illustrate the relationship between two or more similar variables, it is known as a ____ bar chart. When it is used to illustrate the parts of something that add to a total, it is known as a ____ bar chart. (21-3)

comparative, component

7. To construct a pie chart, we multiply each component's percent by ____ degrees to determine how many degrees of the circle each component's slice will be. (21-4)

360

8. A numerical value that is representative of a whole set of values is known as a(n) ____. It is also known as the mean or the arithmetic mean. Write the formula for the mean of ungrouped data. (21-5)

average, $\text{Mean of ungrouped data} = \dfrac{\text{Sum of values}}{\text{Number of values}}$

9. The ____ is the midpoint value of a set of data which is listed in ascending or descending order. Write the formula for this midpoint value when there is an even number of values in the data set. (21-6)

median, $\text{Median} = \dfrac{\text{Middle value} + \text{Middle value}}{2}$

10. The ____ is the value or values in a set of data that occur most often. (21-7)

mode

11. The difference between the lowest and the highest values in a data set are known as the ____. This useful statistic is a measure of ____. (21-8)

range, dispersion

12. When dealing with large amounts of data in a set, it is often easier to represent the data by dividing the values into equal-size groups known as ____. The chart obtained by this procedure is known as a frequency ____ or frequency table. (21-9)

classes, distribution

13. Write the formula for the mean of grouped data. (21-10)

$\text{Mean of grouped data} = \dfrac{\text{Sum of (frequency} \times \text{midpoint)}}{\text{Sum of frequency}}$

14. A(n) ____ is a special type of bar chart, without space between the bars, which is used to display the data from a frequency distribution. (21-11)

histogram

ASSESSMENT TEST

CHAPTER 21

Name

Class

Answers

1. a. and b.

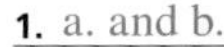

1. The following data represent the monthly sales figures, in thousands of dollars, for the New York and California branches of the Discovery Corporation:

	April	May	June	July	August	September
New York	121	254	218	156	255	215
California	88	122	211	225	248	260

a. Construct a multiple-line chart depicting the monthly sales for the two branches. Show the New York branch as a solid line and the California branch as a dashed line.

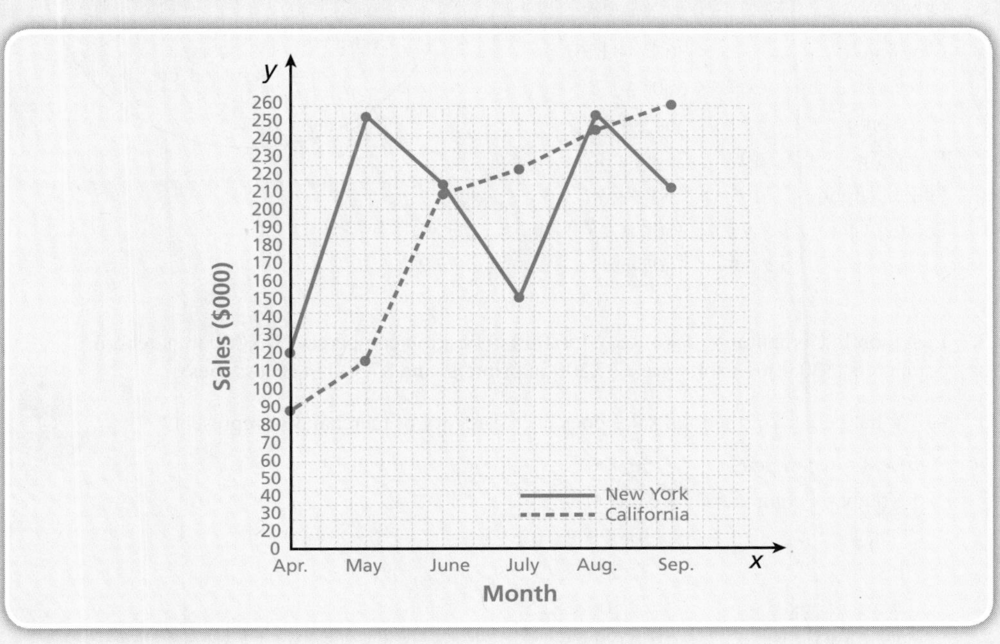

b. Construct a comparative bar chart for the same data. Highlight the bars for each branch differently.

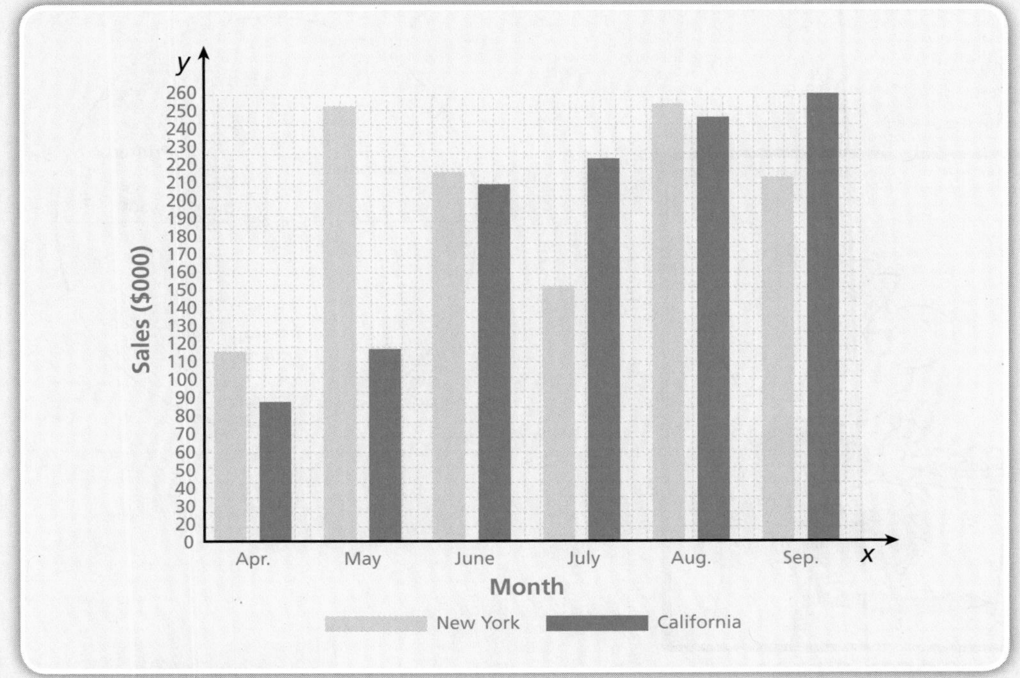

Name

Class

Answers

3. a. Desktop computers 50%

Notebook computers 25%

Software 10%

Printers 12.5%

Accessories 2.5%

2. Construct a pie chart from the following information compiled in a recent survey of the buying habits of children aged 8 to 17.

Category	Percentage
Clothing	35%
Fast food, snacks, candy	20%
Electronics products	15%
Entertainment	10%
School supplies	10%
Personal care	7%
Other	3%

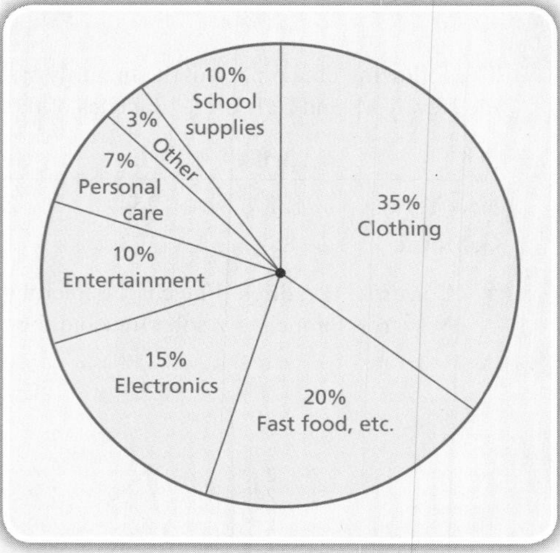

Clothing	35% × 360° = 126°
Fast food, etc.	20% × 360° = 72°
Electronics	15% × 360° = 54°
Entertainment	10% × 360° = 36°
School supplies	10% × 360° = 36°
Personal care	7% × 360° = 25°
Other	3% × 360° = 11°

3. Last month, Computer Village sold $150,000 in desktop computers, $75,000 in notebook computers, $30,000 in software, $37,500 in printers, and $7,500 in accessories.

a. What percent of the total sales does each category of merchandise represent?

EXCEL

Desktop computers	$150,000 =	50%
Notebook computers	75,000 =	25%
Software	30,000 =	10%
Printers	37,500 =	12.5%
Accessories	7,500 =	2.5%
Total sales	$300,000	

b. Construct a pie chart showing the percentage breakdown of sales by merchandise category.

Desktop	50% × 360° = 180°
Notebook	25% × 360° = 90°
Software	10% × 360° = 36°
Printers	12.5% × 360° = 45°
Accessories	2.5% × 360° = 9°

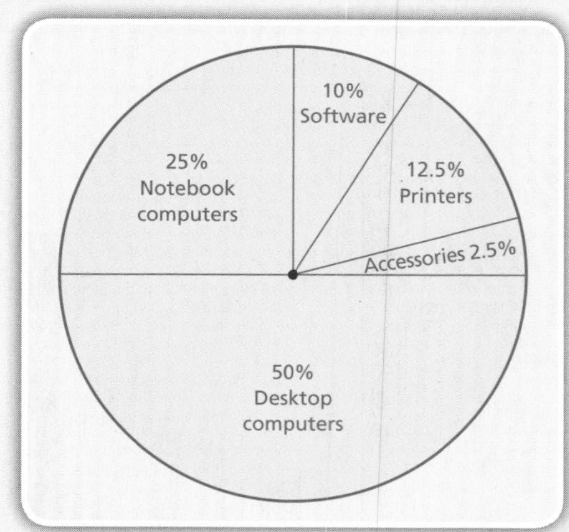

"THIS PIE WOULD MAKE A GOOD CHART."

Name

Class

Answers

4\. a. 14.1

14

13 occurs six times

11

b. 9.1

9

8 and 9

6

c. $1,057.50

$682.50

d. $112,500

e. $16,875

5\. a. 78

72 is the mode

4. You have just been hired as the quality control manager by Blue Diamond Manufacturing, a company producing fuel injection systems for General Motors, Ford, and Chrysler. Top management has requested a status report on the number of defective units produced each day. You decide to keep track of the number of defects each day for 30 days. The following are the results of your survey:

Blue Diamond Manufacturing—Defects per day—Survey 1

11	13	17	13	15	9	14	11	13	15	11	10	14	12	15
19	15	13	17	9	20	13	14	18	16	15	14	17	18	13

a. Find the mean, median, mode, and range of these data for your report to top management.

Mean: $424 \div 30 = \underline{14.1}$

Median: $\frac{14+14}{2} = \underline{14}$

Mode: 13 occurs six times; it is the mode.

Highest 20
Lowest −9
Range 11

After implementing your suggestions for improved quality on the production line, you decide to survey the defects for another 30 days with the following results:

Blue Diamond Manufacturing—Defects per day—Survey 2

11	9	12	7	8	10	12	8	9	10	9	7	11	12	8
7	9	11	8	6	12	10	8	8	7	9	6	10	9	11

b. Find the mean, median, mode, and range of the new data.

Mean: $\frac{274}{30} = \underline{9.1}$

Mode: 8 and 9 occur six times each; they are the modes.

Range:
Highest 12
Lowest −6
Range 6

Median: $\frac{9+9}{2} = \underline{9}$

c. If defective units cost the company $75 each to fix, use the *means* of each survey to calculate the average cost per day for defects, before and after your improvements.

Before: 75 × 14.1 = $1,057.50 Per day
After: 75 × 9.1 = $682.50 Per day

d. Theoretically, how much will your improvements save the company in a 300-day production year?

Savings over 300 days

1,057.50
−682.50
375.00 × 300 = $112,500

e. Congratulations! The company has awarded you a bonus amounting to 15% of the first year's savings. How much is your bonus check?

Bonus check = 112,500 × 15% = $16,875

5. You are the human resource director for Apollo Industries. Forty applicants for employment were given an assessment test in math and English with the following results:

87	67	81	83	94	72	84	68	33	56
91	79	88	95	84	75	46	27	69	97
69	57	66	81	87	19	76	54	78	91
78	72	75	89	74	92	45	59	85	72

a. What are the range and mode of these scores?

Range: Highest 97
Lowest −19
Range 78

Mode: 72 is the mode. It occurs three times.

Name

Class

Answers

5. b. See solution below problem

c. 72.5

d. 14 Persons

b. Group the data into nine classes of equal size (11–20, 21–30, etc.) and construct a frequency distribution.

Class	Tally	Frequency
11–20	I	1
21–30	I	1
31–40	I	1
41–50	II	2
51–60	IIII	4
61–70	~~IIII~~	5
71–80	~~IIII~~ ~~IIII~~	10
81–90	~~IIII~~ ~~IIII~~	10
91–100	~~IIII~~ I	6

c. Calculate the mean of the grouped data by using 15.5, 25.5, etc., as the midpoints.

Class	Tally	Frequency (f)	Midpoint (m)	$f \times m$
11–20	I	1	15.5	15.5
21–30	I	1	25.5	25.5
31–40	I	1	35.5	35.5
41–50	II	2	45.5	91.0
51–60	IIII	4	55.5	222.0
61–70	~~IIII~~	5	65.5	327.5
71–80	~~IIII~~ ~~IIII~~	10	75.5	755.0
81–90	~~IIII~~ ~~IIII~~	10	85.5	855.0
91–100	~~IIII~~ I	6	95.5	573.0
		40		2,900.0

$$\text{Mean} = \frac{2{,}900}{40} = \underline{\underline{72.5}}$$

d. If company policy is to consider only those who score *10 points higher* than the mean of the data or better, how many from this group are still being considered for the job?

72.5 + 10 points = 82.5

14 persons scored higher than 82.5.

e. Construct a histogram of the assessment test scores frequency distribution.

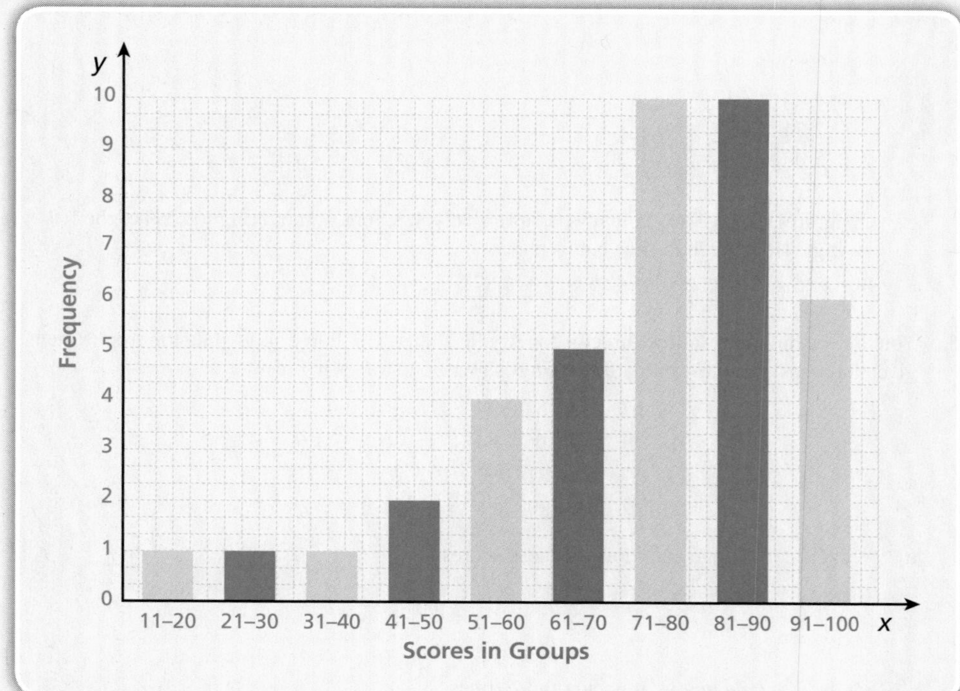

BUSINESS DECISION BEAT THE MEAN BONUS!

CHAPTER

Name

Class

Answers

6. $550

$550

$300

$1,350

$2,450

6. You are the owner of Supreme Imports, Inc., a car dealership specializing in expensive pre-owned automobiles, such as Mercedes Benz, BMW, and Lexus. You have a unique and quite motivating bonus plan that has worked well over the years.

Each quarter, the mean number of cars sold is calculated. The first time a salesperson sells more cars than the mean, he or she earns a $100 bonus for each car *over the mean* in that quarter. If a salesperson beats the mean a second time in a year, the bonus increases to $150 per car for that quarter. Three times over the mean in 1 year and the bonus is $200 per car for that quarter. If anyone beats the mean all four quarters, the fourth quarter bonus is $300 per car. Remember, the bonus is paid only for the number of cars over the mean.

Each year, the program starts all over again. All bonuses are paid once per year, in January, for the previous year. The following table represents the number of cars sold by your five salespeople for each quarter last year. Calculate the bonus each person should receive for last year.

	First Quarter	Second Quarter	Third Quarter	Fourth Quarter
Baxter	16	23	14	23
Anderson	12	20	16	25
Lima	15	13	26	19
Stanford	22	20	27	19
Wilson	25	19	32	24

Mean, 1st Quarter

$$\frac{16+12+15+22+25}{5}=18$$

Mean, 2nd Quarter

$$\frac{23+20+13+20+19}{5}=19$$

Mean, 3rd Quarter

$$\frac{14+16+26+27+32}{5}=23$$

Mean, 4th Quarter

$$\frac{23+25+19+19+24}{5}=22$$

Baxter

Beat mean: 2Q + 4Q

Bonus: (4 × 100) + (1 × 150)
400 + 150 = $550

Anderson

Beat mean: 2Q + 4Q

Bonus: (1 × 100) + (3 × 150)
100 + 450 = $550

Lima

Beat mean: 3Q

Bonus: (3 × 100) = $300

Stanford

Beat mean: 1Q + 2Q + 3Q

Bonus: (4 × 100) + (1 × 150) + (4 × 200)
400 + 150 + 800 = $1,350

Wilson

Beat mean: 1Q + 3Q + 4Q

Bonus: (7 × 100) + (9 × 150) + (2 × 200)
700 + 1,350 + 400 = $2,450

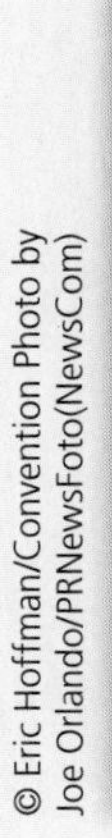

Luxury Cars

According to MarketResearch.com, in the United States, about 1,500 of the over 20,000 new car dealerships sell mainly luxury cars, with combined annual revenue of about $50 billion. Luxury cars (those costing more than $40,000) account for 10 to 15 percent of all cars sold. Major luxury brands sold in the United States include BMW, Lexus, Cadillac, Mercedes Benz, Infiniti, Audi, and Lincoln.

COLLABORATIVE LEARNING ACTIVITY

Conducting a Marketing Research Survey

You and your team have been hired to conduct a marketing research survey by a company that is interested in advertising its products to college students in your area. They want to know the news media preferences of the students at your school and specifically would like answers to the following questions:

- What radio station, if any, do you listen to for news in the morning?
- What television local news program, if any, do you watch in the evening?
- What newspaper, if any, do you read each day?
- What Internet sites, if any, do you log on to for news each week?

a. As a team, design a questionnaire for this research survey. For each media question, list all of the local choices, with a place for easy check-off responses. Be sure to include "no preference" and "none of the above" as choices. For the Internet question, list the most popular news sites, and include some spaces for students to list other responses. In addition to the survey questions, design some easy check-off demographic information questions, such as gender, age group, ethnic group, income range, and marital status.

b. Individually, have each member of the research team personally interview about 25 or 30 students. Questionnaires can be handed out and then collected.

c. Individually, tabulate the results of the surveys you conducted. As a team, total the results of each team member's surveys to arrive at the survey totals.

d. Convert the totals for each question to percents.

e. Calculate the mean, median, and mode for each of the demographic questions.

f. Using different types of charts, prepare a visual presentation for the class illustrating the results of the survey questions.

g. As a team, do you think the results of your survey are valid? Why or why not?

http://www.contemporarymath.com

Contemporary Math

ContemporaryMath.com

All the Math That's Fit to Learn

ETFs –Growing Investment Tool

Exchange Traded Funds (ETFs) are similar to mutual funds in that they hold a variety of stocks, giving you a diversified portfolio with just one purchase. But unlike mutual funds, they are traded on exchanges, where you can buy and sell them throughout the day, like stocks. Despite their rapid growth, ETFs still claim a relatively small share of investors' dollars. In 2007, there was about $550 billion invested in ETFs, vs. $10.5 trillion in the roughly 6,500 conventional stock and bond mutual funds.

Think of exchange-traded funds as mutual funds that trade like stocks. Just like an index fund, an ETF represents a basket of stocks that reflect an index such as the S&P 500. Unlike a mutual fund that has its net-asset value (NAV) calculated at the end of each trading day, an ETF's price changes throughout the day, fluctuating with supply and demand.

Quote...UnQuote

- If you want to make money, really big money, do what nobody else is doing. Buy when everyone else is selling and hold until everyone else is buying. This is not merely a catchy slogan; it is the very essence of successful investment. **–J. Paul Getty**
- Twenty years from now you will be more disappointed by the things you didn't do than by the ones you did do. So throw off the bow lines, sail away from the safe harbor, and catch the trade winds in your sails. Explore, Dream, Discover **–Mark Twain**

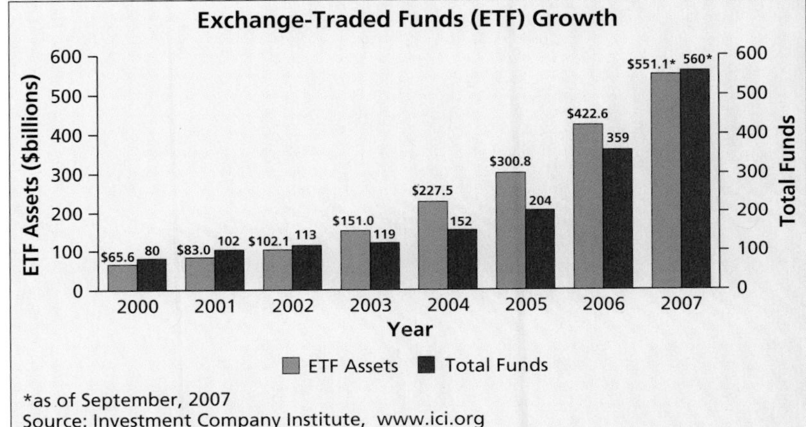

Varieties of ETFs

The first exchange-traded fund was the S&P 500 index fund (nicknamed spiders because of their SPDR ticker symbol), which began trading on the American Stock Exchange (AMEX) in 1993. Today - tracking a wide variety of sector-specific, country-specific and broad-market indexes - there are hundreds of ETFs trading on the open market.

Some of the more popular ETFs have nicknames like cubes (QQQQ), vipers (VIPERs) and diamonds (DIAs). Listed here are some of the more popular ETFs:

Nasdaq-100 Index Tracking Stock (QQQQ)

This ETF represents the Nasdaq-100 Index, which consists of the 100 largest and most actively traded non-financial stocks on the Nasdaq, QQQQ offers broad exposure to the tech sector.

SPDRs

Usually referred to as spiders, these investment instruments bundle the benchmark S&P 500 and give you ownership in the index. Imagine the trouble and expenses involved in trying to buy all 500 stocks in the S&P 500! SPDRs allow individual investors to own the index's stocks in a cost-effective manner.

iShares

iShares is Barclay's (Barclay's Global Investors "BGI") brand of ETFs. In 2007 there were approximately 140 iShares trading on more than 10 different stock exchanges.

Diamonds

These ETF shares, Diamonds Trust Series I, track the Dow Jones Industrial Average. The fund is structured as a unit investment trust. The ticker symbol of the Dow Diamonds is DIA, and it trades on the AMEX.

Sources: Investment Company Institute: www.ici.org
Investopedia: www.investopedia.com

Vipers

Just like iShares are Barclay's brand of ETFs, VIPERs are Vanguard's brand of the financial instrument. Vipers, or Vanguard Index Participation Receipts, are structured as share classes of open-end funds.

"No, Harliss, you can't take a 'family leave' day to spend with your family of mutual funds."

Internet 100%

Appendix A

Answers to Odd-Numbered Exercises

(Except Business Decisions)

WHOLE NUMBERS

CHAPTER 

Review Exercises

SECTION I 

1. 22,938—twenty-two thousand, nine hundred thirty-eight **3.** 184—one hundred eighty-four **5.** 2,433,590—two million, four hundred thirty-three thousand, five hundred ninety **7.** 183,622 **9.** 1,936 **11.** d **13.** a **15.** 1,760 **17.** 235,400 **19.** 8,000,000 **21.** 1,300,000,000 **23.** 19,000,000,000

Review Exercises

SECTION II 

1. 91 **3.** 19,943 **5.** 37,648 **7.** 70,928 **9.** 43,100 estimate—41,844 exact **11a.** 7,000 **11b.** 6,935 **13.** 3,236 grand total **15.** $1,627 **17.** 4,629 **19.** 278,091 **21.** $138 **23.** $139 **25.** 3,490,700 **27a.** 43 **27b.** 22 **27c.** 94 **29.** 378

Review Exercises

SECTION III 

1. 11,191 **3.** 294,300 **5.** 56,969,000 **7.** 13,110 **9.** 100,000 estimate—98,980 exact **11.** 200 estimate—187 exact **13.** 12,960 **15.** Micro Systems by $160 **17.** 13 R 67 **19.** 55 **21.** 2 R 300 estimate—2 R 339 exact **23.** 6 **25.** $924

ASSESSMENT TEST

CHAPTER 

1. 200,049—two hundred thousand, forty-nine **3.** 316,229 **5.** 18,300 **7.** 260,000 **9.** 99 **11.** 44 R 28 **13.** 22,258 **15.** 714 **17.** $53,950 **19a.** 19 **19b.** 25 **21a.** $11,340 **21b.** $36 **23.** $1,003 **25.** $49,260 **27a.** $7,119,770 **27b.** $17,990,230 **29.** 15 **31.** $20

2 CHAPTER FRACTIONS

2 SECTION I Review Exercises

1. mixed fraction, twenty-three and four-fifths **3.** improper fraction, fifteen-ninths **5.** mixed fraction, two and one-eighth **7.** $3\frac{1}{3}$ **9.** $4\frac{4}{15}$ **11.** $1\frac{2}{31}$ **13.** $\frac{59}{5}$ **15.** $\frac{149}{8}$ **17.** $\frac{1,001}{4}$ **19.** $\frac{3}{4}$ **21.** $\frac{27}{115}$ **23.** $\frac{1}{8}$ **25.** $\frac{19}{65}$ **27.** $\frac{13}{16}$ **29.** $\frac{5}{18}$ **31.** $\frac{36}{48}$ **33.** $\frac{44}{64}$ **35.** $\frac{42}{98}$ **37.** $\frac{40}{64}$ **39.** $\frac{126}{182}$ **41.** $\frac{16}{72}$ **43.** $\frac{3}{5}$

2 SECTION II Review Exercises

1. 15 **3.** 12 **5.** 300 **7.** $1\frac{1}{3}$ **9.** $1\frac{7}{16}$ **11.** $1\frac{13}{20}$ **13.** $2\frac{3}{20}$ **15.** $11\frac{13}{24}$ **17.** $10\frac{17}{40}$ **19.** $10\frac{19}{30}$ **21.** $\frac{2}{3}$ **23.** $\frac{11}{18}$ **25.** $8\frac{4}{15}$ **27.** $26\frac{29}{45}$ **29.** $35\frac{13}{15}$ **31.** $21\frac{1}{8}$ **33.** $1\frac{13}{16}$

2 SECTION III Review Exercises

1. $\frac{8}{15}$ **3.** $\frac{2}{9}$ **5.** $\frac{10}{19}$ **7.** $\frac{12}{5}$ **9.** $21\frac{13}{15}$ **11.** $\frac{1}{125}$ **13a.** $\frac{5}{8}$ **13b.** 2,750 **15.** $43\frac{15}{16}$ **17.** 15 **19.** $2\frac{2}{9}$ **21.** $1\frac{1}{15}$ **23.** $\frac{2}{5}$ **25.** $5\frac{17}{35}$ **27.** 19 **29.** $\frac{5}{14}$ **31.** 46 **33a.** 240 **33b.** 90 **35.** 185 **37.** 55 **39.** $23\frac{3}{11}$

CHAPTER ASSESSMENT TEST

1. improper fraction, eighteen-elevenths **3.** proper fraction, thirteen-sixteenths **5.** 25 **7.** $\frac{86}{9}$ **9.** $\frac{2}{5}$ **11.** $\frac{18}{78}$ **13.** $\frac{25}{36}$ **15.** $5\frac{1}{3}$ **17.** $4\frac{3}{10}$ **19.** $13\frac{1}{3}$ **21.** 69 **23.** $23\frac{5}{8}$ **25.** $10\frac{7}{16}$ **27a.** \$588,000 **27b.** \$49,000 **29a.** 275 sq. ft. each bath and kitchen **29b.** 495 total sq. ft. **31.** pasta: 15 ounces; garlic: 4 tablespoons; tomatoes: $3\frac{1}{8}$ cups; cheese: $6\frac{1}{4}$ tablespoons.

DECIMALS

CHAPTER 3

Review Exercises

SECTION I

1. twenty-one hundredths **3.** ninety-two thousandths **5.** ninety-eight thousand forty-five and forty-five thousandths **7.** nine hundred thirty-eight hundred-thousandths **9.** fifty-seven and one-half hundred-thousandths **11.** .8 **13.** 67,309.04 **15.** 183,000.0183 **17.** 123.007 **19.** 0.01004 **21.** $14.60 **23.** 43.01 **25.** 46

Review Exercises

SECTION II

1. 58.033 **3.** $45.27 **5.** 152.784494 **7.** 16.349 **9.** $.87 **11.** 779.75 **13.** 80.482 **15a.** $30.25 **15b.** $27.75 **17.** $11.14 **19a.** 6.0012, 6.0122, 6.102, 6.12, 6.122 **19b.** .1208 **21.** 400.2129 **23.** 1,120,050 **25.** 15.152256 **27.** 33,090 **29.** .07 **31.** $2.72 **33.** 6 **35.** 217.39 **37a.** $2,480.98 **37b.** $15,590.00 **37c.** $230 **39a.** 3,632.00 **39b.** 454 **41a.** $2,104.32 **41b.** $920.06 **43.** $16.00 **45.** $5,919 **47.** $70,284

Review Exercises

SECTION III

1. $\frac{1}{8}$ **3.** $\frac{1}{125}$ **5.** $14\frac{41}{50}$ **7.** 5.67 **9.** 1.22 **11.** 58.43 **13.** 5 **15a.** 16 **15b.** $190.24 **17a.** $489.26 **17b.** 32.7¢ **19.** $13.10

ASSESSMENT TEST

CHAPTER 3

1. sixty-one hundredths **3.** one hundred nineteen dollars and eighty-five cents **5.** four hundred ninety-five ten-thousandths **7.** 5.014 **9.** $16.57 **11.** 995.070 **13.** 4.7 **15.** $37.19 **17.** 7.7056 **19.** .736 **21.** .000192 **23.** .4 **25.** $20.06 **27.** $\frac{441}{10,000}$ **29.** 3.11 **31.** The box of 40 DVD/Rs and box of 40 cases by $4.93 **33.** $19.89 **35a.** $0.98 **35b.** $0.25 **35c.** Sale price **37.** $2,161.19 **39a.** 23 **39b.** $41.17

CHAPTER 4 CHECKING ACCOUNTS

SECTION I Review Exercises

1. \$345.54 **3.** for deposit only, your signature, #099-506-8 Restrictive Endorsement **5.** Pay to the order of, David Sporn, your signature, #099-506-8 Full Endorsement **7.** \$501.03 net deposit **9a.** \$479.20 bal. forward **9b.** \$1,246.10 bal. forward **9c.** \$1,200.45 bal. forward **9d.** \$1,075.45 bal. forward **9e.** \$205.45 bal. forward **9f.** \$1,555.45 bal. forward **9g.** \$691.05 bal. forward

SECTION II Review Exercises

1. \$1,935.90 reconciled balance **3.** \$471.84 reconciled balance

CHAPTER ASSESSMENT TEST

1. \$24,556.00 **3.** \$935.79 net deposit **5a.** \$463.30 bal. forward **5b.** \$395.52 bal. forward **5c.** \$145.52 bal. forward **5d.** \$270.97 bal. forward **5e.** \$590.97 bal. forward **5f.** \$467.87 bal. forward **7.** \$1,538.32 reconciled balance

CHAPTER 5 USING EQUATIONS TO SOLVE BUSINESS PROBLEMS

SECTION I Review Exercises

1. $B = 13$ **3.** $S = 90$ **5.** $K = 3$ **7.** $Y = 7\frac{1}{2}$ **9.** $G = 4$ **11.** $A = 3$ **13.** $X = 4$ **15.** $D = 5$ **17.** $Q = 1$ **19.** $5F + 33$ **21.** $HP + 550$ **23.** $8Y - 128$ **25.** $\frac{3}{4}B + 40$ **27.** $X = 5B + C$ **29.** $\$5.75R = \$28.75$ **31.** $5X + 4 + 2X = X + 40$

Review Exercises

SECTION II 5

1. 47 Karen, 39 Kathy **3.** $21,700 **5.** 8 iPod Nanos, 24 iPod Shuffles **7a.** 280 Small size **7b.** Large size $3,400, Small size $3,920 **9.** $5,000 = Each grandchild's share, $15,000 = Each child's share, $60,000 = Wife's share, **11.** $396 Cost of standard oven, $838 Cost of deluxe oven **13.** 3—Age of Ohio plant, 12—Age of Michigan plant **15.** $5,400,000 **17.** $2.60 per piece **19.** $275 **21.** $777 **23.** 18,850 **25.** 27 **27.** $114.10 **29a.** 256 **29b.** $9.52

ASSESSMENT TEST

CHAPTER 5

1. $T = 65$ **3.** $K = 15$ **5.** $X = 8$ **7.** $B = 8$ **9.** $X = 15$ **11.** $4R - 108$ **13.** $ZW + 24$ **15.** $X = 4C + L$ **17.** $3F - 14 = 38$ **19.** Century Marine: 14 Boats, Marine Max: 19 Boats **21.** $55 **23.** 95 watts **25.** $1.15 **27.** $430 **29.** $104,000 **31.** $3\frac{1}{3}$ Quarts **33a.** 45 Pizzas **33b.** 180 People Served

PERCENTS AND THEIR APPLICATIONS IN BUSINESS

Review Exercises

SECTION I

1. .28 **3.** .134 **5.** .4268 **7.** .0002 **9.** 1.2517 **11.** 350% **13.** 4,600% **15.** .935% **17.** 16,400% **19.** 533% **21.** $\frac{1}{20}$ **23.** $\frac{89}{100}$ **25.** $\frac{19}{50}$ **27.** $\frac{5}{8}$ **29.** $1\frac{1}{4}$ **31.** 75% **33.** 240% **35.** 125% **37.** 18.75% **39.** 35%

Review Exercises

SECTION II

1. 57 **3.** 90 **5.** 85.5 **7.** 64.77 **9.** 56.88 **11.** 32% **13.** 250% **15.** 13.5% **17.** 29.9% **19.** 26.0% **21.** 460 **23.** 34.86 **25.** 363.64 **27.** 400 **29.** $53.65 **31a.** $59,200 **31b.** $594.50 **33.** $165,000 **35.** $13,650 **37.** 2,820 **39.** 10 **41.** 1,700 **43.** $61,230.75 **45.** $32.3 billion **47.** 20

Review Exercises

SECTION III

1. 37.5% **3.** 25.2% **5.** 60 **7.** 15 **9.** 10,000 **11.** 7% **13a.** 1,105 racquets **13b.** 442 metal alloy, 663 graphite **15.** 29.4% **17.** $658,762 **19.** 22.7%

CHAPTER 6 ASSESSMENT TEST

1. .88 **3.** .5968 **5.** .005625 **7.** 68.1% **9.** 2,480% **11.** $\frac{19}{100}$ **13.** $\frac{93}{1,250}$ **15.** $\frac{127}{500}$
17. 55.56% **19.** 5,630% **21.** 408 **23.** 103.41 **25.** 180% **27.** 69 **29.** 2,960
31. 1,492 **33.** $122.48 **35a.** $72,000 **35b.** $.24 Per mile **35c.** 25% Savings per mile
37. 21.0% **39.** $3.4 Billion **41.** 18.1% **43.** $33.3 Billion **45.** $40,583.33 **47.** 115%
49. $23.3 Million

CHAPTER 7 INVOICES, TRADE DISCOUNTS, AND CASH DISCOUNTS

SECTION I Review Exercises

1. box **3.** drum **5.** gross **7.** thousand **9.** Frasier Mfg. **11.** June 16, 20XX **13.** J. M. Hardware Supply **15.** 2051 W. Adams Blvd, Lansing, MI 48901 **17.** Gilbert Trucking **19.** $61.45 **21.** $4,415.12

SECTION II Review Exercises

1. $258.00 **3.** $7.93 **5.** $44.13 **7.** $53.92, $80.87 **9.** $527.45, $431.55 **11.** 76%, $429.65 **13.** 87.25%, $4.01 **15.** $120.50, $34.9% **17.** $239.99 **19.** $1,950 **21a.** $8,653 **21b.** $16,797 **23.** $1,512 **25a.** Pro-Chef, $233.75 **25b.** $7,125

SECTION III Review Exercises

1. .792, $285.12 **3.** .648, $52.97 **5.** .57056, $4.14 **7.** .765, .235 **9.** .59288, .40712 **11.** .51106, .48894 **13.** .6324, .3676, $441.12, $758.88 **15.** .65666, .34334, $303.34, $580.16 **17.** .5292, .4708, $1,353.53, $1,521.42 **19.** .49725 **21a.** .6 **21b.** $54,300 **23a.** .57375 **23b.** .42625 **25a.** $324.19 **25b.** .53687 **27a.** $232.96 **27b.** $291.20 **29a.** $1,494.90 **29b.** $687.65 **29c.** $807.25

SECTION IV Review Exercises

1. $474, $15,326.00 **3.** $96.84, $2,324.16 **5.** $319.25, $8,802.19 **7.** $474.23, $870.37 **9.** $5,759.16, $1,472.92 **11.** May 8, June 22 **13.** 2%, Feb 8, 1%, Feb 18, Mar 30 **15.** Jan 10, Jan 30 **17.** Oct 23, Nov 12 **19.** June 25, July 15 **21a.** April 27, May 27 **21b.** $21.24 **21c.** $1,148.76 **23a.** Mar 22 **23b.** Apr 11 **25a.** $32,931.08 **25b.** May 19

ASSESSMENT TEST

CHAPTER 7

1. Leisure Time Industries **3.** 4387 **5.** $46.55 **7.** $2,558 **9.** $11,562.45 **11.** $1,485 **13.** 33.76% **15.** Fancy Footwear **17a.** .6052 **17b.** .3948 **19a.** April 24 **19b**. May 9 **19c.** May 15 **19d.** June 4 **21.** $14,563.80

MARKUP AND MARKDOWN

CHAPTER

Review Exercises

SECTION I

1. $138.45, 85.7% **3.** $6,944.80, 77.8% **5.** $156.22, $93.73 **7.** $2,149, 159.2% **9.** $.75, $1.33 **11.** $85.90 **13.** $195 **15a.** $4.19 **15b.** 71.7% **17a.** 60.63 **17b.** 104.1% **19.** $583.92 **21a.** $81.58 **21b.** 119.3% **23a.** $11.76 **23b.** $8.23

Review Exercises

SECTION II

1. $115, 43.5% **3.** $61.36, $136.36 **5.** 37.5% **7.** $94.74, 133%, 57.1% **9.** $9,468.74, $24,917.74, 61.3% **11.** 60% **13a.** $455.99 **13b.** 45.6% **15.** $366.12 **17a.** $2.87 **17b.** $1.12 **17c.** 39% **19.** 75.4% **21a.** $30.49 **21b.** 141.8% **21c.** 58.6% **23a.** 58.3% **23b.** 60.2% **23c.** $15,576 **23d.** Answers will vary.

Review Exercises

SECTION III

1. $161.45, 15% **3.** $1.68, 23.2% **5.** $41.10, $16.44 **7.** $80.27, 30.7% **9.** $559.96, $1,039.92 **11a.** $1,750 **11b.** 18.0% **13a.** $.70 **13b.** 41.4% **13c.** $1.39 **15.** $30 **17.** $6,018.75 **19.** $469.68 **21.** $233.99 **23a.** 20% **23b.** $159.99

ASSESSMENT TEST

CHAPTER 8

1. $152.60 **3.** $18.58 **5a.** $66.99 **5b.** 44.2% **5c.** 79.1% **7.** $15.95 **9a.** $778 **9b.** 21.3% **11.** $216.06 **13a.** $56.25 **13b.** $64.68 **15a.** $2,499.99 **15b.** $1,000 **15c.** 60% **15d.** 36%

9 CHAPTER PAYROLL

9 SECTION I Review Exercises

1. $1,250, $625, $576.92, $288.46 **3.** $8,333.33, $4,166.67, $3,846.15, $1,923.08 **5.** $34,800, $2,900, $1,338.46, $669.23 **7.** $17,420, $1,451.67, $725.83, $670 **9.** $1,115.38 **11.** $1,329.23 **13.** 36, 0, $313.20, 0, $313.20 **15.** 48, 8, $290, $87, $377 **17.** $711.90 **19.** $320.25 **21.** $1,170.90 **23.** $5,790.40 **25.** $1,565 **27.** $352.66

9 SECTION II Review Exercises

1. $51.15, social security; $11.96, Medicare **3a.** $545.60, social security; $127.60, Medicare **3b.** December **3c.** $43.40, social security; $127.60, Medicare **5.** $212.16, $49.62 **7.** $142.60, $68.15 **9.** $31.64 **11.** $623.12 **13.** $166.24 **15.** $2,174.51 **17.** $124.53 **19.** $611.21

9 SECTION III Review Exercises

1a. $806, social security; $188.50, Medicare **1b.** $10,478, social security; $2,450.50, Medicare **3.** $5,282.40, social security; $1,235.40, Medicare **5a.** $378 **5b.** $56 **7a.** $950.13, SUTA; $140.76, FUTA **7b.** $183.87, SUTA; $27.24, FUTA **9a.** $23,197.50 **9b.** 1040-ES

9 CHAPTER ASSESSMENT TEST

1a. $67,200 **1b.** $2,584.62 **3.** $898.70 **5.** $656.25 **7.** $1,011.71 **9.** $6,963 **11.** $2,284.10 **13.** $44.95, social security, $10.51, Medicare **15a.** $2,001.82 **15b.** $2,140.94 **15c.** $2,428.33 **17.** $1,112.19 **19a.** $1,693.03, social security, $395.95, Medicare **19b.** $44,018.78, social security, $10,294.70, Medicare **21a.** $378 **21b.** $56 **23a.** $58,589.20 **23b.** 20.8% **23c.** $3,046,638.40

10 CHAPTER SIMPLE INTEREST AND PROMISSORY NOTES

10 SECTION I Review Exercises

1. $800 **3.** $19,050 **5.** $206.62 **7.** $1,602.74, $1,625 **9.** $1,839.79, $1,865.34 **11.** $15.16, $15.38 **13.** $60.82, $61.67 **15.** $882.88, $895.15 **17.** $12,852, $66,852 **19.** $2,362.50, $36,112.50 **21.** $1,770 **23.** $1,330,000 **25.** 98 **27.** 289 **29.** Dec. 3 **31.** June 24 **33.** Feb. 23 **35.** $62,005.48 **37.** $403.89 **39.** $14.97

Review Exercises — SECTION II 10

1. $1,250 **3.** $50,000 **5.** $12,000 **7.** 14% **9.** 12.8% **11.** 158 days **13.** 308 days **15.** 180 days **17.** $13,063.16, $13,403.16 **19.** $2,390.63, $27,890.63 **21a.** 166 days **21b.** Sept. 29 **23.** $10,000 **25.** 11.6% **27.** $6,147.56 **29a.** $33,441.59 **29b.** June 13

Review Exercises — SECTION III 10

1. $292.50, $4,207.50 **3.** $231.25, $1,618.75 **5.** $232.38, $7,567.62 **7.** 84 days, $171.50, $4,828.50 **9.** 100 days, $34.31, $1,265.69 **11.** $132.30, $2,567.70, 14.72% **13.** $214.28, $3,585.72, 15.37% **15.** $4,683.85, $52,816.15, 13.88% **17.** Jan. 31, $4,057.78, 12 days, $4,037.49 **19.** $195, $14,805, 5.27% **21.** $964, $79,036, 4.88% **23.** 13.61% **25a.** $484.62 **25b.** $149,515.38 **25c.** 4.21%

ASSESSMENT TEST

CHAPTER 10

1. $641.10 **3.** $672.93 **5.** $24,648 **7.** 107 **9.** Jan. 24 **11.** $11,666.67 **13.** 9.1% **15.** 72 days **17.** 190 days, $13,960 **19.** 15.2%, $2,795 **21.** Jan. 20, $20,088.54, $854,911.46 **23.** $10,544.72, $279,455.28, 12.35% **25.** Aug. 25, $5,642.31, 34 days, $5,569.30 **27.** $686, $27,314, 5.02% **29.** $99.37 **31.** 15.3% **33.** $9,393.88 **35a.** $28,970.83 **35b.** Nov. 12 **35c.** 13.46% **37a.** $752 **37b.** $63,248 **37c.** 4.76%

COMPOUND INTEREST AND PRESENT VALUE — CHAPTER 11

Review Exercises — SECTION I

1. 3, 13% **3.** 24, 4% **5.** 16, 3.5% **7.** 3, 3% **9.** $11,255.09, $1,255.09 **11.** $11,413.29, $4,413.29 **13.** $6,721.67, $1,421.67 **15.** $119,614.75, $94,614.75 **17.** $29,799.88, $20,999.88 **19.** 12.17218, $231,271.42 **21.** 132.78160, $1,327,816 **23.** $512.50, 10.25% **25.** $4,565.88, 12.68% **27a.** 6.14% **27b.** $4,288.50 **29.** $673,925 **31.** 97

Review Exercises — SECTION II

1. $4,633.08, $1,366.92 **3.** $437.43, $212.57 **5.** $3,680.50, $46,319.50 **7.** $6,107.07, $3,692.93 **9.** $209.10, $40.90 **11.** .20829, $2,499.48 **13.** .24200, $338.80 **15.** .26355, $28,990.50 **17a.** $2,549.58 **17b.** $950.42 **19.** $15,742,200 **21.** 47 million

CHAPTER 11 ASSESSMENT TEST

1. $31,530.66, $17,530.66 **3.** $3,586.86, $586.86 **5.** 5.61652, $112,330.40 **7.** $1,078.06, 12.68% **9.** $6,930, $143,070 **11.** $658.35, 241.65 **13.** .62027, $806.35 **15.** $81,392.40, $45,392.40 **17.** $17,150.85, compound amount; $2,150.85, compound interest **19.** $92,727.70 **21a.** 12.55% **21b.** $17,888.55 **23.** $48,545.40 **25a.** $37,243.34 **25b.** $14,243.34 **27.** 3.7 million

CHAPTER 12 ANNUITIES

12 SECTION I Review Exercises

1. $18,639.29 **3.** $151,929.30 **5.** $74,951.37 **7.** $13,680.33 **9.** $100,226.90 **11.** $2,543.20 **13.** $2,956.72 **15.** $15,934.37 **17a.** $39,620.37 **17b.** $104,157.75 **17c.** $209,282.37 **17d.** $42,122.67

12 SECTION II Review Exercises

1. $2,969.59 **3.** $27,096.86 **5.** $79,773.10 **7.** $16,819.32 **9.** $110,997.88 **11.** $9,025.15 **13.** $380,773 **15.** $7,900.87

12 SECTION III Review Exercises

1. $2,113.50 **3.** $55.82 **5.** $859.13 **7.** $336.36 **9.** $1,087.48 **11a.** $245,770.96 **11b.** $2,135,329.28 **13a.** $3,769.04 **13b.** $2,385.76 **15.** $418.24 **17a.** $12,244.45 **17b.** $265,333

ASSESSMENT TEST

1. \$121,687.44 **3.** \$86,445.14 **5.** \$42,646.92 **7.** \$11,593.58 **9.** \$993.02 **11.** \$255.66 **13.** \$20,345.57 **15.** \$6,081.72 **17.** \$368.62 **19.** \$40,012.45 **21a.** \$19,496.56 **21b.** \$19,351.43 **23.** \$1,678.39

CONSUMER AND BUSINESS CREDIT

Review Exercises

1. 1.5%, \$2.52, \$335.90 **3.** 21%, \$7.96, \$544.32 **5a.** \$1.20 **5b.** \$259.13 **7.** \$636.17, \$11.13, \$628.75 **9.** \$817.08, \$14.30, \$684.76 **11.** \$152.29 **13a.** \$6.89 **13b.** \$728.23 **15a.** \$157.14 **15b.** \$9,957.14 **15c.** \$20,042.86

Review Exercises

1. \$1,050, \$582, \$1,982 **3.** \$10,800, \$2,700, \$14,700 **5.** \$7,437.50, \$2,082.34, \$10,832.34 **7.** \$1,350, \$270, \$67.50 **9.** \$15,450, \$8,652, \$502.13 **11.** \$322, \$14, 13% **13.** \$223.50, \$12.02, 14.75% **15.** \$31, 11.25% **17.** \$4,940, 16.6% **19.** 29.97, \$1,498.50, \$135.39 **21.** 6.20, \$111.60, \$159.30 **23.** 8, 36, 78, $\frac{36}{78}$ **25.** 15, 120, 300, $\frac{120}{300}$ **27.** $\frac{120}{300}$, \$360, \$2,077.50 **29.** $\frac{78}{1,176}$, \$219.94, \$2,984.06 **31a.** \$411.30 **31b.** \$2,310.30 **33.** \$68.75 **35a.** \$729.52 **35b.** \$8,329.52 **37.** \$216.45, finance charge, \$63.19, monthly payment **39a.** 300 **39b.** 465 **41a.** \$504 **41b.** \$152.25 **41c.** formula, 14.64%; table, 14.75% **41d.** \$1,157.52

ASSESSMENT TEST

1a. 1.33% **1b.** \$4.59 **1c.** \$440.38 **3a.** \$4.46, \$724.12 **3b.** \$724.12, \$12.09, \$839.64 **3c.** \$839.64, \$14.02, \$859.61 **5a.** \$694.76 **5b.** \$7.50 **5c.** \$864.74 **7a.** \$9,920 **7b.** \$39,120 **9a.** \$10,384 **9b.** 19.25% **11a.** \$66,300 **11b.** \$4,646.67 **13a.** \$14,144 **13b.** \$1,428 **13c.** 11.75% **13d.** \$32,906.45 **15a.** \$30,686.75 **15b.** \$24,686.75 **15c.** \$8,733.25 **15d.** \$39,420 **15e.** 12.75%

14 CHAPTER MORTGAGES

14 SECTION I Review Exercises

1. 80, 9.00, \$720, \$92,800 **3.** 130.9, 8.06, \$1,055.05, \$185,615 **5.** 96.8, 7.17, \$694.06, \$153,061.60 **7.** \$639.47, \$821.39 **9.** \$1,189.79, \$1,601.21 **11a.** \$1,736.46 **11b.** \$275,328 **13a.** Fortune Bank, \$115,950; Northern Trust Bank, \$120,000 **13b.** Fortune Bank, \$121,950, Northern Trust Bank, \$120,000 (better deal by \$1,950) **15a.** 7.25% **15b.** 15.25% **17a.** \$2,512.08 **17b.** \$150,400 **17c.** \$51,495 **17d.** \$15,275

14 SECTION II Review Exercises

1. \$89,025, \$21,125 **3.** \$112,960, \$13,860 **5.** \$63,700, 0 **7.** 14.32%, 24.05% **9.** 26.04%, 35% **11a.** Parker and Martin **11b.** Parker and Martin **13.** \$210,928 **15a.** 20.6% **15b.** 49.6% **15c.** neither **15d.** \$835.18

14 CHAPTER ASSESSMENT TEST

1. 134.9, 7.56, \$1,019.84, \$171,052 **3.** Month 1: \$146,052.28; Month 2: \$146,004.10; Month 3: \$145,955.46 **5.** \$1,321, \$1,596.67 **7.** \$41,200, \$13,800 **9.** 24.3%, 40.15% **11.** Perkins, FHA; Drake, FHA and conventional **13a.** \$5,194.80 **13b.** Month 1 loan bal. \$519,355.20; Month 2 loan bal. \$518,704.76 **13c.** \$6,147.30 **13d.** \$13,652.70 **15a.** Spring Creek Bank, \$946,368; Foremost Savings & Loan, \$919,584 **15b.** Foremost is a better deal by \$9,346.50 **17a.** \$1,230.98 **17b.** \$120,236 **17c.** \$22,557.40 **17d.** \$80,060 **19.** 0 **21a.** 27.86% **21b.** 39.53% **21c.** FHA

15 CHAPTER FINANCIAL STATEMENTS AND RATIOS

15 SECTION I Review Exercises

1. \$161,600 **3.** \$29,000 **5.** current asset **7.** owner's equity **9.** long-term liability **11.** current liability **13.** current asset **15.** current asset **17.** fixed asset **19.** current asset **21.** owner's equity **23.** owner's equity **25.** current liability

27a.

Flagship Industries, Inc.
Balance Sheet
June 30, 2008

Assets		
Current Assets		**Percent***
Cash	$ 44,300	5.5%
Accounts Receivable	127,600	15.8
Merchandise Inventory	88,100	10.9
Prepaid Maintenance	4,100	.5
Office Supplies	4,000	.5
Total Current Assets	268,100	33.2
Property, Plant and Equipment		
Land	154,000	19.0
Buildings	237,000	29.3
Fixtures	21,400	2.6
Vehicles	64,000	7.9
Computers	13,000	1.6
Total Property, Plant and Equipment	489,400	60.4
Investments and Other Assets		
Investments	32,000	4.0
Goodwill	20,000	2.5
Total Assets	$809,500	100.0%

Liabilities and Stockholders' Equity		
Current Liabilities		
Accounts Payable	55,700	6.9%
Salaries Payable	23,200	2.9
Notes Payable	38,000	4.7
Total Current Liabilities	116,900	14.5
Long-Term Liabilities		
Mortgage Payable	91,300	11.3
Debenture Bonds	165,000	20.4
Total Long-Term Liabilities	256,300	31.7
Total Liabilities	373,200	46.2
Stockholders' Equity		
Common Stock	350,000	43.2
Retained Earnings	86,300	10.7
Total Stockholders' Equity	436,300	53.9
Total Liabilities and Stockholders' Equity	$809,500	100.0%

*Percents may vary by .1 due to rounding

27b.

Flagship Industries, Inc.
Comparative Balance Sheet
June 30, 2008 and 2009

			Increase (Decrease)	
Assets	**2009**	**2008**	**Amount**	**Percent**
Current Assets				
Cash	$ 40,200	$ 44,300	($4,100)	(9.3)%
Accounts Receivable	131,400	127,600	3,800	3.0
Merchandise Inventory	92,200	88,100	4,100	4.7
Prepaid Maintenance	3,700	4,100	(400)	(9.8)
Office Supplies	6,200	4,000	2,200	55.0
Total Current Assets	273,700	268,100	5,600	2.1
Property, Plant and Equipment				
Land	154,000	154,000	0	0.0
Buildings	231,700	237,000	(5,300)	(2.2)
Fixtures	23,900	21,400	2,500	11.7
Vehicles	55,100	64,000	(8,900)	(13.9)
Computers	16,800	13,000	3,800	29.2
Total Property, Plant and Equipment	481,500	489,400	7,900	1.6
Investments and Other Assets				
Investments	36,400	32,000	4,400	13.8
Goodwill	22,000	20,000	2,000	10.0
Total Assets	$813,600	$809,500	4,100	.5
Liabilities and Stockholders' Equity				
Current Liabilities				
Accounts Payable	51,800	55,700	(3,900)	(7.0)
Salaries Payable	25,100	23,200	1,900	8.2
Notes Payable	19,000	38,000	(19,000)	(50.0)
Total Current Liabilities	95,900	116,900	(21,000)	(18.0)
Long-Term Liabilities				
Mortgage Payable	88,900	91,300	(2,400)	(2.6)
Debenture Bonds	165,000	165,000	0	0.0
Total Long-Term Liabilities	253,900	256,300	(2,400)	(.9)
Total Liabilities	349,800	373,200	(23,400)	(6.3)
Stockholders' Equity				
Common Stock	350,000	350,000	0	0.0
Retained Earnings	113,800	86,300	27,500	31.9
Total Stockholders' Equity	463,800	436,300	27,500	6.3
Total Liabilities and Stockholders' Equity	$813,600	$809,500	4,100	.5

Review Exercises

SECTION II 15

1. $202,200, $94,200 **3.** $675,530, $334,160 **5a.** $316,120 **5b.** $122,680
5c. $212,320 **5d.** $45,120

7a.

Sweets & Treats Candy Company, Inc.
Income Statement
For the year ended December 31, 2008

Revenue		
Gross Sales	$2,249,000	109.6
Less: Sales Returns and Allowances	143,500	7.0
Sales Discounts	54,290	2.6
Net Sales	$ 2,051,210	100.0
Cost of Goods Sold		
Merchandise Inventory, Jan.1	875,330	42.7
Net Purchases	546,920	26.7
Freight In	11,320	.6
Goods Available for Sale	1,433,570	69.9
Less: Merchandise Inventory, Dec. 31	716,090	34.9
Cost of Goods Sold	717,480	35.0
Gross Margin	1,333,730	65.0
Operating Expenses		
Salaries	319,800	15.6
Rent	213,100	10.4
Depreciation	51,200	2.5
Utilities	35,660	1.7
Advertising	249,600	12.2
Insurance	39,410	1.9
Administrative Expenses	91,700	4.5
Miscellaneous Expenses	107,500	5.2
Total Operating Expenses	1,107,970	54.0
Income before Taxes	225,760	11.0
Income Tax	38,450	1.9
Net Income	$ 187,310	9.1

7b.

Sweets & Treats Candy Company, Inc.
Comparative Income Statement
For the years ended December 31, 2008 and 2009

			Increase (Decrease)	
Assets	**2009**	**2008**	**Amount**	**Percent**
Revenue				
Gross Sales	$2,125,000	$2,249,000	($124,000)	(5.5)
Less: Sales Returns and Allowances	126,400	143,500	(17,100)	(11.9)
Sales Discounts	73,380	54,290	19,090	35.2
Net Sales	1,925,220	2,051,210	(125,990)	(6.1)
Cost of Goods Sold				
Merchandise Inventory, Jan. 1	716,090	875,330	(159,240)	(18.2)
Net Purchases	482,620	546,920	(64,300)	(11.8)
Freight In	9,220	11,320	(2,100)	(18.6)
Goods Available for Sale	1,207,930	1,433,570	(225,640)	(15.7)
Less: Merchandise Inventory, Dec. 31	584,550	716,090	(131,540)	(18.4)
Cost of Goods Sold	623,380	717,480	(94,100)	(13.1)
Gross Margin	1,301,840	1,333,730	(31,890)	(2.4)
Operating Expenses				
Salaries	340,900	319,800	21,100	7.0
Rent	215,000	213,100	1,900	.9
Depreciation	56,300	51,200	5,100	10.0
Utilities	29,690	35,660	(5,970)	(16.7)
Advertising	217,300	249,600	(32,300)	(13.0)
Insurance	39,410	39,410	0	0.0
Administrative Expenses	95,850	91,700	4,150	4.5
Miscellaneous Expenses	102,500	107,500	(5,000)	(4.7)
Total Operating Expenses	1,096,950	1,107,970	(11,020)	(1.0)
Income before Income Tax	204,890	225,760	(20,870)	(9.2)
Income Tax	44,530	38,450	6,080	15.8
Net Income	$ 160,360	$ 187,310	(26,950)	(14.4)

15 SECTION III Review Exercises

1. $51,160, 1.69:1 **3.** $2,350, 2.88:1 **5.** $95,920, 1.29:1 **7.** $2,165, 1.73:1 **9.** 44 days **11.** $105,650, 6.2 times **13.** $74,447.50, 6.6 times **15.** .58:1 **17.** $155,390, .70:1, 2.30:1 **19.** $253,940, $78,530, 34.2%, 10.6% **21.** $113,080, $27,159, 35.7%, 8.6% **23.** 8.2%

25.

Hook, Line, and Sinker Fishing Supply
Trend Analysis Chart

	2008	2007	2006	2005	2004
Net Sales	107.5	127.3	108.0	97.1	100.0
Net Income	124.3	128.5	99.4	104.2	100.0
Total Assets	109.7	107.4	105.0	97.7	100.0
Stockholders' Equity	105.9	120.3	106.4	94.5	100.0

ASSESSMENT TEST

CHAPTER 15

1a.

Mountain Magic Tire Company
Balance Sheet
December 31, 2008

Assets		**Percent**
Current Assets	$132,500	52.2
Property, Plant and Equipment	88,760	35.0
Investments and Other Assets	32,400	12.8
Total Assets	$253,660	100.0%
Liabilities		
Current Liabilities	51,150	20.2
Long-Term Liabilities	87,490	34.5
Total Liabilities	138,640	54.7
Owner's Equity		
Paul Provost, Equity	115,020	45.3
Total Liabilities and Owner's Equity	$253,660	100.0%

1b.

Mountain Magic Tire Company
Comparative Balance Sheet
December 31, 2008 and 2009

			Increase (Decrease)	
	2009	**2008**	**Amount**	**Percent**
Assets				
Current Assets	$154,300	$132,500	$21,800	16.5
Property, Plant and Equipment	124,650	88,760	35,890	40.4
Investments and Other Assets	20,000	32,400	(12,400)	(38.3)
Total Assets	$298,950	$253,660	45,290	17.9
Liabilities				
Current Liabilities	65,210	51,150	14,060	27.5
Long-Term Liabilities	83,800	87,490	(3,690)	(4.2)
Total Liabilities	149,010	138,640	10,370	7.5
Owner's Equity				
Paul Provost, Equity	149,940	115,020	34,920	30.4
Total Liabilities and Owner's Equity	$298,950	$253,660	45,290	17.9

3. $185,772

5a.

Woof & Meow Pet Supply
Income Statement
Third Quarter, 2009

Revenue		
Gross Sales	$224,400	106.8
Less: Sales Returns and Allowances	14,300	6.8
Net Sales	210,100	100.0
Cost of Goods sold		
Merchandise Inventory, July 1	165,000	78.5
Net Purchases	76,500	36.4
Goods Available for Sale	241,500	114.9
Less: Merchandise Inventory, Sept. 30	143,320	68.2
Cost of Goods Sold	98,180	46.7
Gross Margin	111,920	53.3
Operating Expenses	68,600	32.7
Income before Taxes	43,320	20.6
Income Tax	8,790	4.2
Net Income	$ 34,530	16.4

5b.

Woof & Meow Pet Supply
Comparative Income Statement
Third and Fourth Quarters, 2009

			Increase (Decrease)	
	4th Qtr.	**3rd Qtr.**	**Amount**	**Percent**
Revenue				
Gross Sales	$218,200	$224,400	($6,200)	(2.8)
Less: Sales Returns and Allowances	9,500	14,300	(4,800)	(33.6)
Net Sales	208,700	210,100	1,400	.7
Cost of Goods Sold				
Merchandise Inventory, Beginning	143,320	165,000	(21,680)	(13.1)
Net Purchases	81,200	76,500	4,700	6.1
Goods Available for Sale	224,520	241,500	(16,980)	(7.0)
Less: Merchandise Inventory, Ending	125,300	143,320	(18,020)	(12.6)
Cost of Goods Sold	99,220	98,180	1,040	1.0
Gross Margin	109,480	111,920	(2,440)	(2.2)
Operating Expenses	77,300	68,600	8,700	12.7
Income before Income Tax	32,180	43,320	(11,140)	(25.7)
Income Tax	11,340	8,790	2,550	29.0
Net Income	$ 20,840	$ 34,530	(13,690)	(39.6)

7. $653,300 **9.** 1.51:1 **11.** 1.74 times **13.** 37.9% **15.** 48.3% **17.** 4.2%

19.

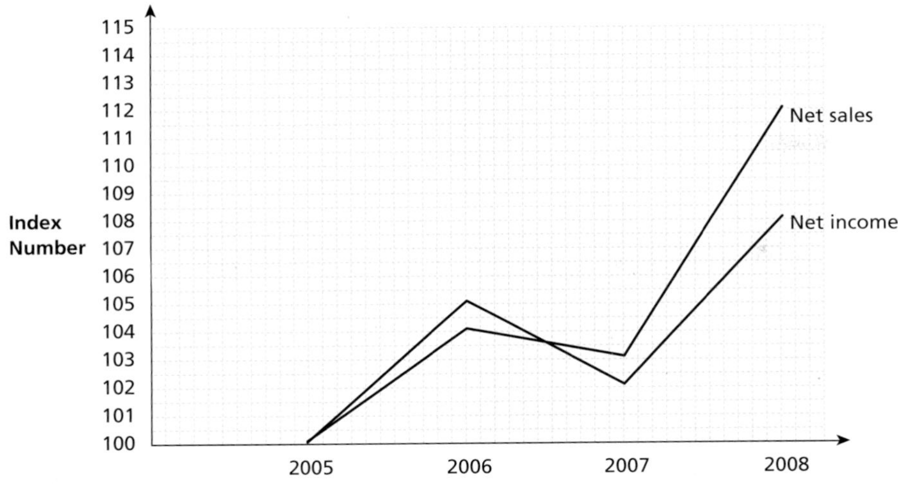

INVENTORY

Review Exercises

1. 1,110 units available, $1,798.30, cost of goods **3a.** 600 **3b.** $86,230 **3c.** $24,765.20 **3d.** $23,380 **3e.** $24,001.24 **5.** $2,610.28 Total value of inventory

Review Exercises

1. $108,225 **3.** $157,350 **5.** $61,716

Review Exercises

1. $60,000, 8.3 times, $50,000 **3.** $486,500, 2.5 times, $342,857.14 **5a.** $28,450 **5b.** 5.1 Times **7a.** $77,650 **7b.** 5.9 Times **9a.** 4.8 Times **9b.** $134,309.09 **11a.** $38,150, 3.8 Times **11b.** $29,591.84

ASSESSMENT TEST

CHAPTER 16

1. 454 units, $22,053.65 cost of goods **3.** $178,159 **5.** $394,885 **7.** $153,500, 5 times, $111,764.71 **9a.** $173,200 **9b.** 2.5 times **9c.** $114,710.53

17 CHAPTER DEPRECIATION

17 SECTION I Review Exercises

1. \$45,650, \$42,150, \$4,215 **3.** \$160,000, \$140,000, \$28,000

5.

Fluffy Laundromat
Straight-Line Depreciation Schedule
Laundry Equipment

End of Year	Annual Depreciation	Accumulated Depreciation	Book Value
		(new)	\$57,970
1	\$11,194	\$11,194	46,776
2	11,194	22,388	35,582
3	11,194	33,582	24,388
4	11,194	44,776	13,194
5	11,194	55,970	2,000

7. 15, $\frac{5}{15}, \frac{3}{15}, \frac{1}{15}$ **9.** 55, $\frac{10}{55}, \frac{8}{55}, \frac{6}{55}$ **11.** 25%, 31.25% **13.** 10%, 15% **15.** \$.122

17. \$.25 **19a.** \$85,000 **19b.** \$2,100,000 **19c.** \$132,000

17 SECTION II Review Exercises

1a. \$45,500 **1b.** \$9,100 **3a.** \$150,000 **3b.** 10-year property **3c.** 7.37%
3d. \$4,920 **5a.** \$.48 **5b.** \$375,360

CHAPTER ASSESSMENT TEST

1. \$5,864, \$5,264, \$877.33

3.

Oxford Manufacturing, Inc.
Straight-Line Depreciation Schedule
Manufacturing Equipment

End of Year	Annual Depreciation	Accumulated Depreciation	Book Value
		(new)	\$652,000
1	\$154,750	\$154,750	497,250
2	154,750	309,500	342,500
3	154,750	464,250	187,750
4	154,750	619,000	33,000

5. 45, $\frac{8}{45}, \frac{6}{45}, \frac{4}{45}$ **7.** 11.111%, 13.889%

9.

Award Makers
125% Declining-Balance Depreciation Schedule
Computerized Engraving Machine

End of Year	Beginning Book Value	Depreciation Rate	Depreciation for the Year	Accumulated Depreciation	Ending Book Value
					(new) $33,800.00
1	$33,800.00	.20833	$7,041.55	$7,041.55	26,758.45
2	26,758.45	.20833	5,574.59	12,616.14	21,183.86
3	21,183.86	.20833	4,413.23	17,029.37	16,770.63

11. $.024 **13a.** Business-use basis = $344,000; Tentative basis = $320,000; No special allowances available. Basis for depreciation = $320,000

13b.

Stone Age Concrete, Inc.
MACRS Depreciation Schedule
Cement Manufacturing Equipment

End of Year	Original Basis (cost)	Cost Recovery Percentage	Cost Recovery (depreciation)	Accumulated Depreciation	Book Value
					(new) $320,000
1	$320,000	5.00	$16,000	$16,000	304,000
2	320,000	9.50	30,400	46,400	273,600
3	320,000	8.55	27,360	73,760	246,240
4	320,000	7.70	24,640	98,400	221,600
5	320,000	6.93	22.176	120,576	199,424

15a. $375,000 **15b.** $415,500

TAXES

CHAPTER 18

Review Exercises

SECTION I

1. $.59, $9.54 **3.** $.32, $5.20 **5.** $100.80, $15.84, $1,556.64 **7.** $9.90, $22, $251.85 **9.** $17,847.98, $937.02 **11a.** $70.19 **11b.** $1,045.09 **13a.** $54,871.09 **13b.** $3,017.91 **15.** $287,760

Review Exercises

SECTION II

1. $76,000, $2,614.40 **3.** $198,400, $5,138.56 **5.** $106,440, $2,267.17 **7.** $264,033, $13,993.75 **9.** 4.92%, $4.92, $49.20, 49.2 **11.** 3.68%, $3.68, $36.80, 36.8 **13a.** $87,500 **13b.** $1,701

18 SECTION III Review Exercises

1. $32,180, $5,150, $3,300, $23,730 **3.** $43,910, $10,300, $6,600, $27,010 **5.** $6,780, $5,150, $3,300, $50,980 **7.** $4,080, $7,550, $21,230, $9,900, $53,390 **9.** $31,407 **11.** $14,064 **13.** $10,596 **15.** $68,305.77 **17.** $103,705.50 **19.** refund, $651 **21.** refund, $1,438 **23.** $18,494.70, $70,460.30 **25.** $334,250,000, $620,750,000

18 CHAPTER ASSESSMENT TEST

1. $1.17, $19.05 **3.** $6.62, $141.62 **5.** $1,184.63, $755, $19,489.63 **7a.** $25.42 **7b.** $471.30 **9a.** $3.83, $2,221.40 **9b.** $7.50, $4,350 **9c.** $55,871.40 **11.** $52,101, $662.72 **13.** $82,615, $2,394.18 **15.** 1.64%, $1.64, $16.40, 16.4 **17a.** .07% **17b.** $.07 **17c.** $.70 **17d.** .7 **19.** $66,003, $10,300, $9,900, $43,623 **21.** $44,351.96 **23.** $2,984 **25.** $61,273.25 **27.** owe, $228 **29a.** $35,150 **29b.** $23,400 **29c.** $1,371 **29d.** refund, $2,529

19 CHAPTER INSURANCE

19 SECTION I Review Exercises

1. $79.50, $41.34, $20.67, $7.16 **3.** $842, $437.84, $218.92, $75.78 **5.** $270, $140.40, $70.20, $24.30 **7.** $1,125.25, $585.13, $292.57, $101.27 **9.** $4,900, $9,300, 17 years, 54 days **11.** $5,495, $10,990, 21 years, 218 days **13a.** $5,240.40 **13b.** $2,725.01 **15.** $14,325 cash value; $37,200 reduced paid-up ins.; 30 years, 206 days extended term

19 SECTION II Review Exercises

1. $668.80, $174.30, $843.10 **3.** $451.50, $69.60, $521.10 **5.** $2,132.10, $438.90, $2,571 **7.** $89.60, $470.40 **9.** $134.17, $187.83 **11.** $75,000 **13.** $37,000 **15.** $150,000 **17.** $202.50 **19.** Aetna: $57,000, State Farm: $23,750, Liberty Mutual: $14,250

19 SECTION III Review Exercises

1. $343 **3.** $1,125 **5.** $625.60 **7.** $1,146.60 **9.** $1,412 **11a.** Hart: $13,500, Black: $11,700, Garner: $4,140, Williams: $50,000, Morgan: $3,590, Bus: $12,230, Camper: $3,530, total: $98,690 **11b.** Williams: $7,800, deductible: $250, total: $8,050

ASSESSMENT TEST

CHAPTER 

1. $2,521.60, $1,311.23, $655.62, $226.94 **3.** $148.20, $77.06, $38.53, $13.34 **5.** $20,410 cash value, $40,820 reduced paid-up ins.; 21 years, 218 days extended term **7a.** $1,088 **7b.** $97.92 **7c.** $87.04 **9.** $512.000 **11.** $475, $672, $1,147 **13.** $173.33, $86.67 **15.** $6,057.69 **17.** $12,392 **19.** $153,000 **21.** $361.80 **23.** $564.40 **25a.** Goya: $45,000, Truman: $50,000, Copeland: $5,000, Kelly: 0, Blake's car: $3,650, total: $103,650 **25b.** Truman: $18,000, Copeland: $11,000, Kelly: $11,000, deductible: $250, total: $40,250

INVESTMENTS

CHAPTER 

Review Exercises

SECTION I 20

1. none, $.60 **3.** $5.00, 0 **5.** 0, 0 **7.** HPQ, $52.03, 21 **9.** $53.90, 3%, 0.6% **11.** 3.5%, 7 **13.** $1.31, 1.6% **15.** $1.41, $.30 **17.** $6,585.15, $9,997.57, $3,412.42 **19.** $29,723.41, $26,310.56, ($3,412.85) **21.** $.85 **23a.** $27,000,000 **23b.** $1.74 **25a.** $29,658.56 **25b.** $36,078.38 **25c.** $6,419.82

Review Exercises

SECTION II 20

1. 9.98%, $94.95 **3.** BAC.XQ, up $0.345 **5.** Citicorp **7.** 8.25%, 9.188% **9.** Baal/A-/A-, 5.26%, **11.** $9.17, $876.67 **13.** $34.90, $7,959.20 **15.** $16.56, $11,433.10 **17.** $28.33, $4,429.32 **19.** $8.13, $6,262.41 **21.** $66.25, 7.3% **23.** $75, 6% **25.** $53.75, 6.4%

Review Exercises

SECTION III 20

1. OAKVX, $26.43 **3.** Oak Associates Funds, BlkOakEmrg, $2.87 **5.** Delaware Invest B, CorPlsBd t, 2% **7.** Int Ret p, 29% **9.** $.53, 4.1% **11.** $1.28, 5% **13.** $15.54, 621.118 **15.** $10.68, 4,484.305 **17.** $1,530, $1,880, $395, 25.8% **19.** $4,850, $6,120, $2,520, 52% **21a.** $.75 **21b.** 6.1% **23.** 689.655

ASSESSMENT TEST

CHAPTER 20

1. none, $.36 **3.** $15, $.09 **5.** 3M Company, 2,101,200 shares **7.** Honeywell Int'l. Inc. $33.9% **9.** $2.09, 3.3% **11.** $8.98, $1.71 **13.** $15,665.20, $12,142.70, ($3,522.50) **15.** $39,277.88, $44,975.31, $5,697.43 **17a.** $13,000,000 **17b.** $.71 **19a.** $4,472.28 **19b.** $3,346.85 **19c.** ($1,125.43) **21.** A3/A-/A, 5.2% **23.** Merrill Lynch, down $3.385 **25.** Baal/A-/A-, up $0.029, 5.26% **27.** $20.49, $4,074.95 **29.** $2.05, $9,410.50 **31.** $21.84, $4,969.20 **33.** $95, 9% **35.** Harper Funds, Intl Ret p. $75.62 **37.** $11.62, down $0.01 **39.** $.52, 5% **41.** $7.05, 6,410.256 **43.** $1,340, $1,180, ($85), (6.3%) **45.** $9,400, $12,820, $4,380, 46.6% **47.** $9.04 **49.** 33.6%

CHAPTER 21 BUSINESS STATISTICS AND DATA PRESENTATION

SECTION I Review Exercises

1.

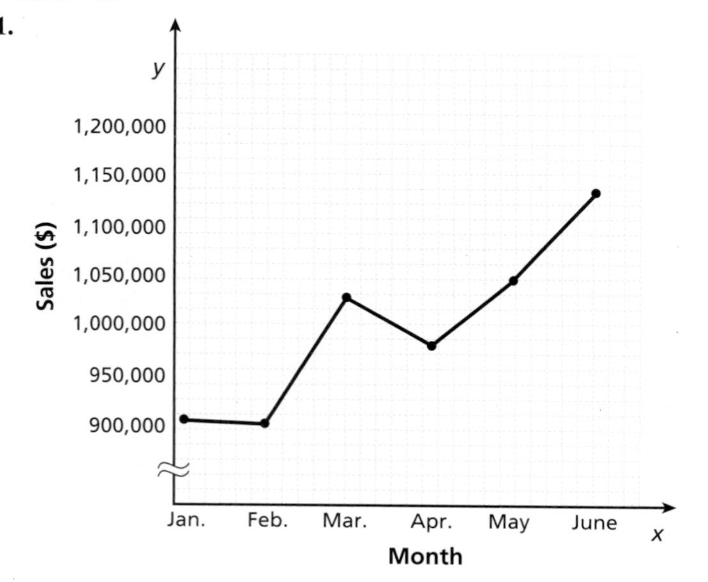

3.

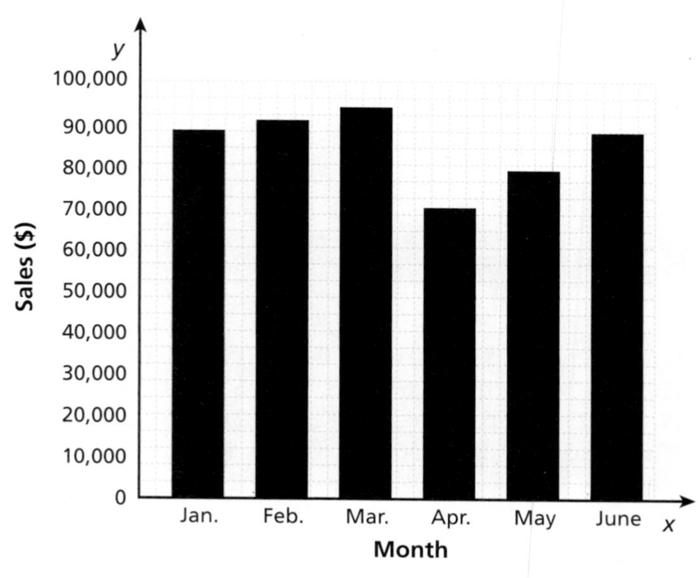

5.

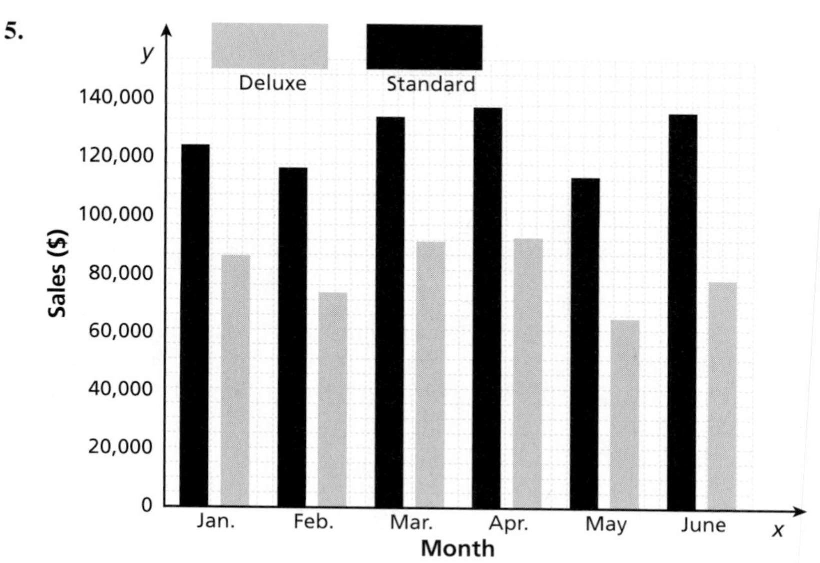

SECTION II Review Exercises

1. 5.8 **3.** 2 **5.** \$2.88 **7.** 21 **9.** 4 and 9 **11.** \$3.66 **13a.** 339.9 **13b.** 343 **13c.** 425 **13d.** 221

SECTION III Review Exercises

1a.

Class	Tally	Frequency
0–99	IIII	4
100–199	~~IIII~~	5
200–299	~~IIII~~ I	6
300–399	~~IIII~~ IIII	9
400–499	III	3
500–599	II	2
600–699	I	1

1b.

Class	Tally	Frequency (f)	Midpoint (m)	$f \times m$
0–99	IIII	4	49.5	198.0
100–199	~~IIII~~	5	149.5	747.5
200–299	~~IIII~~ I	6	249.5	1,497.0
300–399	~~IIII~~ IIII	9	349.5	3,145.5
400–499	III	3	449.5	1,348.5
500–599	II	2	549.5	1,099.0
600–699	I	1	649.5	649.5
		30		8,685.0

$$\text{Mean} = \frac{8{,}685}{30} = \underline{\underline{289.5}}$$

1c.

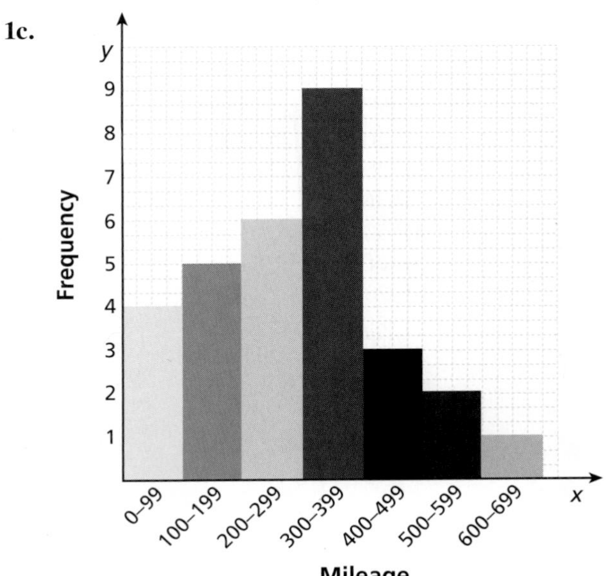

ASSESSMENT TEST

CHAPTER 21

1a.

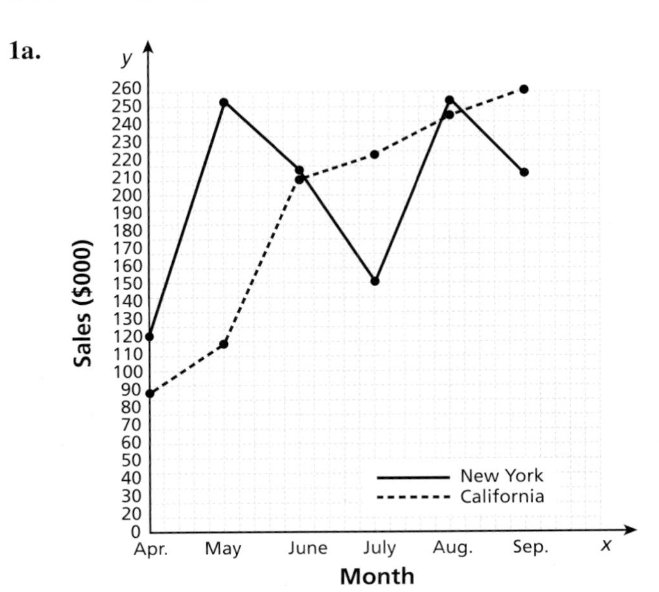

1b.

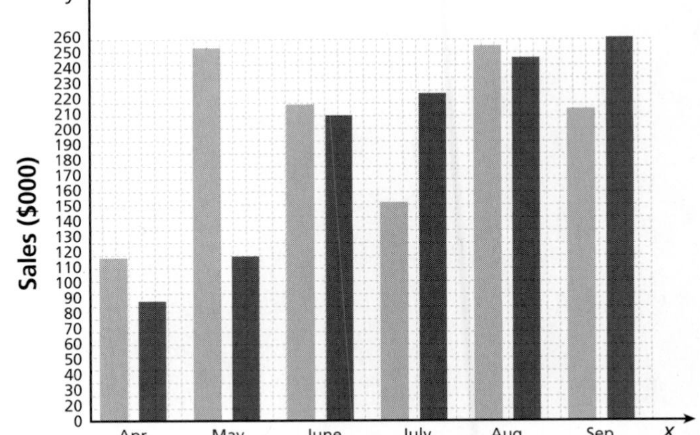

3a. desktop computers: 50%, notebook computers: 25%, software: 10%, printers: 12.5%, accessories: 2.5%

3b.

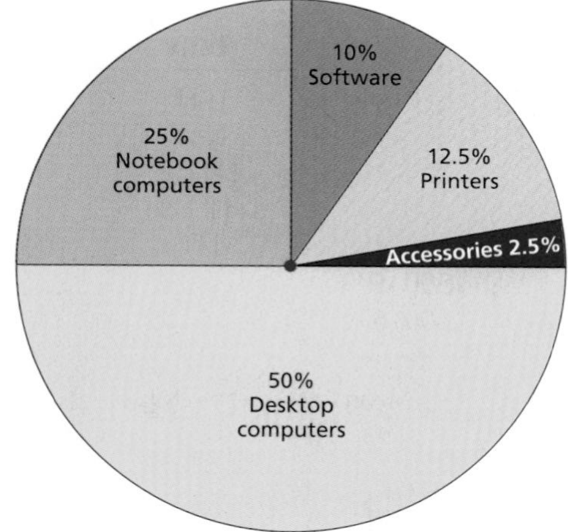

5a. range: 78, mode: 72

5b.

Class	Tally	Frequency
11–20	|	1
21–30	|	1
31–40	|	1
41–50	||	2
51–60	||||	4
61–70	𝍸	5
71–80	𝍸 𝍸	10
81–90	𝍸 𝍸	10
91–100	𝍸 |	6

5c.

Class	Tally	Frequency (f)	Midpoint (m)	$f \times m$
11–20	|	1	15.5	15.5
21–30	|	1	25.5	25.5
31–40	|	1	35.5	35.5
41–50	||	2	45.5	91.0
51–60	||||	4	55.5	222.0
61–70	𝍸	5	65.5	327.5
71–80	𝍸 𝍸	10	75.5	755.0
81–90	𝍸 𝍸	10	85.5	855.0
91–100	𝍸	6	95.5	573.0
		40		2,900.0

$$\text{Mean} = \frac{2{,}900}{40} = \underline{\underline{72.5}}$$

5d. 14

5e.

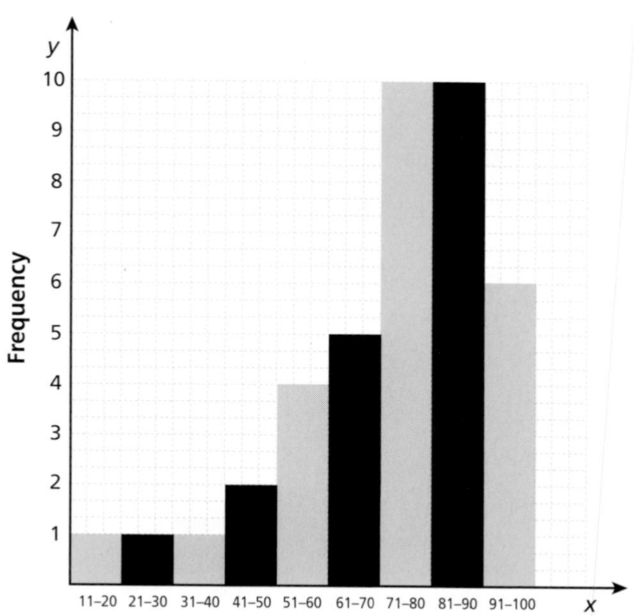

Index

A

B

M

N

T

U

V

W

X

Y

Z

Appendix B

Worked-out Solutions

USING EQUATIONS TO SOLVE BUSINESS PROBLEMS

CHAPTER

Review Exercises

SECTION I

1. $$\begin{array}{l} B + 11 = 24 \\ \quad -11 \;\; -11 \\ \hline B \qquad = 13 \end{array}$$ *Proof:* $$\begin{array}{r} 13 + 11 = 24 \\ 24 = 24 \end{array}$$

2. $$\begin{array}{l} C - 16 = \;\; 5 \\ \quad +16 \;\; +16 \\ \hline C \qquad = 21 \end{array}$$ *Proof:* $$\begin{array}{r} 21 - 16 = 5 \\ 5 = 5 \end{array}$$

3. $$\begin{array}{l} S + 35 = 125 \\ \quad -35 \;\; -35 \\ \hline S \qquad = 90 \end{array}$$ *Proof:* $$\begin{array}{r} 90 + 35 = 125 \\ 125 = 125 \end{array}$$

4. $$\begin{array}{l} M - 58 = \;\; 12 \\ \quad +58 \;\; +58 \\ \hline M \qquad = 70 \end{array}$$ *Proof:* $$\begin{array}{r} 70 - 58 = 12 \\ 12 = 12 \end{array}$$

5. $$\begin{array}{c} 21K = 63 \\ \dfrac{\cancel{21}K}{\cancel{21}} = \dfrac{63}{21} \\ K = 3 \end{array}$$ *Proof:* $$\begin{array}{r} 21(3) = 63 \\ 63 = 63 \end{array}$$

6. $$\begin{array}{c} \dfrac{Z}{3} = 45 \\ (\cancel{3})\dfrac{Z}{\cancel{3}} = 45(3) \\ Z = 135 \end{array}$$ *Proof:* $$\begin{array}{r} \dfrac{135}{3} = 45 \\ 45 = 45 \end{array}$$

7. $$\begin{array}{c} 50Y = 375 \\ \dfrac{\cancel{50}Y}{\cancel{50}} = \dfrac{375}{50} \\ Y = 7\frac{1}{2} \end{array}$$ *Proof:* $$\begin{array}{r} 50\left(7\frac{1}{2}\right) = 375 \\ 375 = 375 \end{array}$$

8. $$\begin{array}{c} \dfrac{L}{5} = 8 \\ (\cancel{5})\dfrac{L}{\cancel{5}} = 8(5) \\ L = 40 \end{array}$$ *Proof:* $$\begin{array}{r} \dfrac{40}{5} = 8 \\ 8 = 8 \end{array}$$

9. $$\begin{array}{l} 6G + 5 = \;\; 29 \\ \quad -5 \;\; -5 \\ \hline 6G \qquad = 24 \\ \dfrac{\cancel{6}G}{\cancel{6}} = \dfrac{24}{6} \\ G = 4 \end{array}$$ *Proof:* $$\begin{array}{r} 6(4) + 5 = 29 \\ 24 + 5 = 29 \\ 29 = 29 \end{array}$$

10. $$\begin{array}{l} \dfrac{D}{3} - 5 = 15 \\ \quad +5 \;\; +5 \\ \hline \dfrac{D}{3} \qquad = 20 \end{array}$$ $$\begin{array}{c} (\cancel{3})\dfrac{D}{\cancel{3}} = 20(3) \\ D = 60 \end{array}$$ *Proof:* $$\begin{array}{r} \dfrac{60}{3} - 5 = 15 \\ 20 - 5 = 15 \\ 15 = 15 \end{array}$$

11. $$\begin{array}{l} 25A - 11 = \;\; 64 \\ \quad +11 \;\; +11 \\ \hline 25A \qquad = 75 \end{array}$$ $$\begin{array}{c} \dfrac{\cancel{25}A}{\cancel{25}} = \dfrac{75}{25} \\ A = 3 \end{array}$$ *Proof:* $$\begin{array}{r} 25(3) - 11 = 64 \\ 75 - 11 = 64 \\ 64 = 64 \end{array}$$

12. $$\begin{array}{l} \dfrac{R}{5} + 33 = 84 \\ \quad -33 \;\; -33 \\ \hline \dfrac{R}{5} \qquad = 51 \end{array}$$ $$\begin{array}{c} (\cancel{5})\dfrac{R}{\cancel{5}} = 51(5) \\ R = 255 \end{array}$$ *Proof:* $$\begin{array}{r} \dfrac{255}{5} + 33 = 84 \\ 51 + 33 = 84 \\ 84 = 84 \end{array}$$

13. $$\begin{array}{l} 3(4X + 5) = 63 \\ 12X + 15 = 63 \\ \quad -15 \;\; -15 \\ \hline 12X \qquad = 48 \end{array}$$ $$\begin{array}{c} \dfrac{\cancel{12}X}{\cancel{12}} = \dfrac{48}{12} \\ X = 4 \end{array}$$ *Proof:* $$\begin{array}{r} 3(4(4) + 5) = 63 \\ 3(16 + 5) = 63 \\ 3(21) = 63 \\ 63 = 63 \end{array}$$

14.
$$\begin{aligned} C + 5 &= 26 - 2C \\ +2C \quad & \quad +2C \\ \hline 3C + 5 &= 26 \end{aligned} \qquad \begin{aligned} 3C + 5 &= 26 \\ -5 \quad & -5 \\ \hline 3C &= 21 \end{aligned} \qquad \frac{\cancel{3}C}{\cancel{3}} = \frac{21}{3} \quad \underline{\underline{C = 7}}$$

Proof:
$$\begin{aligned} 7 + 5 &= 26 - 2(7) \\ 12 &= 26 - 14 \\ \underline{\underline{12}} &\underline{\underline{= 12}} \end{aligned}$$

15.
$$\begin{aligned} 12(2D - 4) &= 72 \\ 24D - 48 &= 72 \\ +48 \quad & +48 \\ \hline 24D \quad &= 120 \end{aligned} \qquad \frac{\cancel{24}D}{\cancel{24}} = \frac{120}{24} \quad \underline{\underline{D = 5}}$$

Proof:
$$\begin{aligned} 12(2(5) - 4) &= 72 \\ 12(10 - 4) &= 72 \\ 12(6) &= 72 \\ \underline{\underline{72}} &\underline{\underline{= 72}} \end{aligned}$$

16.
$$\begin{aligned} 14V + 5 - 5V &= 4(V + 5) \\ 9V + 5 &= 4V + 20 \\ -4V \quad & \quad -4V \\ \hline 5V + 5 &= 20 \end{aligned} \qquad \begin{aligned} 5V + 5 &= 20 \\ -5 \quad & -5 \\ \hline 5V &= 15 \end{aligned} \qquad \frac{\cancel{5}V}{\cancel{5}} = \frac{15}{5} \quad \underline{\underline{V = 3}}$$

Proof:
$$\begin{aligned} 14(3) + 5 - 5(3) &= 4(3 + 5) \\ 42 + 5 - 15 &= 4(8) \\ \underline{\underline{32}} &\underline{\underline{= 32}} \end{aligned}$$

17.
$$\begin{aligned} Q + 20 &= 3(9 - 2Q) \\ Q + 20 &= 27 - 6Q \\ +6Q \quad & \quad +6Q \\ \hline 7Q + 20 &= 27 \end{aligned} \qquad \begin{aligned} 7Q + 20 &= 27 \\ -20 \quad & -20 \\ \hline 7Q &= 7 \end{aligned} \qquad \frac{\cancel{7}Q}{\cancel{7}} = \frac{7}{7} \quad \underline{\underline{Q = 1}}$$

Proof:
$$\begin{aligned} 1 + 20 &= 3(9 - 2(1)) \\ 21 &= 3(7) \\ \underline{\underline{21}} &\underline{\underline{= 21}} \end{aligned}$$

CHAPTER ASSESSMENT TEST

1.
$$\begin{aligned} T + 45 &= 110 \\ -45 \quad & -45 \\ \hline \underline{\underline{T}} &\underline{\underline{= 65}} \end{aligned}$$

Proof:
$$\begin{aligned} 65 + 45 &= 110 \\ \underline{\underline{110}} &\underline{\underline{= 110}} \end{aligned}$$

2.
$$\begin{aligned} G - 24 &= 75 \\ +24 \quad & +24 \\ \hline \underline{\underline{G}} &\underline{\underline{= 99}} \end{aligned}$$

Proof:
$$\begin{aligned} 99 - 24 &= 75 \\ \underline{\underline{75}} &\underline{\underline{= 75}} \end{aligned}$$

3.
$$\frac{\cancel{11}K}{\cancel{11}} = \frac{165}{11} \quad \underline{\underline{K = 15}}$$

Proof:
$$\begin{aligned} 11(15) &= 165 \\ \underline{\underline{165}} &\underline{\underline{= 165}} \end{aligned}$$

4.
$$\begin{aligned} 3(2C - 5) &= 45 \\ 6C - 15 &= 45 \\ +15 \quad & +15 \\ \hline 6C \quad &= 60 \end{aligned} \qquad \frac{\cancel{6}C}{\cancel{6}} = \frac{60}{6} \quad \underline{\underline{C = 10}}$$

Proof:
$$\begin{aligned} 3(2(10) - 5) &= 45 \\ 3(20 - 5) &= 45 \\ 3(15) &= 45 \\ \underline{\underline{45}} &\underline{\underline{= 45}} \end{aligned}$$

5.
$$\begin{aligned} 8X - 15 &= 49 \\ +15 \quad & +15 \\ \hline 8X \quad &= 64 \end{aligned} \qquad \frac{\cancel{8}X}{\cancel{8}} = \frac{64}{8} \quad \underline{\underline{X = 8}}$$

Proof:
$$\begin{aligned} 8(8) - 15 &= 49 \\ 64 - 15 &= 49 \\ \underline{\underline{49}} &\underline{\underline{= 49}} \end{aligned}$$

6.
$$\begin{aligned} \frac{S}{7} &= 12 \\ (\cancel{7})\frac{(S)}{\cancel{7}} &= 12(7) \\ \underline{\underline{S}} &\underline{\underline{= 84}} \end{aligned}$$

Proof:
$$\begin{aligned} \frac{84}{7} &= 12 \\ \underline{\underline{12}} &\underline{\underline{= 12}} \end{aligned}$$

7.
$$\begin{aligned} B + 5 &= 61 - 6B \\ +6B \quad & \quad +6B \\ \hline 7B + 5 &= 61 \end{aligned} \qquad \begin{aligned} 7B + 5 &= 61 \\ -5 \quad & -5 \\ \hline 7B &= 56 \end{aligned} \qquad \frac{\cancel{7}B}{\cancel{7}} = \frac{56}{7} \quad \underline{\underline{B = 8}}$$

Proof:
$$\begin{aligned} 8 + 5 &= 61 - 6(8) \\ 13 &= 61 - 48 \\ \underline{\underline{13}} &\underline{\underline{= 13}} \end{aligned}$$

8.
$$\begin{aligned} \frac{N}{4} - 7 &= 8 \\ +7 \quad & +7 \\ \hline \frac{N}{4} \quad &= 15 \end{aligned} \qquad (\cancel{4})\frac{N}{\cancel{4}} = 15(4) \quad \underline{\underline{N = 60}}$$

Proof:
$$\begin{aligned} \frac{60}{4} - 7 &= 8 \\ 15 - 7 &= 8 \\ \underline{\underline{8}} &\underline{\underline{= 8}} \end{aligned}$$

9.
$$\begin{aligned} 4(3X + 8) &= 212 \\ 12X + 32 &= 212 \\ -32 \quad & -32 \\ \hline 12X \quad &= 180 \end{aligned} \qquad \frac{\cancel{12}X}{\cancel{12}} = \frac{180}{12} \quad \underline{\underline{X = 15}}$$

Proof:
$$\begin{aligned} 4(3(15) + 8) &= 212 \\ 4(45 + 8) &= 212 \\ 4(53) &= 212 \\ \underline{\underline{212}} &\underline{\underline{= 212}} \end{aligned}$$

INVOICES, TRADE DISCOUNTS, AND CASH DISCOUNTS

CHAPTER 7

Review Exercises — SECTION II

10. 100% − 37% = 63% $3,499.00 × .63 = $2,204.37

11. 100% − 24% = 76% $565.33 × .76 = $429.65

12. 100% − 45.8% = 54.2% $1,244.25 × .542 = $674.38

13. 100% − 12.75% = 87.25% $4.60 × .8725 = $4.01

14. $4,500.00 − 3,565.00 = $935.00 $\frac{935.00}{4,500.00} = .2077 = 20.8\%$

15. $345.50 − 225.00 = $120.50 $\frac{120.50}{345.50} = .3487 = 34.9\%$

16. $2.89 − 2.15 = $.74 $\frac{.74}{2.89} = .2560 = 25.6\%$

Review Exercises — SECTION III

1. Net price factor = (100% − 12%) .88 × (100% − 10%) .90 = .792
Net price = 360.00 × .792 = $285.12

2. Net price factor = .82 × .85 × .95 = .66215
Net price = 425.80 × .66215 = $281.94

3. Net price factor = .80 × .90 × .90 = .648
Net price = 81.75 × .648 = $52.97

4. Net price factor = .85 × .90 × .95 = .72675
Net price = 979.20 × .72675 = $711.63

5. Net price factor = .75 × .85 × .895 = .57056
Net price = 7.25 × .57056 = $4.14

6. Net price factor = .80 × .91 × .92 = .66976
Net price = .39 × .66976 = $.26

12.

Net Price Factor	Single Equivalent Discount	Trade Discount	Net Price
.85 × .95 × .95	1.00 − .76713	$7,800.00	$7,800.00
.76713	.23287	× .23287	× .76713
		$1,816.39	$5,983.61

Review Exercises — SECTION IV

1. CD = $15,800.00 × .03 = $474.00
NAD = $15,800.00 − $474.00 = $15,326.00

2. CD = $12,660.00 × .02 = $253.20
NAD = $12,660.00 − $253.20 = $12,406.80

3. CD = $2,421.00 × .04 = $96.84
NAD = $2,421.00 − $96.84 = $2,324.16

4. CD = $6,940.20 × .02 = $138.80
NAD = $6,940.20 − $138.80 = $6,801.40

5. CD = $9,121.44 × .035 = $319.25
NAD = $9,121.44 − $319.25 = $8,802.19

6. Credit for partial payment $= \frac{\$2,500}{.98} = \$2,551.02$
NAD = $8,303.00 − $2,551.02 = $5,751.98

7. Credit for partial payment $= \frac{\$460}{.97} = \$474.23$
NAD = $1,344.60 − $474.23 = $870.37

8. Credit for partial payment $= \frac{\$3,200}{.96} = \$3,333.33$
NAD = $5,998.20 − $3,333.33 = $2,664.87

9. Credit for partial payment $= \frac{\$5,500}{.955} = \$5,759.16$
NAD = $7,232.08 − $5,759.16 = $1,472.92

CHAPTER MARKUP AND MARKDOWN

SECTION I Review Exercises

1. $M = SP - C = 299.95 - 161.50 = \underline{\underline{\$138.45}}$

$$\%M_C = \frac{M}{C} = \frac{138.45}{161.50} = .8572 = \underline{\underline{85.7\%}}$$

2. $SP = C + M = 32.40 + 21.50 = \underline{\underline{\$53.90}}$

$$\%M_C = \frac{M}{C} = \frac{21.50}{32.40} = .6635 = \underline{\underline{66.4\%}}$$

3. $C = SP - M = 12{,}344.80 - 5{,}400.00 = \underline{\underline{\$6{,}944.80}}$

$$\%M_C = \frac{M}{C} = \frac{5{,}400.00}{6{,}944.80} = .7775 = \underline{\underline{77.8\%}}$$

4. $SP = C(100\% + \%M_C) = 75(100\% + 80\%) = 75(1.8) = \underline{\underline{\$135.00}}$

$M = SP - C = 135.00 - 75.00 = \underline{\underline{\$60.00}}$

5. $$C = \frac{SP}{100\% + \%M_C} = \frac{249.95}{100\% + 60\%} = \frac{249.95}{1.6} = \underline{\underline{\$156.22}}$$

$M = SP - C = 249.95 - 156.22 = \underline{\underline{\$93.73}}$

6. $SP = C + M = 46.25 + 50.00 = \underline{\underline{\$96.25}}$

$$\%M_C = \frac{M}{C} = \frac{50.00}{46.25} = 1.081 = \underline{\underline{108.1\%}}$$

7. $M = SP - C = 3{,}499.00 - 1{,}350.00 = \underline{\underline{\$2{,}149.00}}$

$$\%M_C = \frac{M}{C} = \frac{2{,}149.00}{1{,}350.00} = 1.592 = \underline{\underline{159.2\%}}$$

8. $C = SP - M = 2{,}335.00 - 880.00 = \underline{\underline{\$1{,}455.00}}$

$$\%M_C = \frac{M}{C} = \frac{880.00}{1{,}455.00} = .6048 = \underline{\underline{60.5\%}}$$

9. $SP = C(100\% + \%M_C) = .58(100\% + 130\%) = .58(2.3) = \underline{\underline{\$1.33}}$

$M = SP - C = 1.33 - .58 = \underline{\underline{\$.75}}$

10. $$C = \frac{SP}{100\% + \%M_C} = \frac{44.95}{100\% + 75\%} = \frac{44.95}{1.75} = \underline{\underline{\$25.69}}$$

$M = SP - C = 44.95 - 25.69 = \underline{\underline{\$19.26}}$

SECTION II Review Exercises

1. $SP = C + M = 65.00 + 50.00 = \underline{\underline{\$115.00}}$

$$\%M_{SP} = \frac{M}{SP} = \frac{50.00}{115.00} = .4347 = \underline{\underline{43.5\%}}$$

2. $M = SP - C = 51.50 - 34.44 = \underline{\underline{\$17.06}}$

$$\%M_{SP} = \frac{M}{SP} = \frac{17.06}{51.50} = .3312 = \underline{\underline{33.1\%}}$$

3. $$SP = \frac{C}{100\% - \%M_{SP}} = \frac{75.00}{100\% - 45\%} = \frac{75.00}{.55} = \underline{\underline{\$136.36}}$$

$M = SP - C = 136.36 - 75.00 = \underline{\underline{\$61.36}}$

4. $C = SP(100\% - \%M_{SP}) = 133.50(100\% - 60\%) = 133.50(.4) = \underline{\underline{\$53.40}}$

$M = SP - C = 133.50 - 53.40 = \underline{\underline{\$80.10}}$

5. $$\%M_{SP} = \frac{\%M_C}{100\% + \%M_C} = \frac{60\%}{100\% + 60\%} = \frac{.6}{1.6} = .375 = \underline{\underline{37.5\%}}$$

6. $$\%M_C = \frac{\%M_{SP}}{100\% - \%M_{SP}} = \frac{35\%}{100\% - 35\%} = \frac{.35}{.65} = .5384 = \underline{\underline{53.8\%}}$$

7. $M = SP - C = 165.99 - 71.25 = \underline{\underline{\$94.74}}$

$$\%M_C = \frac{M}{C} = \frac{94.74}{71.25} = 1.3296 = \underline{\underline{133\%}}$$

$$\%M_{SP} = \frac{M}{SP} = \frac{94.74}{165.99} = .5707 = \underline{\underline{57.1\%}}$$

8. $SP = C + M = 1.18 + .79 = \underline{\underline{\$1.97}}$

$$\%M_C = \frac{M}{C} = \frac{.79}{1.18} = .6694 = \underline{\underline{66.9\%}}$$

$$\%M_{SP} = \frac{M}{SP} = \frac{.79}{1.97} = .4010 = \underline{\underline{40.1\%}}$$

9. $$SP = \frac{C}{100\% - \%M_{SP}} = \frac{15,449.00}{100\% - 38\%} = \frac{15,449.00}{.62} = \underline{\underline{\$24,917.74}}$$

$M = SP - C = 24,917.74 - 15,449.00 = \underline{\underline{\$9,468.74}}$

$$\%M_C = \frac{M}{C} = \frac{9,468.74}{15,449.00} = .6129 = \underline{\underline{61.3\%}}$$

10. $C = SP(100\% - \%M_{SP}) = 1,299.00(100\% - 55\%) = 1,299(.45) = \underline{\underline{\$584.55}}$

$M = SP - C = 1,299.00 - 584.55 = \underline{\underline{\$714.45}}$

$$\%M_C = \frac{M}{C} = \frac{714.45}{584.55} = 1.2222 = \underline{\underline{122.2\%}}$$

11. $$\%M_{SP} = \frac{\%M_C}{100\% + \%M_C} = \frac{150\%}{100\% + 150\%} = \frac{1.5}{2.5} = .60 = \underline{\underline{60\%}}$$

12. $$\%M_C = \frac{\%M_{SP}}{100\% - \%M_{SP}} = \frac{47\%}{100\% - 47\%} = \frac{.47}{.53} = .8867 = \underline{\underline{88.7\%}}$$

Review Exercises

SECTION III

1. Sale price = Original price − Markdown = 189.95 − 28.50 = $\underline{\underline{\$161.45}}$

$$MD\% = \frac{MD}{\text{Original price}} = \frac{28.50}{189.95} = .1500 = \underline{\underline{15\%}}$$

2. MD = Original price − Sale price = 53.88 − 37.50 = \$16.38

$$MD = \frac{MD}{\text{Original price}} = \frac{16.38}{53.88} = .3040 = \underline{\underline{30.4\%}}$$

3. Original sale price = Sale price + MD = 1.29 + .39 = $\underline{\underline{\$1.68}}$

$$MD\% = \frac{MD}{\text{Original price}} = \frac{.39}{1.68} = .2321 = \underline{\underline{23.2\%}}$$

4. Sale price = Original price (100% − MD%) = 264.95(.7) = $\underline{\underline{\$185.47}}$

MD = Original price − Sale price = 264.95 − 185.47 = $\underline{\underline{\$79.48}}$

5. $$\text{Original price} = \frac{\text{Sale price}}{100\% - MD\%} = \frac{24.66}{100\% - 40\%} = \frac{24.66}{.6} = \underline{\underline{\$41.10}}$$

MD = Original price − Sale price = 41.10 − 24.66 = $\underline{\underline{\$16.44}}$

6. MD = Original price − Sale price = 68.00 − 51.99 = $\underline{\underline{\$16.01}}$

$$MD\% = \frac{MD}{\text{Original price}} = \frac{16.01}{68.00} = .2354 = \underline{\underline{23.5\%}}$$

7. Sale price = Original price − MD = 115.77 − 35.50 = $\underline{\underline{\$80.27}}$

$$MD\% = \frac{MD}{\text{Original price}} = \frac{35.50}{115.77} = .3066 = \underline{\underline{30.7\%}}$$

8. Original price = Sale price + MD = 235.00 + 155.00 = $\underline{\underline{\$390.00}}$

$$MD\% = \frac{MD}{\text{Original price}} = \frac{155.00}{390.00} = .3974 = \underline{\underline{39.7\%}}$$

9. Sale price = Original price(100% − MD%) = 1,599.88(.65) = $\underline{\underline{\$1{,}039.92}}$

MD = Original price − Sale price = 1,599.88 − 1,039.92 = $\underline{\underline{\$559.96}}$

10. $$\text{Original price} = \frac{\text{Sale price}}{100\% - MD\%} = \frac{15.90}{100\% - 25\%} = \frac{15.90}{.75} = \underline{\underline{\$21.20}}$$

MD = Original price − Sale price = 21.20 − 15.90 = $\underline{\underline{\$5.30}}$

9 CHAPTER PAYROLL

9 SECTION I Review Exercises

18.
50 × 3.60 = 180.00
50 × 4.25 = 212.50
9 × 4.50 = +40.50
109 — $\underline{\underline{\$433.00}}$

19.
50 × 3.60 = 180.00
33 × 4.25 = +140.25
83 — $\underline{\underline{\$320.25}}$

20.
50 × 3.60 = 180.00
50 × 4.25 = 212.50
50 × 4.50 = 225.00
24 × 5.10 = +122.40
174 — $\underline{\underline{\$739.90}}$

9 SECTION II Review Exercises

9.
65.38 × 2 = 130.76
594.00 − 130.76 = 463.24
463.24 − 449.00 = 14.24
Tax = 29.50 + .15(14.24)
29.50 + 2.14 = $\underline{\underline{\$31.64}}$

10.
1,227.00 − 422.00 = 805.00
Tax = 31.20 + .15(805.00)
31.20 + 120.75 = $\underline{\underline{\$151.95}}$

11. $4{,}150.00 - 283.33 = 3{,}866.67$
$3{,}866.67 - 2{,}793.00 = 1{,}073.67$
$\text{Tax} = 354.70 + .25(1{,}073.67)$
$354.70 + 268.42 = \underline{\underline{\$623.12}}$

12. $130.77 \times 4 = 523.08$
$1{,}849.00 - 523.08 = 1{,}325.92$
$1{,}325.92 - 898.00 = 427.92$
$\text{Tax} = 59.00 + .15(427.92)$
$59.00 + 64.19 = \underline{\underline{\$123.19}}$

SIMPLE INTEREST AND PROMISSORY NOTES

Review Exercises

1. $I = PRT = 5{,}000 \times .08 \times 2 = \underline{\underline{\$800}}$

2. $I = PRT = 75{,}000 \times .1075 \times \dfrac{6}{12} = \underline{\underline{\$4{,}031.25}}$

3. $I = PRT = 100{,}000 \times .127 \times \dfrac{8}{12} = \underline{\underline{\$19{,}050.00}}$

4. $I = PRT = 80{,}000 \times .15 \times 3.5 = \underline{\underline{\$42{,}000.00}}$

5. $I = PRT = 6{,}440 \times .055 \times \dfrac{7}{12} = \underline{\underline{\$206.62}}$

6. $I = PRT = 13{,}200 \times .092 \times 4.75 = \underline{\underline{\$5{,}768.40}}$

7. $I = PRT$

Exact: $45{,}000 \times .13 \times \dfrac{100}{365} = \underline{\underline{\$1{,}602.74}}$

Ordinary: $45{,}000 \times .13 \times \dfrac{100}{360} = \underline{\underline{\$1{,}625.00}}$

8. $I = PRT$

Exact: $184{,}500 \times .155 \times \dfrac{58}{365} = \underline{\underline{\$4{,}544.26}}$

Ordinary: $184{,}500 \times .155 \times \dfrac{58}{365} = \underline{\underline{\$4{,}607.38}}$

9. $I = PRT$

Exact: $32{,}400 \times .086 \times \dfrac{241}{365} = \underline{\underline{\$1{,}839.79}}$

Ordinary: $32{,}400 \times .086 \times \dfrac{241}{360} = \underline{\underline{\$1{,}865.34}}$

10. $I = PRT$

Exact: $7{,}230 \times .09 \times \dfrac{18}{365} = \underline{\underline{\$32.09}}$

Ordinary: $7{,}230 \times .09 \times \dfrac{18}{360} = \underline{\underline{\$32.54}}$

11. $I = PRT$

Exact: $900 \times .1025 \times \dfrac{60}{365} = \underline{\underline{\$15.16}}$

Ordinary: $900 \times .1025 \times \dfrac{60}{360} = \underline{\underline{\$15.38}}$

12. $I = PRT$

Exact: $100{,}000 \times .1 \times \dfrac{1}{365} = \underline{\underline{\$27.40}}$

Ordinary: $100{,}000 \times .1 \times \dfrac{1}{360} = \underline{\underline{\$27.78}}$

13. $I = PRT$

Exact: $2{,}500 \times .12 \times \dfrac{74}{365} = \underline{\underline{\$60.82}}$

Ordinary: $2{,}500 \times .12 \times \dfrac{74}{360} = \underline{\underline{\$61.67}}$

14. $I = PRT$

Exact: $350 \times .141 \times \dfrac{230}{365} = \underline{\underline{\$31.10}}$

Ordinary: $350 \times .141 \times \dfrac{230}{360} = \underline{\underline{\$31.53}}$

15. $I = PRT$

Exact: $50{,}490 \times .0925 \times \dfrac{69}{365} = \underline{\underline{\$882.88}}$

Ordinary: $50{,}490 \times .0925 \times \dfrac{69}{360} = \underline{\underline{\$895.15}}$

16. $I = PRT$

Exact: $486{,}000 \times .135 \times \dfrac{127}{365} = \underline{\underline{\$22{,}828.68}}$

Ordinary: $486{,}000 \times .135 \times \dfrac{127}{360} = \underline{\underline{\$23{,}145.75}}$

17. $I = PRT = 54{,}000 \times .119 \times 2 = \underline{\underline{\$12{,}852.00}}$

$MV = P + I = 54{,}000 + 12{,}852 = \underline{\underline{\$66{,}852.00}}$

18. $I = PRT = 125{,}000 \times .125 \times \dfrac{5}{12} = \underline{\underline{\$6{,}510.42}}$

$MV = P + I = 125{,}000 + 6{,}510.42 = \underline{\underline{\$131{,}510.42}}$

19. $I = PRT = 33{,}750 \times .084 \times \dfrac{10}{12} = \underline{\underline{\$2{,}362.50}}$

$MV = P + I = 33{,}750.00 + 2{,}362.50 = \underline{\underline{\$36{,}112.50}}$

20. $I = PRT = 91{,}000 \times .0925 \times 2.5 = \underline{\underline{\$21{,}043.75}}$

$MV = P + I = 91{,}000.00 + 21{,}043.75 = \underline{\underline{\$112{,}043.75}}$

21. $MV = P(1 + RT) = 1{,}500(1 + .09 \times 2) = \underline{\underline{\$1{,}770.00}}$

22. $MV = P(1 + RT) = 18{,}620\left(1 + .105 \times \dfrac{30}{12}\right) = \underline{\underline{\$23{,}507.75}}$

23. $MV = P(1 + RT) = 1{,}000{,}000(1 + .11 \times 3) = \underline{\underline{\$1{,}330{,}000.00}}$

24. $MV = P(1 + RT) = 750{,}000\left(1 + .1335 \times \dfrac{11}{12}\right) = \underline{\underline{\$841{,}781.25}}$

25.
$$\begin{array}{rl} 30 & \\ -\ 5 & \\ \hline 25 & \text{Sept} \\ 61 & \text{Oct–Nov} \\ +\ 12 & \text{Dec} \\ \hline 98 & \text{Days} \end{array}$$

26.
$$\begin{array}{rl} 30 & \\ -\ 27 & \\ \hline 3 & \text{June} \\ 92 & \text{July–Sept} \\ +\ 15 & \text{Oct} \\ \hline 110 & \text{Days} \end{array}$$

27.
$$\begin{array}{rl} 31 & \\ -\ 23 & \\ \hline 8 & \text{Jan} \\ 273 & \text{Feb–Oct} \\ +\ 8 & \text{Nov} \\ \hline 289 & \text{Days} \end{array}$$

28.
$$\begin{array}{rl} 31 & \\ -\ 9 & \\ \hline 22 & \text{Mar} \\ 91 & \text{Apr–June} \\ +\ 30 & \text{July} \\ \hline 143 & \text{Days} \end{array}$$

29.
$$\begin{array}{rl} 31 & \\ -\ 19 & \\ \hline 12 & \text{Oct} \\ 30 & \text{Nov} \\ +\ 3 & \text{Dec} \longrightarrow \underline{\underline{\text{December 3}}} \\ \hline 45 & \text{Days} \end{array}$$

30.
$$\begin{array}{rl} 28 & \\ -\ 5 & \\ \hline 23 & \text{Feb} \\ 61 & \text{Mar–Apr} \\ +\ 26 & \text{May} \longrightarrow \underline{\underline{\text{May 26}}} \\ \hline 110 & \text{Days} \end{array}$$

31.
$$\begin{array}{rl} 31 & \\ -\ 26 & \\ \hline 5 & \text{May} \\ +\ 24 & \text{June} \longrightarrow \underline{\underline{\text{June 24}}} \\ \hline 29 & \text{Days} \end{array}$$

32.
$$\begin{array}{rl} 31 & \\ -\ 21 & \\ \hline 10 & \text{July} \\ 184 & \text{Aug–Jan} \\ +\ 6 & \text{Feb} \longrightarrow \underline{\underline{\text{February 6}}} \\ \hline 200 & \text{Days} \end{array}$$

33.
$$\begin{array}{rl} 31 & \\ -\ 6 & \\ \hline 25 & \text{Dec} \\ 31 & \text{Jan} \\ +\ 23 & \text{Feb} \longrightarrow \underline{\underline{\text{February 23}}} \\ \hline 79 & \text{Days} \end{array}$$

10 SECTION II Review Exercises

1. $P = \dfrac{I}{RT} = \dfrac{300}{.12 \times 2} = \underline{\underline{\$1{,}250.00}}$

2. $P = \dfrac{I}{RT} = \dfrac{675}{.09 \times 1.5} = \underline{\underline{\$5{,}000.00}}$

3. $P = \dfrac{I}{RT} = \dfrac{3{,}000}{.08 \times \frac{9}{12}} = \underline{\underline{\$50{,}000.00}}$

4. $P = \dfrac{I}{RT} = \dfrac{5{,}350}{.107 \times \frac{90}{360}} = \underline{\underline{\$200{,}000.00}}$

5. $P = \dfrac{I}{RT} = \dfrac{917}{.131 \times \frac{210}{360}} = \underline{\underline{\$12{,}000.00}}$

6. $R = \dfrac{I}{PT} = \dfrac{1{,}200}{5{,}000 \times 3} = \underline{\underline{8\%}}$

7. $R = \dfrac{I}{PT} = \dfrac{105}{1{,}800 \times \frac{5}{12}} = \underline{\underline{14\%}}$

8. $R = \dfrac{I}{PT} = \dfrac{728}{48{,}000 \times \frac{60}{360}} = \underline{\underline{9.1\%}}$

9. $R = \dfrac{I}{PT} = \dfrac{275}{4{,}600 \times \frac{168}{360}} = \underline{\underline{12.8\%}}$

10. $R = \dfrac{I}{PT} = \dfrac{18{,}750}{125{,}000 \times 2} = \underline{\underline{7.5\%}}$

11. $T = \dfrac{I}{PR} = \dfrac{948}{18{,}000 \times .12} = .4388889$

$$\begin{array}{r} .4388889 \\ \times 360 \\ \hline \underline{\underline{158 \text{ Days}}} \end{array}$$

12. $T = \dfrac{I}{PR} = \dfrac{228}{7{,}900 \times .104} = .2775073$

$$\begin{array}{r} .2775073 \\ \times 360 \\ \hline \underline{\underline{100 \text{ Days}}} \end{array}$$

13. $T = \frac{I}{PR} = \frac{375}{4{,}500 \times .0975} = .8547009$
$\times 360$
$\underline{\underline{308 \text{ Days}}}$

14. $T = \frac{I}{PR} = \frac{4{,}450}{25{,}000 \times .089} = \underline{\underline{2 \text{ Years}}}$

15. $T = \frac{I}{PR} = \frac{51}{680 \times .15} = .5$
$\times 360$
$\underline{\underline{180 \text{ Days}}}$

16. $T = \frac{I}{PR} = \frac{760}{16{,}000 \times .13} = .3653846$
$\times 360$
$\underline{\underline{132 \text{ Days}}}$

$MV = P + I = 16{,}000 + 760 = \underline{\underline{\$16{,}760.00}}$

17. $P = \frac{I}{RT} = \frac{340}{.095 \times \frac{100}{365}} = \underline{\underline{\$13{,}063.16}}$

$MV = P + I = 13{,}063.16 + 340.00 = \underline{\underline{\$13{,}403.16}}$

18. $R = \frac{I}{PT} = \frac{225}{3{,}600 \times \frac{160}{365}} = \underline{\underline{14.3\%}}$

$MV = P + I = 3{,}600 + 225 = \underline{\underline{\$3{,}825.00}}$

19. $I + PRT + 25{,}500 \times .1125 \times \frac{300}{360} = \underline{\underline{\$2{,}390.63}}$

$MV = P + I = 25{,}500 + 2{,}390.63 = \underline{\underline{\$27{,}890.63}}$

20. $P = MV - I = 59{,}000 - 4{,}000 = \underline{\underline{\$55{,}000}}$

$T = \frac{I}{PR} = \frac{4{,}000}{55{,}000 \times .104} = .6993007$
$\times \quad 365$
$\underline{\underline{256 \text{ Days}}}$

Review Exercises

1. Bank Discount $= FV \times R \times T = 4{,}500 \times .13 \times \frac{6}{12} = \underline{\underline{\$292.50}}$

Proceeds $= FV -$ Discount $= 4{,}500 - 292.50 = \underline{\underline{\$4{,}207.50}}$

2. Bank Discount $= FV \times R \times T = 235 \times .113 \times \frac{50}{360} = \underline{\underline{\$3.69}}$

Proceeds $= FV -$ Discount $= 235.00 - 3.69 = \underline{\underline{\$231.31}}$

3. Bank Discount $= FV \times R \times T = 1{,}850 \times .125 \times 1 = \underline{\underline{\$231.25}}$

Proceeds $= FV -$ Discount $= 1{,}850.00 - 231.25 = \underline{\underline{\$1{,}618.75}}$

4. Bank Discount $= FV \times R \times T = 35{,}000 \times .0965 \times \frac{11}{12} = \underline{\underline{\$3{,}096.04}}$

Proceeds $= FV -$ Discount $= 35{,}000 - 3{,}096.04 = \underline{\underline{\$31{,}903.96}}$

5. Bank Discount $= FV \times R \times T = 7{,}800 \times .0825 \times \frac{130}{360} = \underline{\underline{\$232.38}}$

Proceeds $= FV -$ Discount $= 7{,}800 - 232.38 = \underline{\underline{\$7{,}567.62}}$

6. Maturity date = 30
− 3
27 Days → 27 June
31 July
22 Aug ⟶ $\underline{\underline{\text{August 22}}}$
80 Days

Bank Discount $= FV \times R \times T = 16{,}800.00 \times .10 \times \frac{80}{360} = \underline{\underline{\$373.33}}$

Proceeds $= FV -$ Discount $= 16{,}800.00 - 373.33 = \underline{\underline{\$16{,}426.67}}$

7. Term = 30 − 16 = 14 Days

14	Apr
61	May–June
9	July
84	Days

$$\text{Bank Discount} = FV \times R \times T = 5{,}000.00 \times .147 \times \frac{84}{360} = \underline{\underline{\$171.50}}$$

$$\text{Proceeds} = FV - \text{Discount} = 5{,}000.00 - 171.50 = \underline{\underline{\$4{,}828.50}}$$

8. Maturity date = 30 − 3 = 27 Days

27	Sept
61	Oct–Nov
21	Dec ⟶ December 21
109	Days

$$\text{Bank Discount} = FV \times R \times T = 800 \times .121 \times \frac{109}{360} = \underline{\underline{\$29.31}}$$

$$\text{Proceeds} = FV - \text{Discount} = 800.00 - 29.31 = \underline{\underline{\$770.69}}$$

9. Term = 31 − 19 = 12 Days

12	Aug
61	Sept–Oct
27	Days
100	Days

$$\text{Bank Discount} = FV \times R \times T = 1{,}300 \times .095 \times \frac{100}{360} = \underline{\underline{\$34.31}}$$

$$\text{Proceeds} = FV - \text{Discount} = 1{,}300.00 - 34.31 = \underline{\underline{\$1{,}265.69}}$$

10. Maturity date = 31 − 7 = 24 Days

24	May
29	June ⟶ June 29
53	

$$\text{Bank Discount} = FV \times R \times T = 75{,}000 \times .15 \times \frac{53}{360} = \underline{\underline{\$1{,}656.25}}$$

$$\text{Proceeds} = FV - \text{Discount} = 75{,}000.00 - 1{,}656.25 = \underline{\underline{\$73{,}343.75}}$$

11. $$\text{Bank discount} = FV \times R \times T = 2{,}700 \times .14 \times \frac{126}{360} = \underline{\underline{\$132.30}}$$

$$\text{Proceeds} = FV - \text{Discount} = 2{,}700.00 - 132.30 = \underline{\underline{\$2{,}567.70}}$$

$$\text{Effective rate} = \frac{\text{Discount}}{P \times T} = \frac{132.30}{2{,}567.70 \times \frac{126}{360}} = \underline{\underline{14.72\%}}$$

12. $$\text{Bank discount} = FV \times R \times T = 6{,}505.00 \times .1039 \times \frac{73}{360} = \underline{\underline{\$137.05}}$$

$$\text{Proceeds} = FV - \text{Discount} = 6{,}505.00 - 137.05 = \underline{\underline{\$6{,}367.95}}$$

$$\text{Effective rate} = \frac{\text{Discount}}{P \times T} = \frac{137.05}{6{,}367.95 \times \frac{73}{360}} = \underline{\underline{10.61\%}}$$

13. $$\text{Bank discount} = FV \times R \times T = 3{,}800 \times .145 \times \frac{140}{360} = \underline{\underline{\$214.28}}$$

$$\text{Proceeds} = FV - \text{Discount} = 3{,}800.00 - 214.28 = \underline{\underline{\$3{,}585.72}}$$

$$\text{Effective rate} = \frac{\text{Discount}}{P \times T} = \frac{214.28}{3{,}585.72 \times \frac{140}{360}} = \underline{\underline{15.37\%}}$$

14. $\text{Bank discount} = FV \times R \times T = 95{,}000 \times .097 \times \dfrac{45}{360} = \underline{\underline{\$1{,}151.88}}$

$\text{Proceeds} = FV - \text{Discount} = 95{,}000.00 - 1{,}151.88 = \underline{\underline{\$93{,}848.12}}$

$\text{Effective rate} = \dfrac{\text{Discount}}{P \times T} = \dfrac{1{,}151.88}{93{,}848.12 \times \dfrac{45}{360}} = \underline{\underline{9.82\%}}$

15. $\text{Bank discount} = FV \times R \times T = 57{,}500 \times .1275 \times \dfrac{230}{360} = \underline{\underline{\$4{,}683.85}}$

$\text{Proceeds} = FV - \text{Discount} = 57{,}500.00 - 4{,}683.85 = \underline{\underline{\$52{,}816.15}}$

$\text{Effective rate} = \dfrac{\text{Discount}}{P \times T} = \dfrac{4{,}683.85}{52{,}816.15 \times \dfrac{230}{360}} = \underline{\underline{13.88\%}}$

16. Maturity date =

31	27 Mar	
− 4	30 Apr	
27 Days	13 May	→ May 13
	70 Days	

$MV = FV(1 + RT) = 2{,}500\left(1 + .12 \times \dfrac{70}{360}\right) = \$2{,}558.33$

Discount Period =

30	15 Apr
− 15	13 May
15 Days	28 Days

$\text{Bank discount} = MV \times R \times T = 2{,}558.33 \times .13 \times \dfrac{28}{360} = \$25.87$

$\text{Proceeds} = MV - \text{Discount} = 2{,}558.33 - 25.87 = \underline{\underline{\$2{,}532.46}}$

17. Maturity date =

31	19 Dec	
− 12	31 Jan	→ January 31
19 Days	50 Days	

$MV = FV(1 + RT) = 4{,}000\left(1 + .104 \times \dfrac{50}{360}\right) = \underline{\underline{\$4{,}057.78}}$

Discount Period =

31
−19
12 Days

$\text{Bank discount} = MV \times R \times T = 4{,}057.78 \times .15 \times \dfrac{12}{360} = \$20.29$

$\text{Proceeds} = MV - \text{Discount} = 4{,}057.78 - 20.29 = \underline{\underline{\$4{,}037.49}}$

18. Maturity date =

31	23 June	
− 7	92 July–Sept	
23 Days	10 Oct	→ October 10
	125 Days	

$MV = FV(1 + RT) = 850\left(1 + .135 \times \dfrac{125}{360}\right) = \underline{\underline{\$889.84}}$

Discount Period =

30	27 Apr
− 3	10 May
27 Days	37 Days

$\text{Bank discount} = MV \times R \times T = 889.84 \times .165 \times \dfrac{37}{360} = \$15.09$

$\text{Proceeds} = MV - \text{Discount} = 889.84 - 15.09 = \underline{\underline{\$874.75}}$

19. Interest = Face value × Discount rate × Time = $15{,}000 \times .052 \times \frac{13}{52} = \underline{\underline{\$195}}$

Purchase price = Face value − Interest = 15,000 − 195 = $\underline{\underline{\$14{,}805}}$

$$\text{Effective interest rate} = \frac{\text{Interest}}{\text{Purchase price} \times \text{Time}} = \frac{195}{14{,}805 \times \frac{13}{52}} = .05268 = \underline{\underline{5.27\%}}$$

20. Interest = Face value × Discount rate × Time = $50{,}000 \times .044 \times \frac{26}{52} = \underline{\underline{\$1{,}100}}$

Purchase price = Face value − Interest = 50,000 − 1,100 = $\underline{\underline{\$48{,}900}}$

$$\text{Effective interest rate} = \frac{\text{Interest}}{\text{Purchase price} \times \text{Time}} = \frac{1{,}100}{48{,}900 \times \frac{26}{52}} = .04499 = \underline{\underline{4.50\%}}$$

21. Interest = Face value × Discount rate × Time = $80{,}000 \times .0482 \times \frac{13}{52} = \underline{\underline{\$964}}$

Purchase price = Face value − Interest = 80,000 − 964 = $\underline{\underline{\$79{,}036}}$

$$\text{Effective interest rate} = \frac{\text{Interest}}{\text{Purchase price} \times \text{Time}} = \frac{964}{79{,}036 \times \frac{13}{52}} = .04879 = \underline{\underline{4.88\%}}$$

10 CHAPTER ASSESSMENT TEST

1. $I = PRT = 15{,}000 \times .13 \times \frac{120}{365} = \underline{\underline{\$641.10}}$

2. $I = PRT = 1{,}700 \times .125 \times \frac{33}{365} = \underline{\underline{\$19.21}}$

3. $I = PRT = 20{,}600 \times .12 \times \frac{98}{360} = \underline{\underline{\$672.93}}$

4. $I = PRT = 286{,}000 \times .135 \times \frac{224}{360} = \underline{\underline{\$24{,}024.00}}$

5. $MV = P(1 + RT) = 15{,}800(1 + .14 \times 4) = \underline{\underline{\$24{,}648.00}}$

6. $MV = P(1+RT) = 120{,}740\left(1 + .1175 \times \frac{7}{12}\right) = \underline{\underline{\$129{,}015.72}}$

7.
30
− 16
14 Days → 14 Apr
92 May–July
1 Aug
107 Days

8.
31
− 20
11 Days → 11 Oct
30 Nov
18 Dec
59 Days

9.
30
− 30
0 Days → 0 Nov
31 Dec
24 Jan → January 24
55 Days

10.
31
− 15
16 Days → 16 May
92 June–Aug
3 Sept → September 3
111 Days

11. $P = \frac{I}{RT} = \frac{2{,}800}{.12 \times 2} = \underline{\underline{\$11{,}666.67}}$

12. $P = \frac{I}{RT} = \frac{5{,}900}{.105 \times \frac{10}{12}} = \underline{\underline{\$67{,}428.57}}$

13. $R = \frac{I}{PT} = \frac{800}{2{,}200 \times 4} = \underline{\underline{9.1\%}}$

14. $R = \frac{I}{PT} = \frac{4{,}500}{50{,}000 \times \frac{9}{12}} = \underline{\underline{12\%}}$

15. $T = \frac{I}{PR} = \frac{350}{13{,}500 \times .13} = .1994301$
× 360
71.7 = 72 Days

16. $T = \frac{I}{PR} = \frac{625}{7,900 \times 1.04} = .7607108$

$\times 360$

$273.8 = \underline{\underline{274 \text{ Days}}}$

17. $T = \frac{I}{PR} = \frac{960}{13,000 \times .14} = .5274725$

$\times 360$

$189.8 = \underline{\underline{190 \text{ Days}}}$

$MV = P + I = 13,000 + 960 = \underline{\underline{\$13,960.00}}$

18. $P = \frac{I}{RT} = \frac{1,790}{.122 \times \frac{133}{365}} = \underline{\underline{\$40,265.62}}$

$MV = P + I = 40,265.62 + 1,790.00 = \underline{\underline{\$42,055.62}}$

19. $R = \frac{I}{PT} = \frac{295}{2,500 \times \frac{280}{360}} = \underline{\underline{15.2\%}}$

$MV = P + I = 2,500 + 295 = \underline{\underline{\$2,795.00}}$

20.
```
 30           25 Apr
− 5           92 May–July
 25 Days      14 Aug
             131 Days
```

Bank Discount $= FV \times R \times T = 50,000 \times .13 \times \frac{131}{360} = \underline{\underline{\$2,365.28}}$

Proceeds $= FV -$ Discount $= 50,000.00 - 2,365.28 = \underline{\underline{\$47,634.72}}$

21.
```
 31            6 Oct
− 25          61 Nov–Dec
  6 Days      20 Jan       January 20
              87 Days
```

Bank Discount $= FV \times R \times T = 875,000 \times .095 \times \frac{87}{360} = \underline{\underline{\$20,088.54}}$

Proceeds $= FV -$ Discount $= 875,000.00 - 20,088.54 = \underline{\underline{\$854,911.46}}$

22. Bank discount $= FV \times R \times T = 22,500 \times .105 \times \frac{60}{360} = \underline{\underline{\$393.75}}$

Proceeds $= FV -$ Discount $= 22,500.00 - 393.75 = \underline{\underline{\$22,106.25}}$

Effective rate $= \frac{\text{Discount}}{P \times T} = \frac{393.75}{22,106.25 \times \frac{60}{360}} = \underline{\underline{10.69\%}}$

23. Bank discount $= FV \times R \times T = 290,000 \times .119 \times \frac{110}{360} = \underline{\underline{\$10,544.72}}$

Proceeds $= FV -$ Discount $= 290,000.00 - 10,544.72 = \underline{\underline{\$279,455.28}}$

Effective rate $= \frac{\text{Discount}}{P \times T} = \frac{10,544.72}{279,455.28 \times \frac{110}{360}} = \underline{\underline{12.35\%}}$

24. Maturity date =
```
 30           19 Jan
− 12          59 Feb–Mar
 19 Days       5 Apr       April 5
              83 Days
```

$MV = FV(1 + RT) = 8,000\left(1 + .11 \times \frac{83}{360}\right) = \underline{\underline{\$8,202.89}}$

Discount Period =
```
 31           30 Mar
− 1            5 Apr
 30 Days      35 Days
```

Bank discount $= MV \times R \times T = 8,202.89 \times .15 \times \frac{35}{360} = \underline{\underline{\$119.63}}$

Proceeds $= MV -$ Discount $= 8,202.89 - 119.63 = \underline{\underline{\$8,083.26}}$

25. Maturity date =
```
 30           13 June
− 17          31 July
 13 Days      25 Aug       August 25
              69 Days
```

$MV = FV(1 + RT) = 5,500\left(1 + .135 \times \frac{69}{360}\right) = \underline{\underline{\$5,642.31}}$

Discount Period =
```
 31            9 July
− 22          25 Aug
  9 Days      34 Days
```

$$\text{Bank discount} = MV \times R \times T = 5{,}642.31 \times .137 \times \frac{34}{360} = \$73.01$$

$$\text{Proceeds} = MV - \text{Discount} = 5{,}642.31 - 73.01 = \underline{\underline{\$5{,}569.30}}$$

26. $\text{Interest} = \text{Face value} \times \text{Discount rate} \times \text{Time} = 75{,}000 \times .0515 \times \frac{4}{52} = \underline{\underline{\$297.12}}$

$\text{Purchase price} = \text{Face value} - \text{Interest} = 75{,}000 - 297.12 = \underline{\underline{\$74{,}702.88}}$

$$\text{Effective interest rate} = \frac{\text{Interest}}{\text{Purchase price} \times \text{Time}} = \frac{297.12}{74{,}702.88 \times \frac{4}{52}} = .05171 = \underline{\underline{5.17\%}}$$

27. $\text{Interest} = \text{Face value} \times \text{Discount rate} \times \text{Time} = 28{,}000 \times .049 \times \frac{26}{52} = \underline{\underline{\$686}}$

$\text{Purchase price} = \text{Face value} - \text{Interest} = 28{,}000 - 686 = \underline{\underline{\$27{,}314}}$

$$\text{Effective interest rate} = \frac{\text{Interest}}{\text{Purchase price} \times \text{Time}} = \frac{686}{27{,}314 \times \frac{26}{52}} = .05023 = \underline{\underline{5.02\%}}$$

CHAPTER 11 COMPOUND INTEREST AND PRESENT VALUE

11 SECTION I Review Exercises

1. $\text{Periods} = \text{Years} \times \text{Periods/Year} = 3 \times 1 = \underline{\underline{3}}$

$\text{Rate per period} = \frac{\text{Nominal Rate}}{\text{Periods/Year}} = \frac{13}{1} = \underline{\underline{13\%}}$

2. $\text{Periods} = \text{Years} \times \text{Periods/Year} = 5 \times 4 = \underline{\underline{20}}$

$\text{Rate per period} = \frac{\text{Nominal Rate}}{\text{Periods/Year}} = \frac{16}{14} = \underline{\underline{4\%}}$

3. $\text{Periods} = \text{Years} \times \text{Periods/Year} = 12 \times 2 = \underline{\underline{24}}$

$\text{Rate per period} = \frac{\text{Nominal Rate}}{\text{Periods/Year}} = \frac{8}{2} = \underline{\underline{4\%}}$

4. $\text{Periods} = \text{Years} \times \text{Periods/Year} = 6 \times 12 = \underline{\underline{72}}$

$\text{Rate per period} = \frac{\text{Nominal Rate}}{\text{Periods/Year}} = \frac{18}{12} = \underline{\underline{1.5\%}}$

5. $\text{Periods} = \text{Years} \times \text{Periods/Year} = 4 \times 4 = \underline{\underline{16}}$

$\text{Rate per period} = \frac{\text{Nominal Rate}}{\text{Periods/Year}} = \frac{14}{4} = \underline{\underline{3.5\%}}$

6. $\text{Periods} = \text{Years} \times \text{Periods/Year} = 9 \times 2 = \underline{\underline{18}}$

$\text{Rate per period} = \frac{\text{Nominal Rate}}{\text{Periods/Year}} = \frac{10.5}{2} = \underline{\underline{5.25\%}}$

7. $\text{Periods} = \text{Years} \times \text{Periods/Year} = .75 \times 4 = \underline{\underline{3}}$

$\text{Rate per period} = \frac{\text{Nominal Rate}}{\text{Periods/Year}} = \frac{12}{4} = \underline{\underline{3\%}}$

8.

4,000	Original principal
+ 400	Interest period 1 ($I = PRT$) (4,000 × .1 = 400)
4,400	Principal period 2
+ 440	Interest period 2 ($I = PRT$) (4,400 × .1 = 440)
$4,840	Compound amount

Compound interest =	Compound amount	4,840
	− Principal	−4,000
		$840

9.

10,000.00	Original Principal
+ 300.00	Interest period 1 (10,000 × .12 × .25 = 300)
10,300.00	Principal period 2
+ 309.00	Interest period 2 (10,300 × .12 × .25 = 309)
10,609.00	Principal period 3
+ 318.27	Interest period 3 (10,609 × .12 × .25 = 318.27)
10,927.27	Principal period 4
+ 327.82	Interest period 4 (10,927.27 × .12 × .25 = 327.82)
$11,255.09	Compound amount

Compound interest = Compound amount $11,255.09
− Principal − 10,000.00
$1,255.09

10.

8,000.00	Original principal
+ 320.00	Interest period 1 (8,000 × .08 × .5 = 320)
8,320.00	Principal period 2
+ 332.80	Interest period 2 (8,320 × .08 × .5 = 332.80)
8,652.80	Principal period 3
+ 346.11	Interest period 3 (8,652.80 × .08 × .5 = 346.11)
8,998.91	Principal period 4
+ 359.96	Interest period 4 (8,998.91 × .08 × .5 = 359.96)
9,358.87	Principal period 5
+ 374.35	Interest period 5 (9,358.87 × .08 × .5 = 374.35)
9,733.22	Principal period 6
+ 389.33	Interest period 6 (9,733.22 × .08 × .5 = 389.33)
$10,122.55	Compound amount

Compound interest = Compound amount 10,122.55
− Principal − 8,000.00
$2,122.55

11. 13%, 4 Periods

Compound amount = Table factor × Principal
1.63047 × 7,000 = $11,413.29

Compound interest = Compound amount − Principal
11,413.29 − 7,000.00 = $4,413.29

12. 7%, 12 Periods

Compound amount = Table factor × Principal
2.25219 × 11,000 = $24,774.09

Compound interest = Compound amount − Principal
24,774.09 − 11,000.00 = $13,774.09

13. 2%, 12 Periods

Compound amount = Table factor × Principal
1.26824 × 5,300 = $6,721.67

Compound interest = Compound amount − Principal
6,721.67 − 5,300.00 = $1,421.67

14. $1\frac{1}{2}$%, 24 Periods

Compound amount = Table factor × Principal
1.42950 × 67,000 = $95,776.50

Compound interest = Compound amount − Principal
95,776.50 − 67,000.00 = $28,776.50

15. 11%, 15 Periods

Compound amount = Table factor × Principal
4.78459 × 25,000 = $119,614.75

Compound interest = Compound amount − Principal
119,614.75 − 25,000.00 = $94,614.75

16. $\frac{1}{2}$%, 24 Periods

Compound amount = Table factor × Principal
1.12716 × 400 = $450.86

Compound interest = Compound amount − Principal
450.86 − 400.00 = $50.86

17. 5%, 25 Periods

Compound amount = Table factor × Principal
3.38635 × 8,800 = $29,799.88

Compound interest = Compound amount − Principal
29,799.88 − 8,800.00 = $20,999.88

18. Table factor required = 1%, 36 Periods

1%, 18 Periods: 1.19615
1%, 18 Periods: × 1.19615
36 Periods 1.4307748 = 1.43077 "New" factor 1%, 36 Periods

Compound amount = Table factor × Principal
1.43077 × 13,000 = $18,600.01

19. Table factor required = 9%, 29 Periods

9%, 15 Periods: 3.34173
9%, 14 Periods: × 3.64248
29 Periods 12.172184 = 12.17218 "New" factor 9%, 29 Periods

Compound amount = Table factor × Principal
12.17218 × 19,000 = $231,271.42

20. Table factor required = 4%, 44 Periods

4%, 22 Periods: 2.36992
4%, 22 Periods: × 2.36992
44 Periods 5.6165208 = 5.61652 "New" factor 4%, 44 Periods

Compound amount = Table factor × Principal
5.61652 × 34,700 = $194,893.24

21. Table factor required = 13%, 40 Periods

13%, 20 Periods: 11.52309
13%, 20 Periods: × 11.52309
40 Periods 132.7816 = 132.78160 "New" factor 13%, 40 Periods

Compound amount = Table factor × Principal
132.78160 × 10,000 = $1,327,816.00

22. Table factor required = 7%, 32 Periods

7%, 16 Periods: 2.95216
7%, 16 Periods: × 2.95216
32 Periods 8.7152486 = 8.71525 "New" factor 7%, 32 Periods

Compound amount = Table factor × Principal
8.71525 × 1,000 = $8,715.25

23. 5%, 2 Periods

Compound amount = Table factor × Principal
1.10250 × 5,000 = $5,512.50

Compound interest = Compound amount − Principal
$5,512.50 − 5,000 = $512.50

$$\text{Annual percentage yield (APY)} = \frac{\text{1 year interest}}{\text{Principal}} = \frac{512.50}{5{,}000.00} = 10.25\%$$

24. 13%, 1 Period

Compound amount = Table factor × Principal
1.13000 × 2,000 = $2,260.00

Compound interest = Compound amount − Principal
2,260.00 − 2,000.00 = $260.00

$$\text{Annual percentage yield (APY)} = \frac{\text{1 year interest}}{\text{Principal}} = \frac{260.00}{2{,}000.00} = 13\%$$

25. 1%, 12 Periods

Compound amount = Table factor × Principal
1.12683 × 36,000 = $40,565.88

Compound interest = Compound amount − Principal
40,565.88 − 36,000.00 = $4,565.88

$$\text{Annual percentage yield (APY)} = \frac{\text{1 year interest}}{\text{Principal}} = \frac{4,565.88}{36,000.00} = \underline{\underline{12.68\%}}$$

26. 2%, 4 Periods

Compound amount = Table factor × Principal
1.08243 × 1,000 = $1,082.43

Compound interest = Compound amount − Principal
1,082.43 − 1,000.00 = $82.43

$$\text{Annual percentage yield (APY)} = \frac{\text{1 year interest}}{\text{Principal}} = \frac{82.43}{1,000.00} = \underline{\underline{8.24\%}}$$

Review Exercises

SECTION II

1. 9%, 3 Periods

Present value = Table factor × Compound amount
.77218 × 6,000 = $4,633.08

Compound interest = Compound amount − Present value
6,000.00 − 4,633.08 = $1,366.92

2. 7%, 12 Periods

Present value = Table factor × Compound amount
.44401 × 24,000 = $10,656.24

Compound interest = Compound amount − Present value
24,000.00 − 10,656.24 = $13,343.76

3. 2%, 20 Periods

Present value = Table factor × Compound amount
.67297 × 650 = $437.43

Compound interest = Compound amount − Present value
650.00 − 437.43 = $212.57

4. 3%, 24 Periods

Present value = Table factor × Compound amount
.49193 × 2,000 = $983.86

Compound interest = Compound amount − Present value
2,000.00 − 983.86 = $1,016.14

5. 11%, 25 Periods

Present value = Table factor × Compound amount
.07361 × 50,000 = $3,680.50

Compound interest = Compound amount − Present value
50,000.00 − 3,680.50 = $46,319.50

6. 5%, 3 Periods

Present value = Table factor × Compound amount
.86384 × 14,500 = $12,525.68

Compound interest = Compound amount − Present value
14,500.00 − 12,525.68 = $1,974.32

7. 3%, 16 Periods

Present value = Table factor × Compound amount
.62317 × 9,800 = $6,107.07

Compound interest = Compound amount − Present value
9,800.00 − 6,107.07 = $3,692.93

8. 9%, 10 Periods

Present value = Table factor × Compound amount
.42241 × 100,000 = $42,241.00

Compound interest = Compound amount − Present value
100,000.00 − 42,241.00 = $57,759.00

9. 1%, 12 Periods

Present value = Table factor × Compound amount
.83639 × 250 = $209.10

Compound interest = Compound amount − Present value
250.00 − 209.10 = $40.90

10. 2%, 9 Periods

Present value = Table factor × Compound amount
.83676 × 4,000 = $3,347.04

Compound interest = Compound amount − Present value
4,000.00 − 3,347.04 = $652.96

11. Table factor required = 4%, 40 Periods

4%, 20 Periods: .45639
4%, 20 Periods: × .45639
40 Periods .2082918 = .20829 "New" factor 4%, 40 Periods

Present value = Table factor × Compound amount
.20829 × 12,000 = $2,499.48

12. Table factor required = 7%, 38 Periods

7%, 19 Periods: .27651
7%, 19 Periods: × .27651
38 Periods .0764577 = .07646 "New" factor 7%, 38 Periods

Present value = Table factor × Compound amount
.07646 × 33,000 = $2,523.18

13. Table factor required = 3%, 48 Periods

3%, 24 Periods: .49193
3%, 24 Periods: × .49193
48 Periods .2419951 = .24200 "New" factor 3%, 48 Periods

Present value = Table factor × Compound amount
.24200 × 1,400 = $338.80

14. Table factor required = 13%, 45 Periods

13%, 23 Periods: .06014
13%, 22 Periods: × .06796
45 Periods .0040871 = .00409 "New" factor 13%, 45 Periods

Present value = Table factor × Compound amount
.00409 × 1,000 = $4.09

15. Table factor required = 4%, 34 Periods

17 Periods:	.51337		
17 Periods:	× .51337		
34 Periods	.2635487 = .26355	"New" factor 4%, 34 Periods	

Present value = Table factor × Compound amount
.26355 × 110,000 = $28,990.50

ASSESSMENT TEST

CHAPTER 

1. 7%, 12 Periods

Compound amount = 2.25219 × 14,000 = $31,530.66

Compound interest = 31,530.66 − 14,000 = $17,530.66

2. $1\frac{1}{2}$%, 20 Periods

Compound amount = 1.34686 × 7,700 = $10,370.82

Compound interest = 10,370.82 − 7,700 = $2,670.82

3. $1\frac{1}{2}$%, 12 Periods

Compound amount = 1.19562 × 3,000 = $3,586.86

Compound interest = 3,586.86 − 3,000.00 = $586.86

4. 11%, 19 Periods

Compound amount = 7.26334 × 42,000 = $305,060.28

Compound interest = 305,060.28 − 42,000.00 = $263,060.28

5. Table factor required = 4%, 44 Periods

4%, 22 Periods:	2.36992	
4%, 22 Periods:	× 2.36992	
44 Periods	5.6165208 = 5.61652	"New" factor 4%, 44 Periods

Compound amount = 5.61652 × 20,000 = $112,330.40

6. Table factor required = $\frac{1}{2}$%, 48 Periods

$\frac{1}{2}$%, 24 Periods:	1.12716	
$\frac{1}{2}$%, 24 Periods:	× 1.12716	
48 Periods	1.2704897 = 1.27049	"New" factor $\frac{1}{2}$%, 48 Periods

Compound amount = 1.27049 × 10,000 = $12,704.90

7. 1%, 12 Periods

Compound amount = 1.12683 × 8,500 = $9,578.06

1 year interest = 9,578.06 − 8,500.00 = $1,078.06

$$\text{Annual percentage yield (APY)} = \frac{\text{1 year interest}}{\text{Principal}} = \frac{1{,}078.06}{8{,}500.00} = \underline{\underline{12.68\%}}$$

8. 2%, 4 Periods

Compound amount = 1.08243 × 1,000,000 = $1,082,430.00

1 year interest = 1,082,430.00 − 1,000,000.00 = $82,430.00

$$\text{Annual percentage yield (APY)} = \frac{\text{1 year interest}}{\text{Principal}} = \frac{82{,}430.00}{1{,}000{,}000.00} = \underline{\underline{8.24\%}}$$

9. 15%, 22 Periods

Present value = .04620 × 150,000 = $6,930.00

Compound interest = 150,000.00 − 6,930.00 = $143,070.00

10. 7%, 5 Periods

Present value = .71299 × 20,000 = $14,259.80

Compound interest = 20,000.00 − 14,259.80 = $5,740.20

11. $1\frac{1}{2}$%, 21 Periods

Present value = .73150 × 900 = $658.35

Compound interest = 900.00 − 658.35 = $241.65

12. 2%, 5 Periods

Present value = .90573 × 5,500 = $4,981.52

Compound interest = 5,500.00 − 4,981.52 = $518.48

13. Table factor required = 1%, 48 Periods

1%, 24 Periods:	.78757		
1%, 24 Periods:	× .78757		
48 Periods	.6202665 = .62027	"New" factor 1%, 48 Periods	

Present value = .62027 × 1,300 = $806.35

14. Table factor required = 5%, 50 Periods

5%, 25 Periods:	.29530	
1%, 25 Periods:	× .29530	
50 Periods	.0872021 = .08720	"New" factor 5%, 50 Periods

Present value = .08720 × 100,000 = $8,720.00

12 CHAPTER ANNUITIES

12 SECTION I Review Exercises

1. R = 2% P = 16 F = 18.6329

Future value = 1,000 × 18.6329 = $18,632.90

2. R = 5% P = 10 F = 12.57789

Future value = 2,500 × 12.57789 = $31,444.73

3. $R = 9\%$ $P = 10$ $F = 15.19293$
Future value = 10,000 × 15.19293 = $151,929.30

4. $R = 1\%$ $P = 24$ $F = 26.97346$
Future value = 200 × 26.97346 = $5,394.69

5. $R = 4\%$ $P = 28$ $F = 49.96758$
Future value = 1,500 × 49.96758 = $74,951.37

6. $R = 5\%$ $P = 24 + 1 = 25$ $F = 47.72710 - 1.00000 = 46.72710$
Future value = 400 × 46.72710 = $18,690.84

7. $R = 2\%$ $P = 12 + 1 = 13$ $F = 14.68033 - 1.00000 = 13.68033$
Future value = 1,000 × 13.68033 = $13,680.33

8. $R = 1.5\%$ $P = 30 + 1 = 31$ $F = 39.10176 - 1.00000 = 38.10176$
Future value = 50 × 38.10176 = $1,905.09

9. $R = 5\%$ $P = 25 + 1 = 26$ $F = 51.11345 - 1.00000 = 50.11345$
Future value = 2,000 × 50.11345 = $100,226.90

10. $R = 3\%$ $P = 16 + 1 = 17$ $F = 21.76159 - 1.00000 = 20.76159$
Future value = 4,400 × 20.76159 = $91,351.00

Review Exercises

SECTION II

1. $R = 5\%$ $P = 14$ $F = 9.89864$
Amount = 300.00 × 9.89864 = $2,969.59

2. $R = 7\%$ $P = 20$ $F = 10.59401$
Amount = 2,000.00 × 10.59401 = $21,188.02

3. $R = 3\%$ $P = 24$ $F = 16.93554$
Amount = 1,600.00 × 16.93554 = $27,096.86

4. $R = \frac{1}{2}\%$ $P = 21$ $F = 19.88798$
Amount = 1,000.00 × 19.88798 = $19,887.98

5. $R = 4\%$ $P = 12$ $F = 9.3850$
Amount = 8,500.00 × 9.38507 = $79,773.10

6. $R = 11\%$ $P = 9$ $F = 5.53705 + 1.00000$
Amount = 1,400.00 × 6.53705 = $9,151.87

7. $R = 3\%$ $P = 15$ $F = 11.93794 + 1.00000$
Amount = 1,300.00 × 12.93794 = $16,819.32

8. $R = 1\frac{1}{2}\%$ $P = 26$ $F = 21.39863 + 1.00000$
Amount = 500.00 × 22.39863 = $11,199.32

9. $R = 4\%$ $P = 23$ $F = 14.85684 + 1.00000$
Amount = 7,000.00 × 15.85684 = $110,997.88

10. $R = 7\%$ $P = 17$ $F = 9.76322 + 1.00000$
Amount = 4,000.00 × 10.76322 = $43,052.88

Review Exercises

SECTION III 12

1. $R = 5\%$ $P = 16$ $FV = 50,000.00$
Table factor = 23.65749

$$\text{Payment} = \frac{50,000.00}{23.65749} = \$2,113.50$$

2. $R = 9\%$ $P = 14$ $FV = 250,000.00$
Table factor = 26.01919

$$\text{Payment} = \frac{250,000.00}{26.01919} = \$9,608.29$$

3. $R = 3\%$ $P = 20$ $FV = 1{,}500.00$
Table factor = 26.87037
$$\text{Payment} = \frac{1{,}500.00}{26.87037} = \underline{\underline{\$55.82}}$$

4. $R = 1\%$ $P = 18$ $FV = 4{,}000.00$
Table factor = 19.61475
$$\text{Payment} = \frac{4{,}000.00}{19.61475} = \underline{\underline{\$203.93}}$$

5. $R = 4\%$ $P = 16$ $FV = 18{,}750.00$
Table factor = 21.82453
$$\text{Payment} = \frac{18{,}750.00}{21.82453} = \underline{\underline{\$859.13}}$$

6. $R = 9\%$ $P = 12$ $PV = 30{,}000.00$
Table factor = 7.16073
$$\text{Payment} = \frac{30{,}000.00}{7.16073} = \underline{\underline{\$4{,}189.52}}$$

7. $R = 2\%$ $P = 20$ $PV = 5{,}500.00$
Table factor = 16.35143
$$\text{Payment} = \frac{5{,}500.00}{16.35143} = \underline{\underline{\$336.36}}$$

8. $R = 1\frac{1}{2}\%$ $P = 21$ $PV = 10{,}000.00$
Table factor = 17.90014
$$\text{Payment} = \frac{10{,}000.00}{17.90014} = \underline{\underline{\$558.65}}$$

9. $R = 3\%$ $P = 16$ $PV = 13{,}660.00$
Table factor = 12.56110
$$\text{Payment} = \frac{13{,}660.00}{12.56110} = \underline{\underline{\$1{,}087.48}}$$

10. $R = 1\%$ $P = 18$ $PV = 850.00$
Table factor = 16.39827
$$\text{Payment} = \frac{850.00}{16.39827} = \underline{\underline{\$51.83}}$$

CHAPTER 12 ASSESSMENT TEST

1. $R = 2\%$ $P = 24$ Payment = 4,000.00
Table factor = 30.42186 × 4,000.00
FV = $\underline{\underline{\$121{,}687.44}}$

2. $R = 5\%$ $P = 20$ Payment = 10,000.00
Table factor = 33.06595 × 10,000.00
FV = $\underline{\underline{\$330{,}659.50}}$

3. $R = 5\%$ $P = 25$ Payment = 1,850.00
Table factor = 47.72710 − 1.00000
= 46.72710 × 1,850.00
FV = $\underline{\underline{\$86{,}445.14}}$

4. $R = 1\%$ $P = 22$ Payment = 200.00
Table factor = 24.47159 − 1.00000
= 23.47159 × 200.00
FV = $\underline{\underline{\$4{,}694.32}}$

5. $R = 5\%$ $P = 9$ Payment = 6,000.00
Table factor = 7.10782 × 6,000.00
PV = $\underline{\underline{\$42{,}646.92}}$

6. $R = 1\frac{1}{2}\%$ $P = 12$ Payment = 125,000.00
Table factor = 10.90751 × 125,000.00
PV = $\underline{\underline{\$1{,}363{,}438.75}}$

7. $R = 1\%$ $P = 17$ Payment = 700.00
Table factor = 15.56225 + 1.00000
PV = 16.56225 × 700.00 = $\underline{\underline{\$11{,}593.58}}$

8. $R = 2\%$ $P = 11$ Payment = 2,000.00
Table factor = 9.78685 + 1.00000
PV = 10.78685 × 2,000.00 = $\underline{\underline{\$21{,}573.70}}$

9. $R = 7\%$ $P = 13$ $FV = 20{,}000.00$
Table factor = 20.14064
$$\text{Payment} = \frac{20{,}000.00}{20.14064} = \underline{\underline{\$993.02}}$$

10. $R = 1\%$ $P = 27$ $FV = 7{,}000.00$
Table factor = 30.82089
$$\text{Payment} = \frac{7{,}000.00}{30.82089} = \underline{\underline{\$227.12}}$$

11. $R = 2\%$ $P = 32$ Loan amount = 6,000.00
Table factor = 23.46833
$$\text{Payment} = \frac{6{,}000.00}{23.46833} = \underline{\underline{\$255.66}}$$

12. $R = 1\%$ $P = 30$ Loan amount = 20,000.00
Table factor = 24.01584
$$\text{Payment} = \frac{20{,}000.00}{24.01584} = \underline{\underline{\$832.78}}$$

24.c. Ann

Annuity due: \$1,200, 10%, 15 years

Number of periods = (1 × 15) + 1 = 16

Interest rate per period = nominal rate ÷ periods per year

= 10 ÷ 1 = 10

Table factor, annuity due = 35.94973 − 1.00000 = 34.94973

Future value, annuity due = 34.94973 × 1,200 = \$41,939.68

Compound interest: 10%, 25 periods = 10.83471 × 41,939.68 = \$454,404.27

Boyd

Annuity due: \$1,200, 10%, 15 years

Number of periods = (1 × 15) + 1 = 16

Interest rate per period = nominal rate ÷ periods per year

= 10 ÷ 1 = 10

Table factor, annuity due = 35.94973 − 1.00000 = 34.94973

Future value, annuity due = 34.94973 × 1,200 = \$41,939.68

Compound interest: 10%, 10 periods = 2.59374 × 41,939.68 = \$108,780.63

Sam

Annuity due: \$1,200, 10%, 25 years

Number of periods = (1 × 25) + 1 = 26

Interest rate per period = nominal rate ÷ periods per year

= 10 ÷ 1 = 10

Table factor, annuity due = 109.18177 − 1.00000 = 108.18177

Future value, annuity due = 108.18177 × 1,200 = \$129,818.12

Nancy

Annuity due: \$1,500, 10%, 15 years

Number of periods = (1 × 15) + 1 = 16

Interest rate per period = nominal rate ÷ periods per year

= 10 ÷ 1 = 10

Table factor, annuity due = 35.94973 − 1.00000 = 34.94973

Future value, annuity due = 34.94973 × 1,500 = \$52,424.60

Compound interest: 10%, 15 periods = 4.17725 × 52,424.60 = \$218,990.66

Lindsey

Annuity due: \$1,500, 10%, 30 years

Number of periods = (1 × 30) + 1 = 31

Interest rate per period = nominal rate ÷ periods per year

= 10 ÷ 1 = 10

Table factor, annuity due = 181.94342 − 1,00000 = 180.94342

Future value, annuity due = 180.94342 × 1,500 = \$271,415.13

CHAPTER 13 CONSUMER AND BUSINESS CREDIT

SECTION I Review Exercises

11.

Dates	Number of Days	Activity	Unpaid Balance	Daily Balance
Oct 1–12	2	Previous balance	$140.00	$ 280.00
Oct 3–6	4	+ 50.00	190.00	760.00
Oct 7–9	3	− 75.00	115.00	345.00
Oct 10–15	6	+ 26.69	141.69	850.14
Oct 16–24	9	− 40.00	101.69	915.21
Oct 25–31	7	+ 122.70	224.39	1,570.73
Days in cycle:	31			$4,721.08

$$\text{Average daily balance} = \frac{4,721.08}{31} = \underline{\underline{\$152.29}}$$

12.

Dates	Number of Days	Activity	Unpaid Balance	Daily Balance
Feb 1–5	5	Previous balance	$ 69.50	$ 347.50
Feb 6–8	3	− 58.00	11.50	34.50
Feb 9–14	6	+ 95.88	107.38	644.28
Feb 15–23	9	+ 129.60	236.98	2,132.82
Feb 24–26	3	− 21.15	215.83	647.49
Feb 27–28	2	+ 100.00	315.83	631.66
Days in cycle:	28			$4,438.25

$$\text{Average daily balance} = \frac{4,438.25}{28} = \underline{\underline{\$158.51}}$$

13.

Dates	Number of Days	Activity	Unpaid Balance	Daily Balance
Mar 1–4	4	Previous balance	$324.45	$ 1,297.80
Mar 5–10	6	+ 156.79	481.24	2,887.44
Mar 11–14	4	− 150.00	331.24	1,324.96
Mar 15–16	2	+ 45.60	376.84	753.68
Mar 17–31	15	+ 344.50	721.34	10,820.10
Days in cycle:	31			$17,083.98

$$\text{Average daily balance} = \frac{17,083.98}{31} = \underline{\underline{\$551.10}}$$

$$\text{Periodic rate} = \frac{15\%}{12} = .0125$$

16a. SILVER Periodic Rate $= \frac{18\%}{12} = 1.5\%$

Date	Activity	Interest	New Balance
Oct 22	Purchase + $3,000.00		$3,000.00
Nov 1			3,000.00
Nov 10	Payment $1,000.00		2,000.00
Dec 1		$30.00	2,030.00
Dec 10	Payment $1,000.00		1,030.00
Jan 1		$15.45	1,045.45
Jan 10	Payment $1,045.45		0

Total Interest 30.00 + 15.45 = $45.45

GOLD Periodic Rate $= \frac{18\%}{12} = 1.5\%$

Dates	Number of Days	Activity	Unpaid Balance	Daily Balance
Oct 1–21	21	Purchase	0	0
Oct 22–31	10	$3,000.00	$3,000.00	$30,000.00
	31			30,000.00

ADB $= \frac{30,000.00}{31} = \$967.74$ Fin. Charge = 967.74 × 1.5% = $14.52

Dates	Number of Days	Activity	Unpaid Balance	Daily Balance
Nov 1–9	9	Fin. Ch. $14.52	3014.52	27,130.68
Nov 10–30	21	Payment 1,000.00	2014.52	42,304.92
	30			69,435.60

ADB $= \frac{69,435.60}{30} = \$2,314.52$ Fin. Charge = 2314.52 × 1.5% = $34.72

Dates	Number of Days	Activity	Unpaid Balance	Daily Balance
Dec 1–9	9	Fin. Ch. $34.72	2,049.24	18,443.16
Dec 10–31	22	Payment 1,000.00	1,049.24	23,083.28
	31			41,526.44

ADB $= \frac{41,526.44}{31} = \$1,339.56$ Fin. Charge = 1,339.56 × 1.5% = $20.09

Dates	Number of Days	Activity	Unpaid Balance	Daily Balance
Jan 1–9	9	Fin. Ch. $20.09	1,069.33	9,623.97
Jan 10–31	22	Payment 1,069.33	0	0
	31			9,623.97

ADB $= \frac{9,623.97}{31} = \$310.45$ Fin. Charge = $310.45 × 1.5% = $4.66

TOTAL INTEREST   14.52 + 34.72 + 20.09 + 4.66 = $73.99

CHAPTER

ASSESSMENT TEST

4.

Dates	Number of Days	Activity	Unpaid Balance	Daily Balance
Jan 1–6	6	$480.94	$480.94	2,885.64
Jan 7–11	5	+ 80.00	560.94	2,804.70
Jan 12–17	6	−125.00	435.94	2,615.64
Jan 18–23	6	+ 97.64	533.58	3,201.48
Jan 24–28	5	− 72.00	461.58	2,307.90
Jan 29	1	+109.70	571.28	571.28
Jan 30–31	2	+ 55.78	627.06	1,254.12
	31			$15,640.76

$$\text{Average daily balance} = \frac{\$15{,}640.76}{31} = \underline{\underline{\$504.54}}$$

5a.

Dates	Number of Days	Activity	Unpaid Balance	Daily Balance
Sept 1–3	3	$686.97	$686.97	$2,060.91
Sept 4–7	4	+ 223.49	910.46	3,641.84
Sept 8–11	4	− 350.00	560.46	2,241.84
Sept 12–20	9	+ 85.66	646.12	5,815.08
Sept 21–23	3	− 200.00	446.12	1,338.36
Sept 24–27	4	+ 347.12	793.24	3,172.96
Sept 28–30	3	+ 64.00	857.24	2,571.72
	30			$20,842.71

$$\text{Average daily balance} = \frac{\$20{,}842.71}{30} = \underline{\underline{\$694.76}}$$

6a. Periodic rate $= 7.75\% + 3.25\% = \dfrac{11\%}{12} = .92\%$

Dates	Number of Days	Activity	Unpaid Balance	Daily Balance
Jun 1–7	7	$52,900.00	52,900.00	370,300.00
Jun 8–17	10	+ 30,600.00	83,500.00	835,000.00
Jun 18–27	10	+ 12,300.00	95,800.00	958,000.00
Jun 28–30	3	+ 35,000.00	60,800.00	182,400.00
	30			2,345,700.00

$$\text{Average daily balance} = \frac{2{,}345{,}700.00}{30} = \underline{\underline{\$78{,}190.00}}$$

14a. Amount financed = 29,000 − 6,000 = $23,000

Total of payments = 379 × 120 = $45,480

Interest = 45,480 − 23,000 = $22,480

$$\text{APR} = \frac{72 \times 22{,}480}{(3 \times 23{,}000 \times 121) + (22{,}480 \times 119)}$$

$$= \frac{1{,}618{,}560}{8{,}349{,}000 + 2{,}675{,}120}$$

$$= \frac{1{,}618{,}560}{11{,}024{,}120} = .14681 = \underline{\underline{14.68\%}}$$

16a.

$19,995.00	Cost of car
1,229.68	6.5% sales tax
75.00	Tag and title
$21,369.68	Total purchase price

16b.

$21,369.68	Total purchase price
−3,800.00	Down payment
$17,569.68	Amount financed

APR table factor for 10.25%, 36 periods is 16.58

$$\text{Finance charge} = \frac{17{,}569.68 \times 16.58}{100} = 2{,}913.05$$

$$\text{Monthly payment} = \frac{17{,}569.68 + 2{,}913.05}{36} = \underline{\underline{\$568.96}}$$

MORTGAGES

CHAPTER 

Review Exercises

SECTION I

6. 9%, 15 years table factor = 10.15

Number of 1,000s financed $= \frac{78{,}500}{1{,}000} = 78.5$

Monthly payment = 78.5 × 10.15 = $\underline{\underline{\$796.78}}$

Month 1

$I = 78{,}500 \times .09 \times \frac{1}{2} = \underline{\underline{\$588.75}}$

\$796.78 − \$588.75 = $\underline{\underline{\$208.03}}$ to reduce principal

\$78,500 − 208.03 = $\underline{\underline{\$78{,}291.97}}$ Loan balance

7. $\frac{76{,}400.00}{1{,}000} = 76.4$

8% for 20 years = 8.37 × 76.4

Monthly PI	= \$639.47	
Annual insurance	866.00	
Annual taxes	= 1,317.00	
Annual TI	\$2,183.00 ÷ 12 =	181.92
		+ 639.47
Monthly PITI		\$821.39

8. $\frac{128{,}800.00}{1{,}000} = 128.8$

10% for 15 years = 10.75 × 128.8

Monthly PI	= \$1,384.60	
Annual insurance	1,215.00	
Annual taxes	= 2,440.00	
	\$3,655.00 ÷ 12 =	304.58
		+ 1,384.60
Monthly PITI		\$1,689.18

9. $\frac{174{,}200.00}{1{,}000} = 174.2$

$7\frac{1}{4}\%$ for 30 years = 6.83 × 174.2

Monthly PI	= \$1,189.79	
Annual insurance	1,432.00	
Annual taxes	= 3,505.00	
	\$4,937.00 ÷ 12 =	411.42
		+ 1,189.79
Monthly PITI		\$1,601.21

10. $\frac{250{,}000}{1{,}000} = 250$

$9\frac{1}{2}\%$ for 25 years = 8.74 × 250

Monthly PI	= \$2,185.00	
Annual insurance	2,196.00	
Annual taxes	= 6,553.00	
	\$8,749.00 ÷ 12 =	729.08
		+ 2,185.00
Monthly PITI		\$2,914.08

ASSESSMENT TEST

1. Number of 1,000s financed $= \frac{134{,}900.00}{1{,}000} = \underline{\underline{134.9}}$

Table factor, $7\frac{3}{4}\%$ for 25 years = $\underline{\underline{7.56}}$

Monthly payment = 134.9 × 7.56 = $\underline{\underline{\$1{,}019.84}}$

Total interest = (25 × 12 × 1,019.84) − 134,900.00 = $\underline{\underline{\$171{,}052.00}}$

2. Number of 1,000s financed $= \frac{79,500.00}{1,000} = \underline{\underline{79.5}}$

Table factor, $8\frac{1}{4}\%$ for 20 years $= \underline{\underline{8.53}}$

Monthly payment $= 79.5 \times 8.53 = \underline{\underline{\$678.14}}$

Total interest $= (20 \times 12 \times 678.14) - 79{,}500.00$
$= \underline{\underline{\$83{,}253.60}}$

4. Monthly PI $= 54.2 \times 8.40 = \underline{\underline{\$455.28}}$

Monthly PITI $= 455.28 + \frac{719.00 + 459.00}{12} = \underline{\underline{\$553.45}}$

5. Monthly PI $= 132.1 \times 10.00 = \underline{\underline{\$1{,}321.00}}$

Monthly PITI $= 1{,}321.00 + \frac{2{,}275.00 + 1{,}033.00}{12} = \underline{\underline{\$1{,}596.67}}$

6. Percent of appraised value $= 114{,}500.00 \times .65 = \underline{\underline{\$74{,}425.00}}$

Potential credit $=$

$$\begin{array}{r} 74{,}425.00 \\ -\ 77{,}900.00 \\ \hline -\ \$3{,}475.00 \end{array} = \underline{\underline{0}}$$

7. Percent of appraised value $= 51{,}500.00 \times .8$
$= \underline{\underline{\$41{,}200.00}}$

Potential credit $=$

$$\begin{array}{r} 41{,}200.00 \\ -\ 27{,}400.00 \\ \hline \underline{\underline{\$13{,}800.00}} \end{array}$$

8. Percent of appraised value $= 81{,}200.00 \times .7$
$= \underline{\underline{\$56{,}840.00}}$

Potential credit $=$

$$\begin{array}{r} 56{,}840.00 \\ -\ 36{,}000.00 \\ \hline \underline{\underline{\$20{,}840.00}} \end{array}$$

9. Housing expense ratio $= \frac{1{,}288.00}{5{,}300.00} = \underline{\underline{24.3\%}}$

Total obligations ratio $= \frac{1{,}288.00 + 840.00}{5{,}300.00} = \underline{\underline{40.15\%}}$

10. Housing expense ratio $= \frac{952.00}{3{,}750.00} = \underline{\underline{25.39\%}}$

Total obligations ratio $= \frac{952.00 + 329.00}{3{,}750.00} = \underline{\underline{34.16\%}}$

15 CHAPTER FINANCIAL STATEMENTS AND RATIOS

15 SECTION I Review Exercises

26a.

Victory Lane Sporting Goods
Balance Sheet
December 31, 2008

Assets		
Current Assets	$157,600	67%
Property, Plant, Equipment	42,000	17.8%
Investments & Other Assets	35,700	15.2%
Total Assets	$235,300	100.0%
Liabilities & Owner's Equity		
Current Liability	$ 21,200	9%
Long-Term Liability	53,400	22.7%
Total Liabilities	$ 74,600	31.7%
Owners Equity	$160,700	68.3%
Total Liabilities & Owner's Equity	$235,300	100.0%

26b.

Victory Lane Sporting Goods
Comparative Balance Sheet
December 31, 2008 and 2009

			Increase (Decrease)	
Assets	**2009**	**2008**	**Amount**	**Percent**
Current Assets	$175,300	$157,600	$ 17,700	11.2%
Property, Plant, Equipment	43,600	42,000	1,600	3.8
Invest. & Other Assets	39,200	35,700	3,500	9.8
Total Assets	$258,100	$235,300	$22,800	9.7
Liabilities & Owner's Equity				
Current Liabilities	$ 27,700	$ 21,200	$ 6,500	30.7
Long Term Liabilities	51,000	53,400	(2,400)	(4.5)
Total Liabilities	$ 78,700	$ 74,600	$ 4,100	5.5
Owners Equity	$179,400	$160,700	$ 18,700	11.6
Total Liability & Owner's Equity	$258,100	$235,300	$22,800	9.7

27a.

Flagship Industries, Inc.
Balance Sheet
June 30, 2008

Assets		**Percent**
Current Assets		
Cash	$ 44,300	5.5%
Accounts Receivable	127,600	15.8
Merchandise Inventory	88,100	10.9
Prepaid Maintenance	4,100	.5
Office Supplies	4,000	.5
Total Current Assets	268,100	33.2
Property, Plant, and Equipment		
Land	154,000	19.0
Buildings	237,000	29.3
Fixtures	21,400	2.6
Vehicles	64,000	7.9
Computers	13,000	1.6
Total Property, Plant, and Equipment	489,400	60.4
Investments and Other Assets		
Investments	32,000	4.0
Goodwill	20,000	2.5
Total Assets	$809,500	100.0%
Liabilities and Stockholders' Equity		
Current Liabilities		
Accounts Payable	$55,700	6.9%
Salaries Payable	23,200	2.9
Notes Payable	38,000	4.7
Total Current Liabilities	116,900	14.5
Long-Term Liabilities		
Mortgage Payable	91,300	11.3
Debenture Bonds	165,000	20.4
Total Long-Term Liabilities	256,300	31.7
Total Liabilities	373,200	46.2
Stockholders' Equity		
Common Stock	350,000	43.2
Retained Earnings	86,300	10.7
Total Stockholders' Equity	436,300	53.9
Total Liabilities and Stockholders' Equity	$809,500	100.0%

*Percents may vary by .1 due to rounding

27b.

Flagship Industries, Inc.
Comparative Balance Sheet
June 30, 2008 and 2009

			Increase (Decrease)	
Assets	**2009**	**2008**	**Amount**	**Percent**
Current Assets				
Cash	$ 40,200	$ 44,300	($4,100)	(9.3)%
Accounts Receivable	131,400	127,600	3,800	3.0
Merchandise Inventory	92,200	88,100	4,100	4.7
Prepaid Maintenance	3,700	4,100	(400)	(9.8)
Office Supplies	6,200	4,000	2,200	55.0
Total Current Assets	273,700	268,100	5,600	2.1
Property, Plant, and Equipment				
Land	154,000	154,000	0	0
Buildings	231,700	237,000	(5,300)	(2.2)
Fixtures	23,900	21,400	2,500	11.7
Vehicles	55,100	64,000	(8,900)	(13.9)
Computers	16,800	13,000	3,800	29.2
Total Property, Plant, and Equipment	481,500	489,400	7,900	1.6
Investments and Other Assets				
Investments	36,400	32,000	4,400	13.8
Goodwill	22,000	20,000	2,000	10.0
Total Assets	$813,600	$809,500	$4,100	.5
Liabilities and Stockholders' Equity				
Current Liabilities				
Accounts Payable	$51,800	$55,700	($3,900)	(7.0)
Salaries Payable	25,100	23,200	1,900	8.2
Notes Payable	19,000	38,000	(19,000)	(50.0)
Total Current Liabilities	95,900	116,900	(21,000)	(18.0)
Long-Term Liabilities				
Mortgage Payable	88,900	91,300	(2,400)	(2.6)
Debenture Bonds	165,000	165,000	0	0
Total Long-Term Liabilities	253,900	256,300	(2,400)	(.9)
Total Liabilities	349,800	373,200	(23,400)	(6.3)
Stockholders' Equity				
Common Stock	350,000	350,000	0	0
Retained Earnings	113,800	86,300	27,500	31.9
Total Stockholders' Equity	463,800	436,300	27,500	6.3
Total Liabilities and Stockholders' Equity	$813,600	$809,500	$ 4,100	.5

28a.

Kellogg Company
Comparative Balance Sheet
December 30, 2005 and 2006

			Increase (Decrease)	
(Amounts in millions)	**2006**	**2005**	**Amount**	**Percent**
Current assets				
Cash and cash equivalents	$ 410.6	$ 219.1	$ 191.5	87.4%
Accounts receivable, net	944.8	879.1	65.7	7.5
Inventories	823.9	717.0	106.9	14.9
Other current assets	247.7	381.3	(133.6)	(35.0)
Total current assets	$2,427.0	$2,196.5	$230.5	10.5

28b.

Kellogg Company
Balance Sheet
December 30, 2006

		Percent
Current liabilities		
Current maturities of long-term debt	$ 723.3	18.0%
Notes payable	1,268.0	31.5
Accounts payable	910.4	22.6
Other current liabilities	1,118.5	27.8
Total current liabilities	$4,020.2	100.0%

Review Exercises

SECTION II 15

6a.

Jefferson Airplane Parts, Inc.
Income Statement
January 1 to March 31, 2008

Revenue		
Gross Sales	$240,000	122.1%
Less: Sales Discounts	43,500	22.1
Net Sales	$196,500	100.0
Cost of Goods Sold		
Merchandise Inventory, Jan. 1	86,400	44.0
Net Purchases	76,900	39.1
Goods Available for Sale	163,300	83.1
Less: Merchandise Inventory, Mar. 31	103,200	52.5
Cost of Goods Sold	60,100	30.6
Gross Margin	136,400	69.4
Operating Expenses	108,000	55.0
Income before Taxes	28,400	14.5
Income Tax	14,550	7.4
Net Income	$ 13,850	7.0

6b.

Jefferson Airplane Parts, Inc.
Comparative Income Statement
First and Second Quarter, 2008

	2nd Qtr.	1st Qtr.	Increase (Decrease) Amount	Percent
Revenue				
Gross Sales	$297,000	$240,000	$57,000	23.8%
Less: Sales Discounts	41,300	43,500	(2,200)	(5.1)
Net Sales	255,700	196,500	59,200	30.1
Cost of Goods Sold				
Merchandise Inventory, Beginning	103,200	86,400	16,800	19.4
Net Purchases	84,320	76,900	7,420	9.6
Goods Available for Sale	187,520	163,300	24,220	14.8
Less: Merchandise Inventory, Ending	96,580	103,200	(6,620)	(6.4)
Cost of Goods Sold	90,940	60,100	30,840	51.3
Gross Margin	164,760	136,400	28,360	20.8
Operating Expenses	126,700	108,000	18,700	17.3
Income before Income Tax	38,060	28,400	9,660	34.0
Income Tax	16,400	14,550	1,850	12.7
Net Income	$ 21,660	$ 13,850	$ 7,810	56.4

7a.

Sweets & Treats Candy Company, Inc.
Income Statement
For the year ended December 31, 2008

Revenue		
Gross Sales	$2,249,000	109.6%
Less: Sales Returns and Allowances	143,500	7.0
Sales Discounts	54,290	2.6
Net Sales	$ 2,051,210	100.0
Cost of Goods Sold		
Merchandise Inventory, Jan.1	875,330	42.7
Net Purchases	546,920	26.7
Freight In	11,320	.6
Goods Available for Sale	1,433,570	69.9
Less: Merchandise Inventory, Dec. 31	716,090	34.9
Cost of Goods Sold	717,480	35.0
Gross Margin	1,333,730	65.0
Operating Expenses		
Salaries	319,800	15.6
Rent	213,100	10.4
Depreciation	51,200	2.5
Utilities	35,660	1.7
Advertising	249,600	12.2
Insurance	39,410	1.9
Administrative Expenses	91,700	4.5
Miscellaneous Expenses	107,500	5.2
Total Operating Expenses	1,107,970	54.0
Income before Taxes	225,760	11.0
Income Tax	38,450	1.9
Net Income	$ 187,310	9.1

7b.

Sweets & Treats Candy Company, Inc.
Comparative Income Statement
For the years ended December 31, 2008 and 2009

			Increase (Decrease)	
	2009	2008	Amount	Percent
Revenue				
Gross Sales	$2,125,000	$2,249,000	($124,000)	(5.5)%
Less: Sales Returns and Allowances	126,400	143,500	(17,100)	(11.9)
Sales Discounts	73,380	54,290	19,090	35.2
Net Sales	1,925,220	2,051,210	(125,990)	(6.1)
Cost of Goods Sold				
Merchandise Inventory, Jan. 1	716,090	875,330	(159,240)	(18.2)
Net Purchases	482,620	546,920	(64,300)	(11.8)
Freight In	9,220	11,320	(2,100)	(18.6)
Goods Available for Sale	1,207,930	1,433,570	(225,640)	(15.7)
Less: Merchandise Inventory, Dec. 31	584,550	716,090	(131,540)	(18.4)
Cost of Goods Sold	623,380	717,480	(94,100)	(13.1)
Gross Margin	1,301,840	1,333,730	(31,890)	(2.4)
Operating Expenses				
Salaries	340,900	319,800	21,100	7.0
Rent	215,000	213,100	1,900	.9
Depreciation	56,300	51,200	5,100	10.0
Utilities	29,690	35,660	(5,970)	(16.7)
Advertising	217,300	249,600	(32,300)	(13.0)
Insurance	39,410	39,410	0	0
Administrative Expenses	95,850	91,700	4,150	4.5
Miscellaneous Expenses	102,500	107,500	(5,000)	(4.7)
Total Operating Expenses	1,096,950	1,107,970	(11,020)	(1.0)
Income before Income Tax	204,890	225,760	(20,870)	(9.2)
Income Tax	44,530	38,450	6,080	15.8
Net Income	$ 160,360	$ 187,310	$ (26,950)	(14.4)

8a.

FedEx Corporation
Comparative Income Statement
May 31, 2006 and 2007

			Increase (Decrease)	
(in millions)	2007	2006	Amount	Percent
REVENUES	$35,214	$32,294	2,920	9.0%
Operating expenses:				
Salaries and employee benefits	13,740	12,571	1,169	9.3
Purchased transportation	3,873	3,251	622	19.1
Rentals and landing fees	2,343	2,390	(47)	(2.0)
Depreciation and amortization	1,742	1,550	192	12.4
Fuel	3,533	3,256	277	8.5
Maintenance and repairs	1,952	1,777	175	9.8
Other	4,755	4,485	270	6.0
Total operating expenses	31,938	29,280	2,658	9.1
OPERATING INCOME	$3,276	$3,014	$262	8.7

8b.

FedEx Corporation
Income Statement
May 31, 2007

Operating expenses:		Percent
Salaries and employee benefits	$13,740	43.0%
Purchased transportation	3,873	12.1
Rentals and landing fees	2,343	7.3
Depreciation and amortization	1,742	5.5
Fuel	3,533	11.1
Maintenance and repairs	1,952	6.1
Other	4,755	14.9
Total Operating Expenses	$31,938	100.0%

CHAPTER 15 ASSESSMENT TEST

1a.

Mountain Magic Tire Company
Balance Sheet
December 31, 2008

Assets		Percent
Current Assets	$132,500	52.2%
Property, Plant, and Equipment	88,760	35.0
Investments and Other Assets	32,400	12.8
Total Assets	$253,660	100.0%
Liabilities		
Current Liabilities	51,150	20.2%
Long-Term Liabilities	87,490	34.5
Total Liabilities	138,640	54.7
Owner's Equity		
Paul Provost, Equity	115,020	45.3
Total Liabilities and Owner's Equity	$253,660	100.0%

1b.

Mountain Magic Tire Company
Comparative Balance Sheet
December 31, 2008 and 2009

			Increase (Decrease)	
Assets	**2009**	**2008**	**Amount**	**Percent**
Current Assets	$154,300	$132,500	$21,800	16.5%
Property, Plant, and Equipment	124,650	88,760	35,890	40.4
Investments and Other Assets	20,000	32,400	(12,400)	(38.3)
Total Assets	$298,950	$253,600	$45,290	17.9
Liabilities				
Current Liabilities	$ 65,210	$ 51,150	$ 14,060	27.5
Long-Term Liabilities	83,800	87,490	(3,690)	(4.2)
Total Liabilities	149,010	138,640	10,370	7.5
Owner's Equity				
Paul Provost, Equity	149,940	115,020	34,920	30.4
Total Liabilities and Owner's Equity	$298,950	$253,660	$45,290	17.9

2a.

Sticks & Stones Builder's Mart
Balance Sheet
October 31, 2008

Assets		
Current Assets		**Percent***
Cash	$ 45,260	4.1%
Accounts Receivable	267,580	24.5
Merchandise Inventory	213,200	19.5
Prepaid Expenses	13,400	1.2
Office Supplies	5,300	.5
Total Current Assets	544,740	49.8
Property, Plant, and Equipment		
Land	87,600	8.0
Building	237,200	21.7
Equipment	85,630	7.8
Vehicles	54,700	5.0
Computers	31,100	2.8
Total Property, Plant, and Equipment	496,230	45.4
Investments and Other Assets		
Investments	53,100	4.8
Total Assets	$1,094,070	100.0%

Liabilities and Stockholders' Equity		
Current Liabilities		
Accounts Payable	$ 43,200	3.9%
Salaries Payable	16,500	1.5
Notes Payable (6-months)	102,400	9.4
Total Current Liabilities	162,100	14.8
Long-Term Liabilities		
Mortgage Payable	124,300	11.4
Notes Payable (3 years)	200,000	18.3
Total Long-Term Liabilities	324,300	29.6
Total Liabilities	486,400	44.5
Stockholders' Equity		
Common Stock	422,000	38.6
Retained Earnings	185,670	17.0
Total Stockholders' Equity	607,670	55.5
Total Liabilities and Stockholders' Equity	$1,094,070	100.0%

*Percents may vary by .1 due to rounding

2b.

Sticks & Stones Builder's Mart
Comparative Balance Sheet
October 31, 2008 and 2009

			Increase (Decrease)	
Assets	**2009**	**2008**	**Amount**	**Percent**
Current Assets				
Cash	$ 47,870	$ 45,260	$ 2,610	5.8%
Accounts Receivable	251,400	267,580	(16,180)	(6.0)
Merchandise Inventory	223,290	213,200	10,090	4.7
Prepaid Maintenance	8,500	13,400	(4,900)	(36.6)
Supplies	6,430	5,300	1,130	21.3
Total Current Assets	537,490	544,740	7,250	1.3
Property, Plant, and Equipment				
Land	87,600	87,600	0	0
Building	234,500	237,200	(2,700)	(1.1)
Equipment	88,960	85,630	3,330	3.9
Vehicles	68,800	54,700	14,100	25.8
Computers	33,270	31,100	2,170	7.0
Total Property, Plant and Equipment	513,130	496,230	16,900	3.4
Investments and Other Assets				
Investments	55,640	53,100	2,540	4.8
Total Assets	$1,106,260	$1,094,070	$12,190	1.1
Liabilities and Stockholders' Equity				
Current Liabilities				
Accounts Payable	$ 48,700	$ 43,200	$ 5,500	11.3
Salaries Payable	9,780	16,500	(6,720)	(40.7)
Notes Payable (6-month)	96,700	102,400	(5,700)	(5.6)
Total Current Liabilities	155,180	162,100	(6,920)	(4.3)
Long-Term Liabilities				
Mortgage Payable	121,540	124,300	(2,760)	(2.2)
Notes Payable (3-years)	190,000	200,000	(10,000)	(5.0)
Total Long-Term Liabilities	311,540	324,300	(12,760)	(3.9)
Total Liabilities	466,720	486,400	(19,680)	(4.0)
Stockholders' Equity				
Common Stock	450,000	422,000	28,000	6.6
Retained Earnings	189,540	185,670	3,870	2.1
Total Stockholders' Equity	639,540	607,670	31,870	5.2
Total Liabilities and Stockholders' Equity	$1,106,260	$1,094,070	$12,190	1.1

5a.

Woof & Meow Pet Supply
Income Statement
Third Quarter, 2009

Revenue		
Gross Sales	$224,400	106.8%
Less: Sales Returns and Allowances	14,300	6.8
Net Sales	210,100	100.0
Cost of Goods sold		
Merchandise Inventory, July 1	165,000	78.5
Net Purchases	76,500	36.4
Goods Available for Sale	241,500	114.9
Less: Merchandise Inventory, Sept. 30	143,320	68.2
Cost of Goods Sold	98,180	46.7
Gross Margin	111,920	53.3
Operating Expenses	68,600	32.7
Income before Taxes	43,320	20.6
Income Tax	8,790	4.2
Net Income	$ 34,530	16.4

5b.

Woof & Meow Pet Supply
Comparative Income Statement
Third and Fourth Quarter—2009

			Increase (Decrease)	
	4th Qtr.	**3rd Qtr.**	**Amount**	**Percent**
Revenue				
Gross Sales	$218,200	$224,400	$ (6,200)	(2.8)%
Less: Sales Returns and Allowances	9,500	14,300	(4,800)	(33.6)
Net Sales	208,700	210,100	1,400	.7
Cost of Goods Sold				
Merchandise Inventory, Beginning	143,320	165,000	(21,680)	(13.1)
Net Purchases	81,200	76,500	4,700	6.1
Goods Available for Sale	224,520	241,500	(16,980)	(7.0)
Less: Merchandise Inventory, Ending	125,300	143,320	(18,020)	(12.6)
Cost of Goods Sold	99,220	98,180	1,040	1.0
Gross Margin	109,480	111,920	(2,440)	(2.2)
Operating Expenses	77,300	68,600	8,700	12.7
Income before Income Tax	32,180	43,320	(11,140)	(25.7)
Income Tax	11,340	8,790	2,550	29.0
Net Income	$ 20,840	$ 34,530	$(13,690)	(39.6)

6a.

Touchstone Jewelers
Income Statement
For the year ended December 31, 2008

Revenue		
Gross Sales	$1,243,000	108.5%
Less: Sales Returns and Allowances	76,540	6.7
Sales Discounts	21,300	1.9
Net Sales	$ 1,145,160	100.0
Cost of Goods Sold		
Merchandise Inventory, Jan. 1	654,410	57.1
Net Purchases	318,000	27.8
Freight In	3,450	.3
Goods Available for Sale	975,860	85.2
Less: Merchandise Inventory, Dec. 31	413,200	36.1
Cost of Goods Sold	562,660	49.1
Gross Margin	582,500	50.9
Operating Expenses		
Salaries	92,350	8.1
Rent	83,100	7.3
Depreciation	87,700	7.7
Utilities	21,350	1.9
Advertising	130,440	11.4
Insurance	7,920	.7
Miscellaneous Expenses	105,900	9.2
Total Operating Expenses	528,760	46.2
Income before Taxes	53,740	4.7
Income Tax	18,580	1.6
Net Income	$ 35,160	3.1

6b.

Touchstone Jewelers
Comparative Income Statement
For the years ended December 31, 2008 and 2009

	2009	2008	Increase (Decrease) Amount	Increase (Decrease) Percent
Revenue				
Gross Sales	$1,286,500	$1,243,000	$43,500	3.5%
Less: Sales Returns and Allowances	78,950	76,540	2,410	3.1
Sales Discounts	18,700	21,300	(2,600)	(12.2)
Net Sales	1,188,850	1,145,160	43,690	3.8
Cost of Goods Sold				
Merchandise Inventory, Jan. 1	687,300	654,410	32,890	5.0
Net Purchases	325,400	318,000	7,400	2.3
Freight In	3,980	3,450	530	15.4
Goods Available for Sale	1,016,680	975,860	40,820	4.2
Less: Merchandise Inventory, Dec. 31	401,210	413,200	(11,990)	(2.9)
Cost of Goods Sold	615,470	562,660	52,810	9.4
Gross Margin	573,380	582,500	(9,120)	1.6
Operating Expenses				
Salaries	99,340	92,350	6,990	7.6
Rent	85,600	83,100	2,500	3.0
Depreciation	81,200	87,700	(6,500)	(7.4)
Utilities	21,340	21,350	(10)	(0.05)
Advertising	124,390	130,440	(6,050)	(4.6)
Insurance	8,700	7,920	780	9.8
Miscellaneous Expenses	101,230	105,900	(4,670)	(4.4)
Total Operating Expenses	521,800	528,760	(6,960)	(1.3)
Income before Income Tax	51,580	53,740	(2,160)	(4.0)
Income Tax	12,650	18,580	(5,930)	(31.9)
Net Income	$ 38,930	$ 35,160	$ 3,770	10.7

20.

Apple Computer
Vertical Analysis
Fiscal year 2006

	Percent
Net Sales	100.0%
Cost of Sales	71.0
Gross Margin	29.0
Operating Expenses:	
Research and Development	3.7
Selling, General, and Administrative	12.6
Restructuring Costs	—
Total Operating Expenses	16.3
Operating Income	12.7
Other Income and Expense	1.9
Income Before Provision for Income Taxes	14.6
Provision for Income Taxes	4.3
Net Income	10.3%

CHAPTER 16 INVENTORY

CHAPTER 16 ASSESSMENT TEST

10a.

Date	Number of Units	Price per Unit	Total Cost
Beginning inventory, Jan. 1	10,000	5.00	50,000
Purchase, April 15	15,000	6.00	90,000
Purchase, July 19	20,000	7.00	140,000
Purchase, November 2	25,000	8.00	200,000
Units for sale	70,000		$480,000

	Units		Price		Amount
Value of 40,000 units using FIFO	25,000	@	8.00	=	200,000
	15,000	@	7.00	=	105,000
	40,000				$305,000
Value of 40,000 units using LIFO	10,000	@	5.00	=	50,000
	15,000	@	6.00	=	90,000
	15,000	@	7.00	=	105,000
	40,000				$245,000

Value of 40,000 units using average cost

$$\frac{480{,}000}{70{,}000} = \$6.86 \text{ Each}$$

$40{,}000 \times 6.86 = \underline{\underline{\$274{,}400}}$

CHAPTER 17 DEPRECIATION

SECTION II Review Exercises

4.

End of Year	Orig. Cost	Cost Recov. %	Depreciation	Accum. Depreci.	Book Value
					$2,400,000
1	$2,400,000	14.29	$342,960	$ 342,960	2,057,040
2	2,400,000	24.49	587,760	930,720	1,469,280
3	2,400,000	17.49	419,760	1,350,480	1,049,520
4	2,400,000	12.49	299,760	1,650,240	749,760
5	2,400,000	8.93	214,320	1,864,560	535,440
6	2,400,000	8.92	214,080	2,078,640	321,360
7	2,400,000	8.93	214,320	2,292,960	107,040
8	2,400,000	4.46	107,040	2,400,000	0

INSURANCE

CHAPTER

Review Exercises

SECTION I

1. Face value $5,000 Male-24

$$\text{Number of 1,000s} = \frac{5{,}000}{1{,}000} = 5$$

Whole life annual premium = 15.90 × 5
= $79.50

Semiannual premium = 79.50 × .52
= $41.34

Quarterly premium = 79.50 × .26
= $20.67

Monthly premium = 79.50 × .09
= $7.16

9. Nonforfeiture options:
Face value $50,000 10 years in force, Whole life
Number of 1,000s = 50

Option 1, Cash value $ 98.00 per 1,000
= 98.00 × 50
= $4,900.00

Option 2, Reduced, Paid up $ 186.00 per 1,000
= 186.00 × 50
= $9,300.00 ins. for life

Option 3, Extended terrm 17 years, 54 days

Review Exercises

SECTION II

1. Building value $88,000, Contents value $21,000
Area 4, Class B

$$\text{Building, number of 100s } \frac{88{,}000}{100} = 880$$

$$\text{Contents, number of 100s } \frac{21{,}000}{100} = 210$$

Building .76 × 880 = $668.80 Annual premium
Contents .83 × 210 = $174.30 Annual premium
Total annual premium = 668.80 + 174.30 = $843.10

6. Annual premium $450 after 3 months by insurance company

$$\text{Premium} = 450.00 \times \frac{3}{12} = \$112.50$$

Refund due = 450.00 − 112.50
= $337.50

7. Annual premium $560 after 20 days by insured

Short-rate premium = 560 × 16%
= $89.60

Refund due = 560.00 − 89.60
= $470.40

11. Replacement cost = $200,000 Face value = $160,000
Coinsurance = 80% Loss = $75,000
Insurance required = 200,000 × 80% = $160,000

$$\text{Amount of loss paid} = \frac{160{,}000}{160{,}000} \times 75{,}000$$

= $75,000

19.

$$\text{Aetna: } \frac{300{,}000}{500{,}000} = 60\% \qquad .6 \times 95{,}000 = \$57{,}000$$

$$\text{State Farm: } \frac{125{,}000}{500{,}000} = 25\% \qquad .25 \times 95{,}000 = \$23{,}750$$

$$\text{Liberty Mutual: } \frac{95{,}000}{500{,}000} = 15\% \qquad .15 \times 95{,}000 = \$14{,}250$$

CHAPTER ASSESSMENT TEST

1. M-29, Face value $80,000, 20 payment life

Number of 1,000s $\frac{80,000}{1,000} = 80$

Annual premium = 31.52 × 80
= $2,521.60

Semiannual = 2,521.60 × 52%
= $1,311.23

Quarterly = 2,521.60 × 26%
= $655.62

Monthly = 2,521.60 × 9%
= $226.94

5. Nonforfeiture options:

Face value $130,000 15 years in force, Whole life

Number of 1,000s $\frac{130,000}{1,000} = 130$

Option 1, Cash value = 157 × 130 = $20,410

Option 2, Reduced, Paid up = 314 × 130 = $40,820

Option 3, Extended term = 21 years, 218 days

6. Face value $60,000 5 years in force, 20 payment life

Number of 1,000s $\frac{60,000}{1,000} = 60$

Option 1, Cash value = 73 × 60 = $4,380

Option 2, Reduced, Paid up = 212 × 60 = $12,720

Option 3, Extended term = 14 years, 86 days

10. Number of 100s, Building $\frac{47,000}{100} = 470$

Building premium 470 × .76 = $357.20

Number of 100s, Contents $\frac{93,000}{100} = 930$

Contents premium 930 × .83 = $771.90

Total premium = 771.90 + 357.20 = $1,129.10

13. Short-term premium = $260.00 \times \frac{8}{12}$ = $173.33

Refund = 260.00 − 173.33 = $86.67

15. Insurance needed = 260,000 × 80% = $208,000

Amount of loss paid by insurance = $\frac{105,000}{208,000} \times 12,000$
= $6,057.69

21.

Bodily injury	50/100	99.00
Property damage	25	74.00
Collision	$500 deductible	116.00
Comprehensive	$100 deductible	+ 113.00
Rating factor	.9	402.00 × .9
	Annual Premium	$361.80

22.

Bodily injury	10/20	61.00
Property damage	5	46.00
Collision	$250 deductible	100.00
Comprehensive	Full coverage	+ 79.00
Rating factor	2.2	286.00 × 2.2
	Annual Premium	$629.20

23.

Bodily injury	100/300	122.00
Property damage	100	84.00
Collision	$500 deductible	76.00
Comprehensive	$100 deductible	+ 50.00
Rating factor	1.7	332.00 × 1.7
	Annual Premium	$564.40

INVESTMENTS

Review Exercises

1. Common dividend per share $= \dfrac{3,000,000}{5,000,000} = .6 = \underline{\underline{\$.60 \text{ per share}}}$

2. Total preferred dividend $= 3,000,000 \times 5.50 = \$16,500,000$

Total common dividend $= 25,000,000 - 16,500,000 = \$8,500,000$

Common dividend per share $= \dfrac{8,500,000}{10,000,000} = .85 = \underline{\underline{\$.85 \text{ per share}}}$

11. Current yield $= \dfrac{\text{Annual dividend}}{\text{Current price}}$

$= \dfrac{1.60}{46.13} = .0346 = \underline{\underline{3.5\%}}$

Price earnings ratio $= \dfrac{\text{Current price per share}}{\text{Earnings per share}}$

$= \dfrac{46.13}{6.59} = \underline{\underline{7}}$

13. Earnings per share $= \dfrac{\text{Current price}}{\text{PE ratio}} = \dfrac{27.5}{21} = \underline{\underline{\$1.31}}$

14. Current price $= \dfrac{\text{Dividend}}{\text{Yield}} = \dfrac{1.60}{2.5\%} = \underline{\underline{\$64}}$

15. Dividend = Price × Yield $= 42.38 \times .7\% = \underline{\underline{\$.30}}$

16.

Cost of shares	= 100 × 47.20	=	$4,720.00
Commission	= 100 × 47.20 × 3%	=	+ 141.60
	Total cost	=	$4,861.60
Value of shares	= 100 × 56.06	=	$5,606.00
Commission	= 100 × 56.06 × 3%	=	− 168.16
	Proceeds	=	$5,437.82
Gain (loss)	= 5,437.82 − 4,861.60	=	$576.22

17.

Cost of shares	= 350 × 18.42	=	$6,447.00
Commission	= 300 × 18.42 × 2%	=	+ 110.52
	= 50 × 18.42 × 3%	=	+ 27.63
	Total cost	=	$6,585.15
Value of shares	= 350 × 29.19	=	$10,216.50
Commission	= 300 × 29.19 × 2%	=	− 175.14
	= 50 × 29.19 × 3%	=	− 43.79
	Proceeds	=	$9,997.57
Gain (loss)	= 9,997.57 − 6,585.15	=	$3,412.42

18. Cost of shares = 900 × 28.37 = $25,533.00
Commission = 900 × 28.37 × 3% = + 765.99
Total cost $26,298.99
Value of shares = 900 × 36.25 = $32,625.00
Commission = 900 × 36.25 × 3% = − 978.75
Proceeds $31,646.25
Gain (loss) = 31,646.25 − 26,298.99 = $5,347.26

19. Cost of shares = 775 × 37.75 = $29,256.25
Commission = 700 × 37.75 × 1.5% = + 396.38
= 75 × 37.75 × 2.5% = + 70.78
Total cost $29,723.41
Value of shares = 775 × 34.50 = $26,737.50
Commission = 700 × 34.50 × 1.5% = − 362.25
= 75 × 34.50 × 1.5% = − 64.69
Proceeds $26,310.56
Gain (loss) = $26,310.50 − 29,723.41 = ($3,412.85)

20. Cost of shares = 500 × 25.11 = $12,555.00
Commission = 500 × 25.11 × 3% = + 376.65
Total cost $12,931.65
Value of shares = 500 × 28.86 = $14,430.00
Commission = 500 × 28.86 × 3% = − 432.90
Proceeds $13,997.10
Gain (loss) = 13,997.10 − 12,931.65 = $1,065.45

20 SECTION III Review Exercises

9. Mutual fund sales charge = Offer price − Net asset value
Sales charge = 13.35 − 12.82 = $.53
Sales charge % = Sales charge ÷ Net asset value

$$\text{Sales charge \%} = \frac{.53}{12.82} = 4.1\%$$

13. $$\text{Net asset value} = \frac{\text{Total assets} - \text{Total liabilities}}{\text{Number of shares outstanding}}$$

$$= \frac{80{,}000{,}000 - 2{,}300{,}000}{5{,}000{,}000}$$

$$= \$15.54$$

$$\text{Shares purchased} = \frac{\text{Total investment}}{\text{Offer price}}$$

$$= \frac{10{,}000}{16.10}$$

$$= 621.118 \text{ Shares}$$

17. Gain (or loss) on investment = Proceeds − Total cost

Total gain (or loss) = Gain (or loss) + Dividends

$$\text{Return on investment} = \frac{\text{Total gain}}{\text{Total cost of purchase}}$$

Total cost = 100 × 15.30 = $\underline{\underline{\$1,530.00}}$

Proceeds = 100 × 18.80 = $\underline{\underline{\$1,880.00}}$

1,880.00 − 1,530.00 + (.45 × 100)

Total gain = $\underline{\underline{\$395.00}}$

$$\text{Return on investment} = \frac{395.00}{1,530.00} = \underline{\underline{25.8\%}}$$

ASSESSMENT TEST

CHAPTER 20

1. $\text{Common dividend} = \frac{\text{Dividend}}{\text{Shares}} = \frac{7,900,000}{22,000,000} = .359 = \underline{\underline{\$.36}} \text{ per share}$

2. Preferred dividend = 3.20 current + 3.20 arrears = $\underline{\underline{\$6.40}}$ per share

Total preferred = 1,000,000 × 6.40 = $6,400,000

Total common = 8,500,000 − 6,400,000 = $2,100,000

$$\text{Common dividend} = \frac{2,100,000}{5,000,000} = .42 = \underline{\underline{\$.42}} \text{ per share}$$

8. $\text{Current yield} = \frac{\text{Dividend}}{\text{Price}} = \frac{1.50}{69.25} = .0216 = \underline{\underline{2.2\%}}$

$$\text{Price-earnings ratio} = \frac{\text{Price}}{\text{Earnings}} = \frac{69.25}{3.20} = 21.6 = \underline{\underline{22}}$$

9. $\text{Earnings per share} = \frac{\text{Price}}{\text{PE Ratio}} = \frac{33.50}{16} = \underline{\underline{\$2.09}}$

10. $\text{Current price} = \frac{\text{Dividend}}{\text{Yield}} = \frac{.48}{1.2\%} = \underline{\underline{\$40.00}}$

11. Dividend = Price × Yield = 89.75 × 1.9% = $\underline{\underline{\$1.71}}$

12.

Cost of shares	= 400 × 39.25	=	$15,700
Commission	= 400 × 39.25 × 2%	=	+ 314
	Total cost		$16,014
Value of shares	= 400 × 44.75	=	$17,900
Commission	= 400 × 44.75 × 2%	=	− 358
	Proceeds		$17,542

Gain (loss) = 17,542 − 16,014 = $\underline{\underline{\$1,528}}$

13. Cost of shares $= 630 \times 24.13 = \$15{,}201.90$

Commission $= 600 \times 24.13 \times 3\% = 434.34$

$30 \times 24.13 \times 4\% = +\ 28.96$

Total cost $\underline{\underline{\$15{,}665.20}}$

Value of shares $= 630 \times 19.88 = \$12{,}524.40$

Commission $= 600 \times 19.88 \times 3\% = -\ 357.84$

$30 \times 19.88 \times 4\% = -\ 23.86$

Proceeds $\underline{\underline{\$12{,}142.70}}$

Gain (loss) $= 12{,}142.70 - 15{,}665.20 = \underline{\underline{(\$3{,}522.50)}}$

27. Interest $= 1{,}000 \times .07375 \times \frac{100}{360} = \underline{\underline{\$20.49}}$

Total cost $= (785.00 + 20.49 + 9.50) \times 5 = \underline{\underline{\$4{,}074.95}}$

28. Interest $= 1{,}000 \times .05625 \times \frac{3}{12} = \underline{\underline{\$14.06}}$

Total cost $= (1{,}057.50 + 14.06 + 7.00) \times 15 = \underline{\underline{\$16{,}178.40}}$

30. Interest $= 1{,}000 \times .08875 \times \frac{4}{12} = \underline{\underline{\$29.58}}$

Proceeds $= (1{,}092.50 + 29.58 - 5.00) \times 20 = \underline{\underline{\$22{,}341.60}}$

31. Interest $= 1{,}000 \times .0925 \times \frac{85}{360} = \underline{\underline{\$21.84}}$

Proceeds $= (980.00 + 21.84 - 8.00) \times 5 = \underline{\underline{\$4{,}969.20}}$

33. Annual interest $= 1{,}000 \times 9.5\% = \underline{\underline{\$95.00}}$

Current yield $= \frac{95.00}{1{,}057.50} = \underline{\underline{9\%}}$